QUANTUM CHEMISTRY

QUANTUM CHEMISTRY

SIXTH EDITION

R K PRASAD
Ex-Professor
Department of Chemistry
B R A Bihar University, Bihar
India

Committed to Educate the Nation

NEW AGE

Publishing Globally

IN INDIA

NEW AGE INTERNATIONAL (P) LIMITED, PUBLISHERS

LONDON • NEW DELHI

Bangalore • Chennai • Cochin • Guwahati • Hyderabad • Kolkata • Mumbai

Visit us at **www.newagepublishers.com**

Published by New Age International (P) Ltd., Publishers
First Edition: 1992
Sixth Edition: 2025
Reprint: 2026

GLOBAL OFFICES

- **New Delhi** **NEW AGE INTERNATIONAL (P) LIMITED, PUBLISHERS**
7/30 A, Daryaganj, New Delhi-110002, (INDIA), **Tel.:** (011) 23253472, 23253771, **Mob.:** 9315905300
E-mail: contactus@newagepublishers.com • Visit us at www.newagepublishers.com

- **London** **NEW AGE INTERNATIONAL (UK) LTD.**
27 Old Gloucester Street, London, WC1N 3AX, UK
E-mail: info@newacademicscience.co.uk • Visit us at www.newacademicscience.co.uk

BRANCHES

- **Bangalore** 37/10, 8th Cross (Near Hanuman Temple), Azad Nagar, Chamarajpet, Bangalore- 560 018
Tel.: (080) 26756823, **Mob.:** 9315905288, **E-mail: bangalore@newagepublishers.com**

- **Chennai** 26, Damodaran Street, T. Nagar, Chennai-600 017, **Tel.:** (044) 24353401, **Mob.:** 9315905309
E-mail: chennai@newagepublishers.com

- **Cochin** CC-39/1016, Carrier Station Road, Ernakulam South, Cochin-682 016
Tel.: (0484) 4051304, **Mob.:** 9315905289, **E-mail: cochin@newagepublishers.com**

- **Guwahati** Hemsen Complex, Mohd. Shah Road, Paltan Bazar, Near Starline Hotel
Guwahati-781 008, **Tel.:** (0361) 2513881, **Mob.:** 9315905296, **E-mail: guwahati@newagepublishers.com**

- **Hyderabad** 105, 1st Floor, Madhiray Kaveri Tower, 3-2-19, Azam Jahi Road, Near Kumar Theater
Nimboliadda Kachiguda, Hyderabad-500 027, **Tel.:** (040) 24652456, **Mob.:** 9315905326
E-mail: hyderabad@newagepublishers.com

- **Kolkata** RDB Chambers (Formerly Lotus Cinema) 106A, 1st Floor, S N Banerjee Road
Kolkata-700 014, **Tel.:** (033) 22273773, **Mob.:** 9315905319, **E-mail: kolkata@newagepublishers.com**

- **Mumbai** 142C, Victor House, Ground Floor, N.M. Joshi Marg, Lower Parel, Mumbai-400 013
Tel.: (022) 24927869, 24915415, **Mob.:** 9315905282, **E-mail: mumbai@newagepublishers.com**

- **New Delhi** 22, Golden House, Daryaganj, New Delhi-110 002, **Tel.:** (011) 23262368, 23262370
Mob.: 9315905300, **E-mail: sales@newagepublishers.com**

C-25-12-15224

Printed in India at Glorious Printers, Delhi.
Typeset at In-house, Delhi.

NEW AGE INTERNATIONAL (P) LIMITED, PUBLISHERS
7/30 A, Daryaganj, New Delhi - 110002
Visit us at **www.newagepublishers.com**
(CIN: U74899DL1966PTC004618)

Foreword

Quantum Mechanics, Thermodynamics and Kinetics are important theoretical tools for understanding the behaviour of chemical systems. Quantum Mechanics yields vital information about structural chemistry of atoms and molecules including chemical bond. Hence, the subject becomes quite basic for the entire spectrum of chemical studies. The present text by the author is welcome, particularly in view of the need to present suitable material in appropriate manner to Indian students keeping in view their background.

It is a fairly detailed and comprehensive text. The subject matter has been divided into four parts. Part I dealing with Fundamental Principles of Quantum Mehanics along with its formalims. Part II deals with Applications to some Simple Systems such as translational, vibrational and rotational motion of hydrogen and hydrogen-like atoms. Polyelectronic atoms are discussed in Part II along with the mathematical background relating to approximation methods and the Theory of Angular Momentum. Part III deals with Atomic Structure. Part IV deals with Molecular Structure and Chemical Bond for diatomic as well as polyatomic molecules. Principles of Symmetry and Group theory have been discussed in a separate chapter. Basic methematical principles relating to Determinants, Matrices and Vectors have been presented in appendices.

Professor Prasad has had a long teaching experience and hence the subject matter has been presented as clearly as possible. An important feature of the book is that detailed steps of mathematical derivations have been given which are likely to prove useful to teachers and students alike. Similar is the case with problems, sufficient hints for which have been provided. Problems have been suitably chosen.

R.P. RASTOGI

Ex-Vice Chancellor

Banaras Hindu University

Varanasi

India

Preface to the Sixth Edition

The sixth revised and updated edition of this textbook incorporates several comments and suggestions offered by faculties and students all over the country. The concepts explained in this book are well established concepts in this field. Yet the spirit of the first edition of the book which appeared in 1992 with its pedagogical features has been preserved.

In this edition four appendices Greek Alphabet, Masses and Natural Abundances for Selected Isotopes, Conversion Table for Units and Equation List have been included at the end of the book. This will help the students in their study and understanding the subject in a better way.

Updates in the text have been made wherever necessary.

Publisher & Author

Preface to the First Edition

Dirac had once said that the whole of chemistry is implicit in the laws of quantum mechanics. Today, quantum mechanics is accepted as a legitimate tool for the study of almost all chemical phenomena as well as molecular and atomic properties.

A gradual realisation of the necessity of the knowledge of the principles of quantum mechanics and their applicability of chemical problems for students undergoing postgraduate chemistry courses has led to the introduction of the subject in the curricula of almost all the Indian Universities. The present text is accordingly a humble attempt to fulfil the needs of such students and is the outcome of the author's desir e to present the subject to the students in as simple a manner as possible without sacrificing the rigour.

Though the scope of quantum chemistry is unlimited, the author has restrained himself from being too ambitious, but has taken the care to ensure that the prepared text covers all the topics being commonly taught today. The material presented in the book is divided into four parts and thirteen chapters. Part I begins with the developments leading to the formulation of quantum theory (Chapter one). This is followed by descriptions of the theory of matter waves and the quantum mechanical laws in Chapters two and three, respectively. Having gained familiarity with the concepts of operators, eigenvalue, eigenfunction, expectation values, normalization, orthogonality etc., in Part one, the reader will pass on to Part II of the book where applicability of these principles to simple system, viz., particle in a box, harmonic oscillator, a rotating particle and one-electron atomic systems (Chapters 4-7) is discussed. Part III begins with approximation methods of finding wave functions and energies. The quantum mechanics of polyelectronic atoms including the HF SCF theory and the theory of angular momentum of electrons in atoms are treated in Chapter 9 and 10, respectively. Part IV comprising three chapters deals mainly with theories of chemical bond. Principle of symmetry, group theory and their relation to quantum mechanics, which are known to have wide applications in molecular structure, are treated first (Chapter 11) in this part of the book. These are followed by molecular orbital and valence bond treatments of diatomic molecules (Chapter 12) and polyatomic molecules (Chapter 13) wherein the importance and applicability of symmetry principles have been demonstrated. The material in the last two chapters has been presented in such a manner that the reader is able to see the parallel nature of the two theories of bonding and is able to compare the two approaches.

The author has taken care to keep the language simple and presentation unambiguous. Further, the reader may find that a background of advanced mathematics (beyond degree level) is not a prerequisite in following the material presented in this book. Necessary mathematical details, wherever needed, have been explained in the text. Mathematical appendices provided at the end of the text are also useful aids.

Exposition of principles in each chapter has been extensively backed by exercises and problems for which hints are also provided.

**It is hoped that the book will prove to be a self-educator for students undergoing the quantum chemistry courses and for teachers a helpful aid for the classroom.

—Author

Contents

Part II

APPLICATIONS TO SIMPLE SYSTEMS

Part III

ATOMIC STRUCTURE

Part IV

MOLECULAR STRUCTURE AND CHEMICAL BOND

Part I

Fundamental Principles of Quantum Mechanics

CHAPTER 1

Quantum Theory

Quantum mechanics is the science of motion of micro (atomic and subatomic) particles. Its study is of great importance in chemistry because physicochemical properties of atoms and molecules, their structures, spectral behaviour and even reactions may be interpreted in terms of the motion of micro particles like electrons and protons.

The dynamical properties (position, momentum, energy, etc.) of a particle are determined by laws of mechanics. Classical mechanics does not put any restrictions on the values, large or small, of a dynamical property of a particle. However, experimental measurements for atomic and molecular systems show that an electron moving around the nucleus of an atom has only a discrete set of values of energy. This discreteness, termed "quantisation", cannot be explained on the basis of classical laws of mechanics, and to understand this behaviour, it is necessary to postulate a new system of mechanics, called quantum mechanics.

The formal methods of quantum mechanics will be described later (Chapter 3). Before that, it is necessary to know the origin of the quantum theory and quantisation.

1.1 BLACK BODY RADIATION AND QUANTUM THEORY

Radiation is defined as a wave that consists of oscillating electric and magnetic fields; hence, it is also called electromagnetic wave. It is characterised by its wavelength (λ) and frequency (ν) (number of oscillations per second) which are related as $c = \lambda\nu$, where, c is the velocity of the wave. The value of c is generally 3×10^8 ms^{-1}.

Radiation is emitted by any solid at any temperature as a result of the vibrations of its particles. At low temperatures the emitted radiation is of low frequency (large wavelength) infrared (human body also gives off infrared radiation, but the amount of radiation is very small). As the temperature is raised, not only the amount of radiation increases but also more radiations of smaller frequencies are emitted. At any temperature the radiation from a solid has a continuous range of frequencies (in contrast to gases which produce line spectra).

Different solids emit radiation at different rates at the same temperature; the rate is maximum when the solid is perfectly black (black body). By definition, a black body can absorb all the radiation that falls on it. In practice, a hollow enclosure having a small hole is the nearest approach to a black body because the radiation entering the chamber through the hole is absorbed completely due to repeated reflections inside the enclosure. Radiation emerging through the small hole of such a hollow enclosure is, therefore, called "black body radiation". The intensity of radiation, *i.e.*, the total radiation emitted per unit surface area, from a black body depends only on temperature (*T*) and is independent of the nature of the solid.

1.1.1 Distribution of Energy in the Black Body Radiation

The radiation emitted by a black body is not confined to a single wavelength but is spread over a wide spectrum of wavelengths. The distribution of the radiant energy over the different frequencies is described in terms of a function $\rho(\nu)\,d\nu$ which denotes the amount of radiation in the frequency range ν and $\nu + d\nu$. Experimentally, it is found that at any temperature T, the energy density $\rho(\nu)$ increases with ν, reaches a maximum and then falls off to zero. As T increases, the point of maximum shifts to higher frequency (shorter wavelength) side.

Lord Rayleigh (1900) was the first to make an attempt at deriving an equation for distribution of radiation density in terms of the classical laws of mechanics. He based his derivations on two theorems:

(*i*) Theorem of stationary waves in a hollow space, and

(*ii*) Theorem of equipartition of energy.

If the walls of the black body chamber are assumed to be composed of a large number of harmonic oscillators that emit and absorb radiations continuously and are in equilibrium with the radiation field, then the radiation density $\rho(\nu)$ is given by Equation (1.1),

$$\rho(\nu)\,d\nu = \bar{E}\,n(\nu)\,d\nu \qquad \text{... (1.1)}$$

where, $\bar{E}$ is the average energy of the oscillators and $n(\nu)$ is the number of possible vibrations or wave motions per unit volume in the frequency range ν and $\nu + d\nu$ in the black body chamber. Rayleigh first calculated* that,

$$n(\nu)\,d\nu = \frac{8\pi\nu^2}{c^3}\,d\nu \qquad \text{... (1.2)}$$

which is independent of the volume, shape and size of the chamber. Now, the energy of a single harmonic oscillator is given by,

$$E = \frac{p^2}{2m} + \frac{kx^2}{2} \qquad \text{... (1.3)}$$

where, p is the momentum, m is the mass of the oscillator, x is the displacement caused in it and k is the force constant (see Chapter 5). According to classical theories, x and p can have any value between $-\infty$ to ∞. The average energy $(\bar{E})$ of an oscillator ** is, therefore, calculated by taking the average over the Boltzmann distribution as follows:

$$\bar{E} = \frac{\int E\exp\left(-E/k_BT\right)d\tau}{\int \exp\left(-E/k_BT\right)d\tau} \qquad \text{... (1.4)}$$

* The derivation is lengthy. The interested reader is referred to *Treatise on Heat* by M.N. Saha and B.N. Srivastava (Indian Press, Allahabad), 5th Edn., 1969, pp. 534–537.

** Harmonic Oscillator is discussed in detail in Chapter 5.

where, k_B is the Boltzmann constant whose value is known to be 1.38×10^{-23} JK^{-1} and $d\tau = dp\,dx$. Using Equation (1.3) for E in Equation (1.4), we get

$$\overline{E} = \frac{\iint (p^2/2m + kx^2/2)\exp(-p^2/2mk_BT).\exp(-kx^2/2k_BT)\,dp\,dx}{\iint \exp(-p^2/2mk_BT).\exp(-kx^2/2k_BT)\,dp\,dx}$$

where, the double integral $\iint$ stands for integration over p and x-coordinates, and the limits are from $-\infty$ to ∞.

$$\overline{E} = \frac{\frac{1}{2m}\int_{-\infty}^{\infty} p^2 \exp(-p^2/2mk_BT)\,dp}{\int_{-\infty}^{\infty} \exp(-p^2/2mk_BT)\,dp} + \frac{\frac{1}{2}k\int_{-\infty}^{\infty} x^2 \exp(-kx^2/2k_BT)\,dx}{\int_{-\infty}^{\infty} \exp(-kx^2/2k_BT)\,dx}$$

The above equation can be simplified using the table of integrals (see Appendix 5).

$$\overline{E} = \frac{(2mk_BT)^{3/2}}{2m(2mk_BT)^{1/2}} + \frac{k(2k_BT)^{3/2}}{2\left(\frac{2k_BT}{k}\right)^{1/2}}$$

$$= \frac{k_BT}{2} + \frac{k_BT}{2} = k_BT \qquad \text{... (1.5)}$$

The density of radiation [Equation (1.6)] is obtained by substituting Equation (1.5) for $\overline{E}$ and Equation (1.2) for n (ν) in Equation (1.1),

$$\rho(\nu)\,d\nu = \frac{8\pi\nu^2}{c^3} k_BT\,d\nu \qquad \text{... (1.6)}$$

or $\rho(\nu) = A\nu^2 T$, where, A contains all the constants of Equation (1.6). This is Rayleigh-Jean's law of radiation. The law is quite consistent with the classical theories but it leads to an absurdity—if we plot ρ (ν) against ν, it runs to infinity as ν increases without showing any maximum. Moreover, as Rayleigh himself pointed out, the law could hold only for the low frequency radiations and failed miserably as ν became large.

1.1.1.1 Planck's Law of Radiation

In October 1900, the German physicist Max Planck proposed a new empirical formula which agreed remarkably well with the observed energy curves of the black body radiation. The formula could be written as,

$$\rho(\nu)\,d\nu = \frac{a\nu^3}{\exp(b\nu/T) - 1} \qquad \text{... (1.7)}$$

where, a and b are numerical constants. This formula had no theoretical background and was obtained empirically by trial and error method to explain the observed results. However, a few weeks later (December, 1900) Planck announced the theoretical derivation of his radiation law Equation (1.7). For this, he proposed that a black body chamber was filled not only with radiation but also with molecules of a perfect gas, and dipole oscillators of molecular dimensions constituting the black body absorbed energy from the radiation and transferred it partly or wholly to the gas molecules when the latter collided with them. This was a roundabout way of explaining the emission and absorption of radiation by the black body and there was no other way of explaining the mechanism of emission and absorption of radiation by atoms and molecules by direct exchange known at the time. Planck calculated that the number of oscillators per unit volume was $\frac{8\pi\nu^2}{c^3}$, so that the radiation density was given by Equation (1.8).

$$\rho(\nu) = \frac{8\pi\nu^2}{c^3}\,\bar{E}(\nu) \qquad \text{... (1.8)}$$

where, $\bar{E}(\nu)$ is the mean energy of the oscillator emitting radiation of frequency ν. Now if $\bar{E}(\nu)$ were to be determined by equipartition law, *i.e.*, $\bar{E}(\nu) = k_B T$, the Equation (1.8) would lead to the same Rayleigh-Jeans law. Planck gave up the hypothesis of continuous emission of radiation by oscillators and assumed that they emitted energy only when they acquired certain minimum energy E or an integral multiple of it, nE. That is to say, an oscillator having an amount of energy nE could emit only after it had absorbed the amount $(n + 1)$ E, and after emitting the amount of energy E it reverted back to the previous state of energy nE. Thus, the radiation of energy E could be emitted by only those oscillators which had energy E, 2E, 3E, ..., nE *i.e.*, an integral multiple of a minimum E. Further, E was directly proportional to ν, *i.e.*,

$$E = h\nu \qquad \text{... (1.9)}$$

where, the constant of proportionality, h, was called the Planck's constant. In the light of this hypothesis, Planck calculated the mean energy $\bar{E}$ of the oscillators as follows:

According to the Maxwell-Boltzmann distribution law of energy, which applies to any system of particles, oscillators, etc., the probability that an oscillator will have energy E is exp $(-E/k_B T)$. Now let $N_0, N_1, N_2, \ldots, N_n, \ldots$ be the number of oscillators having the energy 0, E, 2E, ..., nE, ... etc., then

$$N = N_0 + N_1 + N_2 + \ldots\ldots + N_n + \ldots\ldots \qquad \text{... (1.10)}$$

$$E_T = E\,(N_1 + 2N_2 + 3N_3 + \ldots\ldots + nN_n + \ldots\ldots) \qquad \text{... (1.11)}$$

where, N = total number of oscillators, and
E_T = total energy.

By Boltzmann's law,

$$N_n = N_0 \exp(-nE/k_B T) \qquad \text{... (1.12)}$$

The mean energy of the oscillators is

$$\bar{E} = \frac{E_T}{N} \qquad \text{... (1.13)}$$

Putting $y = \exp(-E/k_B T)$,

$$N = \sum_{n=0}^{\infty} N_0\, y^n$$

$$= N_0\left(1 + y + y^2 + ...\right) = N_0\left(\frac{1}{1-y}\right) \quad ...(1.14)$$

Similarly,

$$E_T = EN_0 \sum_{n=0}^{\infty} ny^n$$

$$= EN_0\,(y + 2y^2 + 3y^3 + ...)$$

$$= EN_0\,y\,(1 + 2y + 3y^2 + ...)$$

$$= \frac{EN_0\,y}{(1-y)^2} \quad ...(1.15)$$

Hence,

$$\overline{E} = \frac{yE}{1-y} = \frac{E\exp\left(-E/k_B T\right)}{1-\exp\left(-E/k_B T\right)}$$

$$= \frac{E}{\exp\left(E/k_B T\right) - 1} \quad ...(1.16)$$

Using Equation (1.16) for $\overline{E}$, the energy relation density Equation (1.8) becomes,

$$\rho(\nu)\,d\nu = \frac{8\pi\nu^2}{c^3}\cdot\frac{E}{\exp\left(E/k_B T\right) - 1}\,d\nu$$

Since

$$E = h\nu$$

$$\rho(\nu)\,d\nu = \frac{8\pi h\nu^3}{c^3}\cdot\frac{1}{\exp\left(h\nu/k_B T\right) - 1}\,d\nu \quad ...(1.17)$$

Equation (1.17) is known as the Planck's radiation law. This has the same form as Equation (1.7) if a is equal to $\frac{8\pi h}{c^3}$ and b is equal to $\frac{h}{k_B}$.

Planck's derivation introduced a new constant, h, the value of which was obtained by fitting the formula (1.17) to the observed curves for black body radiation. The value of h is 6.626×10^{-34} Js.

The most important aspect of Planck's hypothesis was the new idea of discontinuous emission of radiation. According to classical physics, a system can absorb or emit any amount of energy, but in Planck's hypothesis energy emitted by a black body is restricted to an integral number of a certain minimum E, where $E = h\nu$. To this definite amount of energy, $h\nu$, Planck gave the name "quantum".

Planck had to introduce the idea of quantisation in order to explain the phenomenon of black body radiation. In the beginning most physicists were reluctant to accept this idea. But in the following years this idea led to some of the most significant discoveries in physics, particularly photoelectricity (Einstein, 1905).

1.2 PHOTOELECTRIC EFFECT : WAVE-PARTICLE DUALITY OF RADIATION

The importance of the Planck's idea of energy quantisation was quickly realised by Albert Einstein. In the year 1905 he made a discovery known as "photoelectric effect". According to this effect, when a beam of electromagnetic radiation of a particular frequency falls on a metal surface, the latter emits electrons. This happens because electrons on metal surface absorb energy from the light beam and ultimately overcome binding energy. There are two very significant experimental observations concerning photoelectric effect:

(*i*) Photoelectric emission of electron is possible only with a light of certain minimum frequency ν; this "threshold frequency" varies from metal to metal, and for most metals it lies in the ultraviolet region.

(*ii*) Kinetic energy of the emitted electrons increases on increasing the frequency, but remains unaffected on increasing the intensity of the light.

These observations could not be understood in terms of classical wave theory of light. According to the wave theory, the energy in a wave is proportional to its intensity and is independent of its frequency; so the kinetic energy of the emitted electrons should increase with intensity of the light irrespective of the frequency. Moreover, light of any frequency, provided it was sufficiently intense, could emit electrons; this was contrary to the experimental observations.

Einstein picked up the Planck's idea of quantisation. It is to be noted that Planck had proposed that material oscillators could absorb or emit radiation not continuously but in units of quanta ($h\nu$) but considered radiation as a continuous wave. Einstein proposed that radiation itself is quantised. He called each quantum of radiation ($h\nu$) a photon.

When a light photon of a particular frequency (ν) hits an electron in a metal, it transfers its energy $h\nu$ to the electron. The electron uses this quantum of energy to overcome the energy (w) that binds it in the metal and to increase its own kinetic energy $\left(\frac{1}{2}m\nu^2\right)$.

i.e.,

$$h\nu = w + \frac{1}{2}m\nu^2 \qquad ...(1.18)$$

If $h\nu < w$, the photon will not have sufficient energy to eject the electron from the metal and no photoelectric effect would be observed. Further, Equation (1.18) shows that as frequency (ν) increases, the kinetic energy of the emitted electron increases. Increase in intensity of light would mean increase in the number of photons per unit volume thereby increasing the number of electrons emitted and not their kinetic energy. The successful explanation of experimental observation regarding photoelectric effect brought back the particle concept of light into active consideration. Thus, certain phenomena, *e.g.*, diffraction, interference, etc., of light could be explained only in terms of the wave concept while photoelectric effect could be explained in terms of particle (photon) concept.

This confusion was ultimately solved by the proposition that electromagnetic radiation has a dual character, particle and wave. The duality was supposed to be inherent in the Planck's equation, $E = h\nu$, E being the energy of the photon (a particle property) and ν is frequency (a wave property).

If it could be at rest, the photon would have zero mass; but, it is hardly ever at rest. It always has a velocity c ($\approx 3 \times 10^{10}$ cm s^{-1}). Einstein, in his special theory of relativity, pointed out that the photon travelling with the speed of light has a mass (m) and that its energy is related to it by the equation

$$E = mc^2 \quad \text{... (1.19)}$$

or

$$h\nu = mc^2 \quad \text{... (1.20)}$$

In wave theory of light, the frequency ν is related to the wavelength λ by the equation $\nu\lambda = c$. Therefore,

$$\lambda = \frac{c}{\nu} = \frac{h}{mc} = \frac{h}{p} \quad \text{... (1.21)}$$

where, p is the momentum of the photon, λ, the wavelength is a wave property and p, the momentum, is a particle property and Equation (1.21) correlates the two properties of a photon.

1.3 QUANTUM THEORY AND ATOMIC SPECTRA

Perhaps the theory of quantisation achieved its most decisive victory in the interpretation of the atomic spectral lines. During the period 1885–1908, many spectroscopists (Ritz, Rhydberg, Balmer, etc.) had shown that spectra of hydrogen atoms consisted of lines whose frequency could be expressed as a difference of two terms, *i.e.*,

$$\bar{\nu} = \frac{\nu}{c} = \frac{1}{\lambda} = R\left(\frac{1}{n_1^2} - \frac{1}{n_2^2}\right) \quad \text{... (1.22)}$$

where, $\bar{\nu}$ and λ are the wavenumber (number of waves per cm) and the wavelength of the spectral line respectively, n_1 and n_2 are integers which can assume the values:

$$n_1 = 1, 2, 3, ..., n_2 = 2, 3, 4, ...$$

Equation (1.22) gives rise to various series of spectral lines in the spectrum of H atom; these series of lines are designated after the names of their discoverers, as shown below:

Lyman series : $n_1 = 1, n_2 = 2, 3, 4, ...$

Balmer series : $n_1 = 2, n_2 = 3, 4, 5, ...$

Paschen series : $n_1 = 3, n_2 = 4, 5, 6, ...$

Brackett series : $n_1 = 4, n_2 = 5, 6, 7, ...$

Pfund series : $n_1 = 5, n_2 = 6, 7, 8, ...$

The lines of Lyman series occur in the ultraviolet region of the spectrum while the lower members of the Balmer series and those of all the other series occur in the visible region. In Equation (1.22), R is a constant (Rydberg constant) whose value is 109677.6 cm^{-1}. This formula was obtained empirically and lacked theoretical support. The classical (Rutherford) picture of the structure of atom predicted continuous band spectra and not spectral lines, as according to the electromagnetic theory, an electron rotating round the nucleus could emit radiation whose frequency changed continuously.

1.3.1 The Bohr Model

Neils Bohr (1913) used quantum theory to interpret the spectral lines of hydrogen. He argued that if according to quantum theory (E = $h\nu$) only certain frequencies of light are emitted by H-atoms, then in contrast to the classical ideas, an Hatom can exist only in certain discrete energy states. He then postulated as follows:

(*i*) Even though electron revolves round the nucleus, "stationary states" exist for the atom when it does not emit radiation violating the classical electromagnetic theory.

(*ii*) Atoms radiate only when an electron undergoes transition from one stationary state to another state of lower energy; in the case of transition to a higher energy stationary state, energy is absorbed; the frequency of the light emitted or absorbed is in accordance with the relation given by the quantum theory,

$$\Delta E = E_2 - E_1 = h\nu \qquad \text{... (1.23)}$$

Equations (1.22) and (1.23) give the relation,

$$\Delta E = Rhc\left(\frac{1}{n_1^2} - \frac{1}{n_2^2}\right) \qquad \text{... (1.24)}$$

where, R is called Rhydberg constant having the value $1.09678 \times 10^7\ m^{-1}$, h is Planck's constant and c is velocity of light.

The energies of the stationary states of H-atom are given by,

$$E = -\frac{Rhc}{n^2},\ n \text{ being an integer as } 1, 2, 3, ... \qquad \text{... (1.25)}$$

The units of energy (erg, Joule etc.) will depend on those of h.

(*iii*) The orbits of electronic motion are circular and well-defined and are such that the angular momentum (mvr) of the electron is quantized in units of $\frac{h}{2\pi}$, *i.e.*,

$$mvr = \frac{nh}{2\pi}, \quad n \text{ is a simple integer} \qquad \text{... (1.26)}$$

where, m is the mass of electron, v its velocity and r is the radius of the orbit. On squaring Equation (1.26) and rearranging,

$$v^2 = \frac{n^2 h^2}{4\pi^2 m^2 r^2} \qquad \text{... (1.27)}$$

For a stable orbit the centrifugal force is equal to the coulombic force of attraction between the nucleus and the electron; thus, for a nucleus of charge Ze (e = electronic charge).

$$\frac{mv^2}{r} = \frac{Ze^2}{4\pi\varepsilon_0 r^2} \qquad \text{... (1.28)}$$

where, ε_0 is called permittivity of the medium in vacuum and has the value 8.85×10^{-12}. In C.G.S. system $\frac{1}{4\pi\varepsilon_0} = 1$.

From Equations (1.27) and (1.28), we get

$$r = \frac{(4\pi\varepsilon_0)\, n^2 h^2}{4\pi^2 m Z e^2} \qquad \text{... (1.29)}$$

For H-atom (Z = 1), the radius of the first Bohr orbit (n = 1) is,

$$r = (4\pi\varepsilon_0)\, h^2 / 4\pi^2 m e^2 \qquad \text{... (1.30)}$$

In quantum theory, this is often denoted as a_0 and is taken as the atomic unit of length. The total energy of the electron is the sum of its kinetic and potential energies, *i.e.*,

$$E = \frac{1}{2} mv^2 - \frac{Ze^2}{(4\pi\varepsilon_0) r} = -\frac{2\pi^2 Z^2 e^4 m}{(4\pi\varepsilon_0)^2 n^2 h^2} \qquad \text{... (1.31)}$$

[By using Equations (1.27) and (1.29)].

Equation (1.31) shows that the energy of the electron in H-atom is quantised, the integer n being called "quantum number" of the electron. In other words, discrete energy levels exist for the electron (Fig. 1.1).

Various series of emission spectral lines arise when an electron falls from a higher energy ($n \geq 2$) to a lower level. The series corresponding to transitions from $n > 1$ to $n = 1$ could be recognised as the Lyman series ; those corresponding to transition from $n > 2$ to $n = 2$ as the Balmer series and so on.

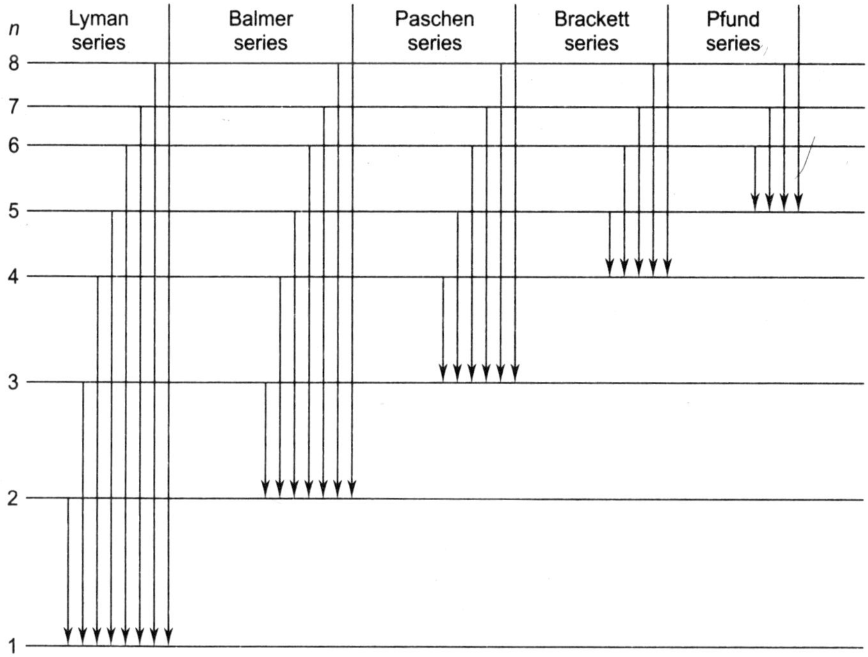

Fig. 1.1 *Energy levels and spectrum of hydrogen atom*

According to Bohr's theory,

$$Rhc = \frac{2\pi^2 me^4}{(4\pi\varepsilon_0)^2 h^2} \text{ and } R = \frac{2\pi^2 me^4}{(4\pi\varepsilon_0)^2 h^3 c}$$

On substituting the values of

$$\pi = 3.1416, m = 9.109 \times 10^{-31} \text{ kg}, e = 1.602 \times 10^{-19} \text{ C},$$

$$4\pi\varepsilon_0 = 1.11265 \times 10^{-10} \text{ J}^{-1} c^2 \text{ m}^{-1}$$

$$h = 6.62 \times 10^{-34} \text{ J and } c = 3 \times 10^8 \text{ ms}^{-1}$$

in the above relation, the value of R is found to be 1.09737×10^7 m^{-1} and is in excellent agreement with the experimental value 1.09678×10^7 m^{-1}. This was a very big triumph for the quantum theory as it provided a theoretical basis for the empirical formula (1.22) for the frequency of spectral lines.

Bohr's theory proved to be of great significance. For the first time the theory was used to construct a satisfactory model of atomic structure. It was later extended by Sommerfeld and others to construct superior models taking into consideration the deviations of electronic motion from circular paths to elliptical paths. Later developments, however, proved that the postulate (*iii*) of Bohr was wrong; electron had no defined path, circular or elliptical. Bohr-Sommerfeld theory was ultimately superseded in 1926 by Schrödinger's quantum mechanical model. In subsequent chapters we deal with quantum mechanics of atomic and molecular systems.

PROBLEMS

1.1. Assuming that a heated hollow cavity with a small hole is made up of a large number of harmonic oscillators which are in thermal equilibrium with the radiation in the cavity (black body), derive the expression for the average energy of the oscillators using (*i*) classical theory, and (*ii*) quantum theory. Explain the term equipartition of energy.
[**Hint :** See text].

1.2. Calculate the average energy of an oscillator with frequency 10 Hz (s^{-1}) at a temperature 1000 K.

$$\left[\textbf{Hint: } \text{Use the formula } \bar{E} = \frac{h\nu}{\exp(h\nu/k_B T) - 1}; \ \textbf{Ans.} = 5.5 \times 10^{-13} \text{ erg.}\right]$$

1.3. Planck's law of distribution of energy in the black body radiation is given by the equation,

$$E(\nu)\, d\nu = \frac{8\pi h\nu^3}{c^3} \cdot \frac{d\nu}{\exp(h\nu/k_B T) - 1}$$

where E (ν) is the energy associated with the radiation of frequency ν.
Show that (*i*) the total energy of all radiations from the black body is proportional to the fourth power of the temperature of the body (Stefan-Boltzmann law) ; and (*ii*) the wavelength corresponding to the maximum energy density is inversely proportional to the temperature (Wien's law).

[**Hint:** (*i*)

$$\nu = \frac{c}{\lambda}, d\nu = -\frac{c}{\lambda^2} d\lambda$$

$$E(\lambda)\, d\lambda = -\frac{8\pi hc}{\lambda^5} \frac{d\lambda}{\exp(hc/\lambda k_B T) - 1}$$

Put

$$x = \frac{hc}{\lambda k_B T}; dx = -\frac{hc}{\lambda^2 . k_B T} . d\lambda$$

or

$$\lambda = \frac{hc}{x k_B T}; d\lambda = -\frac{hc}{k_B T} \frac{dx}{x^2}$$

$$E(x)\,dx = -\frac{8\pi hc}{(hc/xk_BT)^5(e^x-1)}\left(-\frac{hc}{k_BT}\right)\cdot\frac{dx}{x^2}$$

$$= \frac{8\pi(k_BT)^4}{(hc)^3}\cdot\frac{x^3}{e^x-1}\,dx$$

Total energy, $$E = \int_0^\infty E(x)\,dx$$

$$= \frac{8\pi(k_BT)^4}{(hc)^3}\int_0^\infty\frac{x^3}{e^x-1}\,dx$$

$$= \frac{8\pi(k_BT)^4}{(hc)^3}\cdot\frac{\pi^4}{15};\left[\text{because}\int_0^\infty\frac{x^3}{e^x-1}\,dx = \frac{\pi^4}{15}\right]$$

or $$E \propto T^4$$

(*ii*) At maximum energy density, $\frac{dE}{d\lambda} = 0$

$$\frac{dE}{d\lambda} = -\frac{5}{\lambda^6}\left(\frac{1}{\exp(hc/\lambda k_BT)-1}\right)+\frac{1}{\lambda^7}\left[\frac{(hc/k_BT)\exp(hc/\lambda k_BT)}{(\exp(hc/\lambda k_BT)-1)^2}\right] = 0$$

or $$\lambda\ (i.e., \lambda_{max}) = \frac{hc}{5k_BT}\left(\frac{\exp hc/\lambda k_BT}{\exp(hc/\lambda k_BT)-1}\right)$$

Assuming that $\frac{h\nu}{k_BT}\left(=\frac{hc}{\lambda k_BT}\right) \gg 1$

$$\lambda_{max} = \left(\frac{hc}{5k_B}\right)\frac{1}{T} \text{ or } \lambda_{max} \propto \frac{1}{T} \text{ (Wien's law)].}$$

1.4. A plot of the energy density of the radiation, in equilibrium with a black body, versus λ exhibits a maximum (λ_{max}). The energy density of the solar radiation shows maximum at λ_{max} = 480 nm. Assuming the Sun to be a black body, calculate the temperature of the Sun's surface.

[Hint : $T = hc/5k_B\,\lambda_{max}$ = 5900 K].

1.5. The diameter of the Sun is 1.4×10^9 m and the temperature of its surface is 5800 K. Assuming it a black body, estimate the energy loss per second by radiation from the Sun, given that the total radiant energy emitted per second by unit area of a black body is

$$\frac{(2\pi^5 k_B^4)}{15c^2h^3}T^4.$$

[**Hint :** On substitution for k_B, c and h.

$$\sigma = \frac{2\pi^5 k_B^4}{15c^2 h^3} = 5.67 \times 10^{-8}\,\text{Jm}^{-2}\,\text{s}^{-1}\,\text{K}^{-4} \text{ (Stefan-Boltzmann constant)}$$

Total energy loss per second from the surface of the Sun

$$= 4\pi r^2 \times 5.67 \times 10^{-8} \times (5800)^4\,\text{Js}^{-1}$$

$$= 4 \times 3.14 \times (0.7 \times 10^9)^2 \times 5.67 \times 10^{-8} \times (5800)^4\,\text{Js}^{-1}$$

$$= 4 \times 10^{26}\,\text{Js}^{-1}.$$

1.6. The work function for the platinum metal is 8×10^{-19} J. Will a radiation of wavelength 200 nm be able to cause photoelectric effect in it ? If so, what will be the velocity of the electron ejected from the surface ? (Given 10^{-19} J = 5035.7 cm^{-1}, and mass of the electron = 9.1×10^{-31} kg, $c = 3 \times 10^{10}$ cm s^{-1}).

[**Hint :** 8×10^{-10} J = 8×5035.7 cm^{-1} = 40280 cm^{-1}.

Therefore,
$$\nu_0 = \frac{c}{\lambda} = c\bar{\nu}_0 = 3 \times 10^{10}\ \text{cm s}^{-1} \times 40341.5\,\text{cm}^{-1}$$

$$= 1.21 \times 10^{15}\,\text{s}^{-1}$$

$$\nu = \frac{c}{\lambda} = \frac{3.0 \times 10^{10}\ \text{cm s}^{-1}}{200 \times 10^{-7}\ \text{cm}} = 1.5 \times 10^{15}\ \text{s}^{-1}$$

$\nu > \nu_0$, therefore, photoelectric effect is possible.

Using
$$h\nu = h\nu_0 + \frac{1}{2}m\nu^2, \text{ and } m = 9.1 \times 10^{-31}\,\text{kg}$$

$$u^2 = \frac{2h(\nu - \nu_0)}{m}, \nu = 3.3 \times 10^5\,\text{ms}^{-1}].$$

1.7. The following data for the photoelectric effect in Na were found by Millikan:

$10^{19}\,T_{max}$ (J)	3.41	2.56	1.95	0.75
λ/nm	312.5	365.0	404.7	546.1

where T_{max} is the maximum kinetic energy of emitted electrons and λ is the wavelength of the incident light. Plot T_{max} vs ν and calculate from the slope and intercept the values of h and the work function for Na.

[**Hint :** T = $h\nu - h\nu_0$; slope = h, intercept = $h\nu_0$].

1.8. The emission spectrum of H-atom is analysed between 100 nm and 400 nm. What spectral lines are seen in this region ?

$$\left[\textbf{Hint :} \ \bar{\nu}\left(\text{cm}^{-1}\right) = R\left(\frac{1}{n_1^2} - \frac{1}{n_2^2}\right)\right.$$

$$\lambda\,(\text{nm}) = \left(\frac{1}{\bar{\nu}\left(\text{cm}^{-1}\right)} \cdot \frac{1\,(\text{nm})}{10^{-7}\ \text{cm}}\right) = \frac{1}{\text{R} \times 10^{-7}} \frac{\left(n_1^2\, n_2^2\right)}{n_2^2 - n_1^2}\ \text{nm}$$

$$= 91.13 \times \left(\frac{n_1^2\, n_2^2}{n_2^2 - n_1^2}\right) \text{nm}$$

Lyman series ($n_1 = 1, n_2 = 2, 3, 4 \ldots$)

For $n_1 = 1, n_2 = 2$ $\quad \lambda = 121.5$ nm
$n_1 = 1, n_2 = 3$ $\quad \lambda = 102.5$ nm] these two lines will be seen.

$n_1 = 1, n_2 = 3$ $\quad \lambda < 100$ nm | will not be seen.

Balmer series ($n_1 = 2, n_2 = 3, 4, 5, \ldots$)

For $n_1 = 2, n_2 = 3$ $\quad \lambda = 656.1$ nm
$n_1 = 2, n_2 = 4$ $\quad \lambda = 486.0$ nm
$n_1 = 2, n_2 = 5$ $\quad \lambda = 433.9$ nm
$n_1 = 2, n_2 = 6$ $\quad \lambda = 410.1$ nm] will not be seen.

$n_1 = 2, n_2 = 7$ $\quad \lambda = 396.9$ nm | will be seen.

and all other lines will be seen as for $n_2 = \infty$, $\lambda = 364.5$ nm. No other series will be observed.]

CHAPTER 2

Matter Waves

2.1 WAVE-PARTICLE DUALITY OF MATERIAL PARTICLES AND de BROGLIE'S HYPOTHESIS

Quantisation is inherent in wave motion. For example, a string fixed at the two ends can vibrate at frequencies ν, 2ν, 3ν, etc., *i.e.*, its frequencies are quantised, and a vibration is synonymous with wave motion.

These considerations led a young French physicist, Louis de Broglie, in 1924 to propose that it was possible to explain quantisation of energy in an atom if one considered that some sort of wave motion was associated with electronic motion, that is, if electrons too, like electromagnetic light, exhibited the dual behaviour of particles and waves.

The wavelength or frequency of electron could be derived in analogy with that of photons whose wavelength is given by the relation $\lambda = \frac{h}{p}$ [see Chapter 1, Equation (1.21)], where λ is the wavelength and p is the momentum of a photon. de Broglie proposed that the wavelength of a material particle is likewise given by

$$\lambda = \frac{h}{mv} \text{ or } \frac{h}{p} \qquad \text{... (2.1)}$$

where, m = mass and v = velocity of the particle. For example, an electron ($m = 9.109 \times 10^{-31}$ kg) having a velocity of 10^6 ms^{-1} would have a wavelength,

$$\lambda = \frac{6.625 \times 10^{-34} \text{ Js}}{9.109 \times 10^{-31} \text{ kg} \times 10^6 \text{ ms}^{-1}} = 7.3 \times 10^{-10} \text{ m} = 0.73 \text{ nm}$$

The order of magnitude of the wavelength shows that the wave effects can be felt in electrons; for larger particles, however, the wavelength will be too small to lead to observable wave effects. For example, a particle of mass 1 g moving with a velocity 10 cm s^{-1} will have the wavelength,

$$\lambda = \frac{6.625 \times 10^{-34} \text{ Js}}{1.0 \times 10^{-3} \text{ kg} \times 10 \times 10^{-2} \text{ ms}^{-1}} = 6.625 \times 10^{-30} \text{ m}$$

de Broglie's hypothesis was verified experimentally by Davisson and Germer, working independently, three years later through electron diffraction experiments. If electrons were waves then they would produce diffraction patterns, similar to light waves when passed through a thin diffraction grating. This was exactly what they observed when electrons were passed through a crystal of nickel. Diffraction effects are also observed with neutrons, protons, helium atoms, etc., establishing that the de Broglie hypothesis of wave-particle duality is applicable to all subatomic particles as also to very small atoms.

2.2 ELECTRON WAVES AND DIFFRACTION

The wave nature of light was established through interference experiments. If a beam of light is passed through an aperture screen on to a photographic film it produces a band when the film is developed. But if it passes through two slits close to each other it produces a pattern with alternate bands of maximum and minimum intensity; this is called diffraction pattern. This occurs because of the cancellation and reinforcement of the waves when they are out of phase and in-phase respectively. On being sketched the band intensities appear as in Figures 2.1 and 2.2.

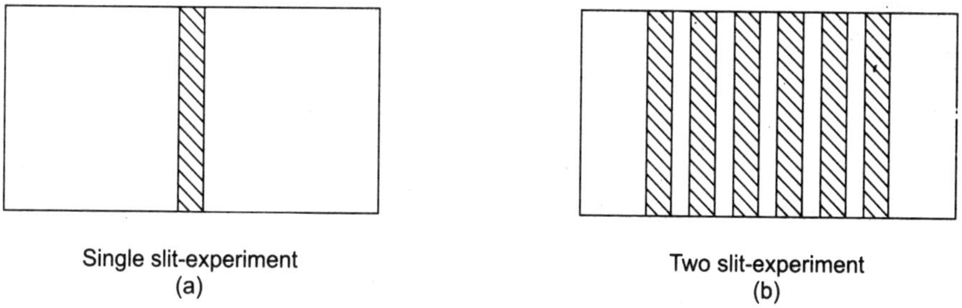

Fig. 2.1

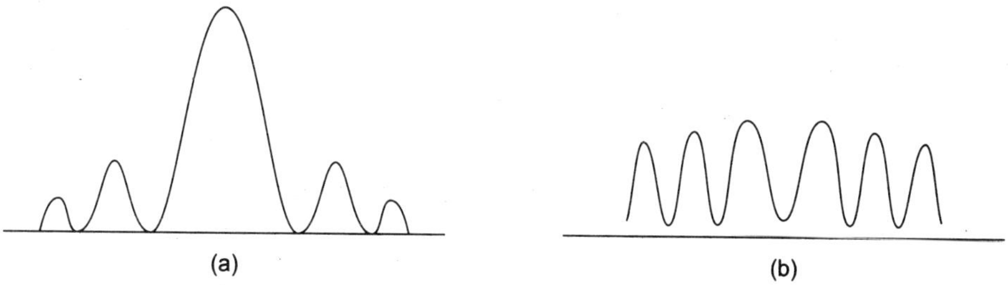

Fig. 2.2 *Intensity curves*

If electrons have wave properties they are expected to show similar behaviour. Three years after de Broglie hypothesis, Davisson and Germer observed diffraction of electron waves by passing a beam of electrons through a nickel grating. The wave nature of electrons was thus established.

2.3 THE HEISENBERG'S PRINCIPLE OF UNCERTAINTY

The paradox of electron diffraction lies, however, in the fact that if you try to observe it the diffracting pattern is washed out and if you do not, it occurs. In the words of W. Heisenberg, "Peculiar though it may appear, it is in the very nature of electrons. (An elegant discussion on it may be found in the "Breakthrough-Quantum Revolution" by Venkat Raman, Universities press India Limited, 1994). Heisenberg devised a thought (gedanken) experiment. To observe a tiny particle we have to use a microscope with a light source and the accuracy of measurement depends on the wavelength (λ) of the light. For an electron ordinary light (≈ 5000 Å) cannot be used as the wavelength is many times larger than the size of the electron due to which the uncertainty of its position (Δx) will be large ($\Delta x \sim \lambda$). A light of much shorter wavelength, say X-rays or γ-rays ($\lambda \approx 0.1$ to 1 Å) may be used for accurate measurement. But in the process, the electron while colliding with X-ray photon suffers a recoil and, due to Compton effect, suffers a change in momentum. Thus the accuracy of measurement of position offsets that of momentum. Heisenberg concluded, "it is not possible, even in principle, to determine both the position and momentum of an electron with equal exactness; the more exactly we determine the position the less exact becomes the momentum, and vice-versa. Here is a situation where the very act of observing disturbs. This is known as the "principle of uncertainty"; it is a law of nature and this very principle forms the basis of quantum mechanics.

The principle of uncertainty is expressed mathematically as,

$$\Delta x \cdot \Delta p_x \approx h \quad \text{... (2.2)}$$

Equation (2.2) may be derived in various ways. Heisenberg derived it theoretically. Consider, however, an electron moving along the y-axis; let it pass through a slit of width d to fall on a fluorescent screen where its position is recorded by production of a spot.

When the electron enters the slit, it suffers diffraction, *i.e.*, it bends round the corners of the slit. A classical electron would go straight through the slit on to the screen; a beam of electrons would spread on the screen covering the length d. This would mean that the uncertainty in the position of a single electron along the x-coordinate would be d. But waves associated with the beam will spread out to give a diffraction pattern wherein the intensity of the waves will vary from point to point. There will be points of minimum and maximum intensity due to the destructive and constructive interferences, respectively, of the waves originating from the different parts of the slit. When two waves originate from two points such that their path lengths to the screen differ by $\frac{\lambda}{2}$, they will be out of phase and the intensity of the waves will be minimum (points P and Q on the screen), and when the path lengths differ by λ (in phase) the intensity will be maximum [point E on the screen (see Fig. 2.3)]. Let two such waves originating from the points A and D in the slit $\left(AD = \frac{d}{2}\right)$ travelling along AP and DP interfere destructively to produce the intensity minimum at P. Cutting from DP a distance CP equal to AP gives $DP - AP = DC = \frac{\lambda}{2}$. But the distances AP and DP are so large compared to the size (d) of the slit that the $\angle APC \approx 0$ or $\angle PAC = \angle ACP \approx 90°$.

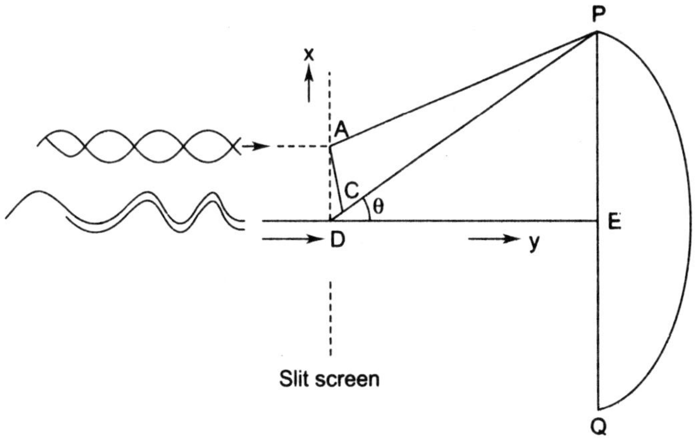

Fig. 2.3

Then, $\angle PDE = \angle DAC \approx 90° - \angle ADC = \theta$ (say)

$$\sin\theta = \frac{DC}{AD} = \frac{\lambda/2}{d/2} = \frac{\lambda}{d}\ ;\text{ or } d = \frac{\lambda}{\sin\theta}$$

The uncertainty in the x-coordinate of the position of a single electron is given by Equation (2.3).

$$\Delta x = d = \frac{\lambda}{\sin\theta} \qquad \text{... (2.3)}$$

Near the slit, where the electron is moving along the y-axis, the x-component of p, *i.e.*, p_x is zero. On diffraction, angular range is 2θ; but

$$p_x = p\sin\theta \qquad \text{... (2.4)}$$

at the point P or Q, [Fig. 2.3 (*a*)] *i.e.*, the value of p_x is governed by the angle of diffraction θ: hence, the uncertainty Δp_x is

$$p\sin\theta - 0 = p\sin\theta$$

Hence, $$\Delta x \,.\, \Delta p_x = \frac{\lambda}{\sin\theta}\,.\,p\sin\theta$$

$$= \lambda\frac{h}{\lambda} = h$$

which is same as Equation (2.2).

Before measurement, Δx, was infinite and Δp_x was zero (there was no motion along the x-coordinate). Diffraction through the slit produced uncertainties $\Delta x = d$ and $\Delta p_x = \frac{h}{d}$. As Δx is made smaller, Δp_x becomes larger.

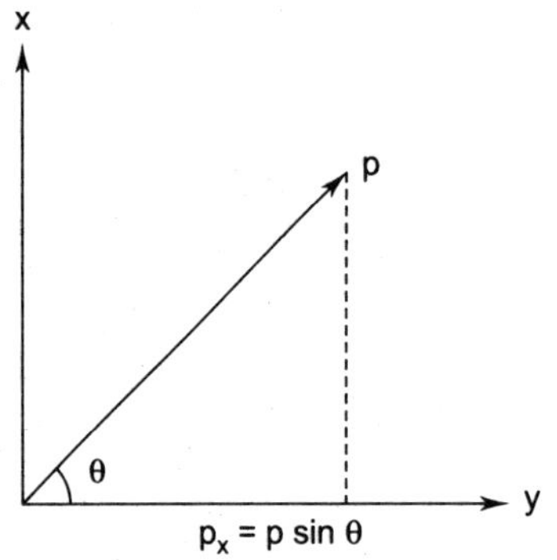

Fig. 2.3 *(a) x and y components of momentum*

The uncertainty relation explains the inadequacy of the Bohr theory of well-defined orbits. Consider an electron (mass = 9.109×10^{-31} kg) moving in an H-atom in the first orbit with a speed of 2×10^6 ms^{-1}. The momentum (p) will be $9.109 \times 10^{-31} \times 2 \times 10^6 = 18.218 \times 10^{-25}$ kg ms^{-1}. If this is measured with an accuracy of 1%, the uncertainty of momentum will be $18.218 \times 10^{-25} \times 0.01 = 18.218 \times 10^{-27}$. Then, the uncertainty of position is,

$$\Delta x = \frac{h}{\Delta p}$$

$$= \frac{6.625 \times 10^{-34}\ \text{Js}}{18.218 \times 10^{-27}\ \text{kg ms}^{-1}} = 3.64 \times 10^{-8}\ \text{m or 36 nm}$$

The radius of the first orbit in H-atom is only 0.529 Å or 0.0529 nm. This means that the uncertainty of electron's position in the H-atom will be 36/0.0529 ≈ 700 times the radius of the atom itself—it is not even known whether at the given instance the electron is within the atom or not ! This is contrary to the Bohr's concept of electron orbits; the path of the electron is not defined at all, it is spread out due to uncertainty.

The principle of uncertainty, however, does not apply to larger bodies or particles. Consider, for example, a ball of mass 0.2 kg moving with a speed of 10 m per second. The momentum (p) is 2 kg ms^{-1}. If the error in this measurement is 0.1%, $\Delta p = 2 \times 10^{-3}$ kg ms^{-1}. The uncertainty of position,

$$\Delta x = \frac{h}{\Delta p} = \frac{6.625 \times 10^{-34}\ \text{Js}}{2 \times 10^{-3}\ \text{kg ms}^{-1}} = 3.31 \times 10^{-31}\ \text{m}$$

which is negligible, *i.e.*, both momentum and position can be determined sufficiently accurately.

It should be immediately obvious that failure of uncertainty principle in the case of larger bodies is due to the very small value of h.

2.3.1 Uncertainty of Energy and Time

The product of uncertainties of position and momentum, which has the dimensions of h (Js), may be extended to any pair of conjugate variables. Two variables will be said to be conjugate to each other if the dimensions of their product are the dimensions of h. For example, energy and time, angular momentum and angular position, etc., are conjugate variables. One such relationship of interest is,

$$\Delta E \, . \, \Delta t \approx h \qquad \text{... (2.5)}$$

where, ΔE is the uncertainty in the measurement of energy and Δt that of time. The Equation (2.5) can also be derived directly from the concept of wave particle duality. A particle is assumed to have a packet of waves associated with it; let it occupy a region Δx along x-axis and let the velocity of the group of waves be v. The time in which it passes through a given point in the x-axis has an uncertainty.

$$\Delta t = \frac{\Delta x}{v} \qquad \text{... (2.6)}$$

If the wave packet is localised in the region Δx, then the momentum will be spread out by,

$$\Delta p_x \approx \frac{h}{\Delta x} \quad \text{[from Equation (2.2)]}$$

$$\Delta x \approx \frac{h}{\Delta p_x}$$

Substituting for Δx in Equation (2.6), we get

$$\Delta t \approx \frac{h}{v \Delta p_x} \qquad \text{... (2.7)}$$

Since $$E = \frac{p_x^2}{2m}, \frac{\Delta E}{\Delta p_x} = \frac{dE}{dp_x} = \frac{p_x}{m} = v \qquad \text{... (2.8)}$$

Hence, $$\Delta E = \frac{dE}{dp_x} \cdot \Delta p_x = v \Delta p_x \qquad \text{... (2.9)}$$

Combining Equations (2.7) and (2.9), we arrive at Equation (2.5).

The energy-time uncertainty relation, however, has a different physical interpretation. It implies that if a system can exist in a certain state for a period not longer than Δt, the energy of the system in that state will be uncertain by at least $\Delta E \approx \frac{h}{\Delta t}$. An atom, for example, may exist in an excited state for about 10^{-8} s after which it reemits the energy. This implies that the energy of excitation can be determined with uncertainty ΔE, where,

$$\Delta E = \frac{h}{\Delta t} = \frac{6.625 \times 10^{-34} \text{ Js}}{10^{-8} \text{ s}} = 6.625 \times 10^{-26} \text{ J}$$

Since $\Delta E = h \Delta v$, we have

$$\Delta v = \frac{1}{\Delta t} = 10^8 \text{ s}^{-1}$$

which is called the linewidth of the corresponding spectrum.

If $\Delta t = \infty$, then $\Delta E = 0$, *i.e.*, if the atom in any state can exist for an infinite time, its energy will have a very precise value; the atom is said to be in a "stationary state".

2.4 THEORY OF WAVE MOTION

The de Broglie and Heisenberg principles, besides the electron diffraction experiments, established that electrons are not ordinary particles; they are also waves. A particle is after all essentially localised; it cannot be in more than one place at the same time. A wave, on the other hand, cannot be localised at a point; it is a kind of disturbance which varies from point to point in space. So, in order to have an insight into the behaviour of electrons or any microparticle, we have to be acquainted with the characteristics of wave motion.

2.4.1 Classical Waves and the Wave Equation

All waves originate from some kind of vibratory (oscillatory) motion, the simplest of which is the simple harmonic motion. A simple harmonic vibration is a periodic motion in which a certain physical quantity regularly assumes a definite value after a definite period of time. In a water wave, for example, this quantity is the height of the water, and in the vibration of a string, it is the vertical displacement of the string from its mean position, often called amplitude of the vibration (or wave). This quantity (amplitude) is a function of position (x) and time (t) and may be denoted by $\psi(x, t)$.

A simple harmonic wave travels as shown in Fig. 2.4.

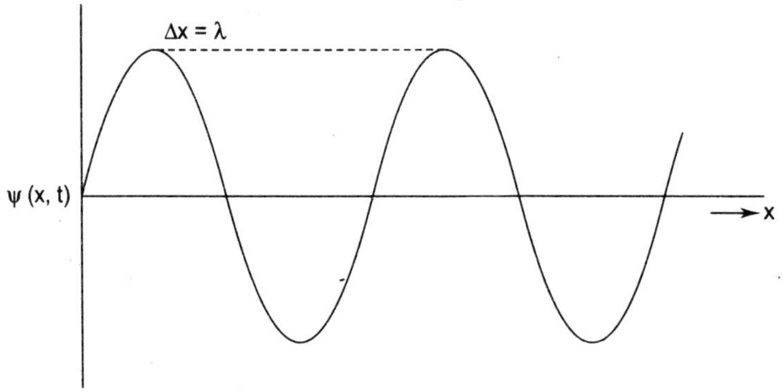

Fig. 2.4 *A progressing simple harmonic wave*

It can be seen that as the wave progresses, the curve assumes the same height (amplitude) at regular intervals of position Δx, representing the wavelength (λ) of the wave. The time taken by the wave in travelling the distance λ is the time period (T), the velocity (c) of the wave being $\frac{\lambda}{T}$. At a particular point the number of waves passing per unit time (*i.e.*, the frequency ν of the wave) will be $\frac{1}{T} = \frac{c}{\lambda}$ and the number of waves passing per unit distance (*i.e.*, the wave number $\bar{\nu}$) will be $\frac{1}{\lambda}$.

The periodic nature of $\psi(x, t)$ suggests that analytical expression for it will be a sine or cosine function of x and t, where, x is the position coordinate and t is the time. Such expressions are obtained by solving the equation of the wave motion,

$$\frac{\partial^2 \psi}{\partial x^2} = \frac{1}{c^2} \frac{\partial^2 \psi}{\partial t^2} \quad ...(2.10)$$

where ψ has been written for $\psi(x, t)$. The derivation, which is not given here*, involves nothing more than Newton's second law of motion together with the consideration that each wave propagates along the medium continuously, each segment of the medium being "attached" to its neighbouring segments so that as it is displaced it drags along its neighbour.

2.4.1.1 Separation of Variables

Equation (2.10) which is a second order partial differential equation containing two variables, x and t can be separated into single variable ordinary equations by a standard procedure shown below.

Assume that the function $\psi(x, t)$ is a product of two functions

$$\psi(x, t) = \psi(x) \,.\, \phi(t) \quad ...(2.11)$$

where, $\psi(x)$ is a function of x only and $\phi(t)$ a function of t only.

Now substitute the function (2.11) in the wave Equation (2.10) and subsequently divide by $\psi(x) \,.\, \phi(t)$ on both sides. This gives,

$$\frac{c^2}{\psi} \cdot \frac{d^2 \psi}{dx^2} = \frac{1}{\phi} \cdot \frac{d^2 \phi}{dt^2} \quad ...(2.12)$$

The left hand side of Equation (2.12) depends only on x while the right hand side depends only on t and yet the two sides are equal. This is possible only if both are equal to a constant. Let this constant be denoted by $-k^2$, *i.e.*,

$$\frac{c^2}{\psi} \cdot \frac{d^2 \psi}{dx^2} = \frac{1}{\phi} \cdot \frac{d^2 \phi}{dt^2} = -k^2 \quad ...(2.13)$$

Thus, we get two separate and ordinary differential equations for ψ and ϕ,

$$\frac{d^2 \psi}{dx^2} = -\frac{k^2}{c^2} \psi \quad ...(2.14)$$

and

$$\frac{d^2 \phi}{dt^2} = -k^2 \phi \quad ...(2.15)$$

(This technique of obtaining ordinary differential equations containing single variables from a partial differential equation containing more than one variable, called the method of separation of variables, will often be used in subsequent chapters).

Equation (2.14) is the time-independent wave equation, often called the "amplitude equation,". One can predict by inspection as to what sort of functions will satisfy Equations (2.14) and (2.15).

* For the derivation see *Quantum Chemistry* by John P. Lowe (Acad. Press, New York), 1978, p. 5-6 or *Contemporary Quantum Chemistry* by J. Goodishman (Plenium Press, New York, 1977 pp. 15-17

These must be such that when differentiated twice they yield the same function multiplied by a constant, $-\frac{k^2}{c^2}$ in Equation (2.14) and $-k^2$ in Equation (2.15). Obviously, sine and cosine functions will serve the purpose. The most general solutions for Equations (2.14) and (2.15) will be,

$$\psi(x) = A \sin\left(\frac{kx}{c}\right) + B\cos\left(\frac{kx}{c}\right) \qquad \text{... (2.16)}$$

$$\phi(t) = C\sin(kt) + D\cos(kt) \qquad \text{... (2.17)}$$

respectively, where A, B, C and D are arbitrary constants. Such functions are periodic in nature and are consistent with wave behaviour. For example, when t is increased by $\frac{2\pi}{k}$, $\phi(t)$ repeats its value, *i.e.*, $\phi(t) = \phi\left(t + \frac{2\pi}{k}\right)$; thus, we should call $\frac{2\pi}{k}$ the time period (T) and $\frac{k}{2\pi}$ the frequency (ν) of the wave. Similarly, when x increases by $\frac{2\pi c}{k}$, the function $\psi(x)$ is repeated, *i.e.*, $\psi(x) = \psi\left(x + \frac{2\pi c}{k}\right)$; so, $\frac{2\pi c}{k} = \lambda$ is the wavelength of the wave.

Therefore, Equations (2.16) and (2.17) can also be written as

$$\psi(x) = A\sin\left(\frac{2\pi}{\lambda}x\right) + B\cos\left(\frac{2\pi}{\lambda}x\right) \qquad \text{... [2.17 (a)]}$$

$$\phi(t) = C\sin(2\pi\nu t) + D\cos(2\pi\nu t)$$

$$= C\sin\left(\frac{2\pi c}{\lambda}t\right) + D\cos\left(\frac{2\pi c}{\lambda}t\right) \qquad \text{... [2.17 (b)]}$$

Two points have to be noted here. First, there are several other functions that would satisfy the Equation (2.14). For example, function

$$\psi(x) = A\exp\left(\frac{2\pi ix}{\lambda}\right) \text{ or } \psi(x) = A\exp\left(-\frac{2\pi ix}{\lambda}\right)$$

would be quite suitable. But, these two exponential functions are not independent of the trigonometric functions in view of the following trigonometric theorem,

$$\exp(\pm ikx) = \cos kx \pm i\sin kx \qquad \text{... (2.18)}$$

Any complex exponential function can be expressed in terms of trigonometric functions and vice-versa.

Second, for a given value of the constants A and B, the function described by Equation (2.16) is a single wave with wavelength λ. On altering the ratio of A to B, the wave shifts to the left or right with respect to the origin. For example, for A = 1 and B = 0, $\psi(x) = \sin\left(\frac{2\pi x}{\lambda}\right)$ which shows no displacement ($\psi = 0$) at $x = 0$ (origin). On the other hand, for A = 0 and B = 1, $\psi = \cos\left(\frac{2\pi}{\lambda}x\right)$ which shows maximum displacement at $x = 0$.

2.4.2 Stationary Waves in a Clamped String

Waves described by Fig. 2.4 or Equation (2.10) are called running waves for which ψ is also a function of time. However, waves of interest to us, *i.e.*, electron waves in atoms and molecules are of stationary type for which ψ does not change with time. The classical example of a stationary wave is the wave in a vibrating string which is clamped at two points.

Writing ψ for $\psi(x)$, we may write Equation (2.14) as,

$$\frac{d^2\psi}{dx^2} = -\frac{4\pi^2}{\lambda^2}\psi \left(\text{because } \frac{k}{c} = \frac{2\pi}{\lambda c}\right) \quad \text{... (2.14)}$$

This equation can be used to predict the nature of stationary waves in a string that is clamped at $x = 0$ and $x = \text{L}$ which means that the string is not allowed to vibrate at these points, *i.e.*,

$$\psi = 0 \text{ at } x = 0 \text{ or L} \quad \text{... (2.19)}$$

Conditions like Equation (2.19) are called boundary conditions. The condition that $\psi = 0$ at $x = 0$ gives,

$$0 = \text{A} \sin\left(\frac{2\pi}{\lambda}\cdot 0\right) + \text{B} \cos\left(\frac{2\pi}{\lambda}\cdot 0\right) = \text{B}$$

Thus, the first boundary condition forces B to be zero. The condition that $\psi = 0$ at $x = \text{L}$ gives,

$$0 = \text{A} \sin\left(\frac{2\pi}{\lambda}\cdot \text{L}\right)$$

This may be satisfied in two ways:

(*i*) A = 0, but then ψ would be zero for all values of x, *i.e.*, there will be no wave at all; this solution is trivial.

(*ii*) $\frac{2\pi}{\lambda}\cdot \text{L} = n\pi$, n being 0, ± 1, ± 2, ± 3,...

or
$$\lambda = \frac{2\text{L}}{n} \text{ or } \nu = \frac{nc}{2\text{L}}$$

This has two important implications:

(*a*) Only certain frequencies $\nu = \frac{c}{2\text{L}}, \frac{2c}{2\text{L}}, \frac{3c}{2\text{L}}$ and so on of vibrations are allowed for this system; this is quantisation of frequency, the integer n being the quantum number, $n = 0$ is again trivial as it would mean $\nu = 0$, *i.e.*, no vibration. The origin of frequency quantisation lies in the boundary conditions.

(*b*) An integral number of half wavelengths just fit into the length of the string, *i.e.*, between the points at which it is clamped. This leads to the solution,

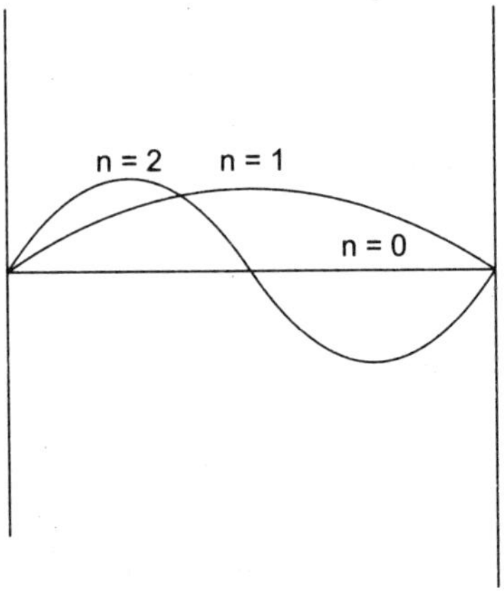

Fig. 2.5 *Quantised frequencies of vibration in a clamped string*

$$\psi = A \sin \frac{n\pi x}{L} \qquad \text{... (2.20)}$$

Some of these solutions are sketched in Fig. 2.5.

Further, since sin $(-x) = -\sin x$, the functions corresponding to positive integers n are not physically different from the set of functions corresponding to negative integers n.

The constant A in Equation (2.20) gives the maximum amplitude of the wave.

2.4.3 Stationary Waves and Nodes

Equation (2.20) shows that in the states of vibration corresponding to $n > 1$ there are points other than the boundaries where $\psi = 0$; such points are called "nodes". For $n = 2$, for example, $\psi = 0$ when $x = \frac{L}{2}$, *i.e.*, the node lies in the centre of the string; for $n = 3$, nodes exist at $x = \frac{L}{3}$ and $\frac{2L}{3}$, and so on.

In a stationary wave the nodes do not move. On the other hand, in a running wave the nodes are functions of time. For example, $\psi = A \sin (ax + bt)$ is a running wave whose node occurs at $x = \dfrac{n\pi - bt}{a}$ which is a function of time.

2.5 THE SCHRÖDINGER EQUATION FOR PARTICLE WAVES

E. Schrödinger, an Austrian scientist, argued that if particles like electrons could behave like waves, the equations of wave motion could be successfully applied to them. Schrödinger used the classical time-independent wave equation to describe the particle wave, substituting de Broglie's relation for λ. Thus, for a particle of wavelength λ moving along x-coordinate,

$$\frac{d^2\psi}{dx^2} = -\frac{4\pi^2}{\lambda^2}\psi$$

$$= -\frac{4\pi^2 m^2 v^2}{h^2}\psi$$

$$= -\frac{8\pi^2 m T\psi}{h^2}, \text{(T = kinetic energy)}$$

$$= -\frac{8\pi^2 m(E - V)}{h^2}\psi \qquad \text{... (2.21)}$$

where, $\psi = \psi(x)$ represents a quantity analogous to the amplitude function in a classical wave, T is the kinetic energy, V is the potential energy and E is the total energy (= T + V) of the particle.

This is the Schrödinger equation for the particle of mass m moving in one dimension. For three-dimensional motion, the Schrödinger equation will be a partial differential equation with variables x, y and z.

$$\frac{\partial^2\psi}{\partial x^2} + \frac{\partial^2\psi}{\partial y^2} + \frac{\partial^2\psi}{\partial z^2} = -\frac{8\pi^2 m(E - V)}{h^2}\psi$$

or written briefly,

$$\nabla^2\psi = -\frac{8\pi^2 m(E - V)}{h^2}\psi \qquad \text{... (2.22)}$$

where, the symbol ∇^2 (del squared), called the Laplacian operator, stands for $\frac{\partial^2}{\partial x^2} + \frac{\partial^2}{\partial y^2} + \frac{\partial^2}{\partial z^2}$

and $\psi = \psi(x, y, z)$

The formulation of the Schrödinger equation marked the beginning of the quantum mechanics of subatomic particles.

2.5.1 Classical Equation and Schrödinger Equation

Thus, whereas in classical mechanics we have separate equations for particle motion and wave motion, in quantum mechanics we have only one equation—the Schrödinger equation in which the de Broglie relation $\lambda = \frac{h}{mv}$ acts as the link between the particle and the wave properties.

2.5.1.1 Operators

In classical mechanics, the total energy of a particle of mass m is given by

$$\frac{1}{2m}\left(p_x^2 + p_y^2 + p_z^2\right) + V = E \qquad \text{... (2.23)}$$

where, p_x, p_y and p_z are the three cartesian components of the momentum p, and V is the potential energy.

In quantum mechanics, the Schrödinger Equation (2.22) can be written as,

$$\left[-\frac{h^2}{8\pi^2 m}\left(\frac{\partial^2}{\partial x^2}+\frac{\partial^2}{\partial y^2}+\frac{\partial^2}{\partial z^2}\right)+V\right]\psi = E\psi \qquad \text{... (2.24)}$$

Had it not been for ψ, one would be tempted to write, from Equations (2.23) and (2.24),

$$\frac{1}{2m}\left(p_x^2+p_y^2+p_z^2\right) = -\frac{h^2}{8\pi^2 m}\left(\frac{\partial^2}{\partial x^2}+\frac{\partial^2}{\partial y^2}+\frac{\partial^2}{\partial z^2}\right) \qquad \text{... (2.25)}$$

This would mean putting,

$$p_x^2 = -\frac{h^2}{4\pi^2}\frac{\partial^2}{\partial x^2},\; p_y^2 = -\frac{h^2}{4\pi^2}\frac{\partial^2}{\partial y^2} \text{ and } p_z^2 = -\frac{h^2}{4\pi^2}\frac{\partial^2}{\partial z^2}$$

The important thing to note here is that while the expression on the left hand side of Equation (2.25) represents a definite physical quantity—the kinetic energy of a particle—that on the right hand side is just a symbol for a mathematical operation—the second order partial differential operator. In general, any physical quantity in classical mechanics (kinetic energy, momentum, potential energy, total energy, position, dipole moment of a molecule, etc.) can be represented in quantum mechanics by a mathematical operator.

Operator of interest in quantum chemistry are those associated with momentum, kinetic, potential and total energies, position, etc. These can be derived in a straightforward manner; for example, since,

$$p_x^2 = -\frac{h^2}{4\pi^2}\frac{\partial^2}{\partial x^2},\; i.e., \left(\frac{h}{2\pi i}\frac{\partial}{\partial x}\right)\left(\frac{h}{2\pi i}\frac{\partial}{\partial x}\right),$$

$$\therefore \qquad p_x = \left(\frac{h}{2\pi i}\frac{\partial}{\partial x}\right)$$

and so on for p_y and p_z. In classical mechanics, the quantity on the left hand side of Equation (2.23) is called the Hamiltonian. Therefore, in quantum mechanics the operator within the square brackets of Equation (2.24) is called the Hamiltonian operator with the symbol $\hat{H}$. The Schrödinger equation is, therefore, often written in a compact form as,

$$\hat{H}\psi = E\psi \qquad \text{... (2.26)}$$

where, $\hat{H}$ stands for

$$\frac{-h^2}{8\pi^2 m}\left(\frac{\partial^2}{\partial x^2}+\frac{\partial^2}{\partial y^2}+\frac{\partial^2}{\partial z^2}\right)+V$$

V is the potential energy operator and not the potential energy itself. This operator (V) is just a multiplier meaning that any function (ψ, for example) when combined with it gets multiplied by it.

The Schrödinger Equations (2.24) or (2.26) does not contain the time variable and, therefore, represents only the stationary waves. A time-dependent Schrödinger equation in which the potential energy and, hence, the Hamiltonian depends on time also exists for material particles and describes 'running' waves. The Equation (2.24) is just a special case of such a time-dependent wave equation. However, physical quantities of interest in atomic and molecular problems, *e.g.*, energy, charge density, dipole moment, etc., do not depend on time; hence, the time-independent Equation (2.24) is sufficient for the purpose.

Systems for which Hamiltonian is independent of time are called 'conservative systems'.

2.6 THE WAVE FUNCTION (ψ) AND ITS PHYSICAL MEANING

In the Schrödinger equation we have used the function ψ as a quantity analogous to amplitude in a classical wave. But the ψ is not a physically observable quantity although it can be used to determine all the observable physical quantities of the system through certain recipes. This function (ψ) is called "wave function".

A physical interpretation is given to ψ^2 (if ψ is real) or $\psi^* \psi$ (if ψ is complex and ψ^* its complex conjugate) rather than ψ itself. The product function $\psi^* \psi$ is always a real quantity (let $\psi = Ae^{ix}$, then $\psi^* = A^* e^{-ix}$ and $\psi^* \psi = A^* e^{-ix} \cdot Ae^{ix} = |A|^2$). The conventional interpretation that the square of the amplitude at a point of a classical wave represents energy density at that point is not acceptable here because energy of a microparticle is a discontinuous function (it consists of photons) while ψ, as we shall see later, must be a continuous function.

For an electromagnetic wave, Einstein interpreted ψ^2 at a point as "probability density", *i.e.*, probability per unit space of finding the photon at that point. A similar interpretation was given by Max Born to ψ^2 for a particle wave. If a particle is moving in one dimension, ψ^2 or $\psi^* \psi$ represents the probability of finding it within unit distance. Then in an infinitesimal interval dx around a point, the probability is $\psi^2\, dx$ or $\psi^* \psi\, dx$, ψ being a function of x. In three dimensional space, this probability is $\psi^2\, dx\, dy\, dz$ or $\psi^* \psi\, dx\, dy\, dz$, where $\psi = \psi\,(x, y, z)$ and it refers to the probability that the x, y and z-coordinates of the particle lie within x and $x + dx$, y and $y + dy$, and z and $z + dz$ respectively. For a system of n particles in three dimensions, each will have its own set of three coordinates—a total of $3n$ coordinates ($x_1, y_1, z_1, \ldots\ldots, x_n, y_n, z_n$). Then the probability that the particle 1 has the coordinates (x_1, y_1, z_1), particle 2 has (x_2, y_2, z_2) and so on, is given as $\psi^2\, dx_1\, dy_1\, dz_1, \ldots, dx_n\, dy_n\, dz_n$. Here $dx\, dy\, dz$, or $dx_1\, dy_1\, dz_1, \ldots, dx_n\, dy_n\, dz_n$, is called "volume element of space" and is usually given the symbol $d\tau$.

For an electron wave, an alternative and more useful interpretation of ψ^2 or $\psi^* \psi$ is given in terms of "electron density, *i.e.*, electronic charge per unit space". This arises from the concept that the electron being a wave may be supposed to behave like a cloud of negative electricity with non-uniform charge distribution.

2.6.1 Conditions for Acceptable Wave Function

The interpretation given to ψ or ψ^2 imposes certain restrictions on acceptable values of ψ.

First, the function ψ must always remain finite; an infinite value of ψ at any point would mean infinite probability of finding the particle at that point, which would be an absurdity in view of the earlier discussions.

Second, ψ must be single-valued at all points, *i.e.*, it must have one and only one value at a particular point. This restriction arises because the probability at any given point must be unambiguous.

Third, the function ψ and its first derivative must be continuous at all points, in the space specified for the system, *i.e.*, they must not change abruptly at any point for a slight change in coordinates. The continuity of $\frac{d\psi}{dx}$ means that there must not be an inflexion in the ψ vs x curve at any point. Expressed mathematically, function $\psi(x)$ is continuous at the point $x = a$ if $\underset{h \to 0}{\text{Lt}}\, \psi(a+h) = \underset{h \to 0}{\text{Lt}}\, \psi(a-h)$, where, h is an infinitesimal change in the value of x at $x = a$.

2.6.2 Condition of Normalisation of Wave Functions

If $\psi^2\, dx$ or $\psi^*\, \psi\, dx$ represents the probability of finding the particle at any point x, then the integration over the entire range of possible locations, *i.e.*, the total probability must be unity because the particle has to be somewhere within that range, *i.e.*,

$$\int \psi^2\, dx = 1 \text{ or } \int \psi^*\, \psi\, dx = 1 \qquad \text{... (2.27)}$$

If the space available is only a small length L, then

$$\int_0^L \psi^*\, \psi\, dx = 1$$

In three dimensions,

$$\int \psi^2\, d\tau = 1\ (d\tau = dx\, dy\, dz) \qquad \text{... (2.28)}$$

A wave function which satisfies an equation of the type (2.27) or (2.28) is called a normalised wave function, and this condition is called "normalisation condition", which every wave function must fulfil.

If after solving the Schrödinger equation, the wave function does not satisfy the Equation (2.27), it must be multiplied by a factor, called the normalisation factor. For example, if a function $\phi(x)$ satisfies the Schrödinger equation and if,

$$\int \phi^2\, dx = c\,(c \neq 1)$$

then the normalisation factor will be $\frac{1}{\sqrt{c}}$ and the normalised wave function will be $\frac{1}{\sqrt{c}}\phi$. [It is not difficult to see that $\frac{1}{\sqrt{c}}\phi$ will be as good a wave function as ϕ itself; see Problems 2.14 and 2.16].

2.6.3 Condition of Orthogonality

There may be many acceptable solutions to Schrödinger equation $\hat{H}\psi = E\,\psi$ for a particular system. Each wave function ψ corresponds to an energy value E. For any two wave functions ψ_i and ψ_j corresponding to the energy values E_i and E_j, respectively, the following condition must be fulfilled.

$$\int \psi_i \psi_j \, d\tau = 0 \qquad \text{... (2.29)}$$

Such a condition is called condition of "orthogonality" of the wave functions; the two functions ψ_i and ψ_j are said to be orthogonal to each other. More about the orthogonality property will be discussed in a later Chapter (see Problem 2.15).

2.6.3.1 Degeneracy

There may, however, be situations when two wave functions ψ_j and ψ_k correspond to the same energy E. This is a case of "degeneracy"; the system in such an energy state is said to be in a degenerate state. In such a situation, the degenerate wave functions ψ_j and ψ_k will not necessarily be orthogonal.

2.6.3.2 Orthonormal Set

The normalisation and orthogonality conditions may be combined as follows:

$$\int \psi_i \psi_j \, d\tau = 1, \text{ if } i = j \qquad \text{... (2.30)}$$

$$= 0, \text{ if } i \neq j$$

Wave functions satisfying the Equation (2.30) are said to form "orthonormal set of wave functions" (see Problem 2.17).

PROBLEMS

2.1. Show that the wavelength of an electron depends on the accelerating potential (V).

[**Hint:** $\frac{1}{2} mv^2 = \text{V}e, v = \text{velocity and } e = \text{electronic charge}$

$$\lambda = \frac{h}{mv} = \frac{h}{\sqrt{2m\text{V}e}} = \frac{1}{\sqrt{2\text{V}}} \times 10^{-8} \text{ cm (V in C.G.S. units)}$$

$$= \sqrt{\frac{150}{\text{V}}} \times 10^{-8} \text{ cm (V in volts)}.$$

2.2. What is the wavelength of an H^+ ion (mass = 1.7×10^{-27} kg) moving with a velocity equal to $\frac{1}{100}$th of light ?

$$\left[\textbf{Hint: } \lambda = \frac{h}{m \cdot \frac{(c)}{100}} = 13 \times 10^{-14} \text{ m } \left(c = 3 \times 10^8 \text{ m s}^{-1}\right)\right]$$

2.3. Find the wavelength of:
(*a*) An electron with kinetic energy (*i*) 1.0 eV, (*ii*) 10 eV.
(*b*) An H^+ ion with kinetic energy 1.0 eV.
(*c*) A UF_6 molecule with kinetic energy 1.0 eV.

2.4. Calculate the wavelength of an electron ($m = 9.1 \times 10^{-31}$ kg) accelerated through a potential of 100 volt.

[**Hint:** $\frac{1}{2} mv^2 = \frac{eV}{300}$, $e = 4.8 \times 10^{-10}$ e.s.u., V = volts

$$\lambda = h\left(\frac{150}{meV}\right)^{1/2} = \frac{12.27}{\sqrt{V}} \times 10^{-8} \text{ cm} = 1.227 \times 10^{-8} \text{ cm}]$$

2.5. Calculate the wavelength of an electron ($m = 9.109 \times 10^{-31}$ kg) having energy equal to 1000 eV in SI units.

[**Hint:** $\lambda = \frac{h}{p} = \frac{h}{\sqrt{2mE}}$

$$1 \text{ eV} = 1.6 \times 10^{-16} \text{ J}$$
$$= 0.39 \times 10^{-10} \text{ m} = 0.039 \text{ nm}]$$

2.6. Calculate the wavelength of an electron in an H atom in the ground state.

[**Hint:** $\text{v} = \frac{2\pi Ze^2}{hn} = 2.19 \times 10^6 \text{ ms}^{-1} \ (n = 1, Z = 1)$

$$\lambda = \frac{6.625 \times 10^{-34} \text{ Js}}{9.109 \times 10^{-31} \text{ kg} \times 2.19 \times 10^6 \text{ ms}^{-1}} = 3.32 \times 10^{-10} \text{ m}]$$

2.7. If the position of the electron ($m = 9.109 \times 10^{-31}$ kg) in H-atom could be determined with an accuracy of 0.01 nm, what would be the uncertainty in its velocity ? Comment on the result.

[**Hint:** $\Delta p_x = \frac{h}{\Delta x} = \frac{6.625 \times 10^{-34} \text{ Js}}{0.01 \times 10^{-9} \text{ m}} = 6.625 \times 10^{-23} \text{ kg ms}^{-1}$

$$= m\Delta \text{v}_x$$

or
$$\Delta \text{v}_x = \frac{6.625 \times 10^{-23} \text{ kg ms}^{-1}}{9.109 \times 10^{-31} \text{ kg}} = 0.727 \times 10^8 \text{ ms}^{-1}$$

The uncertainty in velocity is fantastically high; hence, the path of the electron (orbit) cannot be specified, *i.e.*, Bohr model is false.]

2.8. A base ball ($m = 200$ g) is moving with a velocity of 3000 cm s^{-1}. If its position is located with an uncertainty of 500 nm, what will be the uncertainty in its velocity ? Comment upon the result.

[**Hint:** $\Delta v_x = \frac{h}{m\Delta x} = \frac{6.625 \times 10^{-34}\ \text{Js}}{0.200\ \text{kg} \times 500 \times 10^{-9}\ \text{m}} = 6.625 \times 10^{-25}\ \text{ms}^{-1}$

Δv_x is negligible in comparison to v, the velocity of the ball; so, the uncertainty principle will not apply.]

2.9. Calculate the width of the spectral line resulting when an atom in an excited state of life time 10^{-10} s returns to the ground state.

$$\left[\textbf{Hint: } \Delta v = \frac{1}{\Delta t} = \frac{1}{10^{-10}} = 10^{10}\ \text{s}^{-1} = \frac{10^{10}\ \text{s}^{-1}}{3 \times 10^{8}\ \text{ms}^{-1}} = 0.0033\ \text{m}^{-1} = 0.33\ \text{cm}^{-1}\right]$$

2.10. Show that in a wave represented by $\psi = A \exp\left(\frac{2\pi i x}{\lambda}\right)$, the wavelength corresponds to one complete cycle of vibration.

$$\left[\textbf{Hint: } \psi = A \exp\left(\frac{2\pi i x}{\lambda}\right) = A\left(\cos\frac{2\pi x}{\lambda} + i \sin\frac{2\pi x}{\lambda}\right)\right.$$

Put $\frac{2\pi x}{\lambda} = \theta$; for $x = 0$, $\theta = 0$ and for $x = \lambda$, $\theta = 2\pi$, *i.e.*, one cycle is completed when x is changed by λ. The function repeates itself after an interval $\Delta x = \lambda$.]

2.11. The equation for a standing wave in a string has the form

$$\psi(x, t) = \psi(x) . \cos(\omega t),$$

(*a*) Calculate the time-averaged potential energy and kinetic energy for this motion.
(*b*) Show that $E \propto \psi^2(x)$.

$$\left[\textbf{Hint: } \text{P.E.} = -\int F\, d\psi,\ F = ma,\ a = \frac{d^2\psi(x,t)}{dt^2} = -\omega^2 \psi(x) \cos \omega t\right.$$

$$= -\omega^2 \psi(x, t)$$

or $$\text{P.E.} = -\int F\, d\psi = -\int -m\omega^2 \psi(x,t)\, d\psi = \frac{1}{2} m\omega^2 \psi^2(x,t)$$

$$= \frac{1}{2} m\omega^2 \psi^2(x) \cos^2 \omega t$$

$$\text{K.E.} = \frac{1}{2} mv^2 = \frac{1}{2} m(-\omega\psi(x) \sin \omega t)^2 = \frac{1}{2} m\omega^2 \psi^2(x) \sin^2 \omega t \quad \left(v = \frac{d\psi(x,t)}{dt}\right)$$

Hence, $$\left.E = \text{K.E.} + \text{P.E.} = \frac{1}{2} m\omega^2 \psi^2(x)\right]$$

2.12. Indicate which of the following functions are acceptable as wave functions :

(*i*) $\psi = x$, (*ii*) $\psi = x^2$, (*iii*) $\psi = \sin x$, (*iv*) $\psi = e^x$

(*v*) $\psi = e^{-x}$, (*vi*) $\psi = e^{-x^2}$, (*vii*) $\psi = \tan x$.

[**Hint:** (*i*) not acceptable, as $\psi \to \infty$ as $x \to \infty$
(*ii*) not acceptable
(*iii*) acceptable
(*iv*) not acceptable, $\psi \to \infty$ as $x \to \infty$
(*v*) not acceptable, $\psi \to \infty$ as $x \to -\infty$
(*vi*) acceptable, $\psi \to 0$ as $x \to \pm \infty$
(*vii*) not acceptable, as $\psi \to \infty$ as $x = \frac{\pi}{2}$.]

2.13. A wave function is given as $\psi = \sin x$.
(*i*) Is it acceptable?
(*ii*) Is it normalised? Explain.

$\left[\textbf{Hint: } (i) \text{ Yes, } (ii) \int \sin^2 x\, dx \neq 1.\right]$

2.14. The functions given below are defined in the interval $x = -a$ and $x = a$ as follows:
(*i*) $F_1(x) = N_1 (a^2 - x^2)$
(*ii*) $F_2(x) = N_2\, x\, (a^2 - x^2)$
(*iii*) $F_3(x) = N_3 (a^4 - x^4)$.
Assuming the value of the functions to be zero for $x < -a$ and $x > a$, calculate the normalisation constants, N_1, N_2 and N_3.

[**Hint:** (*i*) $N_1^2 \int_{-a}^{a} \left(a^2 - x^2\right)^2 dx = 1$

$$\text{or } N_1^2 \left[a^4 x - \frac{2}{3} a^2 x^3 + \frac{x^5}{5}\right]_{-a}^{a} = 1$$

$$\text{or} \quad N_1^2\, a^5 \left(2 - \frac{4}{5} + \frac{2}{5}\right) = 1$$

$$\text{or} \quad N_1 = \left(\frac{15}{16a^5}\right)^{1/2}$$

(*ii*) $N_2 = \left(\dfrac{105}{16a^7}\right)^{1/2}$

(*iii*) $N_3 = \left(\dfrac{45}{64a^9}\right)^{1/2}$]

2.15. Show that the functions $F_1(x)$ and $F_2(x)$ in the above problem are orthogonal.

$$\left[\textbf{Hint: } \int_{-a}^{a} N_1 N_2 \left(a^2 - x^2\right).x\left(a^2 - x^2\right)dx\right.$$

$$= N_1 N_2 \left[\frac{a^4 x^2}{2} - \frac{a^2 x^4}{2} + \frac{x^6}{6}\right]_{-a}^{a}$$

$$\left. = N_1 N_2 a^6 \left(\frac{1}{2} - \frac{1}{2} + \frac{1}{6} - \frac{1}{2} + \frac{1}{2} - \frac{1}{6}\right) = 0\right]$$

2.16. Show that the functions,

$$\psi = \left(\frac{1}{2\pi}\right)^{1/2}$$

$$\psi = \left(\frac{1}{\pi}\right)^{1/2} \cos nx$$

$$\psi = \left(\frac{1}{\pi}\right)^{1/2} \sin nx$$

in the interval 0 to 2π are orthogonal; n is an integer.

$$\left[\textbf{Hint: } \int_0^{2\pi} \left(\frac{1}{2\pi}\right)^{1/2} \left(\frac{1}{\pi}\right)^{1/2} \cos nx \, dx = \frac{1}{\sqrt{2\pi}} \left[\sin nx\right]_0^{2\pi} = 0\right]$$

CHAPTER 3

Quantum Mechanical Formalism

The formal treatment of quantum mechanics begins with the concept and properties of operators, eigenvalues, eigenfunctions and a set of basic postulates, also known as quantum mechanical laws and expressing the physical interpretation of the mathematical operations in a straightforward manner. Since an understanding of the properties of operators is necessary for following quantum mechanical postulates, we start with an introduction to quantum mechanical operators.

3.1 OPERATORS

An operator is a symbol for a rule for transforming a given mathematical function into another function. It has no physical meaning if written alone. For example, √ is an operator which in itself does not mean anything, but if a quantity or a number is put under it, it transforms that quantity into its square root, another quantity. Similarly, $\frac{d}{dx}$ is an operator which transforms a function into its first derivative with respect to x; for example, $\frac{d}{dx}$ transforms the function $\sin x$ into the function $\cos x$.

In general, if $\hat{A}$ denotes an operator which transforms the function $f(x)$ into the function $g(x)$, then we write $\hat{A} f(x) = g(x)$. For example,

(*i*) Let $\hat{A}$ be $\frac{d}{dx}$, and $f(x) = ax^2$; then $\hat{A} f(x) = \frac{d}{dx}\left(ax^2\right) = 2ax$, *i.e.*, $g(x) = 2ax$.

(*ii*) Let $\hat{A}$ be a and $f(x) = x^2 + c$, then $\hat{A} f(x) = a \cdot (x^2 + c) = ax^2 + ac$, *i.e.*, $g(x) = ax^2 + ac$.

3.1.1 Algebra of Operators

Although operators do not have any physical meaning, they can be added, subtracted, multiplied, and have some other properties.

3.1.1.1 Addition and Subtraction

The addition or subtraction of operators yields new operators, the sum or the difference of operators being defined by,

$$(\hat{A} \pm \hat{B})\, f(x) = \hat{A} f(x) \pm \hat{B} f(x)$$

For example, let $\hat{A}$ be $\log_e$ and $\hat{B}$ be $\frac{d}{dx}$, and $f(x)$ be x^2; then,

$$(\hat{A} \pm \hat{B})\, f(x) = \left(\log_e \pm \frac{d}{dx}\right) x^2 = \log_e x^2 \pm \frac{d}{dx}(x^2)$$

$$= 2 \log_e x \pm 2x = \hat{A} f(x) + \hat{B} f(x).$$

3.1.1.2 Multiplication

Multiplication of two operators means operations by the two operators one after the other, the order of operation being from right to left; for example, $\hat{A}\hat{B} f(x)$ means that the function $f(x)$ is first operated on by $\hat{B}$ to yield a new function $g(x)$ which is then operated on by $\hat{A}$ to yield the final function $h(x)$.

$$\hat{A}\hat{B} f(x) = \hat{A}\left[\hat{B} f(x)\right] = \hat{A} g(x) = h(x)$$

For example, let $\hat{A}$ be $4x^2$, $\hat{B}$ be $\frac{d}{dx}$, and $f(x) = ax^3$, then,

$$\hat{A}\hat{B} f(x) = 4x^2 \cdot \frac{d}{dx}\left(ax^3\right) = 4x^2 \cdot \left(3ax^2\right) = 12ax^4$$

The square of an operator means that the same operator is applied successively twice, *i.e.*, $\hat{A}^2 f(x) = \hat{A}\hat{A} f(x)$. For example,

let $$\hat{A} = \frac{d}{dx} \text{ and } f(x) = \sin x, \text{ then } \hat{A}^2 f(x) = \left(\frac{d}{dx}\right)^2 \sin x$$

or $$\frac{d^2}{dx^2}(\sin x) = \frac{d}{dx}\left[\frac{d}{dx}(\sin x)\right] = \frac{d}{dx}(\cos x) = -\sin x.$$

3.1.2 Commutative Property

When a series of operations are performed on a function successively the result depends on the sequence in which the operations are performed; in other words, in operator algebra it is not necessary that $\hat{A}\hat{B} f(x) = \hat{B}\hat{A} f(x)$. For example, let $\hat{A}$ denote $\frac{d}{dx}$, $\hat{B}$ stand for $3x^2$ and the function $f(x)$ be $\sin x$; then,

$$\hat{A}\hat{B}f(x) = \frac{d}{dx}\left[3x^2 . (\sin x)\right] = \frac{d}{dx}\left(3x^2 \sin x\right) = 6x \sin x + 3x^2 \cos x \text{ and}$$

$$\hat{B}\hat{A}f(x) = 3x^2 \cdot \frac{d}{dx}\left(\sin x\right) = 3x^2 \cos x.$$

If two operators are such that the result of their successive applications is the same irrespective of the order of operations then the two operators are said to be *commutative.* In the above example, the two operators are non-commutative.

Now let $\hat{A}$ be $\frac{d}{dx}$ and $\hat{B}$ be $\frac{d^2}{dx^2}$ and $f(x) = \sin x$

$$\hat{A}\hat{B}f(x) = \frac{d}{dx}\left(\frac{d^2}{dx^2}\sin x\right) = -\cos x$$

$$\hat{B}\hat{A}f(x) = \frac{d^2}{dx^2}\left(\frac{d}{dx}\sin x\right) = -\cos x$$

Here $\hat{A}$ and $\hat{B}$ commute.

The significance of the commuting operators, as will be seen later, lies in the fact that the "observables" corresponding to their eigenvalues can be determined precisely simultaneously.

3.1.3 Commutator Operator

If two operators $\hat{A}$ and $\hat{B}$ do not commute then $\hat{A}\hat{B} - \hat{B}\hat{A}$ is called 'commutator'. Let $\hat{A} = \hat{p}_x$ (linear momentum operator) and $\hat{B} = \hat{x}$ (position operator) and a function be $f(x)$. Then,

$$[\hat{p}_x, \hat{x}]f(x) = \frac{h}{2\pi i}\cdot\frac{d}{dx}\left[x \cdot f(x)\right] = \frac{h}{2\pi i}\left[f(x) + x f'(x)\right]$$

$$[\hat{x}, \hat{p}_x]f(x) = x \cdot \frac{h}{2\pi i}\frac{d}{dx}f(x) = \frac{h}{2\pi i}. x f'(x)$$

$$[\hat{p}_x, \hat{x} - \hat{x}, \hat{p}_x]f(x) = \frac{h}{2\pi i}f(x)$$

Therefore, the commutator is $[\hat{p}_x, \hat{x} - \hat{x}, \hat{p}_x] = \frac{h}{2\pi i}$.

This means that $\hat{p}_x$ and $\hat{x}$ do not commute and it is not possible to determine precise values of the position and momentum of a particle simultaneously, quite in line with the principle of uncertainty.

3.1.4 Linear Operator

An operator $\hat{A}$ is said to be linear if its application on the sum of two functions gives the result which is equal to the sum of the operations on the two functions separately, *i.e.*, if

$$\hat{A}[f(x)+g(x)] = \hat{A}f(x)+\hat{A}g(x)$$

or

$$\hat{A}Cf(x) = C\cdot\hat{A}f(x), C = \text{constant}$$

Example: (*i*) $\frac{d}{dx}$ is a linear operator because $\frac{d}{dx}\left(ax^m + bx^n\right)$

$$= \frac{d}{dx}\left(ax^m\right) + \frac{d}{dx}\left(bx^n\right).$$

(*ii*) $\sqrt{}$ (square root), is not a linear operator because

$$\sqrt{f(x)+g(x)} \neq \sqrt{f(x)} + \sqrt{g(x)}.$$

3.1.5 The Operator ∇ and ∇^2

So far we have given the examples of simple one-dimensional operators, *viz.*, $\frac{d}{dx}$, $4x$, etc., which operate on functions of a single variable like $f(x)$ or $f(x) + g(x)$. But there may be two or three-dimensional operators which operate on functions of more than one variable, *i.e.*, $f(x, y, z)$. Thus, the operator $\frac{\partial}{\partial x} + \frac{\partial}{\partial y} + \frac{\partial}{\partial z}$ when applied to a function f, where f stands for $f(x, y, z)$, gives the result,

$$\left(\frac{\partial}{\partial x} + \frac{\partial}{\partial y} + \frac{\partial}{\partial z}\right)f = \frac{\partial f}{\partial x} + \frac{\partial f}{\partial y} + \frac{\partial f}{\partial z}$$

A very important differential operator, known as "del" or ∇-operator, or a vector operator, is defined as,

$$\nabla = \vec{i}\,\frac{d}{dx} + \vec{j}\,\frac{d}{dy} + \vec{k}\,\frac{d}{dz} \qquad \text{...(3.1)}$$

where, $\vec{i}, \vec{j}$ and $\vec{k}$ are unit vectors along the x, y and z-axes (see section 3.4.2). This is a vector operator in the sense that when applied to a scalar function it transforms it into its gradient which is a vector

$$\nabla f = \vec{i}\,\frac{\partial f}{\partial x} + \vec{j}\,\frac{\partial f}{\partial y} + \vec{k}\,\frac{\partial f}{\partial z} \qquad \text{...(3.2)}$$

The square of the ∇-operator, ∇^2, also called Laplacian operator, is defined as

$$\nabla^2 = \frac{\partial^2}{\partial x^2} + \frac{\partial^2}{\partial y^2} + \frac{\partial}{\partial z^2} \qquad \text{...(3.3)}$$

3.2 EIGENVALUES AND EIGENFUNCTIONS

If an operator $\hat{A}$ operates on a well-behaved (*i.e.*, finite, continuous and single-valued) function f to give the same function but multiplied by a constant, then the constant is called the "eigenvalue" of the operator and the function f is called the "eigenfunction". The equation is called "eigenvalue equation". For example, if the function $f = e^{-ax}$ is acted upon by the operator $\frac{d}{dx}$, the result is $\frac{d}{dx}\left(e^{-ax}\right) = -a\,(e^{-ax})$. Therefore, $(-a)$ is the eigenvalue and e^{-ax} is the eigenfunction of the operator $\frac{d}{dx}$.

[**Exercises:** (*i*) Show that sin 2*x* is not an eigenfunction of the operator $\frac{d}{dx}$ but of $\frac{d^2}{dx^2}$; what is the eigenvalue ?

$$\frac{d}{dx}(\sin 2x) = 2 \cos 2x$$

$$\frac{d^2}{dx^2}(\sin 2x) = -4\,(\sin 2x)$$

The eigenvalue is -4.

(*ii*) Show that if ψ is an eigenfunction of a linear operator $\hat{A}$ with an eigenvalue λ, then $C\,\psi$, where C is an arbitrary constant, is also an eigenfunction of $\hat{A}$ with the same eigenvalue.

$$\hat{A}\psi = \lambda\psi$$

Since $\hat{A}$ is linear, $\hat{A}\,(C\,\psi) = C\,.\,\hat{A}\,\psi = C\,.\,\lambda\,\psi = \lambda\,(C\,\psi)$ (C and λ are just numbers).]

3.2.1 Hermitian Property of Operators

It is very important to note that a quantum mechanical operator satisfies the following condition known as Hermitian condition:

"If an operator $\hat{A}$ has two eigenfunctions ψ and ϕ, and if

$$\int \psi\left(\hat{A}\phi\right) d\tau = \int \left(\hat{A}\psi\right).\phi\, d\tau, \qquad \text{... (3.4)}$$

when ψ and ϕ are real,

or

$$\int \psi^*\left(\hat{A}\phi\right) d\tau = \int \left(\hat{A}\psi\right)^*.\phi\, d\tau, \qquad \text{... (3.5)}$$

when ψ and ϕ are complex, ψ^* is the complex conjugate of ψ and $d\tau$ is the volume element of space in which the function is defined, then the operator $\hat{A}$ is called Hermitian operator."

[**Exercise:** Examine if $\frac{d^2}{dx^2}$ is a Hermitian operator.

Let $\psi = e^{ix}$ and $\phi = \sin x$ be the two acceptable eigenfunctions. Then,

$$\int \psi^* (\hat{A}\phi)\, d\tau = \int e^{-ix} \frac{d^2}{dx^2} (\sin x)\, dx = -\int e^{-ix} \sin x\, dx$$

$$\int \phi (\hat{A}\psi)^*\, d\tau = \int \sin x \left[\frac{d^2}{dx^2} (e^{ix})^* \right] dx = \int \sin x \,(i^2 e^{ix})^*\, dx$$

$$= -\int \sin x\, e^{-ix}\, dx$$

The two integrals are the same; therefore, $\frac{d^2}{dx^2}$ is Hermitian.]

Operators of interest in chemistry are Hermitian.

3.2.1.1 Properties of a Hermitian Operator

There are two very important characteristics of a Hermitian operator: (*i*) The eigenvalues are real (positive or negative) and (*ii*) Eigenfunctions corresponding to different eigenvalues are orthogonal to each other.

These two important theorems about Hermitian operators can be proved easily as follows:

(*i*) *Eigenvalues of a Hermitian operator are real.*

Let $\hat{A}$ be a Hermitian operator, ψ its eigenfunction and λ is the eigenvalue; then,

$$\hat{A}\psi = \lambda \psi \text{ and also } (\hat{A}\psi)^* = \lambda^* \psi^*$$

Multiplying the first equation by ψ^* and the second by ψ, and then integrating

$$\int \psi^* \hat{A}\psi\, d\tau = \int \psi^* \lambda \psi\, d\tau = \lambda \int \psi^* \psi\, d\tau$$

and $$\int \psi (\hat{A}\psi)^*\, d\tau = \int \psi \lambda^* \psi^*\, d\tau = \lambda^* \int \psi \psi^*\, d\tau$$

But since $\hat{A}$ is Hermitian,

$$\int \psi^* (\hat{A}\psi)\, d\tau = \int \psi (\hat{A}\psi)^*\, d\tau$$

Therefore, $$\lambda \int \psi^* \psi\, d\tau = \lambda^* \int \psi \psi^*\, d\tau$$

or $$\lambda = \lambda^*, \text{ i.e., } \lambda \text{ is real.} \qquad \text{... (3.6)}$$

(*ii*) *Eigenfunctions of a Hermitian operator corresponding to different eigenvalues are orthogonal.*

Let ψ_1 and ψ_2 be two eigenfunctions of a Hermitian operator $\hat{A}$ corresponding to two eigenvalues λ_1 and λ_2 respectively. The condition of orthogonality is,

$$\int \psi_1 \psi_2\, d\tau = 0 \quad \text{or} \quad \int \psi_1 \psi_2^*\, d\tau = 0$$

or $$\int \psi_1^* \psi_2 \, d\tau = 0$$

The eigenvalue equations are :

$$\hat{A}\psi_1 = \lambda_1 \psi_1 \quad \text{... (3.7)}$$

$$\hat{A}\psi_2 = \lambda_2 \psi_2 \quad \text{... (3.8)}$$

Multiplying Equation (3.7) by ψ_2^* and integrating,

$$\int \psi_2^* \hat{A} \psi_1 \, d\tau = \int \psi_2^* \lambda_1 \psi_1 \, d\tau = \lambda_1 \int \psi_2^* \psi_1 \, d\tau$$

But since $\hat{A}$ is Hermitian,

$$\int \psi_2^* \hat{A} \psi_1 \, d\tau = \int \psi_1 \left(\hat{A}\psi_2\right)^* d\tau = \int \psi_1 \left(\lambda_2 \psi_2\right)^* d\tau$$

$$= \lambda_2^* \int \psi_1 \psi_2^* \, d\tau$$

$$= \lambda_2 \int \psi_1 \psi_2^* \, d\tau \quad \text{... (by 3.6)}$$

Thus, $$\lambda_1 \int \psi_2^* \psi_1 \, d\tau = \lambda_2 \int \psi_1 \psi_2^* \, d\tau$$

or $$(\lambda_1 - \lambda_2) \int \psi_1 \psi_2^* \, d\tau = 0$$

But $$\lambda_1 \neq \lambda_2, \int \psi_1 \psi_2^* \, d\tau = 0 \quad \text{... (3.9)}$$

If, however, $\lambda_1 = \lambda_2$ (*i.e.*, ψ_1 and ψ_2 are degenerate), then the integral $\int \psi_1 \psi_2^* \, d\tau$ need not be zero, *i.e.*, ψ_1 and ψ_2 may not be orthogonal.

3.2.1.2 Schmidt Orthogonalisation Process

However, we can always construct an orthogonal pair ϕ_1 and ϕ_2 by taking suitable linear combinations of ψ_1 and ψ_2 as shown below.

Let ψ_1 and ψ_2 be the two linearly independent degenerate functions which are normalised but not orthogonal. Let $\phi_1 = \psi_1$ and $\phi_2 = a_1 \psi_1 + a_2 \psi_2$. Let $\int \psi_1 \psi_2 \, d\tau = S$, the task is then to determine a_1 and a_2, such that

$$\int \phi_1 \phi_2 \, d\tau = 0$$

and $$\int \phi_2^2 \, d\tau = 1$$

or $$\int \psi_1 (a_1 \psi_1 + a_2 \psi_2) \, d\tau = 0$$

or $$a_1 \int \psi_1^2 \, d\tau + a_2 \int \psi_1 \psi_2 \, d\tau = 0$$

or $$a_1 + a_2 S = 0$$

or $$a_1 = -a_2 S \qquad ...(3.10)$$

$$\int (a_1 \psi_1 + a_2 \psi_2)^2 \, d\tau = 1$$

or $$a_1^2 \int \psi_1^2 \, d\tau + a_2^2 \int \psi_2^2 \, d\tau + 2a_1 a_2 \int \psi_1 \psi_2 \, d\tau = 1$$

or $$a_1^2 + a_2^2 + 2a_1 a_2 S = 1 \qquad ...(3.11)$$

Substituting for a_1 in Equation (3.11), we get

$$a_2^2 S^2 + a_2^2 - 2a_2^2 S^2 = 1$$

or $$a_2 = (1 - S^2)^{-1/2} \qquad ...(3.12)$$

Therefore, $$a_1 = -S\left(1 - S^2\right)^{-1/2} \qquad ...(3.13)$$

The desired orthogonal pair will be

$$\phi_1 = \psi_1$$

$$\phi_2 = a_1 \psi_1 + a_2 \psi_2 = -S(1 - S^2)^{-1/2} \psi_1 + (1 - S^2)^{-1/2} \psi_2$$

$$= (1 - S^2)^{-1/2} (\psi_2 - \psi_1 S) \qquad ...(3.14)$$

This is called "Schmidt orthogonalisation" process.

Eigenfunctions of a Hermitian operator form a complete orthonormal set.

A series of functions $\psi_1, \psi_2, ...,$ which are subject to certain restrictions (*e.g.*, finiteness, single-valuedness, continuity, boundary conditions), is said to form a complete set if any arbitrary function F having the same restrictions can be expressed as a linear combination of these functions,

$$F = a_1 \psi_1 + a_2 \psi_2 + ... = \sum_i a_i \psi_i \quad (i = 1, 2, ...) \qquad ...(3.15)$$

The proof of this relation exists, but it is difficult and will not be given here.

3.3 BASIC POSTULATES OF QUANTUM MECHANICS

There is no unique set of postulates. However, some very important ones which briefly provide mathematical language and formalism to quantum mechanics are stated below:

3.3.1 Postulate I

"The state of a microsystem is described in terms of a function of position coordinates and time, called wave function ψ."

This postulate follows from the quantum mechanical concept of state based on experiments and expresses an act of faith in quantum mechanics by asserting that the ψ-function contains all the information that can be obtained about the system.

3.3.2 Postulate II

To every 'observable', *i.e.*, a quantity that can be experimentally measured (*e.g.*, position, momentum, energy etc.), there corresponds a quantum mechanical operator. The operators corresponding to the above quantities are listed in Table 3.1 below.

TABLE 3.1 Quantum Mechanical Operators Corresponding to Various Physical Quantities

Physical Quantity	*Quantum Mechanical Operator*
Position (x)	x
Position (r)	r
x-Component of momentum (p_x)	$\frac{h}{2\pi i}\frac{\partial}{\partial x}$
Momentum (p)	$\frac{h}{2\pi i}\nabla$
Kinetic energy (T)	$-\frac{h^2}{8\pi^2 m}\nabla^2$
x-Component of K.E. (T_x)	$-\frac{h^2}{8\pi^2 m}\frac{\partial^2}{\partial x^2}$
Potential energy (V)	V
Total energy (H)	$-\frac{h^2}{8\pi^2 m}\nabla^2 + V$

3.3.2.1 *Rules for Setting up Quantum Mechanical Operators*

(*i*) Operator for a coordinate of position (say x) is the multiplier $x.$, where the dot stands for multiplication.

(*ii*) Operator for a coordinate of momentum, say p_x is $\frac{h}{2\pi i}\frac{d}{dx}$, where $i = \sqrt{-1}$.

(*iii*) For any other physical quantity we have to write its expression in terms of coordinates of position (x, y and z) and of momenta (p_x, p_y and p_z), and then replace these coordinates by their operators.

Take for example the kinetic energy (T_x) of a single particle moving in one direction (x).

$$T_x = \frac{1}{2} m v_x^2 = \frac{p_x^2}{2m}$$

Therefore, the K.E. operator

$$\hat{T}_x = \frac{1}{2m}\left(\frac{h}{2\pi i}\frac{\partial}{\partial x}\right)^2$$

$$= -\frac{h^2}{8\pi^2 m}\frac{\partial^2}{\partial x^2} \quad \text{... (3.16)}$$

Similarly, potential energy operator $\hat{V}(x) = V(x)$. The total energy (H) is $\frac{P_x^2}{2m} + V(x)$; hence, the total energy operator

$$\hat{H} = -\frac{h^2}{8\pi^2 m}\frac{d^2}{dx^2} + V(x). \qquad \text{... (3.17)}$$

3.3.3 Some Operators of Interest

3.3.3.1 Momentum Operator

The kinetic, potential and total energies are derived from coordinates of momentum and position. But how is momentum operator to be derived ? This is done by using a more fundamental property of electron wave itself. For an electron wave the wave function may be represented by the function,

$$\psi = A \exp\left(\pm \frac{2\pi i x}{\lambda}\right) \qquad \text{... (3.18)}$$

Differentiating with respect to x,

$$\frac{d\psi}{dx} = \pm \frac{2\pi i}{\lambda}\left(A \exp\left(\pm 2\pi i x/\lambda\right)\right) = \pm \frac{2\pi i}{\lambda}\psi$$

But by de Broglie relationship,

$$\lambda = \frac{h}{p_x}$$

Therefore,

$$\frac{d\psi}{dx} = \pm \frac{2\pi i}{h} p_x \psi$$

or

$$p_x \psi = \pm \frac{h}{2\pi i}\frac{d\psi}{dx} \qquad \text{... (3.19)}$$

But ψ is a function which on being removed from the equation reduces it to a differential operator,

$$\hat{p}_x = \pm \frac{h}{2\pi i}\frac{d}{dx} \qquad \text{... (3.20)}$$

The operator p_x in the $+x$ direction is $\frac{h}{2\pi i}\frac{d}{dx}$ and in the $-x$ direction it is $-\frac{h}{2\pi i}\frac{d}{dx}$.

3.3.3.2 Hamiltonian Operator

The operator corresponding to the total energy of a system, written as a sum of kinetic and potential energies, is called Hamiltonian operator $(\hat{H})$. The total energy of a single particle of mass m is

$$H = \frac{p^2}{2m} + V(x, y, z) = \frac{1}{2m}\left(P_x^2 + P_y^2 + P_z^2\right) + V \qquad ...(3.21)$$

where, V is written for V (x, y and z).

The corresponding operator will, therefore, be

$$\hat{H} = \frac{1}{2m}\left(\hat{p}_x^2 + \hat{p}_y^2 + \hat{p}_z^2\right) + \hat{V}$$

But $$\hat{p}_x^2 = \left(\frac{h}{2\pi i}\frac{\partial}{\partial x}\right)\left(\frac{h}{2\pi i}\frac{\partial}{\partial x}\right) = -\frac{h^2}{4\pi^2}\frac{\partial^2}{\partial x^2};$$

similarly, $$\hat{p}_y^2 = -\frac{h^2}{4\pi^2}\frac{\partial^2}{\partial y^2} \text{ and } \hat{p}_z^2 = -\frac{h^2}{4\pi^2}\frac{\partial^2}{\partial z^2}$$

Thus, $$\hat{H} = -\frac{h^2}{8\pi^2 m}\left(\frac{\partial^2}{\partial x^2} + \frac{\partial^2}{\partial y^2} + \frac{\partial^2}{\partial z^2}\right) + \hat{V}$$

$$= -\frac{h^2}{8\pi^2 m}\nabla^2 + \hat{V} \qquad ...(3.22)$$

For a system of n particles,

$$\hat{H} = -\frac{h^2}{8\pi^2}\sum_i \frac{1}{m_i}\nabla_i^2 + \hat{V} \qquad ...[3.22\,(a)]$$

where, m_i is the mass and ∇_i^2 the Laplacian operator of the ith particle.

3.3.3.3 *Angular Momentum Operator*

The angular momentum (L) is a very important physical quantity for rotating systems. Classically, it is given by the vector product (see section 3.4.3.2) of position $(\vec{r})$ and linear momentum $(\vec{p})$,

$$\vec{L} = \vec{r} \times \vec{p} \qquad ...(3.23)$$

If $\vec{i}, \vec{j}$ and $\vec{k}$ are unit vectors along x, y and z-coordinates respectively, we have

$$\vec{r} = \vec{i}x + \vec{j}y + \vec{k}z,$$

and $$\vec{p} = \vec{i}p_x + \vec{j}p_y + \vec{k}p_z$$

Therefore, $$\vec{L} = \left(\vec{i}x + \vec{j}y + \vec{k}z\right) \times \left(\vec{i}p_x + \vec{j}p_y + \vec{k}p_z\right)$$

$$= \vec{i}\left(yp_z - zp_y\right) + \vec{j}\left(zp_x - xp_z\right) + \vec{k}\left(xp_y - yp_x\right) \qquad \text{(See Appendix 4)}$$

Also, by definition,

$$\vec{L} = \vec{i}L_x + \vec{j}L_y + \vec{k}L_z \qquad ...(3.24)$$

where, L_x, L_y and L_z represent the three components of L. Replacing p_x, p_y and p_z by their corresponding operators we obtain the operators for the three components of angular momentum. Thus,

$$\left.\begin{aligned}\hat{L}_x &= \left(y\hat{p}_z - z\hat{p}_y\right) = \frac{h}{2\pi i}\left(y\frac{\partial}{\partial z} - z\frac{\partial}{\partial y}\right)\\ \hat{L}_y &= \left(z\hat{p}_x - x\hat{p}_z\right) = \frac{h}{2\pi i}\left(z\frac{\partial}{\partial x} - x\frac{\partial}{\partial z}\right)\\ \hat{L}_z &= \left(x\hat{p}_y - y\hat{p}_x\right) = \frac{h}{2\pi i}\left(x\frac{\partial}{\partial y} - y\frac{\partial}{\partial x}\right)\end{aligned}\right\} \quad \text{... (3.25)}$$

3.3.4 Postulate III

The possible values of any physical quantity of a system (*e.g.*, energy, angular momentum etc.) are given by the eigenvalues a in the operator equation,

$$\hat{A}\psi = a\psi \quad \text{... (3.26)}$$

where, $\hat{A}$ is the operator corresponding to that physical quantity and ψ is the eigenfunction. In other words, each single measurement of a physical quantity A gives an eigenvalue a of the operator $\hat{A}$.

The eigenvalues and eigenfunctions for a system can be obtained by solving the operator equation. While the eigenfunctions and the operator may be real or complex, the eigenvalues must be real because they represent observable physical quantities. Moreover, quantum mechanical operators of interest, *e.g.*, momentum, energy, etc., are Hermitian operators which have been shown earlier to have real eigenvalues.

Consider, for example, the operator equation for momentum p_x (in one dimension),

$$\hat{p}_x\psi(x) = \frac{h}{2\pi i}\frac{d\psi(x)}{dx} = p_x\psi(x) \quad \text{... (See 3.19)}$$

This is an ordinary differential equation whose solution may be easily obtained as

$$\psi(x) = A\exp\left(\pm\frac{2\pi i p_x x}{h}\right) \quad \text{(See 3.18)}$$

where, A is a constant. Now, any value of p_x is allowed that keeps the function $\psi(x)$ well-behaved, *i.e.*, finite, single-valued and continuous. If we put $\frac{2\pi p_x}{h} = k$, then the eigenfunction of momentum operator becomes,

$$\psi = A\exp(\pm ikx) \quad \text{... (3.27)}$$

with eigenvalue

$$p_x = \frac{kh}{2\pi} \quad \text{... (3.28)}$$

3.3.4.1 Schrödinger Equation as an Eigenvalue Equation

A particularly important eigenvalue equation is the equation for energy of a system. The operator for energy E (K.E. + P.E.) is the Hamiltonian operator. For a single particle in three dimensions, the Hamiltonian is

$$\hat{H} = -\frac{h^2}{8\pi^2 m}\nabla^2 + \hat{V}(x, y \text{ and } z) \qquad \text{... (3.29)}$$

The eigenvalue equation is

$$\hat{H}\psi\ (x, y \text{ and } z) = E\,\psi\,(x, y \text{ and } z) \text{ or simply } \hat{H}\psi = E\,\psi$$

i.e.,

$$-\frac{h^2}{8\pi^2 m}\nabla^2\psi + \hat{V}\psi = E\,\psi \qquad \text{... (3.30)}$$

This is the familiar Schrödinger equation.

Since energy is a very important observable property of a system, and can often be measured experimentally, a thing of major importance in the quantum chemistry is solving of Schrödinger equation.

3.3.5 Postulate IV

The expected average (expectation) value of a physical quantity (M) of a system, whose state function is ψ, is given by

$$\overline{M} = \frac{\int \psi^* \hat{M}\psi\, d\tau}{\int \psi^* \psi\, d\tau} \qquad \text{... (3.31)}$$

$$= \int \psi^* \hat{M}\psi\, d\tau, \text{ if } \psi \text{ is normalised,}$$

where, $\hat{M}$ is the operator for M.

If ψ is an eigenfunction of $\hat{M}$ with the eigenvalue m, then

$$\overline{M} = \frac{\int \psi^* \hat{M}\psi\, d\tau}{\int \psi^* \psi\, d\tau} = \frac{\int \psi^* m\psi\, d\tau}{\int \psi^* \psi\, d\tau} = \frac{m\int \psi^* \psi\, d\tau}{\int \psi^* \psi\, d\tau} = m$$

which means that the observable M has precisely the same value as the eigenvalue m.

If ψ is not an eigenfunction of $\hat{M}$, even though $\hat{M}$ has a set of its own orthonormal eigenfunctions (φ_i), then ψ can be expressed as

$$\psi = a_1\hat{\phi}_1 + a_2\phi_2 + \ldots$$

$$\psi = \sum_i a_i\varphi_i \ (i = 1, 2, \ldots)$$

Hence,

$$\overline{M} = \int\left(\sum_i a_i\varphi_i\right)^* \hat{M}\left(\sum_i a_i\varphi_i\right) d\tau, \text{ if } \psi \text{ is normalised}$$

$$= \sum_i \sum_j a_i^* a_j \int \varphi_i^* \hat{M} \varphi_j \, d\tau$$

But $\hat{M}\varphi_j = \lambda_j \varphi_j$, where λ_j is eigenvalue corresponding to ϕ_j.

Therefore,
$$\overline{M} = \sum_i \sum_j (a_i^* a_j) \int \varphi_i^* \lambda_j \varphi_j \, d\tau$$

$$= \sum_i \sum_j (a_i^* a_j) \lambda_j \int \varphi_i^* \varphi_j \, d\tau$$

Since $\int \varphi_i^* \varphi_j \, d\tau = 0$ for $i \neq j$, (φ_i and φ_j are orthogonal)

$= 1$ for $i = j$ (φ_i and φ_j are normalised)

$$\overline{M} = \sum_i a_i^* a_i \lambda_i \text{ or } \sum_i |a_i|^2 \lambda_i$$

This expression means that each measurement of M must give one of the eigenvalues λ_i (postulate II) and the average of many such measurements is equal to $\overline{M}$. Further, $a_i^* a_i$ or $|a_i|^2$ represents the fraction of the total number of measurements that give the eigenvalue λ_i and $\sum |a_i|^2 = 1.0$. If ψ were an eigenfunction of $\hat{M}$ the result of each measurement would be an eigenvalue.

Thus the expectation value of position x, for a particle moving in one dimension, is given by

$$\bar{x} = \int_{-\infty}^{\infty} \psi^* x \psi \, dx$$

Similarly, the expected average value of momentum for the above system is,

$$\bar{p}_x = \frac{h}{2\pi i} \int_{-\infty}^{\infty} \psi^* \frac{d\psi}{dx} dx \qquad \text{... (3.32)}$$

and K.E.,
$$\overline{T}_x = -\frac{h^2}{8\pi^2 m} \int_{-\infty}^{\infty} \psi^* \frac{d^2\psi}{dx^2} dx \qquad \text{... (3.33)}$$

The limits of integration in each case will depend on the total length available for the particle's motion.

3.3.6 Postulate V

For every system, time-dependent Schrödinger equation exists which is given by,

$$\hat{H}\psi = \frac{ih}{2\pi} \frac{\partial \psi}{\partial t} \qquad \text{... (3.34)}$$

where, $\hat{H}$ is the Hamiltonian operator, ψ is a function of position (x, y and z) as well as time (t) and V is a function of position only.

Since this is a partial differential equation involving both position and time variables, it can be solved only by separating it into two differential equations, one containing position variable and the other containing time variable only. This can be done if we assume that,

$$\psi = \psi(q, t) = \psi(q) \cdot \phi(t) \qquad \text{... (3.35)}$$

where, q is the collective symbol for the three coordinates of position x, y and z; dropping q and t for simplicity,

$$\psi = \psi \, \phi$$

Then,

$$\frac{\partial \psi}{\partial q} = \varphi \frac{\partial \psi}{\partial q}$$

or

$$\frac{\partial^2 \psi}{dq^2} = \varphi \frac{\partial^2 \psi}{\partial q^2} \qquad \text{... (3.36)}$$

and

$$\frac{\partial \psi}{\partial t} = \psi \frac{\partial \phi}{\partial t} \qquad \text{... (3.37)}$$

Substituting Equations (3.35), (3.36) and (3.37) into (3.34) and dividing the resulting equation by $\psi\varphi$, we get

$$\left[-\frac{h^2}{8\pi^2 m} \cdot \frac{\partial^2 \psi}{\partial q^2} + \hat{V} \psi \right] \frac{1}{\psi} = \frac{ih}{2\pi} \frac{1}{\varphi} \cdot \frac{\partial \varphi}{\partial t} \qquad \text{... (3.38)}$$

where V is potential energy.

Now the left hand side of Equation (3.38) is independent of t and the right hand side is independent of q. Each side of this equation may be equated to a constant, say E, *i.e.*,

$$-\frac{h^2}{8\pi^2 m} \frac{\partial^2 \psi}{\partial q^2} + \hat{V} \psi = E\psi \qquad \text{... (3.39)}$$

and

$$\frac{ih}{2\pi} \frac{\partial \varphi}{\partial t} = E\varphi \qquad \text{... (3.40)}$$

Equation (3.39) is the familiar time-independent Schrödinger equation, also called the amplitude equation of the type

$$\hat{H}\psi = E\psi$$

Equation (3.40) has a solution,

$$\phi = a \exp\left(-\frac{2\pi i E t}{h} \right) \qquad \text{... (3.41)}$$

where, a is a constant.

So, the time-dependent wave function $\psi\ (q,\ t)$ is given by,

$$\psi = a\psi \exp\left(-\frac{2\pi i Et}{h}\right) \qquad \text{... (3.42)}$$

Stationary States : States for which ψ is given by Equation (3.42) are called *stationary states*. A stationary state does not imply that the particle, or particles, of the system are at rest. It is stationary in the sense that the probability density $|\psi|^2$ and the energy are independent of time as long as the state of the system is being described by the function ψ. The probability density is given by,

$$\psi\psi^* = |\psi|^2 = a\psi \exp\left(-\frac{2\pi i Et}{h}\right) \cdot a^* \psi^* \exp\left(\frac{2\pi i Et}{h}\right)$$

$$= aa^* \psi\psi^* \qquad \text{... (3.43)}$$

which is independent of time. Thus, we see that the factor $\exp\left(-\frac{2\pi i Et}{h}\right)$ is of no significance and the essential part of the state function for a stationary state is the time-independent wave function ψ.

A knowledge of stationary states is of prime importance in understanding chemical problems. If the state of a system corresponds to one of these stationary states, every physical property of the system *e.g.*, energy, charge density, dipole moment, etc., will be independent of time. Atomic and molecular spectra arise due to transitions between these stationary states brought about by the action of radiation.

3.3.7 Some Typical Theorems Relating to Basic Postulates

(*i*) If two operators commute, then it is possible to find out a set of functions that are simultaneously the eigenfunctions of both the operators.

Suppose ψ is an eigenfunction of operator $\hat{A}$ with eigenvalue λ, and $\hat{B}$ is another operator that commutes with $\hat{A}$. We can write,

$$\hat{A}\left(\hat{B}\psi\right) = \hat{B}\hat{A}\psi = \hat{B}\lambda\psi = \lambda\left(\hat{B}\psi\right) \qquad \text{... (3.44)}$$

because λ is a constant. Equation (3.44) says that $\left(\hat{B}\psi\right)$ is an eigenfunction of $\hat{A}$ with the same eigenvalue λ. This is possible only if the function $\hat{B}\psi$ is obtained by multiplying ψ with a factor μ, say, *i.e.*, $\hat{B}\psi = \mu\lambda$ *i.e.*, ψ is also eigenfunction of B with eigenvalue μ.

(*ii*) A physical quantity (*e.g.*, E, p_x, etc.) of a system can be represented in quantum mechanics by its Hermitian operator. If two Hermitian operators commute, it is possible to determine accurately both the corresponding quantities simultaneously.

(*iii*) Any well behaved arbitrary function f can be expressed in terms of a complete set of eigenfunctions ϕ having the same variables, of a Hermitian operator, provided it obeys the same boundary conditions as the eigenfunction.

$$f = \sum c_i \phi_i \qquad \text{... (3.45)}$$

where, the c_i's are the linear combination coefficients of the individual ϕ_i's ; for example, the amplitude functions

$$\psi_n = A \sin \frac{n\pi x}{L}, n = 1, 2, 3, ...$$

for a vibrating string of length L (see Chapter) having the boundary condition $\psi_n = 0$ at $x = 0$ and L form a discrete but complete set and any arbitrary function $f(x)$ can be expressed as

$$f(x) = \sum_{n=1}^{\infty} c_n \,.\, A \sin\left(\frac{n\pi x}{L}\right)$$

only if $0 \leq x \leq L$.

The eigenfunctions of the momentum operator $\hat{p}_x$

$$\phi_k = e^{2\pi ikx/h}, -\infty < k < \infty$$

form a continuous but complete set; the summation has to be replaced by integration, that is

$$f(x) = \int_{-\infty}^{\infty} c_k \,.\, e^{2\pi ikx/h}\, dx$$

The discrete set of eigenfunctions of an electron in a hydrogen atom is not complete as in the ionized state it has a different and continuous set.

The coefficients c_i in Equation (3.45) can be determined as follows. Multiply both sides of the equation by a coefficient ϕ_j^* and integrate,

$$\int \phi_j^* f\, d\tau = \int \phi_j^* \sum_i c_i \phi_i\, d\tau$$

$$= \sum_i c_i \int \phi_j^* \phi_i\, d\tau = c_j \qquad [\because \text{ for } i = j,\ c_i = c_j, \text{ and } \int \phi_j^* \phi_i\, d\tau = 1$$

(normalization), and for $i \neq j$, $\int \phi_j^* \phi_i\, d\tau = 0$ (orthogonality)]

Thus, $c_j = \int \phi_j^* f\, d\tau$, and therefore,

$$f = \sum_i \left[\int \phi_j^* f\, d\tau\right] \phi_i \qquad ...(3.46)$$

3.4 MATRIX, VECTOR AND QUANTUM MECHANICS

The early development of quantum mechanics followed two very different lines. Schrödinger, to interpret the observed discreteness in the atomic phenomena, based his method on calculus using operators and wave functions. Heisenberg, on the other hand, dealt directly with collection of discrete numbers in the form of matrices and vectors. Later, it became evident that the two formulations are alternate expressions of the same mathematical structure. Schrödinger's wave functions and linear operators could be regarded as representatives of Heisenberg's vectors and matrices respectively. Both wave functions and vectors represent different states of a physical system and the principle of superposition could be applied to both through linear combination.

Matrices and vectors provide key mathematical tool in doing modern day quantum mechanical calculations. In the section below matrix methods are described to formulate rules of quantum mechanics to be used in later Chapters wherever needed.

3.4.1 Matrices

A collection of numbers arranged in p rows and q columns is called a $(p \times q)$, read as p by q, matrix. Each number is called "element of the matrix". Consider the following two equations:

$$x - y + 2z = 0$$

$$3x + y - 3z = 0$$

Here the coefficients of x, y and z constitute a 2×3 matrix which is written as

$$\begin{bmatrix} 1 & -1 & 2 \\ 3 & 1 & -3 \end{bmatrix}$$

An element in a matrix is located by specifying first its row and then its column. For example, if a matrix [A] is defined as

$$[A] = \begin{bmatrix} a_{11} & a_{12} & \cdots\cdots & a_{1j} & \cdots\cdots & a_{1q} \\ a_{21} & a_{22} & \cdots\cdots & a_{2j} & \cdots\cdots & a_{2q} \\ \vdots & \vdots & & \vdots & & \vdots \\ a_{i1} & a_{i2} & \cdots\cdots & a_{ij} & \cdots\cdots & a_{iq} \\ \vdots & \vdots & & \vdots & & \vdots \\ a_{p1} & a_{p2} & \cdots\cdots & a_{pj} & \cdots\cdots & a_{pq} \end{bmatrix}$$

then a_{ij} is one of its elements which occurs in the ith row and jth column.

The elements can be pure or algebraic numbers, real or complex. A matrix having a complex number will have conjugate matrix for example,

$$[A] = \begin{bmatrix} 1 & 2 \\ 4 & i \end{bmatrix} \text{ has conjugate } \begin{bmatrix} 1 & 2 \\ 4 & -i \end{bmatrix}.$$

A matrix can be rectangular $(p \times q)$ or square $(p \times p$ or $q \times q)$, or one containing a single row $(1 \times q)$ or a single column $(p \times 1)$. A row or column matrix is called a 'vector'.

3.4.1.1 *Determinant of a Matrix*

The array of numbers constituting a square matrix can also give the determinant of the numbers when expanded as per rules ; for example, if

* In the present text a matrix will be denoted by square brackets, in most books it is indicated by thick letters.

$$[A] = \begin{bmatrix} 1 & 2 \\ 3 & 4 \end{bmatrix}; \text{ then } \| A \| = \begin{vmatrix} 1 & 2 \\ 3 & 4 \end{vmatrix} = (1 \times 4) - (3 \times 2) = 6$$

where, [A] is matrix and $\| A \|$ is the determinant. Matrix differs from the determinant in that a matrix is an array of numbers and determinant is essentially a number. The determinants of matrices $\begin{bmatrix} 1 & 2 \\ 3 & 4 \end{bmatrix}$ and $\begin{bmatrix} 1 & 3 \\ 2 & 4 \end{bmatrix}$ are same and equal to −2 though the matrices are different.

3.4.1.2 *Diagonal Matrix*

A square matrix is said to be diagonal if all its off-diagonal elements are zero. For example,

$\begin{bmatrix} 1 & 0 & 0 \\ 0 & 2 & 0 \\ 0 & 0 & 3 \end{bmatrix}$ is a diagonal matrix.

3.4.1.3 *Unit Matrix*

A diagonal matrix whose diagonal elements are all equal to 1 is called 'unit matrix' ; for example,

$$\begin{bmatrix} 1 & 0 & 0 \\ 0 & 1 & 0 \\ 0 & 0 & 1 \end{bmatrix}$$

3.4.1.4 *Symmetric Matrix*

A square matrix is symmetric if the elements $a_{ij} = a_{ji}$, for example,

$$\begin{bmatrix} 1 & 2 & 3 \\ 2 & 1 & 4 \\ 3 & 4 & 1 \end{bmatrix}$$

3.4.2 Algebra of Matrices

Matrices can be combined (added, subtracted and multiplied). Three operations are important—addition (or subtraction), scalar multiplication and matrix multiplication.

3.4.2.1 *Addition*

Two matrices [A] and [B] can be added, provided they are of same dimensions (same number of rows and columns) by adding each individual element of [A] to the element in the corresponding position in [B] ; for example,

$$\begin{bmatrix} 1 & 2 \\ 3 & 4 \end{bmatrix} + \begin{bmatrix} 1 & 3 \\ 2 & 4 \end{bmatrix} = \begin{bmatrix} 1+1 & 2+3 \\ 3+2 & 4+4 \end{bmatrix} = \begin{bmatrix} 2 & 5 \\ 5 & 8 \end{bmatrix}$$

For subtraction, simply *+ve* is replaced by *–ve* sign.

3.4.2.2 *Scalar Multiplication*

This means multiplication of a matrix by a simple number and is accomplished by multiplying each element by that number; for example,

$$3\times\begin{bmatrix}1 & 2\\ 3 & 4\end{bmatrix}=\begin{bmatrix}3 & 6\\ 9 & 12\end{bmatrix}.$$

3.4.2.3 *Matrix Multiplication*

Two matrices [A] and [B] can be multiplied to give a product [C] in which the elements are obtained by the rule

$$c_{ij}=\sum_n a_{in}b_{nj} \qquad \text{... (3.47)}$$

where, c_{ij} is the element in the ith row and jth column of [C] and the summation extends over the elements a_{in} of all the n columns of the ith row of [A] and b_{nj} of all the n rows of the jth column of [B]. For example, let

$$[A]=\begin{bmatrix}1 & 2\\ 3 & 4\end{bmatrix} \text{ and } [B]=\begin{bmatrix}1 & 3\\ 2 & 4\end{bmatrix} \text{ and}$$

$$[A]\times[B]=[C]\text{; then,}$$

$$[C]=\begin{bmatrix}1 & 2\\ 3 & 4\end{bmatrix}\times\begin{bmatrix}1 & 3\\ 2 & 4\end{bmatrix}=\begin{bmatrix}(1\times1)+(2\times2) & (1\times3)+(2\times4)\\ (3\times1)+(4\times2) & (3\times3)+(4\times4)\end{bmatrix}.$$

$$=\begin{bmatrix}5 & 11\\ 11 & 25\end{bmatrix}$$

The elements of the new matrix [C] are obtained by the rule

$$c_{11}=a_{11}\,b_{11}+a_{12}\,b_{21}=(1\times1)+(2\times2)=5$$

$$c_{12}=a_{11}\,b_{12}+a_{12}\,b_{22}=(1\times3)+(2\times4)=11$$

and so on.

For multiplication of two matrices, the two must conform to each other, that is, the number of columns in [A] must be equal to the number of rows in [B].

It is not necessary that the product [B] × [A] be equal to [A] × [B]. In the present example,

$$[B]\,[A]=\begin{bmatrix}1 & 3\\ 2 & 4\end{bmatrix}\times\begin{bmatrix}1 & 2\\ 3 & 4\end{bmatrix}=\begin{bmatrix}10 & 14\\ 14 & 20\end{bmatrix}$$

which is not the same as [A] [B]. When [A] [B] = [B] [A] the matrices are said to be commutative. Two matrtices [C] and [D] will be equal only if $C_{ij} = D_{ij}$.

3.4.2.4 *Transpose of a Matrix* $[\tilde{A}]$

The matrix obtained by interchanging rows and columns in [A] is called the transpose $[\tilde{A}]$ of the matrix [A] ; for example, if

$$[A] = \begin{bmatrix} 1 & 2 \\ 3 & 4 \end{bmatrix}, \text{then } [\tilde{A}] = \begin{bmatrix} 1 & 3 \\ 2 & 4 \end{bmatrix}.$$

3.4.2.5 *Inverse of a Matrix* $[A]^{-1}$

The inverse $[A]^{-1}$ of the matrix [A] is defined by the relation

$$[A]\,[A]^{-1} = [A]^{-1}\,[A] = [1]$$

where, [1] is the unit matrix, or identity matrix. If [B] is the inverse of [A], then

$$[A]\,[B] = [B]\,[A] = [1]$$

A matrix can have inverse only if its determinant $\| A \| \neq 0$.

The inverse [B] of [A] can be constructed by the formula

$$[B] = [A]^{-1} = \frac{[\tilde{A}]'}{\| A \|} \qquad \text{... (3.48)}$$

where, $[\tilde{A}]'$ is the transpose of the matrix of cofactors of $\| A \|$ (for co-factors of a determinant see Appendix 3). For example, let

$$[A] = \begin{bmatrix} 1 & 2 \\ 3 & 4 \end{bmatrix}, \text{then } [\tilde{A}]' = \begin{bmatrix} 4 & -2 \\ -3 & 1 \end{bmatrix} \text{ and } |A| = -2$$

So,

$$[B] = [A]^{-1} = \frac{1}{-2}\begin{bmatrix} 4 & -2 \\ -3 & 1 \end{bmatrix} = \begin{bmatrix} -2 & 1 \\ \frac{3}{2} & -\frac{1}{2} \end{bmatrix}$$

The reader can check if $[A]\,[A]^{-1} = 1$

Matrix inversion for larger matrices is a very tedious process and is often done by computer.

3.4.2.6 *Orthogonal Matrix*

Matrix whose inverse is equal to its transpose is called orthogonal matrix, *i.e.*,

$$[A]^{-1} = [\tilde{A}];\ \text{if } [A] \text{ is orthogonal.}$$

3.4.2.7 *Conjugate Transpose*

If [A] is a complex matrix, $[A]^*$ is its complex conjugate, *e.g.*,

$$[A] = \begin{bmatrix} 1 & 2 \\ 3 & 4i \end{bmatrix}, [A]^* = \begin{bmatrix} 1 & 2 \\ 3 & -4i \end{bmatrix}$$

and the transpose of $[A]^*$ is conjugate transpose, A^+, *i.e.*,

$$A^+ = [\tilde{A}]^* = \begin{bmatrix} 1 & 3 \\ 2 & -4i \end{bmatrix}$$

3.4.2.8 *Unitary Matrix*

If the inverse of a matrix is equal to its conjugate transpose, the matrix is unitary, *i.e.*, if [U] is unitary matrix, then

$$[U]^{+} = [U]^{-1}$$

From the definition of unitary matrix

$$[U]^{+}[U] = [1] \text{ (unit matrix)}$$

This means that $\sum_k u_{ki}^{+} u_{kj} = \delta_{ij}$ (= 1 for $i = j$ and = 0 for $i \neq j$)

where, i and j are columns of a unitary matrix. In other words, the columns of a unitary, matrix are orthogonal and normalised. Conversely, if the above relation is true for all columns, then [U] is a unitary matrix. If the unitary matrix is real then $[u]^{+} = [\tilde{U}]$

3.4.2.9 *Singular and Non-Singular Matrices*

A matrix [A] is singular if its determinant $\| A \| = 0$ and non singular if $\| A \| \neq 0$. Only non-singular matrices can have inverse.

3.4.3 Vectors

An array of numbers arranged in a single row or a single column is a vector in the algebraic sense. The numbers in the row or the column are called 'elements'. Thus each row and each column of a matrix is a vector.

$$(a_1, a_2, \ldots\ldots, a_n) \qquad \begin{pmatrix} a_1 \\ a_2 \\ \vdots \\ a_n \end{pmatrix}$$

row vector

column vector

In the geometrical sense a vector has both magnitude and direction and is represented by an arrow over a symbol which stands for the array of numbers, *e.g.*, $\vec{A}^{*}$.

A physical quantity which has magnitude but no direction, *e.g.*, energy, mass, density etc., or a single number, is called 'scalar'.

It is easy to visualise a vector in a real space of two or three dimensions where it may be represented by an arrow whose length is the magnitude and direction is the direction of the vector. In cartesian coordinate system a vector $\vec{A}$ has three components A_x, A_y and A_z and the vector is represented as $\vec{A} = (A_x, A_y, A_z)$. It is related to the components through the equation

$$\vec{A} = A_x \vec{i} + A_y \vec{j} + A_z \vec{k} \qquad \ldots (3.49)$$

* In most textbooks thick letter is used in place of an overhead arrow.

where, $\vec{i}$, $\vec{j}$ and $\vec{k}$ are called 'unit vectors' *i.e.*, vectors of unit length, along the three Cartesian axes.

However, there is nothing in vector algebra to prevent a vector with n components ($n > 3$) in an n-dimensional abstract space or vector space, $\vec{A} = (A_1, A_2, \ldots\ldots, A_n)$. On the other hand, such vectors have profound use in quantum mechanics.

3.4.4 Algebra of Vectors

3.4.4.1 *Addition*

If $\vec{A} = (A_x, A_y, A_z)$

and $\vec{B} = (B_x, B_y, B_z)$, then

$$\vec{A} \pm \vec{B} = [(A_x \pm B_x), (A_y \pm B_y), (A_z \pm B_z)]$$

The two vectors $\vec{A}$ and $\vec{B}$ will be equal if $A_x = B_x$, $A_y = B_y$ and $A_z = B_z$.

The addition of two vectors may be represented geometrically in three dimensional space as follows. Let $\vec{A}$ and $\vec{B}$ be represented by two arrows (Fig. 3.1). Bring the head of $\vec{B}$ to touch the tail of $\vec{A}$ without changing the direction of the either, then draw another vector $\vec{C}$ from the tail of $\vec{B}$ to the head of $\vec{A}$, the resultant $\vec{C} = \vec{A} + \vec{B}$.

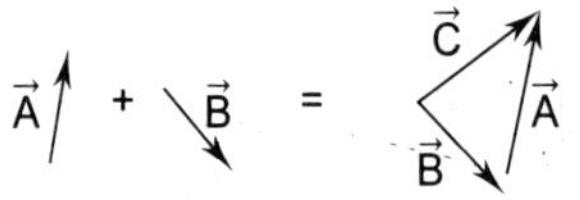

Fig. 3.1 *Addition of two vectors*

3.4.4.2 *Multiplication*

There are two types of multiplication in vector algebra—'scalar' or 'dot' multiplication and 'vector' or 'cross' multiplication.

Scalar product of two vectors is defined as

$$\vec{A} \cdot \vec{B} = |A|\ |B| \cos\theta \qquad \ldots (3.50)$$

where, $|A|$ and $|B|$ are the magnitudes of the vectors and θ is the angle between the two, all three being scalar quantities, the dot product is a scalar. If $\theta = 90°$, the product is zero and in that case the vectors will be called 'orthogonal'.

The unit vectors $\vec{i}, \vec{j}$ and $\vec{k}$ along the cartesian axes are orthogonal, *i.e.*,

$$\vec{i} \cdot \vec{j} = \vec{j} \cdot \vec{k} = \vec{k} \cdot \vec{i} = 0$$

If $\theta = 0$, we have 'normal' vectors, *i.e.*,

$$\vec{i} \cdot \vec{i} = 1,\ \vec{j} \cdot \vec{j} = 1 \text{ and } \vec{k} \cdot \vec{k} = 1$$

The product of two vectors $\vec{A} \cdot \vec{B}$ may be written analytically as

$$\vec{A}.\vec{B} = \left(A_x\vec{i} + A_y\vec{j} + A_z\vec{k}\right).\left(B_x\vec{i} + B_y\vec{j} + B_z\vec{k}\right)$$

$$= A_x B_x + A_y B_y + A_z B_z \qquad \text{... (3.51)}$$

Because in view of the 'orthonormality' of the unit vectors, six of the nine terms in the dot product are zero.

The product of $\vec{A}$ with itself ($\theta = 0$) is

$$\vec{A}.\vec{A} = |A|\,|A| \cos 0 = |A|^2$$

Also, $\qquad \vec{A}.\vec{A} = A_x^2 + A_y^2 + A_z^2$

$$|A| = \left(A_x^2 + A_y^2 + A_z^2\right)^{1/2} \qquad \text{... (3.52)}$$

$|A|$ is the 'norm' of the vector $\vec{A}$.

The scalar product applies to vectors of any dimension, for example, for n-dimensional vectors

$$\vec{A}.\vec{B} = A_1 B_1 + A_2 B_2 + \ldots\ldots + A_n B_n \qquad \text{... (3.53)}$$

where, A'_i s and B'_i s ($i = 1, 2, \ldots\ldots, n$) are the components of the vectors in the vector space.

For three dimensional vectors, there is another type of product, the vector or cross product, defined as

$$\vec{A} \times \vec{B} = |A|\,|B| \sin\theta\,.\,\vec{n} \qquad \text{... (3.54)}$$

where, $\vec{n}$ is the unit vector which makes the cross product also a vector. The product vector has the direction perpendicular to the plane defined by $\vec{A}$ and $\vec{B}$ such that the three vectors $\vec{A}$, $\vec{B}$ and $\vec{A} \times \vec{B}$ form a right-handed screw system rotating from $\vec{A}$ to $\vec{B}$. It follows that $\vec{A} \times \vec{B} = -\vec{B} \times \vec{A}$, and $\vec{A} \times \vec{A} = 0$. The unit vectors are related as

$$\vec{i} \times \vec{j} = \vec{k}, \vec{j} \times \vec{k} = i, \vec{k} \times \vec{i} = \vec{j};$$

$$\vec{j} \times \vec{i} = -\vec{k} \times \vec{j} = -\vec{i}, \vec{i} \times \vec{k} = -\vec{j};$$

Also, $\qquad \vec{i} \times \vec{i} = \vec{j} \times \vec{j} = \vec{k} \times \vec{k} = 0.$

The cross-product can also be written analytically as

$$\vec{A} \times \vec{B} = \left(A_x\vec{i} + A_y\vec{j} + A_z\vec{k}\right) \times \left(B_x\vec{i} + B_y\vec{j} + B_z\vec{k}\right)$$

$$= (A_y B_z - A_z B_y)\,\vec{i} + (A_z B_x - A_x B_z)\,\vec{j} + (A_x B_y - A_y B_x)\,\vec{i} \qquad \text{... (3.55)}$$

which can also expressed as a determinant

$$A \times B = \begin{vmatrix} \vec{i} & \vec{j} & \vec{k} \\ A_x & A_y & A_z \\ B_x & B_y & B_z \end{vmatrix}$$

$$= \vec{i}\begin{vmatrix} A_y & A_z \\ B_y & B_z \end{vmatrix} - \vec{j}\begin{vmatrix} A_x & A_z \\ B_x & B_z \end{vmatrix} + \vec{k}\begin{vmatrix} A_x & A_y \\ B_x & B_y \end{vmatrix} \qquad \text{... (3.56)}$$

3.4.4.3 Vector Operator

A vector operator, also called 'del' operator $\vec{\nabla}$ is defined as

$$\vec{\nabla} = \vec{i}\,\frac{\partial}{\partial x} + \vec{j}\,\frac{\partial}{\partial y} + \vec{k}\,\frac{\partial}{\partial z} \qquad \text{... (3.57)}$$

when applied to a scalar function it is called 'gradient' of the function and is given as

$$\text{grad } f = \vec{\nabla} f = \vec{i}\,\frac{\partial f}{\partial x} + \vec{j}\,\frac{\partial f}{\partial y} + \vec{k}\,\frac{\partial f}{\partial z} \qquad \text{... (3.58)}$$

The second order differential operator 'del square' ∇^2 becomes a scalar given as

$$\nabla^2 = \vec{\nabla}\,.\,\vec{\nabla} = \frac{\partial^2}{\partial x^2} + \frac{\partial^2}{\partial y^2} + \frac{\partial^2}{\partial z^2}. \qquad \text{... (3.59)}$$

3.5 VECTOR REPRESENTATION OF WAVE FUNCTIONS

Schrödinger equation for a one dimensional system leads to an infinite set of orthonormal wave functions defined by

$$\int \psi_m^*(x)\,\psi_n(x)\,dx = \delta_{mn} \qquad \text{... (3.60)}$$

where, $\delta_{mn} = 1$ for $m = n$ (normalised) and 0 for $m \neq n$ (orthogonal). The terms orthogonality, normalisation and orthonormality are adapted from the language of vector anlaysis. A set of M vectors $\vec{X}_1, \vec{X}_2, \ldots\ldots, \vec{X}_M$ is orthonormal if the scalar product

$$\left(\vec{X}_i\,.\,\vec{X}_j\right) = \delta_{ij}\ (= 1 \text{ for } i = j \text{ and } 0 \text{ for } i \neq j) \qquad \text{... (3.61)}$$

Orthonormal vectors, like orthonormal wave functions, are linearly independent, that is, they form coordinate bases for the vector space. Any vector $\vec{X}$ can be expressed as a linear combination of the orthonormal set of vectors,

$$\vec{X} = \sum_m a_m\,\vec{e}_m \qquad \text{... (3.62)}$$

where, a_m's are the coefficients of the linear combination (scalar quantities) and $\vec{e}_m$ is the unit vector. (In 3-dimensions, $\vec{X} = a_1\,\vec{i} + a_2\,\vec{j} + a_3\,\vec{k}$). The coefficients can be obtained from the relation

$$a_m = \left(\vec{e}_m\,.\,\vec{X}\right) \qquad \text{... (3.63)}$$

Compare with a wave function ϕ as a linear combination of orthonormal set of wave functions

$$\phi = \sum_m a_m\,\psi_m \qquad \text{... (3.64)}$$

where

$$a_{\text{m}} = \int \psi_m\,\phi\,d\tau \qquad \text{... (3.65)}$$

The analogy is complete if the wave functions ψ_m and ψ_n in Equation (3.60) are made to correspond to the vectors $\overline{X}_m$ and $\overline{X}_n$ respectively, that is, if the wave functions are regarded as vectors in a vector space of infinite dimensions.

The scalar product of two vectors $\vec{A}_m$ and $\vec{A}_n$, by definition, is given by

$$\left(\vec{A}_m \,.\, \vec{A}_n\right) = \sum_{\alpha=1}^{N} A_m(\alpha) \,.\, A_n(\alpha) \qquad \text{... (3.66)}$$

where, the $A_m(\alpha)$ and $A_n(\alpha)$ are the components of the vectors $\vec{A}_m$ and $\vec{A}_n$ respectively in the direction α and N is the dimension of the vector space (For $N = 3$, $\alpha = x, y$ and z), and where integration in section (3.6) has been replaced by summation because the integration variable x is continuous while the summation variable α is discrete.

For orthonormal vectors

$$\left(\vec{A}_m \,.\, \vec{A}_n\right) = \delta_{mn} \qquad \text{... (3.67)}$$

$$= 1 \text{ for } m = n$$

$$= 0 \text{ for } m \neq n.$$

3.6 MATRIX REPRESENTATION OF OPERATORS

A matrix may be used to represent a geometrical operation, for example rotation. Consider, for example, a vector $\vec{A}\,(x_1, y_1)$ of length r in an X-Y plane (Fig. 3.2). Let the vector be rotated clockwise through an angle θ. How to represent this rotation algebraically ?

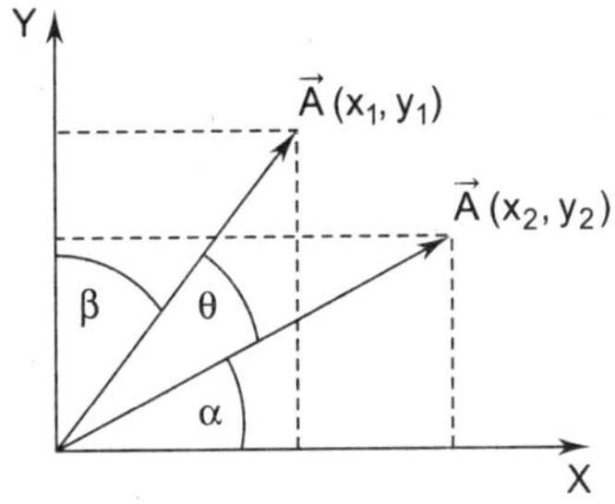

Fig. 3.2 *Rotation of a vector*

The vector has changed its direction, from the position (x_1, y_1) to (x_2, y_2) but not its length (r). Let α be the angle between the vector (x_2, y_2) and the X-axis, and β be the angle between the vector (x_1, y_1) and the Y-axis. By inspection,

$$x_2 = r\cos\alpha = r\cos[90 - (\beta + \theta)] = r\sin(\beta + \theta)$$

$$= r\sin\beta\cos\theta + r\cos\beta\sin\theta$$

$$= x_1\cos\theta + y_1\sin\theta \qquad \text{... (3.68)}$$

Similarly,

$$y_2 = -x_1\sin\theta + y_1\cos\theta \qquad \text{... (3.69)}$$

The two Equations (3.68) and (3.69) can be written as a single matrix equation as

$$\begin{pmatrix} x_2 \\ y_2 \end{pmatrix} = \begin{bmatrix} \cos\theta & \sin\theta \\ -\sin\theta & \cos\theta \end{bmatrix} \begin{pmatrix} x_1 \\ y_1 \end{pmatrix} \qquad \text{... (3.70)}$$

Hence the matrix representative of the rotation operator R is

$$\begin{bmatrix} \cos\theta & \sin\theta \\ -\sin\theta & \cos\theta \end{bmatrix}$$

For an anticlockwise rotation, the operator R^{-1} would be

$$\begin{bmatrix} \cos\theta & -\sin\theta \\ \sin\theta & \cos\theta \end{bmatrix}$$

which is just the transpose $\tilde{R}$ of R, and it can be easily seen that the matrix product

$$R^{-1}R = \tilde{R}R = \begin{bmatrix} 1 & 0 \\ 0 & 1 \end{bmatrix} \qquad \text{... (3.71)}$$

meaning no rotation. Thus we have a just parallel between the geometrical operator and matrix as well as a geometrical vector and algebraic vector.

How are quantum mechanical operators represented through matrices? A linear operator in quantum mechanics is represented by a square matrix ($n \times n$) where, n is the number of rows or columns. If $\psi_1, \psi_2, \ldots\ldots, \psi_n$ form *a* complete set of wave functions and $\hat{A}$ is the linear operator then each integral of the type $\int \psi_i \hat{A} \psi_j \, d\tau$, given the symbol A_{ij}, is an element of the matrix [A] which is constructed as

$$\begin{bmatrix} A_{11} & A_{12} & \ldots\ldots & A_{1n} \\ A_{21} & A_{22} & \ldots\ldots & A_{2n} \\ \vdots & \vdots & & \vdots \\ A_{n1} & A_{n2} & \ldots\ldots & A_{nn} \end{bmatrix} \qquad \text{... (3.72)}$$

We call this matrix a representative of the linear operator $\hat{A}$ in the complete basis set of $\{\psi_i\}$. (In principle, number of matrix elements may be infinite but in practice it is usually not).

If the basis set consists of orthonormal eigenfunctions of $\hat{A}$, the elements are

$$A_{ij} = \int \psi_i \hat{A} \psi_j \, d\tau = \int \psi_i \left(\hat{A}\psi_j\right) d\tau = \int \psi_i \left(\lambda_j \psi_j\right) d\tau$$

$$= \lambda_j \int \psi_i \psi_j \, d\tau = \lambda_j \,.\, \delta_{ij}$$

where, $\delta_{ij} = 1$ for $i = j$ and 0 for $i \neq j$, λ_j is one of the eigenvalues of the operator $\hat{A}$. This makes the matrix [A] diagonal, *i.e.*,

$$\begin{bmatrix} A_{11} & 0 & 0 & \ldots\ldots & 0 \\ 0 & A_{22} & 0 & \ldots\ldots & 0 \\ 0 & 0 & A_{33} & \ldots\ldots & 0 \\ \vdots & \vdots & \vdots & & \vdots \\ 0 & 0 & 0 & \ldots\ldots & A_{nn} \end{bmatrix} \quad \text{... (3.73)}$$

whose diagonal elements A_{jj} are the set of eigenvalues (λ_j).

Conversely, if the matrix is in diagonal form, the basis functions are orthonormal eigenfunctions of $\hat{A}$. Then the basis functions can be used to construct any arbitrary function ϕ as a linear combination function

$$\phi = \sum_i a_i \psi_i \quad \text{... (3.74)}$$

where, a_i is the coefficient of ψ_i in the linear combination determined by the formula

$$a_i = \int \psi_i \phi \, d\tau \quad \text{... (3.75)}$$

The set of coefficients $a_1, a_2, \ldots\ldots, a_i, \ldots\ldots, a_n$ can be arranged as a column vector $\vec{a}$ and then the vector $\vec{a}$ will be representative of the function ϕ in the basis $\{\psi_i\}$.

An operator $\hat{A}$ transforms a function ϕ into another function ω,

$$\hat{A}\,\phi = \omega$$

which just parallels the matrix-vector equation

$$[A]\,\vec{a} = \vec{\omega} \quad \text{... (3.76)}$$

If the transformation results in the same vector with a constant multiplied to it we have an eigenvalue equation

$$[A]\,\vec{a} = \lambda\,\vec{a} \quad \text{... (3.77)}$$

λ is eigenvalue and $\vec{a}$ is called 'eigenvector'.

Thus the effect of any linear operator $\hat{A}$ on an arbitrary function ϕ can be found if the matrix representing the operator is known.

Consider now the Schrödinger equation

$$\hat{H}\,\psi_n = E_n\,\psi_n \quad \text{... (3.78)}$$

The Hamiltonian matrix will be

$$[H] = \begin{bmatrix} H_{11} & H_{12} & \ldots\ldots & H_{1n} \\ H_{21} & H_{22} & \ldots\ldots & H_{2n} \\ \vdots & \vdots & & \vdots \\ H_{n1} & H_{n2} & \ldots\ldots & H_{nn} \end{bmatrix}$$

The set of n eigenfunctions ψ_n have eigenvectors as representatives: $\vec{a}_1, \vec{a}_2, \ldots\ldots, \vec{a}_n$ each of which is a column vector like

$$\vec{a}_1 = \begin{bmatrix} a_{11} \\ a_{21} \\ a_{31} \\ \vdots \\ a_{n1} \end{bmatrix}$$ and so on in which the first index denotes the row number and the second index the column number and the n Schrödinger equation may be written as :

$$[\mathrm{H}]\vec{a}_n = \mathrm{E}_n \vec{a}_n = \vec{a}_n \mathrm{E}_n \qquad (\because \ \mathrm{E}_n \text{ is a scalar}) \qquad \ldots (3.79)$$

However, the n equations of the type (3.79) may be written as a single matrix equation if we construct the matrix of the n eigenvectors [A]. The equation is

$$[\mathrm{H}]\,[\mathrm{A}] = [\mathrm{A}]\,[\mathrm{E}] \qquad \ldots (3.80)$$

where each column in [A] is an eigenvector, [E] is a diagonal matrix each diagonal element of which is an eigenvalue corresponding to the eigenvector of that column of [A]. The equation becomes

$$\begin{bmatrix} \mathrm{H}_{11} & \mathrm{H}_{12} & \cdots\cdots & \mathrm{H}_{1n} \\ \mathrm{H}_{21} & \mathrm{H}_{22} & \cdots\cdots & \mathrm{H}_{2n} \\ \vdots & \vdots & & \vdots \\ \mathrm{H}_{n1} & \mathrm{H}_{n2} & \cdots\cdots & \mathrm{H}_{nn} \end{bmatrix} \begin{bmatrix} a_{11} & a_{12} & \cdots\cdots & a_{1n} \\ a_{21} & a_{22} & \cdots\cdots & a_{2n} \\ \vdots & \vdots & & \vdots \\ a_{n1} & a_{n2} & \cdots\cdots & a_{nn} \end{bmatrix} = \begin{bmatrix} \mathrm{E}_1 & 0 & 0 & 0 & \cdots\cdots \\ 0 & \mathrm{E}_2 & 0 & 0 & \cdots\cdots \\ 0 & 0 & \mathrm{E}_3 & 0 & \cdots\cdots \\ \vdots & \vdots & \vdots & \vdots & \\ 0 & 0 & 0 & \vdots & \mathrm{E}_n \end{bmatrix}$$

$$\begin{bmatrix} a_{11} & a_{12} & \cdots\cdots & a_{1n} \\ a_{21} & a_{22} & \cdots\cdots & a_{2n} \\ \vdots & \vdots & & \vdots \\ a_{n1} & a_{n2} & \cdots\cdots & a_{nn} \end{bmatrix} \qquad \ldots (3.81)$$

or in abbreviated form

$$[\mathrm{H}]\,[\mathrm{A}] = [\mathrm{E}]\,[\mathrm{A}] = [\mathrm{A}]\,[\mathrm{E}] \qquad \ldots (3.82)$$

Each column of [A] is an eigenvector and the vector $\vec{a}_i$ corresponds to the eigenvalue E_i ($i = 1, 2, \ldots\ldots, n$).

The Equation (3.82) is the matrix representation of the Schrödinger Equation (3.78). The matrix [H] is known but [A] and [E] are unknown. To solve for them we search for the inverse $[\mathrm{A}]^{-1}$ of [A] and multiply both sides of the Equation (3.82) by $[\mathrm{A}]^{-1}$ from the left (matrix multiplication is not necessarily commutative, so we have to multiply both sides either from the left or from the right). This leads to

$$[\mathrm{A}]^{-1}\,[\mathrm{H}]\,[\mathrm{A}] = [\mathrm{A}]^{-1}\,[\mathrm{A}]\,[\mathrm{E}] = [\mathrm{E}] \qquad \ldots (3.83)$$

Since the matrix [E] is essentially diagonal, if the left hand side product matrix is made out to be diagonal we have the eigenvalues coming directly from the latter. The task lies in finding the unitary inverse of the [H] matrix.

PROBLEMS

3.1. What are the expressions for the following operators ?

(*a*) $\left(\frac{d}{dx}+x\right)^2$

(*b*) $\left(x\frac{d}{dx}\right)^2$

(*c*) $\left(\frac{d}{dx}x\right)^2$

[**Hint :** (*a*)
$$\left(\frac{d}{dx}+x\right)^2\psi = \left(\frac{d}{dx}+x\right)\left(\frac{d}{dx}+x\right)\psi$$
$$= \left(\frac{d}{dx}+x\right)\left(\frac{d\psi}{dx}+x\psi\right)$$
$$= \left(\frac{d^2\psi}{dx^2}+2x\frac{d\psi}{dx}+x^2\psi+\psi\right)$$
$$= \left(\frac{d^2}{dx^2}+2x\frac{d}{dx}+x^2+1\right)\psi$$

or
$$\left(\frac{d}{dx}+x\right)^2 = \left(\frac{d^2}{dx^2}+2x\frac{d}{dx}+x^2+1\right)$$

(*b*)
$$\left(x\frac{d}{dx}\right)^2\psi = \left(x\frac{d}{dx}\right)\left(x\frac{d}{dx}\right)\psi = \left(x\frac{d}{dx}\right)\left(x\frac{d\psi}{dx}\right)$$
$$= x\left(x\frac{d^2\psi}{dx^2}+\frac{d\psi}{dx}\right) = \left(x^2\frac{d^2}{dx^2}+x\frac{d}{dx}\right)\psi$$

(*c*)
$$\left(\frac{d}{dx}x\right)^2\psi = \left(\frac{d}{dx}x\right)\left(\frac{d}{dx}x\right)\psi = \left(\frac{d}{dx}x\right)\frac{d}{dx}(x\psi)$$
$$= \left(\frac{d}{dx}x\right)\left(x\frac{d\psi}{dx}+\psi\right) = \frac{d}{dx}\left(x^2\frac{d\psi}{dx}+x\psi\right)$$
$$= x^2\frac{d^2\psi}{dx^2}+2x\frac{d\psi}{dx}+\frac{d\psi}{dx}+\psi$$
$$= \left(x^2\frac{d^2}{dx^2}+2x\frac{d}{dx}+\frac{d}{dx}+1\right)\psi\Bigg].$$

3.2. Which of the following operators are linear ?

(*i*) $\hat{A}\varphi = \lambda\varphi$ $\quad$ (λ = constant)

(*ii*) $\hat{C}\varphi = \varphi^2$

(*iii*) $\hat{D}\psi = \dfrac{d\psi}{dx}$

[Hints : (*i*) $\hat{A}(\varphi + \psi) = \lambda(\varphi + \psi) = \lambda\varphi + \lambda\psi$

$$\hat{A}\ (\varphi) = \lambda\,(C\varphi) = C\lambda\varphi\,;\ \hat{A}\ \text{is linear.}$$

(*ii*) $\hat{C}\ (\varphi + \psi) = (\varphi + \psi)^2 = \varphi^2 + 2\varphi\psi + \psi^2$

But $\quad \hat{C}\varphi + \hat{C}\psi = \varphi^2 + \psi^2$

Therefore, $\hat{C}$ is not linear.

(*iii*) $\hat{D}\ (u + v) = \dfrac{du}{dx} + \dfrac{dv}{dx} = \hat{D}u + \hat{D}v$

or $\quad \hat{D}\ (Cu) = C\,\dfrac{du}{dx} = C\left(\hat{D}u\right)$

3.3. Verify that the operator ∇^2 + V, is linear.

[Hint : $\nabla^2 (u + v) = \dfrac{\partial^2 (u + v)}{\partial x^2} + \dfrac{\partial^2 (u + v)}{\partial y^2} + \dfrac{\partial^2 (u + v)}{\partial z^2}$

$$= \frac{\partial^2 (u + v)}{\partial x^2} + \frac{\partial^2 (u + v)}{\partial y^2} + \frac{\partial^2 (u + v)}{\partial z^2}$$

$$= \nabla^2 u + \nabla^2 v\,\big].$$

3.4. Which of the functions $\sin 3x, 6\cos 4x, 5x^3, \dfrac{1}{x}, 3e^{-5x}, \ln 2x$ are eigenfunctions of $\dfrac{d^2}{dx^2}$?

For each eigenfunction state the eigenvalue.

$\Big[$**Hint :** $\dfrac{d^2}{dx^2}(\sin 3x) = -9(\sin 3x)$,

sin 3*x* is the eigenfunction of $\dfrac{d^2}{dx^2}$ with eigenvalue –9.

$\dfrac{d^2}{dx^2}\left(5x^3\right) = 30\ (x)$, $5x^3$ is not the eigenfunction of $\dfrac{d}{dx^2}\Big]$.

3.5. If φ_1 and φ_2 are the two degenerate eigenfunctions of the linear operator $\hat{H}$ show that $\psi = C_1\,\varphi_1 + C_2\,\varphi_2$ is an eigenfunction of $\hat{H}$ with the same eigenvalue as that for φ_1 and φ_2.

[**Hint:** $\hat{H}\varphi_1 = \lambda\varphi_1$; $\hat{H}\varphi_2 = \lambda\varphi_2$

$$\hat{H}(C_1\varphi_1 + C_2\varphi_2) = \hat{H}(C_1\varphi_1) + \hat{H}(C_2\varphi_2) = C_1\hat{H}\varphi_1 + C_2\hat{H}\varphi_2$$
$$= C_1\lambda\varphi_1 + C_2\lambda\varphi_2 = \lambda(C_1\varphi_1 + C_2\varphi_2)].$$

3.6. Consider the operator $\hat{R} = -\dfrac{d^2}{dx^2}$ and the eigenvalue equation $\hat{R}\varphi = \lambda\varphi$. Write out the possible eigenfunctions and discuss the condition under which they are well-behaved and when λ is an eigenvalue.

[**Hint:** $-\dfrac{d^2\varphi}{dx^2} = \lambda\varphi$

General solution: $\varphi = A\exp(\sqrt{-\lambda}x) + B\exp(-\sqrt{-\lambda}x)$ for $\lambda \neq 0$

and $\phi = Cx + D$, for $\lambda = 0$

Three cases are to be considered:

(*i*) $\lambda < 0$; ϕ is not well-behaved as it does not remain finite as $|x| \to \infty$; so λ is not an eigenvalue.

(*ii*) $\lambda = 0$; ϕ is well-behaved only if C = 0.

(*iii*) $\lambda > 0$; $\phi = (A + B)\cos\sqrt{\lambda}x + i(A - B)\sin\sqrt{\lambda}x$

which is well-behaved for all values of x.

Hence, λ represents an eigenvalue].

3.7. Find the eigenfunctions and eigenvalues of linear momentum operator $\hat{p}_x$. Show that in the absence of any restriction there is a continuous series of eigenvalues of $\hat{p}_x$.

[**Hint:** $\hat{p}_x\,\psi = \lambda\psi$

or $$\frac{h}{2\pi i}\frac{d\psi}{dx} = \lambda\psi$$

or $$\frac{d\psi}{dx} = ik\psi \left(\text{putting } k = \frac{2\pi\lambda}{h}\right)$$

or $$\psi = Ae^{ikx} \text{ (eigenfunction)}$$

$$\lambda = \frac{kh}{2\pi} \text{ (eigenvalues)}$$

λ depends on k; if there is no restriction on k there will be no restriction on λ provided ψ is finite, single-valued and continuous for all values of x].

3.8. Show that the function $\psi(x) = -A\exp(ikx)$ represents a de Broglie wave.

[**Hint:** As x changes to $x + \lambda$ (λ = wavelength of the de Broglie wave);

$$\psi(x+\lambda) = A\exp(ik(x+\lambda)) = A\exp(ikx)\,.\exp(ik\lambda)$$
$$= A\exp(ikx)\exp(ikh/p) = A\exp(ikx)\,.\exp(2\pi i)$$
$$= A\exp(ikx)(\cos 2\pi + i\sin 2\pi)\left(\because p = \frac{kh}{2\pi}\right)$$

$$= \text{A} \exp(ikx) = \psi$$

That is, the function $\psi(x)$ repeats after an interval of λ which is the wavelength].

3.9. Show that sin $m\varphi$ or cos $m\varphi$ are not eigenfunctions of the angular momentum operator $\hat{L}_z$ but exp $(im\varphi)$ is.

$$\left[\textbf{Hint: } \frac{h}{2\pi i}\frac{d}{d\varphi}(\sin m\varphi) = \frac{mh}{2\pi i}(\cos m\varphi)\right.$$

$$\left.\frac{h}{2\pi i}\frac{d}{d\varphi}(\exp(im\varphi)) = \frac{mh}{2\pi}(\exp(im\varphi))\right].$$

3.10. Find the eigenfunctions and eigenvalues of the angular momentum operator, $\hat{L}_z$. Show that the eigenvalues of $\hat{L}_z$ form a discrete set.

[Hint: $$\hat{L}_z\,\psi = \lambda\psi,\ \hat{L}_z = \frac{h}{2\pi i}\frac{d}{d\varphi j}$$

where φ is the angle which the angular momentum vector makes with the z-axis. Therefore,

$$\frac{h}{2\pi i}\frac{d\psi}{d\varphi} = \lambda\psi$$

or $$\frac{d\psi}{d\varphi} = \frac{2\pi i\lambda}{h}\psi = im\psi\left(\text{Putting } m = \frac{2\pi\lambda}{h}\right)$$

or $$\psi = \text{C}\exp(im\varphi),\quad \text{C} = \text{constant}$$

ψ has to be single-valued for all values of φ (*i.e.*, $0 < \varphi < 2\pi$)

i.e., $$\psi(\varphi) = \psi(\varphi + 2\pi)$$

or $$\exp(im\varphi) = \exp(im(\varphi + 2\pi)) \text{ or } \exp(2\pi im) = 1$$

or $$\cos(2\pi m) + i\sin(2\pi m) = 1$$

This is true only if $m = 0, \pm 1, \pm 2, \pm 3, \ldots$

Thus, $$\lambda = \frac{mh}{2\pi}\left[(\text{the eigenvalues}) \text{ form a discrete } (\textit{i.e.}, \text{quantised}) \text{ set}\right]\Big]$$

3.11. Show that :

$$[x^n, p_x] = \frac{1}{2\pi i}nx^{n-1},$$

where n is a positive integer.

[Hint: $$\hat{x}^n\,\hat{p}_x\,\psi = \hat{x}^n \cdot \frac{h}{2\pi i}\frac{d\psi}{dx} = x^n\,\frac{h}{2\pi i}\cdot\frac{d\psi}{dx}$$

$$\hat{p}_x\,\hat{x}^n\,\psi = \frac{h}{2\pi i}\frac{d}{dx}\left[\hat{x}^n(\psi)\right] = \frac{h}{2\pi i}nx^{n-1}\psi + \frac{h}{2\pi i}x^n\frac{d\psi}{dx}$$

Therefore, $\hat{x}^n \hat{p}_x \psi - \hat{p}_x \hat{x}^n \psi = \left(\hat{x}^n \hat{p}_x - \hat{p}_x \hat{x}^n\right) \psi = \frac{h}{2\pi i} . nx^{n-1} \psi \Big]$.

3.12. Evaluate the commutators

$$\left[x, \frac{d}{dx}\right], \left[y, \frac{d}{dx}\right], \left[\frac{d}{dx}, \frac{d^2}{dx^2}\right]$$

[Hint: $\left[x, \frac{d}{dx}\right]\psi = x . \left[\frac{d\psi}{dx}\right] - \frac{d}{dx}[x . \psi]$

$$= x\frac{d\psi}{dx} - \psi - x\frac{d\psi}{dx} = -\psi$$

Therefore, $\left[x, \frac{d}{dx}\right] = -1$

$$\left[y, \frac{d}{dx}\right]\psi = y . \frac{d\psi}{dx} - \frac{d}{dx}(y\psi) = y . \frac{d\psi}{dx} - y\frac{d\psi}{dx} = 0 . \psi = 0$$

Therefore, $\left[y, \frac{d}{dx}\right] = 0$

$$\left[\frac{d}{dx}, \frac{d^2}{dx^2}\right]\psi = \frac{d}{dx}\left(\frac{d^2}{dx^2}\right)\psi - \frac{d^2}{dx^2}\left(\frac{d\psi}{dx}\right) = \frac{d^3\psi}{dx^3} - \frac{d^3\psi}{dx^3} = 0 . \psi \Bigg].$$

3.13. If $\hat{A} = 3x^2$, and $\hat{B} = \frac{d}{dx}$, then show that

$$\hat{A}\hat{B} \neq \hat{B}\hat{A}.$$

3.14. Show that the function sin $(k_1 x)$ sin $(k_2 y)$ sin $(k_3 z)$ is an eigenfunction of

$$\nabla^2 = \frac{\partial^2}{\partial x^2} + \frac{\partial^2}{\partial y^2} + \frac{\partial^2}{\partial z^2};$$

what is the eigenvalue ?

[Hint : Take the partial differentials

$$\frac{\partial^2}{\partial x^2}, \frac{\partial^2}{\partial y^2} \text{ and } \frac{\partial^2}{\partial z^2};$$

eigenvalue $= -\left(k_1^2 + k_2^2 + k_3^2\right)\Big]$.

3.15. Show that the function

$$\psi = \exp(i(k_x x + k_y y + k_z z))$$

is simultaneously an eigenfunction of both operators

$$\hat{p} = \frac{h}{2\pi i}\nabla \text{ and } \frac{-h^2}{4\pi^2}\nabla^2$$

Find the eigenvalues.

[Hint:

$$\hat{p}\psi = \frac{h}{2\pi i}\left\{\vec{i}\frac{\partial}{\partial x}+\vec{j}\frac{\partial}{\partial y}+\vec{k}\frac{\partial}{\partial z}\right\}\left[\exp\left(i\left(k_x x + k_y y + k_z z\right)\right)\right]$$

$$= \frac{h}{2\pi}\left(\vec{i}\,k_x + \vec{j}\,k_y + \vec{k}\,k_z\right)\left[\exp\left(i\left(k_x x + k_y y + k_z z\right)\right)\right]$$

eigenvalue $= \frac{h}{2\pi}\left(\vec{i}\,k_x + \vec{j}\,k_y + \vec{k}\,k_z\right).$

$$\frac{-h^2}{4\pi^2}\nabla^2\left[\exp\left(i\left(k_x x + k_y y + k_z z\right)\right)\right]$$

$$= -\frac{h^2}{4\pi^2}\left\{-\left(k_x^2 + k_y^2 + k_z^2\right)\exp\left(i\left(k_x x + k_y y + k_z z\right)\right)\right\}$$

eigenvalue $= -\frac{h^2}{4\pi^2}\left(k_x^2 + k_y^2 + k_z^2\right)\Bigg].$

3.16. Show that the operator $\hat{p}_x$ for linear momentum is Hermitian. What is its physical significance ?

[Hint: It is required to prove that

$$\int_{-\infty}^{\infty}\psi^*\left(\frac{h}{2\pi i}\frac{d}{dx}\right)\varphi\,d\tau = \int_{-\infty}^{\infty}\varphi\left(\frac{h}{2\pi i}\frac{d}{dx}\right)^*\psi^*\,dx$$

Integrate by parts; the L.H.S. is equal to

$$\frac{h}{2\pi i}\left[\psi^*\varphi\right]_{-\infty}^{\infty} - \frac{h}{2\pi i}\int_{-\infty}^{\infty}\varphi\frac{d\psi^*}{dx}\,dx$$

$$= 0 + \int_{-\infty}^{\infty}\varphi\left(-\frac{h}{2\pi i}\frac{d}{dx}\right)\psi^*\,dx$$

$$= \int_{-\infty}^{\infty}\varphi\left(\frac{h}{2\pi i}\frac{d}{dx}\right)^*\psi^*\,dx\Bigg].$$

3.17. Show that if two operators $\hat{A}$ and $\hat{B}$ are Hermitian, then their product $(\hat{A}\hat{B})$ is also Hermitian if and only if $\hat{A}$ and $\hat{B}$ commute.

[**Hint:** Since $\hat{A}\hat{B} = \hat{B}\hat{A}$, the integral

$$\int \psi^* (\hat{A}\hat{B})\varphi \, d\tau = \int \psi^* (\hat{B}\hat{A})\varphi \, d\tau = \int \psi^* \hat{B}(\hat{A}\varphi)\, d\tau$$

{Because $(\hat{B}\hat{A})\varphi$ means $\hat{B}$ operating on the function $(\hat{A}\varphi)$}.

Since $\hat{B}$ is Hermitian, the integral is equal to

$$\int (\hat{A}\varphi)(\hat{B}\psi)^* \, d\tau = \int (\hat{B}\psi)^* (\hat{A}\varphi)\, d\tau = \int \varphi \hat{A}^* (\hat{B}\psi)^* \, d\tau$$

$$= \int \varphi (\hat{A}\hat{B})^* \psi^* \, d\tau \qquad \text{(because } \hat{A} \text{ is Hermitian)}$$

Therefore, $(\hat{A}\hat{B})$ is also Hermitian.

3.18. Prove that the operator $\frac{h}{2\pi i} x\left(-\frac{d}{dx}\right)$ is not Hermitian.

$\hat{A}\left[\textbf{Hint: } x, \text{ and } \frac{d}{dx} \text{ do not commute}\right].$

3.19. Prove that the Hamiltonian operator for the total energy of a system is Hermitian provided that the wave-function is well behaved.

[**Hint:**

$$\hat{H} = \frac{-h^2}{8\pi^2 m}\frac{d^2}{dx^2} + \hat{V}(x) \qquad \text{(in one dimension)}$$

Assuming the wave functions to be real, it is required to prove that,

$$\int_{-\infty}^{\infty} \psi \hat{H} \phi \, d\tau = \int_{-\infty}^{\infty} \varphi \hat{H} \psi \, d\tau$$

For the potential energy part,

$$\int_{-\infty}^{\infty} \psi V(x)\, \varphi \, d\tau = \int_{-\infty}^{\infty} \varphi V(x)\, \psi \, d\tau \qquad \text{(because V } (x) \text{ is just as multiplier)}$$

For the K.E. part,

$$\int_{\infty}^{\infty} \psi \frac{d^2}{dx^2} \varphi \, dx = \left[\psi \frac{d\varphi}{dx}\right]_{-\infty}^{\infty} - \int_{-\infty}^{\infty} \frac{d\varphi}{dx} \cdot \frac{d\psi}{dx} dx \qquad \text{(integration by parts)}$$

Also,

$$\int_{-\infty}^{\infty} \varphi \frac{d^2}{dx^2} \psi\, dx = \left[\varphi \frac{d\psi}{dx} \right]_{-\infty}^{\infty} - \int_{-\infty}^{\infty} \frac{d\psi}{dx} \cdot \frac{d\varphi}{dx}\, dx$$

If the functions are well-behaved, then ψ, $\frac{d\psi}{dx}$, φ, $\frac{d\varphi}{dx}$, must vanish at infinity making the first term in each integral zero; the second terms in both are identical since they differ only in the order of multiplication of $\frac{d\psi}{dx}$ and $\frac{d\varphi}{dx}$. Thus, both V(x) and $\frac{d^2}{dx^2}$ are Hermitian while $\frac{-h^2}{8\pi^2 m}$ is just a constant factor].

3.20. Given operator $\frac{d}{dr}$ with a set of eigenfunctions exp (– ar) (a being real and positive) and real eigenvalues. Is the operator necessarily Hermitian ?

[**Hint :** $\frac{d}{dr}\left(\exp\left(-ar\right)\right) = -a \exp(-ar)$; eigenvalue = $-a$

Let two of the eigenfunctions be with $a_1 = 1$ and $a_2 = 2$.

$$\psi_1 = \exp(-r), \text{ eigenvalue} = -1$$

$$\psi_2 = \exp(-2r), \text{ eigenvalue} = -2$$

$$\int_0^{\infty} \exp\left(-r\right) \frac{d}{dr}\left(\exp\left(-2r\right)\right) r^2\, dr$$

$$= -2 \int_0^{\infty} r^2 \left(\exp\left(-3r\right)\right) dr = \frac{-4}{27} \qquad \text{(using the table of integrals)}$$

and $\int_0^{\infty} \exp\left(-2r\right) \frac{d}{dr}\left(\exp\left(-2r\right)\right) r^2 dr$

$$= -2 \int_0^{\infty} r^2 \exp\left(-4r\right) dr = -\frac{1}{16}$$

$\frac{d}{dr}$ is not Hermitian unless $a_1 = a_2$].

3.21. Two functions φ_1 and φ_2 are given which are degenerate eigenfunctions of $\hat{H}$ and which are linearly independent and normalised but not orthogonal. Construct two linear combinations of φ_1 and φ_2 which may be orthogonal to each other, and hence demonstrate that there is always sufficient freedom to choose degenerate functions which are orthogonal.
[**Hint :** First set $u_1 = \varphi_1$, and $u_2 = c_1\, \varphi_1 + c_2\, \varphi_2$

The task is then to determine c_1 and c_2, so that

$$\int u_1 u_2 \, d\tau = 0, \text{ and } \int u_1^2 \, d\tau = \int u_2^2 \, d\tau = 1$$

(assuming φ_1 and φ_2 to be real)].

3.22. A certain system is described by the Hamiltonian operator

$$\hat{H} = -\frac{d^2}{dx^2} + x^2$$

(*a*) Show that $\psi = Ax \exp\left(-\frac{x^2}{2}\right)$ is eigenfunction of $\hat{H}$; determine the eigenvalue.

(*b*) Determine A so that the function is normalised.

(*c*) What is the expectation value of x for the state described by

$$\psi = Ax \exp\left(-\frac{x^2}{2}\right)?$$

[**Hint:** By inspection it is apparent that ψ is well-behaved.

(*a*) $$-\frac{d^2}{dx^2}\left[Ax \exp\left(-\frac{x^2}{2}\right)\right] = -A\frac{d}{dx}\left[\left(1 - x^2\right)\exp\left(-\frac{x^2}{2}\right)\right]$$

$$= A\,(3 - x^2)\, x \exp\left(-\frac{x^2}{2}\right)$$

Therefore, $$\hat{H}\psi = \left(-\frac{d^2}{dx^2} + x^2\right)\left(Ax \exp\left(-\frac{x^2}{2}\right)\right)$$

$$= 3\left(Ax \exp\left(-\frac{x^2}{2}\right)\right)$$

Eigenvalue = 3.

(*b*) $$\int_{-\infty}^{\infty} \psi^2 \, dx = \int_{-\infty}^{\infty} A^2 x^2 \exp\left(-x^2\right) dx = A^2\left(\frac{\pi}{4}\right)^{1/2}$$

(from the table of integrals, Appendix 1)

= 1 (from normalisation condition)

Therefore, $$A = \left(\frac{4}{\pi}\right)^{1/4}.$$

(*c*) The time-independent state function is

$$\psi = Ax \exp\left(-\frac{x^2}{2}\right)$$

$$\bar{x} = \int_{-\infty}^{\infty} Ax \exp\left(-\frac{x^2}{2}\right) \hat{x} \, . \, Ax \exp\left(-\frac{x^2}{2}\right) dx$$

$$= \int_{-\infty}^{0} A^2 x^3 \exp\left(-x^2\right) dx + \int_{0}^{\infty} A^2 x^3 \exp\left(-x^2\right) dx = 0.$$

3.23. Prove that if a normalized function is expanded in terms of an orthonormal set of functions the sum of the squares of the coefficients is unity.
[**Hint :** Let $\psi = a_1 \varphi_1 + a_2 \varphi_2 + a_3 \varphi_3 + ...$

$$\int \psi^2 \, d\tau = \left[a_1^2 \int \varphi_1^2 \, d\tau + a_2^2 \int \varphi_2^2 \, d\tau + a_3^2 \int \varphi_3^2 \, d\tau + \ldots\right]$$

$$+ 2a_1 a_2 \int \varphi_1 \varphi_2 \, d\tau + 2a_1 a_3 \int \varphi_1 \varphi_3 \, d\tau + 2a_2 a_3 \int \varphi_2 \varphi_3 \, d\tau + \ldots\Big]$$

$$= 1$$

or, $a_1^2 + a_2^2 + a_3^2 + \ldots = 1$(because $\varphi_1, \varphi_2, \varphi_3, \ldots\ldots$ are normalised and orthogonal)].

3.24. A particle in a ring is in a state with

$$\psi = \frac{1}{\sqrt{\pi}} \cos 2\varphi$$

(*a*) Calculate the average value of the angular momentum (p_φ) where the operator is

$$\bar{p}_\varphi = \frac{h}{2\pi i} \frac{d}{d\varphi}$$

(*b*) Express ψ as a linear combination of exponentials and evaluate the average value of the angular momentum using formula,

$$\bar{p}_\varphi = \sum_i |\, c_n \,|^2 \, p_{\varphi_n} \, ,$$

where p_{φ_n} is the eigenvalue for the nth exponential, C_n is the appropriate coefficient.

[**Hint :** (*a*)
$$\bar{p}_{\varphi_n} = \int_0^{2\pi} \frac{1}{\sqrt{\pi}} \cos 2\varphi \frac{h}{2\pi i} \frac{d}{d\varphi} \left(\frac{1}{\sqrt{\pi}} \cos 2\varphi\right) d\varphi$$

$$= - \frac{h}{2\pi^2 i} \int_0^{2\pi} 2 \cos 2\varphi \sin 2\varphi \, d\varphi$$

$$= - \frac{h}{2\pi^2 i} \int_0^{2\pi} \sin 4\varphi \, d\varphi = 0$$

(*b*) Normalised eigenfunctions of

$$\hat{p}_\varphi\left(=\frac{h}{2\pi i}\frac{d}{d\varphi}\right)\text{ are }\frac{1}{\sqrt{2\pi}}\exp(\pm im\varphi)$$

with eigenvalues $\pm\dfrac{mh}{2\pi}$ (vide Problem 3.8).

So, $$\psi=\frac{1}{\sqrt{2}}\left[\frac{1}{\sqrt{2\pi}}e^{im\varphi}+\frac{1}{\sqrt{2\pi}}e^{-im\varphi}\right],$$

$$\frac{1}{\sqrt{2}}=\text{normalisation factor}$$

and $$\bar{p}_\varphi=\int_0^{2\pi}\psi^*\,\hat{p}_\varphi\,\psi\,d\varphi$$

$$=\left(\frac{1}{\sqrt{2}}\right)^2\frac{mh}{2\pi}+\left(\frac{1}{\sqrt{2}}\right)^2\cdot\left(-\frac{mh}{2\pi}\right)=0\Bigg].$$

3.25. Given that ψ and φ are two nonorthogonal eigenfunctions of an operator, find the normalisation constant for a wave function ψ' expressed in terms of ψ and φ.

[**Hint :** Use a definition $\psi'=\varphi-S\,\psi$,

where $$S=\int\psi^*\,\varphi\,d\tau$$

If N = normalisation constant for ψ',

$$N^2\left[\int\varphi^2\,d\tau+\int S^2\,\psi^2\,d\tau-\int 2S\varphi\psi\,d\tau\right]=1$$

or $$N^2\,[1+S^2-2S^2]=1$$

or $$N=(1-S^2)^{-1/2}].$$

3.26. Given the two normalised but nonorthogonal eigenfunctions

$$\psi=\frac{1}{\sqrt{\pi}}e^{-r}$$

and $$\varphi=\frac{1}{\sqrt{3\pi}}re^{-r},$$

construct a new function ψ' which is orthogonal to the first function and is normalised.

$$[\textbf{Hint}: S=\int\psi\varphi\,d\tau=\int_0^\infty\frac{1}{\sqrt{\pi}}e^{-r}\,\frac{1}{\sqrt{3\pi}}re^{-r}\,r^2\,dr\int_0^\pi\sin\theta\,d\theta\int_0^{2\pi}d\varphi$$

$$= \frac{4}{\sqrt{3}} \int_0^\infty r^3 e^{-2r}\, dr \qquad \left[\because \int_0^\pi \sin\theta\, d\theta \int_0^{2\pi} d\varphi = 4\pi\right]$$

$$= \frac{\sqrt{3}}{2} \text{ [using the table of integrals]}$$

The new function ψ' is orthogonal to

$$\psi = \frac{1}{\sqrt{\pi}} e^{-r}$$

Therefore,

$$\psi' = \varphi - S\psi = \frac{1}{\sqrt{3\pi}} re^{-r} - \frac{\sqrt{3}}{2} \frac{1}{\sqrt{\pi}} e^{-r}$$

$$= \frac{1}{\sqrt{3\pi}} \left(r - \frac{3}{2}\right) e^{-r}$$

Let N = normalised factor. Then,

$$\int (N\psi')^2 d\tau = N^2 \int_0^\infty \left[\frac{1}{\sqrt{3\pi}} \left(r - \frac{3}{2}\right) e^{-r}\right]^2 r^2\, dr \int_0^\pi \sin\theta\, d\theta \int_0^{2\pi} d\phi$$

$$= 1$$

or $$\frac{N^2 \cdot 4\pi}{3\pi} \int_0^\infty \left[\left(r^2 - 3r + \frac{9}{4}\right) r^2 e^{-2r}\right] dr = 1$$

or $$\frac{4N^2}{3} \left[\frac{3}{4} - \frac{9}{8} + \frac{9}{16}\right] = 1 \text{(using the table of integrals)}$$

or $N^2 = 4$

or $N = 2$

Therefore, the normalised wave function is

$$\left.\psi' = \frac{2}{\sqrt{3\pi}} \left(r - \frac{3}{2}\right) e^{-r}\right].$$

3.27. The state of a system is described by the function $\Psi(x, t)$ which is a function of both position and time, but the average value of any physical quantity is independent of time ; why ?

[Hint: $$\Psi(x, t) = \psi(x)\, \varphi(t) = \psi(x)\, a \exp\left(-\frac{2\pi i\, Et}{h}\right)$$

$$\bar{A} = \int \psi^*(x)\, a\exp\left(\frac{2\pi i Et}{h}\right) \cdot \hat{A}\,\psi(x)\, a\exp\left(\frac{-2\pi i Et}{h}\right) d\tau$$

$$= a^2 \int \psi^*(x)\, \hat{A}\,\psi(x)\, dx$$

which is independent of time].

3.28. The uncertainty in measurement of a physical quantity A is defined as $\Delta A = \left[\hat{A}^2 - \left(\hat{A}\right)^2\right]^{1/2}$

Show that inspite of the uncertainty of time (Δt), the total ground state energy (E_0) of a system can be determined exactly.

[Hint:

$$\bar{E} = \int \psi_0 \hat{H} \psi_0\, d\tau = \int \psi_0 E_0 \psi_0\, d\tau = E_0 \int \psi_0^2\, d\tau = E_0$$

(if ψ_0 is normalised)

$$\bar{E}^2 = \int \psi_0 \hat{H}^2 \psi_0\, d\tau = \int \psi_0 \hat{H}\left(\hat{H}\psi_0\right) d\tau$$

$$= \int \psi_0 \hat{H}\left(E_0 \psi_0\right) d\tau$$

$$= E_0 \int \psi_0 \hat{H} \psi_0\, d\tau$$

$$= E_0 \int \psi_0 E_0 \psi_0\, d\tau$$

$$= E_0^2$$

Therefore,

$$\Delta E = \left[\bar{E}_0^2 - \left(\bar{E}_0\right)^2 = 0\right].$$

PART II

APPLICATIONS TO SIMPLE SYSTEMS

CHAPTER 4

Translational Motion of a Particle

The most common type of motion that a particle can undergo is translational or linear (motion in a line). Kinetic motion of atoms and molecules is, in general, translational. However, electrons in atoms and molecules can execute translational, rotational and vibrational motions, but when free they move only linearly.

In this Chapter we deal with the linear motion of a particle when free and when under quantum mechanical constraints.

4.1 FREE PARTICLE SYSTEM

A free particle is one which is not subjected to any force or potential barrier and is free to move in limitless space. For a linear motion of the particle, the Hamiltonian $\hat{H}$ is given as,

$$\hat{H} = -\frac{h^2}{8\pi^2 m}\frac{d^2}{dx^2} + V$$

and the wave function ψ (which is also eigenfunction of $\hat{H}$ here) is $\psi(x)$.

Since the particle is not subjected to any external force, its potential energy V is constant which, for convenience, may be assumed to be zero. Thus, the Schrödinger equation for the free particle may be written explicitly as,

$$\frac{d^2\psi}{dx^2} + \frac{8\pi^2 m}{h^2}E\psi = 0 \qquad \text{... (4.1)}$$

Equation (4.1) has the general solution,

$$\psi = A\sin kx + B\cos kx \qquad \text{... (4.2)}$$

where, A and B are arbitary constants introduced while integrating Equation (4.1), and

$$k^2 = \frac{8\pi^2 mE}{h^2} \qquad \text{... (4.3)}$$

A, B and k (and hence E) can have any value without restriction.

The function (4.2) represents the sinusoidal wave associated with the particle. But it is difficult to draw information regarding the wavelength of the sinusoidal wave from this relation. It can, however, be transformed into a form more useful for the purpose by a theorem of trigonometry.

$$\cos x \pm i \sin x = e^{\pm ix}$$

from which it follows that

$$\cos x = \frac{e^{ix} + e^{-ix}}{2}, \text{ and } \sin x = \frac{e^{ix} - e^{-ix}}{2i}$$

Thus, the function (4.2) can be expressed as,

$$\psi = \text{C}e^{ikx} + \text{D}e^{-ikx} \qquad \text{... (4.4)}$$

where, C and D are the other constants.

The functions $e^{\pm ikx}$ are eigenfunctions of the linear momentum operator, $\frac{h}{2\pi i}\frac{d}{dx}$, with eigenvalues $\frac{\pm kh}{2\pi}$ [see Chapter 3, Equations (3.27) and (3.28)].

Thus, a physical meaning can be ascribed to the imaginary exponential function ψ. The quantities

$$\frac{\pm kh}{2\pi} = \pm\sqrt{2m\text{E}} \qquad \text{... (4.5)}$$

are equal to the classical linear momentum (p_x) of a free particle having energy E. Therefore, λ, given by Equation (4.6),

$$\lambda = \frac{h}{p_x} = \frac{h}{\pm\sqrt{2m\text{E}}} \qquad \text{... (4.6)}$$

is the wavelength of the wave associated with the particle (by de Broglie relationship). The state in which D = 0,

$$\psi = \text{C}e^{ikx} \qquad \text{... (4.7)}$$

represents a particle wave travelling in the $+x$ direction with wavelength $\lambda = \frac{h}{\sqrt{2m\text{E}}}$ and momentum $\sqrt{2m\text{E}}$; on the other hand, for the state C = 0.

$$\psi = \text{D}e^{-ikx} \qquad \text{... (4.8)}$$

represents particle wave in the $-x$ direction with wavelength $\lambda = -\frac{h}{\sqrt{2m\text{E}}}$ and momentum $\sqrt{2m\text{E}}$. For all other values of C and D, the waves are superpositions of two waves moving in opposite directions.

So it is apparent that either of the two functions A sin kx and B cos kx represents a superposition of two waves of equal intensity moving in opposite directions.

Since the wave function has appreciable values at all values of x from $-\infty$ to ∞, it cannot be normalised.

4.1.1 Position, Momentum and Uncertainty Relations

The function $\psi^* \psi$ represents the probability density, *i.e.*, probability of finding the particle in unit length. For the free particle, use of either of the wave functions [$\psi = Ce^{ikx}$ or De^{-ikx}], gives $\psi^* \psi$ = constant (independent of x) which means that the probability of finding the particle at all points is the same, *i.e.*, the position is completely uncertain ($\Delta x = \infty$). On the other hand, the momentum of the particle is exactly determined and is equal to $\pm\sqrt{2mE}$ (as discussed earlier); therefore, the uncertainty in momentum is nil ($\Delta p_x = 0$).

4.1.2 Energy of the Particle

From Equation (4.3), the energy (E) of the particle can be obtained as,

$$E = \frac{k^2 h^2}{8\pi^2 m} \qquad \text{... (4.9)}$$

The function $\psi = A \sin kx + B \cos kx$, is always finite, single valued and continuous, so no restrictions can be placed on the value of k and hence on that of E. In other words, the free particle can have any value of energy.

Exercise 1: Show that the energy of the free particle is always positive.

Exercise 2: Show that the average kinetic energy is equal to E. Use the wave function $\psi = Ae^{ikx}$

$$\overline{T}_x = \int \psi^* \hat{T}_x \psi \, dx$$

$$= -\frac{h^2}{8\pi^2 m} \int A^* \exp(-ikx) \cdot \frac{d^2}{dx^2} \left(A \exp(ikx)\right) dx$$

$$= -\frac{h^2}{8\pi^2 m} \int A^* \exp(-ikx) \left(-k^2 A \exp(ikx)\right) dx$$

$$= \int \psi^* E \psi \, dx = E \int \psi^* \psi \, dx = E \qquad \text{[by Equation (4.3)]}$$

Exercise 3: Show that the average momentum is zero.

4.2 PARTICLE IN A BOX : INFINITE POTENTIAL BARRIERS

Now consider the particle which is allowed to move in a limited space. Such a model, usually called "particle in a box" model, serves as the simplest case for the treatment of bound electrons in atoms and molecules.

4.2.1 One Dimensional Box

Consider a particle moving in a one-dimensional box of length L with infinitely high walls at the two ends; inside the box the potential energy (V) is zero (the particle is not acted upon by any force) and outside the box it is infinite. In other words, the particle is confined to move in the length L. The model, also called "particle in a potential well", is shown in Fig. 4.1.

The Schrödinger Equation: Since the potential is discontinuous (suddenly rises) at $x = 0$ and $x = L$, it is convenient to consider the Schrödinger equation inside and outside the box separately.

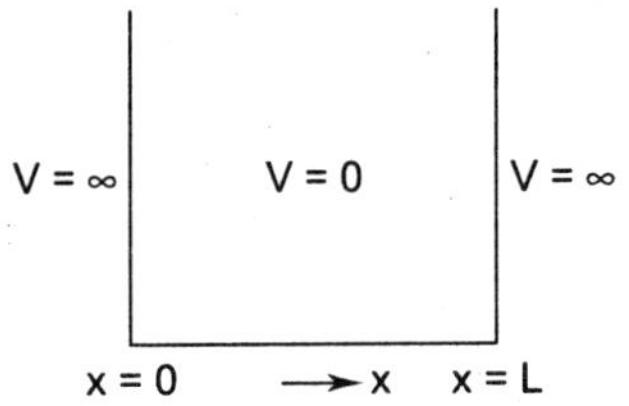

Fig. 4.1 *Particle in a one dimensional box of length L*

The Schrödinger equation outside the box (where V = ∞) will be,

$$-\frac{h^2}{8\pi^2 m}\frac{d^2\psi}{dx^2} + \infty\psi = E\psi \qquad \text{... (4.10)}$$

The Schrödinger equation inside the box, *i.e.*, at $0 \le x \le L$ (where, V = 0) will be,

$$-\frac{h^2}{8\pi^2 m}\frac{d^2\psi}{dx^2} = E\psi \qquad \text{... (4.11)}$$

Due to infinitely large potential energy beyond the boundary of the box, the particle has no chance of being found in regions $x < 0$ and $x > L$, *i.e.*, ψ^2 and hence $\psi = 0$ in these regions.

Since ψ must be continuous (it cannot rise or fall suddenly by large amounts), ψ must be 0 at $x = 0$ and $x = L$. This is the "boundary condition" for the system.

The Schrödinger equation inside the box, Equation (4.11) may be written as

$$\frac{d^2\psi}{dx^2} + k^2\psi = 0 \qquad \text{... (4.12)}$$

where,

$$k^2 = \frac{8\pi^2 mE}{h^2} \qquad \text{... (4.13)}$$

Equation (4.12) is the same as Equation (4.1) which is satisfied by any of the functions like sin kx, cos kx, e^{ikx} and e^{-ikx}, all of which are finite, single-valued and continuous, fulfilling the necessary criteria of an acceptable wave function.

The Wave Function and the Energy of the Particle: The wave function ψ may be expressed in terms of $e^{\pm ikx}$ or in terms of sin kx and cos kx. Both the complex and the real forms have their own advantages.

In terms of the real form of the wave function, the general solution is,

$$\psi = A \sin kx + B \cos kx \qquad \text{... (4.14)}$$

where, A and B are arbitrary constants introduced during the integration; the values of A, B and k are determined by the boundary conditions as follows:

At $x = 0$, $\psi = 0$; therefore, from Equation (4.14)

$$0 = A \sin (k \,.\, 0) + B \cos (k \,.\, 0)$$

or

$$B = 0, \text{ and hence,}$$

$$\psi = A \sin kx \text{ for all values of } x$$

Also, at $x = \mathrm{L}, \psi = 0$; therefore,

$$0 = \mathrm{A} \sin k\mathrm{L} \quad \text{... (4.15)}$$

Equation (4.15) is satisfied if either (*i*) A = 0 or (*ii*) $k\mathrm{L} = n\pi$. However, if both A and B become zero, ψ will be zero at all values of x, which will make little sense. The other solution *i.e.*, $k\mathrm{L} = n\pi$ is acceptable.

Hence

$$k = \frac{n\pi}{\mathrm{L}} \quad \text{... (4.16)}$$

where, n is a simple integer (1, 2, 3, ...) but not zero, (if n were to be zero, k would become zero and ψ would again be zero everywhere).

These considerations lead to the solutions,

$$\psi = \mathrm{A} \sin \frac{n\pi}{\mathrm{L}} x \text{ and} \quad \text{... (4.17)}$$

$$\mathrm{E} = \frac{k^2 h^2}{8\pi^2 m} = \frac{n^2 h^2}{8m\mathrm{L}^2} \quad \text{... (4.18)}$$

Quantisation and Quantum Number: In Equation (4.18), h, m and L are constant. Therefore, there can be only a discrete set of values of E dictated only by the integer n. In other words, the energy is quantised and the integer n is the quantum number. This situation is in contrast with that in the case of the free particle which can have any positive value of energy. (This conclusion is universal—whenever a particle is confined to move in a limited space, its energy is quantised).

[**Exercise** : Verify that $\psi = \mathrm{A} \sin kx$ and $\psi = \mathrm{A}e^{ikx}$ are eigenfunctions of the Hamiltonian operator for particle in a box. What is the eigenvalue ?

$$\hat{\mathrm{H}}\psi = -\frac{h^2}{8\pi^2 m} \frac{d^2 (\mathrm{A} \sin kx)}{dx^2} = \frac{k^2 h^2}{8\pi^2 m} (\mathrm{A} \sin kx)$$

$$= \left(\frac{n^2 h^2}{8m\mathrm{L}^2}\right) \psi$$

Eigenvalue,

$$\mathrm{E} = \frac{n^2 h^2}{8m\mathrm{L}^2} \Bigg]$$

Similarly, momentum is also quantised, since

$$p_x^2 = 2m\mathrm{E}$$

$$p_x = \left(\frac{2mn^2 h^2}{8m\mathrm{L}^2}\right)^{1/2}$$

or

$$p_x = \pm \frac{nh}{2\mathrm{L}} \quad \text{... (4.19)}$$

The Energy Levels: The quantisation of energy is shown graphically in Fig. 4.2. The allowed energy levels are shown as horizontal lines.

That these lines are straight emphasises the fact that energy (E) is the same irrespective of the position (x) of the particle. Since for a particular value of n, the energy (E) does not change with x, the latter is often termed as "constant of motion"; further, since the $\hat{H}$ or E is independent of time (t) the system under consideration is a good and simple example of "conservative system" (see page 29, Chapter 2).

The lowest value of E is not zero but $\frac{h^2}{8mL^2}$ (when $n = 1$). Evidently, the particle in a box will continue to move to and fro in the region 0 to L even at the temperature of absolute zero; for this reason it is called the "zero point energy". This conclusion is universal and valid for any system under restricted to and fro motion.

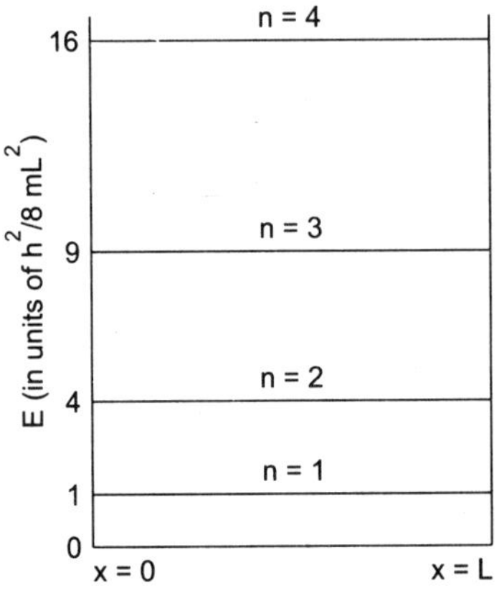

Fig. 4.2 *Energy levels for the particle in a one dimensional box*

The dependence of E on n^2 results in the increased spacing between energy levels as n increases [Equation (4.20)].

$$\Delta E = E_{n+1} - E_n = [(n+1)^2 - n^2]\, E_1 = (2n+1)\, E_1 \qquad \text{... (4.20)}$$

Since the energy E_1 is proportional to $\frac{1}{L^2}$, the smaller the box the greater are the energy spacings (ΔE), *i.e.*, the quantisation is more pronounced. Alternatively, as the box is made wider, ΔE decreases and in the limiting case of $L \to \infty$ (free particle) the quantisation vanishes.

ΔE is also proportional to $\frac{1}{m}$ which means that for macroscopic bodies (large m) the levels are closely spaced (there is no quantisation).

Exercise 1: Calculate and draw the energy levels E_1 to E_6 in eV for an electron in a one-dimensional box of length 12 Å. How large is the energy difference $E_6 - E_5$ in cm^{-1} ?

$$E_n = \frac{n^2 h^2}{8mL^2} = \frac{n^2 \left(6.62 \times 10^{-34}\ \text{Js}\right)^2}{8 \times \left(9.1 \times 10^{-31}\ \text{kg}\right) \times \left(12 \times 10^{-10}\ \text{m}\right)^2}$$

$$= 4.16 \times 10^{-20}\, n^2\ \text{J}$$

$$= (4.16 \times 10^{-20} \times 6.24 \times 10^{18})\, n^2 \text{ eV}$$
$$= 0.26\, n^2 \text{ eV } (1 \text{ J} = 6.24 \times 10^{18} \text{ eV})$$
$$E_6 - E_5 = 0.26 \times (36 - 25) = 2.86 \text{ eV} = 23000 \text{ cm}^{-1}$$
$$(1 \text{ eV} = 8.06 \times 10^3 \text{ cm}^{-1}).$$

Exercise 2: Calculate the spacings between energy levels for (*i*) an electron (mass ≈ 10^{-30} kg) in a one-dimensional box of 1.0 Å length, and (*ii*) a ball bearing (mass = 1 g) in a box of 10 cm length. Comment on the energy gaps in the two cases.

By Equation (4.19), $$E_{n+1} - E_n = (2n + 1)\, E_1 = (2n + 1)\, \frac{h^2}{8mL^2}$$

For (*i*) $$E_2 - E_1 = \frac{3h^2}{8mL^2} = \frac{3 \times (6.62 \times 10^{-34} \text{ Js})^2}{8 \times 10^{-30} \text{ kg} \times (10^{-10} \text{ m})^2}$$
$$= 16.33 \times 10^{-18} \text{ J}$$
$$= 16.33 \times 10^{-18} \times 6.24 \times 10^{18} = 102 \text{ eV}$$

For (*ii*) $$E_2 - E_1 = \frac{3 \times (6.62 \times 10^{-34} \text{ Js})^2}{8 \times 10^{-3} \text{ kg} \times (0.1 \text{ m})^2}$$
$$= 16.43 \times 10^{-63} \text{ J}$$
$$= 10.2 \times 10^{-44} \text{ eV}.$$

In case (*i*) the energy gap is large while in (*ii*) it is too small for the quantisation to be observed.

Normalisation of the Wave Function : The wave function given by Equation (4.17), *i.e.*,

$$\psi = A \sin\left(\frac{n\pi x}{L}\right)$$

is still incomplete in as much as the constant A is not determined. It can be determined by making use of the condition of normalisation,

$$\int_0^L \psi^2\, d\tau = \int_0^L A^2 \sin^2 \frac{n\pi x}{L}\, dx = 1$$

By reference to the table of standard integrals,

$$A^2 \int_0^L \sin^2 \frac{n\pi x}{L}\, dx = \frac{A^2}{2} \int_0^L \left(1 - \cos \frac{2n\pi x}{L}\right) dx$$
$$= \frac{A^2}{2} \left\{ [x]_0^L - \left[\frac{\sin 2n\pi x/L}{2n\pi/L} \right]_0^L \right\}$$
$$= \frac{A^2 L}{2}$$

That is, $$\frac{A^2 L}{2} = 1 \text{ or } A = \sqrt{\frac{2}{L}}$$

The normalised wave function is thus,*

$$\psi = \sqrt{\frac{2}{L}} \sin \frac{n\pi x}{L} \qquad \text{... (4.21)}$$

It can be seen that the ψ has the dimension $cm^{-1/2}$.

Exercise 3: Find the values of the normalised wave function at

$$x = 0, \frac{L}{4}, \frac{L}{2}, \frac{3L}{4} \text{ and L corresponding to } n = 1, 2.$$

$$\psi_1 = \sqrt{\frac{2}{L}} \sin \frac{\pi x}{L};$$

at $x = 0$, $\psi_1 = 0$

$x = \frac{L}{4}$, $\psi_1 = \frac{1}{\sqrt{L}}$

$x = \frac{L}{2}$, $\psi_1 = \sqrt{\frac{2}{L}}$

$x = \frac{3L}{4}$, $\psi_1 = \sqrt{\frac{1}{L}}$

$x = L$, $\psi_1 = 0$

$$\psi_2 = \sqrt{\frac{2}{L}} \sin \frac{2\pi x}{L};$$

at $x = 0$, $\psi_2 = 0$

$x = \frac{L}{4}$, $\psi_2 = \sqrt{\frac{2}{L}}$

$x = \frac{L}{2}$, $\psi_2 = 0$

$x = \frac{3L}{4}$, $\psi_2 = -\sqrt{\frac{2}{L}}$

$x = L$, $\psi_2 = 0$

Orthogonality of the Wave Function: We have shown in Chapter 3 that eigenfunctions of a Hermitian operator corresponding to different eigenvalues are necessarily orthogonal to each other, and that Hamiltonian is a Hermitian operator.

For the problem of particle is a one-dimensional box, it can be demonstrated easily.

Let $\psi_1 = \sqrt{\frac{2}{L}} \sin \frac{\pi x}{L}$, and $\psi_2 = \sqrt{\frac{2}{L}} \sin \frac{2\pi x}{L}$

be the two normalised eigenfunctions corresponding to the two eigenvalues E_1 and E_2 (characterised by quantum numbers 1 and 2). Then,

---

* Actually $\psi = \pm \sqrt{\frac{2}{L}} \sin \frac{n\pi x}{L}$. However, since probability is given by $|\psi|^2$ and not by ψ, it is immaterial whether it is positive or negative

$$\int_0^L \psi_1 \psi_2 \, dx = \frac{2}{L} \int_0^L \sin \frac{nx}{L} \sin \frac{2\pi x}{L} \, dx$$

$$= \frac{2}{L} \int_0^L \left[\frac{\cos \frac{(2-1)\pi x}{L} - \cos \frac{(2+1)\pi x}{L}}{2} \right] dx$$

$$= \frac{1}{L} \left[\frac{L}{(2-1)} \sin \frac{(2-1)\pi x}{L} - \frac{L}{(2+1)} \sin \frac{(2+1)\pi x}{L} \right]_0^L$$

$$= \frac{1}{L}(0-0) = 0.$$

Wavelength of the ψ Waves—Analogy with Vibrations of a Stretched String: For the particle confined to move in a one-dimensional box of length L, what will be the wavelength of the wave associated with it ? It can easily be derived by using the de Broglie relationship,

$$\lambda = \frac{h}{p} = \frac{2L}{n} \qquad \text{... (4.22)}$$

Thus, the allowed wavelengths are 2L, L, $\frac{2L}{3}$, $\frac{L}{2}$ ... But since $L = \frac{n\lambda}{2}$, it means that an integral number (n) of half waves fits exactly into the length of the box. The situation is analogous to that involving vibrations of a string which is fixed at $x = 0$ and $x = L$, discussed in Chapter 2. As n increases, p_x and E increase, λ decreases and the waves oscillate more rapidly.

Forms of the Wave Functions: The expression for the real form of the wave function can be used conveniently to draw its graphical representations. Some of the sketches, for several values of n are shown in Fig. 4.3.

It may be seen that the graphical representations of ψ are exactly like those showing the displacements of a vibrating string clamped at $x = 0$ and $x = L$.

Nodes: In addition to the two ends, there are points inside the box where $\psi = 0$. Such points are called "nodes". For the energy state $n = 1$ (the minimum energy) there is no node. As n increases, nodes appear and it can be seen that the number of nodes for any state n is equal to $n - 1$. It should be obvious to the reader that the increasing number of nodes is consistent with increasing energy of the system.

Symmetry of the Wave Functions: The wave functions $\psi = \sqrt{\frac{2}{L}} \sin \frac{n\pi x}{L}$ belong to one of the two classes: (*i*) symmetric or (*ii*) antisymmetric. The function is symmetric when n is odd, *e.g.*, ψ_1, ψ_3, ψ_5, ..., all of which satisfy the condition

$$\psi(x) = \psi(-x)$$

The function, on the other hand, is antisymmetric if n is even, *e.g.*, ψ_2, ψ_4, ψ_6, ... which satisfy the condition, $\psi(x) = -\psi(-x)$.

Qualitatively, the symmetry of the functions can be demonstrated by taking the origin at the middle of the box and imagining a vertical mirror placed exactly at the mid-point of the box (shown by dotted vertical line in Fig. 4.4). The wave functions can be seen to be symmetrical with respect to reflection in this mirror when n is odd (*i.e.*, the left half is the mirror image of the right half) while they are antisymmetric when n is even (left half is exactly opposite to the right half).

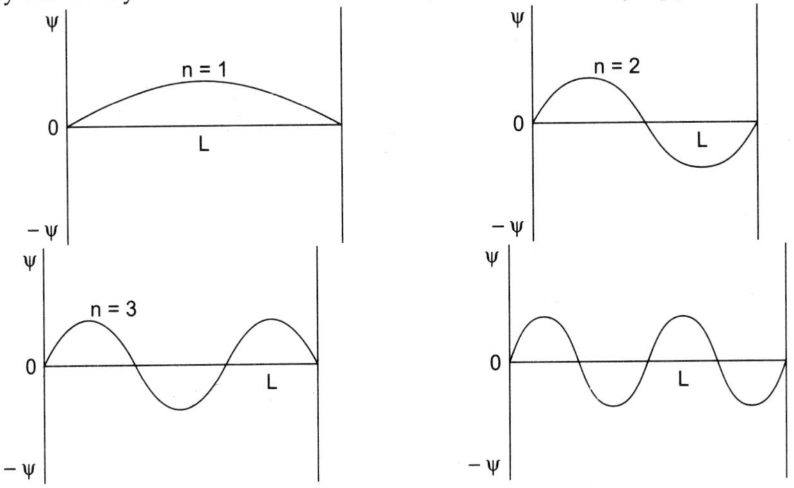

Fig. 4.3 *Forms of the ψ wave of a particle in a one dimensional box*

The boundaries of the box now lie at $-\frac{L}{2}$ and $+\frac{L}{2}$, while the length of the box remains equal to L (see Fig. 4.4).

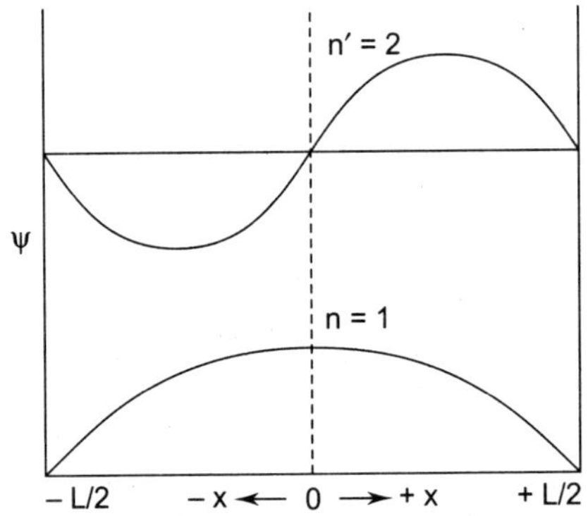

Fig. 4.4 *One dimensional box with origin at the centre; symmetric and antisymmetric wave functions*

Now the boundary conditions become $\psi\left(\pm\frac{L}{2}\right) = 0$. Using Equation (4.14),

$$\psi = A \sin kx + B \cos kx,$$

We obtain two relations at $x = \pm\frac{L}{2}$ where $\psi = 0$,

$$\psi\left(+\frac{L}{2}\right) = A \sin\left(\frac{kL}{2}\right) + B \cos\left(\frac{kL}{2}\right) = 0 \qquad \text{... (4.23)}$$

$$\psi\left(-\frac{L}{2}\right) = A\sin\left(-\frac{kL}{2}\right) + B\cos\left(-\frac{kL}{2}\right) = 0$$

or
$$-A\sin\left(\frac{kL}{2}\right) + B\cos\left(\frac{kL}{2}\right) = 0 \qquad \text{... (4.24)}$$

[because sin (– x) = – sin x, and cos (– x) = cos x]

From Equations (4.23) and (4.24) we obtain,

$$2B\cos\left(\frac{kL}{2}\right) = 0,$$

or
$$\frac{kL}{2} = \frac{n\pi}{2}, \text{ or } k = \frac{n\pi}{L}$$

(where, n is an odd integer),

and
$$2A\sin\left(\frac{kL}{2}\right) = 0$$

or
$$\frac{kL}{2} = n\pi \text{ or } k = \frac{n'\pi}{L}$$

(where, $n' = 2n$ is an even integer).

For the same value of k both sine and cosine functions cannot be zero; hence, we obtain two sets of solution:

$$\psi = B\cos\frac{n\pi x}{L} \text{ (where, } n = 1, 3, 5, \ldots\ldots) \qquad \text{... (4.25)}$$

and
$$\psi = A\sin\frac{n\pi x}{L} \text{ (where, } n = 2, 4, 6, \ldots\ldots) \qquad \text{... (4.26)}$$

n or n' = 0 is not acceptable because that will make the sine function zero everywhere and the cosine function constant. The values of both A and B, found by normalisation, are equal to $\sqrt{\frac{2}{L}}$.

With respect to the middle point (x = 0), the cosine functions are symmetric and sine functions antisymmetric.

Exercise 1: Draw the list of the first four eigenfunctions along with the eigenvalues for a particle in a one-dimensional box whose length is L and origin (x = 0) of the coordinate system is in the middle.

$$\psi_n : \sqrt{\frac{2}{L}}\cos\frac{\pi x}{L}\,(n = 1), \sqrt{\frac{2}{L}}\sin\frac{2\pi x}{L}\,(n = 2), \sqrt{\frac{2}{L}}\cos\frac{3\pi x}{L}\,(n = 3), \sqrt{\frac{2}{L}}\sin\frac{4\pi x}{L}\,(n = 4).$$

The corresponding values of E_n are:

$$\frac{h^2}{8mL^2}, \frac{4h^2}{8mL^2}, \frac{9h^2}{8mL^2} \text{ and } \frac{16h^2}{8mL^2}.$$

Exercise 2: For the first two states (n = 1 and 2) in the above problem, find the values of the eigenfunctions at several values of x between $-\frac{L}{2}$ and $+\frac{L}{2}$. Draw the corresponding plots and indicate the symmetry of the wave functions.

$\psi_1 = \sqrt{\frac{2}{L}} \cos \frac{\pi x}{L}$ (symmetric) $\qquad \psi_2 = \sqrt{\frac{2}{L}} \sin \frac{2\pi x}{L}$ (antisymmetric)

$x = -\frac{L}{2}, \psi_1 = 0 \qquad x = -\frac{L}{2}, \psi_2 = 0$

$x = -\frac{L}{4}, \psi_1 = \sqrt{\frac{2}{L}} \cos\left(-\frac{\pi}{4}\right) \qquad x = -\frac{L}{4}, \psi_2 = \sqrt{\frac{2}{L}} \sin\left(-\frac{\pi}{2}\right)$

$= \sqrt{\frac{1}{L}} \qquad = -\sqrt{\frac{2}{L}}$

$x = 0, \psi_1 = \sqrt{\frac{2}{L}} \qquad x = 0, \psi_2 = 0$

$x = +\frac{L}{4}, \psi_1 = \sqrt{\frac{1}{L}} \qquad x = +\frac{L}{4}, \psi_2 = +\sqrt{\frac{2}{L}}$

$x = +\frac{L}{2}, \psi_1 = 0 \qquad x = +\frac{L}{2}, \psi_2 = 0$

The plots are shown in Figures 4.5 and 4.6.

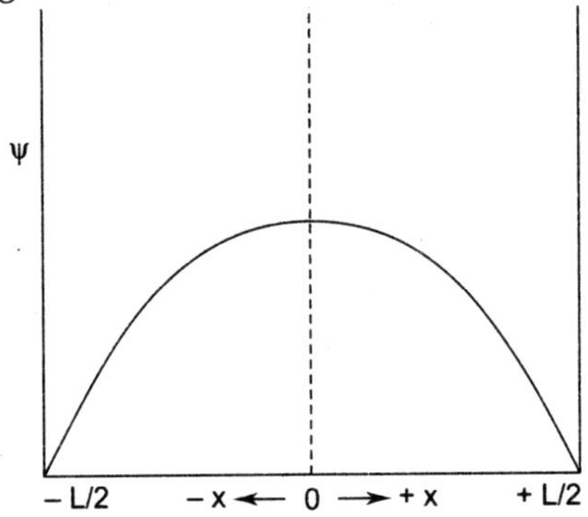

Fig. 4.5 *Symmetry properties of cosine waves when the origin is in the middle; cosine waves are symmetric*

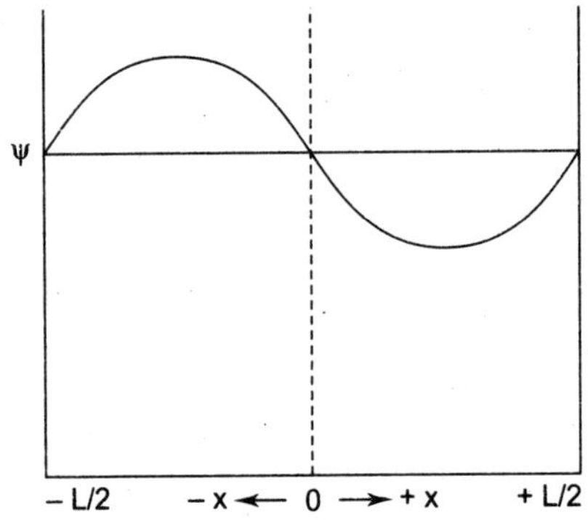

Fig. 4.6 *Symmetry properties of sine waves when the origin is in the middle; sine waves are anti-symmetric*

Physical Meaning of the Wave Functions—Probability Density: The normalised expression for the wave function enables us to calculate the probabilities of finding the particle at various points in the box. The probability density,

$$\psi^2 = \frac{2}{L}\sin^2\frac{n\pi x}{L} \qquad \text{... (4.27)}$$

varies between 0 and $\frac{2}{L}$. In a region between $x = a$ and $x = b$, the probability is given by

$$P = \int_a^b \psi^2\, dx = \frac{2}{L}\int_a^b \sin^2\frac{n\pi x}{L}\, dx \qquad \text{... (4.28)}$$

This shows that in contrast to the free particle, for which there is equal probability (ψ^2 = constant) of finding the particle at every point, the particle in a box is "delocalised" within the ends of the box, but it has maximum probability at certain specified points depending on the energy state (value of n). For $n = 1$, the maximum probability $\left(\frac{2}{L}\right)$ occurs at $x = \frac{L}{2}$; for $n = 2$, the probability at $x = \frac{L}{2}$ is zero, while it is maximum at $x = \frac{L}{4}$ and $x = \frac{3L}{4}$, *i.e.*, on either side of the middle point. Being ψ^2, the probability can never be negative, and so the probability curves are always symmetric about the reflection plane at the middle of the box (see Fig. 4.7).

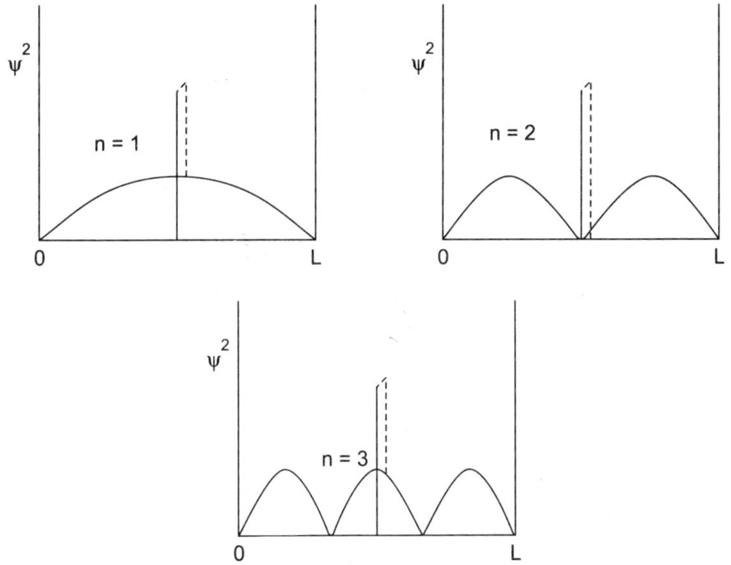

Fig. 4.7 *Probability curves for particle in a box*

One point deserves special consideration. In the $n = 2$ state, there is a finite (through varying) probability of finding the particle at all points on either side of the middle point of the box, but there is absolutely no chance of finding it in just the middle. Does it mean that the particle can move to and fro from one end to the other end without actually even touching the middle point ? Surprising though it may appear, it is precisely the conclusion based on quantum mechanical considerations.

There is one way to understand it: The particle may be considered to be a smeared out cloud of varying density with zero density at the middle of the box and maximum on either side of it.

Average or Expectation Values: We can use the wave function to determine, in any state n, the average or expectation values of any physical quantity, *e.g.*, position, momentum, energy, etc., (see Chapter 3). Consider, for example, the position. Since the particle can be anywhere in the box, the average of a series of measurements can be computed by the formula,

$$\bar{x} = \int_0^L \psi \hat{x} \psi \, dx = \frac{2}{L} \int_0^L x \sin^2 \frac{n\pi x}{L} dx \qquad \text{... (4.29)}$$

Let $u = \frac{n\pi x}{L}$, or $x = \frac{Lu}{n\pi}$, $dx = \frac{L}{n\pi} du$;

when $x = 0, u = 0$ and when $x = L, u = n\pi$ ... (4.30)

Therefore,

$$\bar{x} = \frac{2}{L} \int_0^{n\pi} \frac{Lu}{n\pi} \sin^2 u \left(\frac{L}{n\pi}\right) du$$

$$= \frac{2L}{(n\pi)^2} \int_0^{n\pi} u \sin^2 u \, du \qquad \text{... (4.31)}$$

Using the table of integrals

$$\bar{x} = \frac{2L}{(n\pi)^2} \left[\left(\frac{u^2}{4} - \frac{u \sin 2u}{4} - \frac{\cos 2u}{8}\right)\right]_0^{n\pi}$$

$$= \frac{2L}{(n\pi)^2} \left[\left\{\frac{(n\pi)^2}{4} - \frac{(n\pi)\sin(2n\pi)}{4} - \frac{\cos(2n\pi)}{8}\right\} - \left\{0 - 0 - \frac{1}{8}\right\}\right]$$

$$= L - \frac{2L}{(n\pi)^2} \times \frac{(n\pi)^2}{4} = \frac{L}{2} \qquad \text{... (4.32)}$$

Thus, quantum mechanical considerations show that the average value of the position of the particle in any state (n) lies in the middle of the box, which is the same as that obtained from classical point of view. This should not be surprising as the probability density curves [Fig. 4.7] indicate that the probability of finding the particle at a distance d to the left of the centre is exactly the same as that at the distance d to the right.

We can likewise calculate other quantities. A quantity of interest is $\bar{x}^2$.

$$\bar{x}^2 = \frac{2}{L}\left(\frac{L}{n\pi}\right)^3 \int_0^{n\pi} u^2 \sin^2 u \, du$$

$$= \frac{2}{L}\left(\frac{L}{n\pi}\right)^3 \left[\frac{u^3}{6} - \left(\frac{u^2}{4} - \frac{1}{8}\right)\sin 2u - \frac{u \cos 2u}{4}\right]_0^{n\pi}$$

$$= \frac{2}{L}\left(\frac{L}{n\pi}\right)^3 \left[\left(\frac{n^3\pi^3}{6} - 0 - \frac{n\pi}{4}\right) - (0 - 0 - 0)\right]$$

$$= \frac{2}{L}\left(\frac{L}{n\pi}\right)^3 (n\pi)\left[\frac{n^2\pi^2}{6} - \frac{1}{4}\right]$$

$$= \frac{L^2}{3} - \frac{L^2}{2n^2\pi^2} = \frac{L^2}{3}\left[1 - \frac{3}{2n^2\pi^2}\right] \quad \text{... (4.33)}$$

Uncertainties in Position and Momentum: Since the particle can be anywhere within the length L, the error (uncertainty) involved in any single measurement of position, $\Delta x = L$. The momentum lies betwen $+\frac{nh}{2L}$ and $-\frac{nh}{2L}$; so, the uncertainty,

$$\Delta p_x = \frac{nh}{2L} - \left(-\frac{nh}{2L}\right) = \frac{nh}{L}; \text{ for } n = 1, \Delta p_x = \frac{h}{L},$$

and the product $\Delta x \,.\, \Delta p_x = h$ ... (4.34)

which satisfies the Heisenberg uncertainty relation.

4.2.2 Utility of the Particle-in-a-Box Model

1. **Quantisation effects:** The problem of particle in a one-dimensional box can serve as a good model for the calculation of approximate energies in atomic and molecular systems, besides accounting for the effect of quantisation.
   Firstly, let us estimate the quantisation effects in energy of gaseous molecules. For a gas molecule of molecular weight 50, for example, in a "box" of size 1 cm the lowest energy gap

$$\Delta E_1 = \frac{3h^2}{8mL^2} = \frac{3 \times \left(6.625 \times 10^{-34} \text{ Js}\right)^2}{8 \times \left(\frac{50 \times 10^{-3}}{1000 \times 6.02 \times 10^{23}} \text{ kg}\right) \times (0.01 \text{ m})^2}$$

$$= 3.5 \times 10^{-38} \text{ J}.$$

   On comparison with the thermal energy, KT, of the molecule (~ 5×10^{-21} J) at room temperature, it can be seen that there is practically no quantisation of translational energy. If now we assume that in atoms and molecules the bound electrons ($m = 9.1 \times 10^{-30}$ g) move in "boxes" of lengths 1 – 10 Å, the minimum energy gap between two levels is of the order of 10^{-18} to 10^{-20} J, which is greater than the thermal energy (KT) at ordinary temperatures. Hence, the quantisation of electronic energy may be observed in atoms and molecules.

2. **Electronic spectra:** Such calculations also provide satisfactory interpretation of electronic spectra of atoms and molecules. An electron in an atom or molecule can jump from a lower energy level to a higher energy level by absorption of light of appropriate wavelength, or it can jump from a higher to a lower level by emission of light. The wavelength (λ) of the light absorbed or emitted is related to the energy gap between the two levels.

$$\Delta E = \frac{hc}{\lambda}, (c = \text{velocity of light}) \qquad \text{... (4.35)}$$

The model is most suitable for explaining the electronic spectra (UV or visible): of conjugated organic molecules. Spectral data available for polyenes, cyanine dyes, etc., agree fairly well with the calculated values. Such linear molecules are treated as one-dimensional boxes in which π electrons move freely (*i.e.*, V = 0) from one end of the conjugated chain to the other end. The π electrons are distributed in the various energy levels in accordance with the rules of electronic distribution in atom and molecules. Ignoring the interelectronic repulsion as a first approximation, the energy of each π electron in each level is calculated by the formula (4.18), *i.e.*, $E_n = \frac{n^2 h^2}{8mL^2}$. L, the length of the box, is taken as roughly equal to the sum of all the C—C bond distances. The wavelength of the light absorbed depends on the length of the box, *i.e.*, length of the conjugated chain. For molecules of small chain length (*e.g.*, butadiene) the absorption takes place in ultraviolet region, while for molecules having longer chains the energy gap (ΔE) becomes lower and, hence, the wavelength of the absorbed light larger. The following exercise will explain the idea.

Exercise 1: What is the wavelength of the light absorbed when an electron in a linear molecule 10 Å long makes a transition from the energy level, $n = 1$ to the level $n = 2$.

$$\Delta E = E_2 - E_1 = \left(2^2 - 1^2\right)\frac{h^2}{8mL^2}$$

$$= \frac{3 \times \left(6.625 \times 10^{-34}\right)^2}{8 \times \left(9.109 \times 10^{-31}\right) \times \left(10 \times 10^{-10}\right)^2}$$

$$= 1.8 \times 10^{-19}\ \text{J}$$

$$\lambda = \frac{hc}{\Delta E}$$

$$= \frac{6.62 \times 10^{-34}\ \text{J} \times 3 \times 10^{8}\ \text{ms}^{-1}}{18.0 \times 10^{-20}\ \text{J}}$$

$$= 1.1 \times 10^{-6}\ \text{m} = 1100\ \text{nm}.$$

Exercise 2: Treating the π electrons in a conjugated system as particles moving in a one-dimensional box, calculate the lowest absorption frequency (in cm^{-1}) and the wavelength (in nm) of absorbed light for the molecule of butadiene; the length of the molecule is 0.56 nm. What is the total ground state energy of the molecule ?

The lowest absorption frequency (greatest wavelength of the absorption) corresponds to the transition from the highest occupied energy level (E_n) to the lowest unoccupied energy level (E_{n+1}). Since π electrons are distributed in these levels by aufbau rule, the former has the quantum number $n = \frac{N_\pi}{2}$, where, N_π is the number of π electrons, and the latter has the quantum number $n + 1 = \frac{N_\pi}{2} + 1$. In butadiene there are 4π electrons (see Fig. 4.8). (For π electrons in butadiene see Chapter 13).

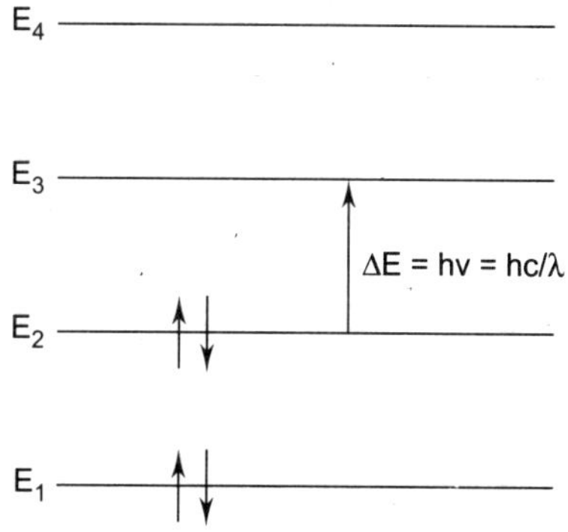

Fig. 4.8 *Energy levels and electron distribution in butadiene ($H_2C{=}CH{-}CH{=}CH_2$) molecule*

$$\bar{\nu}\left(cm^{-1}\right) = \frac{\Delta E}{hc} = \left\{\left(\frac{N_\pi}{2}+1\right)^2 - \left(\frac{N_\pi}{2}\right)^2\right\}\frac{h^2}{8mL^2} \times \frac{1}{hc}$$

or

$$\bar{\nu} = \frac{\left(3^2 - 2^2\right) \times 6.62 \times 10^{-34}\ \text{Js}}{8 \times 9 \times 10^{-31}\ \text{kg} \times \left(0.56 \times 10^{-19}\ \text{m}\right)^2 \times \left(3 \times 10^8\ \text{ms}^{-1}\right)}$$

$$= 0.484 \times 10^5\ \text{cm}^{-1} = 48400\ \text{cm}^{-1}$$

$$\lambda = \frac{1}{\bar{\nu}} = \frac{1}{48400} = 207 \times 10^{-7}\ \text{cm} = 207\ \text{nm}.$$

Total ground state energy, $E_0 = \sum_i \nu_i E_i$, where, ν_i is the number of electrons and E_i the energy of a single electron in the ith energy level; that is,

$$E_0 = \sum_{i=1}^{N_{\pi/2}} \nu_i \left(\frac{n^2 h^2}{8mL^2}\right) \qquad \text{... (4.36)}$$

N_π is the total number of π electrons and the summation extends over all the occupied energy levels. The value of ν_i in any level i can be either 1 or 2 (in accordance with Pauli's exclusion principle). In the butadiene molecule,

$$E_0 = \left(2\times 1^2 + 2\times 2^2\right)\frac{h^2}{8mL^2}$$

$$= \frac{10\times\left(6.625\times 10^{-34}\ \text{Js}\right)^2}{8\times 9\times 10^{-31}\ \text{kg}\times\left(0.56\times 10^{-10}\ \text{m}\right)^2}$$

$$= 1.5\times 10^{-18}\ \text{J}.$$

4.2.3 Three Dimensional Box

Electronic motions in atoms and molecules are three-dimensional and a three-dimensional box model should be more appropriate. Though electronic motions in atoms and molecules are complicated due to some other factors (to be discussed in later chapters), let us see how far the results of quantum mechanical treatment of a single particle moving in a three-dimensional box are of interest.

4.2.4 Rectangular Box

For particle moving in a rectangular box of dimensions L_x, L_y and L_z along the three coordinates x, y and z, the Hamiltonian $\left(\hat{H}\right)$ is given by,

$$\hat{H} = -\frac{h^2}{8\pi^2 m}\left(\frac{\partial^2}{\partial x^2}+\frac{\partial^2}{\partial y^2}+\frac{\partial^2}{\partial z^2}\right)+\hat{V}\ (x, y \text{ and } z) \qquad \text{... (4.37)}$$

If the particle's motion within the box is free (unacted upon by any force) *i.e.*, the potential energy (V) is zero inside and infinite outside the boundaries of the box, the Schrödinger equation is,

$$-\frac{h^2}{8\pi^2 m}\left(\frac{\partial^2}{\partial x^2}+\frac{\partial^2}{\partial y^2}+\frac{\partial^2}{\partial z^2}\right)\psi = E\psi \qquad \text{... (4.38)}$$

where, $\psi = \psi\,(x, y, z)$.

The three-dimensionl Equation (4.38) can be solved by the method of separation of variables (as discussed earlier). Thus, assuming ψ to be a product of three independent functions,

$$\psi\,(x, y, z) = X\,(x)\,.\,Y\,(y)\,.\,Z\,(z) \text{ or simply } \psi = X\,.\,Y\,.\,Z \qquad \text{... (4.39)}$$

substituting for ψ in the Schrödinger equation and then dividing by

$$\psi = X\,.\,Y\,.\,Z,$$

we obtain the following three ordinary differential equations, each comprising a single variable.

$$\left.\begin{aligned} -\frac{h^2}{8\pi^2 m}\frac{1}{X}\frac{d^2X}{dx^2} &= E_x \\ -\frac{h^2}{8\pi^2 m}\frac{1}{Y}\frac{d^2Y}{dy^2} &= E_y \\ -\frac{h^2}{8\pi^2 m}\frac{1}{Z}\frac{d^2Z}{dz^2} &= E_z \end{aligned}\right] \qquad \text{... (4.40)}$$

with $E_x + E_y + E_z = E$

Each of these equations has a form similar to the Schrödinger Equation (4.12) for a particle in one-dimensional box with similar boundary conditions. In other words, the problem of a particle in three-dimensional box is reduced to one of three particles in three separate one-dimensional boxes of lengths L_x, L_y and L_z. Accordingly, the normalised solutions of the three equations will be

$$\left.\begin{aligned} X &= \sqrt{\frac{2}{L_x}} \sin \frac{n_x \pi}{L_x} x \\ Y &= \sqrt{\frac{2}{L_y}} \sin \frac{n_y \pi}{L_y} y \\ Z &= \sqrt{\frac{2}{L_z}} \sin \frac{n_z \pi}{L_z} z \end{aligned}\right] \quad \text{... (4.41)}$$

n_x, n_y and n_z are now the quantum numbers for the three separate boxes.

Hence, by (4.39) $\psi(x, y, z) = X \cdot Y \cdot Z = \sqrt{\frac{8}{L_x L_y L_z}} \sin \frac{n_x \pi x}{L_x} \sin \frac{n_y \pi y}{L_y} \sin \frac{n_z \pi z}{L_z}$ .... (4.42)

Also, $$E_x = \frac{n_x^2 h^2}{8mL_x^2};\ E_y = \frac{n_y^2 h^2}{8mL_y^2};\ E_z = \frac{n_z^2 h^2}{8mL_z^2} \quad \text{... (4.43)}$$

such that $$E = E_x + E_y + E_z = \frac{h^2}{8m}\left(\frac{n_x^2}{L_x^2} + \frac{n_y^2}{L_y^2} + \frac{n_z^2}{L_z^2}\right) \quad \text{... (4.44)}$$

The lowest (ground state) energy (E_1) corresponds to $n_x = n_y = n_z = 1$. Note that the total energy E, and the wave function ψ of such a system (three-dimensional) have to be described in terms of three quantum numbers, n_x, n_y and n_z. (A two-dimensional problem would require two quantum numbers). The probability (ψ^2) of finding the particle in unit space is also a product of three separate probabilities X^2, Y^2 and Z^2.

4.2.5 Cubical Box: A Case of Degeneracy

An interesting situation arises if the box is cubical, *i.e.*,

$$L_x = L_y = L_z = L \text{ (say)}$$

The energy E in such a system is

$$E = \frac{h^2}{8mL^2}\left(n_x^2 + n_y^2 + n_z^2\right) \quad \text{... (4.45)}$$

The lowest energy is given by,

$$E_{111} = \frac{3h^2}{8mL^2} \text{ (when } n_x = n_y = n_z = 1) \quad \text{... (4.46)}$$

which is three times that for a particle in a one-dimensional box of length L.

The corresponding wave function is,

$$\psi_{111} = \sqrt{\frac{8}{L^3}} \sin\frac{\pi x}{L} \sin\frac{\pi y}{L} \sin\frac{\pi z}{L} \quad \text{... (4.47)}$$

(The subscripts in E and ψ denote the three quantum numbers).

Now consider the next higher (excited) level when one of the quantum numbers is 2, while the others are 1 each. There will be three independent states corresponding to the following three combinations of n_x, n_y and n_z : (2, 1, 1), (1, 2, 1) and (1, 1, 2). Each state has the same energy,

$$E_{211} = E_{121} = E_{112} = \frac{6h^2}{8mL^2} \quad \text{... (4.48)}$$

but a different wave function,

$$\left.\begin{aligned} \psi_{211} &= \sqrt{\frac{8}{L^3}} \sin\frac{2\pi x}{L} \sin\frac{\pi y}{L} \sin\frac{\pi z}{L} \\ \psi_{121} &= \sqrt{\frac{8}{L^3}} \sin\frac{\pi x}{L} \sin\frac{2\pi y}{L} \sin\frac{\pi z}{L} \\ \psi_{112} &= \sqrt{\frac{8}{L^3}} \sin\frac{\pi x}{L} \sin\frac{\pi y}{L} \sin\frac{2\pi z}{L} \end{aligned}\right] \quad \text{... (4.49)}$$

Such an energy state having more than one wave function for the same value of energy is called "degenerate state" and the phenomenon is called "degeneracy" (see Chapter 2, Section 2.6.3.1). In this example, the state is triply (three-fold) degenerate.

The first three energy levels of a particle in a cubical box are shown in Fig. 4.9.

The degeneracy arises whenever there is an integral relation among L_x, L_y and L_z. If $n_x = n_y = n_z$, the state will be non-degenerate. A slight distortion of the system may lead to the breakdown of degeneracy. Suppose, for example, the length L_x (= L) along x-axis is increased by a small amount dL. For the undistorted cube, the energy of the particle in the (2, 1, 1), (1, 2, 1) and (1, 1, 2) states is $E = \frac{6h^2}{8mL^2}$. After distortion along x-axis, the energy in the 2, 1, 1 state is

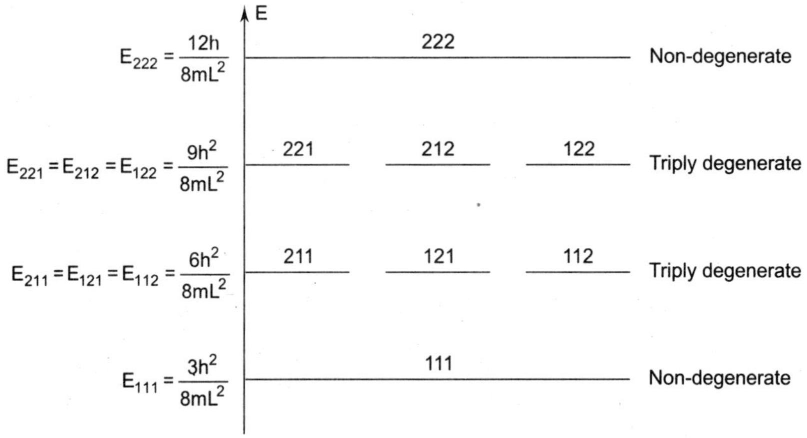

Fig. 4.9 *Energy levels in a cubical box showing degeneracy*

$$E + dE = (E_x + dE_x) + E_y + E_z$$

Since, $$E_x = \frac{4h^2}{8mL^2},$$

$$\frac{dE_x}{dL} = \frac{d\left(\dfrac{h^2}{2mL^2}\right)}{dL} = -\frac{h^2}{mL^3}$$

or $$dE_x = -\frac{h^2}{mL^3}\,dL$$

$$E + dE = \frac{6h^2}{8mL^2} + \left(-\frac{h^2}{mL^3}\,dL\right) \qquad \text{... (4.50)}$$

But in the (1, 2, 1) and (1, 1, 2) states $E_x = \dfrac{h^2}{8mL^2}$ and,

$$E + dE = E_x + dE_x + E_y + E_z = \frac{6h^2}{8mL^2} + \frac{d}{dL}\left(\frac{h^2}{8mL^2}\right)$$

$$= \frac{6h^2}{8mL^2} + \left(-\frac{h^2}{4mL^3}\,dL\right) \qquad \text{... (4.51)}$$

The triply degenerate state is thus split (Fig. 4.10) into a non-degenerate state (ψ_{211}) with energy given by Equation (4.50) and two degenerate states (ψ_{121} and ψ_{112}) with energy given by Equation (4.51).

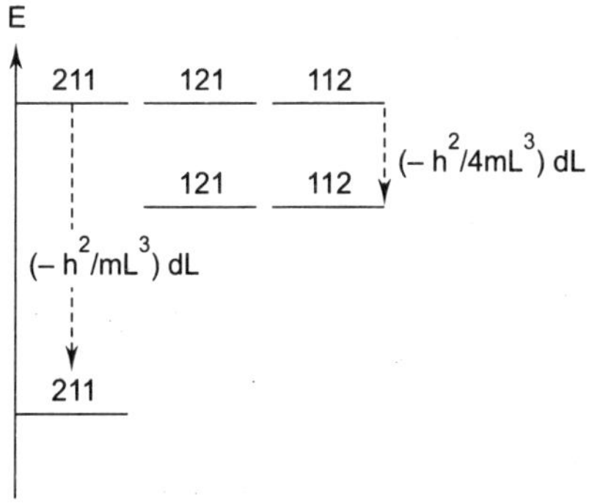

Fig. 4.10 *Breakdown of degeneracy*

4.2.5.1 Physical Representation of the Wave Functions

Because the function ψ involves three variables x, y and z, it cannot be represented graphically. A qualitative understanding of the wave function can be achieved, however, from the nature of the expression (4.42). The value of the function in the ground state ($n_x = n_y = n_z = 1$) is maximum when $x = \frac{L_x}{2}, y = \frac{L_y}{2}$ and $z = \frac{L_z}{2}$ (*i.e.*, at the box centre) and is positive everywhere. In the excited states, the function changes sign and exhibits, nodes in some particular regions. For example, for the state ψ_{211} the function vanishes at $x = \frac{L_x}{2}$ irrespective of the values of y and z, *i.e.*, along the yz plane which is, therefore, the "nodal plane". Similarly, the xz and xy planes passing through $\frac{L_y}{2}$ and $\frac{L_z}{2}$ are nodal planes for the states ψ_{121} and ψ_{112} respectively.

We can arrive at a better picture by considering ψ^2 functions (*i.e.*, probability). For the state ψ_{111} in a cubical box, the probability of finding the particle is maximum at the centre of the box and decreases uniformly towards each side. The probability distribution may be shown pictorially as in Fig. 4.11. In the next higher state, the probability distribution exhibits two equal halves and the probability is zero along the vertical planes passing through the box centre (nodal planes) as described above.

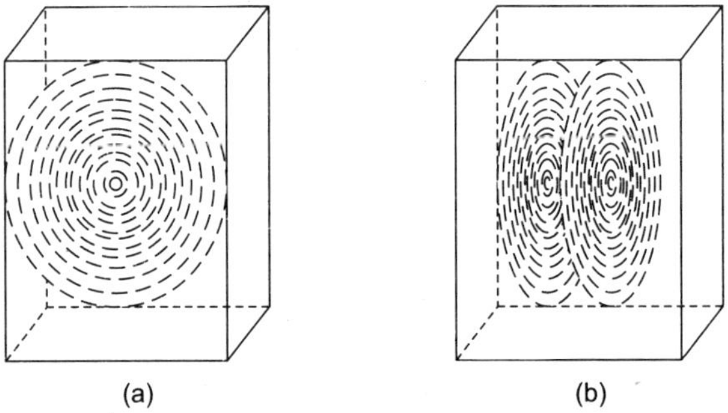

Fig. 4.11 *Probability distribution of a particle in a three dimensional box for the states (a) $n_x = n_y = n_z = 1$; (b) $n_x = 2, n_y = n_z = 1$*

The state (2, 2, 2) has three vertical nodal planes along each side (*i.e.*, *yz*, *xz* and *xy*). It is apparent that as the energy level increases the probability distribution is spread out more and more inside the box and in the limiting case tends to correspond to the classical prediction.

4.3 PARTICLE WITH FINITE POTENTIAL BARRIERS

Now consider that the freely moving particle meets a potential energy barrier of finite height. According to classical laws, it is expected that (*i*) if the energy (E) of the particle is less than the height of barrier (V) it will be reflected back, and (*ii*) if it is greater it will be transmitted to the other side of the barrier. But, somewhat different and highly interesting results are obtained if the system is treated quantum-mechanically.

4.3.1 One Finite Potential Barrier

Consider the particle in a one-dimensional box of length L with the modification that one of the walls at the end x = L has a finite height (V) and the other at the end $x = 0$ has infinite height

(V = ∞). Between $x = 0$ and $x = L$, the potential energy V = 0 (Fig. 4.12). The system which may also be termed as a potential well is now divided into regions I and II where V = 0 and V = V respectively. The Schrödinger equations for the two regions can be conveniently written as follows:

Region I: $$\frac{d^2\psi_I}{dx^2} + \frac{8\pi^2 mE}{h^2}\psi_I = 0 \quad \text{... (4.52)}$$

Region II: $$\frac{d^2\psi_{II}}{dx^2} + \frac{8\pi^2 m(E-V)}{h^2}\psi_{II} = 0 \quad \text{... (4.53)}$$

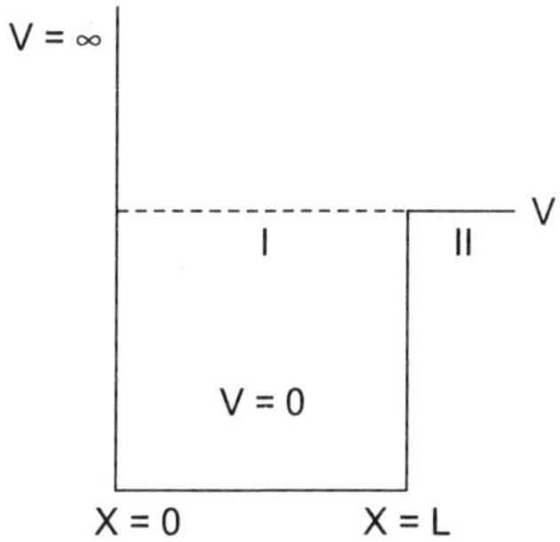

Fig. 4.12 *Potential barriers, one finite and the other infinite, for a particle in a one-dimensional box*

Solutions to these equations have to be obtained under two situations : (*i*) E < V, when the particle, in the classical sense, is unable to escape from the box, and (*ii*) E > V, when it has sufficient energy to cross over the potential wall.

Case I: E < V

Equations (4.52) and (4.53) may be put in the forms

Region I: $$\frac{d^2\psi_I}{dx^2} + k_1^2\psi_I = 0 \quad \text{... (4.54)}$$

Region II: $$\frac{d^2\psi_{II}}{dx^2} - k_2^2\psi_{II} = 0 \quad \text{... (4.55)}$$

where, $k_1^2 = \frac{8\pi^2 mE}{h^2}$, and $k_2^2 = \frac{8\pi^2 m(V-E)}{h^2}$

The solution for Equation (4.54) is,

$$\psi_I = A\sin k_1 x + B\cos k_1 x \text{ (real form)} \quad \text{... (4.56)}$$

or $$\psi_I = A'\exp(ik_1 x) + B'\exp(-ik_1 x) \text{ (complex form)} \quad \text{... (4.57)}$$

and for Equation (4.55) the solution is,

$$\psi_{II} = C\exp(k_2 x) + D\exp(-k_2 x) \quad \text{... (4.58)}$$

where, A, A′, B, B′, C and D are arbitrary constants of integration. The expression (4.58) for ψ_{II} contains all real exponential terms which cannot be converted to sine and cosine terms. This means that ψ_{II} does not represent a periodic (wave) motion and has no wavelength associated with it. The expressions (4.56) and (4.57) for ψ_I, on the other hand, represent the particle waves moving in the positive and negative directions with wavelength,

$$\lambda = \frac{h}{p} = \frac{h}{\sqrt{2mE}} = \frac{2\pi}{k_1} \qquad \text{... (4.59)}$$

Now we may apply the boundary conditions to the functions ψ_I and ψ_{II}. The function ψ_I is finite and single-valued at all points (because it consists of sine and cosine terms). The boundary condition is that $\psi = 0$ at $x = 0$ (where it meets the infinity wall); so B has to be zero so that,

$$\psi_I = A \sin k_1 x \qquad \text{... (4.60)}$$

At $x = L$, we have no such boundary condition (as it exists in the case of the system with both walls of infinite potential).

As regards ψ_{II}, the first term on the right hand side will increase without limit as $x \to \infty$, this is not acceptable and, hence, the arbitrary constant C must be set equal to zero; the function becomes

$$\psi_{II} = D \exp(-k_2 x) \qquad \text{... (4.61)}$$

There is another very important condition to be fulfilled: ψ_I and ψ_{II} must join each other in continuity at $x = L$, that is, there must not be a sudden change in the slope $\frac{d\psi}{dx}$ at $x = L$. This means that at $x = L$,

$$\psi_I = \psi_{II} \text{ and } \frac{d\psi_I}{dx} = \frac{d\psi_{II}}{dx}$$

This leads to the following relationship at $x = L$.

$$A \sin(k_1 L) = D \exp(-k_2 L) \qquad \text{... (4.62)}$$

and

$$k_1 A \cos(k_1 L) = -k_2 D \exp(-k_2 L)$$

$$= -k_2 A \sin(k_1 L) \text{ by (4.62)} \qquad \text{... (4.63)}$$

or

$$\tan(k_1 L) = -\frac{k_1}{k_2} = -\frac{E^{1/2}}{(V-E)^{1/2}} \text{ (by definitions of } k_1 \text{ and } k_2) \qquad \text{... (4.64)}$$

or

$$\tan\left\{\left(\frac{8\pi^2 mE}{h^2}\right)^{1/2} L\right\} = -\frac{E^{1/2}}{(V-E)^{1/2}} \qquad \text{... (4.65)}$$

The only unknown quantity in Equation (4.65) is E. For given values of m, L and V, only certain values of $E < V$ satisfy this equation; in other words, discrete values of E are allowed but are not characterised by any quantum number (as required in previous model where $E \propto n^2$). The allowed values of E can be determined by drawing graphs of the left and right hand sides of the Equation (4.65) for various assumed values of E and noting the points of intersection of the curves. It is only at these points that the Equation (4.65) is satisfied. Fig. 4.13 shows qualitatively the graphical method of solving the equation.

After determining any one value of E, we have to find A and D only. Equation (4.66) gives the ratio,

$$\frac{A}{D} = \frac{\exp(-k_2 L)}{\sin(k_1 L)} \qquad \text{... (4.66)}$$

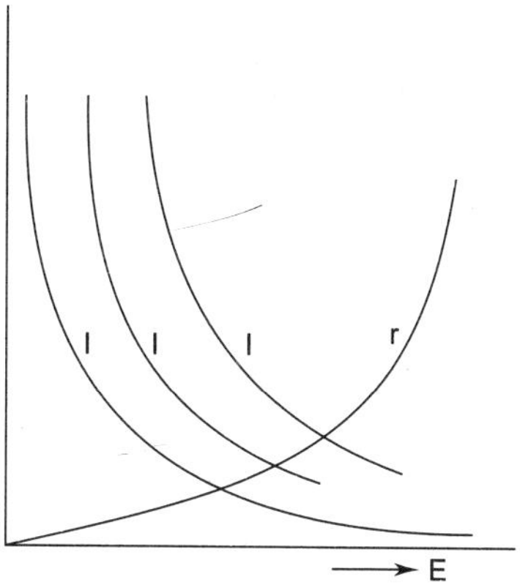

Fig. 4.13 *Graphical solutions for the allowed values of E. l stands for left side and r for right side*

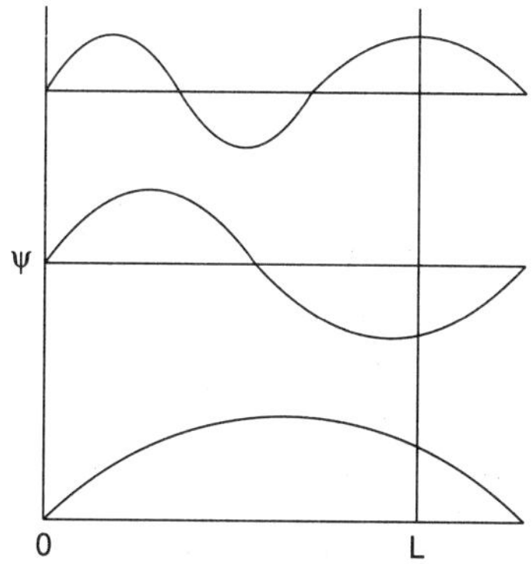

Fig. 4.14 *Forms of the waves in a potential well with one finite potential barrier; it is seen that the waves penetrate through the potential barrier at x = L*

The numerical values of A and D can be obtained by applying the condition of normalisation. The general form of the function is shown in Fig. 4.14.

4.3.1.1 Physical Interpretation

A physical interpretation of the above mathematical treatment can be given as follows. A sine wave ψ_I, having the wavelength $\lambda = \dfrac{h}{\sqrt{2mE}}$ starts from the left wall ($V = \infty$), arrives with a certain magnitude (not zero) at x = L, and as Fig. 4.14 indicates, passes through the barrier into the region-II where it fades out exponentially. The fact that ψ has some finite non-zero value in the region-II indicates that there is a finite probability of finding the particle in the region $x > L$ even though the particle does not have sufficient energy to cross over the potential wall. This is "quantum mechanical penetration" through the barrier which is inconsistent with the classical concept.

Further, it may be seen that for the lowest energy level, slightly less than one-half of a sine wave is accommodated in the box length; that is, the wavelength of the wave is slightly greater than that in the case of a box with infinite barrier, and hence the energy is slightly lower.

Case II: E > V

In this case, the solutions in both regions represent periodic sine waves given by,

$$\psi_I = A \sin k_1 x \quad \text{... (4.67)}$$

$$\psi_{II} = C \sin k_2 x + D \cos k_2 x \quad \text{... (4.68)}$$

or in exponential forms,

$$\psi_I = A' \exp(ik_1 x) + B' \exp(-ik_1 x) \quad \text{... (4.69)}$$

$$\psi_{II} = C' \exp(ik_1 x) + D' \exp(-ik_2 x) \quad \text{... (4.70)}$$

where,

$$k_1 = \left(\frac{8\pi^2 mE}{h^2}\right)^{1/2}$$

and

$$k_2 = \left[\frac{8\pi^2 m(E-V)}{h^2}\right]^{1/2} \quad \text{... (4.71)}$$

and the constants A, A′, etc., are arbitrary constants of integration.

These solutions are analogous to those obtained in the free particle case. The ψ_{II} consists of sine and cosine terms which go on oscillating without being infinite, but it is not zero also as $x \to \infty$. For fixed values of the constants C and D, the waves do not change in amplitude. There are fewer boundary conditions. Therefore, ψ cannot be normalised nor is E quantised. Absolute values of constants A, B, etc., cannot be obtained and only their ratios can be determined.

There is another condition—the condition of continuity of ψ_I and ψ_{II}—to be fulfilled. Since in region II the particle moves only towards the right, away from the box, there is nothing to cause reflection of ψ_{II} ; the term D′ exp $(-ik_2 x)$ is zero which is possible only if D′ = 0. Further, at x = L, since $\psi_I = \psi_{II}$ and $\frac{d\psi_I}{dx} = \frac{d\psi_{II}}{dx}$, from Equations (4.69) and (4.70), we have

$$A' \exp(ik_1 L) + B' \exp(-ik_1 L) = C' \exp(ik_2 L) \quad \text{... (4.72)}$$

and

$$ik_1 A' \exp(ik_1 L) - ik_1 B' \exp(-ik_1 L) = ik_2 C' \exp(ik_2 L) \quad \text{... (4.73)}$$

From Equations (4.72) and (4.73), we have

$$A' = \frac{1}{2} C' \exp(i(k_2 - k_1)L)\left(1 + \frac{k_2}{k_1}\right) \quad \text{... (4.74)}$$

and

$$B' = \frac{1}{2} C' \exp(i(k_2 + k_1)L)\left(1 - \frac{k_2}{k_1}\right). \quad \text{... (4.75)}$$

Since $k_1 \neq k_2$, B′ cannot vanish. This means that the wave can be reflected back after striking the potential wall even though E > V. From Equations (4.74) and (4.75), it is clear that B′ < A′ and, hence, $|B'|^2 < |A'|^2$, *i.e.*, the probability of reflection is less than the probability of propagating over the wall. Such a partial reflection is not expected from classical point of view.

The ratio $\frac{|B'|^2}{|A'|^2}$ is usually called the "reflection coefficient" of the particle. From Equations (4.74) and (4.75),

$$\frac{|B'|^2}{|A'|^2} \text{ or } \frac{B'B'^*}{A'A^*} = \frac{|k_1 - k_2|^2}{|k_1 + k_2|^2} = \frac{\left|\sqrt{E} - \sqrt{E - V}\right|^2}{\left|\sqrt{E} + \sqrt{E - V}\right|^2} \qquad \text{... (4.76)}$$

which is always less than 1.

Exercise: Calculate the percentage of reflection for a particle whose energy E = 2V.

$$\frac{|B'|^2}{|A'|^2} = \frac{\left|\sqrt{2V} - \sqrt{V}\right|^2}{\left|\sqrt{2V} + \sqrt{V}\right|^2} = \frac{\left|\sqrt{2} - 1\right|^2}{\left|\sqrt{2} + 1\right|^2} = 0.025 \text{ or } 2.5\%.$$

4.3.2 Two Finite Barriers

If the origin of the coordinate system lies in the middle of the box, a potential well as shown in Fig. 4.15 will result.

Inside the well, *i.e.*, for $-L \le x \le +L$, the potential, V = 0 and outside it is V. If the energy E < V, two situations arise:

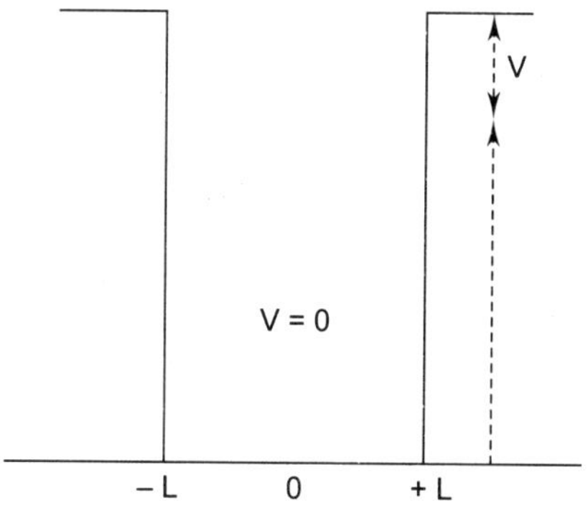

Fig. 4.15 *Potential well with two finite barriers*

(*i*) Inside the well the Schrödinger equation is,

$$\frac{d^2\psi}{dx^2} + \frac{8\pi^2 mE}{h^2}\psi = 0 \qquad \text{... (4.77)}$$

with the solution

$$\psi = A \exp(ik_1 x) + B \exp(-ik_1 x) \qquad \text{... (4.78)}$$

or

$$\psi = A_1 \cos k_1 x + B_1 \sin k_1 x \qquad \text{... (4.79)}$$

where, $k_1^2 = \frac{8\pi^2 mE}{h^2}$.

Basic postulates require that either sine or cosine term be used alone.

(*ii*) Outside the well, the Schrödinger equation is,

$$\frac{d^2\psi}{dx^2} + \frac{8\pi^2 m(E - V)}{h^2}\psi = 0 \quad \text{... (4.80)}$$

Since E – V is negative, here the solution is

$$\psi = C \exp(k_2 x) + D \exp(-k_2 x), k_2 = \frac{8\pi^2 m(E - V)}{h^2} \quad \text{... (4.81)}$$

which is not periodic (no sine or cosine terms are involved) and since ψ has to remain finite as $x \to \pm\infty$, the solution will be

$$\psi = D \exp(-k_2 x) \text{ for } x > L,$$

and

$$\psi = C \exp(k_2 x) \quad \text{for } x < -L \quad \text{... (4.82)}$$

Further, continuity conditions require that at $x = \pm$ L, the sine or cosine functions of Equation (4.79) and their first derivatives must be matched with the exponentials Equation (4.82) and their derivatives respectively.

4.3.2.1 Forms of the Wave Functions

Outside the well the wave functions soon die out as $x \to \pm\infty$. Inside the well, the functions are cosine or sine terms. At the boundaries ($x = \pm$ L) the inside and outside functions join continuously. In Fig. 4.16, the forms of the wave functions are sketched for three different values of k_1. For the central part of ψ_1 and ψ_3, cos $k_1 x$ is used while sin $k_1 x$ is used for ψ_2 in this region. Outer portions of ψ_1, ψ_2 and ψ_3 have exponential terms. The cosine curves are symmetrical about $x = 0$ while the sine curve is antisymmetrical about $x = 0$.

4.3.2.2 Eigenvalues

For ψ_1, the continuity conditions require that at $x = +$ L,

$$A \cos k_1 L = D \exp(-k_2 L) \quad \text{... (4.83)}$$

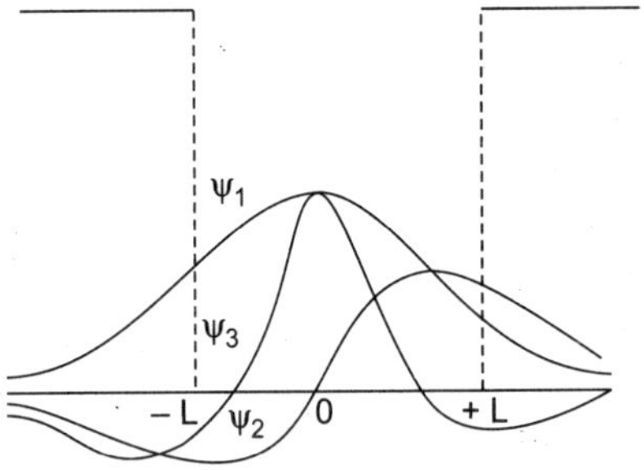

Fig. 4.16 *Forms of three waves in a potential well*

and

$$-Ak_1 \sin(k_1 L) = -Dk_2 \exp(-k_2 L) \quad \text{... (4.84)}$$

At

$$x = -L,$$

$$A \cos(-k_1 L) = C \exp(-k_2 L) \quad \text{... (4.85)}$$

and

$$Ak_1 \sin(-k_1 L) = -Ck_2 \exp(-k_2 L)$$

or $$Ak_1 \sin(k_1 L) = Ck_2 \exp(-k_2 L) \qquad [\because \sin(-k_1 L) = -\sin(k_1 L)] \quad \text{... (4.86)}$$

since $\cos(-k_1 L) = \cos(k_1 L)$ (cos being a symmetric function), from Equations (4.83) and (4.85), C = D. Further,

$$\frac{\exp(-k_2 L)}{\cos k_1 L} = \frac{A}{C} = \frac{k_2 \exp(-k_2 L)}{k_1 \sin k_1 L} \quad \text{... (4.87)}$$

$$\tan(k_1 L) = \frac{k_2}{k_1} \quad \text{... (4.88)}$$

or $$\tan\left[\left(\frac{8\pi^2 mE}{h^2}\right)^{1/2} . L\right] = \frac{\sqrt{V-E}}{\sqrt{E}} \quad \text{... (4.89)}$$

Since L and V are specified, this equation fixes the value of E and thus determines both k_1 and k_2. The equation can be solved by graphical means as described earlier.

Thus, the Equations (4.83) to (4.89) determine the five unknowns and so the wave function is completely specified. A unique value (E_1) is thus selected for the lowest state eigenfunction ψ_1.

For the next higher state E_2, the eigenfunction inside the well is a sine function which must be matched with the exponential functions at $x = \pm$ L.

4.3.3 Potential Barrier of Definite Thickness: The Quantum Mechanical Tunnelling

A much more significant feature is revealed when we consider the case of a particle meeting a finite potential barrier (V) of definite thickness L as shown in Fig. 4.17, the potential at the left (I) and right (III) being zero.

From the classical point of view, as long as E < V, each time the particle strikes the potential well in the region-I, it will be reflected back and there is no chance of its getting into the region-III unless E > V.

However, the quantum mechanical treatment provides a different result. The Schrödinger equations for the three regions are,

Region I: $$\frac{d^2\psi_I}{dx^2} + \frac{8\pi^2 mE}{h^2}\psi_I = 0 \quad \text{... (4.90)}$$

Region II: $$\frac{d^2\psi_{II}}{dx^2} + \frac{8\pi^2 m(E-V)}{h^2}\psi_{II} = 0 \quad \text{... (4.91)}$$

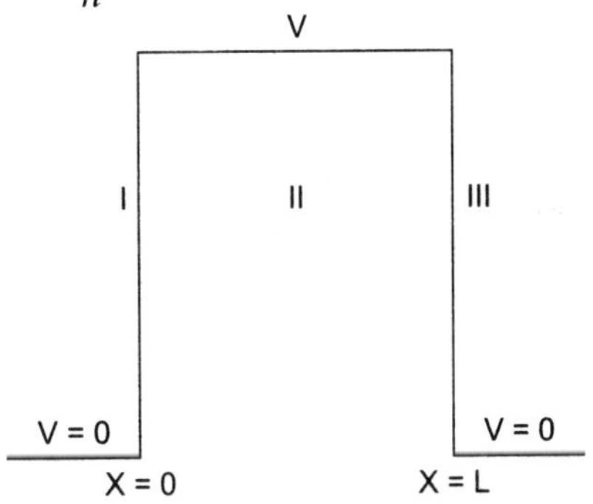

Fig. 4.17 *Barrier of a definite thickness*

Region III: $$\frac{d^2 \psi_{III}}{dx^2} + \frac{8\pi^2 mE}{h^2} \psi_{III} = 0 \qquad \text{... (4.92)}$$

Putting $$k_1^2 = \frac{8\pi^2 mE}{h^2} \qquad \text{... (4.93)}$$

and $$k_2^2 = \frac{8\pi^2 m(E - V)}{h^2} \qquad \text{... (4.94)}$$

We obtain the corresponding solutions

$$\psi_I = A \exp(ik_1 x) + B \exp(-ik_1 x), \text{ for } x < 0 \qquad \text{... (4.95)}$$

$$\psi_{II} = C \exp(k_2 x) + D \exp(-k_2 x), \text{ for } 0 < x < L \qquad \text{... (4.96)}$$

$$\psi_{III} = A' \exp(ik_1 x) + B' \exp(-ik_1 x), \text{ for } x > L \qquad \text{... (4.97)}$$

In region III there is nothing to reflect the wave so that the term $B' \exp(-ik_1 x)$ in Equation (4.97) is zero.

The conditions for continuity at $x = 0$ are that

$$\psi_I = \psi_{II} \text{ and } \frac{d\psi_I}{dx} = \frac{d\psi_{II}}{dx}$$

These lead to the following relations:

$$A + B = C + D \qquad \text{... (4.98)}$$

and $$ik_1 (A - B) = k_2 (C - D)$$

or $$A - B = \frac{k_2 (C - D)}{ik_1} \qquad \text{... (4.99)}$$

Similarly at $x = L$,

$$C \exp(k_2 L) + D \exp(-k_2 L) = A' \exp(ik_1 L) \qquad \text{... (4.100)}$$

and $$k_2 C \exp(k_2 L) - k_2 D \exp(-k_2 L) = ik_1 A' \exp(ik_1 L)$$

or $$C \exp(k_2 L) - D \exp(-k_2 L) = \frac{ik_1}{k_2} A' \exp(ik_1 L) \qquad \text{... (4.101)}$$

From Equations (4.100) and (4.101), we have

$$C = \frac{A' \exp(ik_1 L)}{2 \exp(k_2 L)} \left(1 + \frac{ik_1}{k_2}\right)$$

$$= \frac{A'}{2k_2} \left[\exp\left((ik_1 - k_2) L\right)\right] . (k_2 + ik_1) \qquad \text{... (4.102)}$$

Similarly, $$D = \frac{A'}{2k_2} \exp\left((ik_1 + k_2) L\right) . (k_2 - ik_1) \qquad \text{... (4.103)}$$

From Equations (4.98) and (4.99), we get

$$A = \frac{(C+D) + \dfrac{(C-D)\,k_2}{ik_1}}{2}$$

$$= \frac{(ik_1 + k_2)\,C + (ik_1 - k_2)\,D}{2ik_1} \qquad \text{... (4.104)}$$

In the above equation, values of C and D may be substituted from Equations (4.102) and (4.103), respectively.

$$A = \frac{\left[\dfrac{(ik_1+k_2)\,A'\exp((ik_1-k_2)L)(k_2+ik_1)}{2k_2}\right] + \left[\dfrac{(ik_1-k_2)\,A'\exp((ik_1+k_2)L)(k_2-ik_1)}{2k_2}\right]}{2ik_1}$$

$$= \frac{A'\exp(ik_1 L)}{4ik_1 k_2} \times \left[(ik_1+k_2)^2 \exp(-k_2 L) - (ik_1 - k_2)^2 \exp(k_2 L)\right]$$

$$= \frac{A'\exp(ik_1 L)}{4ik_1 k_2}\left[k_2^2 \exp(-k_2 L) + 2ik_1 k_2 \exp(-k_2 L) - k_1^2 \exp(-k_2 L)\right.$$

$$\left. - k_2^2 \exp(k_2 L) + 2ik_1 k_2 \exp(k_2 L) + k_1^2 \exp(k_2 L)\right]$$

$$= \frac{A'\exp(ik_1 L)}{4ik_1 k_2}\left[(k_1^2 - k_2^2)(\exp(k_2 L) - \exp(-k_2 L))\right.$$

$$\left. + 2ik_1 k_2 (\exp(k_2 L) + \exp(-k_2 L))\right] \qquad \text{... (4.105)}$$

Now we make use of the following two theorems:

$$e^x + e^{-x} = 2\cos hx$$

$$e^x - e^{-x} = 2\sin hx$$

Thus, $$A = \frac{A'\exp(ik_1 L)}{4ik_1 k_2}\left[2(k_1^2 - k_2^2)\sin h(k_2 L) + 4ik_1 k_2 \cos h(k_2 L)\right] \qquad \text{... (4.106)}$$

If A and A′ are the coefficients of the wave functions representing a continuous wave moving forward in regions I and III respectively, then $\dfrac{|A'|^2}{|A|^2}$ represents the relative probability of finding the particle in these two regions which may be called the transmission coefficient (T).

From Equation (4.106)

$$|A|^2 = |A'|^2 (\exp(ik_1 L)\exp(-ik_1 L))\left[\frac{2(k_1^2 - k_2^2)\sin h(k_2 L)}{4ik_1 k_2}\right.$$

$$\left. + \cos h(k_2 L)\right]\left[\cos h(k_2 L) - \frac{2(k_1^2 - k_2^2)\sin h(k_2 L)}{4ik_1 k_2}\right]$$

(using the complex conjugate of A)

$$= |A'|^2 \left[\cos h^2 (k_2 L) + \frac{(k_1^2 - k_2^2)^2 \sin h^2 (k_2 L)}{4k_1^2 k_2^2} \right] \quad \text{... (4.107)}$$

or

$$T = \frac{|A'|^2}{|A|^2} = \frac{1}{\left[\cos h^2 (k_2 L) + \frac{(k_1^2 - k_2^2) \sin h^2 (k_2 L)}{4k_1^2 k_2^2} \right]} \quad \text{... (4.108)}$$

If k_2 L is large (>>1), both cos h (k_2 L) and sin h (k_2 L) become equal to 1/2 exp (k_2 L); then the Equation (4.108) reduces to

$$T = \frac{|A'|^2}{|A|^2} = \frac{16k_1^2 k_2^2 \exp(-2 k_2 L)}{(k_1^2 + k_2^2)^2}$$

Substituting for k_1^2 and k_2^2 from Equation (4.94),

$$T = \frac{16E(V-E)}{V^2} \exp\left(-2 \left[\frac{8\pi^2 m (V-E)}{h^2} \right]^{\frac{1}{2}} L \right) \quad \text{... (4.109)}$$

The right hand side is a definite real quantity which means that there is a definite probability of finding the particle in the region III quite in contradiction to classical predictions. It is as if the particle leaks through the barrier through a "tunnel"—the "quantum mechanical tunnel".

The transmission coefficient or the tunnel effect depends, as is clear from Equation (4.109), on the width (L) and height (V) of the potential barrier in addition to the mass of the particle. The tunnel effect has a great significance in chemistry.

4.3.3.1 Experimental Evidences of Quantum Mechanical Tunnelling

A direct experimental evidence of such a quantum mechanical tunnelling phenomenon comes from emission of α rays from a radioactive nucleus. For example, in the radioactive process,

$$Ra \rightarrow Rn + \alpha$$

the emitting α particle from the radium nucleus has to encounter a strong potential barrier due to coulombic repulsion by the radon nucleus having a large nuclear charge. The energy (E) of the α particle is not sufficient to cross over the barrier. Yet, the particle is able to come out of the radium nucleus by quantum mechanical tunnelling through the barrier.

The movement of electron from one atom to another in several redox reactions as well as reactions at electrodes has been explained in terms of the tunnelling phenomenon. The emission of electrons from metals at low temperatures on applying high voltage has also been explained in terms of tunnelling.

Ammonia has a stable pyramidal structure, but it is capable of inverting into an equivalent "mirror image" pyramid. For this, the H atoms have to pass through a planar configuration having higher potential energy. The vibrational energy of the molecule is not sufficient to allow such an inversion in a classical manner. However, it is presumed that the H atoms in NH_3 are able to tunnel through this barrier. The strong microwave absorption by NH_3 at a wavelength of 1.26×10^7 nm has been explained in terms of this process.

Electrolytic conductance by H^+ and OH^- ions in acidic and basic solutions has also been explained in terms of quantum mechanical tunnelling.

PROBLEMS

4.1. A free particle of mass m is constrained to move in one-dimensional infinite space (x direction). Its potential energy is constant (not zero) at all points.

(*a*) Set up the time-dependent Schrödinger equation and obtain the general solution. Show that this solution can be interpreted as the sum of waves which move in the $+x$ and $-x$ directions.

(*b*) Show that the initial conditions can be so chosen as to make the wave function for the free particle an eigen function of the operator $\hat{p}_x = \frac{h}{2\pi i}\frac{d}{dx}$, *i.e.*, the wave function corresponds to a wave moving in one direction.

(*c*) Show that the initial condition can be so chosen as to make the probability distribution function independent of time, resulting in standing waves.

[Hint: (*a*) $\hat{H} = \frac{ih}{2\pi}\frac{\partial \psi}{\partial t}, \psi = \psi(x, t) = \psi(x), \phi(t)$

Substitution in the wave equation and division by ψ leads to,

$$\frac{\hat{H}\psi}{\psi(x)} \frac{ih}{2\pi} \frac{1}{\phi} \frac{d\phi}{dt} = \text{E (constant, the energy)}$$

Thus, $\frac{ih}{2\pi}\frac{d\phi}{dt} = E\phi, \quad \phi = e^{-2\pi i Et/h}$

and $\hat{H}\psi = E\psi, \quad \text{or } \frac{d^2\psi}{dx^2} + \frac{8\pi^2 m(E - V)}{h^2}\psi = 0$

or

$$\psi = A \exp(ikx) + B \exp(-ikx)$$

$$= A \exp\left(\frac{2\pi i}{h}\sqrt{2m(E - V)}\, x\right) + B \exp\left(-\frac{2\pi i}{h}\sqrt{2m(E - V)}\, x\right)$$

The time-dependent general solution is,

$$\psi(x, t) = \psi \,.\, \phi = A \exp\left(\frac{2\pi i}{h}\left[\sqrt{2m(E - V)}\, x - Et\right]\right)$$

$$+ B \exp\left(\frac{2\pi i}{h}\left[-\sqrt{2m(E - V)}\, x - Et\right]\right)$$

A wave travelling in $\pm x$ directions is classically represented as,

$$A \exp\left(2\pi i\left(\frac{x}{\lambda} - \nu t\right)\right) + B \exp\left(2\pi i\left(-\frac{x}{\lambda} - \nu t\right)\right) \quad \text{(vide Chapter 2)}$$

By comparison, the two expressions will be identical if,

$$\frac{\sqrt{2m(E-V)}}{h} = \frac{1}{\lambda} = \frac{p_x}{h} \text{ and } \frac{E}{h} = \nu, \text{ or } E = h\nu$$

The first term represents the wave moving in the $+x$ direction with crest of the wave corresponding to $\frac{x}{\lambda} = \nu t$ or $x = \nu \lambda t$; the velocity of wave is $C_x = \frac{x}{t} = \nu . \lambda$.

(*b*) At the initial condition $t = 0$

$$\psi(x, 0) = A \exp\left(\frac{2\pi i}{h}\sqrt{2m(E-V)}\, x\right)$$

which requires that $B = 0$

Then, $$\hat{p}_x\, \psi(x, t) = \frac{h}{2\pi i}\frac{d}{dx}\left[A \exp\left(\frac{2\pi i}{h}\left(\sqrt{2m(E-V)}\, x - Et\right)\right)\right]$$

$$= \sqrt{2m(E-V)}\, \psi(x, t)$$

Therefore, $\psi(x, t)$ is an eigenfunction of $\hat{p}_x$ with the eigenvalue $\sqrt{2m(E-V)} = p_x$. Since $p_x > 0$, the wave is in the $+x$ direction. If the initial conditions were chosen so as to set $A = 0$, the wave would be moving in the $-x$ direction.

(*c*) Initial condition can be chosen so that

$$\psi(x, 0) = A\left[\exp\left(\frac{2\pi i}{h}\sqrt{2m(E-V)}\, x\right) + \exp\left(-\frac{2\pi i}{h}\sqrt{2m(E-V)}\, x\right)\right]$$

$$= 2A \cos\left[\frac{2\pi}{h}\sqrt{2m(E-V)}\, x\right]$$

Then, $$\psi(x, t) = 2A \cos\left[\frac{2\pi}{h}\sqrt{2m(E-V)}\, x\right] \exp\left(-\frac{2\pi i Et}{h}\right)$$

Therefore $$\psi\psi^* = 4\,|A|^2 \cos^2\left[\frac{2\pi}{h}\sqrt{2m(E-V)}\, x\right],$$

which is independent of time]

4.2. Show, by considering the origin at the middle point, that for particle in a one-dimensional box of length 2L with ends at ± L, $E_n = \dfrac{n^2 h^2}{32mL^2}$. Determine the first four normalised wave functions.

4.3. An integral number of half wavelengths of a single particle can be fitted between the walls of a one-dimensional box. Use this fact and the de Broglie relation to derive the expression for the quantised energy levels.

$$\left[\textbf{Hint: } \frac{n\lambda}{2} = L;\ \lambda = \frac{h}{\sqrt{2mE}},\ \text{therefore } E = \frac{n^2 h^2}{8mL^2}\right].$$

4.4. Show that the wave functions for a particle in one-dimensional box, $\psi = A \sin \dfrac{n\pi x}{L}$, are not eigenfunction of the linear momentum operator, $\hat{p}_x$, but they can be written as combinations of the eigenfunctions of $\hat{p}_x$.

$$\left[\textbf{Hint: } \sin \frac{n\pi x}{L} = \frac{1}{2i}\left(\exp\left(\frac{in\pi x}{L}\right) - \exp\left(-\frac{in\pi x}{L}\right)\right)\right]$$

Both exponential terms in the right hand side can be easily shown to be eigen function of $\hat{p}_x$ with eigenvalues $\pm \dfrac{nh}{2L}$].

4.5. Show that the wave function $\psi = A \exp(ikx)$ for a free particle cannot be normalised.

4.6. Verify that $\psi = A \sin kx + B \cos kx$ is a general solution for a particle in a one-dimensional box having infinite potential walls.

4.7. Sketch ψ and ψ^2 for the states $n = 4$ and 5 of a particle in a one-dimensional box.

4.8. The size of a nucleus is 10^{-12} cm. Treating it as a one-dimensional box show why electron does not exist in the nucleus.

[**Hint :** Zero point energy, $E_1 = \dfrac{h^2}{8mL^2} = 5.44 \times 10^{-10}$ J. The coulombic attraction energy, on the other hand, is $V = \dfrac{-e^2}{(4\pi\varepsilon_0)\,r} = -2.3 \times 10^{-14}$ J. The coulombic attraction energy is too weak for the nucleus to hold an electron].

4.9. Calculate the length of a one-dimensional box for which the difference between the lowest energy levels of a molecule becomes comparable to its average kinetic energy at a given temperature.

[**Hint:**
$$E_{n+1} - E_n = (2n+1)\frac{h^2}{8mL^2} = \frac{1}{2}k_B T,\ (k_B = \text{Boltzmann constant})$$

$$L = \frac{h}{2}\left(\frac{2n+1}{mk_B T}\right)^{1/2}\Bigg].$$

4.10. For a particle in the states $n = 1, 2$ and 3 of a one-dimensional box of length L, find the probability that the particle is in the region $0 \leq x \leq \frac{L}{4}$.

$$\left[\textbf{Hint: } \text{Probability (P)} = \frac{2}{L}\int_0^{L/4} \sin^2 \frac{n\pi x}{L}\, dx\right.$$

$$= \frac{1}{4} - \frac{\sin \frac{n\pi}{2}}{2n\pi}$$

$$\left(\text{using } \sin^2 x = \frac{1-\cos 2x}{2}\right)$$

For $n = 1, P = \frac{1}{4} - \frac{1}{2\pi} = 0.0908$

$n = 2$, P = 0.25 and for $n = 3$, P = 0.3031].

4.11. A particle of mass $m = 1.0 \times 10^{-26}$ g is confined to move in a box of length 2.0 Å. What is the probability of finding the particle between 1.6000 Å and 1.6001 Å ? Calculate for $n = 1$ and $n = 2$.

[**Hint:** $$P = \frac{2}{L}\int_{1.6000}^{1.6001} \sin^2 \frac{n\pi x}{L}\, dx$$

$$= \frac{1}{L}\left[x - \frac{L\left(\sin \frac{2n\pi x}{L}\right)}{2n\pi}\right]_{1.6000}^{1.6001}$$

for $$n = 1, P = \frac{1}{2.0}\left[0.0001 - \frac{2.0 \times \sin\left(\frac{2\pi \times 1.6001}{2.0}\right) - \sin\left(\frac{2\pi \times 1.6000}{2.0}\right)}{2\pi}\right]$$

$$= 3.41 \times 10^{-5}$$

For $n = 2, P = 1.317 \times 10^{-4}$]

4.12. Show that the probability of finding the particle in the vicinity of the centre of a one-dimensional box of length 1.0 nm is less than the probability of finding it in the range $0 < x < 0.2$ nm corresponding to the state $n = 1$.

[**Hint:** $$P = \psi_1^2\, dx = \frac{2}{L}\sin^2 \frac{\pi x}{L}\, dx$$

In the vicinity of the centre, take $dx \approx 0.51 - 0.49 = 0.02$ (approx)

$$P = \frac{2}{1.0} \times \left(\sin^2 \frac{\pi \times 0.5}{1.0} \right) (0.51 - 0.49) = 0.04 \text{ (approx)}$$

In the range $0 < x < 0.2$ nm, ψ^2 has to be integrated

$$\int_0^{0.2} \psi_1^2 = \frac{2}{1.0} \int_0^{0.2} \frac{1 - \cos 2\pi x/L}{2} dx$$

$$= [x]_0^{0.2} - \left[\frac{\sin\left(\frac{2\pi x}{1.0}\right)}{2\pi} \right]_0^{0.2}$$

$$= \left. \frac{0.2 - \sin \frac{2\pi}{5}}{2\pi} = 0.048 \right].$$

4.13. Show that the probability of finding the particle in a one-dimensional box in the region $\frac{L}{4}$ and $\frac{3L}{4}$ is $\frac{1}{2}$ if n is even, and $\frac{1}{2} + \frac{(-1)^k}{n\pi}$ if n is odd ($= 2k + 1$, where $k = 0, 1, 2, 3, \ldots$)

[Hint:

$$\int_{L/4}^{3L/4} \psi_n^2 \, dx = \frac{2}{L} \int_{L/4}^{3L/4} \sin^2 \frac{n\pi x}{L} dx$$

$$= \frac{1}{2} \times \frac{2}{L} \left[x \right]_{L/4}^{3L/4} - \left[\frac{\sin \frac{2n\pi x}{L}}{2n\pi/L} \right]_{L/4}^{3L/4}$$

$$= \frac{1}{L} \left\{ \left(\frac{3L}{4} - \frac{L}{4} \right) - \frac{1}{2n\pi} \left(\sin \frac{6n\pi}{4} - \sin \frac{2n\pi}{4} \right) \right\}$$

$$= \frac{1}{2} + \frac{1}{2n\pi} \left(\sin \frac{n\pi}{2} - \sin \frac{3n\pi}{2} \right)$$

For even n, both sine terms will be zero; for odd n, if $\sin \frac{n\pi}{2} = 1$, $\sin \frac{3n\pi}{2} = -1$, and vice-versa.

Hence, the term within the bracket can be expressed as $(-1)^k$].

4.14. Using the particle in a box wave function, calculate the average value of p_x^2.

[Hint:

$$\bar{p}_x^2 = \frac{2}{L}\int_0^L \sin\frac{n\pi x}{L}\left[-\frac{h^2}{4\pi^2}\frac{d^2}{dx^2}\left(\sin\frac{n\pi x}{L}\right)\right]dx$$

$$= \frac{2}{L}\times\frac{h^2}{4\pi^2}\times\left(\frac{n\pi}{L}\right)^2\int_0^L \sin^2\frac{n\pi x}{L}\,dx$$

$$= \frac{2}{L}\times\frac{h^2}{4\pi^2}\times\frac{n^2\pi^2}{L^2}\times\frac{L}{2} = \frac{n^2h^2}{4L^2} = 2mE\Bigg].$$

4.15. Calculate the frequency (cm^{-1}) and wavelength of the first ultraviolet band in the spectrum of an organic molecule containing 22 conjugated carbon atoms. The C—C bond length is 0.146 nm while C=C bond length is 0.134 nm, and assumption is made that the length of the molecular chain is equal to $(2n + 1)\,d$ where, $2n$ = number of carbon atoms, d = average C—C bond distance.

$$\left[\textbf{Hint:}\ L = (2n+1)\,d = 23\times\left(\frac{d_{C-C}+d_{C=C}}{2}\right) = 3.22\ \text{nm}\ .\ 22\pi\right]$$

electrons are accommodated in 11 energy levels, the highest occupied level having $n = 11$; so, the next higher level (unoccupied) has $n = 12$.
The first UV band corresponds to the transition from $n = 11$ to $n = 12$.

Using $$\bar{\nu} = \frac{\nu}{c} = \frac{\Delta E}{hc} = \frac{(12^2 - 11^2)\,h}{8mL^2c},$$

and $$m = 9.1\times10^{-31}\ \text{kg for an electron}$$

$$\bar{\nu} = 22000\ \text{cm}^{-1}$$

$$\lambda = \frac{1}{22000}\ \text{cm} = 450\ \text{nm}\Bigg].$$

4.16. Using particle in a box model, find the positions of maximum electron density in the molecule of butadiene, given that the average C—C distance is 0.140 nm. Show graphically the variation of electron density in the molecule.
[Hint: For $C_1{=}C_2{-}C_3{=}C_4$, $L = 4\times0.140 = 0.560$ nm

In the ground state the four π electrons are accommodated in the first two energy levels $n = 1$ and $n = 2$

$$\psi_1^2 = \frac{2}{L}\sin^2\left(\frac{\pi x}{L}\right);\ \psi_2^2 = \frac{2}{L}\sin^2\left(\frac{2\pi x}{L}\right).$$

At $x = \frac{L}{2}$ (*i.e.*, between C_2 and C_3) ψ_1^2 is maximum $\left(\frac{2}{L}\right)$ and $\psi_2^2 = 0$; on the other hand,

at $x = \frac{L}{4}$ and $\frac{3L}{4}$, ψ_2^2 is maximum but ψ_1^2 is not zero.

Therefore, the π electron density $\left(\psi^2 = \psi_1^2 + \psi_2^2\right)$ is maximum between C_1 and C_2, and C_3 and C_4 but minimum between C_2 and C_3].

4.17. For a particle in a cubic box of edge L,

(*i*) how many states have energies in the range 0 to $\frac{16h^2}{8mL^2}$;

(*ii*) how many energy levels lie in this range 0 to $\frac{16h^2}{8mL^2}$;

(*iii*) draw the energy level diagram indicating degenerate states.

[Hint : (*i*) 17 states,

(*ii*) 6 levels,

(*iii*) Energy levels $\left(\text{in terms of } \frac{h^2}{8mL^2}\right)$ see the text].

4.18. A particle is confined to move in a two-dimensional rectangular box having dimensions $L_x = 2L_y$. Draw the energy level for the first 10 lowest levels; give the expressions for the wave function and indicate the degeneracies.

[Hint:

$$E = E_x + E_Y = \frac{h^2}{8mL^2}\left(\frac{n_x^2}{4} + n_y^2\right)$$

$$= \frac{h^2}{32mL^2}\left(n_x^2 + 4n_Y^2\right)$$

$$\psi = \sqrt{\frac{2}{L^2}} \sin\frac{n_x \pi x}{L} \sin\frac{n_y \pi y}{L}\Bigg].$$

4.19. For a particle in a three-dimensional box having the dimensions $L_x = L_y \neq L_z$, tabulate the energies for the quantum numbers 1 and 2. Indicate the degeneracies of the levels.
[Hint: Degenerate levels are (E_{211}, E_{121}), (E_{212}, E_{122}) – see the text].

4.20. For a particle in a three-dimensional box with $L_x = L_y = \frac{L_z}{2}$, what would be the energy when $n_x = 1$, $n_y = 2$, $n_z = 2$, and when $n_x = 1$, $n_y = 1$, $n_z = 4$? Use the calculations to explain the meaning of the term "accidental degeneracy".

[Hint:

$$E_{n_x, n_y, n_z} = \frac{h^2}{32mL^2}\left(4n_x^2 + 4n_y^2 + n_z^2\right)$$

$$E_{122} \frac{24h^2}{32mL^2} = E_{114};$$

The two apparently quite different quantum states are accidentally degenerate].

4.21. For an electron in a three-dimensional rectangular box of dimensions

$$L_x = 1 \times 10^{-15} \text{ m}, L_y = 1.5 \times 10^{-15} \text{ m and } L_z = 2 \times 10^{-15} \text{ m},$$

calculate the zero point energy,

[Hint: Z.P.E. = $E_{111} = 1.01 \times 10^{-7}$ J].

4.22. Calculate the ground state energy of an electron in (*i*) a one-dimensional box of length 3×10^{-10} m and (*ii*) a cubical box of edge length 1×10^{-10} m in eV. Comment on the feasibility of using this cubical box model for an electron in a hydrogen atom.

(*i*)
$$E_I = \frac{h^2}{8mL^2} = \left[\frac{(6.62 \times 10^{-34} \text{ Js})^2}{8 \times 9.1 \times 10^{-31} \text{ kg} \times (3 \times 10^{-10} \text{ m})^2}\right]$$
$$= 4 \text{ eV}.$$

(*ii*)
$$E_{III} = \frac{3h^2}{8mL^2} = 3\left[\frac{(6.62 \times 10^{-34} \text{ Js})^2}{8 \times 9.1 \times 10^{-31} \text{ kg} \times (1 \times 10^{-10} \text{ m})^2}\right]$$
$$= 108 \text{ eV}.$$

Such a model is not acceptable for H atom as the experimental value of ground state energy (E_{III}) is – 13.6 eV.

4.23. For molecules of a gas of molecular weight 60 confined in a cube with each side of 5 cm, what is the quantum number of the stationary state whose energy is equal to the average molecular kinetic energy at 300 K ?

[Hint: $\quad$ $\text{K.E.} = k_B T$

$$E_{n_x, n_y, n_z} = \frac{h^2}{8mL^2}\left(n_x^2 + n_y^2 + n_z^2\right) = k_B T$$

$$m = \frac{\text{M (mol wt)}}{6.03 \times 10^{23}} \text{ g}].$$

4.24. Sketch the following potentials:

(*i*) A single potential step (barrier).
(*ii*) A potential well (two barriers) with origin at one end.
(*iii*) A potential well with origin at the middle.
(*iv*) A potential hill (single barrier of a certain width).
Write the Schrödinger equation for each case and find the eigenfunctions.

4.25. For a particle in a one-dimensional box with one finite and one infinite potential wall, when $E < V$, the energies are discrete and when $E > V$, they are continuous. Is there a solution with $E = V$? What special requirements are there, if any, for such a solution to exist ?

4.26. What is meant by quantum mechanical tunnelling ? Deduce the conditions for a particle to tunnel through a potential barrier.

[Hint : Tunnelling is possible when

$$T = \frac{|A'|^2}{|A|^2} = \frac{1}{\cos h^2 (k_2 L)} = \frac{(k_1^2 - k_2^2) \sin h^2 kL}{4k_1^2 k_2^2} > 0$$

$T = 0$ when the denominator on the right hand side is ∞, *i.e.*, when k_2 L $= \infty$ (because functions are hyperbolic) *i.e.*, when

$$\frac{2\pi}{h}\sqrt{2m(V-E)}\,L=\infty$$

i.e., when

(*i*) either V = ∞

(*ii*) or L = ∞

(*iii*) or *m* is large ($h \approx h^{-34}$ Js, is very small)].

4.27. A beam of electrons strikes an energy barrier of height V = 0.03 eV. What is the percentage of electrons reflected and transmitted if the energy of the electrons is (*i*) 0.025 eV, (*ii*) 0.04 eV ?

[**Hint :** (*i*) For E < V

$$\psi_I = A\exp(ik_1x) + B\exp(-ik_1x)$$
$$\psi_{II} = C\exp(-k_1x) + D\exp(k_2x)$$

Continuity conditions lead to the relations,

$$A + B = C$$

$$A - B = \frac{-Ck_2}{ik_1}\Bigg].$$

CHAPTER 5

Vibrational Motion of a Particle (Harmonic Oscillator)

A characteristic motion often observed in physical systems is simple harmonic motion (vibration or oscillation). It is a back-and-forth motion along the same path, in which the displacement from an equilibrium (rest) position varies periodically with time. The vibration is simple harmonic if it has a fixed time period (τ) and amplitude (a). A pendulum swinging through a very small angle and a mass attached to a weightless spring, restricted to move along the same path, are close approximations to harmonic oscillator. Atoms in a molecule execute vibratory motion along a bond with bond length and bond angles changing periodically; these constitute tiny harmonic oscillators.

In all such oscillators when a particle is displaced from its equilibrium position, a force starts acting on it in the opposite direction in order to restore it to its equilibrium position. If x be the displacement, the restoring force is,

$$f = -kx \qquad \text{... (5.1)}$$

where k, the proportionality constant, is called force constant; the minus sign occurs because the force acts in the opposite direction to the direction of displacement. The Equation (5.1) is known as Hooke's law.

Quantum mechanical treatment of a harmonic oscillator gives different results from those obtained from classical treatment. However, classical treatment is restricted to larger particles (bodies) and the latter to electronic, atomic and molecular particles.

5.1 CLASSICAL MECHANICAL TREATMENT

Combining the Hooke's law Equation (5.1) with Newton's equation of motion (5.2) given below:

$$f = m\frac{d^2x}{dt^2} \qquad \text{... (5.2)}$$

we may obtain the equation for harmonic oscillator,

$$\frac{d^2x}{dt^2} = -\left(\frac{k}{m}\right)x \qquad \text{... (5.3)}$$

where, m is the mass of the particle.

Putting $$\omega = \sqrt{\frac{k}{m}} \quad \text{... (5.4)}$$

we have the general solution for Equation (5.3),

$$x = A \sin \omega t + B \cos \omega t \quad \text{... (5.5)}$$

where, A and B are constants of integration. The Equation (5.5) can also be expressed as,

$$x = a \sin (\omega t + \alpha) \quad \text{... (5.6)}$$

if we put A = a cos α and B = a sin α, where, a and α are two other constants.

The constant a in Equation (5.6) represents the maximum displacement (x) of the vibrating particle from its mean position. The nature of the angle ($\omega t + \alpha$) can be understood if the harmonic vibration is viewed as a projection of the motion of a point on a circle of radius equal to 'a' such that when the particle executes one complete vibration, the point on the circle completes one full rotation $\omega = 2\pi$.

Let AB diameter of the circle, be the path of the vibratory motion and CD, another diameter, perpendicular to it (Fig. 5.1). As the vibrating particle is displaced in time t from its mean position O by OP (= x), a point M on the circle, initially at C, moves through the angle ωt such that x = OP = a sin ωt [Fig. 5.1 (a)], where ω = angular velocity of the point M.

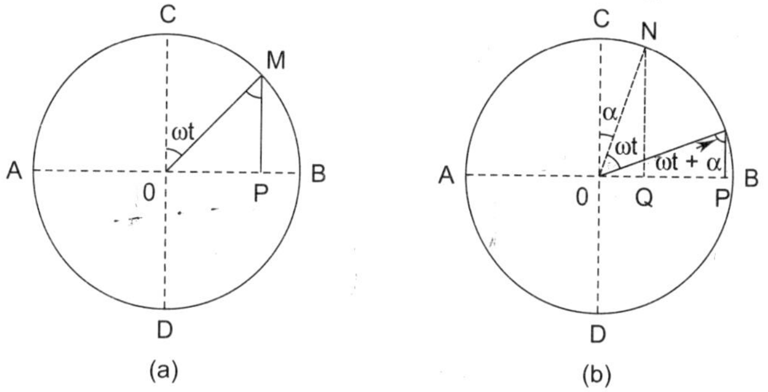

Fig. 5.1 *Geometrical representation of vibratory motion*

We may consider another vibration to begin from the point Q (which is the projection on AB of the point N on the circle) instead of O. The point N makes an angle α with OC so that after time t the displacement OP from O is x = OP = a sin ($\omega t + \alpha$). The angles ωt (in the case of the former) or $\omega t + \alpha$ (in the case of the latter) are phase angles (or simply phases) of the vibrating particle at time t and α is the initial phase (*i.e.*, at t = 0).

It should be clear that if the initial phase be $\frac{\pi}{2}$, the Equation (5.6) will assume the form,

$$x = a \sin \left(\omega t + \frac{\pi}{2} \right)$$

$$= a \cos \omega t \quad \text{... [5.6a]}$$

The motion represented by Equation (5.6) is periodic in t because the sine function repeats itself whenever it goes around an angle of 2π. If the time changes from t to t' in each such round then, $t' - t = \tau$, corresponds to one complete oscillation; it is the time period of oscillation.

$$(\omega t' + \alpha) - (\omega t + \alpha) \text{ or } \omega (t' - t) = 2\pi$$

or $$t' - t \text{ or } \tau = \frac{2\pi}{\omega}, \text{ where, } \tau \text{ is the time period.}$$

or $$\omega = \frac{2\pi}{\tau} = 2\pi\nu \quad \text{... (5.7)}$$

since $\frac{1}{\tau} = \nu$, the frequency of the vibration.

Thus $$x = a \sin (2\pi\nu t + \alpha) \quad \text{... (5.8)}$$

or $$x = a \cos (2\pi\nu t + \alpha') \quad \text{... (5.9)}$$

where, $$\alpha' = \alpha + \frac{\pi}{2}$$

From Equations (5.4) and (5.7), the frequency of oscillation is given by,

$$\nu = \frac{\omega}{2\pi} = \frac{1}{2\pi}\sqrt{\frac{k}{m}} \quad \text{... (5.10)}$$

The potential energy of oscillation at any point x is,

$$V = -\int_0^x f\,dx = \int_0^x kx\,dx = \frac{1}{2}kx^2 \quad \text{... (5.11)}$$

The kinetic energy is

$$T = \frac{1}{2}m\left(\frac{dx}{dt}\right)^2 = 2\pi^2 m\nu^2 a^2 \cos^2(2\pi\nu t + \alpha) \quad \text{... (5.12)}$$

and total energy [using Equations (5.10), (5.11) and (5.12)] is

$$E = \frac{1}{2}kx^2 + \frac{1}{2}m\left(\frac{dx}{dt}\right)^2$$

$$= 2\pi^2\nu^2 ma^2 \sin^2(2\pi\nu t + \alpha) + 2\pi^2 m\nu^2 a^2 \cos^2(2\pi\nu t + \alpha)$$

$$= 2\pi^2\nu^2 ma^2$$

$$= \frac{1}{2}ka^2 \text{ [from Equation (5.10)]} \quad \text{... (5.13)}$$

In Equation (5.13), 'a' represents the amplitude of vibration.

Equation (5.13) shows that the oscillator can have any positive value of E. The path of motion will be a parabola [Fig. (5.2)] which also represents the variation of potential energy.

At the extreme points ($x = \pm a$) of oscillation, all the energy is potential energy $\left(E = V = \frac{1}{2}ka^2\right)$, while at the equilibrium point ($x = 0$), all the energy is kinetic energy. Figure 5.2 shows that at any point within the extremes, the vertical line PQ represents kinetic energy and QR the potential energy; the line PR representing the total energy E.

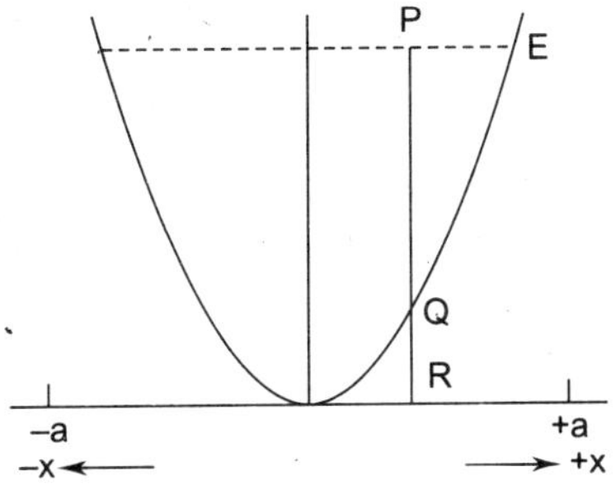

Fig. 5.2

5.2 QUANTUM MECHANICAL TREATMENT

Since the potential energy of oscillation at any point x is,

$$V = \frac{1}{2}kx^2 = 2\pi^2 \nu^2 mx^2 \text{ [from Equations (5.11) and (5.10)]},$$

the Hamiltonian for a harmonic oscillator is given by,

$$\hat{H} = \frac{-h^2}{8\pi^2 m}\frac{d^2}{dx^2} + 2\pi^2 \nu^2 mx^2 \quad \text{... (5.14)}$$

The Schrödinger Equation $\hat{H}\psi = E\psi$, for such a motion may be written as,

$$\frac{d^2\psi}{dx^2} + \frac{8\pi^2 m}{h^2}\left(E - 2\pi^2 \nu^2 mx^2\right)\psi = 0 \quad \text{... (5.15)}$$

Before we attempt to find the expression for ψ and E, let us simplify the Equation (5.15) by on making the following substitutions

$$\alpha = \frac{8\pi^2 mE}{h^2}, \beta = \frac{4\pi^2 \nu m}{h} \quad \text{... (5.16)}$$

Equation (5.15) becomes,

$$\frac{d^2\psi}{dx^2} + \left(\alpha - \beta^2 x^2\right)\psi = 0 \quad \text{... (5.17)}$$

Then we make the following change of variables:

Let $y = \sqrt{\beta}\, x$, so that

$$dx = \frac{dy}{\sqrt{\beta}}, \text{ and } \frac{d^2\psi}{dx^2} = \beta\frac{d^2\psi}{dy^2} \quad \text{... (5.18)}$$

Substituting from Equation (5.18) for x and $\frac{d^2}{dx^2}$ in Equation (5.17), we get

$$\beta\frac{d^2\psi}{dy^2} + \left(\alpha - \beta y^2\right)\psi = 0$$

or
$$\frac{d^2\psi}{dy^2} + \left(\frac{\alpha}{\beta} - y^2\right)\psi = 0 \qquad \text{... (5.19)}$$

The Equation (5.19) is now free of quantities like π, m, h, etc., and since the variable y is dimensionless, the equation is purely algebraic.

5.2.1 Solution of the Equation

It is not as easy to solve Equation (5.19) as in earlier cases. An asymptotic solution can be obtained for very large values of y.

When $y >> \frac{\alpha}{\beta}$, the Equation (5.19) reduces to

$$\frac{d^2\psi}{dy^2} - y^2\psi = 0 \qquad \text{... (5.20)}$$

The solution of Equation (5.20) can be shown to be,

$$\psi = \exp\left(\pm\frac{y^2}{2}\right) \qquad \text{... (5.21)}$$

[This can be verifed as follows:

$$\frac{d^2\psi}{dx^2} = y^2\exp\left(\pm\frac{y^2}{2}\right) \pm \exp\left(\pm\frac{y^2}{2}\right) = \left(y^2 \pm 1\right)\exp\left(\pm\frac{y^2}{2}\right) \qquad \text{... (5.22)}$$

For very large values of y, $y^2 \pm 1 \approx y^2$, so that Equation (5.22) becomes,

$$\frac{d^2\psi}{dx^2} = y^2\exp\left(\pm\frac{y^2}{2}\right)$$

$$= y^2\psi \quad \text{[by Equation (5.21)]} \qquad \text{... (5.23)}$$

However, of the two solutions in Equations (5.21), the solution $\psi = \exp\left(+\frac{y^2}{2}\right)$ is not acceptable because in that case ψ will rapidly increase tending to infinity as y approaches $\pm\infty$. The other solution

$$\psi = \exp\left(-\frac{y^2}{2}\right) \qquad \text{... (5.24)}$$

is the one which is valid for large values of y.

This suggests that the general solution for Equation (5.19) contains the factor $\exp\left(-\frac{y^2}{2}\right)$ and the form of the solution may be written as,

$$\psi = F(y)\exp\left(-\frac{y^2}{2}\right) \qquad \text{... (5.25)}$$

where, F (y) is some function of y whose form has to be determined by finding the differential equation for it. Writing F for F (y), and differentiating Equation (5.25) with respect to y, we obtain,

$$\frac{d^2\psi}{dy^2} = \left\{\frac{d^2F}{dy^2} - 2y\frac{dF}{dy} + \left(y^2 - 1\right)F\right\}\exp\left(-\frac{y^2}{2}\right) \quad \text{... (5.26)}$$

Hence, by substituting for ψ and $\frac{d^2\psi}{dy^2}$ from Equations (5.25) and (5.26), respectively, in the Equation (5.19),

$$\left[\frac{d^2F}{dy^2} - 2y\frac{dF}{dy} + \left(y^2 - 1\right)F\right]\exp\left(-\frac{y^2}{2}\right) + \left[\frac{\alpha}{\beta} - y^2\right]\exp\left(-\frac{y^2}{2}\right)F = 0$$

or

$$\left[\frac{d^2F}{dy^2} - 2y\frac{dF}{dy} + \left(\frac{\alpha}{\beta} - 1\right)F\right]\exp\left(-\frac{y^2}{2}\right) = 0 \quad \text{... (5.27)}$$

Since $\exp\left(\frac{y^2}{2}\right)$ is not zero, except for $y = \pm\infty$, the expression within brackets must be zero, that is,

$$\frac{d^2F}{dy^2} - 2y\frac{dF}{dy} + \left(\frac{\alpha}{\beta} - 1\right)F = 0 \quad \text{... (5.28)}$$

This is the differential equation for function F (y).

Equation (5.28) is known as **Hermite's differential equation.** The solution for equations of this type is obtained by polynomial method, *i.e.*, by assuming that the function F can be expanded as power series in y, *i.e.*,

$$F = a_0 + a_1 y + a_2 y^2 + a_3 y^3 + a_4 y^4 + \ldots \quad \text{... (5.29)}$$

This leads to,

$$\frac{dF}{dy} = a_1 + 2a_2 y + 3a_3 y^2 + 4a_4 y^3 + \ldots \quad \text{... (5.30)}$$

and

$$\frac{d^2F}{dy^2} = (1\times 2)\,a_2 + (2\times 3)\,a_3 y + (3\times 4)\,a_4 y^2 + \ldots \quad \text{... (5.31)}$$

Substituting these equations into Equation (5.28), we get

$$[(1\times 2)\,a_2 + (2\times 3)\,a_3 y + (3\times 4)\,a_4 y^2 + \ldots] - [(2\times 1)\,a_1 y + (2\times 2)\,a_2 y^2 + (2\times 3)\,a_3 y^3 + \ldots]$$

$$+\left[\left(\frac{\alpha}{\beta} - 1\right)a_0 + \left(\frac{\alpha}{\beta} - 1\right)a_1 y + \left(\frac{\alpha}{\beta} - 1\right)a_2 y^2 + \ldots\right] = 0 \quad \text{.. (5.32)}$$

The Equation (5.32) can be satisfied only if the coefficient of each power of y is zero. Thus,

for $y^0 : 1\times 2a_2 + \left(\frac{\alpha}{\beta} - 1\right)a_0 = 0,$

$$\text{for } y^1 : 2 \times 3a_3 + \left(\frac{\alpha}{\beta} - 1 - 2 \times 1\right) a_1 = 0,$$

$$\text{for } y^2 : 3 \times 4a_4 + \left(\frac{\alpha}{\beta} - 1 - 2 \times 2\right) a_2 = 0,$$

... .

... .

$$\text{for } y^k : (k+1)(k+2)\, a_{k+2} + \left(\frac{\alpha}{\beta} - 1 - 2k\right) a_k = 0$$

which leads to a formula for determination of the coefficients,

$$a_{k+2} = \frac{-\left(\frac{\alpha}{\beta} - 1 - 2k\right)}{(k+1)(k+2)} a_k \quad \text{... (5.33)}$$

where, k is an integer. This is known as recursion formula. It permits calculation of the coefficient a_{k+2} of the term y^{k+2} in terms of the coefficient a_k of y^k ; that is if we set $a_1 = 0$ arbitrarily, we can obtain a_2, a_4, a_6, etc., in terms of a_0 (even set) and similarly, if we set $a_0 = 0$, we can obtain a_3, a_5, a_7, etc., in terms of a_1 (odd set).

In any case, the power series will still consist of infinite number of terms and the function F (y) will tend to infinity as $y \to \infty$. So a condition has to be found which will restrict the number of terms in the series. This is possible if for a certain value of k, say n, the numerator in Equation (5.33) vanishes, *i.e.*, when

$$\frac{\alpha}{\beta} - 1 - 2k = \frac{\alpha}{\beta} - 1 - 2n = 0,$$

or
$$\frac{\alpha}{\beta} = 2n + 1 \quad \text{... (5.34)}$$

where, n may be 0, 1, 2, ... The resulting series with finite number of terms is a polynomial, called **"Hermite polynomial"** $H_n(y)$. The Hermite polynomials are defined by the "generating function".

$$H_n(y) = (-1)^n \exp(y^2) \cdot \frac{d^n\left[\exp\left(-y^2\right)\right]}{dy^n} \quad \text{... (5.35)}$$

For example, the Hermite polynomial for $n = 2$ is

$$H_2(y) = (-1)^2 \exp(y^2) \cdot \frac{d^2\left[\exp\left(-y^2\right)\right]}{dy^2}$$

$$= \exp(y^2)\,[(-2\exp(-y^2) + 4y^2(\exp(-y^2))]$$

$$= 4y - 2.$$

5.2.1.1 The Complete Eigenfunctions (Wave Functions)

The complete wave functions of the harmonic oscillator can be now derived (see Table 5.1) corresponding to permissible values of $\frac{\alpha}{\beta}$ or n, and are expressed as

TABLE 5.1 Eigenfunctions of Harmonic Oscillator

$\frac{\alpha}{\beta}$	n	$H_n(y)$	$\psi_n(y)$	$\psi_n(x)$
1	0	1	$N_0 \exp\left(-\frac{y^2}{2}\right)$	$N_0 \exp\left(-\frac{\beta x^2}{2}\right)$
3	1	$2y$	$N_1\, 2y \exp\left(-\frac{y^2}{2}\right)$	$N_1 \left(2\sqrt{\beta}\, x\right) \exp\left(-\frac{\beta x^2}{2}\right)$
5	2	$-2+4y^2$	$N_2 (4y^2-2) \exp\left(-\frac{y^2}{2}\right)$	$N_2 (4\beta x^2-2) \exp\left(-\frac{\beta x^2}{2}\right)$
7	3	$-12y+8y^3$	$N_3 (8y^3-12y) \exp\left(-\frac{y^2}{2}\right)$	$N_3 \left(8\beta^{3/2} x^3 - 12\sqrt{\beta x}\right) \exp\left(-\frac{\beta x^2}{2}\right)$

$$\psi_n(y) = NH_n(y)\, e^{-y^2/2} \qquad \dots (5.36)$$

The normalisation factor N in Equation (5.37) can be determined from the condition,

$$\int_{-\infty}^{\infty} \psi_n(y)^2\, dx = \int_{-\infty}^{\infty} \left[\frac{N}{\sqrt{\beta}} H_n(y) \exp\left(-\frac{y^2}{2}\right)\right]^2 dy = 1 \qquad \dots (5.37)$$

The integral on evaluation leads to *

$$\int_{-\infty}^{\infty} \left[H_n(y)\right]^2 \exp\left(-y^2\right) dy = 2^n\, n!\, \sqrt{\pi} \qquad \dots (5.38)$$

Therefore, from Equation (5.37),

$$\frac{N^2}{\sqrt{\beta}} 2^n\, n! \sqrt{\pi} = 1 \qquad \dots (5.39)$$

$$N = \left(\frac{\sqrt{\beta}}{2^n\, n! \sqrt{\pi}}\right)^{1/2} \qquad \dots (5.40)$$

*The integration is lengthy; interested readers are referred to *Quantum Chemistry and Physics* by C.S. Johnson and L.G. Pederson; Addison-Wesley Pub. Co., 1974, p. 113.

For $\psi_0, N_0 = \left(\frac{\beta}{\pi}\right)^{1/4}$

$$\psi_1, N_1 = \frac{1}{\sqrt{2}}\left(\frac{\beta}{\pi}\right)^{1/4}$$

$$\psi_2, N_2 = \frac{1}{\sqrt{8}}\left(\frac{\beta}{\pi}\right)^{1/4}$$

$$\psi_3, N_3 = \frac{1}{\sqrt{48}}\left(\frac{\beta}{\pi}\right)^{1/4}$$

and so on. The wave functions are necessarily orthogonal to each other.

5.2.1.2 The Energy Eigenvalues

We have seen that satisfactory wave functions for harmonic oscillator are obtained only if for a certain value n of the exponent of y in Equation (5.29), $\frac{\alpha}{\beta} = 2n + 1$. If we use Equation (5.16) for α and β,

$$\frac{2E}{h\nu} = 2n + 1$$

or

$$E = \left(n + \frac{1}{2}\right)h\nu \qquad \text{... (5.41)}$$

where, $n = 0, 1, 2, 3$ and so on. E is regarded as "vibrational energy" and n, the "vibrational quantum number".

This shows that:

(*i*) The energy of the harmonic oscillator is quantised, contrary to the classical view, and this result emerges from the solution of the Schrödinger Equation.

(*ii*) The energies are determined by the parameter n which is called "vibrational quantum number" of the oscillator.

(*iii*) The lowest value of the energy (when $n = 0$ is ½ $h\nu$; this is the "zero point energy", in classical view it is zero).

(*iv*) As n increases by unity, the energy increases by $h\nu$ so that the energy levels are equally spaced as shown in Fig. 5.3.

Fig. 5.3

5.2.2 Physical Interpretation of ψ and ψ^2

The plots of the wave function (ψ) and the probability (ψ^2) against x (Figs. 5.4 and 5.5) reveal several interesting features of the quantum mechanical harmonic oscillator:

(*i*) The wave functions are either symmetric (even) or antisymmetric (odd) with respect to $x = 0$.

We see that the exponential part of the wave function, *i.e.*, $\exp\left(-\frac{\beta x^2}{2}\right)$, is necessarily symmetric because of the quantity x^2; the polynomial part, *i.e.*, $H_n\left(\sqrt{\beta}x\right)$, will be symmetric for x^0, x^2, x^4, ... and anti-symmetric for x, x^3, x^5.

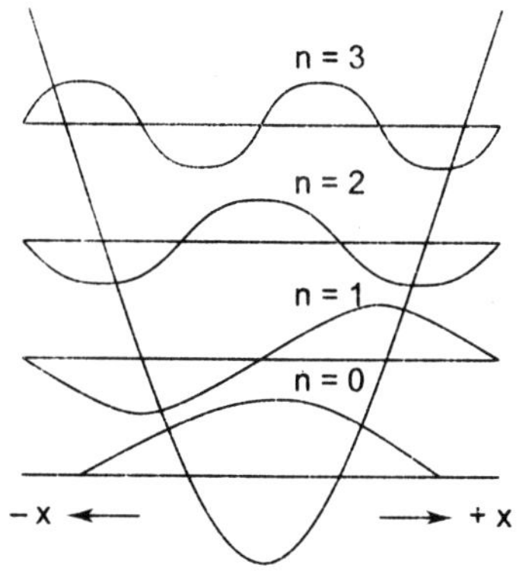

Fig. 5.4

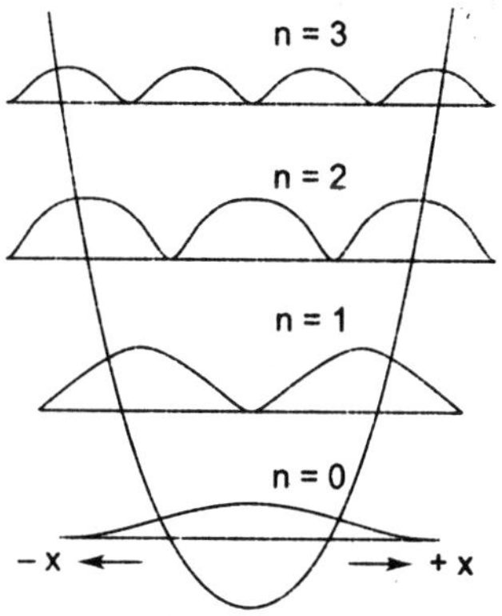

Fig. 5.5

(*ii*) The functions ψ^2 are never negative, and hence, are necessarily symmetric.

(*iii*) In the ground state ($n = 0$), there are no nodes; and each successive state has one additional node.

(*iv*) The presence of nodes indicate the points of zero probability.

(*v*) Still more curious is the fact that ψ and ψ^2 are non-zero even for large values of x, *i.e.*, beyond the classical turning points, *i.e.*, the particle can "penetrate" the potential barrier.

(*vi*) The ψ^2 plot reveals the fact that the particle in the ground state has the maximum probability of being found at the central position ($x = 0$) while in the excited states the probability increases towards the classical turning points (expected from the classical results).

5.2.3 A Comparison of Classical and Quantum Mechanical Results

Certain conclusions derived from the results described above bring the quantum mechanical harmonic oscillator (HO) into sharp contrast with the classical oscillator. In the first place, the energy of the former is quantised, as in the case of particle in a box, and the energy levels are given by a vibrational quantum number. The energy of the classical HO, on the other hand, is continuous. The occurrence of the vibrational energy levels is responsible for the vibrational spectra of molecules which the classical treatment could not explain.

The lowest energy (the zero point energy) of a quantum mechanical HO is $\frac{1}{2}h\nu$, while that of a classical HO is zero (no zero point energy). This means that molecular vibrations around equilibrium bond distances will never stop, not even at absolute zero of temperature. This behaviour is again similar to that of a particle in a box having infinite walls. In fact, the existence of a zero point energy is characteristic of any quantum mechanical system executing to and fro motion.

Wave function (ψ and ψ^2) reveal still more interesting features. Probability calculations show that, in the ground state, the most probable position of a quantum mechanical HO is at the equilibrium point (no displacement) while for a classical HO it lies at the maximum displacement (turning) points. This distinction gradually disappears as the quantum number increases, *i.e.*, in the excited states, when the points of maximum probability even for the former shift more and more towards the classical turning points, reaching these in the limiting case. This again is similar to the case of a particle in a box.

A highly interesting feature of the quantum mechanical HO is its penetration into classically forbidden regions, *i.e.*, regions of E < V. But then, it should not be surprising if one remembers that the potential barrier of the HO is not infinite but $\frac{1}{2}kx^2$ and that the barrier penetration is characteristic of a quantum mechanical system (*e.g.*, particle in a well, see Chapter 4) with finite potential walls.

PROBLEMS

5.1 The wave functions obtained by solving the Schrödinger Equation for simple harmonic oscillator are

$$\psi_n(x) = \left(\frac{1}{2^n n!}\right)^{1/2}\left(\frac{\beta}{\pi}\right)^{1/4} H_n(y)\exp\left(-\frac{y^2}{2}\right)$$

where, $y = \sqrt{\beta}\,x$, $n = 0, 1, 2, 3, \ldots$ are vibrational quantum numbers, and $H_n(y)$ is the Hermite polynomial defined by Equation (5.38).

(*i*) Calculate the first four wave functions, (*ii*) sketch them and sketch ψ^2; and (*iii*) show that the function $\psi_2(x)$ is normalised and that the functions $\psi_1(x)$ and $\psi_2(x)$ are orthogonal.

5.2 The vibrational energy levels of simple harmonic motion are given as,

$$E_n = \left(n + \frac{1}{2}\right)h\nu, n = 0, 1, 2, 3, \ldots$$

Sketch the first four energy levels and find the difference betwen them, ν is the classical frequency given by

$$\nu = \frac{1}{2\pi}\sqrt{\frac{k}{\mu}}.$$

where, k is the force constant and μ is the reduced mass.

5.3 Find the most probable value (s) of x for a harmonic oscillator in the states (*a*) $n = 0$, (*b*) $n = 1$.

5.4 Obtain the asymptotic solution for the ground state of the harmonic oscillator and show that for a diatomic oscillator.

$$\nu = \frac{1}{2\pi}\sqrt{\frac{k}{\mu}}$$

where, ν is the frequency, k the force constant and μ the reduced mass of the diatomic molecule

[Hint: $$\psi(x) = a \exp(-\beta x^2)$$

$$\frac{d\psi}{dx} = -2\beta x\, a \exp(-\beta x^2) = -2\beta x\, \psi$$

$$\frac{d^2\psi}{dx^2} = -2\beta\psi + 4\beta^2 x^2 \psi$$

By substituting in the Schrödinger Equation,

$$\frac{d^2\psi}{dx^2} + \frac{8\pi^2\mu}{h^2}\left(E - \frac{1}{2}kx^2\right)\psi = 0$$

We have, $$\left(-2\beta + 4\beta^2 x^2\right)\psi + \frac{8\pi^2\mu}{h^2}\left(E - \frac{1}{2}kx^2\right)\psi = 0$$

On rearranging so as to collect the terms containing x^2 together and separating them from those independent of it, we get

$$\left[\left(4\beta^2 - \frac{4\pi^2\mu k}{h^2}\right)x^2 + \left(\frac{8\pi^2\mu}{h^2}E - 2\beta\right)\right]\psi = 0$$

Since $\psi \neq 0$ (as it will be a trivial solution), this equation will be satisfied if the coefficients of x^2 and x^0 are separately equal to zero, *i.e.*,

$$4\beta^2 - \frac{4\pi^2\mu k}{h^2} = 0 \qquad \text{...}(i)$$

and $$\frac{8\pi^2\mu E}{h^2} - 2\beta = 0 \qquad \text{...}(ii)$$

From Equations (*i*) and (*ii*)

$$E = \frac{\beta h^2}{4\pi^2\mu} = \frac{1}{2}\frac{h}{2\pi}\sqrt{\frac{k}{\mu}} = \frac{1}{2}h\nu$$

Therefore, $$\nu = \frac{1}{2\pi}\sqrt{\frac{k}{\mu}}\Bigg].$$

5.5 Verify that the following functions are eigenfunctions of the simple harmonic oscillator:

(*a*) $\psi = \exp\left(-\frac{1}{2}\beta x^2\right)$

(*b*) $\psi = x\exp\left(-\frac{1}{2}\beta x^2\right)$ where, $\beta = \frac{2\pi(mk)^{1/2}}{h}$, k = force constant.

What is the eigenvalue in each case ?

[**Hint:** (*a*)
$$\hat{H}\psi = \left[-\frac{h^2}{8\pi^2 m}\frac{d^2}{dx^2} + \frac{1}{2}kx^2\right]\exp\left(-\frac{1}{2}\beta x^2\right)$$
$$= \left[-\frac{h^2}{8\pi^2 m}(\beta^2 x^2 - \beta) + \frac{1}{2}kx^2\right]\exp\left(-\frac{1}{2}\beta x^2\right)$$

Now,
$$\nu = \frac{1}{2\pi}\sqrt{\frac{k}{m}},\ k = 4\pi^2\nu^2 m$$

Therefore,
$$\beta = \frac{2\pi(mk)^{1/2}}{h} = \frac{4\pi^2 \nu m}{h}$$

Substituting for β in the above equation,
$$\hat{H}\psi = \left[-\frac{h^2}{8\pi^2 m}\frac{16\pi^4\nu^2 m^2}{h^2}x^2 + \frac{h^2}{8\pi^2 m}\cdot\frac{4\pi^2\nu m}{h} + \frac{1}{2}kx^2\right]\exp\left(-\frac{1}{2}\beta x^2\right)$$
$$= \left[-\frac{1}{2}kx^2 + \frac{1}{2}h\nu + \frac{1}{2}kx^2\right]\exp\left(-\frac{1}{2}\beta x^2\right)$$
$$= \left[\frac{1}{2}h\nu\right]\exp\left(-\frac{1}{2}\beta x^2\right) = \left[\frac{1}{2}h\nu\right]\psi$$

Eigenvalue is $\frac{1}{2}h\nu$.

(*b*) Eigenvalue in this case will be $\frac{3}{4}h\nu$].

5.6 Say, simply by insection, why $(2 + y - 2y^2)\exp\left(-\frac{y^2}{2}\right)$ cannot be a satisfactory wave function for a harmonic oscillator. What about $2y\exp\left(\frac{y^2}{2}\right)$?

5.7 Calculate the average potential and kinetic energies of a harmonic oscillator in the ground state. Compare the results obtained with the classical results.

[Hint:
$$\overline{V} = \int_{-\infty}^{\infty} \psi_0 \hat{V} \psi_0 \, dx = \left(\frac{\beta}{\pi}\right)^{1/2} \left[-\frac{1}{2} k \int_{-\infty}^{\infty} \left(x^2 \exp\left(-\beta x^2\right) dx\right) \right]$$

$$= \left(\frac{\beta}{\pi}\right)^{1/2} \frac{1}{2} k \frac{1}{2} \left(\frac{\pi}{\beta^3}\right)^{1/2}$$ (from the table of integrals)

$$= \frac{k}{4\beta} = \left(\frac{k}{4}\right) \frac{h}{2\pi (mk)^{1/2}}$$

$$= \frac{h}{8\pi} \sqrt{\frac{k}{m}}$$

The energy, $$E = \frac{h}{4\pi} \sqrt{\frac{k}{m}}.$$

$$\text{P.E.} \left(\overline{V}\right) = \frac{1}{2} \text{E} = \text{average K.E. (because E = P.E. + K.E.)}$$

This is the same as the result obtained from classical considerations].

5.8 (*a*) Write the eigenvalue of the harmonic oscillator for the second excited state.

(*b*) The eigenfunction corresponding to this eigenvalue may be written as

$$\psi_2 = N\,(x^2 + bx + c) \exp\left(-\frac{\beta x^2}{2}\right)$$

where, N is the normalisation factor and

$$\beta = \frac{2\pi\,(mk)^{1/2}}{h}.$$

Knowing that this function must be even (symmetric) and that it is orthogonal to the ground state eigenfunction, determine the values of b and c.

(*c*) Determine the normalisation factor N.

(*d*) Show that the resulting function is an eigenfunction of $\hat{H}$ and calculate the eigenvalue.

[Hint: (*a*) $E = \frac{7}{2} h\nu$

(*b*) The function is even, $\therefore b = 0$

$$\int_{-\infty}^{\infty} \psi_0 \psi_2 \, dx = 0$$

or $$\int_{-\infty}^{\infty} \left(\frac{\beta}{\pi}\right)^{1/4} \exp\left(-\frac{1}{2}\beta x^2\right) N\left(x^2 + c\right) \exp\left(-\frac{\beta x^2}{2}\right) dx = 0$$

or $$N\left(\frac{\beta}{\pi}\right)^{1/4}\int_{-\infty}^{+\infty}\left(x^2+c\right)\exp\left(-\beta x^2\right)dx = 0$$

or $$N\left(\frac{\beta}{\pi}\right)^{1/4}\left[\frac{1}{2\beta}\left(\frac{\pi}{\beta}\right)^{1/2}+c\left(\frac{\pi}{\beta}\right)^{1/2}\right] = 0 \text{ (from the table of integrals)}$$

or $$c = -\frac{1}{2\beta};$$

$$\psi_2 = N\left(x^2-\frac{1}{2\beta}\right)\exp\left(-\frac{\beta x^2}{2}\right)$$

(*c*) $$\int_{-\infty}^{+\infty}\left[N\left(x^2-\frac{1}{2\beta}\right)\exp\left(-\frac{\beta x^2}{2}\right)\right]^2 dx = 1$$

or $$N^2\left[\int_{-\infty}^{+\infty}x^4\exp\left(-\beta x^2\right)dx-\int_{-\infty}^{+\infty}\frac{1}{\beta}x^2\exp\left(-\beta x^2\right)dx+\int_{-\infty}^{+\infty}\frac{1}{4\beta^2}\exp\left(-\beta x^2\right)dx\right] = 1$$

From the table of integrals,

$$\int_0^{\infty}x^{2n}\exp\left(-\beta x^2\right)dx = \frac{1\times3\times5\ldots(2n-1)}{2^{n+1},\beta^n}\left(\frac{\pi}{\beta}\right)^{1/2}$$

Here $n = 2$; therefore,

$$\int_0^{\infty}x^4\exp\left(-\beta x^2\right)dx = \frac{1\times3}{8\beta^2}\left(\frac{\pi}{\beta}\right)^{1/2}$$

Therefore, $$\int_{-\infty}^{\infty}x^4\exp\left(-\beta x^2\right)dx = \frac{2\times3}{8\beta^2}\left(\frac{\pi}{\beta}\right)^{1/2}$$

$$\int_{-\infty}^{\infty}x^2\exp\left(-\beta x^2\right)dx = \frac{1}{2\beta}\left(\frac{\pi}{\beta}\right)^{1/2}$$

and $$\int_{-\infty}^{\infty}\exp\left(-\beta x^2\right)dx = \left(\frac{\pi}{\beta}\right)^{1/2}$$

Therefore, $$N^2\left[\frac{3}{4\beta^2}-\frac{1}{2\beta^2}+\frac{1}{4\beta^2}\right]\left(\frac{\pi}{\beta}\right)^{1/2} = 1$$

or $$N^2 \frac{1}{2\beta^2}\left(\frac{\pi}{\beta}\right)^{1/2} = 1$$

or $$N = \left[2\beta^2\left(\frac{\beta}{\pi}\right)^{1/2}\right]^{1/2}$$

(*d*) $$\psi_2 = \left[2\beta^2\left(\frac{\beta}{\pi}\right)^{1/2}\right]^{1/2}\left(x^2 - \frac{1}{2\beta}\right)\exp\left(-\frac{\beta x^2}{2}\right)$$

$$= \frac{1}{\sqrt{2}}\left(\frac{\beta}{\pi}\right)^{1/4}\left(2\beta x^2 - 1\right)\exp\left(-\frac{\beta x^2}{2}\right)$$

$$\hat{H}\psi_2 = \left[-\frac{h^2}{8\pi^2 m}\frac{d^2}{dx^2} + \frac{1}{2}kx^2\right]\cdot\left[\frac{1}{\sqrt{2}}\left(\frac{\beta}{\pi}\right)^{1/4}\left(2\beta x^2 - 1\right)\exp\left(-\frac{\beta x^2}{2}\right)\right]$$

$$= \left.\frac{5h}{4\pi}\sqrt{\frac{k}{m}}\,\psi_2\right].$$

CHAPTER 6

Rotational Motion of a Particle

There is another basic type of motion that is of great interest in atomic and molecular problems; it is the rotational motion. It crops up whenever we have to deal with motion of a particle under the influence of a central field of force, for example, the motion of an electron around the nucleus of an atom.

For a single particle executing such a motion, the Schrödinger equation can be solved exactly. We shall consider in this chapter first the rotational motion of a particle in a plane (particle in a ring) and then in three-dimensions (particle on a sphere); we shall use these results for the case of a rotating diatomic molecule.

6.1 PARTICLE IN A RING

6.1.1 The Schrödinger Equation and the Wave Functions

Consider a particle of mass m rotating in a circle of radius r in the xy plane. If the potential energy (V) of the particle is zero (*i.e.*, it is unacted upon by any external force), the Hamiltonian in the simplest form can be written as,

$$\hat{H} = \frac{-h^2}{8\pi^2 m}\left(\frac{\partial^2}{\partial x^2} + \frac{\partial^2}{\partial y^2}\right) \quad \text{... (6.1)}$$

Since the motion is circular, it will be more convenient to express $\hat{H}$ in polar coordinates (r, φ). The cartesian coordinates x and y are related to polar coordinates r and φ as,

$$x = r\cos\varphi,\ y = r\sin\varphi \quad \text{... (6.2)}$$

where, φ is the angular variable which varies from 0 to 2π and the radius, r, is constant. Hence, Equation (6.1) in polar coordinates becomes,

$$\hat{H} = -\frac{h^2}{8\pi^2 mr^2}\left(\frac{\partial^2}{\partial\varphi^2}\right) = -\frac{h^2}{8\pi^2 I}\left(\frac{\partial^2}{\partial\varphi^2}\right) \text{(see Appendix 1)} \quad \text{... (6.3)}$$

where, $I = mr^2$ is the moment of inertia. The eigenfunction F (φ), or simply F, will be a function of φ only; so the Schrödinger equation is given by,

$$-\frac{h^2}{8\pi^2 I}\cdot\frac{d^2F}{d\varphi^2} = EF \quad \text{... (6.4)}$$

or

$$\frac{d^2F}{d\varphi^2} + M^2F = 0 \quad \text{... (6.5)}$$

where,

$$M^2 = \frac{8\pi^2 IE}{h^2} \quad \text{... (6.6)}$$

The Equation (6.5) is quite familiar (cf. particle in a one-dimensional box). Its solutions (the wave functions) are:

$$\left.\begin{aligned} F &= N \sin M\varphi \\ F' &= N' \cos M\varphi \end{aligned}\right] \quad \text{... (6.7)}$$

as the real set, and

$$F'' = A \exp(\pm iM\varphi) \quad \text{... (6.8)}$$

as the imaginary set. The trigonometric forms (6.7) are also called "circular harmonics".

Equations (6.7) and (6.8) are equivalent in view of the theorem,

$$\exp(\pm iM\varphi) = \cos M\varphi \pm i \sin M\varphi \quad \text{... (6.9)}$$

The functions (6.7) and (6.8) are finite and continuous for all values of φ and M. They are single-valued too, since the angles φ and $\varphi + 2\pi$ represent the same point, and the property of single-valuedness demands that,

$$F(\varphi) = F(\varphi + 2\pi)$$

Using the real set, Equation (6.7), we get

$$\sin M\varphi = \sin M(\varphi + 2\pi)$$

or

$$\cos M\varphi = \cos M(\varphi + 2\pi)$$

This is possible only if M = 0, ± 1, ± 2, ... [put, for example, M = + 1; then $\sin M\varphi = \sin \varphi$; and $\sin M(\varphi + 2\pi) = \sin \varphi$]. Similarly,

$$A \exp(iM\varphi) = A \exp(iM(\varphi + 2\pi)) = A \exp(iM\varphi).\exp(i2\pi M)$$

$$\exp(i2\pi M) = 1, \text{ or } \cos 2\pi M + i \sin 2\pi M = 1 \text{ only if } M = 0, \pm 1, \pm 2$$

As regards boundary conditions, there is no barrier to the particle's motion as long as it is on the ring, and so there is no condition for the wave function to vanish at any point. (For M = 0, $N \sin M\varphi = 0$ but $N' \cos M\varphi = N'$).

[**Exercise:** Show that $F = N \sin \frac{\phi}{2}$ is not acceptable even though

$$\sin\frac{\phi}{2} = \sin\frac{1}{2}(\phi + 2\pi)$$

Let $F = \sin\frac{\phi}{2}$ and $F' = \sin\frac{1}{2}(\phi + 2\pi)$ then $\frac{dF}{d\varphi} = \frac{1}{2}\cos\frac{\phi}{2}$, and

$$\frac{dF'}{d\varphi} = \frac{1}{2}\cos\left(\frac{\varphi}{2} + \pi\right)$$

$$= \frac{1}{2}\left(\cos\frac{\varphi}{2}\cos\pi - \sin\frac{\varphi}{2}\sin\pi\right) = -\frac{1}{2}\cos\frac{\varphi}{2}$$

Since $\frac{dF}{d\varphi} \neq \frac{dF'}{d\varphi}$, there is discontinuity].

6.1.1.1 Normalisation and Orthogonality

The normalisation factor N can be determined as follows:

$$\int_0^{2\pi} (N \sin M\varphi)^2 \, d\varphi = 1$$

or $$N^2 \int_0^{2\pi} \sin^2 M\varphi \, d\varphi = N^2 \int_0^{2\pi} \left(\frac{1 - \cos 2M\varphi}{2}\right) d\varphi = 1$$

or $$N^2 . \pi = 1 \text{ or } N = \frac{1}{\sqrt{\pi}}$$

Similarly, $$N' = \frac{1}{\sqrt{\pi}}$$

The normalised real set of wave functions are

$$F = \frac{1}{\sqrt{\pi}} \sin M\varphi \text{ and } F = \frac{1}{\sqrt{\pi}} . \cos M\varphi \qquad \text{... (6.10)}$$

For $$M = 0, F' = \frac{1}{\sqrt{\pi}} \qquad \text{... (6.11)}$$

For the imaginary set,

$$\int_0^{2\pi} A^* \exp \pm (iM\varphi), A \exp (\pm iM\varphi) . d\varphi = 1$$

or $$\int_0^{2\pi} |A|^2 \, d\varphi = 1 \text{ or } |A|^2 . 2\pi = 1 \text{ or } |A| = \frac{1}{\sqrt{2\pi}}$$

Hence $$F'' = \frac{1}{\sqrt{2\pi}} \exp (\pm iM\varphi) \qquad \text{... (6.12)}$$

For $$M = 0, F'' = \frac{1}{\sqrt{2\pi}} \qquad \text{... (6.13)}$$

It is not difficult to show that the functions (6.10) and (6.12) are orthogonal sets as, for example,

$$\frac{1}{\pi}\int_0^{2\pi} \sin\varphi \,.\, \cos\varphi \, d\varphi = 0 \qquad \text{(see the table of integrals)}$$

[**Exercise:** Show that $\frac{1}{\sqrt{2\pi}}\exp(i\mathrm{M}\varphi)$ and $\frac{1}{\sqrt{2\pi}}\exp(-i\mathrm{M}\varphi)$ are orthogonal.

$$\int_0^{2\pi} \left(e^{i\mathrm{M}\varphi}\right)^* . e^{-i\mathrm{M}\varphi} . d\varphi = \int_0^{2\pi} e^{-i\mathrm{M}\varphi} . e^{-i\mathrm{M}\varphi} . d\varphi$$

$$= \left[\frac{e^{-2i\mathrm{M}\varphi}}{-2i\mathrm{M}}\right]_0^{2\pi} = 0 \Bigg]$$

It is seen that except for M = 0 the functions (6.10) and (6.12) constitute doubly degenerate real and imaginary sets of wave functions respectively. The degeneracy is inherent in any system that involves rotational motion.

6.1.1.2 Quantisation of Energy

The expression (6.6) can be rearranged to give the expression for energy as

$$\mathrm{E} = \frac{\mathrm{M}^2 h^2}{8\pi^2 \mathrm{I}} \qquad \text{... (6.14)}$$

Thus, the energy is quantised in units of $\frac{h^2}{8\pi^2 \mathrm{I}}$, the parameter M being the "rotational quantum number".

For M = 0, E = 0, *i.e.*, the rotating particle does not have zero point energy.

6.2 PARTICLE ON A SPHERE

6.2.1 The Spherical Angular Coordinates

The position of a particle on the surface of a sphere of radius r is more conveniently determined in terms of two angular variables (coordinates)—φ, called the azimuthal angle, and θ, called the zenith angle. The angle φ is the angle measured in the xy plane between the x-axis and the projection of the line r joining the particle (P) with the centre of the sphere (Fig. 6.1); it varies from 0 to 2π. The angle θ is the angle between the line r and the z-axis; it varies from 0 to π.

6.2.1.1 The Schrödinger Equation

Since the particle rotates in three-dimensions the Hamiltonian in cartesian coordinates, if potential energy V is zero, is

$$\hat{\mathrm{H}} = -\frac{h^2}{8\pi^2 m}\left(\frac{\partial^2}{\partial x^2} + \frac{\partial^2}{\partial y^2} + \frac{\partial^2}{\partial z^2}\right) = -\frac{h^2}{8\pi^2 m}\nabla^2 \qquad \text{... (6.15)}$$

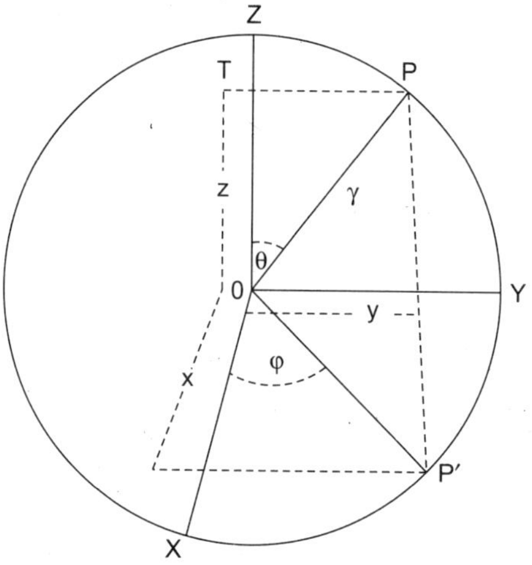

Fig. 6.1 *The angular coordinates θ and φ*

where, x, y and z are the coordinates of the particle at any point. However, with the present form of the Hamiltonian, the Schrödinger equation cannot be solved by the method of separation of variables as the variables x, y and z do not vary independently of each other here. The equation can be solved by transforming Equation (6.15) into one involving θ and φ by making use of the relation betwen cartesian (x, y, z) and angular (θ, φ) variables given below.

$$x = r \sin\theta \cos\varphi,\ y = r \sin\theta \sin\varphi,\ z = r\cos\theta \qquad \text{... (6.16)}$$

The transformation, then, is a straightforward application of the theory of partial derivatives but is lengthy. We give only the final expression here. (For complete derivation see Appendix 1).

$$\nabla^2 = \frac{1}{r^2}\left(\frac{\partial}{\partial r} r^2 \frac{\partial}{\partial r}\right) + \frac{1}{r^2 \sin\theta}\left[\frac{\partial}{\partial\theta}\left(\sin\theta \frac{\partial}{\partial\theta}\right)\right] + \frac{1}{r^2 \sin^2\theta}\left(\frac{\partial^2}{\partial\varphi^2}\right) \qquad \text{... (6.17)}$$

Since r is constant, $\dfrac{\partial}{\partial r} = \dfrac{\partial^2}{\partial r^2} = 0.$

$$\therefore \qquad \hat{H} = -\frac{h^2}{8\pi^2 m}\left[\frac{1}{r^2 \sin\theta}\frac{\partial}{\partial\theta}\left(\sin\theta \frac{\partial}{\partial\theta}\right) + \frac{1}{r^2 \sin^2\theta}\frac{\partial^2}{\partial\varphi^2}\right] \qquad \text{... (6.18)}$$

The Schrödinger equation, $\hat{H}\psi = E\psi$ becomes

$$-\frac{h^2}{8\pi^2 mr^2}\left[\frac{1}{\sin\theta}\frac{\partial}{\partial\theta}\left(\sin\theta \frac{\partial\psi}{\partial\theta}\right) + \frac{1}{\sin^2\theta}\frac{\partial^2\psi}{\partial\varphi^2}\right] = E\psi \qquad \text{... (6.19)}$$

or, on simplification,

$$\frac{\partial^2\psi}{\partial\theta^2} + \frac{\cos\theta}{\sin\theta}\cdot\frac{\partial\psi}{\partial\theta} + \frac{1}{\sin^2\theta}\frac{\partial^2\psi}{\partial\varphi^2} + \frac{8\pi^2 mr^2}{h^2} E\psi = 0 \qquad \text{... (6.20)}$$

where the wave function ψ is ψ (θ, φ).

6.2.1.2 Separation of Variables

The partial differential Schrödinger Equation (6.20) can be solved by separating the variables. For this, suppose that the function $\psi(\theta, \varphi)$ is a product of two functions $P(\theta)$ and $F(\varphi)$, each being a function of a single variable only, *i.e.*,

$$\psi(\theta, \varphi) = P(\theta)\, F(\varphi) \qquad \ldots (6.21)$$

Differentiating partially with respect to θ, we get

$$\frac{\partial \psi}{\partial \theta} = F(\varphi)\frac{dP}{d\theta},\ \frac{\partial^2 \psi}{\partial \theta^2} = F(\varphi)\frac{d^2 P}{d\theta^2}$$

and with respect to φ, we get

$$\frac{\partial \psi}{\partial \varphi} = P(\theta)\frac{dF}{d\varphi},\ \frac{\partial^2 \psi}{\partial \varphi^2} = P(\theta)\frac{\partial^2 F}{\partial \varphi^2}$$

Substituting these relations into Equation (6.20)

$$F.\frac{d^2P}{d\theta^2} + \frac{\cos\theta}{\sin\theta}.F.\frac{dP}{d\theta} + \frac{1}{\sin^2\theta}P\frac{d^2F}{d\varphi^2} + \frac{8\pi^2 mr^2}{h^2}EPF = 0$$

Multiplying through by $\frac{\sin^2\theta}{PF}$,

$$\frac{\sin^2\theta}{P}.\frac{d^2P}{d\theta^2} + \cos\theta.\sin\theta.\frac{1}{P}.\frac{dP}{d\theta} + \frac{1}{F}.\frac{d^2F}{d\varphi^2} + \frac{8\pi^2 mr^2}{h^2}\sin^2\theta\, E = 0$$

where, P and F stand for $P(\theta)$ and $F(\varphi)$ respectively.

or
$$\frac{\sin^2\theta}{P}.\frac{d^2P}{d\theta^2} + \cos\theta.\sin\theta.\frac{1}{P}.\frac{dP}{d\theta} + \frac{8\pi^2 mr^2}{h^2}\sin^2\theta\, E = -\frac{1}{F}.\frac{d^2F}{d\varphi^2} \qquad \ldots (6.22)$$

Now the left hand side (L.H.S.) of Equation (6.22) depends on θ only while the right hand side (R.H.S.) depends on φ only. If φ is maintained constant while θ varies, the R.H.S. will remain constant. Since L.H.S. = R.H.S., the L.H.S. will also remain equal to the same constant even though θ varies. The same argument applies to the situation when θ is kept constant and φ varies. Both sides of Equation (6.22) are, therefore, equal to the same constant. Let the constant be denoted by M^2 for convenience. Thus, Equation (6.22) splits into the following two ordinary differential equations:

$$-\frac{1}{F}.\frac{d^2F}{d\varphi^2} = M^2 \qquad \ldots (6.23)$$

and, after multiplying Equation (6.22) by $\frac{P}{\sin^2\theta}$,

$$\frac{d^2P}{d\theta^2} + \frac{\cos\theta}{\sin\theta} \cdot \frac{dP}{d\theta} + \beta \,.\, P = \frac{M^2 P}{\sin^2\theta} \quad \text{... (6.24)}$$

where, $$\beta = \frac{8\pi^2 mr^2}{h^2} E \quad \text{... (6.25)}$$

6.2.1.3 *The F-equation*

The Equation (6.23) is similar to that for particle in a ring, the solutions of which are

$$\left.\begin{aligned} F &= \frac{1}{\sqrt{\pi}} \sin M\varphi \\ F' &= \frac{1}{\sqrt{\pi}} \cos M\varphi \end{aligned}\right] \quad \text{... (6.10)}$$

and $$F'' = \frac{1}{\sqrt{2\pi}} e^{\pm iM\varphi} \quad \text{... (6.12)}$$

where, M is a quantum number which has values $0, \pm 1, \pm 2, ...$ It differs only in that the eigenvalue here does not contain energy term, E.

6.2.1.4 *The P-equation—Legendre and Associated Legendre Functions*

The Equation (6.24) is known as Legendre differential equation. It is tedious and lengthy to work out its solution. Such equations are solved using polynomial method. Rather than describing the solutions in a rigorous manner, we shall discuss some of the significant properties of the solutions.

It should be obvious that for each value of $|M|$ there will be a corresponding Legendre equation and a new set of solutions. (The symbol $|\;|$ indicates that only the magnitude and not the sign of M is to be used).

Well-behaved solutions are obtained only for some discrete values of β. This is not so obvious but we may examine a few cases.

Consider, first, the case of $|M| = 0$. The Legendre equation is

$$\frac{d^2P}{d\theta^2} + \frac{\cos\theta}{\sin\theta} \cdot \frac{dP}{d\theta} + \beta \,.\, P = 0 \quad \text{... (6.26)}$$

The solutions to this equation exist as polynomials in $\cos\theta$, called "Legendre polynomials", given as

$$P_l(x) = \frac{1}{2^l \,.\, l!} \cdot \frac{d^l}{dx^l}\left(x^2 - 1\right)^l, \quad \text{... (6.27)}$$

where, $x = \cos\theta$ and l is an integer including 0.

Some of these polynomials along with the characteristic values of β are listed in Table 6.1.

TABLE 6.1 Polynomial Solutions of Equation (6.26)

P i.e., f (cos θ)	$\frac{dP}{d\theta}$	$\frac{d^2P}{d\theta^2}$	*L.H.S. of Equation (6.26)*	*β*
$P_0 = 1$	0	0	β	0
$P_1 = \cos\theta$	$-\sin\theta$	$-\cos\theta$	$-2\cos\theta + \beta\cos\theta$	2
$P_2 = 3\cos^2\theta - 1$	$-6\cos\theta\sin\theta$	$-6(\cos^2\theta - \sin^2\theta)$	$-6(3\cos^2\theta - 1)$ $+\beta(3\cos^2\theta - 1)$	6
$P_3 = \frac{5}{3}\cos^3\theta - \cos\theta$	$-5\cos^2\theta\sin\theta$ $+\sin\theta$	$-5(\cos^3\theta - 2\cos\theta)$ $\sin^2\theta + \cos\theta$	$-12\left(\frac{5}{3}\cos^3\theta - \cos\theta\right)$ $+\beta\left(\frac{5}{3}\cos^3\theta - \cos\theta\right)$	12

The indices of the functions P correspond to the highest power of cos θ in the polynomial. It can be seen that

$$\beta = l(l+1) \quad \text{...(6.28)}$$

where, $l = 0, 1, 2, 3$

For $|M| \neq 0$, the solutions have the form,

$$P_l^{|M|}(x) = \left(1 - x^2\right)^{|M|/2} \cdot \frac{d^{|M|}}{dx^{|M|}} \cdot P_l(x) \quad \text{...(6.29)}$$

with $P_l(x)$ defined as earlier. The polynomials (6.29) are called "associated Legendre polynomials".

[We may work out the functions for a few values of $|M|$ and l;

$$|M| = 0, l = 0, P_0^0(x) = 1 = P_0(x) = 1$$

$$l = 1, P_1^0(x) = P_1(x) = \frac{1}{2}(2x) = x = \cos\theta$$

$$l = 2, P_2^0(x) = P_2(x) = \frac{1}{8} \cdot \frac{d^2}{dx^2}\left(x^2 - 1\right)^2 = \frac{1}{2}\left(3x^2 - 1\right)$$

$$= \frac{1}{2}\left(3\cos^2\theta - 1\right)$$

$$|M| = 1, l = 1, P_1^1(x) = \left(1 - x^2\right)^{1/2} \cdot \frac{d}{dx}\{P_1(x)\}$$

$$= \left(1 - x^2\right)^{1/2} \cdot \frac{d}{dx}\left[\frac{1}{2} \cdot \frac{d}{dx}\left(x^2 - 1\right)\right]$$

$$= (1 - x^2)^{1/2} = \sin\theta$$

$$l = 2, P_2^1(x) = (1 - x^2)^{1/2} \cdot \frac{d}{dx}\{P_2(x)\}$$

$$= \left(1 - x^2\right)^{1/2} \cdot \frac{d}{dx} \cdot \left[\frac{1}{8} \cdot \frac{d^2}{dx^2}\left(x^2 - 1\right)^2\right]$$

$$= \left(1-x^2\right)^{1/2} . \frac{d}{dx}\left[\frac{1}{2}\left(3x^2-1\right)\right]$$

$$= (1-x^2)^{1/2} . 3x = 3 \sin\theta . \cos\theta$$

and so on.

Putting cos θ for x, we may write the associated Legendre functions that are solution of Equation (6.24) as

$$P_l^{|M|}(\cos\theta) = \left(1-\cos^2\theta\right)^{|M|/2} . \frac{d^{|M|}}{d(\cos\theta)^{|M|}}\{P_l(\cos\theta)\} \quad ...(6.30)$$

$$= (\sin\theta)^{|M|} . \frac{d^{|M|}}{d(\cos\theta)^{|M|}}\left[\frac{1}{2^l . l!} . \frac{d^l}{d(\cos\theta)^l} . \left(\cos^2\theta - 1\right)^l\right] \quad ...(6.31)$$

The normalisation factor is given as

$$N = \left[\frac{(2l+1)}{2} . \frac{(l-|M|)!}{(l+|M|)!}\right]^{1/2} \quad ...(6.32)$$

It is now easy to tabulate some of the associated Legendre functions $P_l^{|M|}$ (cos θ). The functions and their normalisation factors for various values of | M | and l are given in Table 6.2.

TABLE 6.2 Some Associated Legendre Functions

| M |	l	P_l^M (cos θ)	N
0	0	1	$\frac{1}{\sqrt{2}}$
	1	cos θ	$\sqrt{\frac{3}{2}}$
	2	$\frac{1}{2}(3\cos^2\theta - 1)$	$\sqrt{\frac{5}{2}}$
	3	$\frac{3}{2}\left(\frac{5}{3}\cos^3\theta - \cos\theta\right)$	$\sqrt{\frac{7}{2}}$
1	1	sin θ	$\sqrt{\frac{3}{4}}$
	2	3 sin θ cos θ	$\sqrt{\frac{5}{12}}$
	3	$\frac{3}{2}\sin\theta\left(5\cos^2\theta - 1\right)$	$\sqrt{\frac{7}{24}}$
2	2	$3\sin^2\theta$	$\sqrt{\frac{5}{48}}$
	3	$15\sin^2\theta\cos\theta$	$\sqrt{\frac{7}{240}}$

The associated Legendre functions P_l^M (cos θ) are characterised by two parameters l and M. The value of M is restricted to 0, ± 1, ± 2, ± 3, ... while that of l can be 0, 1, 2, 3, ... The nature of the functions imposes a restriction on the uppermost value of M that $M \leq l$, that is, states with $| M | > l$ cannot exist. It will be clear with the following example. Consider a state with $l = 1$ and M = + 2. The corresponding associated Legendre polynomial derived from Equations [(6.29), (6.30)] will vanish as shown on next page.

$$P_1^2(x) = \left(1 - x^2\right)\frac{d^2}{dx^2}\left[\frac{1}{2}\frac{d}{dx}\left(x^2 - 1\right)\right]$$

$$= \left(1 - x^2\right).\frac{1}{2}\frac{d^2}{dx^2}(2x) = 0$$

This means that for a given value of l, M can be chosen from the set.

$$M = -l, (-l + 1), \ldots 0, \ldots (l - 1), + l$$

We shall see later that l and M are identified with the quantum numbers of energy and angular momentum

Exercise: For $|M| = 1$, verify that the values of l for the first two P (θ) functions are 1 and 2.

For $|M| = 1$, the first Legendre function is

$$P_1^1\ \theta = \sin\theta \times 1$$

Writing P for $P_1^1(\theta)$, $\dfrac{dP}{d\theta} = \cos\theta$; $\dfrac{d^2P}{d\theta^2} = -\sin\theta$.

The Legendre equation becomes

$$-\sin\theta + \frac{\cos\theta}{\sin\theta}.\cos\theta - \frac{\sin\theta}{\sin^2\theta} + \beta\sin\theta = 0$$

or

$$\frac{\cos^2\theta - \sin^2\theta}{\sin\theta} - \frac{1}{\sin\theta} + \beta\sin\theta = 0$$

or

$$-2\sin\theta + \beta\sin\theta = 0, \text{ or } \beta = 2, \therefore l = 1$$

The second Legendre function is $P_2^1(\theta)$ or simply P = sin θ cos θ

A similar procedure will lead to

$$\beta = l(l + 1) = 6 = \text{or } l = 2.$$

6.2.1.5 *Orthonormality of the P (θ) Functions*

The normalisation factor for each P (θ) function can be obtained directly from Equation (6.32). However, it is instructive to normalise P (θ) functions in some simple cases by using the relation.

$$\int_0^\pi \{P(\theta)\}^2\, d\tau = \int_0^\pi \{P(\theta)\}^2 \sin\theta\, d\theta = 1$$

The factor sin θ comes from the volume element $d\tau$ in polar coordinates. Thus, for the function $P_0^0(\theta)$ ($l = 0$, M = 0)

$$\int_0^\pi \{P_0^0(\theta)\}^2 \sin\theta\, d\theta = \int_0^\pi (N.1)^2 \sin\theta\, d\theta = 1$$

or $$N^2 [-\cos\theta]_0^\pi = N^2 . 2 = 1$$

or $$N = \frac{1}{\sqrt{2}}$$

Exercise: Find the normalisation factor for the function $P_2^1(\theta)$

[Hint: $$\int_0^\pi (N \sin\theta \cos\theta)^2 \sin\theta\, d\theta = 1^*$$

or $$N^2 \int_0^\pi \sin^3\theta \cos^2\theta\, d\theta = 1$$

or $$N^2 \int_0^\pi \sin\theta \left(\cos^2\theta - \cos^4\theta\right) d\theta = 1$$

or $$N^2 \left[-\frac{\cos^3\theta}{3} + \frac{\cos^5\theta}{5}\right]_0^\pi = 1$$

or $$N^2 . \frac{4}{15} = 1,$$

or $$N = \sqrt{\frac{15}{4}}\Bigg].$$

P (θ) functions belonging to the same value of M and different values of *l* must be orthogonal. This should be obvious if we write the Legendre equation as an eigenvalue equation

$$\left[\frac{d^2}{d\theta^2} + \frac{\cos\theta}{\sin\theta} \cdot \frac{d}{d\theta} - \frac{M^2}{\sin^2\theta}\right] P = -\beta P$$

Thus, for example,

$$\int_0^\pi P_0^0(\theta) . P_2^0(\theta)\, d\tau = \int_0^\pi \left(\frac{1}{2}\right)^{1/2} \left(\frac{5}{8}\right)^{1/2} \left(3\cos^2\theta - 1\right) \sin\theta\, d\theta$$

$$= \left(\frac{5}{16}\right)^{1/2} \left[-\frac{3\cos^3\theta}{3} + \cos\theta\right]_0^\pi = 0$$

However, P (θ) functions for different values of M will not necessarily be orthogonal because they will not be eigenfunctions of the same operator on account of the term $\frac{M^2}{\sin^2\theta}$ in the operator.

---

*The volume element in spherical polar coordinates is given by $d\tau = r^2\, dr \sin\theta\, d\theta\, d\varphi$ (see chapter 7, page 8). But here we are integrating over θ coordinates only.

6.2.2 The Complete Wave Function (Spherical Harmonics)

The complete wave function of the particle on a sphere (or a rigid rotator) may now be written as

$$\psi_{l,M}(\theta, \varphi) = P_{l,M}(\theta) \,.\, F_M(\varphi) = NP_l^{|M|}(\cos\theta) \,.\, \frac{1}{\sqrt{2\pi}} e^{iM\varphi} \qquad \text{... (6.33)}$$

where, N is normalisation factor given by Equation (6.32) of the associated Legendre function $P_l^{|M|}(\cos\theta)$ given by Equation (6.31). This function is characterised by two quantum numbers l and M. Expressed as trigonometric functions (real form) they represent harmonic waves on the surface of a sphere and are called "spherical harmonics". Spherical harmonics for a few sets of l and M values are listed below.

TABLE 6.3 Spherical Harmonics

l	M	$\psi_{l,M}(\theta, \varphi)$
0	0	$\psi_{0,0} = \frac{1}{2\sqrt{\pi}}$
1	0	$\psi_{1,0} = \left(\frac{3}{4\pi}\right)^{1/2} \cos\theta$
1	+1	$\psi_{1,+1} = \left(\frac{3}{8\pi}\right)^{1/2} \sin\theta\, e^{i\varphi}$
1	−1	$\psi_{1,-1} = \left(\frac{3}{8\pi}\right)^{1/2} \sin\theta\, e^{-i\varphi}$
2	0	$\psi_{2,0} = \left(\frac{5}{16\pi}\right)^{1/2} (3\cos^2\theta - 1)$
2	+1	$\psi_{2,+1} = -\left(\frac{5}{16\pi}\right)^{1/2} \sin\theta\cos\theta\, e^{i\varphi}$
2	−1	$\psi_{2,-1} = \left(\frac{15}{16\pi}\right)^{1/2} \sin\theta\cos\theta\, e^{-i\varphi}$
2	+2	$\psi_{2,+2} = \left(\frac{15}{32\pi}\right)^{1/2} \sin^2\theta\, e^{2i\varphi}$
2	−2	$\psi_{2,-2} = \left(\frac{15}{32\pi}\right)^{1/2} \sin^2\theta\, e^{-2i\varphi}$

6.2.2.1 *Spherical Harmonics in Real Form*

The spherical harmonics listed above have the disadvantage that most of them are complex and no real picture can be drawn of them. They can be transformed into real form which are more convenient to work with by using the following theorem:

$$e^{i\varphi} + e^{-i\varphi} = 2\cos\varphi$$

$$e^{i\varphi} - e^{-i\varphi} = 2i \sin \varphi$$

Then the degenerate functions, for example $\psi_{1,+1}$ and $\psi_{1,-1}$, can be combined to give real functions without altering the eigenvalue

$$\frac{1}{\sqrt{2}}\left(\psi_{1,+1} + \psi_{1,-1}\right), \text{or } \psi_{1+,} = \left(\frac{3}{4\pi}\right)^{1/2} \sin\theta \cos\varphi \quad \text{... (6.34)}$$

$$\frac{1}{i\sqrt{2}}\left(\psi_{1,+1} - \psi_{1,-1}\right), \text{or } \psi_{1-,} = \left(\frac{3}{4\pi}\right)^{1/2} \sin\theta \sin\varphi \quad \text{... (6.35)}$$

The factor $\frac{1}{\sqrt{2}}$ is necessary to keep the functions normalised; ψ_{1+} and ψ_{1-} refer to the + and – combinations respectively.

But a new feature emerges out of these combinations—the significance of the quantum number M is lost. In ψ_{1+} and ψ_{1-}, for example, the quantum number l is 1 but the value of M is undetermined.

6.2.3 Physical Representation of Spherical Harmonics

The spherical harmonics in real form can be visualised pictorially.

The function $\psi_{0,0} = \frac{1}{2\sqrt{\pi}}$ is a constant for all values of θ and φ; so it can be represented by the surface of the sphere and has no specific orientation [Fig. 6.2 (*a*)].

The function $\psi_{1,0} = \left(\frac{3}{4\pi}\right)^{1/2} \cos\theta$ has the largest positive value $\left[= +\left(\frac{3}{4\pi}\right)^{1/2}\right]$ when $\theta = 0$, *i.e.*, along the +*z* axis and gradually decreases as θ increases till it vanishes at $\theta = \frac{\pi}{2}$ *i.e.*, along the *x*-axis. The value becomes increasingly negative till it is maximum negative $\left[= -\left(\frac{3}{4\pi}\right)^{1/2}\right]$ at $\theta = \pi$, *i.e.*, along –*z*-axis. Being independent of φ this function has the same value for all values of φ. As a result, the function $\psi_{1,0}$ looks as sketched in Fig. 6.2 (*b*) which consists of two spherical lobes, one +ve and the other –ve, the *xy* plane being the "nodal plane". In other words, this function is specifically oriented along the *z*-axis.

The function $\psi_{1+} = \left(\frac{3}{4\pi}\right)^{1/2} \sin\theta \cos\varphi$ has the largest positive value for $\theta = \frac{\pi}{2}$, $\varphi = 0$, *i.e.*, along +*x* axis and the largest negative value for $\theta = \frac{3\pi}{2}$, $\varphi = \pi$, *i.e.*, along –*x*-axis. Thus the function is oriented along *x*-axis with *xz* plane as the "nodal plane" [Fig. (6.2) (*c*)].

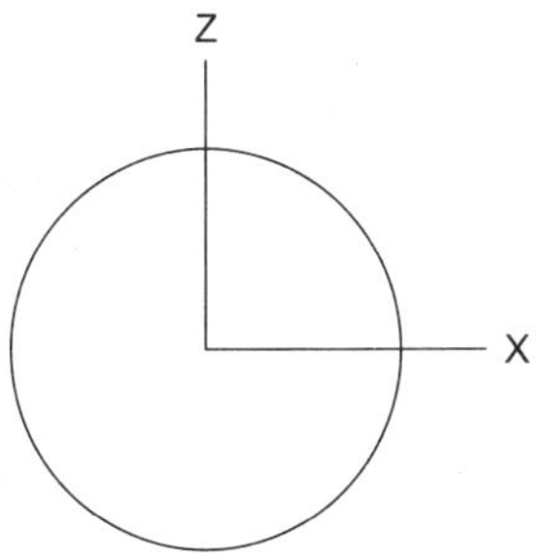

(a) $\psi_{0,0}$: No specific orientation, no node

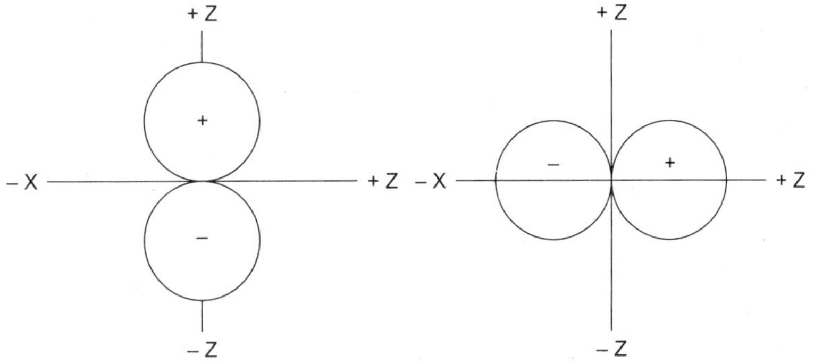

(b) $\psi_{1,0}$: Oriented along z-axis; xy plane is nodal (y-axis is not shown)

(c) ψ_{1+} : Oriented along x-axis; yz plane is nodal; (y-axis is not shown)

Fig. 6.2 *Cross-sections of spherical harmonics*

Similarly, the function $y_{1-} = \left(\dfrac{3}{4\pi}\right)^{1/2} \sin\theta \sin\varphi$ can be seen to be oriented along y-axis with xy plane as the nodal plane.

6.2.4 Introduction to Angular Momentum

Analogous to linear momentum (p) in translational motion, a rotating particle has angular momentum (L) by virtue of its mass and angular velocity. Classically, it is a vector $\vec{L}$ whose direction is along the axis of rotation and the axis is perpendicular to the plane of rotation. Like any other vector it has cartesian components L_x, L_y and L_z in 3-dimensional place.

If the rotation is 2-dimensional, as in the case of a particle in a ring, the axis of rotation may be taken as the z-axis if the plane of rotation is the xy-plane. Then the components $L_x = L_y = 0$, and $L_z = L$. (Fig. 6.3)

In cartesian coordinate system, L_z is expressed as

$$L_z = xp_y - yp_x \qquad \text{(Vide Equation (3.25))}$$

where, p_x and p_y are the components of the linear momentum p associated with the particle at the point (x, y) on the ring. The corresponding operator for L_z is

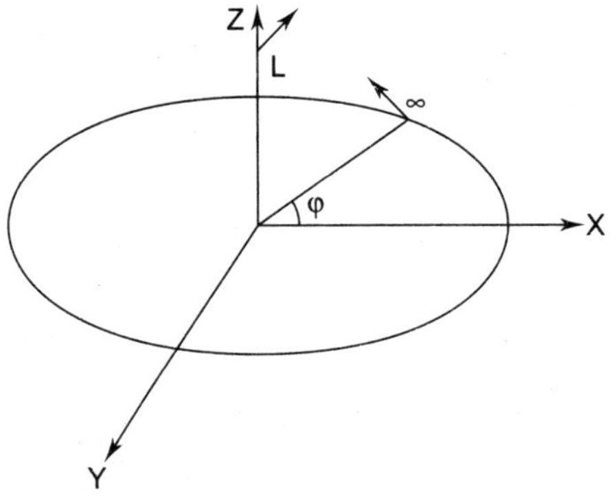

Fig. 6.3 *The direction of the angular momentum vector $\vec{L}$ for a particle in a ring*

$$\hat{L}_z = -\frac{ih}{2\pi}\left(x\frac{\partial}{\partial y} - y\frac{\partial}{\partial x}\right)$$

Since the motion is rotational it is more convenient to use polar coordinates wherein

$$\hat{L}_z = -\frac{ih}{2\pi}\cdot\frac{\partial}{\partial \varphi} \qquad \text{(see Appendix 2)}$$

where, φ is the single polar variable (see Fig. 6.3).

The important feature of it is that the functions

$$\psi = \frac{1}{\sqrt{2\pi}} e^{iM\varphi} \qquad \text{... (6.12)}$$

which are eigenfunctions of the Hamiltonian operator are also the eigenfunctions of $\hat{L}_z$; in the former case we get energy (E) and in the latter case the angular momentum (L_z) as eigenvalue.

$$\hat{H}\psi = -\frac{h^2}{8\pi^2 I}\frac{d^2}{d\varphi^2}\left(\frac{1}{\sqrt{2\pi}}e^{iM\varphi}\right) = \frac{M^2h^2}{8\pi^2 I}\left(\frac{1}{\sqrt{2\pi}}e^{iM\varphi}\right) = \frac{M^2h^2}{8\pi^2 I}\psi = E\psi$$

and $$\hat{L}_z\psi = -\frac{ih}{2\pi}\frac{d}{d\varphi}\left(\frac{1}{\sqrt{2\pi}}e^{iM\varphi}\right) = \frac{Mh}{2\pi}\left[\frac{1}{\sqrt{2\pi}}e^{iM\varphi}\right] = \frac{Mh}{2\pi}\psi = L_z\psi$$

It has to be noted, however, that eigenfunctions of $\hat{H}$ in real form are not the eigenfunctions of $\hat{L}_z$,

$$\hat{L}_z\psi = -\frac{ih}{2\pi}\frac{d}{d\varphi}\left(\frac{1}{\sqrt{\pi}}\sin M\varphi\right) = -\frac{ihM}{2\pi}\left(\frac{1}{\sqrt{\pi}}\cos M\varphi\right)$$

6.2.4.1 Three Dimensional Rotation

When the particle rotates in three dimensional space, as in the case of particle on a sphere, the axis of rotation is still perpendicular to the plane of rotation but now the axis is free to take any orientation and the vector need not be parallel to the z-axis. The components L_x and L_y are no longer zero now and the magnitude of the vector is given by

$$L^2 = L_x^2 + L_y^2 + L_z^2$$

Operators corresponding to these quantities in spherical coordinates are given below (see Appendix 2)

$$\hat{L}_x = -\frac{ih}{2\pi}\left(-\sin\varphi\frac{\partial}{\partial\theta} - \cos\varphi\cot\theta\frac{\partial}{\partial\varphi}\right) \quad \text{... (6.36)}$$

$$\hat{L}_y = -\frac{ih}{2\pi}\left(\cos\varphi\frac{\partial}{\partial\theta} - \sin\varphi\cot\theta\frac{\partial}{\partial\varphi}\right) \quad \text{... (6.37)}$$

$$\hat{L}_z = -\frac{ih}{2\pi}\frac{d}{d\varphi} \quad \text{... (6.38)}$$

$$\hat{L}^2 = -\frac{h^2}{4\pi^2}\left[\frac{1}{\sin\theta}\frac{\partial}{\partial\theta}\left(\sin\theta\frac{\partial}{\partial\theta}\right) + \frac{1}{\sin^2\theta}\frac{\partial^2}{\partial\varphi^2}\right] \quad \text{... (6.39)}$$

The feature of interest here is that there exist eigenfunctions of $\hat{H}$ that are eigenfunctions of $\hat{L}^2$ and of only one of the components. This means that if the system is described by such an eigenfunction then we can obtain definite values of the total energy E, the angular momentum L and one of its components. By convention the component L_z is chosen (perhaps due to the simplicity of its operator in spherical coordinates).

It is easy to see that the spherical harmonics, real or complex, are eigenfunctinos of both $\hat{H}$ and $\hat{L}^2$. For the operator $\hat{L}_z$, however, eigenfunctions exist in complex form only. Take for example the spherical harmonics for $l = 1$, M = 0, *i.e.*, $\psi_{1,0} = \left(\frac{3}{4\pi}\right)^{1/2}\cos\theta$. Then, leaving the normalisation factor,

$$\hat{H}\psi_{1,0} = -\frac{h^2}{8\pi^2 I}\left[\frac{1}{\sin\theta}\frac{\partial}{\partial\theta}\left\{\sin\theta\frac{\partial}{\partial\theta}(\cos\theta)\right\} + \frac{1}{\sin^2\theta}\frac{\partial^2}{\partial\varphi^2}(\cos\theta)\right]$$

$$= \frac{h^2}{8\pi^2 I}\cdot\frac{1}{\sin\theta}\frac{\partial}{\partial\theta}\left(\sin^2\theta\right)$$

$$= \frac{2h^2}{8\pi^2 I}\cos\theta = \frac{2h^2}{8\pi^2 I}\cdot\psi_{1,0}$$

Eigenvaluc (E) $= \dfrac{2h^2}{8\pi^2 I}$

Also $$\hat{L}^2 \psi_{1,0} = -\frac{h^2}{4\pi^2}\left[\frac{1}{\sin\theta}\frac{\partial}{\partial\theta}\left\{\sin\theta\frac{\partial}{\partial\theta}(\cos\theta)\right\} + \frac{1}{\sin^2\theta}\frac{\partial^2}{\partial\varphi^2}(\cos\theta)\right]$$

$$= \frac{2h^2}{4\pi^2}\cos\theta = \frac{2h^2}{4\pi^2}\psi_{1,0}$$

or $$\text{Eigenvalue}\,(L^2) = \frac{2h^2}{4\pi^2}$$

But $$\hat{L}_z \psi_{1,0} = -\frac{ih}{2\pi}\frac{\partial}{\partial\varphi}(\cos\theta) = 0$$

which is not eigenvalue equation. However, we could write

$$\hat{L}_z \psi_{1,0} = -\frac{ih}{2\pi}\frac{\partial}{\partial\varphi}\left(\cos\theta\, e^{i.0.\varphi}\right) = -0\left(\frac{i^2 h}{2\pi}\right)\cos\theta\, e^{i.0.\varphi}$$

$$= 0\,.\cos\theta\, e^{i.0.\varphi} = 0\,.\,\psi_{1,0}$$

or $$\text{Eigenvalue} = 0$$

The eigenvalue equation for $\hat{H}, \hat{L}^2$ and $\hat{L}_z$ may be given, in general, as follows,

$$\hat{H}\psi_{l,M} = \frac{\beta h^2}{8\pi^2 I}\psi_{l,M} = l(l+1)\frac{h^2}{8\pi^2 I}\cdot\psi_{l,M} \quad \text{... (6.40)}$$

$$\hat{L}^2 \psi_{l,M} = \frac{\beta h^2}{4\pi^2}\psi_{l,M} = l(l+1)\frac{h^2}{4\pi^2}\cdot\psi_{l,M} \quad \text{... (6.41)}$$

$$\hat{L}_z \psi_{l,M} = \frac{Mh}{2\pi}\psi_{l,M}. \quad \text{... (6.42)}$$

6.2.5 Quantisation of Energy and Angular Momentum

Spherical harmonics when operated upon by the Hamiltonian $(\hat{H})$ yield energy as eigenvalue expressed as

$$E_l = l(l+1)\frac{h^2}{8\pi^2 I} \quad \text{... (6.43)}$$

where, $I = mr^2$ is the moment of inertia of the rotating particle on the surface of radius r. The energy is quantised in units of $\frac{h^2}{8\pi^2 I}$, l being the "quantum number of energy", and is restricted to the values 0, 2, 6, 12, ... units according as l = 0, 1, 2, 3, ... respectively. The system has no zero point energy ($\because$ E = 0 when l = 0). The energy is determined solely by l and is independent of M. Since for each value of l, there are $2l + 1$ values of M, each energy level is $(2l + 1)$-fold degenerate each state having a definite value of M.

When operated upon by $\hat{L}^2$, the spherical harmonics yield an eigenvalue which represents the square of the length of the angular momentum of the same rotating particle expressed as

$$L^2 = l(l+1)\frac{h^2}{4\pi^2}, \text{ or } L = \sqrt{l(l+1)}\cdot\frac{h}{2\pi} \quad \text{... (6.44)}$$

Therefore, l is also the "quantum number of angular momentum".

The operator $\hat{L}_z$ leads to the magnitude of the z-component of the angular momentum vector $(\vec{L})$, given as

$$L_z = \frac{Mh}{2\pi} \quad \text{... (6.45)}$$

Accordingly, M is the "quantum number of the z-component of angular momentum".

6.2.5.1 *Physical Model of the Angular Momentum*

The foregoing information enables us to devise a physical model of the angular momentum in a three-dimensional rotation of a particle on a sphere. We imagine a classical vector $\vec{L} = (L_x, L_y, L_z)$ drawn from the centre of the sphere. For a given value of the quantum number l, it has a fixed length $\sqrt{l(l+1)}\cdot\frac{h}{2\pi}$. It can take only those directions in which its z-component equals $\frac{Mh}{2\pi}$, where, M, the other quantum number takes any one of the integral values between $+ l$ and $- l$ including 0. The number of such directions is equal to $2l + 1$. The end of the vector lies on the sphere whose radius is $\sqrt{l(l+1)}\cdot\frac{h}{2\pi}$. Since L_x and L_y remain unspecified the vector $\vec{L}$ may lie anywhere on the surface of an inscribed cone whose axis coincides with the z-axis and whose altitude is equal to L_z; in another sense, the vector may be considered to be precessing round the z-axis (Fig. 6.4).

Diagrams representing the situation corresponding to $l = 1$ and $M = + 1, 0$ and $- 1$ are shown in Fig. 6.5.

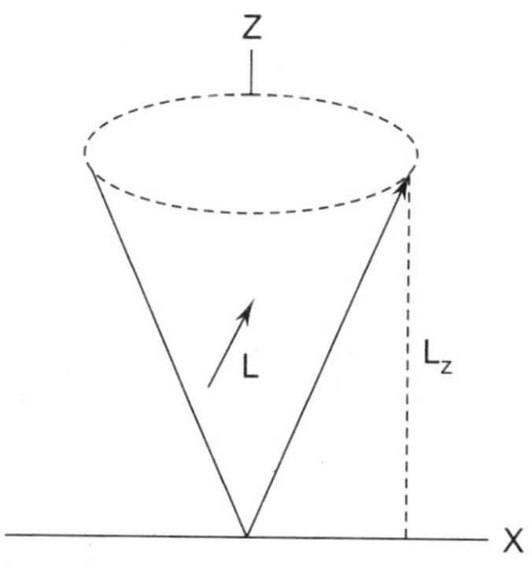

Fig. 6.4 *The precessing angular momentum vector*

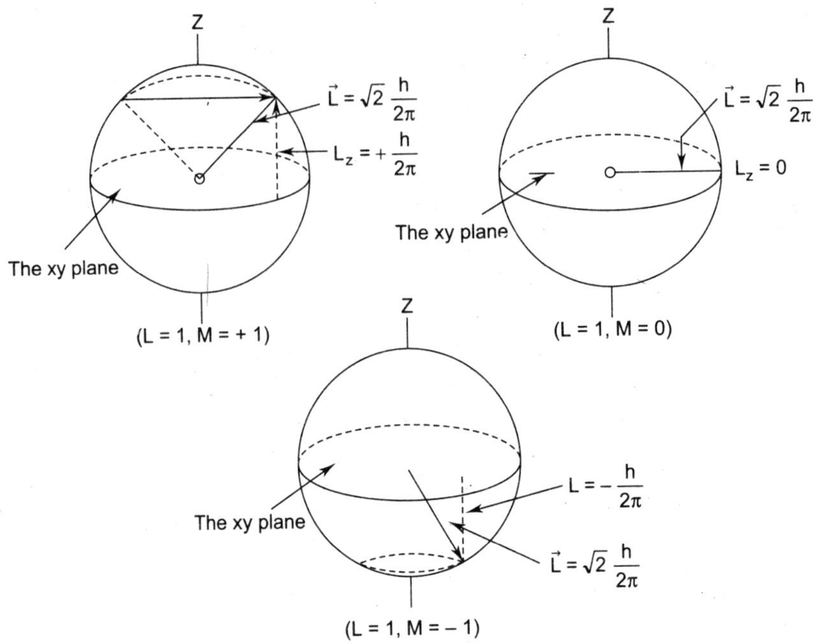

Fig. 6.5 *Three states of the angular momentum vector* $\vec{L} = \sqrt{2}\,\frac{h}{2\pi}$ *corresponding to M = +1, 0 and –1. For the 2 + 1 = 3 values of M,* L_z *assumes values* $+\frac{h}{2\pi}$*, 0 and* $-\frac{h}{2\pi}$ *;* L_x *and* L_y *remain unspecifed*

[**Exercise:** Spherical harmonics for several values of *l* and M are listed in Table 6.3. Verify that they are eigenfunctions of $\hat{H}$, $\hat{L}^2$ and $\hat{L}_z$; give the value of energy and angular momentum in each case.

Take, for example, $\psi_{1,+1} = \sin\theta\, e^{i\varphi}$ (without normalisation)

$$\hat{H}\psi = -\frac{h^2}{8\pi^2 I}\left[\frac{1}{\sin\theta}\frac{\partial}{\partial\theta}\left\{\sin\theta\frac{\partial}{\partial\theta}\left(\sin\theta\, e^{i\varphi}\right)\right\} + \frac{1}{\sin^2\theta}\frac{\partial^2}{\partial\varphi^2}\left(\sin\theta\, e^{i\varphi}\right)\right]$$

$$= -\frac{h^2}{8\pi^2 I}\left[\frac{\cos 2\theta}{\sin\theta} - \frac{1}{\sin\theta}\right]e^{i\varphi}$$

$$= -\frac{h^2}{8\pi^2 I}\left[\frac{\cos^2\theta - \sin^2\theta - 1}{\sin\theta}\right]e^{i\varphi}$$

$$= \frac{h^2}{8\pi^2 I}\,.\,2\sin\theta\, e^{i\varphi} = \frac{2h^2}{8\pi^2 I}\cdot\psi_{1,+1}$$

$\therefore$ Eigenvalue (E) $= \dfrac{2h^2}{8\pi^2 I}$

Similarly, $\hat{L}^2\,\psi_{1,+1} = \dfrac{2h^2}{4\pi^2}\,\psi_{1,+1}$

$$\therefore \qquad \text{Eigenvalue } (L^2) = \frac{2h^2}{4\pi^2} \text{ and } L = \sqrt{2} \cdot \frac{h}{2\pi}$$

$$\hat{L}_z \, \psi_{1,+1} = -\frac{ih}{2\pi}\frac{\partial}{\partial\varphi}\left(\sin\theta \, e^{i\varphi}\right) = -\frac{i^2 h}{2\pi} \sin\theta \, e^{i\varphi}$$

$$= +1 \cdot \frac{h}{2\pi} \psi_{1,+1}$$

$$\therefore \qquad \text{Eigenvalue } (L_z) = \left.\frac{h}{2\pi}\right] .$$

From these observations it may be concluded that if the system is represented by complex spherical harmonics the quantities E, L^2 (hence L) and L_z can be obtained precisely, but if it is represented by a real form of the spherical harmonics, the quantity L_z cannot be determined. But how does the system know as to how it should be represented ? The answer lies in the type of experiment chosen to observe the system as the experiment will disturb the system in such a way as to call forth the appropriate form of the wave function. For example, consider an atom in a uniform magnetic field. The magnetic field disturbs the atom so as to bring it in a state for which its angular momentum is definite; but if we disturb the atom by bringing another atom for chemically combining with it its angular momentum becomes indefinite. Thus the very act of performing an experiment determines the type of information to be obtained. In any case, what remains true is that eigenfunctions (states of the system) exist which permit simultaneous observation of E, L^2 and only one of the components of L, viz L_z.

6.3 ROTATION OF DIATOMIC MOLECULES (RIGID ROTATOR)

We may now apply the concepts developed so far to the more realistic case of rotation of a diatomic molecule. If the masses of the electrons and the vibration of the nuclei are ignored, a diatomic molecule may be compared to a rigid rotator, that is, a system of two masses m_1 and m_2, separated by a fixed (internuclear) distance r. The rotational motion of such a diatomic rotator corresponds to the motion of two masses in such a way that the centre of mass and the internuclear distance remain unchanged. Let the centre of mass be considered at the origin of the coordinate system. If during rotation the two masses m_1 and m_2 move with linear velocities v_1 and v_2 respectively and the distances r_1 and r_2 remain unchanged, then the kinetic energy (T) due to rotation is given by,

$$T = \frac{1}{2} m_1 v_1^2 + \frac{1}{2} m_2 v_2^2$$

Using the relations $x = r \sin\theta \cos\varphi$, $y = r \sin\theta \sin\varphi$, $z = r\cos\theta$

and
$$v^2 = v_x^2 + v_y^2 + v_z^2 = \left(\frac{dx}{dt}\right)^2 + \left(\frac{dy}{dt}\right)^2 + \left(\frac{dz}{dt}\right)^2$$

it can be easily shown that

$$v_1^2 = r_1^2 \left[\left(\frac{d\theta}{dt}\right)^2 + \sin^2\theta \left(\frac{d\varphi}{dt}\right)^2\right] = r_1^2 \, \omega^2$$

and $$v_2^2 = r_2^2 \left[\left(\frac{d\theta}{dt}\right)^2 + \sin^2\theta\left(\frac{d\varphi}{dt}\right)^2\right] = r_2^2\,\omega^2$$

where, ω is angular velocity in 3-dimensions. Therefore,

$$T = \frac{1}{2}\omega^2\left(m_1 r_1^2 + m_2 r_2^2\right)$$

$$= \frac{1}{2}\omega^2 I \qquad \text{... (6.46)}$$

where, I is moment of inertia about the axis passing through the centre of gravity and perpendicular to the internuclear axis of the diatomic molecule.

The Equation (6.46) means that a rigid rotator can be treated in the same way a single particle of mass I moving with angular velocity ω on the surface of a sphere.

6.3.1 Rotation in Plane (Fixed Axis)

If a rigid diatomic molecule rotates in the xy plane the rotational axis coincides with the z-axis. The angular momentum will have only the z-component L_z ($L_x = L_y = 0$). The rotational energy of the molecule will be equal to the kinetic energy ($\because V = 0$). Since $T = \frac{\omega^2 I^2}{2I} = \frac{I_z^2}{2I}$, the Hamiltonian for such a system will be,

$$\hat{H} = \frac{\hat{L}_z^2}{2I} = -\frac{h^2}{8\pi^2 I}\cdot\frac{d^2}{d\varphi^2}$$

and the Schrödinger equation may be written as,

$$\frac{d^2\psi}{d\varphi^2} = -\frac{8\pi^2\mu E}{h^2}\psi = -M^2\psi \qquad \text{... (6.47)}$$

The angle φ is the angle of rotation in the plane, and μ is the reduced mass given by $\mu = \frac{(m_1 m_2)}{(m_1 + m_2)}$.

The eigenfunctions corresponding to Equation (6.47) are known to be,

$$\psi = \frac{1}{\sqrt{2\pi}} e^{iM\varphi}$$

and the eigenvalues as, $$E = \frac{M^2 h^2}{8\pi^2 I}, \; M = 0, \pm 1, \pm 2, \pm 3 \ldots$$

where, $$I = \mu r^2$$

In other words, a diatomic molecule rotating in a plane may be treated as a single particle in a ring.

6.3.2 Rotation in Space (Free Axis)

Rotation in space means that the axis of rotation is free to take any direction in space. In this case, there are two angular variables θ and φ; θ is the angle which the axis of rotation makes with the *z*-axis and φ is the angle in the *xy* plane between the *x*-axis and the projection of the rotational axis in the *xy* plane. Since the internuclear distance does not change, the potential energy V is zero. Then, the rotational energy, which is the same as the kinetic energy, is given by,

$$E = \frac{L^2}{2I} \quad \text{... (6.48)}$$

where, L is the angular momentum.

The Hamiltonian is given by the equation

$$\hat{H} = \frac{\hat{L}^2}{2I} = -\frac{h^2}{8\pi^2 I}\left[\frac{1}{\sin\theta}\cdot\frac{\partial}{\partial\theta}\left(\sin\theta\,.\frac{\partial}{\partial\theta}\right) + \frac{1}{\sin^2\theta}\cdot\frac{\partial^2}{\partial\varphi^2}\right]$$

The Schrödinger equation may be written as,

$$\left[\frac{1}{\sin\theta}\cdot\frac{\partial}{\partial\theta}\left(\sin\theta\,.\frac{\partial}{\partial\theta}\right) + \frac{1}{\sin^2\theta}\cdot\frac{\partial^2}{\partial\varphi^2}\right]\psi(\theta,\varphi) = -\frac{8\pi^2 IE}{h^2}\psi(\theta,\varphi) \quad \text{... (6.49)}$$

This is the same as the Equation (6.19). Therefore, the energy E will be given as,

$$E = \frac{\beta h^2}{8\pi^2 I} = l(l+1)\frac{h^2}{8\pi^2 I}, l = 1, 2, 3, ... \quad \text{... (6.50)}$$

The eigenfunctions ψ (θ, φ) are the spherical harmonics Equation (6.33).

PROBLEMS

6.1 Two masses m_1 and m_2 forming a rigid rotator are restricted to move in a plane.

(*a*) Set up the Schrödinger equation for this rotator and obtain equations for the energy eigenvalues and the normalised eigenfunction.

(*b*) What is the expectation value of the angular momentum for the state of lowest energy for this rotator ?

(*c*) Find an equation for the eigenvalues of the operator $\hat{L}^2 = -\frac{h^2}{4\pi^2}\frac{d^2}{d\varphi^2}$ which corresponds to the square of the angular momentum of the operator.

[**Hint:** (*a*) $I = \mu r^2$, $\mu = \frac{m_1 m_2}{m_1 + m_2}$

This permits the treatment of the rotator as a single particle with mass μ and the radius of circumference of the circle of rotator = *r*. If φ is the single variable to be chosen,

$$-\frac{h^2}{8\pi^2\mu}\cdot\frac{d^2\psi}{d\varphi^2} = E\psi$$

For eigenfunctions and eigenvalues, see the text.

(*b*) For the state of lowest energy (M = 0)

$$\psi = \frac{1}{\sqrt{2\pi}}$$

$$\overline{L} = \int_0^{2\pi} \frac{1}{\sqrt{2\pi}} \left[- \cdot \frac{d}{d\varphi} \left(\frac{1}{\sqrt{2\pi}} \right) \right] d\varphi = 0$$

(*c*) $\hat{L}^2 \psi = -\frac{h^2}{4\pi^2} \cdot \frac{d^2\psi}{d\varphi^2} = +\frac{h^2 M^2}{4\pi^2} \cdot \psi$

(when $\psi = Ae^{\pm iM\varphi}$)

i.e., eigenvalues of $\hat{L}^2$ are $\left.\frac{h^2 M^2}{4\pi^2}\right]$.

6.2 Explain why $\psi = \frac{1}{\sqrt{2\pi}} \cdot \exp\left(i\sqrt{2}\,\varphi\right)$ will not be acceptable function for a particle in a ring.

[**Hint:** Examine the single-valuedness of the function].

6.3 Derive the operator for the angular momentum, $\hat{L}$, for a particle in a ring. Show that

$$\psi = Ae^{iM\varphi} + Be^{-iM\varphi}$$

will be an eigenfunction of $\hat{L}$.

6.4 Verify that $F = \frac{1}{\sqrt{2\pi}} \exp(iM\varphi)$ constitutes an orthonormal set for particle in a ring.

6.5 Confirm that the wave function for a particle on a sphere can be written as $\psi(\theta, \varphi) = P(\theta) \cdot F(\varphi)$.
[**Hint:** Substitute in the Schrödinger equation].

6.6 Confirm that the spherical harmonics, $Y_{1,1}$ and $Y_{2,0}$ are the solutions for the particle on a sphere. Write the normalised wave functions for the two and confirm that they are orthonormal.
[**Hint:** $d\tau = \sin\theta \, d\theta \, d\varphi$].

6.7 In the stationary states $Y_{l,M}(\theta, \varphi)$ found for the rigid rotator, show that there is equal probability of finding the rotator at any value of the coordinate φ.
[**Hint:** $A^* e^{i\varphi} \cdot Ae^{-i\varphi} = A^* \cdot A$ = constant].

6.8 The spherical harmonics $Y_{l,M}(\theta, \varphi)$ are simultaneous eigenfunctions of the angular momentum operators $\hat{L}^2$ and $\hat{L}_2$. Thus,

$$\hat{L}_z Y_{l,M}(\theta, \varphi) = l(l+1) Y_{l,M}(\theta, \varphi)$$

$$\hat{L}_z Y_{l,M}(\theta, \varphi) = MY_{l,M}(\theta, \varphi)$$

(*a*) Separate the variables in the $\hat{L}^2$ equation to obtain equations for $F(\varphi)$ and $P_{l,M}(\theta)$ by assuming that,

$$Y_{l,M}(\theta, \varphi) = F(\varphi) \cdot P(\theta)$$

Determine the normalised function F (φ).

[Hint: $\hat{L}^2 Y_{l,M}(\theta,\varphi) = -\left[\frac{1}{\sin\theta}\cdot\frac{\partial}{\partial\theta}\left(\sin\theta\frac{\partial}{\partial\theta}\right)+\frac{1}{\sin^2\theta}\cdot\frac{\partial^2}{\partial\varphi^2}\right]Y_{l,M}(\theta,\varphi)$

$$= l(l+1)\,Y_{l,M}(\theta,\varphi)$$

Making the substitution $Y_{l,M}(\theta,\varphi) = F(\varphi)\,.\,P(\theta)$ and dividing by $Y_{l,M}(\theta,\varphi)$, one can obtain after rearrangement

$$\sin^2\theta\left[\frac{1}{P(\theta)\sin\theta}\cdot\frac{d}{d\theta}(\sin\theta)\frac{dP}{d\theta}\right]+l(l+1)$$

$$= -\frac{1}{F}\frac{d^2F}{d\varphi^2} = \text{constant } (M^2 \text{ say})$$

Thus, the original equation is separated into

$$\left[\frac{1}{\sin\theta}\cdot\frac{d}{d\theta}\left(\sin\theta\,.\frac{d}{d\theta}\right)-\frac{M^2}{\sin^2\theta}\right]P(\theta)$$

$$= -l(l+1)\,P(\theta)$$

and $$\frac{d^2F}{d\varphi^2} = -M^2F,$$

or $$\hat{L}_z F = MF$$

(*b*) L_z equation is $\frac{h}{2\pi i}\frac{dF}{d\varphi} = MF$

or $$F = Ae^{\frac{2\pi i}{h}}.M\varphi,\ A = \frac{1}{\sqrt{2\pi}}\Bigg].$$

6.9 Show that the spherical harmonics $Y_{1,1}(\theta,\varphi)$ and $Y_{2,0}(\theta,\varphi)$ are orthogonal.
[Hint: $d\tau = \sin\theta\, d\theta\, d\varphi$

$$\int_0^{\pi}\int_0^{2\pi}\left[\left(\frac{3}{4\pi}\right)^{1/2}.\sin\theta\,.\cos\varphi\right].\left[\left(\frac{5}{16}\right)^{1/2}.\left(3\cos^2\theta-1\right)\right]\sin\theta\, d\theta\, d\varphi$$

$$= \left(\frac{15}{64\pi}\right)^{1/2}\int_0^{\pi}\left(3\cos^2\theta-1\right)\sin^2\theta\, d\theta\int_0^{2\pi}\cos\varphi\, d\varphi$$

$$= 0].$$

6.10 Show that the spherical harmonics $Y_{1,1}$; $Y_{1,0}$ and $Y_{1,-1}$ form an orthonormal set.

[Hint: For $Y_{1,1}$ $\int_0^{\pi}\int_0^{2\pi}\left[\left(\frac{3}{4\pi}\right)^{1/2}.\sin\theta\,.\cos\varphi\right]^2\sin\theta\, d\theta\, d\varphi$

$$= \frac{3}{4\pi}\int_0^{\pi}\sin^3\theta\, d\theta \int_0^{2\pi}\cos^2\varphi\, d\varphi$$

$$= \frac{3}{4\pi}\times\frac{4\pi}{3} = 1$$

for $Y_{1,1}$ $\int_0^{\pi}\int_0^{2\pi}\left[\left(\frac{3}{4\pi}\right)^{1/2}\cos\theta\right]^2 \sin\theta\, d\theta\, d\varphi = \frac{3}{4\pi}\times\frac{4\pi}{3} = 1$

for $Y_{1,0}$ $\int_0^{\pi}\int_0^{2\pi}\left[\left(\frac{3}{4\pi}\right)^{1/2}\cos\theta\right]^2 .\sin\theta\, d\theta\, d\varphi = \frac{3}{4\pi}.\frac{2}{3}.2\pi = 1$

For orthogonality,

$$\int_0^{\pi}\int_0^{2\pi}\left[\left(\frac{3}{4\pi}\right)^{1/2}\sin\theta.\cos\varphi\right]\left[\left(\frac{3}{4\pi}\right)^{1/2}.\sin\theta.\sin\varphi\right].\sin\theta\, d\theta\, d\varphi.$$

$$= \frac{3}{4\pi}\int_0^{\pi}\sin^3\theta\, d\theta\int_0^{2\pi}\sin\varphi\cos\varphi\, d\varphi = \frac{3}{4\pi}.\frac{4}{3}.0 = 0$$

Similarly, $\frac{3}{4\pi}\int_0^{\pi}\sin^2\theta\cos\theta\, d\theta\int_0^{2\pi}\sin\varphi\, d\varphi$

$$= \frac{3}{4\pi}.0.0 = 0$$

and $\left.\frac{3}{4\pi}\int_0^{\pi}\sin^2\theta\cos\theta\, d\theta\int_0^{2\pi}\cos\varphi\, d\varphi = 0\right]$

6.11 Show that the spherical harmonics $Y_{2,0}$ and $Y_{2,1}$ are orthogonal to each other. [**Hint:** Use the table of integrals].

6.12 The rotation of an HI molecule may be considered as orbiting of the H atom at a radius of 160 pm with I virtually stationary at the centre. Determine the energy levels considering the rotation to be restricted (*i*) in *x*-*y* plane and (*ii*) in 3-dimensions. Indicate the degeneracies of the energy levels.
What will be the wavelength of radiation emitted for transition from the first excited to the ground state in either case ?

CHAPTER 7

Hydrogen and Hydrogen-like Atoms

Hydrogen, being the simplest of all chemical elements, provides a model for the study of atomic structure of elements in general. Moreover, it constitutes one of the basic examples of chemical systems exhibiting rotational motion. The spatial rotation of an electron around the nucleus in the hydrogen atom can be described in terms of electron's two angular variables θ (zenith angle) and φ (azimuthal angle), and its radial distance r from the nuclear centre. This system is equivalent to a particle moving in an infinite number of concentric spheres.

Positive ions containing only one electron bound to a nucleus of charge + Ze (*e.g.*, He^+, Li^{2+}, B^{3+}, etc.) may be treated quantum mechanically like a hydrogen atom and are accordingly called hydrogen-like atoms.

Spherically Symmetric Potential and the Hamiltonian

Hydrogen-like systems are characterized by a spherically symmetric potential energy given by Equation (7.1),

$$V = -\frac{Ze^2}{(4\pi\varepsilon_0)r} \quad \text{...(7.1)}$$

which means that the potential energy is a function of r only. It is same in all directions, *i.e.*, it is independent of the spherical angular variables θ and φ.

Apparently, a hydrogen-like atom presents a two-particle problem—a nucleus (mass M, charge +Ze where, e = electronic charge) and an electron (mass m, charge – e) interacting by coulombic force of attraction. If x_1, y_1 and z_1 be the cartesian coordinates of the nucleus and x_2, y_2 and z_2 those of the electron, the Hamiltonian operator for the hydrogen-like atom may be written as

$$\hat{H} = -\frac{h^2}{8\pi^2 M}\nabla_1^2 - \frac{h^2}{8\pi^2 m}\nabla_2^2 - \frac{Ze^2}{(4\pi\varepsilon_0)r}$$

where,

$$\nabla_i^2 = \frac{\partial^2}{\partial x_i^2} + \frac{\partial^2}{\partial y_i^2} + \frac{\partial^2}{\partial z_i^2}$$

and i = 1 or 2.

There are two types of motions involved here (*i*) the translational motion of the atom as a whole, and (*ii*) the internal motion of the electron and the nucleus relative to each other. The Schrödinger equation describing the two motions is,

$$\hat{H}\psi_T = E_T\,\psi_T \qquad \text{... (7.2)}$$

where, $\psi_T = \psi\,(x_1, y_1, z_1, x_2, y_2, z_2)$ is the total wave function and E_T is the total energy of the atom (*i.e.*, sum of the translational and the internal energies).

Since the potential energy does not depend on the coordinates of a single particle, it is difficult to solve the Schrödinger equation without separating it into two equations corresponding to the two types of motion. For this we introduce two new sets of variables defined below.

$$\left.\begin{aligned} X &= \frac{Mx_1 + mx_2}{M+m} \\ Y &= \frac{My_1 + my_2}{M+m} \\ Z &= \frac{Mz_1 + mz_2}{M+m} \end{aligned}\right\} \text{ and } \left.\begin{aligned} x &= x_2 - x_1 \\ y &= y_2 - y_1 \\ z &= z_2 - z_1 \end{aligned}\right\}$$

X, Y and Z are called the "coordinates of the centre of mass" of the atom while x, y and z are the "relative coordinates" of the radial distance r of the electron from the nucleus, *i.e.*,

$$r = [(x_2 - x_1)^2 + (y_2 - y_1)^2 + (z_2 - z_1)^2]^{1/2}$$

On transforming to the new variables after carrying out appropriate differentiations*, the Schrödinger equation takes the form,

$$\left[-\frac{h^2}{8\pi^2(M+m)}\,.\,\nabla_q^2 - \frac{h^2}{8\pi^2\mu}\,.\,\nabla_r^2 - \frac{Ze^2}{(4\pi\varepsilon_0)\,r}\right]\psi_T\,(q, r) = E_T\,\psi_T\,(q, r) \qquad \text{... (7.3)}$$

where, $\nabla_q^2 = \dfrac{\partial^2}{\partial X^2} + \dfrac{\partial^2}{\partial Y^2} + \dfrac{\partial^2}{\partial Z^2},\ \nabla_r^2 = \dfrac{\partial^2}{\partial x^2} + \dfrac{\partial^2}{\partial y^2} + \dfrac{\partial^2}{\partial z^2}$

and μ, the reduced mass $= \dfrac{Mm}{M+m}$,

$\psi_T\,(q, r)$ is the total wave function of the two particles in the new sets of coordinates denoted collectively as q and r.

Now assume that, $\psi_T\,(q, r) = \phi\,(q)\,.\,\psi\,(r)$ ... (7.4)

Substituting Equation (7.4) into Equation (7.3), simplifying and rearranging, we obtain,

$$\frac{1}{\phi\,(q)}\left[-\frac{h^2}{8\pi^2(M+m)}\nabla_q^2\,\phi\,(q)\right] = E_T - \frac{1}{\psi(r)}\left[-\frac{h^2}{8\pi^2\mu}\nabla_r^2 - \frac{Ze^2}{4\pi\varepsilon_o r}\right]\psi(r) \qquad \text{... (7.5)}$$

* C.S. Johnson and L.G. Pedersen, *Quantum Chemistry and Physics* (Addison-Wesley, California), 1974, page 174.

In Equation (7.5), the left hand side depends only on the centre of mass coordinates q and the right hand side only on the relative coordinates r; hence, both sides must be equal to the same constant, say W. Thus, we obtain two separate equations,

$$-\frac{h^2}{8\pi^2 (M+m)} \nabla_q^2 \phi(q) = W \phi(q) \qquad \text{... (7.6)}$$

and

$$E_T - \frac{1}{\psi(r)}\left[-\frac{h^2}{8\pi^2 \mu} . \nabla_r^2 - \frac{Ze^2}{4\pi\varepsilon_0 r}\right]\psi(r) = W \qquad \text{... (7.7)}$$

On rearranging, Equation (7.7) takes the form,

$$\left[-\frac{h^2}{8\pi^2 \mu} \nabla_r^2 - \frac{Ze^2}{4\pi\varepsilon_0 r}\right]\psi(r) = (E_T - W)\,\psi(r)$$

$$= E\,\psi(r) \qquad \text{... (7.8)}$$

where, $E = E_T - W$.

The Equation (7.6) represents the Schrödinger equation for the translational motion of a single hypothetical free particle of mass M + m, which is practically the nucleus as M >> m, unacted upon by any external force ; the eigenfunctions and the energy Eigenvalues W (representing the translational energies only) of such a system are well known (see Chapter 4). However, this equation is of little interest as regards the structure of the hydrogen atom.

The Equation (7.8), which contains the potential energy of interaction, is actually the Schrödinger equation for the "internal motion" of the nucleus and the electron. This is equivalent to the Equation of motion of another hypothetical particle of mass μ. However, since M >> m (a hydrogen nucleus is about 2000 times heavier than an electron),

$$\mu = \frac{Mm}{M+m} \approx m$$

such that the Equation (7.8) is, for all practical purposes, the Schrödinger equation for the motion of an electron of mass m in a hydrogen-like atom, and the Eigenvalues, $E = E_T - W$, are the energies of the electron in the atom. The equation may, therefore, be written as,

$$\left[-\frac{h^2}{8\pi^2 m} \nabla^2 - \frac{Ze^2}{4\pi\varepsilon_0 r}\right]\psi = E\psi \qquad \text{... (7.9)}$$

where the subscript r has been dropped, and $\psi = \psi(r)$.

7.1 SPHERICAL COORDINATES

The electron executes rotational motion around the nucleus in three-dimensions, so its position and the wave function must be expressed in spherical coordinates r, θ and φ. The problem is similar to that of the particle on a sphere (see Chapter 6) except that here r is also a variable. Moreover, although the kinetic energy part in Equation (7.9) is in cartesian coordinates, the potential energy depends on r, a spherical coordinate. So, the Equation (7.9) must be transformed into one involving r, θ and φ to solve it by the method of separation of variables. The relationship betwen x, y and z and r, θ and φ can be easily established by referring to Fig. 7.1.

[Let P be a point in space and P'X its projection in the xy plane. Then OP = r, ZOP = θ, XOP' = φ. If PT be perpendicular on the z-axis, then

$$PT = OP' = r \sin\theta,$$

the coordinate $x = OP' \cos\varphi = r \sin\theta \cos\varphi$,

the coordinate $y = OP' \sin\varphi = r \sin\theta \sin\varphi$, and

the coordinate $z = OT = r \cos\theta$.

The limits of variation of these coordinates can be seen to be as

$$-\infty < x, y, z < +\infty \; ; \; 0 < r < \infty \; ; \; 0 < \theta < \pi \text{ and } 0 < \varphi < 2\pi].$$

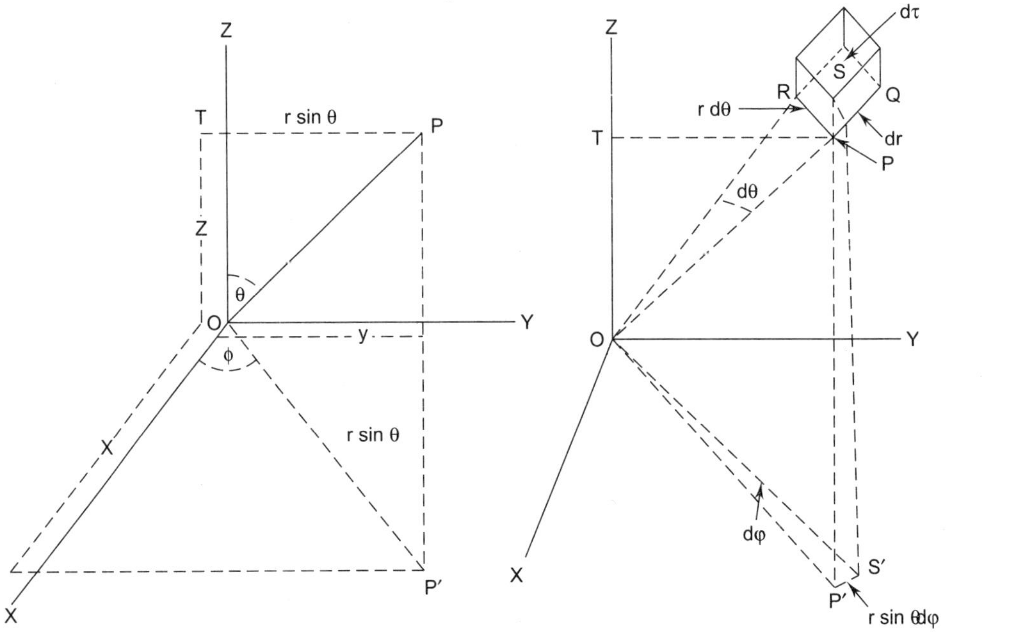

(a) Relation between cartesian and spherical coordinates

(b) The volume element in spherical coordinates dτ = r sin θ dr dθ dφ

Fig. 7.1

Using these relations and applying the theory of partial derivatives, we can transform the Schrödinger Equation (7.9) into one involving r, θ and φ (see Appendix-I) which assumes the form Equation (7.10)

$$-\frac{h^2}{8\pi^2 m}\left[\frac{1}{r^2}\frac{\partial}{\partial r}\left(r^2\frac{\partial}{\partial r}\right)+\frac{1}{r^2\sin\theta}\frac{\partial}{\partial\theta}\left(\sin\theta\frac{\partial}{\partial\theta}\right)+\frac{1}{r^2\sin^2\theta}\frac{\partial^2}{\partial\varphi^2}\right]\psi-\frac{ze^2}{4\pi\varepsilon_0 r}\tilde{\tilde{\psi}}=E\,\psi \qquad \text{... (7.10)}$$

where, $\psi = \psi(r, \theta, \varphi)$.

The physical interpretation of this wave function is that $|\psi|^2$ represents the probability density of finding the electron at the point specified by the coordinates r, θ and φ . $|\psi^2|\, d\tau$, on the other hand, is the probability of finding the electron in an infinitesimal volume element $d\tau$

which is defined such that the distance of the electron from the nucleus is between r and $r + dr$, the zenith angle is between θ and $\theta + d\theta$ and the azimuthal angle is between φ and $\varphi + d\varphi$. The expression for $d\tau$ can be derived by referring to Fig. 7.1 (*b*) as follows. The element of length PQ = dr, for the very small angle $d\theta$, RP = $r\, d\theta$ and the angle RPQ $\approx 90°$. The perpendicular distance PT = OP sin $\theta = r \sin\theta$ = OP′, the projection of PT in the xy-plane. Similarly, for the small angle $d\varphi$, the PS or its projection P′S′ in the xy-plane is $r \sin\theta\, d\varphi$ while PS is almost perpendicular to RP. Thus, the rectangular volume element

$$d\tau = (dr)\,.\,(r\,d\theta)\,.\,(r\sin\theta\,d\varphi) = r^2 \sin\theta\, dr\, d\theta\, d\varphi \qquad \text{...(7.11)}$$

The condition of normalisation, accordingly, is

$$\int \psi^2\, d\tau = \int_{r=0}^{\infty}\int_{\theta=0}^{\pi}\int_{\varphi=0}^{2\pi} |\psi(r,\theta,\varphi)|^2\, r^2\, dr \sin\theta\, d\theta\, d\varphi = 1 \qquad \text{...(7.12)}$$

and where the integration is done thrice covering all possible values of r, θ and φ, where, $\psi = \psi(r, \theta, \varphi)$.

7.1.1 Solving the Schrödinger Equation

Equation (7.10) is a partial differential equation with variables r, θ and φ. Solution to this can be attempted by first separating the variables and obtaining three ordinary differential equation, each involving a single variable. This is effected as follows:

(*i*) We express $\psi(r, \theta, \varphi)$ as a product of three independent functions,

$$\psi(r,\theta,\varphi) = \mathrm{R}(r)\,.\,\mathrm{P}(\theta)\,.\,\mathrm{F}(\varphi) \qquad \text{...(7.13)}$$

(*ii*) We substitute Equation (7.13) into the Schrödinger Equation (7.10) to get

$$-\frac{h^2}{8\pi^2 m}\left[\mathrm{P}\,.\,\mathrm{F}\frac{1}{r^2}\frac{d}{dr}\left(r^2\frac{d\mathrm{R}}{dr}\right) + \mathrm{R}\,.\,\mathrm{F}\frac{1}{r^2\sin\theta}\frac{d}{d\theta}\left(\sin\theta\frac{d\mathrm{P}}{d\theta}\right) + \mathrm{R}\,.\,\mathrm{P}\frac{1}{r^2\sin^2\theta}\frac{d^2\mathrm{F}}{d\varphi^2}\right]$$

$$-\frac{Ze^2}{4\pi\varepsilon_0 r}\mathrm{RPF} = \mathrm{ERPF} \qquad \text{...(7.14)}$$

where, R, P and F have been written for R (r), P (θ) and F (φ), respectively. Since now each differential operator acts on a function of only one variable, total (d) rather than partial (∂) differentials have been written in Equation (7.14).

(*iii*) We multiply Equation (7.14) throughout by $-\dfrac{8\pi^2 m r^2\sin^2\theta}{h^2}$ RPF and rearrange to get,

$$\frac{\sin^2\theta}{\mathrm{R}}\frac{d}{dr}\left(r^2\frac{d\mathrm{R}}{dr}\right) + \frac{8\pi^2 m r^2 \sin^2\theta}{h^2}\left(\mathrm{E} + \frac{Ze^2}{4\pi\varepsilon_0 r}\right) + \frac{\sin\theta}{\mathrm{P}}\frac{d}{d\theta}\left(\sin\theta\frac{d\mathrm{P}}{d\theta}\right) + \frac{1}{\mathrm{F}}\frac{d^2\mathrm{F}}{d\varphi^2} = 0 \qquad \text{...(7.15)}$$

This step isolates the φ part, the θ and r parts are still mixed in the first and second terms of Equation (7.15).

(*iv*) When φ changes, the first three terms do not change so that (7.15) can be written as,

$$\text{constant} + \frac{1}{\mathrm{F}}\frac{d^2\mathrm{F}}{d\varphi^2} = 0$$

or $$\frac{1}{F}\frac{d^2F}{d\varphi^2} = -\text{constant (say } M^2) \qquad ...(7.16)$$

We let the constant in Equation (7.16) be M^2 as we have met such an equation in (Chapter 6) (particle in a ring) whose solutions we know.

(*v*) Substituting Equation (7.16) in Equation (7.15), and dividing by $\sin^2\theta$, we have

$$\frac{1}{R}\frac{d}{dr}\left(r^2\frac{dR}{dr}\right) + \frac{8\pi^2 mr^2}{h^2}\left(E + \frac{Ze^2}{4\pi\varepsilon_0 r}\right) + \frac{1}{P\sin\theta}\frac{d}{d\theta}\left(\sin\theta\frac{dP}{d\theta}\right) - \frac{M^2}{\sin^2\theta} = 0 \qquad ...(7.17)$$

This separates the *r* and θ parts; the first and second terms depend on *r* only while the third and the fourth terms depend on θ only. Hence, by the previous argument used in (*iv*) the sum of the first two terms may be set equal to a constant, say β, so that the sum of the third and fourth terms becomes equal to – β; or

$$\frac{d}{dr}\left(r^2\frac{dR}{dr}\right) + \frac{8\pi^2 mr^2}{h^2}\left(E + \frac{Ze^2}{4\pi\varepsilon_0 r}\right)R = \beta R \qquad ...(7.18)$$

or $$\frac{d^2R}{dr^2} + \frac{2}{r}\frac{dR}{dr} + \left[\frac{8\pi^2 m}{h^2}\left(E + \frac{Ze^2}{4\pi\varepsilon_0 r}\right) - \frac{\beta}{r^2}\right]R = 0 \qquad ...[7.18(a)]$$

and $$\frac{1}{\sin\theta}\frac{d}{d\theta}\left(\sin\theta\frac{dP}{d\theta}\right) - \frac{M^2 P}{\sin^2\theta} = -\beta P \qquad ...(7.19)$$

In this way we have separated the partial differential Equation (7.10) into three ordinary differential Equations (7.16), (7.18) and (7.19); Equations (7.16) and (7.19) are the angular (φ-and θ-dependent, respectively) equations while Equation (7.18) is the radial equation. It can be seen that the energy E appears only in the radial equation. The angular equations are similar to those obtained for a particle on a sphere where $\beta = l(l+1)$, *l* being 0, 1, 2, 3, ... It may be pointed out that such equations will arise whenever we have a system having spherically symmetric potential. *l* is the "angular momentum, usually called azimuthal, quantum number."

7.1.1.1 The φ Equation

The Equation (7.16) is similar to the one for particle in a ring, for which the normalised solutions are,

$$F_M = \frac{1}{\sqrt{2\pi}}e^{iM\varphi}, M = 0, \pm 1, \pm 2, \text{etc.} \qquad ...(7.20)$$

M is a quantum number which, for reasons to be understood later, is regarded as "magnetic quantum number".

7.1.1.2 The θ Equation

The Equation (7.19) is similar to the θ-part of the equation for particle on a sphere (except that it does not contain energy term E). The solutions to this equation appear in the form of "associated Legendre functions" (vide Chapter 6).

$$P_{l,M}(\theta) = NP_l^{|M|}(\cos\theta) \qquad \text{...(7.21)}$$

where N, the normalisation factor, is given as

$$N = \left[\frac{2l+1}{2}\frac{(l-|M|)!}{(l+|M|)!}\right]^{1/2} \qquad \text{...(7.22)}$$

and the function $P_l^{|M|}(\cos\theta)$ is given as

$$P_l^{|M|}(x) = \frac{1}{2^l\, l!}\left(1-x^2\right)^{|M|/2}\frac{d^{l+|M|}}{dx^{l+|M|}}\left(x^2-1\right)^l \qquad \text{...(7.23)}$$

where, $x = \cos\theta$, and $|M|$ denotes the magnitude (without sign) of the magnetic quantum number.

l is "angular momentum" or "azimuthal" quantum number, which can assume the values 0, 1, 2, 3, ... For M = 0, the functions are called Legendre functions (Table 7.1).

TABLE 7.1 Some Legendre Functions

$\|M\| = 0, l = 0, P_0^0(\cos\theta) = 1,$	$N = \frac{1}{\sqrt{2}}$
$\|M\| = 0, l = 1, P_1^0(\cos\theta) = \cos\theta,$	$N = \sqrt{\frac{3}{2}}$
$\|M\| = 0, l = 2, P_2^0(\cos\theta) = \frac{1}{2}\left(3\cos^2\theta - 1\right),$	$N = \sqrt{\frac{5}{2}}$
$\|M\| = 0, l = 3, P_3^0(\cos\theta) = \frac{3}{2}\left(\frac{5}{3}\cos^3\theta - \cos\theta\right),$	$N = \sqrt{\frac{7}{2}}$

Some of the associated Legendre functions are given in Table 7.2.

The product function $P_{l,M}(\theta)\, F_M(\varphi)$ is identified as "spherical harmonics $Y_{l,M}(\theta, \varphi)$", also called angular function.

TABLE 7.2 Some Associated Legendre Functions

$\|M\| = 1, l = 1, P_1^1(\cos\theta) = (1-\cos^2\theta)^{1/2} = \sin\theta,$	$N = \sqrt{\frac{3}{4}}$
$\|M\| = 1, l = 2, P_2^1(\cos\theta) = 3\cos\theta\,(1-\cos^2\theta)^{1/2} = 3\sin\theta\cos\theta,$	$N = \sqrt{\frac{5}{12}}$
$\|M\| = 1, l = 3, P_3^1(\cos\theta) = \frac{3}{2}(1-\cos^2\theta)^{1/2}(5\cos^2\theta - 1) = \frac{3}{2}\,.\,\sin\theta\,(5\cos^2\theta - 1),$	$N = \sqrt{\frac{7}{24}}$
$\|M\| = 2, l = 2, P_2^2(\cos\theta) = 3(1-\cos^2\theta) = 3\sin^2\theta,$	$N = \sqrt{\frac{5}{48}}$
$\|M\| = 2, l = 3, P_3^2(\cos\theta) = 15(1-\cos^2\theta)\cos\theta = 15\sin^2\cos\theta,$	$N = \sqrt{\frac{7}{240}}$

7.1.1.3 The r-Equation

Since $\beta = l\,(l + 1)$, the radial Equation (7.18) (*a*) becomes

$$\frac{d^2R}{dr^2} + \frac{2}{r}\frac{dR}{dr} + \left[\frac{8\pi^2 mE}{h^2} + \frac{8\pi^2 m Ze^2}{(4\pi\varepsilon_0)h^2 r} - \frac{l(l+1)}{r^2}\right]R = 0 \qquad \text{... (7.24)}$$

where, $R = R(r)$.

To make the Equation (7.24) simpler, let us make the following substitutions:

$$n^2 = -\frac{2\pi^2 mZ^2 e^4}{h^2 E(4\pi\varepsilon_0)^2} \qquad \text{... (7.25)}$$

and

$$\rho = \frac{2Zr}{na_0}, \text{ i.e., } R(r) = R\left(\frac{na_0\,\rho}{2Z}\right) \qquad \text{... (7.26)}$$

where, $a_0 = \dfrac{(4\pi\varepsilon_0)h^2}{4\pi^2 me^2}$ is the radius of the first Bohr orbit of hydrogen atom; this makes r dimensionless. The choice of the substituents may seem to be peculiar, but we know from Bohr's theory that,

$$E = -\frac{2\pi^2 mZ^2 e^4}{n^2 h^2 (4\pi\varepsilon_0)^2} \qquad \text{... [7.26 (a)]}$$

where, n is an integer. However, from Equation (7.25) we do not know whether the parameter n is integer or non-integer and now we proceed to establish its nature.

From Equation (7.26),

$$\frac{dR}{dr} = \left(\frac{2Z}{na_0}\right)\frac{dR}{d\rho},$$

and

$$\frac{d^2R}{dr^2} = \left(\frac{2Z}{na_0}\right)^2 \frac{d^2R}{d\rho^2} \qquad \text{... (7.27)}$$

Substituting Equations (7.25), (7.26) and (7.27) in Equation (7.24), one may obtain,

$$\frac{d^2R}{d\rho^2} + \frac{2}{\rho}\frac{dR}{d\rho} + \left[-\frac{1}{4} + \frac{n}{\rho} - \frac{l(l+1)}{\rho^2}\right]R = 0 \qquad \text{... (7.28)}$$

where, R is now $R(\rho)$ and we have used the relations

$$\frac{8\pi^2 mE}{h^2} = -\frac{16\pi^4 m^2 e^4 Z^2}{n^2 h^4 (4\pi\varepsilon_0)^2} = -\frac{1}{4}\left(\frac{2Z}{na_0}\right)^2,$$

and

$$\frac{8\pi^2 mZe^2}{(4\pi\varepsilon_0)h^2 r} = \frac{4Z^2}{na_0^2\,\rho} = \frac{n}{\rho}\left(\frac{2Z}{na_0}\right)^2.$$

The limits for ρ, like those for r, are from zero to infinity. The advantage of the substitutions is that we have now a dimensionless (purely algebraic) equation, which is more convenient to handle.

7.1.1.4 Solving the Radial Equation

But even Equation (7.28) is not easy to solve. Let us examine it for (*i*) very large, (*ii*) very small and (*iii*) intermediate values of ρ.

(*i*) *Very Large* ρ

In such a situation the terms $\frac{n}{\rho}$ and $\frac{l(l+1)}{\rho^2}$ become very small compared to $\frac{1}{4}$ and may, therefore, be dropped. Also, the term $\frac{2}{\rho}\frac{dR}{d\rho}$ may be neglected in comparison to $\frac{d^2R}{d\rho^2}$. The Equation (7.28) thus reduces to an asymptotic equation,

$$\frac{d^2R}{d\rho^2} - \frac{R}{4} = 0 \qquad \text{... (7.29)}$$

This equation has the general solution,

$$R = A\exp\left(-\frac{\rho}{2}\right) + B\exp\left(\frac{\rho}{2}\right) \qquad \text{... (7.30)}$$

where A and B are arbitrary constants of integration. Since R must be finite for $\rho \to \infty$, we must set B = 0. The acceptable solution is, therefore,

$$R = A\exp\left(-\frac{\rho}{2}\right) \qquad \text{... (7.31)}$$

(*ii*) *Very Small Value of* ρ

Here $$\frac{l(l+1)}{\rho^2} >> \frac{n}{\rho} \text{ and } \frac{1}{4}$$

[*e.g.*, if $\rho = 0.01$, then for $n = 1$ and $l = 1$ (say),

$$\frac{n}{\rho} = 100 \text{ but } \frac{l(l+1)}{\rho^2} = 20000].$$

The Equation (7.28) reduces to,

$$\frac{d^2R}{d\rho^2} + \frac{2}{\rho}\frac{dR}{d\rho} - \frac{l(l+1)}{\rho^2}R = 0 \qquad \text{... (7.32)}$$

This equation is unfamiliar to us; let us assume that

$$R = \rho^k \qquad \text{... (7.33)}$$

where, k is the number to be determined. Substituting (7.33) in (7.32), we obtain,

$$[k(k-1) + 2k - l(l+1)]\rho^{k-2} = 0 \qquad \text{... (7.34)}$$

The Equation (7.32) will, therefore, be satisfied by Equation (7.33) if the expression within square brackets in Equation (7.34) equals zero, *i.e.*, $k^2 + k = l^2 + l$, *i.e.*, if $k = l$ or $-(l + 1)$. Correspondingly, the solution to Equation (7.32) may be

$$R = \rho^{l} \text{ or } R = \rho^{-(l+1)}$$

But the latter solution approaches infinity rapidly as $\rho \to 0$, and, hence, is not acceptable. The solution which is acceptable is

$$R = \rho^{l} \qquad \text{... (7.35)}$$

(*iii*) *Intermediate Values of* ρ

We see that for large values of ρ, R behaves as $e^{-\rho/2}$ while for small values of ρ it behaves as ρ^l. It may oscillate in between these two extremes. Therefore, the radial functions at all values of ρ may be given as,

$$R = \rho^{l}\,L(\rho)\exp\left(-\frac{\rho}{2}\right) \qquad \text{... (7.36)}$$

where, L (ρ) is a polynomial, *i.e.*, a power series in ρ. We have to determine the nature of this polynomial.

Differentiating R with respect to ρ and rearranging the terms, we get

$$\frac{dR}{d\rho} = l\rho^{l-1}\,L\exp\left(-\frac{\rho}{2}\right) + \rho^{l}\frac{dL}{d\rho}\exp\left(-\frac{\rho}{2}\right) - \frac{1}{2}\rho^{l}\,L\exp\left(-\frac{\rho}{2}\right) \qquad \text{... (7.37)}$$

$$\frac{d^2R}{d\rho^2} = \left[\rho^{l}\frac{d^2L}{d\rho^2} + \left(2l\rho^{l-1} - \rho^{l}\right)\frac{dL}{d\rho} + \left\{l(l-1)\rho^{l-2} - l\rho^{l-1} + \frac{1}{4}\rho^{l}\right\}L\right]\exp\left(-\frac{\rho}{2}\right) \qquad \text{... (7.38)}$$

where, L has been written for L (ρ).

Substituting for R, $\frac{dR}{d\rho}$ and $\frac{d^2R}{d\rho^2}$ in Equation (7.28), we get

$$\rho^{l}\frac{d^2L}{d\rho^2} + \left(2l\rho^{l-1} + 2\rho^{l-1} - \rho^{l}\right)\frac{dL}{d\rho} + \left[\left\{l(l-1) + 2l\right\}\rho^{l-2} - (l+1)\rho^{l-1} + \frac{n}{\rho}\rho^{l} - \frac{l(l+1)\rho^{l}}{\rho^2}\right]L = 0$$

$$\text{... (7.39)}$$

[the factor $\exp\left(-\frac{\rho}{2}\right)$, being common to all the terms, goes out of the equation in Equation (7.39)].

Dividing Equation (7.39) throughout by ρ^{l-1}, we get

$$\rho\frac{d^2L}{d\rho^2} + \left[2(l+1) - \rho\right]\frac{dL}{d\rho} + (n - l - 1)\,L = 0 \qquad \text{... (7.40)}$$

The solution to this equation appears in terms of what are known as "associated Laguerre polynomials" explained in section 7.1.1.5.

7.1.1.5 Laguerre and Associated Laguerre Polynomials

Consider a function of the type

$$y = x^k e^{-x} \qquad \text{... (7.41)}$$

The kth derivative of Equation (7.41) will be

$$\frac{d^k y}{dx^k} = \frac{d^x\left(x^k e^{-x}\right)}{dx^k}$$

$$= e^{-x} \mathrm{L}_k(x) \qquad \text{... (7.42)}$$

where, $\mathrm{L}_k(x)$ is a polynomial in x in which the highest power of x is k.

or
$$\mathrm{L}_k(x) = e^x \frac{d^k y}{dx^k} = e^x \left[\frac{d^k}{dx^k}\left(x^k e^{-x}\right)\right] \qquad \text{... (7.43)}$$

$\mathrm{L}_k(x)$ is called "Laguerre polynomial" of degree k. The pth derivative of $\mathrm{L}_k(x)$, denoted as $\mathrm{L}_k^p(x)$, is called "associated Laguerre polynomial". It is given by the equation,

$$\mathrm{L}_k^p(x) = \frac{d^p}{dx^p}\left[\mathrm{L}_k(x)\right] = \frac{d^p}{dx^p}\left[e^x \left\{\frac{d^k}{dx^k}\left(x^k e^{-x}\right)\right\}\right] \qquad \text{... (7.44)}$$

This polynomial is of degree $k - p$ and order p. For example, let

$$y = x^3 e^{-x}$$

$$\frac{d^3 y}{dx^3} = (6 - 18x + 9x^2 - x^3)\, e^{-x}$$

The Laguerre polynomial is,

$$\mathrm{L}_3(x) = e^x (6 - 18x + 9x^2 - x^3)\, e^{-x}$$

$$= 6 - 18x + 9x^2 - x^3$$

The associated Laguerre polynomial of the first order will be of degree $3 - 1 = 2$,

$$\mathrm{L}_3^1(x) = \frac{d}{dx}\left[\left(6 - 18x + 9x^2 - x^3\right)\right]$$

$$= -18 + 18x - 3x^2.$$

It follows that $p \le k$. When $p = k$, the associated Laguerre polynomial $\mathrm{L}_k^k(x)$ does not have a term in x and the subsequent members (*i.e.*, for $p > k$) in the power series vanish.

The differential equation whose solution will be an associated Laguerre polynomial L_k^p is

$$x \frac{d^2\left[\mathrm{L}_k^p(x)\right]}{dx^2} + (p + 1 - x)\frac{d\left[\mathrm{L}_k^p(x)\right]}{dx} + (k - p)\,\mathrm{L}_k^p(x) = 0 \qquad \text{... (7.45)}$$

If we replace x by ρ, k by $n + l$ and p by $2l + 1$, the Equation (7.45) becomes,

$$\rho \frac{d^2}{d\rho^2}\left[\mathrm{L}_{n+l}^{2l+1}(\rho)\right] + \left[2(l+1) - \rho\right]\frac{d}{d\rho}\left[\mathrm{L}_{n+l}^{2l+1}(\rho)\right] + (n - l - 1)\,\mathrm{L}_{n+l}^{2l+1}(\rho) = 0 \qquad \text{... (7.46)}$$

Equations (7.46) and (7.40) are identical if we identify the function L in Equation (7.40) with the associated Laguerre polynomial $L_{n+l}^{2l+1}(\rho)$ in Equation (7.46). The polynomial is of order $2l + 1$ and degree

$$(n + 1) - (2l + 1) = n - l - 1.$$

The solution to the radial Equation (7.28) is, therefore,

$$R(\rho) = \rho^l L_{n+l}^{2l+1}(\rho) \exp\left(-\frac{\rho}{2}\right) \qquad \text{... (7.47)}$$

To normalise this function we have to evaluate the integral

$$N^2 \int_0^\infty \left[\rho^l L_{n+l}^{2l+1}(\rho) \exp\left(-\frac{\rho}{2}\right)\right]^2 \rho^2 \, d\rho = 1 \qquad \text{... (7.48)}$$

The limits for ρ are from 0 to ∞. The factor ρ^2 enters the equation because the volume element $d\tau$ is equal to $\rho^2 \, d\rho$. The evaluation of the integral is not easy and we shall give the results only*.

The polynomial $L_{n+l}^{2l+1}(\rho)$ is obtained by evaluating (7.44) after putting $p = 2l + 1$ and $k = n + l$. It is also obtained by evaluating Equation (7.49).

$$L_{n+l}^{2l+1}(\rho) = \left[\sum_{k=0}^{n-l-1} (-1)^{k+1} \frac{\{(n+l)!\}^2}{(n-l-1-k)!\,(2l+1+k)!\,.\,k!}\right] \rho^k \qquad \text{... (7.49)}$$

and the normalisation factor is given as

$$N = -\sqrt{\left(\frac{\rho}{r}\right)^3 \frac{(n-l-1)!}{2n\{(n+l)!\}^3}} \qquad \text{... (7.50)}$$

Since we have put $\rho = \frac{2Zr}{na_0}$ [Equation (7.26)], the normalised radial functions of the hydrogen-like atom, also called radial eigenfunctions, may be expressed as

$$R_{nl}(r) = \sqrt{\left(\frac{2Z}{na_0}\right)^3 \frac{(n-l-1)!}{2n\{(n+l)!\}^3}} \cdot \left(\frac{2Zr}{na_0}\right)^l . L_{n+l}^{2l+1}\left(\frac{2Zr}{na_0}\right) . \exp\left(-\frac{2Zr}{na_0}\right) \qquad \text{... (7.51)}$$

The subscripts n and l are added to R (r) because the function depends on two parameters n and l.

7.1.1.6 Nature of n and l

We have established earlier (Chapter 6) that l, the angular momentum (or azimuthal) quantum number, can have values 0, 1, 2, 3, ... In the associated laguerre polynomial $L_{n+l}^{2l+1}(\rho)$, which is an

---

* See L. Pauling and E.B. Wilson : *Quantum Mechanics*, (McGraw Hill, N.Y.), 1935 Appendix, VII, p. 451.

acceptable solution of the differential Equation (7.46), we know that $(n + l) - (2l + 1) = n - l - 1$ represents the degree (k) of the polynomial which must be an integer or zero. For $n - l - 1 = 0$, $n = l + 1$, which shows that the lowest value of n is 1 when $l = 0$. Moreover, since $n - l - 1$ and l are both integers, n has to be an integer. Further, in the polynomial, $n + l > 2l + 1$ or $n > l + 1$. Thus, to conclude, acceptable solutions for the radial Equation (7.24) or Equation (7.28) exist for certain discrete values of the parameters n and l where n can be 1, 2, 3, ... and l can be 0, 1, 2, ... with the condition $l < n$.

7.1.2 The Radial Eigenfunctions

It is a simple matter to work out the radial eigenfunctions using Equations (7.44) or (7.49), (7.50) and (7.51).

For $n = 1, l = 0$

$$R_{10}(\rho) = N\rho^0 L_{1+0}^{0+1}(\rho)\exp\left(-\frac{\rho}{2}\right) = NL_1^1(\rho)\exp\left(-\frac{\rho}{2}\right)$$

$$L_1^1(\rho) = \frac{d}{d\rho}\left[e^{\rho}\frac{d}{d\rho}(\rho\exp(-\rho))\right]$$

$$= \frac{d}{d\rho}(1-\rho) = -1$$

$$N = -\sqrt{\left[\frac{(1-0-1)!}{2\times 1\times\{(1+0)!\}^3}\right]\left[\frac{2Z}{a_0}\right]^3}$$

$$= -\sqrt{\frac{1}{2}\times\frac{8Z^3}{a_0^3}} = -2\left(\frac{Z}{a_0}\right)^{3/2}$$

Therefore $$R_{10}(\rho) = (-2)(-1)\left(\frac{Z}{a_0}\right)^{3/2}\exp\left(-\frac{\rho}{2}\right)$$

$$= 2\left(\frac{Z}{a_0}\right)^{3/2}\exp\left(-\frac{\rho}{2}\right) \quad \text{... (7.52)}$$

or $$R_{10}(r) = 2\left(\frac{Z}{a_0}\right)^{3/2}\exp\left(-\frac{Zr}{a_0}\right) \quad \text{... [7.52 (a)]}$$

For $n = 2, l = 0$:

$$R_{20}(\rho) = N\rho^0 L_{2+0}^{0+1}(\rho)\exp\left(-\frac{\rho}{2}\right) = NL_2^1(\rho)\exp\left(-\frac{\rho}{2}\right)$$

$$N = -\sqrt{\left[\frac{(2-0-1)!}{2\times 2\times\{(2+0)!\}^3}\right]\left(\frac{2Z}{2a_0}\right)^3} = -\frac{1}{4\sqrt{2}}\left(\frac{Z}{a_0}\right)^{3/2}$$

$$L_2^1(\rho) = \frac{d}{d\rho}\left[e^{\rho}\,\frac{d^2}{d\rho^2}\left(\rho^2\right)\exp\left(-\rho\right)\right]$$

$$= \frac{d}{d\rho}\left[2 - 4\rho + \rho^2\right]$$

$$= 2\rho - 4$$

$\therefore$
$$R_{20}(\rho) = -\frac{1}{4\sqrt{2}}\left(\frac{Z}{a_0}\right)^{3/2} \times 2\left(\rho - 2\right)e^{-\rho/2}$$

$$= \frac{1}{2\sqrt{2}}\left(\frac{Z}{a_0}\right)^{3/2}\left(2 - \rho\right)e^{-\rho/2} \qquad \text{... (7.53)}$$

or
$$R_{20}(r) = \frac{1}{2\sqrt{2}}\left(\frac{Z}{a_0}\right)^{3/2}\left(2 - \frac{Zr}{a_0}\right)\exp\left(-\frac{Zr}{2a_0}\right) \qquad \text{... [7.53 (a)]}$$

For $n = 2, l = 1$:

$$R_{21}(\rho) = N\rho\, L_{2+1}^{2+1}(\rho)\exp\left(-\frac{\rho}{2}\right)$$

$$N = -\sqrt{\left[\frac{(2-1-1)!}{2 \times 2 \times \{(2+1)!\}^3}\left(\frac{2Z}{2a_0}\right)^3\right]} = -\frac{1}{12\sqrt{6}}\left(\frac{Z}{a_0}\right)^{3/2}$$

$$L_3^3(\rho) = \frac{d^3}{d\rho^3}\left[e^{\rho} - \frac{d^3}{d\rho^3}\left(\rho^3 e^{-\rho}\right)\right]$$

$$= \frac{d^3}{d\rho^3}\left[6 - 18\rho + 9\rho^2 - \rho^3\right]$$

$$= \frac{d}{d\rho}\left[18 - 6\rho\right] = -6$$

$\therefore$
$$R_{21}(\rho) = -\frac{1}{12\sqrt{6}}\left(\frac{Z}{a_0}\right)^{3/2} .\rho\left(-6\right)e^{-\rho/2}$$

$$= \frac{1}{2\sqrt{6}}\left(\frac{Z}{a_0}\right)^{3/2} .\rho e^{-\rho/2} \qquad \text{... [7.53 (b)]}$$

or
$$R_{21}(r) = \frac{1}{2\sqrt{6}}\left(\frac{Z}{a_0}\right)^{5/2} \times r\exp\left(-\frac{Zr}{2a_0}\right) \qquad \text{... [7.53 (c)]}$$

[**Exercise:** Work out, using the expression (7.51), the radial functions $R_{30}(r)$, $R_{31}(r)$ and $R_{32}(r)$].

7.1.3 Atomic Units

Before proceeding further it will be convenient to introduce the system of atomic units (a.u.) in which the eigenvalues and eigenfunctions are usually expressed. In this system the units of mass, charge, length, energy, etc., are defined as in Table 7.3.

TABLE 7.3 Values of Some Atomic Properties

Quantity	*Value in S.I. units*	*Value in a.u.*
Mass of an electron (m)	9.11×10^{-31} kg	1 a.u.
Charge of an electron (e)	-1.602×10^{-19} C	-1 a.u.
Bohr radius $\left(a_0 = \dfrac{(4\pi\varepsilon_0)\,h}{4\pi^2 me^2}\right)$	0.529×10^{-10} m	1 a.u.
Angular momentum $\dfrac{h}{2\pi}$	1.055×10^{-34} J	1 a.u.
Energy of the electron in the first Bohr orbit of H atom $\left(= -\dfrac{2\pi^2 me^4}{(4\pi\varepsilon_0)^2 h^2} = -\dfrac{e^2}{2a_0}\right)$	-2.176×10^{-19} J	$-\dfrac{1}{2}$ a.u.
Permittivity constant ($4\pi\,\varepsilon_0$)	1.113×10^{-10} Fm^{-1}	1 a.u.

[For S.I. units see Appendix 6].

7.1.4 The Energy Eigenvalues

The quantity of interest E, the energy appears in the radial Equation (7.18). The equation can be rearranged as below:

$$\left[-\frac{h^2}{8\pi^2 m}\left\{\frac{1}{r^2}\frac{d}{dr}\left(r^2\frac{d}{dr}\right)-\frac{l(l+1)}{r^2}\right\}-\frac{Ze^2}{(4\pi\varepsilon_0)\,r}\right]\mathrm{R} = \mathrm{ER} \qquad \text{... (7.54)}$$

wherein E appears as "energy eigenvalue" and $\mathrm{R} = \mathrm{R}_{nl}(r)$ is the "radial eigenfunction". E is given by Equation [7.26 (*a*)],

$$\mathrm{E} = -\frac{2\pi^2 m \mathrm{Z}^2 e^4}{(4\pi\varepsilon_0)^2 n^2 h^2} \qquad \text{... [7.26 (a)]}$$

In atomic units (where, $\dfrac{h}{2\pi} = \dfrac{h^2}{4\pi^2} = 1$, $m = 1$ and $e = 1$) these equations are

$$\left[-\frac{1}{2}\left\{\frac{1}{r^2}\frac{d}{dr}\left(r^2\frac{d}{dr}\right)-\frac{l(l+1)}{r^2}\right\}-\frac{\mathrm{Z}}{r}\right]\mathrm{R} = \mathrm{ER} \qquad \text{... (7.55)}$$

and

$$\mathrm{E} = -\frac{\mathrm{Z}^?}{2n^2} \qquad \text{... (7.56)}$$

In the case of H atom (Z = 1) in the ground state ($n = 1, l = 0$), $E = -\frac{1}{2}$ a.u., and

$$R = R_{10}(r) = 2e^{-r} \text{ a.u.}$$

For any radial function $R_{nl}(r)$ the eigenvalue can be obtained by solving the Equation (7.55). For example, for H atom in the ground state, the left hand side of Equation (7.55) is

$$-\frac{1}{2r^2}\frac{d}{dr}\left[r^2\frac{d}{dr}\left(2e^{-r}\right)\right]-\frac{2e^{-r}}{r} = -\frac{1}{2r^2}\frac{d}{dr}\left[-2r^2 e^{-r}\right]-\frac{2e^{-r}}{r}$$

$$= -\frac{1}{2r^2}\left[-4re^{-r}+2r^2 e^{-r}\right]-\frac{2e^{-r}}{r} = -\frac{1}{2}\left(2e^{-r}\right);$$

and the right hand side = $E(2e^{-r})$. Therefore, $E = -\frac{1}{2}$ a.u.

[Exercise: Determine the energy Eigenvalues of H-atom corresponding to radial functions $R_{20}(r)$ and $R_{21}(r)$ using atomic units; comment on the results].

7.1.5 Complete Wave Functions or Atomic Orbitals of Hydrogen-like Atoms

We are now in a position to write the complete wave functions of hydrogen-like atoms as

$$\psi_{n,l,M}(r,\theta,\varphi) = R_{n,1}(r)\,P_{l,M}(\theta)\,F_m(\varphi) = R_{n,l}(r)\,.\,Y_{l,M}(\theta,\varphi)$$

where, n, l and M are the three quantum numbers used to characterise the wave functions. For example, for $n = 1, l = 0$, M = 0, the wave function is

$$\psi_{100} = \left[2\left(\frac{Z}{a_0}\right)^{3/2}\exp\left(-\frac{Zr}{a_0}\right)\right]\left(\frac{1}{\sqrt{2}}\right)\left(\frac{1}{\sqrt{2\pi}}\right)$$

$$= \frac{1}{\sqrt{\pi}}\left(\frac{Z}{a_0}\right)^{3/2}\exp\left(-\frac{Zr}{a_0}\right) \quad \text{... (7.57)}$$

or in atomic units ($a_0 = 1$)

$$\psi_{100} = \frac{1}{\sqrt{\pi}}Z^{3/2}e^{-Zr} \quad \text{... (7.58)}$$

For H-atom (Z = 1),

$$\psi_{100} = \frac{1}{\sqrt{\pi}}e^{-r} \quad \text{... (7.59)}$$

[Exercise: Write the hydrogen-like wave functions for all the states corresponding to $n = 4$].

7.1.6 Significance of the Quantum Numbers n, l and M

Each ψ represents a definite state of the electron in the H-atom, characterised by two very important physical quantities, energy (E) and angular momentum (L). These are given in a.u. as

$$E = -\frac{1}{2n^2}$$

$$L = \sqrt{l(l+1)}$$

n is regarded as the "principal quantum number" and l the "angular momentum (commonly known as a azimuthal) quantum number". Vector $\vec{L}$ has L_x, L_y and L_z components, but quantum mechanics permits only the L_z component to be determined which is given by

$$L_z = \frac{Mh}{2\pi} \text{ or M (in a.u.)}$$

M is the "quantum number for the z-component of the vector $\vec{L}$."

TABLE 7.4 Normalised Hydrogen-like Wave Functions

Energy (in a.u.)	ψ_{mln} *(in a.u.)*
$n = 1, E_1 = -\frac{Z^2}{2}$,	$\psi_{100} = \frac{1}{\sqrt{\pi}} Z^{3/2} e^{-Zr}$
$n = 2, E_1 = -\frac{Z^2}{8}$,	$\psi_{200} = \frac{1}{\sqrt{32\pi}} Z^{3/2} [2 - Zr] e^{-Zr/2}$
	$\psi_{210} = \frac{1}{\sqrt{32\pi}} Z^{5/2} re^{-Zr/2} \cos\theta$
	$\psi_{21\pm1} = \frac{1}{\sqrt{64\pi}} Z^{5/2} . re^{-Zr/2} \sin\theta\, e^{\pm i\phi}$
$n = 3, E_3 = -\frac{Z^2}{18}$,	$\psi_{300} = \frac{1}{81\sqrt{3\pi}} Z^{3/2} \left[27 - 18Zr + 2(Zr)^2\right] e^{-Zr/3}$
	$\psi_{310} = \frac{1}{81}\left(\frac{2}{\pi}\right)^{1/2} Z^{5/2} r(6 - Zr) e^{-Zr/3} \cos\theta$
	$\psi_{31\pm1} = \left(\frac{1}{81\sqrt{\pi}}\right) Z^{5/2} r(6 - Zr) e^{-Zr/3} \sin\theta\, e^{\pm i\varphi}$
	$\psi_{320} = \frac{1}{81\sqrt{6\pi}} Z^{7/2} r^2 e^{-Zr/3} (3\cos^2\theta - 1)$
	$\psi_{32\pm1} = \frac{1}{81\sqrt{\pi}} Z^{7/2} r^2 e^{-Zr/3} \sin\theta \cos\theta\, e^{\pm i\varphi}$
	$\psi_{32\pm2} = \frac{1}{162\sqrt{\pi}} Z^{7/2} r^2 e^{-Zr/3} \sin\theta\, e^{\pm 2i\varphi}$

7.1.7 Zeeman Effect and Magnetic Quantum Number

M has been more commonly called the "magnetic quantum number". This arises from the fact that when the H-atom is placed in a magnetic field the degenerate states split up into their $2l + 1$ different energy states, each characterised by its M-value (Zeeman effect). The electron rotating round the nucleus has also magnetic moment (μ) vector collinear with the vector $\vec{L}$ and is proportional to it,

$$\mu = -\beta L$$

where, $\beta = 5.788 \times 10^{-9}$ eV/Gauss $= \frac{1}{2}$ a.u. is called "Bohr magneton". The vector $\vec{\mu}$ interacts with the magnetic field (say H) and if the direction of the field be taken as the z-axis of the coordinate system, then the energy of interaction is given by

$$E_M = -\mu_z H = \beta L_z H = \beta HM \cdot \frac{h}{2\pi}$$

$$= \beta HM \text{ a.u.}$$

As M has $2l + 1$ distinct values, the interaction removes the degeneracy and splits the energy level into $2l + 1$ distinct energy states. The four degenerate states corresponding to $n = 2$, for example, will split up according to the scheme shown in the Fig. 7.2.

Each Zeeman energy level is characterised by the magnetic quantum number value.

	______ 2, 1, + 1 (E_{+1})
— — — —	—— 200, 210, (E_0)
No magnetic field	______ 2, 1, – 1, (E_{-1})

Fig. 7.2 *Zeeman splitting*

7.1.8 Atomic Orbitals

For hydrogen-like (*i.e.*, one-electron) atoms, the wave functions are also called "atomic orbitals". Orbitals of different systems differ only in nuclear charge (Z).

Following a system that grew up much before development of quantum mechanics the atomic orbitals are denoted as *s, p, d, f*, ... for $l = 0, 1, 2, 3, ...$ respectively, the letters being preceded by numbers representing principal quantum number. Thus, we have 1*s*, 2*s*, 2*p* atomic orbitals corresponding to ($n = 1, l = 0$), ($n = 2, l = 0$), ($n = 2, l = 1$) respectively.

Since for H-like atoms, the energy depends only on 'n' and is independent of 'l' and 'M', orbitals having same n and differing in l and M are degenerate. Thus we have the following hierarchy of energy states of H-like atoms:

$$[1s] < [2s, 2p] < [3s, 3p, 3d], ...$$

wherein the degenerate states are bracketted. To specify magnetic quantum numbers we may add the subscripts as follows:

$$[1s_0] < [2s_0, 2p_{+1}, 2p_0, 2p_{-1}] < ...$$

7.1.8.1 Orbitals in Real Form

The hydrogen-like wave functions (or atomic orbitals) listed in Table 7.4 have the disadvantage that except for M = 0, they are complex due to the presence of the terms like $e^{\pm im\varphi}$. No real picture can, therefore, be drawn of them. Equivalent real functions can, however, be obtained by utilising the well-known theorem

$$e^{\pm iM\varphi} = \cos M\varphi + i \sin M\varphi$$

The three $2p$ orbitals ($l = 1$), for example, are

$$2p_{+1} \text{ (for M = + 1)} = \text{A}r \exp\left(-\frac{Zr}{2a_0}\right) \sin\theta\, e^{i\varphi} \quad \text{... (7.60)}$$

$$2p_{-1} \text{ (for M = − 1)} = \text{A}r \exp\left(-\frac{Zr}{2a_0}\right) \sin\theta\, e^{-i\varphi} \quad \text{... (7.61)}$$

$$2p_0 \text{ (for M = 0)} = \text{B}r \exp\left(-\frac{Zr}{2a_0}\right) \cos\theta \quad \text{... (7.62)}$$

where, $$\text{A} = \frac{1}{8\sqrt{\pi}}\left(\frac{Z}{a_0}\right)^{5/2} \text{ and B} = \frac{1}{4\sqrt{2\pi}}\left(\frac{Z}{a_0}\right)^{5/2} \quad \text{(See Table 7.4)}$$

The $2p_0$ function is already a real one. Since

$$z = r\cos\theta$$

$$2p_0 = \text{B}z \exp\left(-\frac{Zr}{2a_0}\right) \quad \text{... (7.63)}$$

$2p_{+1}$ and $2p_{-1}$ functions may be combined linearly to get real functions as given below:

$$2p_{+1} \text{ and } 2p_{-1} = \text{A}r \sin\theta \exp\left(-\frac{Zr}{2a_0}\right)\left(e^{i\varphi} + e^{-i\varphi}\right)$$

$$= 2\text{A}r\, 2\sin\theta\cos\varphi\; e^{-Zr/2a_0} \quad \text{... (7.64)}$$

$$\underline{2p_{+1} - 2p_{-1}} = \text{A}r\sin\theta\exp\left(-\frac{Zr}{2a_0}\right)\left(e^{i\varphi} - e^{-i\varphi}\right)$$

$$= 2\text{A}r\, 2\sin\theta\sin\varphi\exp\left(-\frac{Zr}{2a_0}\right) \quad \text{... (7.65)}$$

The linear combination functions Equations (7.64) and (7.65) can be normalised by introducing the factor $\frac{1}{\sqrt{2}}$, *i.e.*,

$$\frac{1}{\sqrt{2}}(2p_{+1} + 2p_{-1}) = \frac{2}{\sqrt{2}}\text{A}\,.\,r\sin\theta\cos\varphi\exp\left(-\frac{Zr}{2a_0}\right)$$

$$= \text{B}x\exp\left(-\frac{Zr}{2a_0}\right) \quad \text{... (7.66)}$$

$$\frac{1}{i\sqrt{2}}(2p_{+1} - 2p_{-1}) = \frac{2}{\sqrt{2}}\text{A}r\sin\theta\sin\varphi\exp\left(-\frac{Zr}{2a_0}\right)$$

$$= B\,y \exp\left(-\frac{Zr}{2a_0}\right) \quad \text{... (7.67)}$$

where, $$\frac{2A}{\sqrt{2}} = B = \frac{1}{4\sqrt{2\pi}}\left(\frac{Z}{a_0}\right)^{5/2}$$

and $$x = r \sin\theta \cos\varphi$$

and $$y = r \sin\theta \sin\varphi$$

The positive (7.66) and negative (7.67) combinations are functions of x and y respectively while the $2p_0$ function Equation (7.63) is a function of z-coordinate. These real forms of the $2p$ functions are accordingly denoted as $2p_x$, $2p_y$ and $2p_z$ atomic orbitals respectively.

The first few atomic orbitals [Equations (7.68) to (7.72)] are given in Table 7.5.

TABLE 7.5 Real Forms of Atomic Orbitals (in a.u.)

	Ref. equation
$\psi_{1s} = \frac{1}{\sqrt{\pi}} Z^{3/2} e^{-Zr}$	(7.68)
$\psi_{2s} = \frac{1}{4\sqrt{2\pi}} Z^{3/2} (2 - Zr) e^{-Zr/2}$	(7.69)
$\psi_{2p_x} = \frac{1}{4\sqrt{2\pi}} Z^{5/2}\, r\,.\,e^{-Zr/2} \sin\theta \cos\varphi$	(7.70)
$\psi_{2p_y} = \frac{1}{4\sqrt{2\pi}} Z^{5/2}\, r\,.\,e^{-Zr/2} \sin\theta \sin\varphi$	(7.71)
$\psi_{2p_z} = \frac{1}{4\sqrt{2\pi}} Z^{5/2}\, r\,.\,e^{-Zr/2} \cos\theta$	(7.72)

[**Exercise:** Find out the five $3d$ atomic orbitals in the real form by taking suitable linear combinations of the complex wave functions. Also justify the notations attributed to the five real $3d$ wave functions.

$$3d_0 = Ar^2 (3\cos^2\theta - 1) = A\,(3Z^2 - r)^2 \text{ ... } (3d_{z^2})$$
$$3d_1 + 3d_{-1} = Br^2 \sin\theta \cos\varphi \cos\theta = Bxz \text{ ... } (3d_{xz})$$
$$3d_1 - 3d_{-1} = Br^2 \sin\theta \cos\theta \sin\varphi = Byz \text{ ... } (3d_{yz})$$
$$3d_{+2} - 3d_{-2} = Cr^2 \sin^2\theta \cos\varphi \sin\varphi = Cxy \text{ ... } (3d_{xy})$$
$$3d_{+2} - 3d_{-2} = Cr^2 \sin^2\theta\,(\cos^2\varphi - \sin^2\varphi) = C\,(x^2 - y^2) \text{ ... } \left(3d_{x^2-y^2}\right)$$]

The following points are to be noted:

(*i*) Since $2p_{+1}$ and $2p_{-1}$ wave functions are eigenfunctions of the same Hamiltonian operator with the same eigenvalue, their linear combination is also an eigenfunction of the same operator with the same eigenvalue.

(*ii*) The significance of the magnetic quantum number M is lost after taking the linear combinations.

(*iii*) The wave functions of the system, $\psi_{2p_{+1}}$, or $y_{2p_{-1}}$ (complex orbital) are simultaneously the eigenfunctions of $\hat{H}$, $\hat{L}^2$ and $\hat{L}_z$ meaning that if the system is in the state represented by such functions you can obtain definite values of E, L and L_z simultaneously through an experiment. But if the system is represented by functions like ψ_{2p_x} or ψ_{2p_y} (real orbital) you can obtain E and L sharply but not L_z. In other words, the system responds to the type of experiment and calls forth the appropriate wave function.

7.1.9 Graphical Representation of the Orbitals

Analytical expressions for the wave functions (atomic orbitals) in the real form permit their physical visualisation. For $l = 0$ (the *s* states) the functions ψ are functions of *r* only and hence can be plotted against *r* conveniently. For $l \neq 0$, the wave functions contain three variables *r*, θ and φ. In such cases graphical representation is possible either by (*a*) plotting the ψ or R_{nl} (*r*) against *r*, keeping θ and φ fixed or (*b*) plotting the ψ or the angular function Y_{iM} (θ, φ) against θ for a fixed value of *r* and φ, or against φ for a fixed value of *r* and θ; in either case of (*b*) a three dimensional picture can emerge if we carry out the plotting for all values of φ (0 to 2π) in the case of the former and all values of θ (0 to π) in the case of the latter.

Plots of ψ or R_{nl} (*r*) against *r* are called the "radial plots" and those of ψ or $Y_{l, M}$ (θ, φ) against θ or φ are called the "angular" or "polar" plots.

7.1.9.1 *Radial Plots*

Expression for ψ or R_{nl} (*r*) corresponding to $l = 0$ indicates that the functions at $r = 0$ (*i.e.*, at the nucleus) will have non-zero value. Since the functions also contain the factor exp $\left(-\dfrac{Zr}{na_0}\right)$, the values of *s*-functions at $r = 0$ will be maximum. They decrease exponentially tending to be zero for $r = \infty$ (Fig. 7.3). As the principal quantum number (*n*) increases the function oscillates as directed by its polynomial part *i.e.*, "nodal" points appear on the *r*-axis where ψ is zero. The number of nodes for an *s*-function is $n - 1$ (none for ψ_{1s}, 1 for ψ_{2s}, 2 for ψ_{3s} and so on). As the nuclear charge Z increases (*e.g.*, He^+, Li^+ the function falls off more rapidly with *r*.

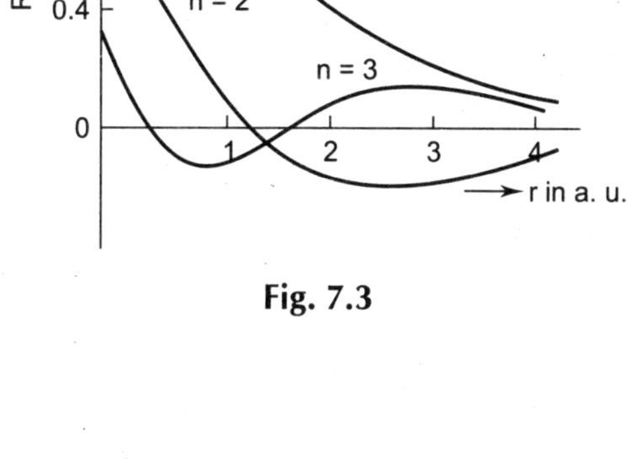

Fig. 7.3

For $l \neq 0$, the function is zero at $r = 0$ because of the factor r^l. The function increases with r but the factor $\exp\left(-\frac{Zr}{na_0}\right)$ has the effect of opposing it. In between $r = 0$ and $r = \infty$, the function is also governed by the nature of the polynomial. For example,

$$R_{21}(x) = \frac{1}{2\sqrt{6}}(Z)^{5/2}\, re^{-Zr/2}$$

suggests that there will be no node in the function whereas in

$$R_{31}(r) = Z^{5/2}\, r\,(6 - Zr)\, e^{-Zr/3}$$

a node will appear at the point $r = \frac{6}{Z}$ a.u.

The number of nodes in any radial function is given by $n - l - 1$ states.

Fig. 7.4 illustrates the radial plots for $l \neq 0$ states.

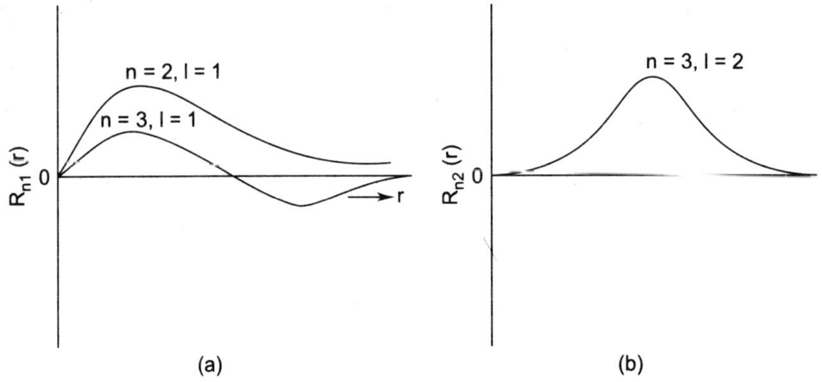

Fig. 7.4

[**Exercise:** Determine the nodal point on the r-axis for the 2s function of H-atom.

$$\psi_{2s} = \frac{1}{\sqrt{32\pi}}(2 - r)\,e^{-r/2} = 0 \text{ for } r = 2 \text{ a.u.}$$]

7.1.9.2 Angular (Polar) Plots

The traditional way of representing is to find values of Y (θ, φ) with R (r) chosen constant. These values are marked off as polar distance '*d*' along radial coordinate. Suppose we are to plot cos θ against θ for a particular value of r and φ. Values of cos θ for θ = 0, 30, 60, 90, 120, 150 and 180 degrees are

$$1, \frac{\sqrt{3}}{2}, \frac{1}{2}, 0, -\frac{1}{2}, -\frac{\sqrt{3}}{2} \text{ and } -1$$

respectively. We mark off these values along the radius r and the particular angle φ and connect the points. Two semi-circles are obtained around the line corresponding to θ = 0° and 180°, known as polar axis (see Fig. 7.5). If the function does not contain ϕ (*e.g.*, the $2p_z$ function) the value of the function will remain unchanged on rotation of the semicircles around the polar axis through 2π (the range of φ). This rotation will produce two spheres (Fig. 7.6) in one of which the function will have positive and in the other the negative sign.

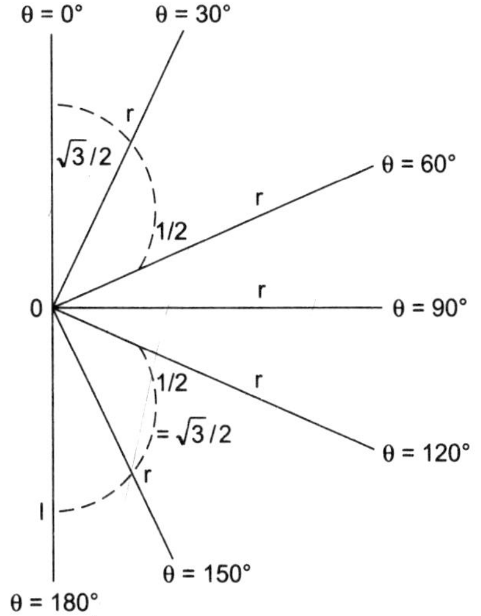

Fig. 7.5

The value of $\cos\theta$ in any direction (*i.e.*, for any value of θ and φ) can then be read off the polar plot by drawing a straight line in that direction from the origin upto the point where it meets the sphere.

A polar plot represents the angular part of the orbital in question. Such plots can be easily drawn for *s*, *p* and *d* orbitals; for others (*f*, *g*, ... orbitals) it is difficult (not impossible) to derive the shapes.

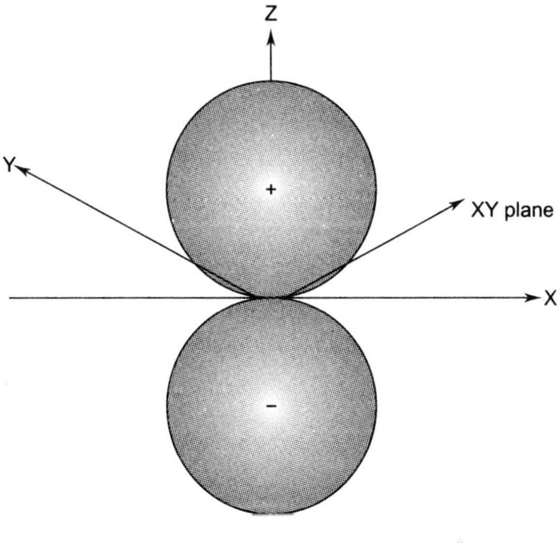

Fig. 7.6

The polar plot for an *s*-orbital (which is independent of θ and φ) is spherical. 1*s* orbital is a single sphere, 2*s* orbital has two concentric spheres, and so on, with nucleus at the centre (Fig. 7.7).

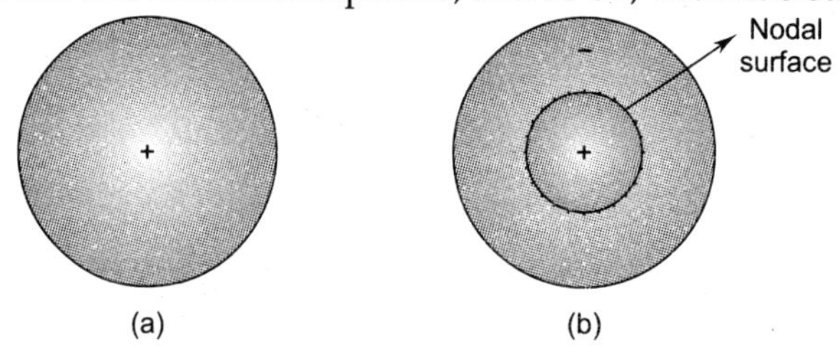

Fig. 7.7

The $2p_z$ function is independent of φ; hence, it is symmetric with respect to the polar (z) axis. For any value of r, the function has the largest positive value in the $+z$ and the largest negative value in the $-z$ direction; xy-plane is the nodal plane (see Fig. 7.6).

The $2p_x$ function contains $\sin\theta\cos\varphi$. First, plot the $\sin\theta$ for $\varphi = 0$ (*i.e.*, along the $+x$ direction). This function goes through 0, $\frac{1}{2}, \frac{\sqrt{3}}{2}, 1, \frac{\sqrt{3}}{2}, \frac{1}{2}$ and 0 as θ moves through 0, 30°, 60°, 90°, 120°, 150° and 180° respectively. The polar plot is a circle (Fig. 7.8). We have another circle for $\varphi = 180°$ (*i.e.*, along $-x$ direction) in which the function is negative. As φ goes from 0 to π and then π to 2π the function changes continuously vanishing for $\varphi = 90°$ and 270°. As φ increases, the value of $\sin\theta\cos\varphi$, for any value of θ, decreases because of the factor $\cos\varphi$. The complete polar plot of the p_x function consists of two spheres along the x-axis (Fig. 7.9) in one of which the function is positive and in the other negative; yz-plane is the nodal plane.

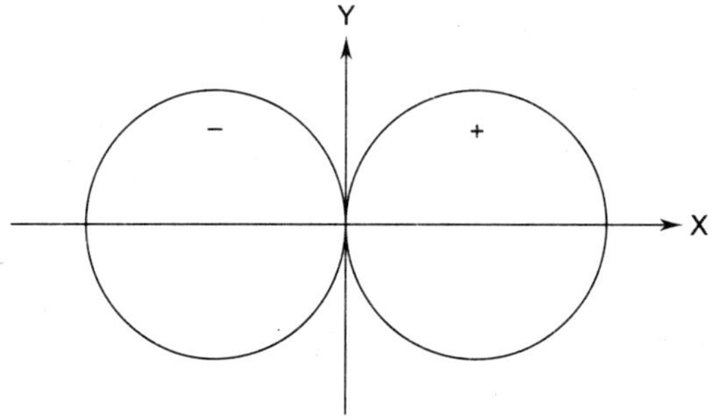

Fig. 7.8

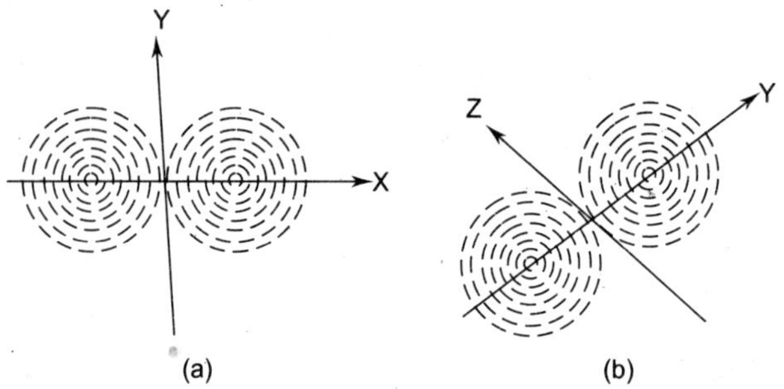

Fig. 7.9

The polar plot of $2p_y$ function (or sin θ sin φ) can likewise be shown to consist of two spheres along the y-axis with xz-plane as the nodal plane.

The three $2p$ functions ($2p_x$, $2p_y$ and $2p_z$) differ only in their orientation.

Polar plots for higher values of n differ only in the size of the spheres.

7.1.9.3 d-Functions

The angular parts of the ψ_{3d} functions in their real form are:

$$d_{z^2} = \left(\frac{5}{16\pi}\right)^{1/2} \left(3\cos^2\theta - 1\right) \quad \text{... (7.73)}$$

$$d_{xz} = \left(\frac{15}{4\pi}\right)^{1/2} \sin\theta\cos\theta\cos\varphi \quad \text{... (7.74)}$$

$$d_{yz} = \left(\frac{15}{4\pi}\right)^{1/2} \sin\theta\cos\theta\sin\varphi \quad \text{... (7.75)}$$

$$d_{x^2-y^2} = \left(\frac{15}{16\pi}\right)^{1/2} \sin^2\theta\cos 2\varphi \quad \text{... (7.76)}$$

$$d_{xy} = \left(\frac{15}{16\pi}\right)^{1/2} \sin^2\theta\sin 2\varphi \quad \text{... (7.77)}$$

The polar plots of these functions can be drawn in the manner described earlier.

The function d_{z^2} has its maximum value (positive) at θ = 0 and 180° ; it vanishes when 3 cos² θ = 1, or θ = 54.74° and 125.26°. In the xy-plane (θ = 90°) it is negative. So the polar plot consists of two lobes along the +z and –z directions. On being multiplied by the radial factor r^2, the function becomes $3z^2 - r^2$ and hence the name d_{z^2}.

The function d_{xz} is zero for θ = 0, 90° and 180°, and for φ = 90° and 270°. The maximum positive value occurs at θ = 45°, φ = 0° and θ = 135°, φ = 180°, while the maximum negative value occurs at θ = 45°, φ = 180° and θ = 135°, φ = 0°. The lines where the planes xy and yz cut the sphere are, therefore, the nodal lines. The function d_{yz} is similar to d_{xz} except that the nodal lines lie in the xy and xz-planes. Multiplication by the radial factor r^2 and use of the definitions of the polar coordinates justify the names d_{xz} and d_{yz}.

The function $d_{x^2-y^2}$ is similar in form, but the two nodal lines are at θ = 0° and 180°, and φ = 45° and 135°. Similarly, the function d_{xy} has the nodal lines lying at φ = 0, 180° and φ = 90°, 270°, *i.e.*, in the xz-and yz-planes. Since cos 2φ = cos² φ – sin² φ, and sin 2φ = 2 sin φ cos φ, multiplication by r^2 leads to $x^2 - y^2$ and xy respectively justifying the names $d_{x^2-y^2}$ and d_{xy} for these functions.

Obviously, all the five d functions are not equivalent in shape. The first (d_{z^2}) is symmetric (positive) with respect to the z-axis. The next two change sign as we go around the z-axis, *i.e.*, as φ increases from 0 to 360°. The last two change sign twice as we go around the z-axis.

7.1.9.4 *Probability Functions and Plots*

The quantity of interest to chemists, however, is ψ^2 rather than ψ itself, ψ^2 is "probability density" of the electron; if the electron is viewed as a cloud of negative charge ψ^2 represents the charge per unit volume (*i.e.*, electron density). Consider, for example, the 1*s* and 2*s* functions of H-atom.

$$\psi_{1s}^2 = \frac{1}{\pi a_0^3} \exp\left(-\frac{2r}{a_0}\right) \quad \text{... (7.78)}$$

$$\psi_{2s}^2 = \frac{1}{32\pi a_0^3} \left(2 - \frac{r}{a_0}\right)^2 \exp\left(-\frac{r}{a_0}\right) \quad \text{... (7.79)}$$

Variation of ψ^2 with r for several states is shown in Fig. 7.10. The expressions (7.78) and (7.79) as well as the plots show that the electron density is maximum at $r = 0$ (at the nucleus) in either case and decays exponentially.

But to say that the probability of electron at the nucleus is maximum seems to negate the very concept of atomic structure. However, it must be borne in mind that ψ^2 is the probability per unit volume (*i.e.*, charge density) and not the actual probability of finding the electron (charge) at a point.

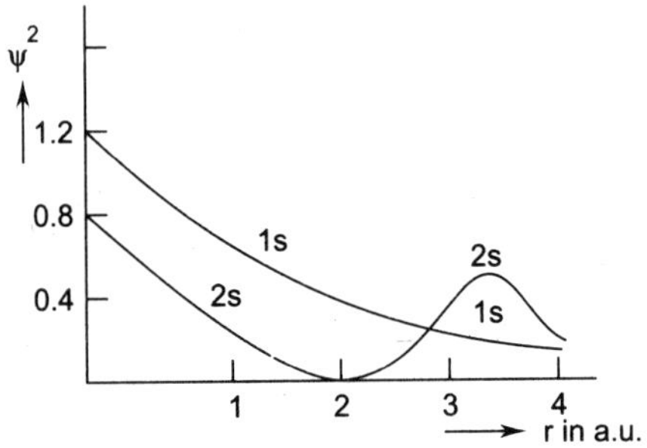

Fig. 7.10

The actual probability of finding the electron at any point is given by $\psi^2\, d\tau$, where $d\tau = r^2\, dr \sin\theta\, d\theta\, d\varphi$. Since it depends on both radial distance (r) and direction (θ, φ) it is more convenient to determine separately the probability distributions at various values of r irrespective of direction (the radial probability distribution) and along the various directions irrespective of distance (the angular probability distribution).

7.1.10 Radial Distribution

A radial distribution function P (r) is obtained by integrating $\psi^2\, d\tau$ over all angles θ and φ but not over r. Since

$$\psi = \psi(r, \theta, \varphi) = R(r) \cdot P(\theta) \cdot F(\varphi),$$

If R (r), P (θ) and F (φ) are normalised functions

$$P(r)\, dr = \int_0^{\pi}\int_0^{2\pi} \{\psi(r, \theta, \varphi)\}^2\, r^2\, dr \sin\theta\, d\theta\, d\varphi$$

$$= \{R(r)\}^2 r^2 dr \int_0^{\pi} \{P(\theta)\}^2 \sin\theta \, d\theta \int_0^{2\pi} \{F(\varphi)\}^2 d\varphi$$

$$= \{R(r)\}^2 . r^2 dr \qquad \text{... (7.80)}$$

or

$$P(r) = r^2 \{R(r)\}^2 \qquad \text{... (7.81)}$$

This gives radial probability density.

Equation (7.80) gives the probability that the electron is at a distance r from the nucleus and within the length dr irrespective of direction. We can formulate an equivalent (not identical) expression for radial probability density in terms of the probability that the electron lies in a spherical shell of radius r and thickness dr centered at the nucleus (as all angular positions are equivalent). Then using R (r) (without normalisation) in place of ψ,

$$dP = R(r)^2 . d\tau = R(r)^2 . d\left(\frac{4}{3}\pi r^3\right) = 4\pi r^2 R(r)^2 dr$$

with the condition of normalisation $N^2 \int 4\pi r^2 R^2 dr \doteq 1$, N = normalisation factor. This gives the radial probability density $= 4\pi r^2 R(r)^2$ ... (7.82)

The two are equivalent if R (r) in Equation (7.82) $= \dfrac{R(r)}{2\sqrt{\pi}}$ in (7.81). Equation (7.81) or (7.82) is the radial distribution function used to compute and plot the radial probability at different values of r (Fig. 7.11).

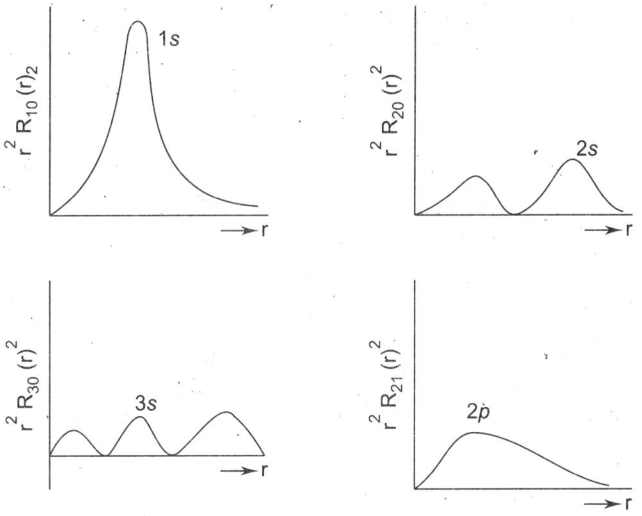

Fig. 7.11

7.1.11 Points of Maximum Probability

The factor r^2 in (7.81) changes the nature of the probability distribution from probability density distribution. Accordingly, the shapes of the graphical plots are changed. While the latter has maximum value at the nucleus ($r = 0$), the former is zero at that point. As we move away from the nucleus R $(r)^2$ decreases but r^2 R $(r)^2$ increases. The factor $\exp\left(-\frac{Zr}{na_0}\right)$, however, in R (r) tends to lower the value of the latter. The result is that for certain value (s) of r, *i.e.*, r_m, P (r) has a maximum value. The r_m can be determined by differentiating the function P (r) with respect to r and setting the resulting expression to zero. Similarly, the direction in which the electron is most likely to be found can be determined by differentiating ψ^2 partially with respect to θ and φ. For example, in the 1s state, the radial function is,

$$R_{10}(r) = 2Z^{3/2} e^{-Zr} \text{ in a.u.}$$

or

$$P(r) = r^2 [R(r)]^2 = 4Z^3 r^2 e^{-2Zr}$$

Therefore

$$\frac{d[P(r)]}{dr} = 8Z^3 re^{-2Zr}(1 - Z_r) \qquad \text{... (7.83)}$$

Setting Equation (7.83) equal to zero, we obtain

$$1 - Zr = 0$$

or

$$r = \frac{1}{Z} \text{ a.u.}$$

For hydrogen atom (Z = 1), r = 1 a.u. *i.e.*, a_0, which is the radius of the first Bohr orbit.

Further, since the ψ_{1s} function is independent of θ and φ, $\frac{\partial\psi}{\partial\theta}$ and $\frac{\partial\psi}{\partial\varphi}$ are zero, and, hence, the probability in all directions is the same. The electron cloud is spherically symmetrical.

This is consistent with Bohr's calculation except that the electron is now "most likely to be found" at a distance of a_0 from the nucleus in any direction rather than rotating in a circular orbit of radius a_0. There is a finite, though small, probability of finding it at other distances also.

Positions of maximum probability in various states (*i.e.*, different values of n and l) can be located also by plotting the function P (r) against r [see Fig. 7.11].

[**Exercise:** For the 2s state of H atom,

$$\psi_{2s} = \frac{1}{4\sqrt{2\pi}}(2 - r)\exp\left(-\frac{r}{2}\right) \text{ in a.u.}$$

find the most probable and the nodal distances of the electron from the nucleus.

$$R_{2,0}(r) = \frac{1}{2\sqrt{2}}(2 - r)\exp\left(-\frac{r}{2}\right)$$

$$P(r) = \frac{1}{8}\left(4r^2 - 4r^3 + r^4\right)\exp(-r)$$

For

$$\frac{dP(r)}{dr} = 0,\ 8 - 16r + 8r^2 - r^3 = 0$$

The cubic equation in r has 3 roots one of which is r = 2 ; but for r = 2, $R_{2,0}(r) = 0$, so this is a nodal point.

Dividing the cubic equation by 2 – r, we get $4 - 6r + r^2 = 0$, which has the solutions,

$$r = 3 \pm \sqrt{5} = 5.23 \text{ and } 0.77 \text{ a.u.}$$

The values of P (r) are 0.191 and 0.052, respectively].

7.1.12 Angular Probability Distribution

Angular probability distribution function can likewise be obtained by integrating $\psi^2\, d\tau$ over all values of r. The integration is, however, complicated and it is more convenient to determine the angular distribution graphically by plotting $[P(\theta)]^2$ against θ for fixed values of r and φ. The probability of finding the electron at any angle θ is then obtained by the magnitude of the straight line drawn from the centre up to the point where it meets the curve along the angle. The magnitude of the line will be greatest in the direction which gives the maximum value of $[P(\theta)]^2$. Let us see a few examples.

The s-wave functions do not contain θ or φ, so the angular distribution is the same in all directions. The electron cloud is, accordingly, spherically symmetrical.

The $2p_z$ wave function is given by,

$$\psi_{2p_z} = \frac{1}{4\sqrt{2\pi}}\, r \exp\left(-\frac{r}{2}\right) \cos\theta \text{ (in a.u.)}$$

The angular distribution is, therefore, proportional to $\cos^2\theta$. Now values of $\cos^2\theta$ for various values of θ are marked off along the radial (r) axis (Fig. 7.12). The maximum and minimum values of $\cos^2\theta$ are +1 (when $\theta = 0$ or π) and 0 (when $\theta = \frac{\pi}{2}$) respectively and are never negative. For any value of θ lying in the xz-plane, the dependence of the function on r will be the same (*i.e.*, $r^2 \exp(-r)$ with maximum at $r = 2$ a.u., but the value of the function will be less than that at $\theta = 0$ or π with zero at $\theta = \frac{\pi}{2}$. Also, at any other value of θ, $\cos^2\theta < \cos\theta$ such that the polar plot of $\cos^2\theta$ against θ in the xz-plane will consist of two semi-ellipses [Fig. 7.12 (*a*)] instead of semicircles (as in the plot of $\cos\theta$ vs θ) and rotation of the curve around the polar axis, which amounts to plotting for other values of φ, will produce two ellipsoids [Fig. 7.12 (*b*)] instead of two spheres. The two ellipsoids represent the electron clouds of the $2p_z$ orbital; each cloud has the maximum density at the centres, each centre lying at the distance $r = 2$ *a.u.* from the nucleus. At the nucleus the density is zero, xy-plane being the nodal plane.

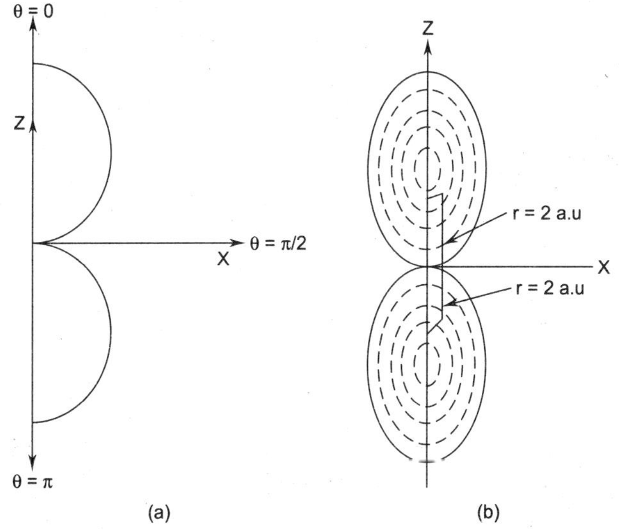

Fig. 7.12

Similar angular probability plots may be drawn for $2p_x$ and $2p_y$ orbitals [Fig. 7.13 (*a*) and (*b*)].

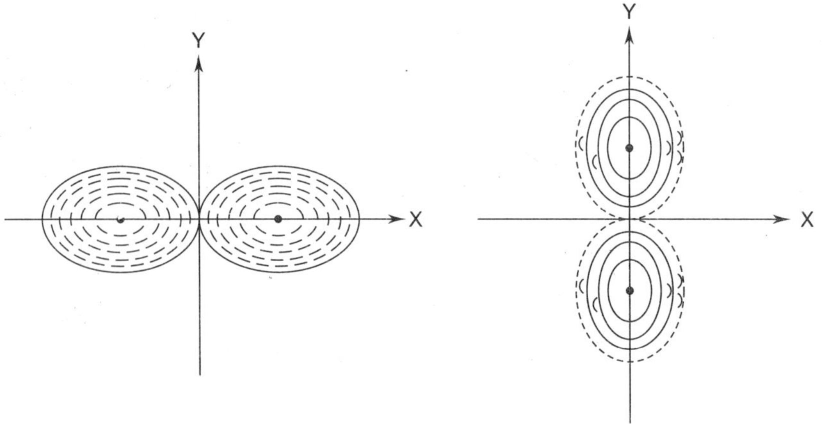

Fig. 7.13

7.1.13 Average Distance ($\bar{r}$) of the Electron from the Nucleus

One is often concerned with the average distance, $\bar{r}$, of the electron from the nucleus as some atomic properties are related to it. For hydrogen in the 1*s* state, this is given by,

$$\bar{r}_{1s} = \int \psi_{1s}\, \hat{r}\, \psi_{1s}\, d\tau \text{ (from the basic postulate III of quantum mechanics, see Chapter 3)}$$

$$= \int_0^\infty \frac{1}{\sqrt{\pi}} \exp(-r)\, \hat{r}\, \frac{1}{\sqrt{\pi}} \exp(-r) r^2\, dr \int_0^\pi \sin\theta\, d\theta \int_0^{2\pi} d\varphi \qquad \text{(using } \psi \text{ in a.u.)}$$

$$= \frac{1}{\pi} \int r^3 \exp(-2r)\,(2)\,(2\pi)$$

$$= 4 \times \frac{3!}{2^4} \qquad \text{(from the table of integrals)}$$

$$= \frac{3}{2} \text{ a.u.}$$

[Instead of ψ we could use $R_{10}(r)$; then,

$$r = \int_0^\infty R_{10}(r)\, \hat{r}\, R_{10}(r)\, r^2\, dr$$

7.2 THE QUANTUM MECHANICAL MODEL

Quantum mechanics provides a new model for representing the structure of hydrogen atom, and hence of other atoms (to be discussed in a later chapter), with sound theoretical basis. The electron rotates round the nucleus but not in a well-defined orbit; the rotation is three-dimensional and the motion is described by a wave equation—the Schrödinger equation. Rather than locating the electron at any instant exactly, this model provides the position of the electron in terms of a probability function, there being a finite, even though small, probability of its being found at all points in the infinite space outside the nucleus. The probability is maximum at a certain distance from the nucleus. Interestingly, in the ground state of H-atom this distance is the same as the radius (a_0) of the first Bohr orbit which is $\frac{h^2}{4\pi^2 me^2}$, *i.e.*, 0.529 Å. This maximum probability is uniformly distributed in all directions at a distance of a_0 from the nucleus (*i.e.*, it is spherically symmetrical). In excited states with non-zero angular momentum of the electron ($l \neq 0$), the maximum lies in certain preferred directions. In each state one can visualise a three-dimensional surface encompassing the nucleus that encloses a large fraction (~ 90%) of the probability; in other words, the electron may be supposed to spend 90% of its time inside this surface. The entire region within this surface is the quantum mechanical analogue of classical orbit and is the physical representation of orbital.

There is an equivalent way of representing the probability distribution by considering the electron as a cloud of negative charge. The density of the electron cloud (probability density) in the ground state of the H atom is maximum at the nucleus and 90% of the charge of the cloud is contained within the surface of the orbital. Although the electron is most likely to be found at a distance a_0 from the nucleus, its average distance is $1.5a_0$.

As in the old planetary model, the stability of the atom, qualitatively, is attributed to (*i*) a force tending to bring the nucleus and the electron together and (*ii*) an opposing force tending to keep the electron away from the nucleus. The former is electrostatic in nature $\left(F = \frac{Ze^2}{r^2}\right)$; for the latter quantum mechanics provides a more consistent picture. We visualise the electron as a diffuse cloud of matter and negative charge around the nucleus. The nucleus tends to make the electron cloud smaller and smaller. This makes the wavelength of the electron wave shorter and shorter and hence the energy greater. Rubinstein* prefers to call it the "energy of confinement" ($E_{conf.}$) Below an optimum distance (a_0) the confinement energy is sufficiently great for the nucleus to pull the electron cloud further towards itself. An equilibrium is ultimately established at the optimum distance for the atom to be stable when the two forces balance.

---

*E. Ley-Keo and S. Rubinstein, J. *Chem. Phys.* 1979, Vol 71, p. 353. For more about energy of confinement and examples, the reader is referred to an article by F. P. Mason and R. W. Richardson, J. Chem. ed. 1983, Vol 60, pp. 40-42.

PROBLEMS

7.1 Using atomic units, write the complete Hamiltonian for electronic motion in hydrogen atom in spherical coordinates. Give the radial and angular parts.

[Hint:
$$\hat{H} = -\frac{1}{2}\nabla^2 - \frac{1}{r}$$

$$\nabla^2 = -\frac{1}{2r^2}\left[\frac{\partial}{\partial r}\left(r^2\frac{\partial}{\partial r}\right) + \frac{1}{\sin\theta}\frac{\partial}{\partial\theta}\left(\sin\theta\frac{\partial}{\partial\theta}\right) + \frac{1}{\sin^2\theta}\frac{\partial^2}{\partial\varphi^2}\right] - \frac{1}{r}$$

Radial part: $-\frac{1}{2r^2}\left[\frac{\partial}{\partial r}\left(r^2\frac{\partial}{\partial r}\right)\right] - \frac{1}{r}$

Second and third terms within the square brackets together constitute the operator for the square of angular momentum, *i.e.*, $\hat{L}^2$. The operator $\hat{L}^2$, however, does not contain r and commutes with $\hat{H}$. This means that both $\hat{H}$ and $\hat{L}^2$ can have the same set of eigenfunctions $\psi(r, \theta, \varphi)$ and that $\psi(r, \theta, \varphi)$ can be expressed as

$$\psi(r, \theta, \varphi) = R(r) \,.\, A(\theta, \varphi)$$

$\psi(r, \theta, \varphi)$ and $A(\theta, \varphi)$ will be the eigenfunctions of $\hat{L}^2$. So the angular operator is,

$$\hat{L}^2 = \frac{1}{\sin\theta}\frac{\partial}{\partial\theta}\left(\sin\theta\frac{\partial}{\partial\varphi}\right) + \frac{1}{\sin^2\theta}\frac{\partial^2}{\partial\varphi^2}\Bigg].$$

7.2 The Hamiltonian for hydrogen atom and the 1s wave function in atomic units are,

$$\hat{H} = -\frac{1}{2}\nabla^2 - \frac{1}{r}$$

$$\psi_{1s} = \frac{1}{\sqrt{\pi}}e^{-r}$$

Calculate the ground state energy of hydrogen atom in S.I. units and also in electron volts.

[Hint:
$$\bar{E}_{1s} = \int \psi_{1s}\hat{H}\psi_{1s}\,d\tau$$

$$= \frac{1}{\pi}\int_0^\infty e^{-r}\left[-\frac{1}{2r^2}\frac{d}{dr}\left(r^2\frac{d}{dr}\right) - \frac{1}{r}\right]e^{-r}r^2\,dr\int_0^\pi \sin\theta\,d\theta\int_0^{2\pi}d\varphi$$

$$= -\frac{4\pi}{2\pi}\int_0^\infty r^2 e^{-2r}\,dr$$

$$= -\frac{1}{2}\text{ a.u.} = -2.18\times10^{-18}\text{ J} = -13.6\text{ eV}\Bigg].$$

7.3 Normalise the following functions,

(*i*) $\psi = e^{-r}$, (*ii*) $\psi = re^{-r/2}\cos\theta$

[Hint : (*i*) $N^2\int_0^\infty e^{-2r}r^2\,dr\int_0^\pi \sin\theta\,d\theta\int_0^{2\pi}d\varphi = 1$

or $$N^2 \frac{2!}{2^3} 4\pi = 1 \text{ or } N = \frac{1}{\sqrt{\pi}}$$

(*ii*) $$N^2 \int_0^\infty r^2 e^{-r} r^2\, dr \int_0^\pi \cos^2\theta \sin\theta\, d\theta \int_0^{2\pi} d\varphi = 1$$

or $$N^2 \frac{4!}{1^5}\left[-\frac{\cos^3\theta}{3}\right]_0^\pi 2\pi = 1 \text{ or } N = \frac{1}{\sqrt{32\pi}}\Bigg].$$

7.4 Using the expressions (7.21), (7.22) and (7.23), work out the functions for the five $3d$ orbitals and write the complete angular functions A (θ, φ).

[Hint: For $$l = 2,\ |M| = 2,\quad N = \sqrt{\frac{(4+1)(2-2)!}{2(2+2)!}} = \sqrt{\frac{5}{48}}$$

$$P_2^2(x) = \frac{1}{2^2 . 2!}\left(1-x^2\right)\frac{d^4}{dx^4}\left(x^4 - 2x^2 + 1\right)$$

$$= \frac{1}{8}\left(1-x^2\right). 24 = 3\sin^2\theta$$

Therefore $$P_{2,\pm 2}(\theta) = \sqrt{\frac{5}{48}} \times 3\sin^2\theta = \sqrt{\frac{15}{16}}\sin^2\theta;$$

$$A(\theta, \varphi) = \sqrt{\frac{15}{32\pi}}\sin^2\theta\, e^{2i\varphi}$$

Similarly, $$P_{2,+1}(\theta) = \sqrt{\frac{15}{4}}\sin\theta\cos\theta;\ A(\theta,\varphi) = \sqrt{\frac{15}{8\pi}}\sin\theta\cos\theta\, e^{2i\varphi}$$

$$P_{2,0}(\theta) = \sqrt{\frac{5}{8}}\left(3\cos^2\theta - 1\right);\ A(\theta,\varphi) = \sqrt{\frac{5}{16\pi}}\left(3\cos^2\theta - 1\right)\Bigg].$$

7.5 Using the expression (7.51), work out the radial functions for $3s$, $3p$ and $3d$ orbitals.

[Hint: $$R_{3,0}(\rho) = \sqrt{\frac{(3-0-1)!}{2\times 3\times\{(3+0)!\}^3}\left(\frac{2}{3a_0}\right)^3}\ \rho^0\, L_3^1(\rho)\, e^{-\rho/2}$$

$$= -\frac{1}{9\sqrt{27}}\left(\frac{1}{a_0}\right)^3 L_3^1(\rho)\, e^{-\rho/2}$$

$$L_3^1(\rho) = \frac{d}{d\rho}\left[e^{\rho}\frac{d^3}{d\rho^3}\left(\rho^3 e^{-\rho}\right)\right]$$

$$= \frac{d}{d\rho}\left(6 - 18\rho + 9\rho^2 - \rho^3\right)$$

$$= -18 + 18\rho - 3\rho^2$$

Therefore $$R_{3,0}(\rho) = \frac{1}{9\sqrt{3a_0^3}}\left(6 - 6\rho + \rho^2\right)e^{-\rho/2}$$

Similarly, $$R_{3,1}(\rho) = \frac{1}{9\sqrt{6a_0^3}}(4 - \rho)\,e^{-\rho/2}$$

$$R_{3,2}(\rho) = \frac{1}{9\sqrt{30a_0^3}}\rho^2\, e^{-\rho/2}\Bigg].$$

7.6 Give the analytical expressions for the ground and the first excited state wave functions of H atom and He^+. Sketch the functions and comment.

[Hint: $$\psi_{1s}^{H} = \frac{1}{\sqrt{\pi}}e^{-r}\,;\ \psi_{2s}^{H} = \frac{1}{4\sqrt{2\pi}}(2 - r)\,e^{-r/2}$$

$$\psi_{1s}^{He^+} = \frac{\sqrt{8}}{\sqrt{\pi}}e^{-2r}\,;\ \psi_{2s}^{He^+} = \frac{1}{\sqrt{\pi}}(1 - r)\,e^{-r}$$

$\psi_{max}^{H}(r = 0) < \psi_{max}^{He^+}(r = 0)$; ψ_{2s}^{He+} decays much faster than ψ_{2s}^{H}, the former showing a node at r = 1 a.u. and the latter at r = 2 a.u.].

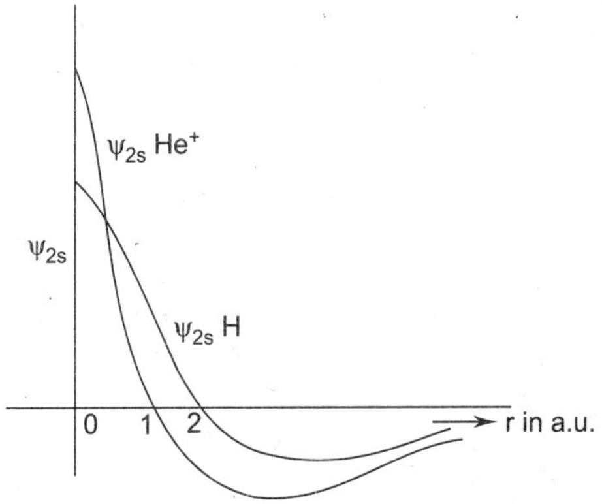

Fig. 7.14

7.7 The ψ_{2s} atomic orbitals for hydrogen-like atoms are given as,

$$\psi_{2s} = \frac{1}{4\sqrt{2\pi}}\left(\frac{Z}{a_0}\right)^{3/2}\left(2 - \frac{Zr}{a_0}\right)\exp\left(-\frac{Zr}{2a_0}\right)$$

Calculate the radii of the nodal surfaces for H, He^+ and Li^{2+} comment.

[**Hint:** $\psi_{2s} = 0$ at $r = \dfrac{2a_0}{Z} = 1.058 \times 10^{-10}$ m for H,

$$\frac{1.058}{2} \times 10^{-10} = 0.529 \times 10^{-10} \text{ m for He}^+$$

and $$\frac{1.058}{3} \times 10^{-10} = 0.352 \times 10^{-10} \text{ m for Li}^{2+}$$

As the nuclear charge increases, the orbital shrinks].

7.8 Derive the atomic orbital for $l = 1$, M = 0

[**Hint:** $$Y_{1,0}(\theta, \varphi) = \left(\frac{3}{2}\right)^{1/2} \cos\theta \frac{1}{\sqrt{2\pi}} \exp(i \,.\, 0 \,.\, \varphi)$$

$$= \sqrt{\frac{3}{2\pi}} \cos\theta = \frac{Z}{r}$$

Therefore, the orbital is p_z].

7.9 The $3d_{x^2-y^2}$ orbital is analytically expressed as

$$\psi = \frac{1}{81\sqrt{2\pi}} \left(\frac{Z}{a_0}\right)^{3/2} \rho^2 e^{-\rho/3} \sin^2\theta \cos 2\varphi$$

Plot the function in the xy-plane and derive the shape of the orbital.

[**Hint:** Find the values of cos 2φ for about 30 values of φ from 0° to 360° using a mathematical table. Calculate ψ for $\theta = \dfrac{\pi}{2}$ using a definite value of ρ; ψ will be positive and maximum for φ = 0, 180° and 360° and negative maximum for φ = 270°. Cut these values along the radial axis for the corresponding values of φ and connect. Repetition of these plots for values of θ between 0° and 180° will produce the three-dimensional picture of the $3d_{x^2-y^2}$ orbital.

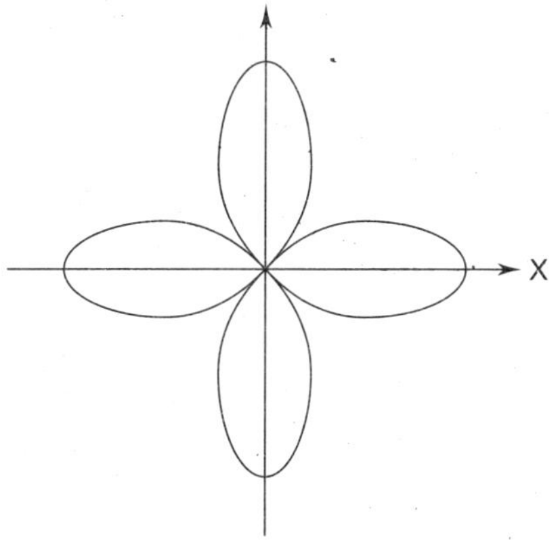

Fig. 7.15

7.10 Plot the radial function of $2p$ orbital of hydrogen atom and He^+, and comment.

[Hint:
$$R_{2,1}(r) = \left(\frac{Z}{a_0}\right)^{3/2} \cdot \frac{1}{\sqrt{24}}\left(\frac{Z}{a_0}\right) r \exp\left(-\frac{Zr}{2a_0}\right)$$

For
$$H, R_{2,1}(r) = \frac{1}{\sqrt{24}}\left(\frac{1}{a_0}\right)^{5/2} r \exp\left(-\frac{r}{2a_0}\right)$$
$$= \sqrt{\frac{1}{24}}\, r \exp\left(-\frac{r}{2}\right) \text{ (in a.u.)}$$

For He^+,
$$R_{2,1}(r) = \frac{2}{\sqrt{3}}\left(\frac{1}{a_0}\right)^{5/2} . r \exp\left(-\frac{r}{a_0}\right)$$
$$= \frac{2}{\sqrt{3}}\, r \exp(-r) \text{ (in a.u.)}$$

Calculate the values of R (r) for various values of r in a.u. using a mathematical table and plot (see Fig. 7.14). The curve for He^+ has a greater height and decays faster than that for H because of the greater nuclear charge.

7.11 Show that wave functions ψ_{2p_x}, ψ_{2p_y} and ψ_{2p_z} have their maximum values along x, y and z-axes respectively. Determine their nodal planes.

[Hint:
$$\psi_{2p_z} = \frac{1}{4\sqrt{2\pi}}\left(\frac{Z}{a_0}\right)^{3/2}\left(\frac{Zr}{a_0}\right)\exp\left(-\frac{Zr}{2}\right)\cos\theta = NR(r)\cos\theta$$

For a definite r, $\cos\theta$ is maximum for $\theta = 0$, and minimum for $\theta = \pi$; this constitutes z-axis. $\cos\theta = 0$ for $\theta = \frac{\pi}{2}$, *i.e.*, the xy-plane is the nodal plane. $\psi_{2p_x} = NR(r)\sin\theta\cos\varphi$ which is maximum for $\theta = \frac{\pi}{2}$, $\varphi = 0$ and minimum for $\theta = \frac{3\pi}{2}$, $\varphi = \pi$, *i.e.*, x-axis; it is zero for $\theta = 0$, π and $\varphi = \frac{\pi}{2}$, *i.e.*, xz-plane is the nodal plane].

7.12 Verify that, $R_{1,0}(r) = 2\left(\frac{Z}{a_0}\right)^{3/2} \exp\left(-\frac{Zr}{a_0}\right)$

$$R_{2,0}(r) = \frac{1}{2\sqrt{2}}\left(\frac{Z}{a_0}\right)^{3/2}\left(2 - \frac{Zr}{a_0}\right)\exp\left(-\frac{Zr}{2a_0}\right)$$

and
$$R_{2,1}(r) = \frac{1}{2\sqrt{6}}\left(\frac{Z}{a_0}\right)^{3/2} r \exp\left(-\frac{Zr}{2a_0}\right)$$

and normalised radial eigenfunctions of hydrogen-like atoms.

[**Hint :** Radial operator is,

$$-\frac{h^2}{8\pi^2 m}\frac{1}{r^2}\frac{d}{dr}\left(r^2\frac{d}{dr}\right)-\frac{Ze^2}{r}$$

and $$\left[-\frac{h^2}{8\pi^2 m}\frac{1}{r^2}\frac{d}{dr}\left(r^2\frac{d}{dr}\right)-\frac{Ze^2}{r}\right]\left\{2\left(\frac{Z}{a_0}\right)^{3/2}\exp\left(-\frac{Zr}{a_0}\right)\right\}$$

$$=-\frac{e^2}{2a_0}\left\{2\left(\frac{Z}{a_6}\right)^{3/2}\exp\left(-\frac{Zr}{a_0}\right)\right\}$$

Eigenvalue $$=-\frac{e^2}{2a_0}$$

$$\int_0^\infty 2\left\{\left(\frac{Z}{a_0}\right)^{3/2}\exp\left(-\frac{Zr}{a_0}\right)\right\}^2 r^2\,dr=4\left(\frac{Z}{a_0}\right)^3\frac{2!}{(2Z/a_0)^3}=1 \quad (d\tau=r^2\,dr)].$$

7.13 Show that ψ_{1s} and ψ_{2s} are orthonormal.

[Hint: $$\psi_{1s}=\frac{1}{\sqrt{\pi}}\left(\frac{Z}{a_0}\right)^{3/2},\exp\left(-\frac{Zr}{a_0}\right)$$

$$d\tau=r^2\,dr\sin\theta\,d\theta\,d\varphi$$

$$\int\psi_{1s}^2\,d\tau=\frac{Z^3}{\pi a_0^3}\int_0^\infty\exp\left(-\frac{2Zr}{a_0}\right)r^2\,dr\int_0^\pi\sin\theta\,d\theta\int_0^{2\pi}d\varphi$$

$$=\frac{4\pi Z^3}{\pi a_0^3}\times\frac{2!}{(2Z/a_0)^3}=1$$

$$\psi_{2s}=\frac{1}{4\sqrt{2\pi}}\left(\frac{Z}{a_0}\right)^{3/2}\left(2-\frac{Zr}{a_0}\right)\exp\left(-\frac{Zr}{2a_0}\right)$$

$$\int\psi_{2s}^2\,d\tau=\frac{1}{32\pi}\left(\frac{Z}{a_0}\right)\int_0^\infty\left(2-\frac{Zr}{a_0}\right)^2\exp\left(-\frac{Zr}{a_0}\right)r^2\,dr\int_0^\pi\sin\theta\,d\theta\int_0^{2\pi}d\varphi$$

$$=\frac{4\pi}{32\pi}\left(\frac{Z}{a_0}\right)^3\left[\int_0^\infty 4r^2\exp\left(-\frac{Zr}{a_0}\right)dr\right.$$

$$\left.-\int_0^\infty\frac{4Zr^3}{a_0}\exp\left(-\frac{Zr}{a_0}\right)dr+\int_0^\infty\frac{Z^2r^4}{a_0^2}\exp\left(-\frac{Zr}{a_0}\right)dr\right]$$

$$= \frac{1}{8}\left(\frac{Z}{a_0}\right)^3 \left[\frac{4\times 2!}{(Z/a_0)^3} - \frac{4\left(\frac{Z}{a_0}\right)^{3!}}{(Z/a_0)^4} + \frac{\frac{Z^2}{a_0^2}\times 4!}{(Z/a_0)^5}\right]$$

$$= 1$$

$$\int \psi_{1s}\,\psi_{2s}\,d\tau = \int_0^\infty \sqrt{\frac{Z^3}{\pi a_0^3}}\exp(-Zr/a_0)\frac{1}{\sqrt{32\pi}}\left(\frac{Z}{a_0}\right)^{3/2}\left(2-\frac{Zr}{a_0}\right)$$

$$.\exp(-Zr/2a_0)\,r^2\,dr\int_0^\infty \sin\theta\,d\theta\int_0^{2\pi} d\varphi$$

$$= \frac{4\pi}{\sqrt{32\,.\,\pi}}\left(\frac{Z}{a_0}\right)^3\int_0^\infty\left(2-\frac{Zr}{a_0}\right)\exp(-3Zr/2a_0)\,r^2\,dr$$

$$= \frac{1}{\sqrt{2}}\left(\frac{Z}{a_0}\right)^3\left[\int_0^\infty 2r^2\exp(-3Zr/2a_0) - \int_0^\infty \frac{Zr^3}{a_0}\exp(-3Zr/2a_0)dr\right]$$

$$= \frac{1}{\sqrt{2}}\left(\frac{Z}{a_0}\right)^3\left[\frac{2\times 2!}{(3Z/2a_0)^3} - \frac{(Z/a_0)\,3!}{\left(\frac{3Z}{2a_0}\right)^4}\right]$$

$= 0]$.

7.14 Show that the functions ψ_{2s} and ψ_{2pz} of H (Z = 1) are orthogonal.
[**Hint:** Using atomic units,

$$\int \psi_{2s}\,\psi_{2pz}\,d\tau = \int_0^\infty\int_0^\pi\int_0^{2\pi}\frac{1}{\sqrt{32\,\pi}}(2-r)\exp(-r/2)$$

$$\frac{1}{\sqrt{32\,\pi}}re^{-r/2}\cos\theta\,r^2\,dr\sin\theta\,d\theta\,d\varphi$$

$$\int_0^\pi \cos\theta\sin\theta\,d\theta = \frac{1}{2}\int_0^\pi \sin 2\theta\,d\theta = \frac{1}{4}[\cos 2\theta]_0^\pi = 0\Bigg].$$

7.15 A hydrogen-like wave function is given below with r in atomic units,

$$\psi = \frac{\sqrt{2}}{81\sqrt{\pi}}Z^{3/2}(6-Zr)\,Zr\exp(-Zr/3)\cos\theta$$

Determine the quantum numbers n, l and M by inspection.

[**Hint:** The exponential factor exp $(-Zr/3)$ show that $n = 3$. The radial factor $r^l = r$ shows that $l = 1$. The angular factor cos θ shows that M = 0].

7.16 Show that the probability of finding the electron in a hydrogen-like atom is independent of the angle φ.

[**Hint:**
$$\psi^* \psi = \left[R(r) P(\theta) \frac{1}{\sqrt{2\pi}} e^{-iM\varphi} \right] \left[R(r) P(\theta) \frac{1}{\sqrt{2\pi}} e^{iM\varphi} \right]$$
$$= \{R(r) P(\theta)\}^2].$$

7.17 Shows that the ψ_{2pz} is antisymmetrical with respect to the xy-plane but its probability distribution is symmetrical.

[**Hint:** (*i*) cos θ changes sign at θ = π/2 but $\cos^2 \theta$ does not].

7.18 Show that the total probability density for any value of n is spherically symmetric irrespective of the value of l.

[**Hint:**
$$\psi_{1s}^2 = \frac{1}{\pi} e^{-2^r} \text{ (in a.u.)}$$
$$\psi_{2s}^2 = \frac{1}{32\pi} (2-r)^2 e^{-r} \text{ (in a.u.)}$$
$$\psi_{2p}^2 = \psi_{2p_x}^2 + \psi_{2p_y}^2 + \psi_{2p_z}^2 = \frac{1}{32\pi} r^2 e^{-r} \left(\sin^2\theta \cos^2\varphi + \sin^2\theta \sin^2\varphi + \cos^2\theta\right)$$
$$= \frac{1}{32\pi} r^2 e^{-r} \left(\sin^2\theta + \cos^2\theta\right)$$
$$= \frac{1}{32\pi} r^2 e^{-r} \text{ (in a.u.)}$$
$$\psi_{3d}^2 = \psi_{3d_{xy}}^2 + \psi_{3d_{yz}}^2 + \psi_{3d_{xz}}^2 + \psi 3d_{x^2-y^2} + \psi 3d_{z^2}$$
= a function of r only].

7.19 For an electron in $2p_z$ orbital of an H-atom what is the probability for θ = π/2 and π/4 at a distance of 1 a.u. from the nucleus ?

[**Hint:**
$$\psi^2 = \frac{1}{32\pi} r^2 \exp(-r) \cos^2\theta$$

For
$$\theta = \frac{\pi}{2}, \psi^2 = 0; \quad \text{for } \theta = \frac{\pi}{4}, \psi^2 = \frac{1}{64\pi} r^2 \exp(-r)$$
$$= \frac{1}{64\pi} \exp(-1) \text{ for } r = 1.$$

7.20 What is the probability of an electron being found at a distance of $r = 0, \frac{1}{2}, 1$ and $\frac{3}{2}$ a.u. from the nucleus of an H in 1s state ?

[**Hint:**
$$P(r) = r^2 R(r)^2 = \frac{1}{\pi} r^2 \exp(-2r)$$

Therefore,

$$P(r) = 0, \frac{1}{4\pi}\exp(-1), \frac{1}{\pi}\exp(-2), \frac{9}{4\pi}\exp(-3)$$

for $$r = 0, \frac{1}{2}, 1, \frac{3}{2}\Big].$$

7.21 Find the points of maximum probability density of the electron in the $2p_x$, $2p_y$ and $2p_z$ states of H atom.

[Hint: $$P_{2p_x} = \psi^2_{2p_x} = \frac{1}{32\pi} r^2 e^{-r} \sin^2\theta \cos^2\varphi$$

$$P_{2p_y} = \psi^2_{2p_y} = \frac{1}{32\pi} r^2 e^{-r} \sin^2\theta \sin^2\varphi$$

$$P_{2y_z} = \psi^2_{2p_z} = \frac{1}{32\pi} r^2 e^{-r} \cos^2\theta$$

In each case, set $\frac{\partial P}{\partial r} = 2re^{-r} - r^2 e^{-r} = 0,$

from which $r = r_m = 2$ a.u. $= 1.05 \times 10^{-10}$ m (the solution $r = 0$ should be rejected as it would lead to $P = 0$ instead of its maximum value)

For $$2p_x, \frac{\partial P}{\partial \theta} = \frac{1}{16\pi} r^2 e^{-r} \sin\theta \cos\theta = 0$$

Solutions are $\sin\theta = 0$, or $\cos\theta = 0$,

$\sin\theta = 0$ will lead to $\psi_{2p_x} = 0$ everywhere; hence the other solution is $\cos\theta = 0$ or $\theta = \pi/2$.

$$\frac{\partial P}{\partial \varphi} = \frac{1}{16\pi} r^2 e^{-r} \sin\varphi \cos\varphi = 0; \textit{i.e.}, \sin\varphi = 0$$

or $$\varphi = 0, \pi.$$

The set of solutions for the $2p_x$ state is $r = 2a_0$, $\theta = \pi/2, 3\pi/2$, $\varphi = 0, \pi$. This corresponds to two points $x = \pm 2$ a.u.

Similarly, for $2p_y$ and $2p_z$, the points are $y = \pm 2$ a.u. and $z = \pm 2$ a.u.].

7.22 Calculate the most probable distance r_m of an electron in the $2p$ state of H atom.

[Hint: $$P(r) = r^2 [R_{21}(r)]^2 = \frac{1}{24} r^4 e^{-r} \text{ (in a.u.)}$$

Setting $$\frac{dP}{dr} = 0, (4r^3 - r^4) e^{-r} = 0;$$

or $$r = 4 \text{ a.u. (or } 4a_0)$$

Note that in the earlier problem, the distance of maximum probability density is 2 a.u. which is different from the most probable distance 4 a.u.].

7.23 What is the maximum electron density in H-atom in the 2*s* and $2p_x$ states ?

[Hint: $$\psi_{2s}^2 = \frac{1}{4\pi a_0^3}\left(2-\frac{r}{a_0}\right)^2 \exp(-r/a_0)$$

This is maximum when $\exp(-r/a_0) = 1$ or $r = 0$, and the value is $\frac{1}{4\pi a_0^3}$, $a_0 = 0.529 \times 10^{-10}$ m.

$$\psi_{2p_x}^2 = \frac{1}{32\pi a_0^3} r^2 \exp(-r/a_0) \sin^2\theta \cos^2\varphi$$

The maximum value corresponds to $\sin^2\theta\cos^2\varphi = 1$ and $r = 2a_0$].

7.24 Calculate the average distance of the electron from the nucleus of H-atom in the 2*s* state.

[Hint: $$\bar{r}_{2s} = \frac{1}{32\pi a_0^3}\int_0^\infty \left(2-\frac{r}{a_0}\right)^2 \exp(-r/a_0)\, r\,.\, r^2\, dr \int_0^\pi \sin\theta\, d\theta \int_0^{2\pi} d\varphi$$

$$= \frac{1}{8a_0^3}\int_0^\infty \left(4r^3 - \frac{4r^4}{a_0} + \frac{r^5}{a_0^2}\right)\exp(-r/a_0)\, dr$$

$$= \frac{1}{8a_0^3}\left[\frac{4\times 3!}{\left(\frac{1}{a_0}\right)^4} - \frac{4\times 4!}{a_0\left(\frac{1}{a_0}\right)^5} + \frac{5!}{a_0^2\left(\frac{1}{a_0}\right)^6}\right]$$

$= 6a_0$].

7.25 Calculate the average distance of the electron in the $2p_z$ state from the nucleus of an H-atom.

[Hint: $$\bar{r} = \frac{1}{32\pi a_0^5}\int_0^\infty \left(r\exp(-r/2a_0)\right)^2 r\,.\, r^2\, dr \int_0^\pi \cos^2\theta \sin\theta\, d\theta \int_0^{2\pi} d\varphi$$

$$= \frac{4\pi}{3\times 32\pi a_0^5}\int_0^\infty r^5 \exp(-r/a_0)\, dr$$

$$\left(\because \int_0^\pi \cos^2\theta \sin\theta\, d\theta = -\left[\frac{\cos^3\theta}{3}\right]_0^\pi = \frac{2}{3}, \text{ see Appendix 5}\right)$$

$$= \frac{1}{24a_0^5}\frac{5!}{\left(\frac{1}{a_0}\right)^6} = 5a_0 \; i.e., 5 \text{ a.u.}$$]

7.26 Calculate $\bar{r}$ and r_m for He^+ (1*s* state) and comment.

[Hint: $$\bar{r} = \frac{3a_0}{2Z};\; r_m = \frac{a_0}{z} = \frac{1}{2}a_0$$

This shows that size of the orbital decreases with Z.

7.27 Calculate the average value of $\bar{x}$ for the 1s electron in H-atom. Is it the same as $\bar{r}$? Explain.

[**Hint:** $$\bar{x} = \int 1s\, x\, 1s\, d\tau$$

$$= \frac{1}{\pi}\int_0^{\infty}\int_0^{\pi}\int_0^{2\pi} e^{-r}\,(r\sin\theta\cos\varphi)\,e^{-r}\,r^2\,dr\,\sin\theta\,d\theta\,d\varphi$$

$$= \frac{1}{\pi}\int r^3 e^{-2r}\,dr\int_0^{\pi}\sin^2\theta\,d\theta\int_0^{2\pi}\cos\varphi\,d\varphi$$

$$= 0\left(\text{because}\int_0^{2\pi}\cos\varphi\,d\varphi = 0\right)$$

But $$\bar{r} = \frac{3}{2}a_0 \text{ i.e., } \bar{x} \neq \bar{r}$$

Because ψ and ψ^2 are spherically symmetrical, there is equal chance of the electron being found at $+x$ and $-x$ distances from the nucleus leading to $\bar{x} = 0$].

7.28 Calculate the average value of $1/r$ for the 1s, and 2p orbitals of an H-atom and obtain the average potential energy. What is the average kinetic energy ? Show that $\left(\overline{\frac{1}{r}}\right) \neq \frac{1}{\bar{r}}$.

[**Hint:** $$\left(\overline{\frac{1}{r}}\right) = \int \psi_{1s}\left(\frac{1}{r}\right)\psi_{1s}\,d\tau$$

$$= \frac{1}{\pi}\int_0^{\infty} e^{-2r}\,r\,dr\int_0^{\pi}\sin\theta\,d\theta\int_0^{2\pi}d\varphi \text{ (in a.u.)}$$

$$= \frac{4\pi}{\pi}\times\frac{1}{2^2} = 1.0$$

$$\text{P.E.} = -\frac{Ze^2}{r} = -1.0 \text{ a.u. for H-atom}$$

$$\text{K.E.} = \text{E} - \text{P.E.} = -\frac{1}{2} - (-1) = +\frac{1}{2} \text{ a.u.}$$

$$\bar{r} = \frac{3}{2} \text{ a.u.; therefore, } \frac{1}{\bar{r}} = \frac{2}{3} \text{ a.u.} \neq \left(\overline{\frac{1}{r}}\right)\Bigg].$$

Part III

Atomic Structure

CHAPTER 8

Approximation Methods

Exact solution of Schrödinger equation is possible in simple one-electron systems only. Even in one-electron atom the solution is obtained after lengthy mathematical manipulations, the difficulty being caused mainly by the presence of a single potential energy term like $-Ze^2/r$. If an atom or molecule has many electrons, interacting with one another, the solution becomes rather impossible because of many potential energy terms. In such cases one has to be contented with approximate values of energies and wave functions.

There are several methods of finding approximate solutions; the most popular are: (a) Method of variation, (b) Method of perturbation.

8.1 METHOD OF VARIATION

In this method a suitable trial function is chosen and is assumed to be the solution of the Schrödinger equation. Using this function, the expectation value of energy of the system in question is calculated by postulate III of quantum mechanics (given in Chapter 3). The principle of variation says that with any trial function ψ the expectation value of energy $\bar{E}$ will be greater than the true value E_0, which is the lowest energy eigenvalue of the Hamiltonian of the system, *i.e.*,

$$E \geq E_0 \quad \text{... (8.1)}$$

The proof for this is based on the following two ideas:

(*i*) Even if the wave function ψ is not an eigenfunction of the Schrödinger equation, it can be expressed as a linear combination of a complete set of normalised and orthogonal eigenfunctions $\phi_1, \phi_2, \phi_3, \ldots$ of the same system with eigenvalues $E_1, E_2, E_3, \ldots$, respectively; that is,

$$\psi = a_1 \phi_1 + a_2 \phi_2 + a_3 \phi_3 + \ldots \quad \text{... (8.2)}$$

and $$\hat{H}\phi_i = E_i \phi_i, \; i = 1, 2, 3, \ldots \quad \text{... (8.3)}$$

Values of the coefficients $a_1, a_2, a_3, \ldots$ are so chosen that the function is normalised. This means that

$$\int \psi^2 \, d\tau = \int [a_1 \phi_1 + a_2 \phi_2 + \ldots]^2 \, d\tau = 1 \quad \text{... (8.4)}$$

or $\left[a_1^2\int\phi_1^2\,d\tau + a_2^2\int\phi_2^2\,d\tau + a_3^2\int\phi_3^2\,d\tau + \ldots\right] + \left[a_1 a_2\int\phi_1\phi_2\,d\tau + a_1 a_3\int\phi_1\phi_3\,d\tau + \ldots + a_2 a_3\int\phi_2\phi_3\,d\tau + \ldots\right] = 1,$ ... (8.5)

or $a_1^2 + a_2^2 + a_3^2 + \ldots = 1$ ... (8.6)

since by definition the ϕ_i's are all normalised and orthogonal.

(*ii*) The energy associated with the linear combination function of the type Equation (8.2) is the weighted average $(\bar{E})$ of the energy eigenvalues of Equation (8.3), $\bar{E}$ is calculated by formula (8.7).

$$\bar{E} = \frac{\int\psi^*\hat{H}\psi\,d\tau}{\int\psi^*\psi\,d\tau} \quad \ldots (8.7)$$

(see postulates of quantum mechanics, Chapter 3).
For example, suppose

$$\psi = a_1\phi_1 + a_2\phi_2 \quad \ldots (8.8)$$

where, a_1 and a_2 are the coefficients introduced to normalise the ψ function. Then,

$$\bar{E} = \frac{\int(a_1\phi_1 + a_2\phi_2)\hat{H}(a_1\phi_1 + a_2\phi_2)\,d\tau}{\int(a_1\phi_1 + a_2\phi_2)^2\,d\tau} \;.\; (\psi \text{ being real})$$

$$= \frac{\int a_1^2\phi_1\hat{H}\phi_1\,d\tau + \int a_2^2\phi_2\hat{H}\phi_2\,d\tau + \int a_1a_2\phi_1\hat{H}\phi_2\,d\tau + \int a_2a_1\phi_2\hat{H}\phi_1\,d\tau}{\int a_1^2\phi_1^2\,d\tau + \int a_2^2\phi_2^2\,d\tau + \int 2a_1a_2\phi_1\phi_2\,d\tau} \quad \ldots (8.9)$$

Since ϕ_1 and ϕ_2 are normalised and orthogonal eigenfunctions of $\hat{H}$.

$$\hat{H}\phi_1 = E_1\phi_1 \text{ and } \hat{H}\phi_2 = E_2\phi_2,$$

$$\int\phi_1^2\,d\tau = \int\phi_2^2\,d\tau = 1 \text{ and } \int\phi_1\phi_2\,d\tau = 0$$

Also, $\int\varphi_1\hat{H}\varphi_2\,d\tau = \int\varphi_1 E\varphi_2\,d\tau = E\int\varphi_1\varphi_2\,d\tau = 0$

Equation (8.9) becomes,

$$\bar{E} = \frac{a_1^2 E_1 + a_2^2 E_2}{a_1^2 + a_2^2} = a_1^2 E_1 + a_2^2 E_2 \text{ (in view of Eqn. (8.6))} \quad \ldots (8.10)$$

If E_0 be the lowest energy then it is easy to show that $\bar{E}$ will be always greater than E_0,

$$\bar{E} - E_0 = \left(a_1^2 E_1 + a_2^2 E_2\right) - \left(a_1^2 + a_2^2\right)E_0$$

$$= a_1^2 (E_1 - E_0) + a_2^2 (E_2 - E_0) \quad ...(8.11)$$

Since E_0 is the lowest energy of the system, $E_1 > E_0$ and $E_2 > E_0$, while a_1^2 and a_2^2 are always positive; hence $\bar{E} - E_0$ is always positive, or $\bar{E} > E_0$.

$\bar{E}$ could utmost be equal to E_0; in that case each term in the numerator must vanish. This would mean that for each term either a_i^2, and hence a_i, would be zero or $E_i = E_0$ (i = 1 or 2). This in turn would mean that the only eigenfunction appearing in Equation (8.8) would be that whose eigenvalue is E_0. In other words, ψ would be an exact eigenfunction with eigenvalue E_0.

The physical significance of Equation (8.10) may be shown as follows. If the energy of the system is measured at any instant, it will be either of the two eigenvalues E_1 and E_2 with the probabilities a_1^2 and a_2^2, respectively, and the weighted average $\bar{E}$ will be given by Equation (8.10).

[**Exercise:** Given the trial function,

$$\psi = \frac{1}{\sqrt{3}} \phi_1 + \sqrt{\frac{2}{3}} \phi_2$$

where, ϕ_1 and ϕ_2 are orthonormal, find the expression for the weighted average of the energy in terms of the eigenvalues.

$$\bar{E} = \left(\frac{1}{\sqrt{3}}\right)^2 E_1 + \left(\sqrt{\frac{2}{3}}\right)^2 E_2 = \frac{1}{3} E_1 + \frac{2}{3} E_2 \Bigg]$$

Thus, in order to apply the variation method, the following steps have to be taken:

(*i*) Make a reasonable guess of a series of trial functions (on the basis of some physical and/or chemical consideration); the function must be well-behaved.

(*ii*) Calculate $\bar{E}$ in each case.

(*iii*) The value of $\bar{E}$ will always be greater than that of $\bar{E}_0$. Pick up the lowest value that would be closest to the true value E_0. The trial function corresponding to that value of $\bar{E}$ will be the best function.

Consider, for example, the wave function for particle in a box system. The true ground state wave function (ψ_0) and energy (E_0) are known to us; however, let us assume that we do not know these and proceed to devise a trial function.

For a one-dimensional box of length L, a reasonable guess would be

$$\psi = Nx (L - x) \quad ...(8.12)$$

as it is finite, continuous and single-valued for all values of x and is zero for $x = 0$ and $x = L$; N is the normalisation factor. Then we calculate the energy,

$$\bar{E} = \frac{\int \psi \hat{H} \psi \, d\tau}{\int \psi^2 \, d\tau} = \frac{\int_0^L Nx(L-x) \left[-\frac{h^2}{8\pi^2 m} \frac{d^2}{dx^2} [Nx(L-x)] \, dx \right]}{\int_0^L N^2 x^2 (L-x)^2 \, dx} \quad ...(8.13)$$

$$= \frac{\frac{h^2}{4\pi^2 m}\int_0^L x(L-x)\,dx}{\int_0^L x^2\left(L^2 - 2Lx + x^2\right)dx}$$

$$= \frac{\frac{h^2}{4\pi^2 m}\cdot\frac{L^3}{6}}{\frac{L^5}{30}} = \frac{5h^2}{4\pi^2 mL^2} = 0.12665\left(\frac{h^2}{mL^2}\right) \qquad \text{... (8.14)}$$

The true ground state energy E is known to us to be,

$$\bar{E} = \frac{h^2}{8mL^2} = 0.125\left(\frac{h^2}{mL^2}\right) \qquad \text{... (8.15)}$$

The calculated energy $\bar{E}$, given by the trial function (8.14) is greater than the true energy (E) vide Equation (8.15) by 1.3%.

In real problems, however, the exact energy may not be known. All that the variation calculation would say is that the exact value is lower than the calculated value. The usual practice is (*i*) to choose a trial function containing one or more variable parameters α, β, etc., then (*ii*) to calculate the energy $\bar{E}$, which will turn out to be a function of α, β, etc., and (*iii*) finally to minimise the $\bar{E}$ with respect to these parameters, *i.e.*, to set the differential coefficients

$$\frac{\partial \bar{E}}{\partial \alpha} = \frac{\partial \bar{E}}{\partial \beta} = \ldots = 0. \qquad \text{... (8.16)}$$

8.1.1 Linear and Non-Linear Variation Functions

If the trial function contains the variable parameters α, β, ... as such, it is linear, *e.g.*,

$$\psi = \alpha\,\phi_1 + \beta\,\phi_2 + \ldots \qquad \text{... (8.17)}$$

If, on the other hand, the variable parameters appear as α^2 or exp (– α) or sin α, etc., the function is non-linear.

8.1.1.1 Non-Linear Variation Functions

As an example, let us consider a harmonic oscillator. We know the exact expressions for its ground state wave function (ψ_0) and energy (E_0) (see Chapter 5); but suppose again that we do not know them and proceed to devise a trial function.

The Schrödinger equation for such a system is,

$$\frac{d^2\psi}{dx^2} + \frac{8\pi^2 m}{h^3}\left(E - \frac{1}{2}kx^2\right)\psi = 0 \qquad \text{... (8.18)}$$

For large values of x, E << $\frac{1}{2}kx^2$; therefore,

$$\frac{d^2\psi}{dx^2} - \frac{4\pi^2 mk}{h^2}x^2\psi = 0$$

or
$$\frac{d^2\psi}{dx^2} = (\text{a constant})\, x^2\psi \qquad \text{... (8.19)}$$

Now we argue as follows. For $x \to \pm\infty$, ψ should tend to zero. The function of the type exp $(-x)$ will not do because for $x \to -\infty$, it will be infinite, but the function exp $(-x^2)$ will behave well. So, a trial function, without normalisation factor, may be written as,

$$\psi = \exp(-\beta x^2) \qquad \text{... (8.20)}$$

where β is a variable parameter. The next step is to calculate $\overline{E}$ using Equation (8.7).

$$\overline{E} = \frac{\int_{-\infty}^{\infty} \exp(-\beta x^2)\left[-\frac{h^2}{8\pi^2 m}\frac{d^2}{dx^2} + \frac{1}{2}kx^2\right]\exp(-\beta x^2)dx}{\int_{-\infty}^{\infty}\exp(-2\beta x^2)dx} \qquad \text{... (8.21)}$$

In Equation (8.21), the numerator (N) is,

$$N = \int_{-\infty}^{\infty} \exp(-\beta x^2)\left[\left(-\frac{h^2}{8\pi^2 m}\right)\left(4\beta^2 x^2 \exp(-\beta x^2)\right)\right.$$

$$\left. -\left(\frac{h^2}{8\pi^2 m}\right)\left(-2\beta \exp(-\beta x^2)\right) + \frac{1}{2}kx^2 \exp(-\beta x^2)\right]dx$$

$$= \int_{-\infty}^{\infty}\left[\frac{h^2}{4\pi^2 m}\beta - \frac{h^2}{2\pi^2 m}\beta^2 x^2 + \frac{1}{2}kx^2\right]\exp(-2\beta x^2)dx$$

Using the table of integrals (Appendix 5), we obtain

$$N = \frac{h^2\beta}{4\pi^2 m}\left(\frac{\pi}{2\beta}\right)^{1/2} - \frac{h^2\beta}{8\pi^2 m}\left(\frac{\pi}{2\beta}\right)^{1/2} + \frac{k}{8\beta}\left(\frac{\pi}{2\beta}\right)^{1/2}$$

The denominator (D) is given by,

$$D = \int_{-\infty}^{\infty}\exp(-2\beta x^2)dx = \left(\frac{\pi}{2\beta}\right)^{1/2}$$

Therefore
$$\overline{E} = \frac{N}{D} = \frac{h^2\beta}{4\pi^2 m} - \frac{h^2\beta}{8\pi^2 m} + \frac{k}{8\beta}$$

$$= \frac{h^2 \beta}{8\pi^2 m} + \frac{k}{8\beta} \qquad \text{... (8.22)}$$

According to the variation method we have to set

$$\frac{d\overline{E}}{d\beta} = \frac{h^2}{8\pi^2 m} - \frac{k}{8\beta^2} = 0$$

or

$$\beta = \frac{\pi (mk)^{1/2}}{h} \qquad \text{... (8.23)}$$

Hence, the trial function (8.20) becomes

$$\psi = \exp\left(-\left[\frac{\pi (mk)^{1/2}}{h} \right] x^2 \right) \qquad \text{... (8.24)}$$

and

$$\overline{E} = \frac{h^2 \pi (mk)^{1/2}}{8\pi^2 mh} + \frac{kh}{8\pi^2 (mk)^{1/2}}$$

$$= \frac{h}{4\pi}\left(\frac{k}{m}\right)^{1/2} \qquad \text{... (8.25)}$$

The functions ψ and $\overline{E}$ turn out to be exactly the same as the true ground state values of ψ_0 and E_0 found by actually solving the Schrödinger equation. If, instead of this, we had used another trial function we would have found a value of $\overline{E}$ greater than E_0.

8.1.1.2 Linear Variation Functions

In chemical problems linear variation functions are more common. A trial function of the type,

$$\psi = a_1 \phi_1 + a_2 \phi_2 \qquad \text{... (8.26)}$$

in which ϕ_1 and ϕ_2 are the orthonormal eigenfunctions, called basis functions, and a_1 and a_2 are the variable parameters also called the mixing coefficients, is a linear variation function. With such a function, it is required to find out the values of a_1 and a_2 that would minimise $\overline{E}$ so that Equation (8.26) would turn out to be the best approximation to the exact wave function ψ_0.

Following the same procedure of variation, we get

$$\overline{E} = \frac{\int (a_1 \phi_1 + a_2 \phi_2)\, \hat{H}\, (a_1 \phi_1 + a_2 \phi_2)\, d\tau}{\int (a_1 \phi_1 + a_2 \phi_2)^2\, d\tau} \qquad \text{... (8.27)}$$

where ψ is assumed to be real. On expanding, the Equation (8.27) will assume the form,

$$\overline{E} = \frac{a_1^2 H_{11} + a_2^2 H_{22} + 2a_1 a_2 H_{12}}{a_1^2 S_{11} + a_2^2 S_{22} + 2a_1 a_2 S_{12}} \qquad \text{... (8.28)}$$

where

$$H_{11} = \int \phi_1 \hat{H} \phi_1\, d\tau, \quad H_{22} = \int \phi_2 \hat{H} \phi_2\, d\tau$$

$$H_{12} = \int \phi_1 \hat{H} \phi_2\, d\tau, \quad H_{21} = \int \phi_2 \hat{H} \phi_1\, d\tau = H_{21} \text{ [because } \hat{H} \text{ is Hermitian]}$$

$$S_{11} = \int \phi_1 \phi_1 \, d\tau, \quad S_{22} = \int \phi_2 \phi_2 \, d\tau$$

and
$$S_{12} = \int \phi_1 \phi_2 \, d\tau, \quad S_{21} = \int \phi_2 \phi_1 \, d\tau$$

For the minimisation of $\bar{E}$, it is necessary that

$$\frac{\partial \bar{E}}{\partial a_1} = \frac{\partial \bar{E}}{\partial a_2} = 0 \qquad \text{... (8.29)}$$

Using N and D for the numerator and denominator respectively, in Equation (8.28), we get

$$\bar{E} = \frac{N}{D} = ND^{-1} \qquad \text{... (8.30)}$$

Differentiating Equation (8.30) with respect to a_1 and a_2 and using Equation (8.29), we get

$$\frac{\partial \bar{E}}{\partial a_1} = \left(\frac{\partial N}{\partial a_1} - \frac{\partial D}{\partial a_1} \frac{N}{D} \right) \frac{1}{D} = 0$$

$$\frac{\partial \bar{E}}{\partial a_2} = \left(\frac{\partial N}{\partial a_2} - \frac{\partial D}{\partial a_2} \frac{N}{D} \right) \frac{1}{D} = 0 \qquad \text{... (8.31)}$$

Since $1/D$ cannot be zero (as that would make D *i.e.*, $\int \psi^2 \, d\tau$ infinite)

$$\frac{\partial N}{\partial a_1} - \frac{\partial D}{\partial a_1} \frac{N}{D} = 0$$

and
$$\frac{\partial N}{\partial a_2} - \frac{\partial D}{\partial a_2} \frac{N}{D} = 0 \qquad \text{... (8.32)}$$

$$\left.\begin{aligned} \frac{\partial N}{\partial a_1} &= 2a_1 H_{11} + 2a_2 H_{12}\,; \\ \frac{\partial N}{\partial a_2} &= 2a_1 H_{12} + 2a_2 H_{12} \end{aligned}\right\}$$

$$\frac{\partial D}{\partial a_1} = 2a_1 S_{11} + 2a_2 S_{12}$$

$$\frac{\partial D}{\partial a_2} = 2a_1 S_{12} + 2a_2 S_{22} \qquad \text{... (8.33)}$$

Substituting the set of Equations (8.33) in the set (8.32), we obtain a set of two homogeneous linear algebraic equations, which are also called "secular equations",

$$a_1 \left(H_{11} - \bar{E}S_{11} \right) + a_2 \left(H_{12} - \bar{E}S_{12} \right) = 0$$

$$a_1 \left(H_{21} - \bar{E}S_{21} \right) + a_2 \left(H_{22} - \bar{E}S_{22} \right) = 0 \qquad \text{... (8.34)}$$

The secular Equations (8.34) have nontrivial solution (*i.e.*, when the coefficients a_1 and a_2 are not zero) only if the determinant of the coefficients of a_1 and a_2 is zero *i.e.*,

$$\begin{vmatrix} H_{11} - \bar{E}S_{11} & H_{12} - \bar{E}S_{12} \\ H_{21} - \bar{E}S_{21} & H_{22} - \bar{E}S_{22} \end{vmatrix} = 0 \qquad \text{... (8.35)}$$

Such a determinant is called secular determinant. Being a determinantal equation of second order, Equation (8.35) will have two roots for $\bar{E}$ viz., E_1 and E_2. The lower of the two values will be the minimum energy corresponding to the trial function (8.26).

To obtain the coefficients a_1 and a_2, the values of E_1 as well as the integrals H_{11}, H_{22}, H_{12}, S_{11}, S_{22} and S_{12} have to be substituted in Equation (8.34). However, these substitutions will lead to only relative values, *i.e.*, a_1 in terms of a_2 or vice-versa. The absolute values may then be obtained from the condition of normalisation, *i.e.*,

$$\int (a_1\phi_1 + a_2\phi_2)^2\, d\tau = a_1^2 \int \phi_1^2\, d\tau + a_2^2 \int \phi_2^2\, d\tau + 2a_1 a_2 \int \phi_1 \phi_2\, d\tau = 1$$

or

$$a_1^2 + a_2^2 = \quad = 1 \qquad = 1 \qquad = 0 \qquad \text{... (8.36)}$$

A linear variation function may consist of several basis eigenfunctions. For the genreal case,

$$\psi = a_1\,\phi_1 + a_2\,\phi_2 + \ldots + a_n\,\phi_n, \qquad \text{... (8.37)}$$

the variation integral Equation (8.7), and the principle of minimisation of $\bar{E}$, *i.e.*,

$$\frac{\partial \bar{E}}{\partial a_1} = \frac{\partial \bar{E}}{\partial a_2} = \ldots = \frac{\partial \bar{E}}{\partial a_n} = 0$$

will lead to a set of n secular equations,

$$a_1\left(H_{11} - \bar{E}S_{11}\right) + a_2\left(H_{12} - \bar{E}S_{12}\right) + \ldots + a_n\left(H_{1n} - \bar{E}S_{1n}\right) = 0$$

$$a_1\left(H_{n1} - \bar{E}S_{n1}\right) + a_2\left(H_{n2} - \bar{E}S_{n2}\right) + \ldots + a_n\left(H_{nn} - \bar{E}S_{nn}\right) = 0 \qquad \text{... (8.38)}$$

and so on and the secular determinant of nth order,

$$\begin{vmatrix} H_{11} - \bar{E}S_{11} & H_{12} - \bar{E}S_{12} \ldots H_{1n} - \bar{E}S_{1n} \\ H_{21} - \bar{E}S_{21} & H_{22} - \bar{E}S_{22} \ldots H_{2n} - \bar{E}S_{2n} \\ \cdots\cdots & \cdots\cdots \\ \cdots\cdots & \cdots\cdots \\ H_{n1} - \bar{E}S_{n1} & H_{n2} - \bar{E}S_{n2} \ldots H_{nn} - \bar{E}S_{nn} \end{vmatrix} = 0 \qquad \text{... (8.39)}$$

Equation (8.39) will have n-roots of $\bar{E}$, viz., E_1, E_2, E_3, ..., E_n.

Specific examples of linear variation function will be found in connection with theories of chemical bonding in later chapters.

8.1.2 Matrix Formulation of the Linear Variation

The Equation (8.38) can be conveniently put in matrix form (8.40)

$$\begin{bmatrix} H_{11} - ES_{11} & H_{12} - ES_{12} & \ldots & H_{1n} - ES_{1n} \\ H_{21} - ES_{21} & H_{22} - ES_{22} & \ldots & H_{2n} - ES_{2n} \\ \vdots & \vdots & & \vdots \\ H_{n1} - ES_{n1} & H_{n2} - ES_{n2} & \ldots & H_{nn} - ES_{nn} \end{bmatrix} \begin{pmatrix} a_1 \\ a_2 \\ \vdots \\ a_n \end{pmatrix} = \begin{pmatrix} 0 \\ 0 \\ \vdots \\ 0 \end{pmatrix} \qquad \text{... (8.40)}$$

The $n \times n$ matrix on the left of the Equation (8.40) is clearly seen to be a difference of two matrices. This enables one to rewrite the Equation (8.40), after rearrangement as

$$\begin{bmatrix} H_{11} & H_{12} & \cdots & H_{1n} \\ H_{21} & H_{22} & \cdots & H_{2n} \\ \vdots & \vdots & & \vdots \\ H_{n1} & H_{n2} & \cdots & H_{nn} \end{bmatrix} \begin{pmatrix} a_1 \\ a_2 \\ \vdots \\ a_n \end{pmatrix} = E \begin{bmatrix} S_{11} & S_{12} & \cdots & S_{1n} \\ S_{21} & S_{22} & \cdots & S_{2n} \\ \vdots & \vdots & & \vdots \\ S_{n1} & S_{n2} & \cdots & S_{nn} \end{bmatrix} \begin{pmatrix} a_1 \\ a_2 \\ \vdots \\ a_n \end{pmatrix} \quad \text{...(8.41)}$$

or in a compact form

$$[H]\, \vec{a}_i = E_i\, [S]\, \vec{a}_i \quad \text{...(8.42)}$$

where, E_i has a set of n values (all scalar quantities) and each E_i value has its own characteristic set of coefficients, a column vector $\vec{a}_i$, the eigenvector and hence there will be n such separate matrix—eigenvector equations. All these can be reduced to a single matrix equation by stacking the n eigenvectors together, side by side, to produce another $n \times n$ matrix [A]. The numbers E_i must also be combined into an appropriate matrix which can be only a diagonal matrix, also called matrix of eigenvalues; [A] is then called matrix of eigenvectors. Each eigenvector corresponds to a wave function of the Schrödinger equation. The matrix equation becomes

$$\begin{bmatrix} H_{11} & H_{12} & \cdots & H_{1n} \\ H_{21} & H_{22} & \cdots & H_{2n} \\ \vdots & \vdots & & \vdots \\ H_{n1} & H_{n2} & \cdots & H_{nn} \end{bmatrix} \begin{bmatrix} a_{11} & a_{12} & \cdots & a_{1n} \\ a_{21} & a_{22} & \cdots & a_{2n} \\ \vdots & \vdots & & \vdots \\ a_{n1} & a_{n2} & \cdots & a_{nn} \end{bmatrix} = \begin{bmatrix} E_1 & 0 & 0 & 0 & 0 & \cdots & 0 \\ 0 & E_2 & 0 & 0 & 0 & \cdots & 0 \\ 0 & 0 & E_3 & 0 & 0 & \cdots & 0 \\ \vdots & \vdots & \vdots & \vdots & \vdots & & \vdots \\ 0 & 0 & 0 & 0 & 0 & \cdots & E_n \end{bmatrix}$$

$$\begin{bmatrix} S_{11} & S_{12} & \cdots & S_{1n} \\ S_{21} & S_{22} & \cdots & S_{2n} \\ \vdots & \vdots & & \vdots \\ S_{n1} & S_{n2} & \cdots & S_{nn} \end{bmatrix} \begin{bmatrix} a_{11} & a_{12} & \cdots & a_{1n} \\ a_{21} & a_{22} & \cdots & a_{2n} \\ \vdots & \vdots & & \vdots \\ a_{n1} & a_{n2} & \cdots & a_{nn} \end{bmatrix}$$

or in the compact form

$$[H]\,[A] = [E]\,[S]\,[A] = [S]\,[A]\,[E] \quad \text{...(8.43)}$$

as [E] is a matrix of eigenvalues (scalars). The matrices are constructed in such a manner that each eigenvalue E_i multiplies only the $\vec{a}_i$ vector in the column i of [A]. Further, the order of the matrices in the Equation (8.42) cannot be altered at will as the matrices are not necessarily commutative with the exception of the matrix [E].

8.2 METHOD OF PERTURBATION

Perturbation method is applied if the system differs only slightly from the unperturbed one and if the energy (E^0) and the wave function (ψ^0) for the unperturbed state are known. For example, a simple harmonic oscillator is an unperturbed system whose Hamiltonian is known to be,

$$\hat{H} = -\frac{h^2}{8\pi^2 m}\frac{d^2}{dx^2} + \frac{1}{2}kx^2$$

On the other hand, an anharmonic oscillator is a perturbed system. If the Hamiltonian for the latter be

$$\hat{H} = -\frac{h^2}{8\pi^2 m}\frac{d^2}{dx^2} + \frac{1}{2}kx^2 + ax^3 + bx^4$$

then, provided a and b are small, the term $(ax^3 + bx^4)$ constitutes a small perturbation ($\hat{H}'$, say). The wave functions and the energies for the former are known (see Chapter 5), Similarly, a normal hydrogen atom is an unpertubed system for which the $\hat{H}^0$, ψ^0 and E^0 are known for each state (see Chapter 7). When placed in an electric or magnetic field, the interaction of the electron with the field causes perturbation.

The perturbation theory, therefore, involves determination of the eigenfunctions (ψ_n) and eigenvalues (E_n) of the perturbed Hamiltonian $\hat{H}$ in terms of those $\left(\psi_0^n \text{ and } E_n^0\right)$ of the unperturbed Hamiltonian $\hat{H}^0$. The perturbed Hamiltonian is given by

$$\hat{H} = \hat{H}^0 + \lambda\hat{H}' \quad \text{... (8.44)}$$

where, $\lambda\hat{H}'$ is very small. It is not always possible to identify λ with a physical quantity.

Exercise: Write the Hamiltonian for a helium atom and identify the perturbation term, if any.

$$\hat{H} = \left[-\frac{h^2}{8\pi^2 m}\left[\hat{\nabla}_1^2 + \hat{\nabla}_2^2\right] - \frac{e^2}{r_1} - \frac{e^2}{r_2}\right] + \frac{e^2}{r_{12}}$$

where, r_1 and r_2 are the distances of the electrons 1 and 2 from the nucleus. The expression within [ ] is $\hat{H}^0$ and $\lambda\hat{H}' = \frac{e^2}{r_{12}}$ where r_{12} is the inter-electronic distance.

8.2.1 The Perturbation Theory

The method is to calculate the correction terms for the eigenfunctions and eigenvalues and add them up to those for the unperturbed system. Expressions for the correction terms are derived as follows:

The Schrödinger equations for the unperturbed and perturbed systems are written as

$$\hat{H}^0\psi_n^0 = E_n^0\psi_n^0 \quad \text{... (8.45)}$$

and

$$\hat{H}\psi_n = E_n\psi_n \quad \text{... (8.46)}$$

or

$$\left(\hat{H}^0 + \lambda\hat{H}'\right)\psi_n = E_n\psi_n \quad \text{... (8.47)}$$

where, the subscript n denotes the state of the system. As $\hat{H}$ depends on λ, both ψ_n and E_n will depend on λ. So, as a first step, we expand these functions as Taylor series assuming that $\lambda\hat{H}' << \hat{H}$

$$\psi_n = \psi_n^0 + \lambda\,\psi_n^{(1)} + \lambda^2\,\psi_n^{(2)} + \ldots \qquad \ldots (8.48)$$

$$E_n = E_n^0 + \lambda\,E_n^{(1)} + \lambda^2\,E_n^{(2)} + \ldots \qquad \ldots (8.49)$$

where, $\psi_n^{(k)}$ and $E_n^{(k)}$ are the kth order correction terms to the ψ_n^0 and E_n^0, respectively.

In most of the chemistry problems, one has not to go beyond the terms $\psi_n^{(2)}$ and $E_n^{(2)}$. Substituting Equations (8.48) and (8.49) in Equation (8.47), we get

$$\left(H^0 + \lambda\hat{H}'\right)\left(\psi_n^0 + \lambda\,\psi_n^{(1)} + \lambda^2\,\psi_n^{(2)} + \ldots\right)$$

$$= \left(E_n^0 + \lambda\,E_n^{(1)} + \lambda^2\,E_n^{(2)} + \ldots\right)\left(\psi_n^0 + \lambda\,\psi_n^{(1)} + \lambda^2\,\psi_n^{(2)} + \ldots\right) \qquad \ldots (8.50)$$

On rearranging the terms in Equation (8.50) according to powers of λ, we get

$$\left(\hat{H}^0\,\psi_n^0 - E_n^0\,\psi_n^0\right) + \lambda\left(\hat{H}^0\,\psi_n^{(1)} + \hat{H}'\,\psi_n^0 - E_n^0\,\psi_n^{(1)} - E_n^{(1)}\,\psi_n^0\right)$$

$$+ \lambda^2\left(\hat{H}^0\,\psi_n^{(2)} + \hat{H}'\,\psi_n^{(1)} - E_n^0\,\psi_n^{(2)} - E_n^{(1)}\,\psi_n^{(1)} - E_n^{(2)}\,\psi_n^0\right) = 0 \qquad \ldots (8.51)$$

The equation holds if the coefficient of each power of λ is zero individually, *i.e.,*

for $$\lambda^0 : \hat{H}^0\,\psi_n^0 = E_n^0\,\psi_n^0 \qquad \ldots (8.52)$$

for $$\lambda^1 : \left(\hat{H}^0 - E_n^0\right)\psi_n^{(1)} = -\,\hat{H}'\,\psi_n^0 + E_n^{(1)}\,\psi_n^0 \qquad \ldots (8.53)$$

for $$\lambda^2 : \left(\hat{H}^0 - E_n^0\right)\psi_n^{(2)} = -\,\hat{H}'\,\psi_n^{(1)} + E_n^{(1)}\,\psi_n^{(1)} + E_n^{(2)}\,\psi_n^0 \qquad \ldots (8.54)$$

and so on for $\lambda^3, \lambda^4, \ldots$

The Equation (8.52) is the Schrödinger equation for the unperturbed system whose solutions are supposed to be known. Equations (8.53) and (8.54) provide first order and second order corrections to the unperturbed wave function ψ_n^0 and energy E_n^0. These correction terms are obtained as follows:

8.2.1.1 First Order Perturbation

Correction to energy: Multiply the Equation (8.53) by ψ_n^{0*} from the left and integrate. This gives on rearrangement.

$$\int \psi_n^{0*}\,\hat{H}'\,\psi_n^0\,d\tau - E_n^{(1)}\int \psi_n^{0*}\,\psi_n^0\,d\tau + \int \psi_n^{0*}\,\hat{H}^0\,\psi_n^{(1)}\,d\tau - E_n^0\int \psi_n^{0*}\,.\,\psi_n^{(1)}\,d\tau = 0 \qquad \ldots (8.55)$$

Since $\hat{H}^0$ is Hermitian.

$$\int \psi_n^{0*}\,\hat{H}^0\,\psi_n^{(1)}\,d\tau = \int \psi_n^{*(1)}\,\hat{H}_n^0\,\psi_n^0\,d\tau = \int \psi_n^{*(1)}\,E_n^0\,\psi_n^0\,d\tau$$

Therefore, the Equation (8.55) becomes,

$$\int \psi_n^{0*}\,\hat{H}'\,\psi_n^0\,d\tau - E_n^{(1)}\int \psi_n^{0*}\,\psi_n^0\,d\tau = 0$$

or $$E_n^{(1)} = \int \psi_n^{0*}\,\hat{H}'\,\psi_n^0\,d\tau \left(\text{because} \int \psi_n^{0*}\,\psi_n^0\,d\tau = 1\right) \qquad \ldots (8.56)$$

Equation (8.55) is often abbreviated as,

$$E_n^{(1)} = H'_{nn} \qquad \text{... (8.57)}$$

The equation says that the first order correction $E_n^{(1)}$ to the energy, is determined as the expectation value of perturbation operator $\hat{H}'$ using the wave function ψ_n^0 of the unperturbed system.

Correction to wave function: For determining the correction to the wave function ψ_n^0, use is made of a well-known theorem of quantum mechanics that any well-behaved function can be expressed as a linear combination of a complete set of orthonormal eigenfunctions. Hence,

$$\psi_n^{(1)} = a_{1n}\,\psi_1^0 + a_{2n}\,\psi_2^0 + a_{3n}\,\psi_n^0 + \ldots = \sum_m a_{mn}\,\psi_m^0 \qquad \text{... (8.58)}$$

Substituting Equation (8.58) in Equation (8.53), and rearranging, we obtain

$$\left(\hat{H}' - E_n^{(1)}\right)\psi_n^0 + \left(\hat{H}^0 - E_n\right)\sum a_{mn}\,\psi_m^0 = 0 \qquad \text{... (8.59)}$$

Multiplying Equation (8.59) from the left by another function ψ_l^0 and integrating, we get

$$\int \psi_l^0\,\hat{H}'\,\psi_n^0\,d\tau - E_n^{(1)}\int \psi_l^0\,\psi_n^0\,d\tau + \sum a_{mn}\left[\int \psi_l^0\,\hat{H}^0\,\psi_m^0\,d\tau - E_n^0\int \psi_l^0\,\psi_m^0\,d\tau\right] \qquad \text{... (8.60)}$$

Now we make use of the facts that (*i*) $\hat{H}^0\,\psi_m^0 = E_m^0\,\psi_m^0$, and (*ii*) the eigenfunctions ψ_l^0, ψ_m^0 and ψ_n^0 are orthonormal. For $l = n$, Equation (8.60) reduces to Equation (8.56) and for $l \neq n$, all terms in the summation vanish except those with $m = l$. Therefore,

$$\int \psi_l^0\hat{H}'\psi_n^0\,d\tau + a_{ln}\left[\int \psi_l^0\hat{H}^0\psi_l^0\,d\tau - E_n^0\int \psi_l^0\psi_l^0\,d\tau\right] = 0$$

or

$$\int \psi_l^0\,\hat{H}'\,\psi_n^0\,d\tau + a_{ln}\left(E_l^0 - E_n^0\right) = 0 \qquad \text{... (8.61)}$$

$$\text{Therefore, } a_{ln} = a_{mn} = -\frac{\int \psi_l^0\hat{H}'\psi_n^0\,d\tau}{E_l^0 - E_n^0} = \frac{\int \psi_m^0\hat{H}'\psi_n^0\,d\tau}{E_n^0 - E_m^0},\ m \neq n, \text{ or } \frac{H'_{mn}}{E_n^0 - E_m^0} \qquad \text{... (8.62)}$$

Therefore, from Equation (8.58),

$$\psi_n^{(1)} = \sum_{m \neq n}\left(\frac{\int \psi_m^0\,H'\,\psi_n^0\,d\tau}{E_n^0 - E_m^0}\right)\psi_m^0 = \sum_{m \neq n}\frac{H'_{mn}}{E_n^0 - E_m^0}\,\psi_m^0 \qquad \text{... (8.63)}$$

Equation (8.63) says that the first order correction $\psi_n^{(1)}$ to the wave function can be determined from the eigenfunctions and eigenvalues of the unperturbed system.

As an example of the applicability of the perturbation theory let us consider an electron in a one-dimensional box of length L to which a uniform electric field of strength F is being applied.

In the absence of the field, the Hamiltonian $\left(\hat{H}_0\right)$, the wave functions $\left(\psi_n^0\right)$ and the energies E_n^0 (unperturbed) are known to be,

$$\hat{H}^0 = -\frac{h^2}{8\pi^2 m}\frac{d^2}{dx^2}$$

$$\psi_n^0 = \sqrt{\frac{2}{L}}\sin\frac{n\pi x}{L}$$

$$E_n^0 = \frac{n^2 h^2}{8mL^2}$$

(see Chapter 4).

The electric field perturbs the system and the electron now experiences a force equal to eF. Suppose the potential energy, $V = eF\,x$, rises continuously as we move along the box, *i.e.*, from $V = 0$ at $x = 0$ to $V = eFL$ at $x = L$ (Figure 8.1); then the perturbed Hamiltonian is

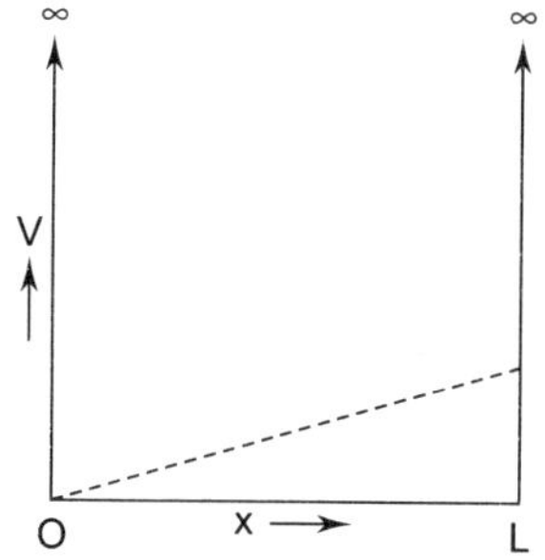

Fig. 8.1

$$\hat{H} = \hat{H}^0 + \hat{H}',$$

$$= -\frac{h^2}{8\pi^2 m}\frac{d^2}{dx^2} + eFx.$$

First order correction to the energy: For the ground state the unperturbed energy is

$$E_1^0 = \frac{h^2}{8mL^2}$$

and the correction,

$$E_1^{(1)} = \int_0^L \psi_1^0 H' \psi_1^0\, d\tau$$

$$= \frac{2}{L}\int_0^L \left[\sin\frac{\pi x}{L}(eFx)\sin\frac{\pi x}{L}\right]dx$$

$$= \frac{2eF}{L}\int_0^L x \sin^2 \frac{\pi x}{L}\, dx$$

Let $\frac{\pi x}{L} = y$ so that $x = \frac{L}{\pi} y$ and $dx = \frac{L}{\pi} dy$. Since for $x = 0$, $y = 0$ and for $x = L$, $y = \pi$, the above equation becomes

$$E_1^{(1)} = \frac{2eFL}{\pi^2}\int_0^{\pi} y \sin^2 y\, dy$$

From the table of integrals, $\int_0^{\pi} y \sin^2 y\, dy = \frac{\pi^2}{4}$. Therefore,

$$E_1^{(1)} = \frac{2eFL}{\pi^2}\frac{\pi^2}{4} = \frac{eFL}{2}$$

and $$E_1 = E_1^0 + E_1^{(1)} = \frac{h^2}{8mL^2} + \frac{eFL}{2}.$$

Correction to the wave function: Correction $\psi_1^{(1)}$ to the ground state wave function ψ_1^0 is calculated as follows:

Using Equation (8.63), we get

$$\psi_1^{(1)} = \sum_{m \neq 1} \frac{\int \psi_m^0 \hat{H}' \psi_1^0\, d\tau}{E_1^0 - E_m^0}\psi_m^0$$

$$= \left[\frac{\int \psi_2^0 \hat{H}' \psi_1^0\, d\tau}{E_1^0 - E_2^0}\psi_2^0 + \frac{\int \psi_3^0 \hat{H}' \psi_1^0\, d\tau}{E_1^0 - E_3^0}\psi_3^0 + \frac{\int \psi_4^0 \hat{H}' \psi_1^0\, d\tau}{E_1^0 - E_4^0}\psi_4^0 + \ldots\right]$$

First term within the brackets in the above equation is,

$$\frac{\int \psi_2^0 \hat{H}' \psi_1^0\, d\tau}{E_1^0 - E_2^0}\psi_2^0 = \frac{\int_0^L \sqrt{\frac{2}{L}} \sin \frac{2\pi x}{L} (eFx) \sqrt{\frac{2}{L}} \sin \frac{\pi x}{L}\, dx}{-\left(\frac{3h^2}{8mL^2}\right)}\psi_2^0$$

$$= \frac{\frac{2eF}{L}\int_0^L \sin \frac{2\pi x}{L} \sin \frac{\pi x}{L}\, x\, dx}{-\left(\frac{3h^2}{8mL^2}\right)}\psi_2^0$$

On letting $\frac{\pi x}{L} = y$, so that $x = \frac{L}{\pi} y$ and $dx = \frac{L}{\pi} dy$, the integral in the numerator becomes,

$$= \left(\frac{L}{\pi}\right)^2 \int_0^{\pi} y \sin 2y \sin y \, dy$$

$$= \left(\frac{L}{\pi}\right)^2 \int_0^{\pi} y \sin y \,(2 \sin y \cos y)\, dy$$

$$= \left(\frac{L}{\pi}\right)^2 \int_0^{\pi} 2y \left(1 - \cos^2 y\right) \cos y \, dy$$

$$= 2\left(\frac{L}{\pi}\right)^2 \left[\int_0^{\pi} y \cos y \, dy - \int_0^{\pi} y \cos^3 y \, dy\right]$$

From the table of integrals (Appendix 5)

$$\int_0^{\pi} y \cos y \, dy = \left[\cos y - y \sin y\right]_0^{\pi}, = -2$$

and

$$\int_0^{\pi} y \cos^3 y \, dy = \left[\frac{y \sin 3y}{12} + \frac{\cos 3y}{36} + \frac{3}{4} y \sin y + \frac{3}{4} \cos y\right]_0^{\pi}$$

$$= -\frac{14}{9}$$

Therefore, the above expression is equal to

$$2\left(\frac{L}{\pi}\right)^2 \left[(-2) - \left(-\frac{14}{9}\right)\right] = -\frac{8}{9}\left(\frac{L}{\pi}\right)^2$$

and the earlier term becomes

$$\frac{\left(\frac{2eF}{L}\right) \times \left(-\frac{8}{9}\right)\left(\frac{L}{\pi}\right)^2}{-\left(\frac{3h^2}{8mL^2}\right)} \psi_2^0 = 0.48\,(eFL)\left(\frac{mL^2}{h^2}\right)\psi_2^0$$

The second, third and subsequent terms can likewise be evaluated. It will be found that whereas the second term vanishes, the contribution of the third term, due to the large value of the difference $E_1^0 - E_4^0$, is very small. The perturbed wave function correct to the first order is, therefore,

$$\psi_1 = \psi_1^0 + 0.48\,(eFL)\left(\frac{mL^2}{h^2}\right)\psi_2^0.$$

8.2.1.2 First Order Perturbation for Degenerate States

The foregoing considerations are not enough to be applicable if the concerned energy level E_n^0 is degenerate. Here we have more than one eigenfunction $\psi_{n1}^0, \psi_{n2}^0, \ldots$ and one does not know to which one the perturbed wave function ψ_n will approximate when the perturbation vanishes except that it will approximate to some arbitrary linear combination χ_n^0.

$$\chi_n^0 = a_1 \psi_{n1}^0 + a_2 \psi_{n2}^0 + \ldots \qquad \ldots (8.64)$$

where, a_1, a_2, ... are the arbitrarily chosen mixing coefficients. Hence our problem is given the operator $\hat{H} = \hat{H}^0 + \lambda \hat{H}$, find the eigenvalues E and eigenfunctions ψ in the equation

$$\left(\hat{H}^0 + \lambda \hat{H}'\right) \psi = E \psi \qquad \ldots (8.65)$$

correct to the first order.

It is convenient to take a simple case of 2-fold degenerate level E_n^0 with ψ_{n1}^0 and ψ_{n2}^0 as the two eigenfunctions in the unperturbed state. Both are orthogonal to all other eigenfunctions ψ^0 but not necessarily orthogonal to each other. As before, we expand

$$E_n = E_n^0 + \lambda E_n^{(1)} + \ldots \qquad \ldots (8.66)$$

$$\psi_n = \chi_n^0 + \lambda \psi_n^{(1)} + \ldots \qquad \ldots (8.67)$$

As the perturbation $\lambda \hat{H}'$ becomes smaller and smaller, $E_n \rightarrow E_n^0$ while $\psi_n \rightarrow \chi_n^0$. The first thing, therefore, is to determine χ_n^0 which is the correct "zero order wave function".

On substituting Equation (8.66) and (8.67) into Equation (8.65) and equating the coefficients of like powers of λ, we have, after suitable rearrangements, the first order equation

$$\hat{H}^0 \psi_n^{(1)} - E_n^0 \psi_1^{(1)} = E^{(1)} \chi_n^0 - \hat{H}' \chi_n^0 \qquad \ldots (8.68)$$

The function $\psi_n^{(1)}$ can be expanded in terms of all the orthonormal eigenfunction ψ_j^0 of the system

$$\psi_n^{(1)} = \sum_j c_j \psi_j^0 \qquad \ldots (8.69)$$

so that

$$\hat{H}^0 \psi_n^{(1)} = \hat{H}^0 \sum_j c_j \psi_j^0 = \sum_j c_j E_j^0 \psi_j^0 \qquad \ldots (8.70)$$

Further, we have

$$\chi_n^0 = a_1 \psi_{n1}^0 + a_2 \psi_{n2}^0 \qquad \ldots (8.71)$$

Substituting Equations (8.69), (8.70) and (8.71) into Equation (8.68),

$$\sum_j c_j \psi_j^0 \left(E_j^0 - E_n^0\right) = E_n^{(1)} \left(a_1 \psi_{n1}^0 + a_2 \psi_{n2}^0\right) - \hat{H}' \left(a_1 \psi_{n1}^0 + a_2 \psi_{n2}^0\right) \qquad \ldots (8.72)$$

In Equation (8.72), the summation on the left hand side involves all the eigenfunctions ψ_j^0 of the unperturbed system while the terms on the right involves only the functions ψ_{ni}^0 belonging to the degenerate level E_n^0. Multiplying both sides of the equation by ψ_{ni}^0 $(i = 1, 2)$ and integrating over the space,

$$\sum c_j\left(E_j^0 - E_n^0\right)\int \psi_{ni}^0\psi_j^0\, d\tau = \int \psi_{ni}^0 E_n^{(1)}\left(a_1\psi_{n1}^0 + a_2\psi_{j2}^0\right) d\tau - \int \psi_{ni}^0 \hat{H}'\left(a_1\psi_{n1}^0 + a_2\psi_{n2}^0\right) d\tau \quad \text{... (8.73)}$$

The left hand side of Equation (8.73) is always zero because for $j \neq n$ (n_1 or n_2), $\int \psi_{ni}^0 \psi_j^0\, d\tau = 0$ due to orthogonality and for $j = n$, $E_j^0 = E_n^0$.

Now, let

$$S_{i1} = \int \psi_{ni}^0\, \psi_{n1}^0\, d\tau,\ S_{i2} = \int \psi_{ni}^0\, \psi_{n2}^0\, d\tau$$

$$H'_{i1} = \int \psi_{ni}^0\, \hat{H}'\, \psi_{n1}^0\, d\tau,\ H'_{i2} = \int \psi_{ni}^0\, \hat{H}'\, \psi_{n2}^0\, d\tau$$

The Equation (8.73) may thus be written, on rearrangement, as

$$a_1\left(H'_{i1} - E_n^{(1)} S_{i1}\right) + a_2\left(H'_{i2} - E_n^{(1)} S_{i2}\right) = 0 \quad \text{... (8.74)}$$

There will be two such equations corresponding to $i = 1$ and 2,

$$\left.\begin{aligned} a_1\left(H'_{11} - E_n^{(1)} S_{11}\right) + a_2\left(H'_{12} - E_n^{(1)} S_{12}\right) = 0 \\ a_1\left(H'_{21} - E_n^{(1)} S_{21}\right) + a_2\left(H'_{22} - E_n^{(1)} S_{22}\right) = 0 \end{aligned}\right\} \quad \text{... (8.75)}$$

If the energy level E_n^0 of the unperturbed system were k-fold degenerate there would be k such equations. These are called "secular equations".

Nontrivial solution of Equation (8.75) is possible only if the determinant of the coefficients of a_1 and a_2 is equal to zero,

$$\begin{vmatrix} H'_{11} - E_n^{(1)} S_{11} & H'_{12} - E_n^{(1)} S_{12} \\ H'_{21} - E_n^{(1)} S_{21} & H'_{22} - E_n^{(1)} S_{22} \end{vmatrix} = 0 \quad \text{... (8.76)}$$

This, on expanding, gives a 2nd degree polynomial yielding two roots of $E_n^{(1)}$, viz., $E_{n1}^{(1)}$ and $E_{n2}^{(1)}$. In other words, the originally doubly degenerate energy level E_n^0 is split into two levels $E_n^0 + E_{n1}^{(1)}$ and $E_n^0 + E_{n2}^{(1)}$ due to perturbation.

In case of k-fold degeneracy there will be $k \times k$ determinant yielding a kth degree polynomial and hence k values of $E_n^{(1)}$, *i.e.*, $E_{n1}^{(1)}, E_{n2}^{(1)}, \ldots E_{nk}^{(1)}$.

We started with the premise that the original eigenfunctions $\psi_{n1}^0, \psi_{n2}^0, \ldots, \psi_{nk}^0$ belonging to the k-fold degenerate level E_n^0 are not necessarily orthogonal. But if they are so, we have the advantage that

$$S_{ik} = 1, \text{ if } i = k \text{ and } = 0 \text{ if } i \neq k$$

Then the $k \times k$ determinant would assume the form

$$\begin{vmatrix} H'_{11} - E_n^{(1)} & H'_{12} & H'_{13} & \ldots\ldots & H'_{ik} \\ H'_{21} & H'_{22} - E_n^{(1)} & H'_{23} & \ldots\ldots & H'_{2k} \\ \cdots & \cdots & \cdots & \cdots & \\ \cdots & \cdots & \cdots & \cdots & \\ H'_{k1} & H'_{k2} & H'_{k3} & \ldots\ldots & H'_{kk} - E_n^{(1)} \end{vmatrix} = 0 \qquad \ldots (8.77)$$

If, in addition, the off diagonal elements H'_{mn} of the determinant are all zero, the initially chosen wave functions $\psi^0_{n1}, \psi^0_{n2}, \ldots$ are themselves the correct zero order wave functions and the roots $E^{(1)}_{n1}, E^{(1)}_{n2}, \ldots$ are obtained directly from the "diagonal elements" as on expansion,

$$\left(H'_{11} - E_n^{(1)}\right)\left(H'_{22} - E_n^{(1)}\right)\ldots\ldots\left(H'_{kk} - E_n^{(1)}\right) = 0 \qquad \ldots (8.78)$$

which gives the roots $\qquad E^{(1)}_{n1} = H'_{11}, E'_{n2} = H'_{22}, \ldots E^{(1)}_{nk} = H'_{kk} \qquad \ldots (8.79)$

Corresponding to each of these new energy states $E^0_n + E^{(1)}_{nk}$ is a distinct eigenfunction expressed as a power series

$$\left.\begin{aligned} \psi_{n1} &= \chi^0_{n1} + \lambda\psi^{(1)}_{n1} + \ldots \\ \psi_{n2} &= \chi^0_{n2} + \lambda\psi^{(1)}_{n2} + \ldots \\ &\ldots\ldots\ldots\ldots\ldots\ldots \\ &\ldots\ldots\ldots\ldots\ldots\ldots \\ \psi_{nk} &= \chi^0_{nk} + \lambda\psi^{(1)}_{nk} + \ldots \end{aligned}\right\} \qquad \ldots (8.80)$$

The first and second terms represent the zero and first order terms respectively. To determine the first term we have to determine the coefficients a_i in the expansion (8.64) and for the second term we need c_j in the expansion (8.69).

Example: *Effect of Perturbation on Excited State of Hydrogen Atom—The Zeeman Effect:* The ground state ($n = 1$) of a hydrogen atom is non-degenerate but the first excited state ($n = 2$) is 4-fold degenerate with

$$\psi^0_{21} = \psi_{2s} = \frac{1}{\sqrt{32\pi}}(r-2)\,e^{-r/2}$$

$$\psi^0_{22} = \psi_{2p_0} = \frac{1}{\sqrt{64\pi}}\,re^{-r/2}\cos\theta$$

$$\psi^0_{23} = \psi_{2p_{+1}} = \frac{1}{\sqrt{64\pi}}\,re^{-r/2}\sin\theta\,e^{i\varphi}$$

$$\psi^0_{24} = \psi_{2p_{-1}} = \frac{1}{\sqrt{64\pi}}\,re^{-r/2}\sin\theta\,e^{-i\varphi}$$

Each corresponding to $E_2^0 = -\frac{1}{8}$ a.u.

When the hydrogen atom is placed in a magnetic field the degenerate E_2^0 state is split into three (not four) energy states. This is known as Zeeman effect. Perturbation theory helps to explain it.

The orbiting electron has a magnetic moment vector associated with it which is collinear with angular momentum vector. In the magnetic field it takes on an additional potential energy due to the coupling of the electron's magnetic moment with the applied magnetic field. Only the z-component of the electronic magnetic moment is of significance. So, if the applied field B is along the z-axis the potential energy due to interaction is proportional to $B \cdot \mu_z$ or εBL_z, where, L_z is the z-component of the angular momentum and ε is a constant.

In terms of perturbation theory this amounts to adding a perturbation operator $\lambda \hat{H}' = \varepsilon B\hat{L}_z$ to the electronic Hamiltonian $\hat{H}$. Then we have to set up the secular equation for which we need the integrals, $H'_{ij} = \int \psi_i^0 \hat{L}_z \psi_j \, d\tau$, S_{ii} and S_{ij}

where i and j refer to all the eigenfunctions of the degenerate state E_2^0. The integrals

$$S_{ii} = 1 \text{ and } S_{ij} = 0$$

if the functions are orthonormal. The operator $\hat{L}_z$ is equal to $\frac{h}{2\pi i}\frac{d}{d\varphi}$. Only the functions $\psi_{2p_{+1}}$ and $\psi_{2p_{-1}}$ contain the variable φ and when operated upon by $\hat{L}'_z$ give the eigenvalues $+\frac{h}{2\pi}$ and $-\frac{h}{2\pi}$ respectively. The resulting secular determinant is

$$\begin{vmatrix} \frac{h}{2\pi} - E^{(1)} & 0 \\ 0 & -\frac{h}{2\pi} - E^{(1)} \end{vmatrix} = 0$$

giving two roots for $E^{(1)}$., viz. $E_1^{(1)} = \frac{h}{2\pi}$ and $E_2^{(1)} = -\frac{h}{2\pi}$. Since the states ψ_{2s} and ψ_{2p} remain unperturbed the net effect of perturbation is to split the energy level E_2^0 into three levels, viz., $E_2^0, E_2^0 + \frac{h}{2\pi}$ and $E_2^0 - \frac{h}{2\pi}$.

8.2.1.3 Second Order Perturbation

Correction to energy: On rearranging the Equation (8.54), we have

$$\hat{H}^0 \psi_n^{(2)} - E_n^0 \psi_n^{(2)} + \hat{H}' \psi_n^{(1)} - E_n^{(1)} \psi_n^{(1)} - E_n^{(2)} \psi_n^0 = 0 \qquad \text{...(8.81)}$$

Multiplying this equation from left by ψ_l^0 and integrating

$$\int \psi_l^0 \hat{H}^0 \psi_n^{(2)}\, d\tau - \int \psi_l^0 E_n^0 \psi_n^{(2)}\, d\tau + \int \psi_l^0 \hat{H}' \psi_n^{(1)}\, d\tau - \int \psi_l^0 E_n^{(1)} \psi_n^{(1)}\, d\tau - \int \psi_l^0 E_n^{(2)} \psi_n^0\, d\tau = 0 \qquad ...(8.82)$$

For $l = n$, since $\hat{H}^0$ is Hermitian, the first and second terms are equal; the Equation (8.82) reduces to

$$E_n^{(2)} = \int \psi_n^0\, \hat{H}'\, \psi_n^{(1)}\, d\tau - \int \psi_n^0\, E_n^{(1)}\, \psi_n^{(1)}\, d\tau \qquad ...(8.83)$$

On substituting Equation (8.63) for $\psi_n^{(1)}$ in Equation (8.83),

$$E_n^{(2)} = \int \psi_n^0 \hat{H}' \left(\sum_{m \neq n} \frac{H'_{mn}}{E_n^0 - E_m^0} . \psi_m^0 \right) d\tau - E_n^{(1)} \int \psi_n^0 \left(\sum_{m \neq n} \frac{H'_{mn}}{E_n^0 - E_m^0} \psi_m^0 \right) d\tau \qquad ...(8.84)$$

The first term in Equation (8.84) may be written as

$$\sum_{m \neq n} \int \psi_n^0\, \hat{H}' \left(\frac{H'_{mn}}{E_n^0 - E_m^0} \right) \psi_m^0\, d\tau = \sum_{m \neq n} \int \psi_n^0\, \hat{H}'\, \psi_m^0\, d\tau . \frac{H'_{mn}}{E_n^0 - E_m^0}$$

$$= \sum_{m \neq n} \frac{H'_{nm} . H'_{mn}}{E_n^0 - E_m^0}$$

The second term $= E_n^{(1)} \sum_{m \neq n} \int \psi_n^0\, \psi_m^0\, d\tau . \dfrac{H'_{mn}}{E_n^0 - E_m^0} = 0$ on account of the orthogonality of ψ_n^0 and ψ_m^0. Hence,

$$E_n^{(2)} = \sum_{m \neq n} \frac{H'_{mn} . H'_{nm}}{E_n^0 - E_m^0} \qquad ...(8.85)$$

Correction to the wave function: We express $\psi_n^{(2)}$ as

$$\psi_n^{(2)} = \sum_m c_{mn}\, \psi_m^0 \qquad ...(8.86)$$

and consider the Equation (8.82) for $l \neq n$. The equation becomes

$$\int \psi_l^0 \hat{H}^0 \left(\sum c_{mn}\, \psi_m^0 \right) d\tau - \int \psi_l^0\, E_n^0 \left(\sum c_{mn}\, \psi_m^0 \right) d\tau + \int \psi_l^0\, \hat{H} \psi_n^{(1)}\, d\tau$$

$$- \int \psi_l^0\, E_n^{(1)}\, \psi_n^{(1)}\, d\tau - \int \psi_l^0\, E_n^{(2)}\, \psi_n^0\, d\tau = 0 \qquad ...(8.87)$$

Because of orthogonality, the last term and all integrals within the summations in the first and second terms of Equation (8.87) vanish except the one for which $m = l$. This leads to

$$c_{ln} \left(E_l^0 - E_n^0 \right) + \int \psi_l^0\, \hat{H}'\, \psi_n^{(1)}\, d\tau - \int \psi_l^0\, E_n^{(1)}\, \psi_n^{(1)}\, d\tau = 0 \qquad ...(8.88)$$

Substituting for $\psi_n^{(1)}$ and $E_n^{(1)}$ in Equation (8.88),

$$c_{ln}\left(E_l^0 - E_n^0\right) + \int \psi_l^0 \hat{H}' \sum_{m \neq n} \frac{H'_{mn}}{E_n^0 - E_m^0} \psi_m^0 \, d\tau - H'_{mn} \int \psi_l^0 \sum_{m \neq n} \frac{H'_{mn}}{E_n^0 - E_m^0} \psi_m^0 \, d\tau = 0 \quad \text{... (8.89)}$$

The second term in Equation (8.89) can be expanded as

$$\int \psi_l^0 \hat{H}' \frac{H'_{1n}}{E_n^0 - E_1^0} \psi_1^0 \, d\tau + \int \psi_l^0 \hat{H}' \frac{H'_{2n}}{E_n^0 - E_2^0} \psi_2^0 \, d\tau + \ldots$$

$$= \frac{H'_{l1} \cdot H'_{1n}}{E_n^0 - E_1^0} + \frac{H'_{l2} \cdot H'_{2n}}{E_n^0 - E_2^0} + \ldots$$

$$= \sum_{k \neq n} \frac{H'_{lk} \cdot H'_{kn}}{E_n^0 - E_k^0}$$

Similarly, the third term in Equation (8.89) can be expanded as

$$H'_{nn}\left[\int \psi_l^0 \frac{H'_{1n}}{E_n^0 - E_1^0} \psi_1^0 \, d\tau + \int \psi_l^0 \frac{H'_{2n}}{E_n^0 - E_2^0} \psi_2^0 \, d\tau + \ldots\right.$$

Because of orthonormality of $\psi_s^{0\prime}$, all terms in this expansion will vanish except for $m = l$; then this expansion reduces to

$$\frac{H'_{nn} \cdot H'_{ln}}{E_n^0 - E_l^0}$$

Therefore, from Equation (8.89)

$$c_{ln} = \sum_{k \neq n} \frac{H'_{lk} H'_{kn}}{\left(E_n^0 - E_k^0\right)\left(E_n^0 - E_l^0\right)} - \frac{H'_{nn} H'_{ln}}{\left(E_n^0 - E_l^0\right)^2} \quad \text{... (8.90)}$$

and

$$\psi_n^{(2)} = \sum c_{mn} \psi_m^0$$

$$= \sum_{m \neq n}\left[\sum_{k \neq n} \frac{H'_{mk} H'_{kn}}{\left(E_n^0 - E_k^0\right)\left(E_n^0 - E_m^0\right)} - \frac{H'_{nn} H'_{mn}}{\left(E_n^0 - E_m^0\right)^2}\right] \psi_m^0 \quad \text{... (8.91)}$$

For an example of the second order effect, see Problem 8.16.

PROBLEMS

(Problems on Variation)

8.1 Devise a trial function for the particle in a one-dimensional box of length L with infinite walls considering that the function shows a single maximum between the ends of the box; use it to calculate the ground state energy.
[**Hint:** Try a parabola: $\psi = ax^2 + bx + c$ where a, b and c are constants. $\psi = 0$ at $x = 0$; therefore c must be zero.

$\psi = 0$ at $x = $ L, leads to $a = -\dfrac{b}{L}$. Thus, the trial function becomes,

$$\psi = -\frac{b}{L}x^2 + bx = \frac{b}{L}\left(Lx - x^2\right)$$

$$E = \frac{\left(\frac{b}{L}\right)^2 \left(-\frac{h^2}{8\pi^2 m}\right) \int_0^L \left(Lx - x^2\right) \frac{d^2}{dx^2}\left(Lx - x^2\right) dx}{\left(\frac{b}{L}\right)^2 \int_0^L \left(Lx - x^2\right)^2 dx}$$

$$= \frac{-\frac{h^2}{8\pi^2 m} \int_0^L \left(Lx - x^2\right)(-2)\, dx}{\int_0^L \left(x^4 - 2Lx^3 + L^2 x^2\right) dx}$$

$$= \frac{\frac{h^2}{4\pi^2 m}\left(\frac{L^3}{2} - \frac{L^3}{3}\right)}{\frac{L^5}{5} - \frac{L^5}{2} + \frac{L^5}{3}}$$

$$= \frac{5h^2}{4\pi^2 mL^2} = 0.12665\left(\frac{h^2}{mL^2}\right)\Bigg].$$

8.2 Apply the variation function $\psi = Nx\,(L^2 - x^2)$ to the particle in a one-dimensional box with infinite potential walls and calculate the energy. Which eigenfunction does this ψ approximate to ? What is the percentage error in the calculated energy ?
[**Hint:** Using Equation (8.7), we get

$$E = 5.25\left(\frac{h^2}{4\pi^2 mL^2}\right)$$

The true eigenfunctions and eigenvalues of such a system are known to be

$$\psi_n = \sqrt{\frac{2}{L}}\sin\frac{n\pi x}{L},\ E_n = \frac{n^2 h^2}{8mL^2}$$

The calculated energy corresponds to $n = 2$ which has the eigenvalue

$$= 4.9348\left(\frac{h^2}{4\pi^2 mL^2}\right).\ \text{The error is } 6.39\%\Bigg].$$

8.3 Use the trial function $\psi = (1 - x^2)\, x^\alpha$ to calculate the ground state energy of a particle in a one-dimensional box of unit length and having infinite potential walls at the two ends; α is a variable parameter.

$$\hat{H}\psi = -\frac{h^2}{8\pi^2 m}\frac{d^2}{dx^2}\left[\left(1-x^2\right)x^\alpha\right]$$

$$= -\frac{h^2}{4\pi^2 m}\left[\alpha(\alpha-1)\,x^{\alpha-2} - (2+\alpha)(1+\alpha)\,x^\alpha\right]$$

$$\bar{E} = \frac{\int_0^1 \psi H \psi\, dx}{\int_0^1 \psi^2\, dx}$$

$$= \frac{-\dfrac{h^2}{8\pi^2 m}\int_0^1 \left[(1-x)\,x^\alpha \,.\, \alpha(\alpha-1)\,x^{\alpha-2} - (2+\alpha)(1+\alpha)\,x^\alpha\right]dx}{\int_0^1 \left(1-x^2\right)^2 x^{2\alpha}\, dx}$$

$$= \frac{h^2}{16\pi^2 m}\left(\frac{2\alpha+5}{2\alpha-1}\right)\left(2\alpha^2+2\alpha-1\right)$$

$$= \frac{h^2}{16\pi^2 m}\left[\frac{4\alpha^3+14\alpha^2+8\alpha-5}{2\alpha-1}\right]$$

$$\frac{d\bar{E}}{d\alpha} = \frac{8\alpha^3+8\alpha^2-14\alpha+1}{8\,(2\alpha-1)^2} = 0$$

$$\left[\text{Using the standard formula: } d\left(\frac{u}{v}\right) = \frac{V\,du - u\,dV}{V^2}\right]$$

or $$8\alpha^3 + 8\alpha^2 - 14\alpha + 1 = 0$$

This is a cubic equation having three roots. Numerical solution yields one of the roots ($\alpha = 0.862$), which is relevant to the present problem. On substituting this value, we get,

$\bar{E} = 5.13$ in a.u. where $\dfrac{h}{2\pi} = m = 1.$

$$\text{The exact value of } E = \frac{n^2 h^2}{8mL^2} = \frac{n^2\pi^2}{2L}\left(\frac{h^2}{4\pi^2}\right)$$

$$= \frac{\pi^2}{2} = 4.94\ (\text{in a.u., } n \text{ and L being equal to 1})\Bigg].$$

8.4 Make a reasonable guess at the ground state wave function for hydrogen atom. Use variation method to calculate the energy and the normalised wave function. Show that the function is an eigenfunction of the Hamiltonian operator.

[**Hint:** Ground state ψ is spherically symmetric; it may be $\psi = Ne^{-\alpha r}$. Hamiltonian in spherical coordinates is

$$\hat{H} = -\frac{1}{2r^2}\frac{d}{dr}\left(r^2\frac{d}{dr}\right) - \frac{1}{r} \text{ (in atomic units)}$$

Therefore
$$\bar{E} = \frac{\int_0^\infty Ne^{-\alpha r}\left[-\frac{1}{2r^2}\frac{d}{dr}r^2\frac{d}{dr}\left(Ne^{-\alpha r}\right) - \frac{N}{r}e^{-\alpha r}\right]r^2\,dr\int_0^\pi \sin\theta\, a\theta\int_0^{2\pi} d\varphi}{\int_0^\infty \left(Ne^{-\alpha r}\right)^2 r^2\,dr\int_0^\pi \sin\theta\, d\theta\int_0^{2\pi} d\varphi}$$

$$= \frac{\int_0^\infty e^{-\alpha r}\left[-\frac{1}{2}\left(\alpha^2 - \frac{2\alpha}{r}\right) - \frac{1}{r}\right]e^{-\alpha r}\, r^2\,dr}{\int_0^\infty e^{-2\alpha r}\, r^2\,dr}$$

$$= \frac{-\frac{\alpha^2}{2}\int_0^\infty e^{-2\alpha r}\, r^2\,dr + \alpha\int_0^\infty e^{-2\alpha r}\, r\,dr - \int_0^\infty e^{-2\alpha r}\, r\,dr}{\int_0^\infty e^{-2\alpha r}\, r^2\,dr}$$

From the table of integrals $\int_0^\infty e^{-\alpha r}x^n\,dx = \frac{n!}{a^{n+1}}$;

$$\bar{E} = \frac{-\frac{\alpha^2}{2}\frac{2}{(2\alpha)^3} + \alpha\frac{1}{(2\alpha)^2} - \frac{1}{(2\alpha)^2}}{\frac{2}{(2\alpha)^3}}$$

$$= \frac{\alpha^2}{2} - \alpha$$

$$\frac{d\bar{E}}{d\alpha} = \alpha - 1 = 0, \text{ or } \alpha = 1,$$

Therefore
$$E = -\frac{1}{2} \text{ a.u. and } \psi = Ne^{-r}.$$

The normalisation condition is,

$$\int_0^{\infty}\left(\mathrm{N}e^{-r}\right)^2 r^2\,dr\int_0^{\pi}\sin\theta\,d\theta\int_0^{2\pi}d\varphi = 1$$

or
$$4\pi\mathrm{N}^2\int_0^{\infty}e^{-2r}\,r^2\,dr = 1$$

or
$$4\pi\mathrm{N}^2\,\frac{2}{8} = 1 \quad\text{or}\quad \mathrm{N} = \frac{1}{\sqrt{\pi}}$$

$$\hat{\mathrm{H}}\psi = -\frac{1}{2r^2}\frac{d}{dr}\left[r^2\frac{d}{dr}\left(\frac{1}{\sqrt{\pi}}e^{-r}\right)\right] - \frac{1.\,e^{-r}}{\sqrt{\pi r}} = \left(-\frac{1}{2}\right)\frac{1}{\sqrt{\pi}}e^{-r}\Bigg].$$

8.5 Use a trial function, $\psi = \mathrm{N}re^{-\alpha r}$ to calculate the ground state energy of the H atom. Compare the result with the true value. Also determine the value of N.

[Hint:
$$\bar{\mathrm{E}} = \frac{\displaystyle\int_0^{\infty} re^{-\alpha r}\left[-\frac{1}{2}\frac{1}{r^2}\frac{d}{dr}\left\{r^2\frac{d}{dr}\left(re^{-\alpha r}\right)\right\} - \frac{1}{r}\left(re^{-\alpha r}\right)\right]r^2\,dr}{\displaystyle\int_0^{\infty} r^2 e^{-2\alpha r}\,r^2\,dr}$$

Numerator
$$= \int_0^{\infty} re^{-\alpha r}\left[-\frac{1}{r}e^{-\alpha r} + \frac{\alpha}{2}e^{-\alpha r} - \frac{\alpha^2}{2}r^2e^{-\alpha r} + \frac{3}{2}\alpha e^{-\alpha r} - e^{-\alpha r}\right].r^2\,dr$$

$$= -\int_0^{\infty} r^2e^{-2\alpha r}\,dr + \frac{\alpha}{2}\int_0^{\infty} r^3e^{-2\alpha r}\,dr - \frac{\alpha^2}{2}\int_0^{\infty} r^4e^{-2\alpha r} + \frac{3\alpha}{2}\int_0^{\infty} r^3e^{-2\alpha r}\,dr - \int_0^{\infty} r^3e^{-2\alpha r}\,dr$$

Using the table of integrals, we get

Numerator
$$= -\frac{1}{4\alpha^3} + \frac{3}{16\alpha^3} - \frac{3}{8\alpha^3} + \frac{9}{16\alpha^3} - \frac{3}{8\alpha^4}$$

and the denominator $= \dfrac{24}{32\alpha^5}$

Therefore
$$\bar{\mathrm{E}} = -\frac{\alpha^2}{3} + \frac{\alpha^2}{4} - \frac{\alpha^2}{2} + \frac{3\alpha^2}{4} - \frac{\alpha}{2} = \frac{\alpha^2}{6} - \frac{\alpha}{2}$$

$$\frac{d\bar{\mathrm{E}}}{d\alpha} = \frac{\alpha}{3} - \frac{1}{2} = 0;\ \text{or}\ \alpha = \frac{3}{2}$$

$$\psi = \mathrm{N}re^{-3r/2},$$

and
$$\bar{\mathrm{E}} = \frac{\left(\frac{3}{2}\right)^2}{6} - \frac{\left(\frac{3}{2}\right)}{2} = -\frac{3}{8}\ \text{(a.u.)}$$

The value is higher than the true ground state energy $\left(-\frac{1}{2}\text{ a.u.}\right)$ of the H atom.

$$N = \sqrt{\frac{243}{96\pi}}\Bigg].$$

8.6 Consider a harmonic oscillator with the following potential energy:

$$V = \frac{1}{2}kx^2 \text{ for } x > 0,$$

and

$$V = \infty \text{ for } x < 0$$

(*i*) Select a trial eigenfunction ψ;

(*ii*) Use it to calculate the lowest energy $\overline{E}_0$; and

(*iii*) Show that ψ is an eigenfunction with $\overline{E}_0$ as an eigenvalue.

[**Hint:** (*i*) For $x \le 0$, and for x very large ψ must vanish.

So a reasonable guess at the trial function can be,

$$\psi = x \exp(-ax^2) \text{ for } x > 0$$

and

$$\psi = 0 \text{ for } x \le 0$$

(*ii*) $$\overline{E} = \frac{\int_0^\infty x\exp\left(-ax^2\right)\left(-\frac{h^2}{8\pi^2 m}\right)\frac{d^2}{dx^2}\left(x\exp\left(-ax^2\right)\right)+\frac{1}{2}kx^2\left(x\exp\left(-ax^2\right)\right)dx}{\int_0^\infty x^2\exp\left(-2ax^2\right)dx}$$

Since for $x \le 0$, $\psi = 0$, the limits of integration range from 0 to ∞, and not $-\infty$ to ∞.

Numerator $$= \left(\frac{h^2 a}{4\pi^2 m}+\frac{h^2 a}{2\pi^2 m}\right)\int_0^\infty x^2\exp\left(-2ax^2\right)dx + \left(-\frac{h^2a^2}{2\pi^2 m}+\frac{k}{2}\right)$$

$$\int_0^\infty x^4\exp\left(-2ax^2\right)dx$$

$$= \left(\frac{h^2}{32\pi^2 m}+\frac{h^2}{16\pi^2 m}-\frac{3h^2}{64\pi^2 m}+\frac{3k}{64a^2}\right)\left(\frac{\pi}{2a}\right)^{1/2}$$

Denominator $$= \frac{1}{8a}\left(\frac{\pi}{2a}\right)^{1/2}$$

(Using the table of integrals, we get

$$\int_0^\infty x^2\exp\left(-2ax^2\right)dx = \frac{1}{4}\times\frac{1}{2a}\left(\frac{\pi}{2a}\right)^{1/2}$$

and $$\int_0^\infty x^2 \exp\left(-2ax^2\right)dx = \frac{1\times 3}{2^3}\left(\frac{\pi}{(2a)^5}\right)^{1/2}\Bigg)$$

Therefore, $$\bar{E} = \frac{3h^2 a}{8\pi^2 m} + \frac{3k}{8a}$$

$$\frac{d\bar{E}}{da} = \frac{3h^2}{8\pi^2 m} - \frac{3k}{8a^2} = 0$$

$$a = \frac{\pi (mk)^{1/2}}{h},$$

$$\bar{E} = \frac{3h}{4\pi}\left(\frac{k}{m}\right)^{1/2}$$

(*iii*) $$\hat{H}\psi = \left[-\frac{h^2}{8\pi^2 m}\frac{d^2}{dx^2} + \frac{1}{2}kx^2\right] x\exp\left(-ax^2\right)$$

$$= \left[\frac{3h^2 a}{4\pi^2 m}x - \frac{h^2 a^2}{2\pi^2 m}x^3 + \frac{1}{2}kx^3\right]\exp\left(-ax^2\right)$$

Putting the value of $$a = \frac{\pi (mk)^{1/2}}{h}$$

$$\hat{H}\psi = \left[\frac{3h}{4\pi}\left(\frac{k}{m}\right)^{1/2} x - \frac{1}{2}kx^3 + \frac{1}{2}kx^3\right]\exp\left(-ax^2\right)$$

$$= \frac{3h}{4\pi}\left(\frac{k}{m}\right)^{1/2} x\exp\left(-ax^2\right) = \frac{3h}{4\pi}\left(\frac{k}{m}\right)^{1/2}$$

Eigenvalue $$= \frac{3h}{4\pi}\left(\frac{k}{m}\right)^{1/2}\Bigg].$$

8.7 Use the trial function $\psi = \exp(-\alpha r^2)$ (without the normalisation factor) for the ground state of the hydrogen atom. (*i*) Apply variation method to find the value of α that would give the minimum energy. (*ii*) Determine that energy, (*iii*) Calculate the average value of r and the most probable value of r using this wave function, and (*iv*) compare these r and the energy values with the exact r and the exact energy values respectively. (*v*) What is the normalisation factor ?

[Hint:

$$\bar{E} = \frac{\int_0^\infty \exp\left(-\alpha r^2\right)\left[-\frac{1}{2r^2}\frac{d}{dr}\left\{r^2\frac{d}{dr}\left(\exp\left(-\alpha r^2\right)\right)\right\} - \frac{e^{-\alpha r^2}}{r}\right] r^2\, dr}{\int_0^\infty \exp\left(-2\alpha r^2\right) r^2\, dr}$$

$$= \frac{\int_0^\infty \exp\left(-\alpha r^2\right)\left[3\alpha - 2\alpha^2 r^2 - \frac{1}{r}\right]\exp\left(-\alpha r^2\right) r^2\, dr}{\int_0^\infty \exp\left(-2\alpha r^2\right) r^2\, dr}$$

$$= \frac{3a\int_0^\infty r^2 \exp\left(-2\alpha r^2\right)dr - 2\alpha^2\int_0^\infty r^4 \exp\left(-2\alpha r^2\right)dr - \int_0^\infty r\exp\left(-\alpha r^2\right)dr}{\int_0^\infty r^2 \exp\left(-2\alpha r^2\right)dr}$$

From the table of integrals,

$$\int_0^\infty r^2 \exp\left(-2\alpha r^2\right) dr = \frac{1}{8\alpha}\left(\frac{\pi}{2\alpha}\right)^{1/2}$$

$$\int_0^\infty r^4 \exp\left(-2\alpha r^2\right) dr = \frac{3}{32\alpha^2}\left(\frac{\pi}{2\alpha}\right)^{1/2}$$

and $$\int_0^\infty r \exp\left(-\alpha r^2\right) dr = \frac{1}{4\alpha}$$

Therefore $$\bar{E} = \frac{\frac{3}{16}\left(\frac{\pi}{2\alpha}\right)^{1/2} - \frac{1}{4\alpha}}{\frac{1}{8\alpha}\left(\frac{\pi}{2\alpha}\right)^{1/2}} = \frac{3}{2}\alpha - 2\left(\frac{2\alpha}{\pi}\right)^{1/2}$$

$$\frac{d\bar{E}}{da} = \frac{3}{2} - \left(\frac{2}{\pi}\right)^{1/2}\alpha^{-1/2} = 0$$

From which $$\alpha = \frac{8}{9\pi}$$

Therefore $$\bar{E} = \frac{4}{3\pi} - \frac{8}{3\pi} = -\frac{4}{3\pi} = -0.4244 \text{ a.u.}$$

(*iii*) $$\bar{r} = \frac{\int_0^\infty \exp\left(-\alpha r^2\right) r \exp\left(-\alpha r^2\right) r^2\, dr}{\int_0^\infty \exp\left(-2\alpha r^2\right) r^2\, dr}$$

From the table of integrals (Appendix 5),

$$\int_0^\infty r^3 \exp\left(-2\alpha r^2\right) dr = \frac{1}{8\alpha^2}$$

and $$\int_0^\infty \exp\left(-2\alpha r^2\right) r^2\, dr = \frac{1}{4}\left(\frac{\pi}{8\alpha^3}\right)^{1/2}$$

$$\bar{r} = \frac{\dfrac{1}{8\alpha^2}}{\dfrac{1}{4}\left(\dfrac{\pi}{8\alpha^3}\right)^{1/2}}$$

Putting $\alpha = \dfrac{8}{9\pi}$, we shall arrive at $\bar{r} = \dfrac{3}{2}$ a.u.

Most probable value of r: $P(r)\, dr = 4\pi r^2 \psi^2\, dr$

$$= 4\pi r^2 \exp(-2\alpha r^2)\, dr$$

For maximum probability,

$$\frac{dP(r)}{dr} = 4\pi\,(2r - 4\alpha r^3) \exp(-2\alpha r^2) = 0$$

or $$r_m = \frac{\sqrt{9\pi}}{4} = 1.329 \text{ a.u.}$$

(*iv*) For exact values, $\psi = \dfrac{1}{\sqrt{\pi}} e^{-r}$,

$$E = -0.5 \text{ a.u.}$$

$$\bar{r} = 1.5 \text{ a.u.}$$

$$r_m = 1.0 \text{ a.u.}$$

(*v*) $$\int_0^\infty N^2 \exp\left(-2\alpha r^2\right) r^2\, dr \int_0^\pi \sin\theta\, d\theta \int_0^{2\pi} d\varphi = 1$$

or $$4\pi N^2 \int_0^\infty r^2 \exp\left(-2\alpha r^2\right) dr = 1$$

$$4\pi N^2 \frac{1}{4}\left(\frac{\pi}{8\alpha^3}\right)^{\frac{1}{2}} = 1$$

Therefore, $$\left. N^2 = \left(\frac{2\alpha}{\pi}\right)^{3/2} \right].$$

8.8 Consider a particle in a one-dimensional box of length 2 atomic units with origin at the centre. Let V = 0 for $-1 \le x \le +1$ and V = ∞ otherwise. Use the functions $\varphi_1 = 1 - x^2$, and $\varphi_2 = 1 - x^4$ to construct the linear trial function,

$$\psi = a_1 \varphi_1 + a_2 \varphi_2$$

(*i*) Calculate the energy with this function and compare with the exact solution, and
(*ii*) Determine the "best" values of a_1 and a_2.
[**Hint:** The secular equation is

$$\begin{vmatrix} H_{11} - ES_{11} & H_{12} - ES_{12} \\ H_{21} - ES_{21} & H_{22} - ES_{22} \end{vmatrix} = 0$$

where $$H_{11} = \int_{-1}^{1} \left(1-x^2\right)\left[-\frac{h^2}{8\pi^2 m}\frac{d^2}{dx^2}\left(1-x^2\right)\right]dx$$

$$= \frac{h^2}{4\pi^2 m}\int_{-1}^{1}\left(1-x^2\right)dx = \frac{h^2}{3\pi^2 m}$$

$$H_{22} = \int_{-1}^{1}\left(1-x^4\right)\left[\frac{h^2}{8\pi^2 m}\frac{d^2}{dx^2}\left(1-x^4\right)\right]dx$$

$$= \frac{6h^2}{4\pi^2 m}\int_{-1}^{1}\left(1-x^4\right)x^2\,dx = \frac{4h^2}{7\pi^2 m}$$

$$H_{12} = H_{21} = \int_{-1}^{1}\left(1-x^4\right)\left[-\frac{h^2}{8\pi^2 m}\frac{d^2}{dx^2}\left(1-x^2\right)\right]dx$$

$$= \frac{h^2}{4\pi^2 m}\int_{-1}^{1}\left(1-x^4\right)dx = \frac{2h^2}{5\pi^2 m}$$

$$S_{11} = \int_{-1}^{1}\left(1-x^2\right)^2 dx = \frac{16}{15}$$

$$S_{22} = \int_{-1}^{1}\left(1-x^4\right)^2 dx = \frac{64}{45}$$

$$S_{12} = S_{21} = \int_{-1}^{1} \left(1 - x^4\right)\left(1 - x^2\right) dx = \frac{128}{105}$$

Thus, $$\begin{vmatrix} \frac{h^2}{3\pi^2 m} - \frac{16}{15}E & \frac{2h^2}{5\pi^2 m} - \frac{128}{105}E \\ \frac{2h^2}{5\pi^2 m} - \frac{128}{105}E & \frac{4h^2}{7\pi^2 m} - \frac{64}{45}E \end{vmatrix} = 0$$

Multiplying throughout by $\frac{\pi^2 m}{h^2}$ and letting $\frac{\pi^2 mE}{h^2} = E'$, we get

$$\begin{vmatrix} \frac{1}{3} - \frac{16}{15}E' & \frac{2}{5} - \frac{128}{105}E' \\ \frac{2}{5} - \frac{128}{105}E' & \frac{4}{7} - \frac{64}{45}E' \end{vmatrix} = 0$$

or $$0.031\ E'^2 - 0.108\ E' + 0.03 = 0$$

The two roots of this equation are

$$E'_+ = 3.19 \text{ and } E'_- = 0.308$$

Therefore, $$E_+ = E'_+ \frac{h^2}{\pi^2 m} = 3.19\left(\frac{h^2}{\pi^2 m}\right) = 12.76\left(\frac{h^2}{4\pi^2 m}\right)$$

and $$E_- = E'_- \frac{h^2}{\pi^2 m} = 0.308\left(\frac{h^2}{\pi^2 m}\right) = 1.23\left(\frac{h^2}{4\pi^2 m}\right)$$

The exact eigenvalues for this problem may be obtained from the formula,

$$E_n = \frac{n^2 h^2}{8m \times 2^2} = \frac{n^2 \pi^2}{8m}\left(\frac{h^2}{4\pi^2 m}\right)$$

$$E_1 = 1.23\left(\frac{h^2}{4\pi^2 m}\right)$$

$$E_3 = 11.10\left(\frac{h^2}{4\pi^2 m}\right)$$

The coefficients a_1 and a_2 are determined from the equations

$$a_1 (H_{11} - ES_{11}) + a_2 (H_{12} - ES_{12}) = 0$$

Using $$E_- = 1.23\left(\frac{h^2}{4\pi^2 m}\right)$$ for E, we get

$$a_1\left(\frac{4h^2}{3\times 4\pi^2 m}-1.23\times\frac{h^2}{4\pi^2 m}\frac{16}{15}\right)+a_2\left(\frac{4\times 2h^2}{4\times 5\pi^2 m}-\frac{1.23\times h^2}{4\pi^2 m}\times\frac{128}{105}\right)=0$$

or $$a_1\left(\frac{4}{3}-1.23\times 1.0666\right)+a_2\left(1.6-1.23\times 1.2191\right)=0$$

or $$a_2 = -\,0.2118\,a_1$$

Then, $$\psi_- = a_1\,(1-x^2)-0.2118\,a_1\,(1-x^4)$$

a_1 can be determined from the condition of normalisation,

$$\int \psi_-^2\,dx = a_1^2\left[S_{11}-2\times 0.2118\,S_{12}+0.0449\,S_{22}\right]=1$$

or $a_1^2\times 0.6141 = 1$; or $a_1 = 1.276$

Therefore $$a_2 = -\,0.2703$$

or $$\psi_- = 1.276\,(1-x^2)-0.2703\,(1-x^4)$$

Similarly, using the value of

$$E = E_+ = 12.77\left(\frac{h^2}{4\pi^2 m}\right)$$

The other wave function can be derived as

$$\psi_+ = 6.6625\,(1-x^2)-5.8285\,(1-x^4)].$$

(Problems on Perturbation)

8.9 The perturbed Hamiltonian $\hat{H}$ is given by the relation

$$\hat{H} = \hat{H}_0+\hat{H}'.$$

where, $\hat{H}_0$ is that for the unperturbed system and $\hat{H}'$ due to a small perturbation operation.

Show that if $\hat{H}$ and $\hat{H}^0$ are Hermitian, $\hat{H}'$ must also be Hermitian.

[Hint: $$\int \psi\hat{H}\varphi\,d\tau = \int \psi\left(\hat{H}_0+\hat{H}'\right)\varphi\,d\tau = \int \psi\hat{H}_0\varphi\,d\tau+\int \psi\hat{H}'\varphi\,d\tau \qquad ...(i)$$

and $$\int \varphi\hat{H}\psi\,d\tau = \int \varphi\left(\hat{H}_0+\hat{H}'\right)\psi\,d\tau = \int \varphi\hat{H}_0\psi\,d\tau+\int \varphi\hat{H}'\psi\,d\tau \qquad ...(ii)$$

Since $\hat{H}$ and $\hat{H}_0$ are Hermitian,

$$\int \psi\hat{H}\varphi\,d\tau = \int \varphi\hat{H}\psi\,d\tau \text{ and}$$

$$\int \psi\hat{H}_0\varphi\,d\tau = \int \varphi\hat{H}_0\psi\,d\tau$$

Therefore, $\int \psi\hat{H}'\varphi\,d\tau$ must be equal to $\int \varphi\hat{H}'\psi\,d\tau$, *i.e.*, $\hat{H}'$ is Hermitian].

8.10 Show that if $\hat{H}'$ is Hermitian, the second order energy correction term will be given by

$$E_n^{(2)} = \sum_n \frac{\left[\int \psi_m \hat{H}' \psi_n \, d\tau\right]^2}{E_n - E_m}$$

[Hint:

$$E_n^{(2)} = \sum_{m+n} \frac{\left(\int \psi_m \hat{H}' \psi_n \, d\tau\right)\left(\int \psi_n \hat{H}' \psi_m \, d\tau\right)}{E_n - E_m}$$

But since $\hat{H}'$ is Hermitian,

$$\left.\int \psi_m \hat{H}' \psi_n \, d\tau = \int \psi_n \hat{H}' \psi_m \, d\tau\right].$$

8.11 Show that

$$\int \psi_i \psi_i^{(1)} \, d\tau = 0 \text{ and } \int \psi_i^{(1)} \hat{H}^0 \psi_i \, d\tau = 0$$

[Hint:

$$\int \psi_i \psi_i^{(1)} \, d\tau = \int \psi_i \left(\sum_{j \neq i} a_{ji} \psi_j \, d\tau\right) = 0$$

$$= \left(\sum_{j \neq i} a_{ji} \int \psi_i \psi_j \, d\tau\right) = 0$$

$$\left.\int \psi_i^{(1)} \hat{H}^0 \psi_i \, d\tau = \int \psi_i^{(1)} E_i \psi_i \, d\tau = E_i \int \psi_i^{(1)} \psi_j \, d\tau = 0\right].$$

8.12 A particle in a one-dimensional infinite potential box is perturbed as shown in Fig. 8.2.

(*i*) Find out the first order energy of the system.

(*ii*) Determine the first three terms in the ground state eigenfunction in terms of the unperturbed functions.

(*iii*) Calculate the second order correction for the lowest eigenvalue.

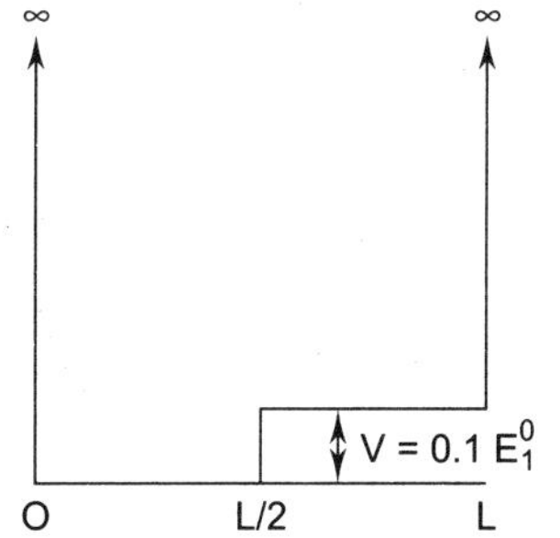

Fig. 8.2

[Hint:

$$E_1^0 = \frac{h^2}{8mL^2}, \; \psi_1^0 = \sqrt{\frac{2}{L}} \sin \frac{\pi x}{L}$$

$$\hat{H}' = 0.1\,E_1 \text{ in the region } \frac{L}{2} \text{ to } L.$$

Therefore, $$E_1^{(1)} = \int_{L/2}^{L} \psi_1^0 \hat{H}' \psi_1^0\, dx = 0.1\,E_1 \int_{L/2}^{L} \left(\psi_1^0\right)^2 dx = 0.1 E \times \frac{1}{2}\int_0^L \left(\psi_1^0\right)^2 dx$$

$$= \frac{0.1 E_1}{2} = 0.05\,E_1$$

$$E = E_1^0 + E_1^{(1)} = \frac{h^2}{8mL^2}(1 + 0.05) = \frac{1.05 h^2}{8mL^2}$$

(*ii*) $$\psi_1 = \psi_1^0 + \sum_{n \neq 1} \frac{\int \psi_n^0 \hat{H}' \psi_1^0\, d\tau}{E_1^0 - E_n^0} \psi_n^0$$

$$= \psi_1^0 + \frac{\int \psi_2^0 \hat{H}' \psi_1^0\, d\tau}{E_1^0 - E_2^0} + \frac{\int \psi_3^0 \hat{H}' \psi_1^0\, d\tau}{E_1^0 - E_3^0} + \frac{\int \psi_4^0 \hat{H}' \psi_1^0\, d\tau}{E_1^0 - E_4^0} + \cdots,$$

Letting $$y = \frac{\pi x}{L},$$

$$\int \psi_m^0 \hat{H}' \psi_n^0\, d\tau = \frac{2}{L}\int_{L/2}^{L} \sin\frac{m\pi x}{L} \sin\frac{n\pi x}{L}\, dx$$

$$= \frac{2}{L}\cdot\frac{L}{\pi}\int_{\pi/2}^{\pi} \sin my \sin ny\, dy$$

$$= \frac{1}{\pi}\left[\frac{\sin(m-n)y}{m-n} - \frac{\sin(m+n)y}{m+n}\right]_{\pi/2}^{\pi} \quad \text{(from table of integrals)}$$

Thus, $$\int \psi_2^0 \hat{H}' \psi_1^0\, d\tau = 0.1\; E_1^0\left(-\frac{4}{3\pi}\right).$$

$$\int \psi_3^0 \hat{H}' \psi_1^0\, d\tau = 0$$

$$\int \psi_4^0 \hat{H}' \psi_1^0\, d\tau = 0.1\,E_1^0\left(\frac{8}{15\pi}\right)$$

and $$\psi_1 = \psi_1^0 + \frac{0.1 E_1^0}{-3E_1^0}\left(-\frac{4}{3\pi}\right)\psi_2^0 + \frac{0.1 E_1^0}{-15 E_1^0}\left(\frac{8}{15\pi}\right)\psi_4^0 + \cdots$$

$$= \psi_1^0 + \frac{2}{45\pi}\psi_2^0 + \frac{4}{1125\pi}\psi_4^0 + \cdots$$

(iii) $$E_1^{(2)} = \sum_{n \neq 1} \frac{\left(\int \psi_n^0 \hat{H}' \psi_1^0 \, d\tau\right)^2}{E_1^0 - E_n^0} = \frac{\left(\int \psi_2^0 \hat{H}' \psi_1^0 \, d\tau\right)^2}{E_1^0 - E_2^0} + \frac{\left(\int \psi_3^0 \hat{H}' \psi_1^0 \, d\tau\right)^2}{E_1^0 - E_3^0} + \frac{\left(\int \psi_4^0 \hat{H}' \psi_1^0 \, d\tau\right)^2}{E_1^0 - E_4^0} + \ldots$$

Using the integrals from (*ii*) above, we get

$$E_1^{(2)} = -\frac{10^{-2}\left(E_1^0\right)^2}{3E_1^0}\left(\frac{4}{3\pi}\right)^2 - \frac{10^{-2}\left(E_1^0\right)^2}{15E_1^0}\left(\frac{8}{15\pi}\right)^2 - \ldots$$

$$= -6.196 \times 10^{-4}\left(\frac{h^2}{8mL^2}\right)$$

Therefore $$E_1 = E_1^0 + E_2^{(1)} + E_1^{(2)} = \frac{h^2}{8mL^2}\left(1 + 0.05 - 6.196 \times 10^{-4}\right)\Bigg].$$

[see L. Melander *J. Chem. Ed.* **49**, 1972, 686].

8.13 A particle in a one-dimensional infinitely deep square potential well is subjected to perturbation as shown in Fig. 8.3.
Evaluate the first order contribution to the energy of the ground state.

[Hint: $$E_1^1 = \int_{L/2}^{L} \psi_1 \left(-V_1\right) \psi_1 \, dx = -\frac{-V_1}{2}\int_0^L \psi_1^2 \, dx = -\frac{V_1}{2}\Bigg].$$

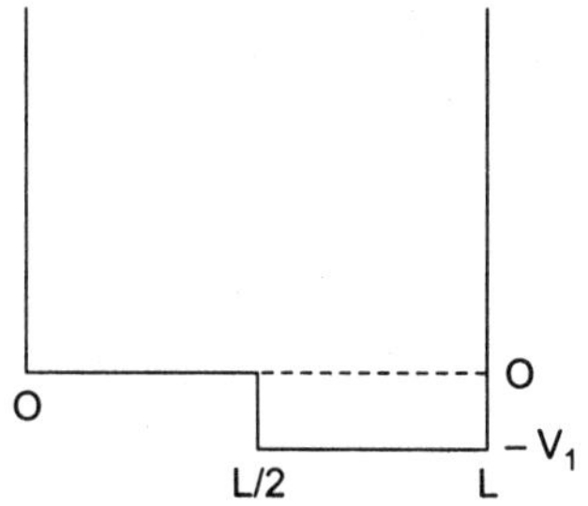

Fig. 8.3

8.14 A particle in a one-dimensional infinitely deep square potential well is subjected to perturbation as shown in Fig. 8.4.

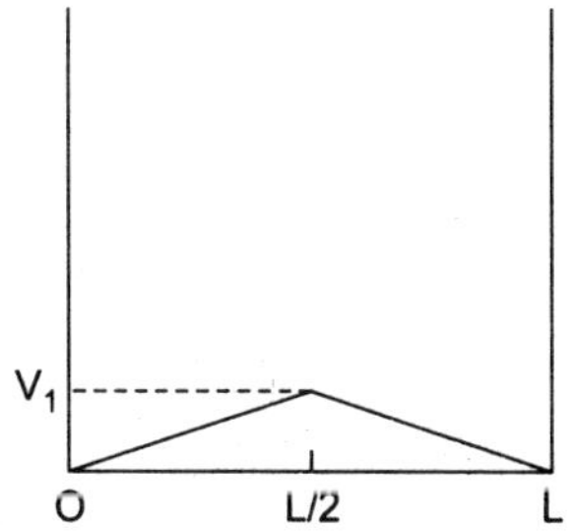

Fig. 8.4

Evaluate the first order correction to the energy in the first excited state.
[**Hint:** Perturbation is not constant but linearly dependent on x. From 0 to L/2.

$$H' = \frac{2V_1}{L}x \text{ and from } \frac{L}{2} \text{ to } L, H' = 2V_1 - \frac{2V_1}{L}x.$$

Therefore,

$$E_2^{(1)} = \int_0^{L/2} \psi_2 \left(\frac{2V_1 x}{L}\right) \psi_2 \, dx + \int_{L/2}^{L} \psi_2 \left(2V_1 - \frac{2V_1 x}{L}\right) \psi_2 \, dx$$

$$= \frac{2V}{L}\frac{2}{L}\int_0^{L/2} x \sin^2 \frac{2\pi x}{L} dx + 2V_1 \frac{2}{L}\int_{L/2}^{L} \sin^2 \frac{2\pi x}{L} dx$$

$$- \frac{2V_1}{L}\frac{2}{L}\int_{L/2}^{L} x \sin^2 \frac{2\pi x}{L} dx$$

Let $\frac{2\pi x}{L} = y$ and $dy = \frac{2\pi}{L} dx$

Integration limits: $x = 0 \rightarrow y = 0; x = \frac{L}{2} \rightarrow y = \pi, x = L \rightarrow y = 2\pi$

Then,

$$E_2^{(1)} = \frac{4V_1}{L^2}\int_0^{\pi}\left(\frac{L}{2\pi}\right)^2 y \sin^2 y \, dy + \frac{4V_1}{L}\int_{\pi}^{2\pi}\left(\frac{L}{2\pi}\right)^2 \sin^2 y \, dy$$

$$- \frac{4V_1}{L^2}\int_{\pi}^{2\pi}\left(\frac{L}{2\pi}\right)^2 y \sin^2 y \, dy$$

$$= \frac{V_1}{\pi^2}\int_0^{\pi} y \sin^2 y \, dy + \frac{2V_1}{\pi}\int_{\pi}^{2\pi} \sin^2 y \, dy - \frac{V_1}{\pi^2}\int_{\pi}^{2\pi} y \sin^2 y \, dy$$

From the table of integrals,

$$\int_a^b y \sin^2 y \, dy = \left[\frac{y^2}{4} - \frac{y \sin 2y}{4} - \frac{\cos 2y}{8}\right]_a^b$$

and

$$\int_a^b \sin^2 y \, dy = \left[\frac{y}{2} - \frac{\sin 2y}{4}\right]_a^b$$

Therefore,

$$E_2^{(1)} = \frac{V_1}{\pi^2}\left[\frac{\pi^2}{4} - 0 - 0\right] + \frac{2V_1}{\pi}\left[\frac{2\pi}{2} - \frac{\pi}{2} - 0 - 0\right] - \frac{V_1}{\pi^2}\left[\frac{4\pi^2}{4} - \frac{\pi^2}{4} - 0 - 0\right]$$

$$= \frac{V_1}{4} + V_1 - \frac{3V_1}{4} = \frac{V_1}{2}\Bigg].$$

8.15 An electron moving in a simple harmonic potential $V = \frac{1}{2}kx^2$ is subjected to a perturbation $\hat{H}' = Ex$ where E is the strength of the electric field which is applied in the x-direction. Determine the effect of first and second order perturbation on the energy.

[Hint: $$E = \left(n + \frac{1}{2}\right)h\nu,\ \psi_n^0 = NH_n(y)\exp(-y^2/2)$$

where, $$H_n(y) = \text{Hermite polynomials},\ y^2 = \beta x^2,$$

$$\beta = (mk)^{1/2}\frac{h}{2\pi},\ x = \frac{y}{\sqrt{\beta}}$$

and $$N = \left(\frac{\beta^{1/2}}{2^n n!\sqrt{\pi}}\right)^{1/2}$$

For the ground state ($n = 0$), $E_0^0 = \frac{1}{2}h\nu$, $H_0(y) = 1$

and $$\psi_0^0 = \left(\frac{\beta}{\pi}\right)^{1/4}\exp\left(-y^2/2\right) = \left(\frac{\beta}{\pi}\right)^{1/4}\exp\left(-\beta x^2/2\right)$$

$$E_0^{(1)} = E\int_{-\infty}^{\infty}\psi_0^0(x)\,x\,\psi_0^0(x)\,dx$$

$$= E\int_{-\infty}^{\infty}\left(\frac{\beta}{\pi}\right)^{1/2}\exp\left(-\beta x^2/2\right)x\exp\left(-\beta x^2/2\right)dx$$

$$= E\left(\frac{\beta}{\pi}\right)^{1/2}\int_{-\infty}^{\infty}x\exp\left(-\beta x^2\right)$$

$$= E\left(\frac{\beta}{\pi}\right)^{1/2}\left(\frac{1}{\beta}\right)^{1/2}\int_{-\infty}^{\infty}y\exp\left(-y^2\right)dy$$

$$= \frac{E}{\sqrt{\pi}}\int_{-\infty}^{\infty}y\exp\left(-y^2\right)dy$$

$$\int_{-\infty}^{\infty}y\exp\left(-y^2\right)dy = \int_{-\infty}^{0}y\exp\left(-y^2\right)dy + \int_{0}^{\infty}y\exp\left(-y^2\right)dy$$

$$= -\int_0^{\infty} y \exp\left(-y^2\right) dy + \int_0^{\infty} y \exp\left(-y^2\right) dy = -\frac{1}{2} + \frac{1}{2} = 0.$$

$$\left(\text{from integration table, } \int_0^{\infty} y \exp\left(-y^2\right) dy = \frac{1}{2}\right)$$

Therefore $\qquad E_0^{(1)} = 0.$

(From symmetry considerations, the integral $\int_{-\infty}^{\infty} y \exp\left(-y^2\right) dy$ is seen to be zero. The function $\exp(-y^2)$ is symmetric, but y is antisymmetric, so the product is antisymmetric)].

8.16 A hydrogen atom is exposed to an electric field of strength F applied in the *z*-direction. Calculate the first order and the second order effects for the ground state of the atom (stark effect).

[Hint: $\qquad H' = eFZ = eFr\cos\theta = Fr\cos\theta$ (in a.u.)

First order effect

$$E_1^0 = -\frac{1}{2} \text{ a.u. } \psi_1^0 = \psi_{1s} = \frac{1}{\sqrt{\pi}} \exp(-r) \text{ (in a.u.)}$$

$$E_1^{(1)} = \int \psi_1^0 H' \psi_1^0 \, d\tau = \frac{F}{\pi} \int_0^{\infty}\int_0^{\pi}\int_0^{2\pi} \exp(-r)\, r\cos\theta \exp(-r)\, r^2 \sin\theta \, d\theta \, d\varphi$$

$$= \frac{F}{\pi}(2\pi) \int_0^{\infty} r^3 \exp(-2r)\, dr \int_0^{\pi} \sin\theta\cos\theta \, d\theta$$

$$\int_0^{\pi} \sin\theta\cos\theta \, d\theta = \left[\frac{1}{2}\sin 2\theta\right]_0^{\pi} = 0.$$

Therefore, $\qquad E_1^{(1)} = 0$

Thus, there is no first order effect.

Second order effect

$$E_1^{(2)} = F^2 \sum_{n \neq 1} \frac{\left[\int \psi_1^0 \, r\cos\theta \, \psi_n^0 \, d\tau\right]^2}{E_1^0 - E_n^0} \text{ (in a.u.)}$$

States closest to ψ_1^0 (*i.e.*, from ψ_2^0) are the

$\psi_{2s}^0, \psi_{2p_x}^0, \psi_{2p_y}^0$ and $\psi_{2p_z}^0$

$$\psi_{2s}^0 = \frac{1}{4\sqrt{2\pi}}(2-r)\exp(-r/2)$$

$$\psi_{2p_x}^0 = \frac{1}{4\sqrt{2\pi}} r \exp(-r/2)\sin\theta\cos\varphi$$

$$\psi_{2p_y}^0 = \frac{1}{4\sqrt{2\pi}} r \exp(-r/2)\sin\theta\sin\varphi$$

$$\psi_{2p_z}^0 = \frac{1}{4\sqrt{2\pi}} r \exp(-r/2)\cos\theta$$

and $$E_2^0 = -\frac{1}{2n^2} = -\frac{1}{8} \text{ a.u.,}$$

$$E_1^0 - E_2^0 = -\frac{1}{2} - \left(-\frac{1}{8}\right) = -\frac{3}{8}$$

Therefore, $$E_1^{(2)} = -\frac{8}{3}F^2\left[\left(\int \psi_{1s}^0 r\cos\theta\,\psi_{2s}^0\,d\tau\right)^2 + \left(\int \psi_{1s}^0 r\cos\theta\,\psi_{2p_x}^0\,d\tau\right)^2 + \left(\int \psi_{1s}^0 r\cos\theta\,\psi_{2p_y}^0\,d\tau\right)^2 + \left(\int \psi_{1s}^0 r\cos\theta\,\psi_{2p_z}^0\,d\tau\right)^2\right]$$

First integral

$$\frac{1}{4\sqrt{2\pi}}\int_0^\infty (2-r)\exp(-3r/2)\,r^3\,dr\int_0^\pi \sin\theta\cos\theta\,d\theta\int_0^{2\pi} d\varphi = 0$$

Second integral

$$\frac{1}{4\sqrt{2\pi}}\int_0^\infty r^4\exp(-3r/2)\,dr\int_0^\pi \sin^2\theta\cos\theta\,d\theta\int_0^{2\pi}\cos\varphi\,d\varphi = 0$$

$$\left[\text{because}\int_0^\pi \sin^2\theta\cos\theta\,d\theta = \left[\frac{\sin^3\theta}{3}\right]_0^\pi = 0\right]$$

Similarly third integral = 0

Third integral

$$\frac{1}{4\sqrt{2\pi}} \int_0^\infty r^4 \exp(-3r/2)\, dr \int_0^\pi \cos^2\theta \sin\theta\, d\theta \int_0^{2\pi} d\varphi$$

$$= \frac{1}{4\sqrt{2\pi}} \frac{4\,!}{\left(\frac{3}{2}\right)^5} \left[-\frac{\cos^3\theta}{3}\right]_0^\pi 2\pi = \frac{2^8}{\sqrt{2} \times 3^5}$$

Therefore, $$E_1^{(2)} = -\frac{8}{3} F^2 \times \frac{2^{15}}{3^{10}} = -\left(\frac{2^{18}}{3^{11}}\right) F^2$$

[Only the $2p_z$ state contributes to the perturbation effect].

CHAPTER 9

Multielectronic Atoms

One-electron systems are only a few; atomic and molecular systems are mostly multielectronic for which Schrödinger equation cannot be solved. We describe in this chapter techniques of obtaining approximate wave functions and energy levels for such systems. First, the method of independent electrons in which we consider a two electron-atom without mutual repulsion (unperturbed system) and then make correction using perturbation and variation methods. For more than two electron-atom, more sophisticated method, the method of self consistent field, is applied in which we rigorously consider the electronic interactions.

9.1 TWO-ELECTRON SYSTEMS—THE HELIUM ATOM

9.1.1 Independent Electron Approximation

For an atom with two electrons (*e.g.*, He) the Hamiltonian is,

$$\hat{H}\ (1,2) \text{ or simply } \hat{H} = \left[-\frac{h^2}{8\pi^2 m}\left(\nabla_1^2 + \nabla_2^2\right)\right] + \left[-\frac{Ze^2}{r_1} - \frac{Ze^2}{r_2} + \frac{e^2}{r_{12}}\right] \quad \text{... (9.1)}$$

where, the terms within the first square brackets represent kinetic energy operator and those within the second square brackets the potential energy operator; the subscripts 1 and 2 in the coordinates refer to the two electrons (Fig. 9.1).

In atomic units, it is

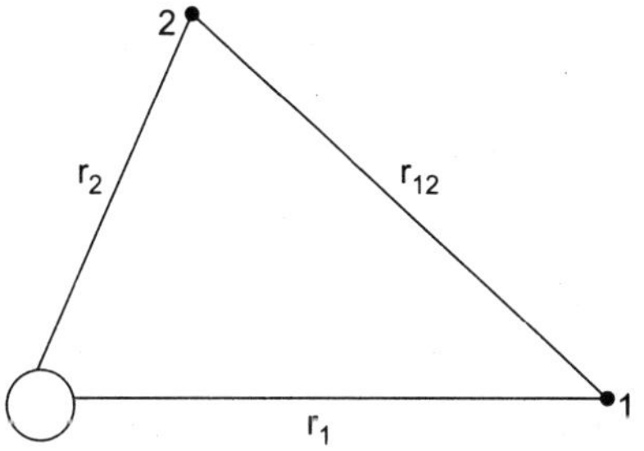

Fig. 9.1

$$\hat{H} = -\frac{1}{2}\nabla_1^2 - \frac{1}{2}\nabla_2^2 - \frac{Z}{r_1} - \frac{Z}{r_2} + \frac{1}{r_{12}} \quad \text{... (9.2)}$$

The Schrödinger equation is

$$\hat{H}\psi = E\psi \quad \text{... (9.3)}$$

where,

$$\psi = \psi(1,2) = \psi(x_1, y_1, z_1, x_2, y_2, z_2) \quad \text{... (9.4)}$$

with a total of six coordinates, three for each electron.

But for the term $\frac{1}{r_{12}}$ in Equation (9.2) the two-electron Hamiltonian would be

$$\hat{H}^0 = \left(-\frac{1}{2}\nabla_1^2 - \frac{Z}{r_1}\right) + \left(-\frac{1}{2}\nabla_2^2 - \frac{Z}{r_2}\right) = \hat{H}^0(1) + \hat{H}^0(2) \quad \text{... (9.5)}$$

This may be taken as the unperturbed (zeroth order) Hamiltonian $(\hat{H}^0)$, $\hat{H}^0$ (1) and $\hat{H}^0$ (2) representing two hydrogen like (*i.e.*, one-electron) Hamiltonians each with nuclear charge Z, the zeroth order eigenfunction and eigenvalue being

$$\psi^0 = \psi^0(1,2) = \phi(1)\,.\,\phi(2) \quad \text{... (9.6)}$$

and

$$E^0 = E^0(1) + E^0(2) \quad \text{... (9.7)}$$

In Equation (9.6), ϕ (1) and ϕ (2) are the "Orbital eigenfunctions" of $\hat{H}^0$ (1) and $\hat{H}^0$ (2) respectively with E^0 (1) and E^0 (2) as the corresponidng "Orbital energy eigenvalues", *i.e.*,

$$\hat{H}(i)\,\phi(i) = E(i)\,\phi(1),\ i = 1 \text{ or } 2 \quad \text{... (9.8)}$$

Since $\hat{H}^0(1)$ and $\hat{H}^0(2)$ operate on electrons 1 and 2 independently,

$$\left[\hat{H}^0\psi = \left[\hat{H}^0(1) + \hat{H}^0(2)\right]\phi(1)\,\phi(2)\right.$$

$$= \hat{H}^0(1)\,\phi(1)\,\phi(2) + \hat{H}^0(2)\,\phi(1)\,\phi(2)$$

$$\left.= \left[E^0(1) + E^0(2)\right]\phi(1)\,\phi(2) = E^0\psi\right]$$

The wave function of the type Equation (9.6) has the physical interpretation that $\psi^2 = \phi(1)^2 . \phi(2)^2$ is the probability that electron 1 is at the point (x_1, y_1, z_1) and electron 2 at the point (x_2, y_2, z_2).

The zeroth order wave function of He atom in atomic units would be written explicitly as

$$\psi^0 = 1s(1)\,1s(2) = \frac{Z^3}{\pi}e^{-Zr_1}\,.\,e^{-Zr_2} \quad \text{... (9.9)}$$

The corresponding zeroth order energy eigenvalue is

$$E^0 = E^0_{1s}(1) + E^0_{1s}(2) = 2 \times \left(-\frac{1}{2}Z^2\right) = -Z^2 \text{ a.u.}$$

$$= -4 \text{ a.u.} = -1.74 \times 10^{-17}\text{ J, or } -108.3 \text{ eV} \quad \text{... (9.10)}$$

taking $Z = 2$

The energy thus calculated is absurd when compared to the experimentally observed value of – 1.25 × 10^{-17} J, – 78.4 eV. Obviously, the gravest error is to neglect the term $\frac{1}{r_{12}}$, the "perturbation" term.

9.1.2 Perturbation Treatment

Now an approximation is made that the function (9.6) or (9.9) can be used as an approximate eigenfunction of the perturbed Hamiltonian

$$\hat{H} = \hat{H}^0 + \frac{1}{r_{12}} = \hat{H}^0(1) + \hat{H}^0(2) + \frac{1}{r_{12}} \quad \text{... (9.11)}$$

The first order correction to energy, by perturbation theory, will be given by

$$E^{(1)} = \int \psi^0 \hat{H}' \psi^0 \, d\tau \qquad (\psi^0 \text{ being normalised and real})$$

$$= \iint \phi(1)\,\phi(2)\,\frac{1}{r_{12}}\,\phi(1)\,\phi(2)\,d\tau_1, d\tau_2 = J\text{ (say)} \quad \text{... (9.12)}$$

The integral J Equation (9.12) represents the average coulombic repulsion energy. Using Equation (9.9), we get

$$J = \left(\frac{Z^3}{\pi}\right)^3 \iint \exp\left[-Z(r_1 + r_2)\right] \frac{1}{r_{12}} \exp\left[-Z(r_1 + r_2)\right] d\tau_1\, d\tau_2 \quad \text{... (9.13)}$$

The integration which has to be performed in spherical coordinates will not be attempted here. It has been evaluated* and found as

$$J = \frac{5}{8} Z \quad \text{... (9.14)}$$

The energy of He atom in the ground state, is therefore

$$E_{1s^2} = -Z^2 + \frac{5}{8} Z \qquad \text{[by Equations (9.10) and (9.14)]}$$

$$= -2.75 \text{ a.u. (because Z = 2)}$$

$$= -74.8 \text{ eV or } -1.196 \times 10^{-17} \text{ J} \quad \text{... (9.15)}$$

This value is in fair agreement with the experimental value, the error being about 5%.

From the point of view of chemical interest, what is more important is ionisation potential. For He atom, the first ionisation and the ionisation potential are defined as

$$\text{He}(1s^2) = \text{He}^+(1s) + e(1s)$$

and

$$\text{I.P.} = E_{1s}^{He+} - E_{1s^2}^{He}$$

$$= -2 - (-2.75) = 0.75 \text{ a.u. or } 20.4 \text{ eV.} \quad \text{... (9.16)}$$

The experimental value is 24.6 eV or J; the error is now about 17%, an amount too large to be ignored.

---

* For example, see J. Goodishman, *Contemporary Quantum Chemistry*, (Plenum Press, New York), p. 154.

9.1.3 Variation Treatment

In this approximation we have to first find a trial function. We argue as follows:

The presence of one electron effectively reduces the nuclear charge (by screening the nucleus partially) for the other electron. Therefore, the value of Z in the function (9.9) should be lower, say Z′; then Z′ may be used as a variable parameter the value of which can be determined by minimising the energy, *i.e.*, by setting

$$\frac{dE_{1s^2}}{dZ'} = 0$$

Using the variation integral [Equation (8.7), Chapter 8], we get

$$\bar{E}_{1s^2} = \frac{\int \psi \hat{H} \psi \, d\tau}{\int \psi^2 \, d\tau} = \int \psi \hat{H} \psi \, d\tau \qquad \text{(if } \psi \text{ is real and normalised)}$$

Using Equation (9.11) for $\hat{H}$ and Equation (9.9) for ψ,

$$\bar{E}_{1s^2} = \iint 1s(1)\, 1s(2) \left[\hat{H}^0(1) + \hat{H}^0(2) + \frac{1}{r_{12}} \right] 1s(1)\, 1s(2)\, d\tau_1\, d\tau_2$$

$$= \iint 1s(1)\, 1s(2)\, \hat{H}^0(1)\, 1s(1)\, 1s(2)\, d\tau_1\, d\tau_2 + \iint 1s(1)\, 1s(2)\, \hat{H}^0(2)\, 1s(1)\, 1s(2)\, d\tau_1\, d\tau_2$$

$$+ \int 1s(1)\, 1s(2) \left(\frac{1}{r_{12}} \right) 1s(1)\, 1s(2)\, d\tau_1\, d\tau_2 \qquad \text{... (9.17)}$$

$\hat{H}^0(1)$ and $\hat{H}^0(2)$ are the Hamiltonians of the He^+ which operate on electrons 1 and 2, respectively, separately $\hat{H}(i)\, 1s(i) = E^{He^+}(i)\, 1s(i), \; i = 1, 2$

Therfore, Equation (9.17) becomes,

$$\bar{E}_{1s^2} = \iint 1s(1)\, 1s(2)\, E_{1s}^{He+}(1)\, 1s(1)\, 1s(2)\, d\tau_1\, d\tau_2$$

$$+ \iint 1s(1)\, 1s(2)\, E_{1s}^{He+}(2)\, 1s(1)\, 1s(2)\, d\tau_1\, d\tau_2 + J \qquad \text{... (9.18)}$$

where

$$J = \iint 1s(1)\, 1s(2) \left(\frac{1}{r_{12}} \right) 1s(1)\, 1s(2)\, d\tau_1\, d\tau_2$$

Since $E_{1s}^{He+}(1) = E_{1s}^{He+}(2) = E_{1s}^0$ (say), Equation (9.18) becomes,

$$\bar{E}_{1s^2} = 2E_{1s}^0 \iint [1s(1)\, 1s(2)]^2\, d\tau_1\, d\tau_2 + J$$

$$= 2E_{1s}^0 + J \qquad \text{(because 1s functions are normalised)} \qquad \text{... (9.19)}$$

E^0_{1s}, the energy of a He^+ in 1s state is given by

$$E^0_{1s} = \int 1s\left(-\frac{1}{2}\nabla^2 - \frac{2}{r}\right)1s\, d\tau \qquad \text{...(9.20)}$$

Equation (9.20) can be written as,

$$E^0_{1s} = \int 1s\left(-\frac{1}{2}\nabla^2 - \frac{Z'}{r} - \frac{2-Z'}{r}\right)1s\, d\tau$$

$$= \int 1s\left(-\frac{1}{2}\nabla^2 - \frac{Z'}{r}\right)1s\, d\tau - \int 1s\left(\frac{2-Z'}{r}\right)1s\, d\tau$$

$$= -\frac{Z'^2}{2}\int (1s)^2\, d\tau - (2-Z')\int 1s\left(\frac{1}{r}\right)1s\, d\tau$$

$$= -\frac{Z'^2}{2} - (2-Z')\int 1s\left(\frac{1}{r}\right)1s\, d\tau \qquad \text{...(9.21)}$$

Since $\quad 1s = \sqrt{\dfrac{Z'^3}{\pi}}\exp(-Z'r)$, and $d\tau = r^2\, dr \sin\theta\, d\theta\, d\varphi$,

$$\int 1s\left(\frac{1}{r}\right)1s\, d\tau = \frac{Z'^3}{\pi}\int_0^{\pi}\frac{1}{r}\exp(-2Z'r)\, r^2\, dr \int_0^{\pi}\sin\theta\, d\theta \int_0^{2\pi} d\varphi$$

$$= \frac{Z'^3}{\pi}\cdot 4\pi\int_0^{\infty} r\exp(-2Z'r)\, dr$$

$$= 4Z'^3\frac{1}{(2Z')^2} = Z' \text{ (using the table of integrals)}$$

Therefore, $$E^0_{1s} = -\frac{Z'^2}{2} - (2-Z')Z' \qquad \text{...(9.22)}$$

and $$\bar{E}_{1s^2} = 2\left[-\frac{Z'^2}{2} - (2-Z')Z'\right] + J \qquad \text{by Equation (9.19)}$$

$$= -Z'^2 - 2Z'(2-Z') + \frac{5}{8}Z' \text{ [using Equation (9.14)]}$$

$$= Z'^2 - \frac{27}{8}Z' \qquad \text{...(9.23)}$$

By the principle of minimisation,

$$\frac{d\bar{E}_{1s^2}}{dZ'} = 2Z' - \frac{27}{8} = 0$$

or $$Z' = \frac{27}{16} \qquad \text{... (9.24)}$$

Therefore, by Equations (9.23) and (9.24), we get

$$\bar{E}_{1s^2} = \left(\frac{27}{16}\right)^2 - \frac{27}{8} \times \frac{27}{16} = -2.84 \text{ a.u.}$$

$$= -77.48 \text{ eV}$$

or $$= -1.24 \times 10^{-17} \text{ J.}$$

The error in total energy of the atom is thus further reduced to less than 2 per cent. The calculated ionisation potential is now 23.06 eV or 0.369×10^{-17} J with an error of 6 per cent.

The value of $Z' = \frac{27}{16}$ represents the "*effective nuclear charge*", *i.e.*, the charge of the nucleus that one electron feels due to the partial screening by the other electron; the difference $2 - \frac{27}{16} = \frac{5}{16}$ represents the *screening effect*. The 1*s* atomic orbitals of He atom should, therefore, be better represented as

$$1s = \sqrt{\frac{Z'^3}{\pi}}\, e^{-Z'r}. \qquad \text{... (9.25)}$$

9.1.4 Symmetric and Antisymmetric Wave Functions: The Ground and Excited States of Helium

In a two-electron atom the orbital functions ϕ (1) and ϕ (2) may be same or different. In the ground state of He, for example, the orbitals for both electrons are the same (1*s*), the combined wave function being

$$\psi(1, 2) = 1s(1)\, 1s(2).$$

In the excited state, one of the electrons may have the orbital 1*s* and the other 2*s*, (configuration 1*s* 2*s*). The complete wave function ψ may be either

$$\psi(1, 2) = 1s(1)\, 2s(2) \qquad \text{... (9.26)}$$

or $$\psi(2, 1) = 1s(2)\, 2s(1) \qquad \text{... (9.27)}$$

both of which are equally good eigenfunctions of the Hamiltonian with the same eigenvalue (doubly degenerate). The two functions differ because of an interchange of the electrons between the two orbitals.

However, the product functions of the type Equations (9.26) and (9.27) suffer from a serious inconsistency; since ψ (1, 2) and ψ (2, 1) differ, their squares are also different, *i.e.*, they lead to different probability distributions for the same two electrons in the same state. This makes no physical sense as the electrons are indistinguishable from each other; the probability must not change on merely interchanging the electron positions. In other words,

$$[\psi(1, 2)]^2 = [\psi(2, 1)]^2 \qquad \text{... (9.28)}$$

This gives $\psi(1, 2) = \pm\psi(2, 1)$ ... (9.29)

This means that the two functions (9.26) and (9.27) ought to be either the same or one be simply the negative of the other. By definition, if the function remains unchanged on interchange of electron positions it is "symmetric" and if it changes sign it is "antisymmetric". The requirement is not met by the expressions (9.26) and (9.27). So, let us take their linear combinations (sum and difference respectively),

$$\psi_+ \text{(symmetric)} = \frac{1}{\sqrt{2}}\,[1s\,(1)\,2s\,(2) + 1s\,(2)\,2s\,(1)] \quad \text{... (9.30)}$$

$$\psi_- \text{(antisymmetric)} = \frac{1}{\sqrt{2}}\,[1s\,(1)\,2s\,(2) - 1s\,(2)\,2s\,(1)] \quad \text{... (9.31)}$$

one (ψ_+) is symmetric, and the other (ψ_-) antisymmetric. Such combinations do not alter the eigenvalue.

It should be clear from Equations (9.30) and (9.31) that on exchange of electrons both ψ_+^2 and ψ_-^2 remain unchanged.

[**Exercise :** Show that the functions $\psi_\pm$ in Equations (9.30) and (9.31) belong to the same eigenvalue of $\hat{H}^0$ as do the functions (9.26) and (9.27) and $\frac{1}{\sqrt{2}}$ is the normalisation factor].

Which of the two wave functions (9.30) and (9.31) is to be used to describe the excited state of He when both lead to the same energy ? Apparently, there is no reason to decide in favour of one against the other. It is necessary at this stage to introduce one more property of the electrons which has no classical counterpart.

9.1.4.1 Electron Spin

While analysing the spectra of alkali metals. Goudsmidt and Uhlenbeck (1926) found it necessary to postulate that an electron has "intrinsic" angular momentum. To explain this, they assumed that the electron spins around its axis. Accordingly, they called it the "spin angular momentum" or simply "spin". Its value (S) could be given by,

$$S = \sqrt{s(s+1)}\,\frac{h}{2\pi} \quad \text{... (9.32)}$$

where s, called the 'spin number', could have only one value, $\frac{1}{2}$.*

The spin angular momentum vector like other vectors has three components S_x, S_y and S_z, but, by quantum mechanics, only one of them can have a specified value ; usually S_z is chosen. In analogy with the orbital angular momentum, the possible orientations that the spin vector can assume correspond to the possible values of the S_z component. The two values of S_z ($\because$ $2s + 1 = 2$)

---

*Subatomic particles have characteristic spin numbers; H^+ has $s = \frac{1}{2}$, photons ($h\nu$) have $s = 1$, and so on.

are $m_s \dfrac{h}{2\pi}$, where $m_s = \dfrac{1}{2}$ or $-\dfrac{1}{2}$. Normally, the two states of the electron corresponding to the two quantum numbers $\pm\dfrac{1}{2}$ are degenerate ; the degeneracy is broken in a magnetic field if the direction of the field is taken as the z-axis.

9.1.4.2 The Eigenvalues and the Eigenfunctions of the Spin Operator

The quantity of interest, *i.e.*, S_z is represented in quantum mechanics by its operator $\hat{S}_z$ and the eigenvalues by $m_s \dfrac{h}{2\pi}$. The eigenvalue equations are,

$$\left.\begin{aligned} \hat{S}_z\, \alpha(s) &= \frac{1}{2}\frac{h}{2\pi}\alpha(s) \\ \hat{S}_z\, \beta(s) &= -\frac{1}{2}\frac{h}{2\pi}\beta(s) \end{aligned}\right\} \qquad \text{... (9.33)}$$

where, $\alpha(s)$ and $\beta(s)$ are the two eigenfunctions corresponding to the two eigenvalues. These are functions of a hypothetical spin coordinate s which is a new variable quite independent of the space coordinates, meaning that an operator depending only on space coordinates does not affect the spin function at all *i.e.*,

$$\nabla^2 [\psi(x, y, z) \,.\, \alpha(s)] = \alpha(s) \,.\, \nabla^2 \psi(x, y, z).$$

Similarly, a spin operator $(\hat{S}_z)$ does not affect the orbital part of a wave function. The operator for spin angular momentum is better represented by $\hat{S}^2$, such that

$$\hat{S}^2\, \alpha = s(s+1)\frac{h^2}{4\pi^2} \,.\, \alpha = \frac{3}{4} \,.\, \frac{h^2}{4\pi^2}\alpha \qquad \left(\because s = \frac{1}{2}\right)$$

The spin eigenfunctions $\alpha(s)$ and $\beta(s)$, usually written as α and β respectively, are taken to be orthonormal, *i.e.*,

$$\left.\begin{aligned} \int \alpha^2\, ds &= \int \beta^2\, ds = 1 \\ \int \alpha\beta\, ds &= \int \beta\alpha\, ds = 1 \end{aligned}\right\} \qquad \text{... (9.34)}$$

ds representing, the hypothetical element of spin coordinate used for integration. No integration and integration limits are, however, ever needed.

9.1.4.3 Matrix Method

Matrices and vectors provide an alternative approach. Electrons have spin angular momentum but the eigenfunctions α and β of the spin operators cannot be expressed in terms of spherical harmonics as no spin coordinate is defined. Pauli represented these functions by column vectors and the spin operators by square matrices as follows:

$$\alpha = \begin{bmatrix} 1 \\ 0 \end{bmatrix}, \beta = \begin{bmatrix} 0 \\ 1 \end{bmatrix} \quad \ldots (9.35)$$

$$\hat{S}_x = \frac{1}{2}\begin{bmatrix} 0 & 1 \\ 1 & 0 \end{bmatrix}, \hat{S}_y = \frac{1}{2}\begin{bmatrix} 0 & -i \\ i & 0 \end{bmatrix}, \hat{S}_z = \frac{1}{2}\begin{bmatrix} 1 & 0 \\ 0 & -1 \end{bmatrix}, \text{and } \hat{S}^2 = \frac{1}{4}\begin{bmatrix} 3 & 0 \\ 0 & 3 \end{bmatrix} \quad \ldots (9.36)$$

This reduces the normalisation and orthogonality integrals to scalar products

$$(\alpha \,.\, \alpha) = (\beta \,.\, \beta) = 1\,; (\alpha \,.\, \beta) = (\beta \,.\, \alpha) = 0$$

The eigenvalue equation becomes

$$\frac{1}{2}\begin{bmatrix} 1 & 0 \\ 0 & -1 \end{bmatrix}\begin{bmatrix} 1 \\ 0 \end{bmatrix} = \frac{1}{2}\begin{bmatrix} 1 \\ 0 \end{bmatrix}$$

$$\hat{S}_z\, \alpha = \frac{1}{2}\alpha\,.$$

9.1.4.4 Spin-Orbitals

In view of the foregoing ideas, an orbital gives an incomplete description of an electron. The complete wave function that represents the actual state of the electron must give not only the probability of finding the electron, at any instant, at the given point in space but also the probability that it is in one or the other spin state, α (*s*) or β (*s*).

If no interaction is supposed to occur between orbital and spin motions, the actual state of an electron is represented by the product of the orbital and the spin functions, the product being called "spin-orbital". Corresponding to an orbital ϕ, there will be two spin-orbitals $\phi\,\alpha$ and $\phi\,\beta$.

For a system of more than one electron the spin state is represented by a product of individual spin functions. The operator for the *z*-component of the total spin angular momentum is then

$$\hat{S}_z = \hat{S}_{1z} + \hat{S}_{2z} + \cdots$$

the operator $\hat{S}_{iz}$ acting on electron *i* only. For a two-electron system we have four possible spin functions viz., α (1) α (2), β (1) β (2), α (1) β (2) and α (2) β (1). The eigenvalue equation for α (1) α (2), for example, is

$$\hat{S}_z\,[\alpha(1)\,\alpha(2)] = \left(\hat{S}_{1z} + \hat{S}_{2z}\right)[\alpha(1)\,\alpha(2)]$$

$$= \hat{S}_{1z}[\alpha(1)\,\alpha(2)] + \hat{S}_{2z}\,[\alpha(1)\,\alpha(2)]$$

$$= \alpha(2)\,\frac{1}{2}\,\alpha(1) + \alpha(1)\,.\,\frac{1}{2}\,\alpha(2) = \alpha(1)\,\alpha(2)$$

(Using atomic units, $\frac{h}{2\pi} = 1$) Eigenvalue (= 1) represents the *z*-component of the "total spin quantum number $M_s \left(= \sum m_{s_i}\right)$" and of the "angular momentum $S_z \left(= M_s \cdot \frac{h}{2\pi}\right)$". The M_s and S_z values of the two-electron system corresponding to the four spin states are given in Table 9.1.

TABLE 9.1

Spin product functions	*Resultant spin quantum number* $\left(M_s = \sum m_{s_i}\right)$	*Resultant angular momentum* $\left(S_z = M_s \cdot \frac{h}{2\pi}\right)$	
$\alpha(1)\,\alpha(2)$	$\frac{1}{2}+\frac{1}{2}=+1$	$+1\,\frac{h}{2\pi}$	... (9.37)
$\beta(1)\,\beta(2)$	$-\frac{1}{2}-\frac{1}{2}=-1$	$-1\,\frac{h}{2\pi}$	... (9.38)
$\alpha(1)\,\beta(2)$	$\frac{1}{2}-\frac{1}{2}=0$	0	... (9.39)
$\alpha(2)\,\beta(1)$	$\frac{1}{2}-\frac{1}{2}=0$	0	... (9.40)

By arguments similar to those used for the two-electron orbital wave function, the spin product functions must be either symmetric or antisymmetric.

The spin combinations Equations (9.37) and (9.38) are symmetric, but Equations (9.39) and (9.40) are neither symmetric nor antisymmetric. In analogy with Equations (9.30) and (9.31), we have symmetric and antisymmetric linear combinations of spins. Accordingly, the four spin functions for a two-electron system are as shown in Table 9.2.

TABLE 9.2

Spin functions	M_s	
$\alpha(1)\,\alpha(2)$	+1	... (9.41)
$\beta(1)\,\beta(2)$	−1	... (9.42)
$\frac{1}{\sqrt{2}}[\alpha(1)\,\beta(2)+\alpha(2)\,\beta(1)]$	0	... (9.43)
$\frac{1}{\sqrt{2}}[\alpha(1)\,\beta(2)-\alpha(2)\,\beta(1)]$	0	... (9.44)

The functions (9.41), (9.42) and (9.43) are symmetric while Equation (9.44) is antisymmetric. The linear combination functions (9.43) and (9.44) can be shown, by the procedure outlined above, to have $M_s = 0$, for example

$$\hat{S}_z\,[\alpha(1)\,\beta(2)+\alpha(2)\,\beta(1)] = \left(\hat{S}_{1z}+\hat{S}_{2z}\right)[\alpha(1)\,\beta(2)+\alpha(2)\,\beta(1)]$$

$$= \frac{1}{2}\alpha(1)\,\beta(2) - \frac{1}{2}\alpha(2)\,\beta(1) - \frac{1}{2}\alpha(1)\,\beta(2) + \frac{1}{2}\alpha(2)\,\beta(1) = 0$$

However, in linear combination functions, the significance of the individual quantum numbers $\left(m_{s_i}\right)$ is lost as one cannot say which electron has which quantum number.

A product of two functions, both of which are symmetric or antisymmetric, will be symmetric, but if one is symmetric and the other antisymmetric, the product must be antisymmetric.

9.1.4.5 *Pauli Principle of Antisymmetric Wave Functions (The Exclusion Rule)*

It is now clear that with two electrons of He atom in the same orbital (the $1s^2$ state) there are the following four possible product combinations of the orbital and spin wave functions:

(*i*) $1s\,(1)\,1s\,(2)\,[\alpha\,(1)\,\alpha\,(2)]$ ... (9.45)

(*ii*) $[1s\,(1)\,1s\,(2)]\,[\beta\,(1)\,\beta\,(2)]$ ... (9.46)

(*iii*) $[1s\,(1)\,1s\,(2)]\,\frac{1}{\sqrt{2}}\,[\alpha\,(1)\,\beta\,(2) + \alpha\,(2)\,\beta\,(1)]$ ... (9.47)

(*iv*) $[1s\,(1)\,1s\,(2)]\,\frac{1}{\sqrt{2}}\,[\alpha\,(1)\,\beta\,(2) - \alpha\,(2)\,\beta\,(1)]$ ... (9.48)

[The explicit form of the orbtial part would be

$$1s\,(1)\,1s\,(2) = \left(\frac{Z'^3}{\pi}\right)^{1/2} e^{-Z'(r_1 + r_2)},$$

Z' = effective nuclear charge].

Which of these four combinations will correctly represent the ground state ($1s^2$) of He atom? The answer is provided by a very important law—the law of antisymmetry of wave functions of electrons. More popularly known as Pauli's exclusion principle, after the name of its discoverer W. Pauli, it states : "For a system of two or more electrons the complete wave function including spin must be antisymmetric with respect to interchange of any two electron positions". Realising that symmetric (+) × symmetric (+), or antisymmetric (–) × antisymmetric (–) is symmetric (+), but symmetric (+) × antisymmetric (–) is antisymmetric (–), we can see that the only antisymmetric combination is Equation (9.48) which, therefore, stands for the ground state of He.

9.1.5 Excited State

In the excited state (1*s* 2*s*) of He, each of the spatial (orbital) functions (9.32) and (9.33) multiplied by the four spin functions (9.41), (9.42), (9.43) and (9.44) yields as many as eight possible product combinations. Of these only the following four are antisymmetric combinations.

$$\Psi_1 = \frac{1}{2}\,[1s\,(1)\,2s\,(2) + 1s\,(2)\,2s\,(1)]\,[\alpha\,(1)\,\beta\,(2) - \alpha\,(2)\,\beta\,(1)] \quad ...\ (9.49)$$

$$\Psi_2 = \frac{1}{\sqrt{2}}\,[1s\,(1)\,2s\,(2) - 1s\,(2)\,2s\,(1)]\,[\alpha\,(1)\,\alpha\,(2)] \quad ...\ (9.50)$$

$$\Psi_3 = \frac{1}{\sqrt{2}}\,[1s\,(1)\,2s\,(2) - 1s\,(2)\,2s\,(1)]\,[\beta\,(1)\,\beta\,(2)] \quad ...\ (9.51)$$

$$\Psi_4 = \frac{1}{2}\,[1s\,(1)\,2s\,(2) - 1s\,(2)\,2s\,(1)]\,[\alpha\,(1)\,\beta\,(2) + \alpha\,(2)\,\beta\,(1)] \quad ...\ (9.52)$$

[An orbital is characterised by three quantum numbers n, l and M and an electron can have any one of the two values $\left(\pm\frac{1}{2}\right)$ of the spin quantum number, m_s. This means that when two electrons are in the same orbital, *e.g.*, $1s^2$ state of He the values of m_s are different $\left(+\frac{1}{2} \text{ and } -\frac{1}{2}\right)$.

If on the other hand they are in different orbitals (1*s* 2*s* of He) at least one of the quantum numbers in the set *n*, *l* and *m* must differ for the two electrons. This qualitative conclusion follows from the Pauli's principle of antisymmetric wave functions. The principle is, therefore, also stated as: "No two electrons in an atom can have all the four quantum numbers identical)."

9.1.5.1 Energy of the Excited State of Helium

The wave functions (9.47) to (9.50) may now be used to calculate the energy of the excited state of He. The energy is given by

$$\bar{E}_{1s\,2s} = \frac{\int \psi^* \hat{H} \psi \, d\tau}{\int \psi^* \psi \, d\tau} \quad \text{... (9.53)}$$

where ψ is the antisymmetric wave function, including spin, of the two-electron system. However, as shown below for the calculation of the energy, the spin part is not relevant.

Since ψ is real and normalised, Equation (9.53) is reduced to

$$\bar{E}_{1s\,2s} = \int \psi \hat{H} \psi \, d\tau \quad \text{... (9.54)}$$

Writing ψ_+ and ψ_- for the orbtial functions, and using Equations (9.49) and (9.52) respectively

$$\bar{E}_{1s\,2s} = \int \psi_\pm \frac{1}{\sqrt{2}} \left[\alpha(1)\,\beta(2) \mp \alpha(2)\,\beta(1)\right] \hat{H} \psi_\pm$$

$$\frac{1}{\sqrt{2}} \cdot \left[\alpha(1)\,\beta(2) \mp \alpha(2)\,\beta(1)\right] dV \quad \text{... (9.55)}$$

where, *d*V is used for integration over all the space and spin coordinates of both the electrons 1 and 2. However, there is no spin coordinate in the Hamiltonian $\hat{H}$ to operate on the spin functions α and β, and so they may be integrated separately. Therefore,

$$\bar{E}_{1s\,2s} = \frac{1}{2}\left[\int \psi_\pm \hat{H} \psi_\pm \, d\tau\right]\left[\iint \alpha(1)\,\beta(2) \mp \alpha(2)\,\beta(1)\right]^2 ds_1\, ds_2 \quad \text{... (9.56)}$$

where, *d*τ is the volume element of space coordinates and ds_1 and ds_2 those of the spin coordinates of electrons 1 and 2 respectively. The double integral over the spin functions in Equation (9.56) may be expanded as

$$\int \alpha(1)^2 ds_1 \cdot \int \beta(2)^2 ds_2 + \int \alpha(2)^2 ds_2 \cdot \int \beta(1)^2 ds_1 \mp 2\int \alpha(1)\,\beta(1)\, ds_1 \cdot \int \alpha(2)\,\beta(2)\, ds_2 \quad \text{... (9.57)}$$

$$= 1 + 1 + 0 = 2$$

because α (1), β (1) and α (2), β (2) are two orthonormal pairs. Hence,

$$\bar{E}_{1s\,2s} = \int \psi_\pm \hat{H} \psi_\pm \, d\tau \quad \text{... (9.58)}$$

The spin part is eliminated. This means that the three functions (9.50) to (9.52) will yield the same energy, which is different from that due to (9.49).

Using the Hamiltonian $\hat{H}$ given by Equation (9.11),

$$\bar{E}_{1s2s} = \left[\int \psi_{\pm} \hat{H}^0(1)\,\psi_{\pm}\,d\tau + \int \psi_{\pm} \hat{H}^0(2)\,\psi_{\pm}\,d\tau + \int \psi_{\pm}\left(\frac{1}{r_{12}}\right)\psi_{\pm}\,d\tau\right] \quad \ldots (9.59)$$

The first integral in Equation (9.59) is

$$\int \psi_{\pm} \hat{H}^0\,(1)\,\psi_{\pm}\,d\tau = \frac{1}{2}\iint\left[1s(1)\,2s(2) \pm 1s(2)\,2s(1)\right]\hat{H}^0\,(1),$$

$$[1s\,(1)\,2s\,(2) \pm 1s\,(2)\,2s\,(1)]\,d\tau_1\,d\tau_2 \quad \ldots (9.60)$$

where, $d\tau_1$ and $d\tau_2$ represent the space coordinates of the two electrons 1 and 2. Expanding the Equation (9.60), we get

$$\int \psi_{\pm} \hat{H}^0\,(1)\,\psi_{\pm}\,d\tau = \frac{1}{2}\Big[\iint 1s(1)\,2s(2)\,\hat{H}^0\,(1)\,1s(1)\,2s(2)\,d\tau_1\,d\tau_2$$

$$\pm \iint 1s(2)\,2s(1)\,\hat{H}^0\,(1)\,1s(2)\,2s(1)\,d\tau_1\,d\tau_2$$

$$\pm \iint 1s(1)\,2s(2)\,\hat{H}^0\,(1)\,1s(2)\,2s(1)\,d\tau_1\,d\tau_2$$

$$\pm \iint 1s(2)\,2s(1)\,\hat{H}^0\,(1)\,1s(1)\,2s(2)\,d\tau_1\,d\tau_2 \quad \ldots (9.61)$$

Since $\hat{H}^0$ (1) operates on electron 1 only, these integrals may be written as products of two separate integrals, each involving a single electron coordinates. Thus, Equation (9.61) may be written as,

$$\int \psi_{\pm} \hat{H}^0\,(1)\,\psi_{\pm}\,d\tau = \int 1s(1)\,\hat{H}^0\,(1)\,1s(1)\,d\tau_1 \int 2s(2)\,2s(2)\,d\tau_2$$

$$\left(= E_{1s}^{He+}\right) \qquad (=1)$$

$$+ \int 2s(1)\,\hat{H}^0\,(1)\,2s(1)\,d\tau_1 \int 1s(2)\,1s(2)\,d\tau_2$$

$$\left(= E_{2s}^{He+}\right) \qquad (=1)$$

$$+ \int 1s(1)\,\hat{H}^0\,(1)\,2s(1)\,d\tau_1 \int 2s(2)\,1s(2)\,d\tau_2$$

$$(=0)$$

$$+ \int 2s(1)\,\hat{H}^0\,(1)\,1s(1)\,d\tau_1 \int 1s(2)\,2s(2)\,d\tau_2$$

$$(=0)$$

Many of the integrals disappear as the 1s and 2s functions are orthonormal.

Therefore, $\int \psi_{\pm} \hat{H}^0(1)\, \psi_{\pm}\, d\tau = E_{1s}^{He+} + E_{2s}^{He+}$ ... (9.62)

Similarly, the second integral in Equation (9.59) gives,

$$\int \psi_{\pm} \hat{H}^0(2)\, \psi_{\pm}\, d\tau = E_{1s}^{He+} + E_{2s}^{He+} \qquad \text{... (9.63)}$$

The third integral in Equation (9.59) becomes

$$\int \psi_{\pm} \left(\frac{1}{r_{12}}\right) \psi_{\pm}\, d\tau = \iint \left[1s(1)\, 2s(2) \pm 1s(2)\, 2s(1)\right]^2 \frac{1}{r_{12}}\, d\tau_1\, d\tau_2$$

$\left(\frac{1}{r_{12}} \text{ is simply a multiplier operator}\right)$

$$= \iint \left[1s(1)\, 2s(2)\right]^2 \frac{1}{r_{12}}\, d\tau_1\, d\tau_2 + \iint \{1s(2)\, 2s(1)\}^2 \frac{1}{r_{12}}\, d\tau_1\, d\tau_2$$

$$\pm 2 \iint 1s(1)\, 2s(2)\, 1s(2)\, 2s(1) \frac{1}{r_{12}}\, d\tau_1\, d\tau_2 \qquad \text{... (9.64)}$$

The first and second integrals in Equation (9.64) represent the expectation average value of $\frac{1}{r_{12}}$ (*i.e.*, the electronic repulsion energy) in the 1*s* 2*s* state. This must be the same whether the configuration is 1*s* (1) 2*s* (2) or 1*s* (2) 2*s* (1), that is, the two integrals are equal.

Therefore, Equation (9.64) becomes,

$$\int \psi_{\pm} \frac{1}{r_{12}} \psi_{\pm}\, d\tau = 2\left[\int \{1s(1)\, 2s(2)\}^2 \frac{1}{r_{12}}\, d\tau_1\, d\tau_2 \pm \int 1s(1)\, 2s(2) \frac{1}{r_{12}}\, 1s(2)\, 2s(1)\, d\tau_1\, d\tau_2\right] \qquad \text{... (9.65)}$$

Putting J for the first and K for the second integral in Equation (9.65), we get

$$\int \psi_{\pm} \frac{1}{r_{12}} \psi_{\pm}\, d\tau = 2\,(J \pm K) \qquad \text{... (9.66)}$$

where the ± signs on the right correspond to the ± signs on the left.

In view of Equations (9.62), (9.63) and (9.66), the expression (9.58) for the total energy of the He in the 1*s* 2*s* state may be written as

$$\bar{E}_{1s\,2s} = E_{1s}^{He+} + E_{2s}^{He+} + J \pm K \qquad \text{... (9.67)}$$

If $\hat{H}^0$ (1) + $\hat{H}^0$ (2) is the unperturbed Hamiltonian, and $\frac{1}{r_{12}}$ the perturbation operator, then J ± K is the first order correction to the unperturbed energy $\left(E_{1s}^{He+} + E_{2s}^{He+}\right)$ which equals (using Table 7.4) – 2.5 a.u.

9.1.5.2 *Coulombic and Exchange Energies*

The integral J stands for the average "coulombic repulsion energy" between electrons in the 1*s* and 2*s* orbitals and the integrals K for the average energy due to interchange of the two-electrons between these orbitals. J has a classical counterpart but K, the "exchange energy", may be termed as "quantum mechanical correction" to the coulombic energy arising due to antisymmetry of the wave function. The evaluation of J and K is very lengthy. Given below are the results:

$$J_{1s\,2s} = \frac{34}{81} \text{ a.u. and } K_{1s\,2s} = \frac{32}{729} \text{ a.u.}$$

$$\therefore \qquad J_{1s\,2s} - K_{1s\,2s} = 0.37\,;\; J_{1s\,2s} + K_{1s\,2s} = 0.46.$$

9.1.5.3 Singlet and Triplet States

From Equation (9.65) it is clear that there will be two energy levels for He in the excited 1*s* 2*s* state (Fig. 9.2) characterised by the perturbation terms J + K and J – K. Since both J and K are positive, the level with the term J + K will be higher and that with J – K lower, the separation between the two levels being 2K. The level having the term J + K corresponds to the symmetric orbital function ψ_+ and an antisymmetric total wave function (9.47) ; the level having the term J – K corresponds to the antisymmetric orbital function ψ_- with three antisymmetric total wave functions (9.50) – (9.52). The former is nondegenerate while the latter is triply degenerate. Accordingly, the former is called the singlet and the latter triplet state. The singlet wave function is denoted by superscript 1 on the left *i.e.*, ${}^1\psi$, and the triplet by ${}^3\psi$, the superscripts.

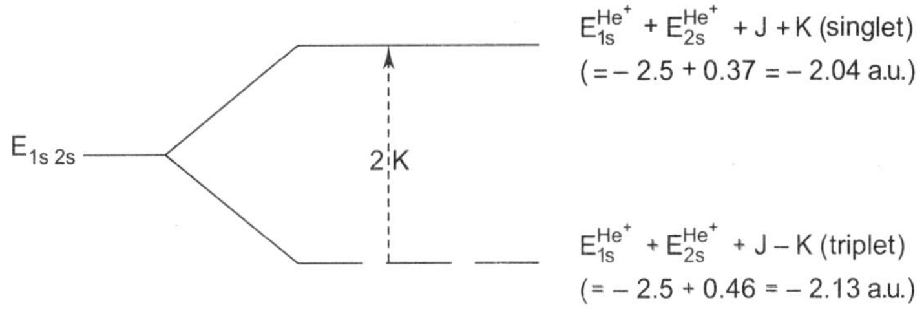

Fig. 9.2

This classification is supported by the observation that in a magnetic field, when the degeneracy is lifted, the lower (triplet) level is split into three sublevels differing only slightly in energy. (For more discussion on singlet-triplet strates see Chapter 10).

9.2 MULTIELECTRON ATOMS

What has been said of a two-electron system can be extended to a multielectron atom. With nucleus at the origin of the coordinate system, the Hamiltonian will consist of a kinetic enegy operator for each electron and potential energy terms due to various nucleus-electron attractions and electron-electron repulsions. There will be as many attraction terms as there are electrons and as many repulsion terms as are the pairs of electrons. For a three-electron atom, for example,

$$V = -\frac{Ze^2}{r_1} - \frac{Ze^2}{r_2} - \frac{Ze^2}{r_3} + \frac{e^2}{r_{12}} + \frac{e^2}{r_{23}} + \frac{e^2}{r_{31}}$$

For an atom with n-electrons, the Hamiltonian in atomic units, is given by

$$\hat{H} = -\frac{1}{2}\left(\nabla_1^2 + \nabla_2^2 + \cdots + \nabla_n^2\right) - \left(\frac{Z}{r_1} + \frac{Z}{r_2} + \cdots + \frac{Z}{r_n}\right) + \frac{1}{2}\left(\frac{1}{r_{12}} + \frac{1}{r_{23}} + \cdots + \frac{1}{r_{mn}}\right)$$

$$= -\frac{1}{2}\sum_{i=1}^{n}\nabla_i^2 - \sum_{i=1}^{n}\frac{Z}{r_i} + \frac{1}{2}\sum_{j}\sum_{i\neq j}^{n}\frac{1}{r_{ij}} \qquad \ldots (9.68)$$

where, Z = nuclear charge, $\nabla_i^2 = \frac{\partial^2}{\partial x_i^2} + \frac{\partial^2}{\partial y_i^2} + \frac{\partial^2}{\partial z_i^2}$, r_i = distance of the electron i from the nucleus, r_{ij} = distance between electrons i and j ; the subscripts i and j can have any value from 1 to n except that $i \neq j$ (because a term like $\frac{1}{r_{ii}}$ or $\frac{1}{r_{jj}}$ would correspond to a nonexistent self-repulsion) and the factor 1/2 has to be included in the third summation term because terms like $\frac{1}{r_{ij}}$ and $\frac{1}{r_{jt}}$ in it would stand for the same electron-electron repulsion. In Equation (9.68) the first and the second terms together is the sum of hydrogen-like Hamiltonians constituting the 'core' Hamiltonian (H^0) of zero order.

Without the respulsion the problem reduces to n one-electron problems. Then, we could use the hydrogen-like atomic orbitals as the basis for contructing the product wave function which would be the approximate (zero order) wave function (ψ^0) for the atom.

This would be a very crude model. Potential energy is highly dependent on repulsion terms. However, before we take to the problem of solution with repulsion included, we describe the method of expressing multi-electron wave functions.

9.2.1 Construction of Antisymmetric Wave Functions

The antisymmetric wave function for n-electron system consists of many terms and it requires some skill to construct it. Consider, for example, a three-electron atom (*e.g.*, Li). Each electron occupies a single spin-orbital. Let the three spin-orbitals be denoted as ϕ_1^α, ϕ_2^β and ϕ_3^α. Now ϕ_1^α can be occupied by any of the three electrons so that we have three choices, $\phi_1^\alpha(1)$, $\phi_1^\alpha(2)$ and $\phi_1^\alpha(3)$ for a single spin-orbital. Corresponding to any one choice for an electron in ϕ_1^α, say ϕ_1^α (1), we have, with the remaining two electrons, only two choices for ϕ_2^β, viz., $\phi_2^\beta(2)$ and $\phi_2^\beta(3)$. Then, with $\phi_2^\beta(2)$, for electron 2, we are left with only one choice for the electron 3, viz., $\phi_3^\alpha(3)$. The total number of ways in which we can arrange the three electrons in the three spin obitals is thus $3 \times 2 \times 1 = 3\,! = 6$. The proper antisymmetric wave function will consist of six terms each with + or – sign. The sign is to be decided as follows. Any two terms which differ by an *odd* number of interchanges will have different signs while those which differ by *even* number of interchanges will have the same sign. Thus, fixing the sign of any term, say

$\phi_1^{\alpha}(1)\,\phi_2^{\beta}(2)\,\phi_3^{\alpha}(3)$ as positive (+), we get negative (–) sign for $\phi_1^{\alpha}(1)\,\phi_2^{\beta}(3)\,\phi_3^{\alpha}(2)$, positive sign (+) for $\phi_1^{\alpha}(2)\,\phi_2^{\beta}(3)\,\phi_3^{\alpha}(1)$, and so on.

Denoting $\phi_1^{\alpha}, \phi_2^{\beta}$ and ϕ_3^{α} by A, B and C respectively, the antisymmetric wave function may be written as,

$$\psi_- = N\,[A(1)\,B(2)\,C(3) - A(1)\,B(3)\,C(2) + A(3)\,B(1)\,C(2) - A(3)\,B(2)\,C(1) + A(2)\,B(3)\,C(1) - A(2)\,B(1)\,C(3)] \quad ...(9.69)$$

where, N is the normalisation factor.

The function (9.69) is antisymmetric with respect to interchange of any pair of electrons. For Li atom, let

$$A(1) = \phi_1^{\alpha}(1) = 1s(1)\,\alpha(1)$$

$$B(2) = \phi_2^{\beta}(2) = 1s(2)\,\beta(2)$$

$$C(3) = \phi_3^{\alpha}(2) = 2s(3)\,\alpha(3), \text{ and so on.}$$

A direct consequence of such an antisymmetric wave function is that any spin orbital cannot be occupied by more than one electron, or any atomic orbital ϕ cannot be occupied by more than two electrons. If the same spin orbital, say ϕ_1^{α} (*i.e.*, A), were to contain two electrons 1 and 2, that would amount to saying that $\phi_2^{\beta} = \phi_1^{\alpha}$, or A = B, then Equation (9.67) would become,

$$\psi_- = A\,[A(1)\,A(2)\,C(3) - A(1)\,A(3)\,C(2) + A(3)\,A(1)\,C(2) - A(2)\,A(3)\,C(1) + A(2)\,A(3)\,C(1) - A(2)\,A(1)\,C(3)] = 0$$

The wave function vanishes, so no such state is possible. This is equivalent to the "Pauli exclusion principle" which states, "an electron in a spin-orbital prevents any other electron from occupying it".

For an n-electron atom, the anti symmetric wave function is constructed by arranging $n\,!$ terms in the manner decribed above.

The normalisation factor can be determined easily if we assume that the individual spin-orbitals are normalised and orthogonal, *i.e.*, terms like

$$\int A(i)^2\,d\tau_i = \int B(j)^2\,d\tau_j = ... = 1 \quad ...(9.70)$$

and $$\int A(i)\,B(j)\,d\tau = 0$$

where, A (i) denotes spin-orbital with electron i. For *a* three-electron atom (Li atom), for example, using Equation (9.67), we get

$$\int \psi_-^2\,d\tau = \int N^2\,A(1)\,B(2)\,C(3) - A(1)\,B(3)\,C(2) + \cdots - A(2)\,B(1)\,C(3)]^2\,d\tau_1\,d\tau_2\,d\tau_3 = 1 \quad ...(9.71)$$

On expanding Equation (9.71), one gets six integrals like,

$$\iiint [A(1)\,B(2)\,C(3)]^2\,d\tau_1\,d\tau_2\,d\tau_3 = \int A(1)^2\,d\tau_1 \int B(2)^2\,d\tau_2 \int C(3)^2\,d\tau_3 = 1 \quad ...(9.72)$$

and several integrals of products of cross terms like,

$$\iiint [\mathrm{A}(1)\,\mathrm{B}(2)\,\mathrm{C}(3)].[\mathrm{A}(1)\,\mathrm{B}(3)\,\mathrm{C}(2)]\,d\tau_1\,d\tau_2\,d\tau_3$$

$$= \int \mathrm{A}(1)\,\mathrm{A}(1)\,d\tau_1 . \int \mathrm{B}(2)\,\mathrm{C}(2)\,d\tau_2 . \int \mathrm{B}(3)\,\mathrm{C}(3)\,d\tau_3 = 0 \quad \text{... (9.73)}$$

if the orbitals, A, B and C are assumed to be orthonormal.

In view of Equations (9.72) and (9.73), the expression (9.71) becomes,

$$\mathrm{N}^2 \times 6 = 1 \text{ or } \mathrm{N} = \frac{1}{\sqrt{6}} = \frac{1}{\sqrt{3!}}$$

For an n-electron atom,

$$\mathrm{N} = \frac{1}{\sqrt{n!}} \quad \text{... (9.74)}$$

9.2.2 Determinantal Form of the Wave Functions (Slater Determinants)

We have laid down the general procedure for constructing antisymmetric wave functions for a multi-electron atom. But with increase in the number of electrons, the number of terms increases in such large proportions (for example, 5 ! *i.e.*, 120 terms for an atom with 5 electrons only) that we must find an abbreviated form to represent a wave function. A short hand form is determinant in which the spin-orbitals are the elements; each row in this determinant is labelled with an electron and each column with a spin-orbital. The normalised wave function, Equation (9.69) for a three electron atom, for example, is written as,

$$\psi_- = \frac{1}{\sqrt{3!}} \begin{vmatrix} \mathrm{A}(1) & \mathrm{B}(1) & \mathrm{C}(1) \\ \mathrm{A}(2) & \mathrm{B}(2) & \mathrm{C}(2) \\ \mathrm{A}(3) & \mathrm{B}(3) & \mathrm{C}(3) \end{vmatrix} \quad \text{... (9.75)}$$

For an n-electron atom, there are n rows and n columns

$$\psi_- = \frac{1}{\sqrt{n!}} \begin{vmatrix} \mathrm{A}(1) & \mathrm{B}(1) & \cdots \\ \mathrm{A}(2) & \mathrm{B}(2) & \cdots \\ \cdots & \cdots & \cdots \\ \cdots & \cdots & \cdots \\ \mathrm{A}(n) & \mathrm{B}(n) & \cdots \end{vmatrix} \quad \text{... (9.76)}$$

Such determinants of spin-orbitals are called "Slater determinants".

The antisymmetry of Equations (9.75) or (9.76) as well as the Pauli principle are guaranteed by two properties of determinants:

(*i*) If two rows or columns of a determinant are interchanged, the resulting determinant is just the negative of the original one, *i.e.*,

$$\begin{vmatrix} \mathrm{A}(1) & \mathrm{B}(1) & \mathrm{C}(1) \\ \mathrm{A}(2) & \mathrm{B}(2) & \mathrm{C}(2) \\ \mathrm{A}(3) & \mathrm{B}(3) & \mathrm{C}(3) \end{vmatrix} = - \begin{vmatrix} \mathrm{A}(2) & \mathrm{B}(2) & \mathrm{C}(2) \\ \mathrm{A}(1) & \mathrm{B}(1) & \mathrm{C}(1) \\ \mathrm{A}(3) & \mathrm{B}(3) & \mathrm{C}(3) \end{vmatrix}$$

(*ii*) If any two rows or two columns of a determinant are the same, the determinant vanishes.

[**Exercise:** *Write the ground and excited state antisymmetric wave function for He atom in the Slater determinantal form, and show that the two electrons cannot have the same spin-orbital.*

$$\Psi_- = 1s(1)\,1s(2)\,[\alpha(1)\,\beta(2) - \alpha(2)\,\beta(1)]$$

$$= 1s(1)\,\alpha(1)\,.\,1s(2)\,\beta(2) - 1s(1)\,\beta(1)\,.\,1s(2)\,\alpha(2)$$

$$= \begin{vmatrix} 1s(1)\,\alpha(1) & 1s(1)\,\beta(1) \\ 1s(2)\,\alpha(2) & 1s(2)\,\beta(2) \end{vmatrix} \quad \text{... (9.77)}$$

where, $1s\,(i)\;\alpha\,(i)$, for example, is the spin-orbital of electron i ($i = 1, 2$).

If both electrons have the same spin-orbitals, the determinant

$$\begin{vmatrix} 1s(1)\,\alpha(1) & 1s(1)\,\alpha(1) \\ 1s(2)\,\alpha(2) & 1s(2)\,\alpha(2) \end{vmatrix} = 0].$$

With increasing number of electrons, the determinant will have large size and further abbreviation is necessary. This is done by using a bar over the orbital which has β-spin; absence of a bar will indicate α spin. Thus, the determinantal wave function for Li atom is,

$$\psi_- = \frac{1}{\sqrt{3\,!}} \begin{vmatrix} 1s(1) & \bar{1}s(1) & 2s(1) \\ 1s(2) & \bar{2}s(2) & 2s(2) \\ 1s(3) & \bar{1}s(3) & 2s(3) \end{vmatrix} \quad \text{... (9.78)}$$

The excited state configuration $1s\,2s$ of He has four Slater determinants corresponding to the four wave functions (9.49) to (9.52),

$$D_1 = \frac{1}{\sqrt{2}} \begin{vmatrix} 1s(1) & 2s(1) \\ 1s(2) & 2s(2) \end{vmatrix} ; D_2 = \frac{1}{\sqrt{2}} \begin{vmatrix} 1s(1) & 2\bar{s}(1) \\ 1s(2) & 2\bar{s}(2) \end{vmatrix}$$

$$D_3 = \frac{1}{\sqrt{2}} \begin{vmatrix} 1\bar{s}(1) & 2s(1) \\ 1\bar{s}(2) & 2s(2) \end{vmatrix} ; D_4 = \frac{1}{\sqrt{2}} \begin{vmatrix} 1\bar{s}(1) & 2\bar{s}(1) \\ 1\bar{s}(2) & 2\bar{s}(2) \end{vmatrix}$$

The wave functions (9.49) to (9.52) may then be written as a Slater determinant or a linear combination of Slater determinants as follows:

$$\Psi_1 = \frac{1}{\sqrt{2}}\,(D_2 - D_3); \Psi_2 = D_1$$

$$\Psi_3 = D_4\,; \Psi_4 = \frac{1}{\sqrt{2}}\,(D_2 + D_3)$$

9.3 SOLVING THE SCHRÖDINGER EQUATION—SELF CONSISTENT FIELD APPROXIMATION

9.3.1 Hartree's Theory

The interelectronic repulsion term in Equation (9.68) does not permit separation of the Schrödinger equation into one-electron equations. Hence the product wave function ψ using

H-like orbitals should not be expected to yield correct energy in the case of many electron atoms. D.R. Hartree proposed the following method which is known as the method of self consistent field (SCF).

The wave function of an n-electron atom is assumed to be a simple product of one electron orbitals.

$$\psi = \phi_1(1) \cdot \phi_2(2) \cdot \phi_3(3) \ldots \phi_n(n) \qquad \ldots (9.79)$$

and the energy

$$E = \int \psi^* \hat{H} \psi \, d\tau \qquad \ldots (9.80)$$

if ψ is normalised which is ensured if each ϕ is normalised, *i.e.*,

$$\int \phi_i^* \phi_j \, d\tau = 1 \text{ for } i = j \text{ and } 0 \text{ for } i \neq j \qquad \ldots (9.81)$$

Each ϕ is the product of a radial function and spherical harmonics and carries effective nuclear charge Z′ in place of Z. $\hat{H}$ is the complete Hamiltonian given by Equation (9.68)

$$\hat{H} = \sum_i \hat{H}^0(i) + \frac{1}{2} \sum_i \sum_{j \neq i} \frac{1}{r_{ij}}$$

where

$$H^0(i) = \frac{1}{2} \nabla_i^2 - \frac{Z}{r_i}$$

The best wave function is that which leads to minimum energy, *i.e.*, which satisfies the equation

$$\delta E = \delta \int \psi^* \hat{H} \psi \, d\tau = 0 \qquad \ldots (9.82)$$

for a small variation $\delta\phi$ in any of the orbitals. The orbitals can be varied at will but their ortho normality must be maintained. The solution of Equation (9.82), subject to the condition Equation (9.81), shows that the best possible wave function (Eqn. 9.79) is obtained by using the set of orbitals ϕ_i which are solution to the n simultaneous Schrödinger equations (Derivation is lengthy and has been avoided. The interested reader is referred to S.M. Blinder, Am. Phys. 1965, 33, 431).

$$\hat{H}(i) \phi_i = E_i \phi_i \, (i = 1, 2, \ldots, n) \qquad \ldots (9.83)$$

where,

$$\hat{H}(i) = -\frac{1}{2} \nabla_i^2 - \frac{Z}{r_i} + \hat{V}_i$$

$$= \hat{H}^0(i) + \hat{V}_i \qquad \ldots (9.84)$$

$\hat{V}_i$ represents the effective potential energy of the electron i due to repulsion by all other electrons.

To determine V_i Hartree assumes that each electron in the atom moves in a potential field due to the nucleus and all other electrons. The Equation (9.83) can be solved by an iterative technique as follows:

We begin with an assumed set of orbitals $\phi_1, \phi_2, \phi_3, \ldots, \phi_n$ which may, for example, be hydrogen like. Now consider the electron 1 moving through the smeared cloud of other electrons. The potential energy of interaction between point charges q_1 and q_2 is $V_{12} = \frac{q_1 q_2}{r_{12}}$. For electron

1, $q_1 = -e$, the electronic charge; electron 2, however is a cloud of varying charge density ρ. The infinitesimal charge in the volume element $d\tau_2$ of the cloud is $\rho_2\, dV_2 = -e\,|\,\phi_2\,|^2\, d\tau_2$. Summing up the interactions of q_1 with infinitesimal elements of charge, we have

$$V_{12} = \frac{\int (-e)(-e)\,|\,\phi_2\,|^2\, d\tau_2}{r_{12}} = \frac{\int |\,\phi_2\,|^2\, d\tau_2}{r_{12}} \qquad \text{... (9.85)}$$

Using atomic units ($e = 1$).

Adding the interactions of electron 1 with all other electrons,

$$V_1 = \sum_{j=2}^{n} \frac{\int |\,\phi_j\,|^2\, d\tau_j}{r_{1j}} \qquad \text{... (9.86)}$$

Under the central force field assumption V_1 averaged over all angles θ and ϕ is a function of r_1 only. Thus the Equation (9.83) for $i = 1$ has the explicit form

$$\left[-\frac{1}{2}\nabla_1^2 - \frac{z}{r_1} + V_1(r_1)\right] = E_1 \qquad \text{... (9.87)}$$

On solving, we obtain an improved orbital ϕ_1'. Now the electron 2 may be considered to move in a charge cloud of density

$$|\,\phi_1'(r_1)\,|^2 + |\,\phi_3(3)\,|^2\;|\,\phi_4(4)\,|^2 + \ldots + |\,(\phi_n(n)\,|^2$$

The effective potential V_2 (2) is calculated as above and the Equation (9.81) solved to obtain ϕ_2'. The process is continued until we have a set of improved orbitals for all n electrons.

The potential energy due to repulsion for any electron i is given by

$$V_i = \sum_{j\neq i}^{n} \int \phi_j^2 \cdot \frac{d\tau_j}{r_{ij}} \qquad \text{... (9.88)}$$

The equations can be solved numerically or by computer.

The new set is now used to recalculate the potential energy and another new set of orbitals.

The cycle of iterations is continued till we have a set not much different from that in the earlier cycle. The orbitals are then consistent with the potential field thus calculated and are accordingly called "self consistent field (SCF) orbitals $\left(\phi_i^S\right)$."

Finally, we have the wave function

$$\psi = \phi_1^s \cdot \phi_2^s \cdot \phi_3^s \cdots \phi_n^s \qquad \text{... (9.89)}$$

The orbitals will be products of radial and angular functions both.

Take the example of helium atom. The wave function in the ground state is

$$\psi = 1s\,(1)\,.\,1s\,(2) \qquad \text{... (9.90)}$$

We start with hydrogen like orbitals

$$1s\,(1) = \sqrt{8/\pi}\,.\,e^{-2r_1}$$

and

$$1s\,(2) = \sqrt{8/\pi}\,.\,e^{-2r_2}$$

with Z = 2. These orbitals would be correct only if the two electrons were independent of each other. Actually they are not ; they repel each other in the atom. The potential energy of repulsion of electron 1 due to electron 2 is

$$V_1 = \int |1s(2)|^2 \cdot \frac{1}{r_{12}} d\tau_2$$

with this potential a better orbital 1s′ (1) for electron 1 is obtained by solving the equation.

$$\left[H_1^0 + \int |1s(2)|^2 \cdot \frac{1}{r_{12}} d\tau_2\right] 1s(1) = E_1(1s(1)) \qquad \text{... (9.91)}$$

Now, the orbital 1s′ (1) is

$$1s'(1) = \sqrt{\frac{\xi^3}{\pi}} \cdot e^{-\xi r}$$

where $\xi < 2$. With this orbital the potential energy of repulsion of electron 2 is

$$V_2 = \int |1s'(1)|^2 \cdot \frac{1}{r_{12}} d\tau_1$$

The equation analogous to Equation (9.91) is solved for 1s′ (2) when

$$1s'(2) = \sqrt{\frac{\xi'^3}{\pi}}\, e^{-\xi' r}$$

where $\xi' < \xi$. The 1s′ (2) is used to recalculate 1s′ (1) and so on until the ξ for both the orbitals become almost the same; the corresponding orbitals are the SCF orbitals.

9.3.1.1 *Orbital Energy and Total Energy*

Avoiding the use of the superscript *s* in Equation (9.89), the orbital energy E_i of the electron *i*, using (9.68), (9.82) and (9.88)

$$E_i = \int \phi_i \hat{H}(i)\, \phi_i\, d\tau_i$$

$$= \int \phi_i \hat{H}^0 \phi_i\, d\tau_i + \int \phi_i \left[\sum_{j \neq i} \int |\phi_j|^2 \frac{1}{r_{ij}} d\tau_j\right] \phi_i\, d\tau_i$$

$$= E_i^0 + \sum_{j \neq i} \iint |\phi_i|^2 \cdot |\phi_j|^2 \cdot \frac{1}{r_{ij}} \cdot d\tau_j\, d\tau_i$$

$$= E_i^0 + \sum_{j \neq i} J_{ij} \qquad \text{... (9.92)}$$

In Equation (9.92), E_i^0 is the orbital energy of the electron *i*, in the absence of all other electrons, and J_{ij} is the average coulombic energy of repulsion between two charges represented by $|\phi_i|^2$ and $|\phi_j|^2$.

The total energy of all the electrons in the atom is

$$E = \int \psi^* \hat{H} \psi \, d\tau$$

$$= \int (\phi_i^* . \phi_2^* . \phi_3^* \cdots \phi_n^*) \sum_i \hat{H}^0 (i) (\phi_i . \phi_2 . \phi_3 \cdots \phi_n) \, d\tau_1 \, d\tau_2 \cdots d\tau_n$$

$$+ \int (\phi_1^* . \phi_2^* . \phi_3^* \cdots \phi_n^*) . \frac{1}{2} \sum_i \sum_{j \neq 1} \frac{1}{r_{ij}} (\phi_1 . \phi_2 . \phi_3 \cdots \phi_n) \, d\tau_1 \, d\tau_2 \cdots d\tau_n$$

$$= \sum_i E_i^0 + \frac{1}{2} \sum_i \sum_{j \neq i} \iint | \phi_i |^2 . | \phi_j |^2 \cdots \frac{1}{r_{ij}} . d\tau_i \, d\tau_j$$

$$= \sum_i E_i^0 + \frac{1}{2} \sum_i \sum_{j \neq i} J_{ij} \quad \text{... (9.93)}$$

as the operator $\hat{H}$ (i) acts on electron i only and $\frac{1}{r_{ij}}$ on electrons i and j, and all orbitals are normalised.

In relation to orbital energies, E_i,

$$E = \sum_i E_i - \frac{1}{2} \sum_i \sum_{j \neq i} J_{ij} \quad \text{... (9.94)}$$

The term $\frac{1}{2} \sum_i \sum_{j \neq i} J_{ij}$ in Equation (9.94) has to be deducted from the sum of the orbital energies otherwise one would be counting J_{ij} and J_{ji} as two separate repulsion terms which actually are physically the same.

Hartree, along with his students, performed numerical calculations for a number of atoms and their ions. His calculations came out to be in good agreement with experimental results for ionisation potentials, but were not very satisfactory for energies of the atoms.

9.4 HARTREE-FOCK SELF CONSISTENT FIELD (HFSCF) THEORY

Hartree's SCF method suffers from a drawback that the orbital product wave function (9.89) is not antisymmetric. V. Fock used antisymmetrised wave function and followed the same iterative procedure is described by Hartree. The orbitals finally obtained are therefore known as Hartree-Fock SCF atomic orbitals (HFSCF AO).

The antisymmetrised product wave function ψ is most conveniently expressed as a determinant. For an n-electron atom with closed shell configuration, that is, in which all atomic orbitals are doubly occupied with paired spins (*e.g.*, Be: $1s^2 \, 2s^2$).

$$\Psi = \frac{1}{\sqrt{n!}} \left| \phi_1 (1) \, \bar{\phi}_1 (2) \, \phi_2 (3) \, \bar{\phi}_2 (4) \cdots \bar{\phi}_{n/2} (n) \right| \quad \text{... (9.95)}$$

where, the determinant has been represented through diagonal elements; ϕ_1 (1) is a spin orbital with electron 1 and α spin, $\bar{\phi}_1(2)$ with electron 2 and β-spin in the same orbital ϕ_1 and so on. The best wave function is that which leads to minimum energy, *i.e.*, which satisfies the equation.

$$\delta E = \delta\left[\int \Psi \hat{H} \Psi \, d\tau\right] = 0 \qquad \text{... (9.96)}$$

The antisymmetry of Ψ led Fock to introduce a new operator, the fock operator $(\hat{F})$, in place of $\hat{H}$ to include electron repulsion as well as electron exchange; the fock operator is defined for any electron i as

$$\hat{F}\,(i) = -\frac{1}{2}\nabla_i^2 - \frac{Z}{r_i} + \sum_{j=1}^{n/2}\left[2\hat{J}_j\,(i) - \hat{K}_j\,(j)\right] \qquad \text{... (9.97)}$$

and the hF equation for the electron i is

$$\hat{F}\,(i)\,\phi_i = E_i\,\phi_i \qquad \text{... (9.97a)}$$

where, j is any orbital and $\frac{n}{2}$ is the number of orbitals for n-electrons. The operators $\hat{J}_j$ and $\hat{K}_j$ are defined, for any pair of electrons 1 and 2, as

$$\hat{J}_j\,(1)\,\phi_i\,(1) = \left[\int \phi_j^*\,(2)\,\frac{1}{r_{12}}\,\phi_j\,(2)\,d\tau_2\right]\phi_i\,(1) \text{ (Coulomb operator)} \qquad \text{... (9.98)}$$

$$\hat{K}_j\,(1)\,\phi_i\,(1) = \left[\int \phi_j^*\,(2)\,\frac{1}{r_{12}}\,\phi_i\,(2)\,d\tau_2\right]\phi_j\,(1) \text{ (Exchange operator)} \qquad \text{... (9.99)}$$

Note that ϕ_i (1) is eigenfunction of J_j (1) but not of $\hat{K}_j$; the effect of K_j is to change ϕ_i (1) to ϕ_j (1). These operators are so named as they yield the average coulomb and exchange energies as

$$\int \phi_i^*\,(1)\,\hat{J}_j(1)\,\phi_i\,(1)\,d\tau = \iint \phi_i^*\,(1)\,\phi_j^*\,(2)\,\frac{1}{r_{12}}\,\phi_j\,(2)\,\phi_i\,(1)\,d\tau_1\,d\tau_2 = J_{ij} \qquad \text{... (9.100)}$$

$$\int \phi_i^*\,(1)\,\hat{K}_j(1)\,\phi_i\,(1)\,d\tau = \iint \phi_i^*\,(1)\,\phi_j^*\,(2)\,\frac{1}{12}\,\phi_i\,(2)\,\phi_j\,(1)\,d\tau_1\,d\tau_2 = K_{ij} \qquad \text{... (9.101)}$$

In the Fock operator, Equation (9.97), the summation term $\sum_i\left(2\hat{J}_j - \hat{K}_j\right)$ includes $\hat{J}_i$ and $\hat{K}_i$ which must be known before we write down the expression for $\hat{F}$ explicitly. But $\hat{J}_i$ and $\hat{K}_i$ involve Equations (9.98) and (9.99) and ϕ_i is an eigenfunction of $\hat{F}$. To know ϕ_i we need $\hat{F}$ and to know $\hat{F}$ we need ϕ_i. So we have to take to iterative procedure. We start with a reasonable set of orbitals (usually the Slater type orbitals, to be discussed in the next section) and apply the Hartree's method of repeated iterations as described, to obtain the HFSCF orbitals ϕ_i.

Using these orbitals, we calculate the "orbital energies" as expectation values of $\hat{F}$; for the orbital ϕ_i

$$E_i = \int \phi_i^* \hat{F} \phi_i \, d\tau$$

$$= \int \phi_i^* \left(-\frac{1}{2}\nabla_1^2 - \frac{Z}{r_1} \right) \phi_i \, d\tau + \int \phi_i^* \left(\sum_{j=1}^{n/2} \left(2\hat{J}_j - \hat{K}_j \right) \phi_i \, d\tau \right)$$

$$= E_i^0 + \sum_{j=1}^{n/2} \left(2J_{ij} - K_{ij} \right) \qquad \text{... (9.102)}$$

In Equation (9.102) E_i^0 represents the one-electron energy of the orbital in absence of all other electrons, also called 'core energy', while the second term is the sum of the coulomb and exchange energies involving all electrons. For a particular value of j other than i, say k,

$$2J_{ik} - K_{ik} = 2\left(\int \phi_i^* (1)\, \phi_k^* (2) \frac{1}{r_{12}} \phi_i (1)\, \phi_k (2)\, d\tau \right) - \int \phi_i^* (1)\, \phi_k^* (2) \frac{1}{r_{12}} \phi_i (2)\, \phi_k (1)\, d\tau \qquad \text{... (9.103)}$$

The factor 2 in first integral occurs as the electron 1 in ϕ_i experiences repulsion by each of the two electrons in ϕ_k. The exchange integral, on the other hand, occurs only once because it arises out of the exchange of electrons and the spin of an electron in ϕ_i can match the spin of only one of the two electrons in ϕ_k. If, for example, the electron 1 with α spin in ϕ_i exchanges with electron 2 of β spin in ϕ_k, then

$$\int \phi_i^* (1)\, \alpha (1)\, \phi_k^* (2)\, \beta (2) \frac{1}{r_{12}} \phi_i (2)\, \alpha (2)\, \phi_k (1)\, \beta (1)\, d\tau . ds_1\, ds_2$$

$$= \int \phi_i^* (1) \phi_k^* (2) \frac{1}{r_{12}} \phi_i (2) \phi_k (1) d\tau . \int \alpha(1)\beta(1) ds_1 \int \alpha(2)\beta(2) ds_2 = 0$$

due to orthogonality of α and β spin functions.

The summation over $2J_{ij} - K_{ij}$ includes the case $j = i$, *i.e.*, $2J_{ii} - K_{ii}$ which is equal to J_{ii} because Equations (9.102) and (9.103) indicate that $J_{ii} = K_{ii}$. In other words, in this case there is no exchange energy (after all, there is no point in exchanging electrons in the same orbital), J_{ii} represents repulsion energy between the two electrons in the same orbital.

Thus, the "orbital energy E_i" Equation (9.102) of an electron in the orbital ϕ_i of an atom is the sum of the hydrogen-like energies $\left(E_i^0\right)$ and the inter-electronic repulsion and exchange energies due to all the other electrons in their orbitals. If all the orbitals are doubly occupied, the sum of the orbital energies of all the electrons is $\sum 2E_i$. But this includes an extra measure of the repulsion and exchange energies due to double counting (see earlier discussion under Hartree's

---

* See John P. Lowe: *Quantum Chemistry* (Academic Press. New York), 1978; page 509.

method). Subtracting from the $\sum 2E_i$, an amount equal to the interelectronic interaction (repulsion and exchange) energy, which has been counted twice, we get the total electronic energy,

$$E = \sum_i 2E_i - \sum_{i=1}^{n/2}\sum_{j=1}^{n/2}\left(2J_{ij} - K_{ij}\right) \quad \text{... (9.104)}$$

$$E = \sum_i 2E_i^0 + \sum_{i=1}^{n/2}\sum_{j=1}^{n/2}\left(2J_{ij} - K_{ij}\right) \quad \text{... (9.105)}$$

[using Equation (9.102)].

The condition that E should be minimum, subject to the condition that the orbitals are orthonormal, leads to HF Equation (9.96) for the best orbitals.

In the case of He ($1s^2$), for example, the orbitals energy E_1 for the electron 1 in 1s orbital is,

$$E_{1s} = E_{1s}^0 + 2J_{1s\,1s} - K_{1s\,1s}$$

$$= E_{1s}^0 + J_{1s\,1s} \text{ (because } J_{1s\,1s} = K_{1s\,1s})$$

The total energy E of the two electrons is

$$E = -2E_{1s} - (2J_{1s\,1s} - K_{1s\,1s}) = 2E_{1s} - J_{1s\,1s} = 2E_{1s}^0 + J_{1s\,1s}$$

where, $\quad E_{1s}^0 = E_{1s}^{He+}$

This is the same expression as derived earlier in the case of He.

[**Exercise :** *Give the expression for potential energy, orbital energy and total energy for Be atom ($1s^2$ $2s^2$).*

Here $\quad \phi_1 = 1s, \phi_2 = 2s$

For a 1s electron the Schrödinger equation is

$$\left[-\frac{1}{2}\nabla_1^2 - \frac{Z'}{r_1} + V_1\right] 1s'(1) = E_1\, 1s'(1);$$

Z' is to be determined by variation method,

$$V_1 = \int \frac{1s(2)'^2}{r_{12}} dV_2 + \int \frac{2s(3)^2}{r_{13}} dV_3 + \int \frac{2s(4)^2}{r_{14}} dV_4$$

$$E^0 = -\frac{Z'^2}{n^2}$$

(n = 1 for 1s and 2 for 2s).

$$E = 2E_{1s}^0 + 2E_{2s}^0 + 2J_{1s\,1s} - K_{1s\,1s} + 2J_{1s\,2s} - K_{1s\,2s} + 2J_{2s\,1s} - K_{2s\,1s} + 2J_{2s\,2s} - K_{2s\,2s}$$

Here E_{1s}^0 and E_{2s}^0 are the energies of 1s and 2s orbitals respectively in the "core". Since

$J_{1s\,1s} = K_{1s\,1s}$ and $J_{2s\,2s} = K_{2s\,2s}$

$$E = 2E^0_{1s} + 2E^0_{2s} + J_{1s\,1s} + J_{2s\,2s} + 2J_{1s\,2s} + 2J_{2s\,1s} - K_{1s\,2s} - K_{2s\,1s}].$$

9.5 SLATER TYPE ORBITALS (STO)

As an initial guess in SCF calculations H-like orbitals are unsuitable because of shielding of the nucleus by inner electrons. J.C. Slater gave a better expression for such orbital functions as,

$$\psi_{nlm}(r, \theta, \varphi) = [Nr^{n'-1}(\exp(-Z'r/n')] [y_{i,M}(\theta, \varphi)] \quad \text{... (9.106)}$$

where, N is the normalisation factor, n' is effective principal quantum number, Z' is effective nuclear charge, and $y_{IM}(\theta, \varphi)$ the angular part, or the spherical harmonics. Functions of the type Equation (9.106) are called "Slater type orbitals (STO)" which differ from hydrogen like orbitals only in the radial part.

9.5.1 Slater Rules

Slater also proposed a set of empirical rules, described below, to calculate n' and Z':

(*i*) The effective principal quantum number n' is related to the quantum number n as follows:

n: 1	2	3	4	5	6
n': 1	2	3	3.7	4.0	4.2

(*ii*) The effective nuclear charge Z' is related to the actual atomic number Z as

$$Z' = Z - S \quad \text{... (9.107)}$$

where, S is the screening constant. The value of S is calculated by the following rules:

The orbitals are first grouped as:

$$(1s)\,;(2s, 2p)\,;(3s, 3p)\,;(3d)\,;(4s, 4p)\,;(4d)\,;(4f) \quad \text{... (9.108)}$$

The screening constant (S) is then calculated by adding the contributions from electrons as follows:

(*a*) No contribution from electrons in groups higher than (*i.e.*, to the right of) the group in question is included.

(*b*) Each electron in the same group contributes 0.35; the electron in 1*s* group, however, contributes 0.30 only.

(*c*) In case of *s* or *p* group, each electron in the next lower group contributes 0.85; for an electron in *d* or *f* group the contribution from each inner electron is 1.00.

(*d*) Each electron in groups lower by two or more numbers from the one in question contributes 1.00.

[**Exercise 1 :** *Determine the effective nuclear charge for the 1s electron in He and 2s electron in C.*

$He\,(1s^2)\,; S = 0.30, Z' = 1.70.$

$C\,(1s^2\,2s^2\,2p^2)$: For each electron in 2*s* or 2*p* group,

$S = 3 \times 0.35$ (due to the remaining three electrons in that group)

$+ 2 \times 0.85$ (due to the two electrons in the next lower group *i.e.*, 1*s*)

$= 2.75$

$Z' = 3.25$].

[Exercise 2 : *Find the expressions for the Slater type orbitals for 2s, $2p_x$, and $2p_z$ electrons in N; ignore the normalisation factor.*

$$N\ (1s^2\,2s^2\,2p^3) : S = 4 \times 0.35 + 2 \times 0.85 = 3.10$$

$$Z' = Z - S = 7 - 3.10 = 3.90$$

$$n' = n = 2$$

Therefore, STO for 2*s* : $\phi_{2s} = [R_{20}(r)]\,[y_{00}(\theta, \varphi)]$

$$= \left[r \exp\left(-\frac{3.90r}{2} \right) \right] \left[\frac{1}{\sqrt{4\pi}} \right]$$

$$\text{STO for } 2p_z : \ \phi_{2p_z} = r \exp\left(-\frac{3.90r}{2} \right) \cdot \frac{1}{2} \left(\frac{3}{\pi} \right)^{1/2} \cos\theta$$

Compared to hydrogen-like orbitals, these STO's will have distorted forms. The orbitals (even 2*s*) vanish at $r = 0$ (contrast with hydrogen-like 2*s* orbitals). They have no nodes. All orbitals are not mutually orthogonal. The orbitals having different l and M quantum numbers can be orthogonal due to their angular terms. Thus, 2*s* and $2p_z$ are orthogonal but 2*s* and 1*s* are not.

9.6 ROOTHAAN'S METHOD

The basic problem in Hartree-Fock calculations is the choice of initial orbitals. A rough estimate can be made by using hydrogen like or Slater type orbitals (STO) CCJ Roothaan, in 1951, proposed that HF orbitals could be best represented as a linear combination of a complete set of known orthornormal functions, called "basis functions" (Any unknown function can be expressed as a linear combination of a complete set of basis functions provided they have the same variables and obey the same boundary conditions (see Chapter 3, Section 3.3.7). Thus the HFR expression for an orbital function ϕ_i is

$$\phi_i = \sum_{s=1}^{k} a_{is}\, \chi_s \qquad \text{... (9.109)}$$

where a_{is} are the expansion coefficients of the basis function χ_s in the orbital ϕ_i, and k is the number of basis functions used (the number of basis functions may be as large as one likes and the more they are the more accurate is the result. However, in practice, the orbital energy E_i reaches a limit with a finite number of basis functions only).

Substituting the Equation (9.109) in the HF Equation (9.97a)

$$\hat{F} \sum_{s=1}^{k} a_{is}\, \chi_s = E_i \sum_{s=1}^{k} a_{is}\, \chi_s$$

or

$$\sum_{s=1}^{k} a_{is}\, \hat{F} \chi_s = E_i \sum_{s=1}^{k} a_{is}\, \chi_s$$

Multiplying both sides by χ_r^* and integrating, we obtain, on rearrangement,

$$\sum_{s=1}^{k} a_{is}\left(F_{rs} - E_i\, S_{rs}\right) = 0 \qquad \text{...(9.110)}$$

where, $F_{rs} = \int \chi_r^* \hat{F} \chi_s \, d\tau$, and $S_{rs} = \int \chi_r^* \cdot \chi_s \, d\tau$.

This gives a set of k simultaneous linear equations known as Roothaan's equations in k unknown coefficients a_{is} to describe the orbital ϕ_i. For a non-trivial solution of these equations we set

$$\det(F_{rs} - E_i\, S_{rs}) = 0 \qquad \text{...(9.111)}$$

This gives k values of E_i the lowest of which is accepted as the orbital energy. The HFR Equation (9.110) are then solved by repeated iteration as the operator $\hat{F}$ depends on its own orbitals ϕ_i which in turn depends on the coefficients a_{is}. (For more about Roothaan treatment see chapter 13, section 13.1.2.2).

The procedure is to begin with an arbitrary but reasonable set of coefficients a_{is} of the basis functions χ_s for the orbitals ϕ_i in Equation (9.109). The initial set of orbitals is used to calculate the operator $\hat{F}$ (1) for the electron 1 which is given by Equation (9.97)

$$\hat{F}(1) = \hat{H}^0(1) + \sum_{j=1}^{n/2}\left[2\hat{J}_j(1) - \hat{K}_j(1)\right]$$

The integrals F_{rs} which are usually called the Fock matrix elements of the secular determinant, are calculated and the secular determinant Eqn. (1.111) is solved to obtain an initial set of E'_i s. The E'_i s are used to solve the Roothaan Equation (9.110) to obtain a better set of coefficients (a_{is}) and hence a better set of orbitals ϕ'_i s. The new orbitals are used to calculate the $\hat{F}$ again and the cycle is repeated again and again till no further improvement is seen in the E'_i s and a_{is}.

To calculate the matrix elements F_{rs} they must be expressed in terms of the basis functions χ_s.

$$F_{rs} = \int \chi_r(1)\, \hat{F}(1)\, \chi_s(1)\, d\tau_1$$

$$= \int \chi_r(1)\, \hat{H}^0(1)\, \chi_s(1)\, d\tau_1 + \sum_{j=1}^{n/2}\left[2\int \chi_r(1)\, \hat{J}_j(1)\, \chi_s(1)\, d\tau_1 - \int \chi_r(1)\, \hat{K}_j(1)\, \chi_s(1)\, d\tau_1\right] \qquad \text{...(9.112)}$$

By definition, $\hat{J}_j(1)\,\chi_s(1) = \chi_s(1)\int \phi_j^*(2)\, \phi_j(2)\,.\,\frac{1}{r_{12}}\, d\tau_2$

$$= \chi_s(1)\int \sum_t a_{jt}^*\, \chi_t^*(2) \sum_u a_{ju}\, \chi_u(2)\,.\,\frac{1}{r_{12}}\, d\tau_2$$

where $\phi_j^* = \sum a_{jt}^*\, x_t^*$ and $\phi_j = \sum a_{ju}\, \chi_u$.

Multiplying by $\chi_r^*(1)$ and integrating over the coordinates of electron 1,

$$\int \chi_r^*(1)\,\hat{J}_j(1)\,\chi_s(1)\,d\tau_1 = \sum_t \sum_u a_{jt}^* a_{ju} \iint \chi_r^*(1)\,\chi_s(1)\,\chi_t^*(2)\,\chi_u(2)\,.\frac{1}{r_{12}}\,d\tau_1\,d\tau_2$$

$$= \sum_t \sum_u a_{jt}^* a_{ju} \left(rs/tu\right) \qquad \ldots (9.113)$$

where, the 2-electron repulsion integral has been denoted by the notation shown in small bracket within the double summation.

Similarly, since

$$\hat{K}_j(1)\,\chi_s(1) = \phi_j(1)\int \phi_j^*(2)\,\chi_s(2)\,\frac{1}{r_{12}}\,d\tau_2$$

$$\int \chi_r^*(1)\,\hat{K}(1)\,\chi_s(1)\,d\tau = \int \chi_r^*(1)\,\phi_j(1)\int \phi_j^*(2)\,\chi_s(2)\,.\frac{1}{r_{12}}\,d\tau_2\,d\tau_1$$

$$= \iint \chi_r^*(1)\sum_u a_{ju}\,\chi_u(1)\sum_t a_{jt}^*\,\chi_t(2)\,x_s(2)\,.\frac{1}{r_{12}}\,d\tau_1\,d\tau_2$$

$$= \sum_u \sum_t a_{ju}\,a_{jt}^* \left(ru/ts\right) \qquad \ldots (9.114)$$

[In the short hand notation for the 2-electron integrals only the indices of the bases are written; those with electron 1 are written on the left and those with electron 2 on the right of the vertical line. Further, if the orbitals are real the star (*) is to be removed].

Substituting these expressions into Equation (9.112)

$$F_{rs} = \int \chi_r^*(1)\,H^0(1)\,\chi_s\,d\tau_1 + \sum_t \sum_u \sum_j a_{jt}^* a_{ju}\left[2\left(rs/tu\right) - \left(ru/ts\right)\right]$$

$$= H_{rs}^0 + \sum_t \sum_u P_{tu}\left[\left(rs/tu\right) - \frac{1}{2}\left(ru/ts\right)\right] \qquad \ldots (9.115)$$

where H_{rs}^0 are the 1-electron core integrals and $P_{tu} = 2\sum_{j=1}^{n/2} a_{jt}^* a_{ju}$ are called elements of electron density matrix.

9.6.1 Electronic Energy

The orbital energy of an electron is given by Eqn. (9.102),

$$E_i = E_i^0 + \sum_{j=1}^{n/2}\left(2J_{ij} - K_{ij}\right) \sum_{i=1}^{n/2} E_i = \sum_{i=1}^{n/2} E_i^0 + \sum_{i=1}^{n/2}\sum_{j=1}^{n/2}\left(2J_{ij} - K_{ij}\right)$$

The total electronic energy by Equations (9.104) or (9.105) is,

$$E = 2\sum_i^{n/2} E_i^0 + \sum_{i=1}^{n/2}\sum_{j=1}^{n/2}\left(2J_{ij} - K_{ij}\right)$$

$$= 2\sum_{i=1}^{n/2} E_i^0 + \left[\sum_{i=1}^{n/2} E_i - \sum_{j=1}^{n/2} E_i^0\right]$$

$$= \sum_i^{n/2} E_i^0 + \sum_i^{n/2} E_i = \sum_i^{n/2} E_i + \sum_i \int \phi_i^* H_i^0 \phi_i \, d\tau$$

$$= \sum_i^{n/2} E_i + \sum_r \sum_s \sum_{i=1}^{n/2} a_{ir}^* a_{is} \int \chi_r^* H_i^0 \chi_s \, d\tau \qquad \text{... (9.116)}$$

$$= \sum_i^{n/2} E_i + \sum_r \sum_s \sum_i a_{ir}^* a_{is} H_{rs}^0 = \sum_i^{n/2} E_i + \frac{1}{2} \sum_r \sum_s P_{rs} H_{rs}^0 \qquad \text{... (9.117)}$$

Case of Helium

The simplest example will be the He atom with two electrons only. One starts with an initial guess for ϕ_{1s}. Roetti and Clementi (J. Chem Phys. 1974, **63**, 4725) expressed the 1s atomic orbital of He as a linear combination of two normalized STO basis functions χ_1 and χ_2.

$$\phi_{1s} = a_1 \chi_1 + a_2 \chi_2$$

where, $\chi_1 = 2\xi_1^{3/2} e^{-\xi_1 r}$ and $\chi_2 = 2\xi_2^{3/2} e^{-\xi_2 r}$ with optimized values of $\xi_1 = 1.45$ and $\xi_2 = 2.91$.

If we were to use a single orbital exponent, the value of ξ (effective nuclear charge) would be $\frac{27}{16} = 1.6875$ (see page 252). In the present case this value is much closer to ξ_1 than to ξ_2. Let us first assume that $a_1 \approx 2a_2$. The condition of normalization for the ϕ_{1s} is

$$\int \phi_{1s}^2 \, d\tau = \int (a_1 \chi_1 + a_2 \chi_2)^2 \, d\tau = 1$$

or $\quad a_1^2 + a_2^2 + 2a_1 a_2 S_{12} = 1$

or $\quad (5 + 4S_{12}) \, a_2^2 = 1$

where, $\quad \int \chi_1^2 \, d\tau = \int \chi_2^2 \, d\tau = 1$

and $\quad \int \chi_1 \chi_2 \, d\tau = S_{12}$

The integral S_{12} has been evaluated and found to be

$$S_{12} = \int \chi_1 \chi_2 \, d\tau = 4 \int \xi_1^{3/2} \xi_2^{3/2} e^{-(\xi_1 + \xi_2) r} . r^2 \, dr = 0.8366$$

This gives $a_2 = 0.34$ and $a_1 = 0.68$ and $P_{11} = 0.958$, $P_{12} = P_{21} = 0.4791$ and $P_{22} = 0.2309$.

To calculate F_{rs} elements, we need the core integrals H_{rs}^0 and the 2-electron integrals (rs/tu) and (ru/ts). The core integrals on evaluation are found to be $H_{11}^0 = -1.8488$, $H_{12}^0 = H_{21}^0 = -1.8826$ and $H_{22}^0 = -1.5860$.

In view of the fact that $\frac{1}{r_{12}}$ is a multiplier, for real basis functions the following equality holds for the 2-electron integrals:

$$(rs/tu) = (sr/tu) = (rs/ut) = (sr/ut) = (tu/rs) = (ut/rs) = (tu/sr) = (ut/sr)$$

This reduces the number of such integrals for evaluation. In the present case, these have been evaluated and found to be as follows:

$$(11/11) = 0.9022; \quad (22/22) = 1.8188$$

$$(11/22) = (22/11) = 1.1826$$

$$(12/12) = (21/12) = (12/21) = (21/21) = 0.9536$$

$$(11/12) = (11/21) = (12/11) = (21/11) = 0.9033$$

$$(12/22) = (22/12) = (22/21) = (21/22) = 1.2980$$

where, for example,

$$(11/12) = \iint \chi_1(1)\,\chi_1(1)\,\chi_1(2)\,\chi_2^{(2)} \cdot \frac{1}{r_{12}}\,d\tau_1 \,.\, d\tau_2$$

Now we are able to calculate the matrix elements as

$$F_{11} = H_{11}^0 + P_{11}(11/11) + P_{12}(11/12) + P_{21}(11/21) + P_{22}(11/22)$$

$$- \frac{1}{2} P_{11}(11/11) - \frac{1}{2} P_{21}(11/21) - \frac{1}{2} P_{12}(12/11) - \frac{1}{2} P_{22}(12/21)$$

$$= H_{11}^0 + \frac{1}{2} P_{11}(11/11) + P_{12}(11/12) + P_{22}\left[(11/22) - \frac{1}{2}(12/21)\right]$$

$\because$ $P_{12} = P_{21}$ and $(11/12) = (11/21) = (12/11)$

$$= -\ 1.8488 + \frac{1}{2} \times 0.9583 \times 0.9022 + 0.4791 \times 0.9033 + 0.2396 \times \left(1.1826 - \frac{1}{2} \times 0.9536\right)$$

$$= -\ 0.815$$

Similarly, $$F_{12} = F_{21} = H_{12}^0 + \frac{1}{2} P_{11}(11/12) + \frac{3}{2} P_{12}(12/12) + \frac{1}{2} P_{22}(12/22) - \frac{1}{2} P_{12}(11/22)$$

$$= -\ 0.892$$

$$F_{22} = H_{22}^0 + P_{11}\left[(22/11) - \frac{1}{2}(22/12)\right] + P_{12}\left[(22/12) + \frac{1}{2} P_{22}(22/22)\right]$$

$$= 0.070$$

The secular determinantal equation becomes

$$\begin{vmatrix} 0.813 - E_i & -0.892 - 0.8366\,E_i \\ -\ 0.892 - 0.8366\,E & -\ 0.813 - E_i \end{vmatrix} = 0$$

On expanding the determinant,

$$0.3001\,E_i^2 - 0.6095E_i - 0.739 = 0$$

or $$E_1 = -0.854 \text{ and } E_2 = 2.885$$

Using the lower value E_1 in the Roothaan's equations are

$$a_1\,(F_{21} - E_1\,S_{21}) + a_2\,(F_{22} - E_1\,S_{22}) = 0$$

or $$-0.177a_1 + 0.784a_2 = 0$$

or $$a_1 = 4.42a_2$$

From the condition of normalization,

$$a_2 = 0.189,\ a_1 = 0.836$$

With these values of a_1 and a_2 we calculate $P_{11} = 1.398$, $P_{12} = P_{21} = 0.316$ and $P_{22} = 0.071$. Then $F_{11} = -0.880$, $F_{12} = F_{21} = -0.940$ and $F_{22} = -0.1246$.

The improved secular determinant is

$$\begin{vmatrix} -0.880 - E_i & -0.940 - 0.8366E_i \\ -0.940 - 0.8366E_i & -0.880 - E_i \end{vmatrix} = 0$$

and $$E_1 = -0.918,\ E_2 = 2.810$$

Using E_1 and the Roothaan equation,

$$\frac{a_1}{a_2} = 4.61$$

From the condition of normalization

$$a_1 = 0.842 \text{ and } a_2 = 0.183$$

Another cycle of calculation will give

$$P_{11} = 1.418,\ P_{12} = P_{21} = 0.308,\ P_{22} = 0.067$$

$$F_{11} = -0.881,\ F_{12} = F_{21} = -0.940,\ F_{22} = -0.124$$

$$E_1 = -0.918 \text{ and } E_2 = 2.809.$$

Using E_1 in the Roothaan equation, $a_1 = 0.842$ and $a_2 = 0.183$, which are the same as in the earlier cycle. Therefore,

$$\phi_{1s}^{SCF} = 0.842x_1 + 0.183x_2$$

The total electronic energy of He is by Equation (9.113)

$$E = -0.918 + \frac{1}{2}\left[1.418 \times (1.8488) + 2 \times 0.308 \times (-1.8826) + 0.067 \times (-1.5860)\right]$$

$$= -2.862 \text{ a.u.} = -77.9 \text{ eV}$$

compared to the true value of -77.9 eV.

9.6.2 Electronic Structure of Atoms

To summarise, an orbital is a wave function of a single electron. In the crudest approximation, where all interelectronic repulsions in an atom are ignored, we have hydrogen like orbitals,

$$\phi_{nlm} = NR_{nl}(r) \cdot Y_l^m(\theta, \varphi) \quad \text{... (9.118)}$$

Slater suggested a better approxmation by taking into consideration the shielding effect of the nucleus by the electrons; the orbital he suggested has the form

$$\phi'_{nlm} = N' r^{n-1} e^{-\xi r/a_0} \cdot Y_l^m(\theta, \varphi) \quad \text{... (9.119)}$$

where ξ is the effective nuclear charge. Slater orbitals differ from the hydrogen-like in their radial part only, the angular—part the spherical harmonics—being the same. The best orbitals are, however, the Hartree-Fock Self consistent field (HFSCF) orbitals.

The electronic structure of atoms can be built up by feeding a pair of electrons with opposite spins in these orbitals in increasing order of orbital energy. The total electronic energy of an atom is the sum of the orbital energies of the electrons minus the energy due to electronic repulsions (J_{ij}) and exchanges (K_{ij}) given by the Equations (9.104) or (9.105). Where small differences in energy levels occur or different levels appear to have the same energy, the ambiguity is resolved by chemical or spectroscopic data.

As the atomic number (Z) increases the increased attraction betwen the nucleus and the "inner electrons" causes decrease in the orbital energies. Orbitals with the same value of the principal quantum number '*n*' but different values of '*l*' then have differnt energies ; for example, for $n = 3$, $E_{3s} < E_{3p} < E_{3d}$, in contrast with hydrogen atom case where $E_{3s} = E_{3p} = E_{3d}$. This splitting arises from perturbation due to interelectronic repulsions. When Z is very large, the relative positions of certain orbitals change. For example, for Potassium (Z = 19) and Calcium (Z = 20) the 4*s* lies below 3*d* and hence their electronic configurations are

$$[KLM]\, 4s^1 \text{ and } [KLM]\, 4s^2$$

where $[KLM] = 1s^2\, 2s^2\, 2p^6\, 3s^2\, 3p^6$, respectively. For $Z > 20$ the $E_{3d} < E_{4s}$. Thus in Vanadium (Z = 23), though the sum of total energies $\left(\sum_i E_i\right)$ for $3d^5$ configurations is less than that for the $3d^3\, 4s^2$ the latter configuration is accepted because the total energy is lessened by electronic repulsions and exchanges which exceed the nuclear attraction.

9.6.3 Electron Correlation and Configuration Interaction

Hartree-Fock method calculates the average potential energy of the electrons. Electrons, on the other hand, due to repulsions, tend to keep out of each others way. If, for example, one electron gets near the nucleus at any time the other electron will remain as far as away as possible. In other words, the electrons in an atom tend to correlate their positions so as to acquire a stable state of minimum potential energy. This is called correlation. The energies of atoms calculated by HF method is, therefore, slightly higher than the true energy. Improvement can be made by including a term in the atomic wave function ψ corresponding to the electron correlation.

To some extent the HF wave function has some electron correlation built into it. Due to antisymmetry requirement two electrons having same spin cannot be in the same orbital. It is therefore that the HF energy is lower than that calculated by Hartree method. The difference between the true energy and the HF energy is called the "correlation energy". For He atom, it is -77.9 (HF) $-$ [-79.0 (true)] = 1.1 eV.

Configuration Interaction: The most common method to incorporate correlation into the wave functions is the "Configuration Interaction (CI) method". This involves expanding a given HF orbital as a linear combination of wave functions arising from various electronic configurations of the atom (ground and excited state), for example, the $1s^2$, $1s\ 2s$, $1s\ 2p$, $2s^2$, ... in He atom. Recall that the ground state ($1s^2$) wave function is $1s\ (1)\ 1s\ (2)\ [\alpha\ (1)\ \beta\ (2) - \alpha\ (2)\ \beta\ (1)]$.

The usual procedure is to start with a complete set of basis function χ (in practice, finite in number), usually STO's. The SCF orbitals ϕ_is are obtained as a linear combination of these. The number of orbitals obtained will be equal to the number of basis functions used. The lowest energy orbitals among these wili be the "occupied orbitals" and the remaining will be the "virtual orbitals".

Using the occupied and virtual orbitals, antisymmetric many-electron wave functions are formed for different electronic configurations. But a single configuration may give rise to a number of functions (*e.g.*, in He $1s\ 2s$ configuration there are four functions, Equations (9.49) to (9.52). Each such function ψ_i is a Slater determinant or a linear combination of Slater determinants. Each ψ_i is called "configuration state function (CSF)". The CI wave function Ψ is then the linear combination of CSF's.

$$\psi = \sum c_i \psi_i \qquad ...(9.120)$$

This is a linear variation function. Variation treatment yields the determinant

$$\det (H_{ij} - E_i S_{ij}) = 0 \qquad ...(9.45)$$

where, $$H_{ij} = \int \psi_i^* \hat{H} \psi_j \, d\tau \text{ and } S_{ij} = \int \psi_i^* \psi_j \, d\tau$$

and E_i is the energy associated with the CSF ψ_i. Associated secular equations are solved to find the coefficients c_i.

Even though the basis set has a finite size, it leads to many CSF's and one has to choose only those CSF's which contribute most (that is, which have substantial values of c_i) to the Ψ. It may be noted that C.F. Bunge (Phys. Rev. A, 1976, 14, 1965) used 650 CSF's for a CI calculation of the ground state energy of Be $(1s\ 1\bar{s}\ 2s\ 2\bar{s})$. This included excited state configurations like $1s\ 1\bar{s}\ 3s\ 3\bar{s}$ and so on. The calculated energy (– 14.6669 hartree) was in close agreement with the true value (– 14.6674 hartree). This incorporated 99.5% of the correlation energy.

9.7 EVALUATION OF MATRIX ELEMENTS: CONDON-SLATER RULES

The HF SCF—CI wave function appears as a Slater determinant or as a linear combination of Slater determinants. Therefore, to calculate the energy of the atom we have to deal with integrals of the form $\int D' \hat{H} D \, d\tau$, where D and D′ are Slater determinants of spin orbitals and $\hat{H}$ is the Hamiltonian operator. D and D′ may be same or different. Condon and Slater provided simplifying rules for their evaluation.

In case $D \neq D'$, arrange the columns of the determinants so as to have as many as possible of their left hand columns match. For example, let $D = |1s\ 1\bar{s}\ 2s\ 2p_z|$ and $D' = |1s\ 1\bar{s}\ 2p_z\ 3s|$, where the determinants have been written through their diagonal elements only. We can write D as $D = -\ |1s\ 1\bar{s}\ 2p_z\ 3s|$ so that the first three columns of the two determinants match.

The operator $\hat{H}$, for n-electron atom, is

$$\hat{H} = \sum_{i=1}^{n} \hat{H}^0(i) + \sum_{i=1}^{n-1}\sum_{j>1} \frac{1}{r_{ij}} \qquad \text{... (9.68)}$$

The first term stands for the zeroth order energy (or the core energy) operator and the second term is the operator for inter-electronic repulsions and exchanges.

$$\sum \hat{H}_i^0 = \sum_i \left(-\frac{1}{2}\nabla_i^2 - \frac{Z}{r_i} \right) \; ; r_{ij} = \text{interelectronic distances}$$

The integral $\int D'\hat{H}D\, d\tau = \int D' \sum_{i=1}^{n} \hat{H}_i^0 D\, d\tau + \int D' \sum_{i=1}^{n-1}\sum_{j>i} \frac{1}{r_{ij}} D\, d\tau$ ... (9.121)

The first term is the sum of the 1-electron integrals like $\int \theta_i \hat{H}^0 \theta_i \, d\tau$ (in view of the orthonormality of the orbitals), and the second term a sum of 2-electron integrals like $\int \theta_i(1)\theta_j(2)\frac{1}{r_{12}}\theta_r(1)\theta_s(2)\, d\tau$, where the θ' s are spin orbitals (*e.g.*, $\theta_i(1) = \phi_i(1)\sigma_i(1)$, ϕ = orbital and σ is α or β spin) ; 1 and 2 refer to any two electrons ; i, j, r and s are subscripts denoting the orbitals that may be same or, partly or wholly, different. If D and D′ are not the same the Codon-Slater rules take the form shown in the Table 9.3.

TABLE 9.3 Condon-Slater Rules

D and D′ differ	$\int D' \sum_{i=1}^{n} \hat{H}^0 D\, d\tau$	$\int D' \sum_{i=1}^{n-1}\sum_{j>1} \frac{1}{r_{ij}} D\, d\tau$
by no spin orbital	$\sum_{i=1}^{n} \int \theta_i(1)\hat{H}^0\theta_i(1)\, d\tau_1$	$\sum_{i=1}^{n-1}\sum_{j>1}\left[\int \theta_i(1)\theta_j(2)\frac{1}{r_{12}}\theta_i(1)\theta_j(2)\, d\tau_1 - d\tau_2 - \int \theta_i(1)\theta_j(2)\frac{1}{r_{12}}\theta_j(1)\theta_i(2)\, d\tau_1\, d\tau_2\right]$
One spin orbital $\theta_n' \neq \theta_n$	$\int \theta_n'(1)\hat{H}^0\theta_n(1)\, d\tau$	$\sum_{j=1}^{n-1}\left[\int \theta_n'(1)\theta_j \frac{1}{r_{12}}\theta_n(1)\theta_j(2)\, d\tau_1\, d\tau_2 - \int \theta_n'(1)\theta_j(2)\frac{1}{r_{12}}\theta_j(1)\theta_n(2)\, d\tau_1\, d\tau_2\right]$
Two spin orbitals $\theta_n' \neq \theta_n$ and $\theta_{n-1}' \neq \theta_{n-1}$	0	$\int \theta_n'(1)\theta_{n-1}'(2)\frac{1}{r_{12}}\theta_n(1)\theta_{n-1}(2)\, d\tau_1\, d\tau_2 - \int \theta_n'(1)\theta_{n-1}'(2)\frac{1}{r_{12}}\theta_{n-1}(1)\theta_n(2)\, d\tau_1\, d\tau_2$
Three or more spin orbitals	0	0

Denoting the spatial part of the spin orbital by ϕ, and the spin part by σ, $\theta_i = \phi_i \cdot \sigma_i$ etc. Then

$$\int \theta_i\,(1)\,\hat{H}^0\,\theta_i\,d\tau = \int \phi_i\,(1)\,\hat{H}^0\,\phi_i\,(1)\,dv_1 \,.\int \sigma_i\,(1)\,\sigma_i\,(1)\,ds_1$$

$$= \int \phi_i\,(1)\,\hat{H}^0\,\phi_i\,(1)\,dv_1\,, \quad \because \quad \sigma_i \text{ is normalised}$$

Similarly, $\int \theta_i\,(1)\,\theta_j\,(2)\,\frac{1}{r_{12}}\,\theta_r\,(1)\,\theta_s\,(2)\,d\tau$

$$= \int \phi_i(1)\phi_j(2)\,\frac{1}{r_{12}}\,\phi_r(1)\phi_s(2)dv_1dv_2 \,.\int \sigma_i(1)\sigma_r(1)ds_1 \,.\int \sigma_i(2)\sigma_s(2)ds_2\,.$$

Since σ's can be either α or β only, and they are ortho normal, the integral will vanish if they are different and will survive only when the spins of the two electrons 1 and 2 are the same. The integral involving spatial orbital only will be of the type

$$\int \phi_i\,(1)\,\phi_j\,\frac{1}{r_{12}}\,\phi_r\,(1)\,\phi_s\,(2)\,dv_1\,dv_2$$

Then the integral $\int D'\,\frac{1}{r_{ij}}\,D\,d\tau = \sum_{j=1}^{n-1}\sum_{j>1}\Big[\int \phi_i\,(1)\,\phi_j\,(2)\,\frac{1}{r_{12}}\,\phi_i\,(1)\,\phi_j\,(2)\,dv_1\,dv_2$

$$-\,\delta_{ij}\int \phi_i\,(1)\,\phi_j\,(2)\,\frac{1}{r_{12}}\,\phi_r\,(1)\,\phi_s\,(2)\,dv_1\,dv_2\Big]$$

where $\delta_{ij} = 1$ if the spins of electrons 1 and 2 in the orbitals i and j are the same, and $\delta_{ij} = 0$ if they are different.

$$\int D\hat{H}D\,d\tau = \sum_{i=1}^{n}\int \phi_i\,(1)\,H^0\,\phi_i\,(1)\,dv + \sum_{j=1}^{n-1}\sum_{j>i}\left(J_{ij} - \delta_{ij}\,K_{ij}\right) \qquad \text{... (9.122)}$$

where

$$J_{ij} = \int \phi_i\,(1)\,\phi_j\,(2)\,\frac{1}{r_{12}}\,\phi_i\,(1)\,\phi_j\,(2)\,dv_1\,dv_2$$

$$K_{ij} = \int \phi_i\,(1)\,\phi_j\,(2)\,\frac{1}{r_{12}}\,\phi_j\,(1)\,\phi_i\,(2)\,dv_1\,dv_2$$

Now consider Be ($1s^2\,2s^2$). Here $n = 4$; the orbitals are $\phi_1 = 1s$ and $\phi_2 = 2s$. The spin orbitals are $\theta_1 = 1s$, $\theta_2 = 1\bar{s}$, $\theta_3 = 2s$ and $\theta_4 = 2\bar{s}$.

$$\sum_{n=1}^{4}\int \phi_i\,(1)\,\hat{H}^0\,\phi_i\,dv = 2\int 1s\hat{H}^0\,1s\,dv + 2\int 2s\,\hat{H}^0\,2s\,dv$$

(∵ there are two electrons in each orbital)

$$\sum_{n=1}^{3}\sum_{j>1}\left(J_{ij} - \delta_{ij}\,K_{ij}\right) = J_{12} + J_{13} + J_{14} + J_{23} + J_{24} + J_{34} - K_{13} - K_{24}$$

$$= J_{1s\,1s} + J_{1s\,2s} + J_{1s\,2s} + J_{1s\,2s} + J_{1s\,2s} - K_{1s\,2s} - K_{1s\,2s}$$

$$\therefore \quad E = J_{1s\,1s} + J_{2s\,2s} + 4J_{1s\,2s} - 2K_{1s\,2s}$$

This expression has the following interpretation. Since J_{ij} and J_{ji} are same, between the two electrons in 1*s* and two electrons in 2*s* orbitals we have two coulombic repulsion terms of the type $J_{1s\,1s}$ and $J_{2s\,2s}$ and four of the type $J_{1s\,2s}$ because each electron in 1*s* interacts with two electrons in 2*s* orbital. The spin in θ_1 matches with that in θ_3 and the spin in θ_2 does with that in θ_4, so we have two exchange terms $K_{1s\,2s}$.

9.8 KOOPMAN'S THEOREM

From the point of view of chemical interest the ionization potential of a molecule or atom is a more important physical quantity than its total energy. Koopman saw that the orbital energies could be easily related to the ionization potential under certain assumptions.

The ionization potential (I.P.) may be defined as

$$\text{I.P.} = E^+ - E$$

where, E and E^+ are the total energies of neutral molecular or atom and the cation resulting from the elimination of an electron respectively. By Equation (9.13)

$$E = \sum_i 2E_i^0 + \sum_i \sum_{j>1} (2J_{ij} - K_{ij})$$

If an electron is removed from the orbital ϕ_k , then

$$E^+ = \sum_i 2E_i^0 + \sum_i \sum_{j>1} (2J_{ij} - K_{ij}) - E_k$$

where E_k is the orbital energy of the ϕ_k. Therefore,

$$\text{I.P.} = E^+ - E = -E_k$$

The assumption made here, which was proved later to be valid, is that the HF wave function resulting after removal of an electron from the orbital ψ_k, or by adding an electron to the virtual orbital ψ_j, remains stable with respect to any variation in ϕ_k or ϕ_j ; that is, it ignores any subsequent variation in all other orbitals containing the electrons.

PROBLEMS

9.1 Write the Hamiltonian for Li atom. Ignoring interelectronic repulsion give the wave function. [**Hint :** See the example of He in the text].

9.2 Take a trial function for helium atom as,

$$\psi = \phi(1)\,\phi(2) \text{ with } \phi(1) = \left(\frac{Z'^3}{\pi}\right)^{1/2} \exp(-Z'r_1) \text{ and}$$

$$\phi(2) = \left(\frac{Z'^3}{\pi}\right)^{1/2} \exp(-Z'r_2)$$

Z' being a variable parameter. Find the best value of Z' and obtain the ground state energy corresponding to the given function ψ. Calculate the first and second ionisation potentials. **[Hint :** See text].

9.3 Write the expression for the average energy of He in 1*s* $2p_x$ state and expand it in terms of the various integrals. What will be the energy in absence of interelectronic repulsion ?

[Hint: Follow the calculations for 1*s* 2*s* state giv n in the text. In the absence of $\frac{1}{r_{12}}$ term,

$$E_{1s\,2p_x} = E_{1s}^{He+} + E_{2p}^{He+} = -\frac{Z^2}{1^2} - \frac{Z^2}{2} = -5 \text{ a.u.}].$$

9.4 Define a spin-orbital. Construct an antisymmetric wave function for Be atom (*i*) as a linear combination of the products of spin-orbitals and (*ii*) as a Slater determinant. Find the expression for its energy in terms of coulomb and exchange integrals.

[Hint:
$$\psi = \frac{1}{\sqrt{4!}}\begin{vmatrix} 1s(1) & \overline{1s}(1) & 2s(1) & \overline{2s}(1) \\ 1s(2) & \overline{1s}(2) & 2s(2) & \overline{2s}(2) \\ 1s(3) & \overline{1s}(3) & 2s(3) & \overline{2s}(3) \\ 1s(4) & \overline{1s}(4) & 2s(4) & \overline{2s}(4) \end{vmatrix}$$

Expand it go get ψ as a linear combination of spin-orbital products.

$$E_{1s}^2\, 2s^2 = 2\,(E_{1s} + E_{2s}) + J_{1s\,1s} + J_{2s\,2s} + 4J_{1s\,2s} - 2K_{1s\,2s}].$$

9.5 Show that if electrons 3 and 4 occupy the same spin-orbital 2*s* in Be atom, the wave function vanishes.

9.6 Verify by the use of determinantal wave function that for Li atom a configuration like $1s^3$ is impossible.

[Hint : Let
$$\psi(1,2,3) = \begin{vmatrix} 1s(1) & \overline{1s}(1) & 1s(1) \\ 1s(2) & \overline{1s}(2) & 1s(2) \\ 1s(3) & \overline{1s}(3) & 1s(3) \end{vmatrix}$$

On expanding it, $\psi = 0$].

9.7 Given the spin-orbital product functions,

$$\left(\phi_{1s}^{\alpha}\,\phi_{1s}^{\beta}\,\phi_{2s}^{\alpha}\right)^* \text{ and } \left(\phi_{2s}^{\alpha}\,\phi_{1s}^{\alpha}\,\phi_{1s}^{\beta}\right),$$

set up the integral product between them; factorise the integral into a product of integrals over one-electron space function and one-electron spin function. Indicate the value of each of the resulting six integrals and of their product.

[Hint: $\int \left(\phi_{1s}^{\alpha}(1)\,\phi_{1s}^{\beta}(2)\,\phi_{2s}^{\alpha}(3)\right)^* \left(\phi_{2s}^{\alpha}(1)\,\phi_{1s}^{\alpha}(2)\,\phi_{1s}^{\beta}(3)\right) d\tau$

$$= \int \left(\phi_{1s}^{\alpha}\right)^* \left(\phi_{2s}^{\alpha}\right) d\tau_1 \cdot \int \left(\phi_{1s}^{\beta}\right)^* \left(\phi_{1s}^{\alpha}\right) d\tau_2 \cdot \int \left(\phi_{2s}^{\alpha}\right)^* \left(\phi_{1s}^{\beta}\right) d\tau_3$$

$$= \int \phi_{1s}^*(1)\,\phi_{2s}(1)\,d\tau_1 \,.\int \alpha(1)\,\alpha(1)\,d\tau_1 \,.\int \varphi_{1s}^*(2)\,\phi_{1s}(2)\,d\tau_2\,.$$

$$\quad(0) \qquad\qquad (1) \qquad\qquad (1)$$

$$\int \beta(2)\,\alpha(2)\,ds_2 \,.\int \phi_{2s}^*(3)\,\phi_{1s}(3)\,d\tau_3 \,.\int \alpha(3)\,\beta(3)\,ds_3$$

$$\quad(0) \qquad\qquad (0) \qquad\qquad (0)$$

$= 0]$.

9.8 Which of the following four functions are symmetric ?

(*i*) $\phi(1)\,\alpha(1)\,\phi(2)\,\alpha(2)$,

(*ii*) $\phi(1)\,\alpha(1)\,\phi(2)\,\beta(2)$,

(*iii*) $\phi(1)\,\beta(1)\,\phi(2)\,\beta(2)$, and

(*iv*) $\phi(1)\,\alpha(2)\,\phi(2)\,\beta(1)$.

Choose the functions and construct symmetric and antisymmetric wave functions. Show that they are mutually orthogonal.

[**Hint :** First and third functions are symmetric].

$$\psi_{\pm} = \frac{1}{\sqrt{2}}\left[\phi(1)\,\alpha(1)\,\phi(2)\,\beta(2) \pm \phi(1)\,\alpha(2)\,\phi(2)\,\beta(1)\right]$$

Orthogonality:

$$\int\left[\phi(1)\,\alpha(1)\,\phi(2)\,\beta(2) + \phi(1)\,\alpha(2)\,\phi(2)\,\beta(1)\right]$$

$$\left[\phi(1)\,\alpha(1)\,\phi(2)\,\beta(2) - \phi(1)\,\alpha(2)\,\phi(2)\,\beta(1)\right]d\tau$$

$$= \int\left[\phi(1)\,\alpha(1)\,\phi(2)\,\beta(2)\right]^2 d\tau - \int\left\{(\phi(1)\,\alpha(2)\,\phi(2)\,\beta(1))\right\}^2 d\tau$$

$$= \int \phi(1)^2\,d\tau_1 \,.\int \phi(2)^2\,d\tau_2 \,.\int \alpha(1)^2\,ds_1 \,.\int \beta(2)^2\,ds_2$$

$$- \int \phi(1)^2\,d\tau_1 \,.\int \phi(2)^2\,d\tau_2 \,.\int \alpha(2)^2\,ds_2 \,.\int \beta(1)^2\,ds_1$$

$= 0]$.

9.9 Use the simple product wave function $1s(1)\,.\,1s(2)$ and the antisymmetric wave function

$$\psi_- = \frac{1}{\sqrt{2}}\,[1s(1)\,\alpha(1)\,1s(2)\,\beta(2) - 1s(2)\,\alpha(2)\,1s(1)\,\beta(1)]$$

of the atom to calculate the electron density. Evaluate it at the nucleus and at a distance $r = a_0$ from the nucleus.

[**Hint:** $\psi^2 = [1s(1)\,1s(2)]^2 = \left(\dfrac{Z^3}{\pi}\right)\exp(-2Z(r_1 + r_2))$].

9.10 Use a trial function for He atom as $\psi = \phi(1)\,\phi(2)$ with

$$\phi(1) = \left(\frac{Z'^3}{\pi}\right)^{1/2} \exp(-Z'r_1) \text{ and } \phi(2) = \left(\frac{Z'^3}{\pi}\right)^{1/2} \exp(-Z'r_2)$$

Z′ being a variable parameter. Find the best value of Z′ so as to obtain the ground state energy. Calculate the first and second ionisation potentials. Given that the electron repulsion integral is

$$J = \frac{5Z'}{8}.$$

[Hint : See the text].

9.11 Calculate the average value $\bar{r}_1$ and $\bar{r}_2$ consistent with He atom wave function

$$\psi(1, 2) = 1s(1)\, 2s(2) \text{ and } \psi(2, 1) = 1s(2)\, 2s(1).$$

Comment on the results.

[Hint:

$$\bar{r}_1 = \frac{\int 1s(1)\, 2s(2)\, \hat{r}_1\, 1s(1)\, 2s(2)\, d\tau_1\, d\tau_2}{\int \{1s(1)\, 2s(2)\}^2\, d\tau_1\, d\tau_2}$$

$$= \frac{\int 1s(1)\, \hat{r}_1\, 1s(1)\, d\tau_1 \,.\, \int 2s(2)\, 2s(2)\, d\tau_2}{\int \{1s(1)^2\}\, d\tau_1 \,.\, \int \{2s(2)\}^2\, d\tau_2}$$

$$= \frac{\int 1s(1)\, \hat{r}_1\, 1s(1)\, d\tau_1}{\int \{1s(1)\}^2\, d\tau_1}$$

Similarly,

$$\bar{r}_2 = \frac{\int 2s(2)\, \hat{r}_2\, 2s(2)\, d\tau_2}{\int \{2s(2)\}^2\, d\tau_2}$$

Using

$$1s(1) = \left(\frac{Z^3}{\pi}\right)^{1/2} \exp(-Zr_1) \text{ and } d\tau_1 = r_1^2\, dr_1 \sin\theta_1\, d\theta_1\, d\varphi_1,$$

We get

$$\bar{r}_1 = \frac{\int_0^\infty \left(\frac{Z^3}{\pi}\right) \exp(-2Zr_1)\, r_1^3\, dr_1 \int_0^\pi \sin\theta_1\, d\theta_1 \int_0^{2\pi} d\varphi_1}{\int_0^\infty \left(\frac{Z^3}{\pi}\right) \exp(-2Zr_1)\, r_1^2\, dr_1 \int_0^\pi \sin\theta_1\, d\theta_1 \int_0^{2\pi} d\varphi_1}$$

$$= \frac{3!}{(2Z)^4} \frac{(2Z)^3}{2!} = \frac{3}{2Z} = \frac{3}{4} \text{ (a.u.)}$$

Using

$$2s(2) = \frac{1}{4}\left(\frac{Z^3}{2\pi}\right)^{1/2} (2 - Zr_2) \exp(-Zr_2),$$

We get
$$\bar{r}_2 = \frac{\int_0^\infty \left[(2 - Zr_2)\exp(-Zr_2)\right]^2 r_3^2\, dr_2}{\int_0^\infty \left[(2 - Zr_2)\exp(-Zr_2)^2\right] r_2^2\, dr_2}$$

$$= \frac{4\int_0^\infty r_2^3 \exp(-2Zr_2)\, dr_2 - 4Z\int_0^\infty r_2^4 \exp(-2Zr_2)\, dr_2 + Z^2\int_0^\infty r_2^5 \exp(-2Zr_2)\, dr_2}{4\int_0^\infty r_2^2 \exp(-2Zr_2)\, dr_2 - 4Z\int_0^\infty r_2^3 \exp(-2Zr_2)\, dr_2 + Z^2\int_0^\infty r_2^4 \exp(-2Zr_2)\, dr_2}$$

$$= \frac{\frac{4\times 3!}{(2Z)^4} - \frac{4Z\times 4!}{(2Z)^5} + \frac{Z^2\times 5!}{(2Z)^6}}{\frac{4\times 2!}{(2Z)^3} - \frac{4Z\times 3!}{(2Z)^4} + \frac{Z^2\times 4!}{(2Z)^5}} = \frac{6}{Z} = 3.0 \text{ (a.u.)}$$

If the electrons are interchanged between 1*s* and 2*s*, *i.e.*,

$$\psi_{(2,1)} = 1s\,(2)\, 2s\,(1)$$

$$\bar{r}_1 = \frac{\int 2s\,(1)\, r_1\, 2s\,(1)\, d\tau_1}{\int \{2s\,(1)\}^2\, d\tau_1} = \frac{6}{Z} = 3 \text{ a.u.}$$

and
$$\bar{r}_2 = \frac{\int 1s\,(2)\, r_2\, 1s\,(2)\, d\tau_2}{\int \{1s\,(2)\}^2\, d\tau_2} = \frac{3}{2Z} = \frac{3}{4} \text{ a.u.}$$

On interchanging the electrons, the expectation values $\bar{r}_1$ and $\bar{r}_2$ of the 1*s* and 2*s* electrons are changed. This does not carry any physical sense as the electrons cannot be labelled].

9.12 Use the four slater determinants of the excited state configuration 1*s*2*s* of Helium and the variation method to derive the energy levels. Point out the singlet and triplet levels.
[**Hint** : See Section 9.2.2 for the slater determinants. The linear variation function is

$$\psi = a_1 D_1 + a_2 D_2 + a_3 D_3 + a_4 D_4$$

where the D's are the determinants. This leads to the scalar equation.

$$\begin{vmatrix} E_0 + J - K - E & 0 & 0 & 0 \\ 0 & E_0 + J - K - E & 0 & 0 \\ 0 & 0 & E + J - K & -K \\ 0 & 0 & -K & E + J - K \end{vmatrix} = 0$$

where $$E_0 = E_{1s} + E_{2s} = -\frac{5}{12} \text{ a.u.},$$

$$J \text{ (coulomb integral)} = \iint 1s(1)\, 1s(1) \frac{1}{r_{12}} 2s(2)\, 2s(2)\, d\tau_1\, d\tau_2$$

$$K \text{ (exchange integral)} = \iint 1s(1)\, 2s(1) \frac{1}{r_{12}} 1s(2)\, 2s(2)\, d\tau_1\, d\tau_2$$

$1s$ and $2s$ are eigenfunctions of the hydrogen like Hamiltonian operator. E is the energy of He in the excited state.
The two $|X|$ blocks give

$$E_1 = E_0 + J - K \quad \text{... (1)}$$

$$E_2 = E_0 + J - K \quad \text{... (2)}$$

and the 2×2 block gives

$$E_3 = E_0 + J + K \quad \text{... (3)}$$

$$E_4 = E_0 + J - K \quad \text{... (4)}$$

(1), (2) and (4) constitute the triplet and (3) the singlet
...... E_3
.... E_1, E_2, E_4

The corresponding determinants are D_1, D_2 and $\frac{1}{\sqrt{2}}(D_3 \pm D_4)$.

9.13 Write the determinantal wave function for the configuration $1s^2\, 2p_z$. Expand it into a linear combination of products.

9.14 Show by calculation of the ground state energy that for Li atom a configuration like $1s^3$ is impossible.
[Hint: If $$\psi(1, 2, 3) = 1s(1)\, 1s(2)\, 1s(3)$$

$$E_{1s^3} = \frac{\int 1s(1)\, 1s(2)\, 1s(3)\, \hat{H}\, 1s(1)\, 1s(2)\, 1s(3)\, d\tau}{\int [1s(1)\, 1s(2)\, 1s(3)]^2\, d\tau}$$

$$\hat{H} = \hat{H}_1 + \hat{H}_2 + \hat{H}_3 + \frac{1}{r_{12}} \cdot \frac{1}{r_{23}} \cdot \frac{1}{r_{31}} \text{ (in a.u.)}$$

where, $$\hat{H}_i = -\frac{1}{2}\nabla_i^2 - \frac{Z}{r_i}, Z = \text{screened nuclear charge } (< 3)$$

But $$E_{1s^3} = 3E_{1s}^{Li^{2+}} + J_{12} + J_{23} + J_{13}$$

$$E_{1s(1)}^{Li^{2+}} = \int 1s\left[-\frac{1}{2}\nabla^2 - \frac{3}{r}\right] 1s\, d\tau$$

$$= \int 1s\left[-\frac{1}{2}\nabla^2 - \frac{Z}{r} - \frac{3-Z}{r}\right] 1s\, d\tau$$

$$= \int 1s\left[-\frac{1}{2}\nabla^2 - \frac{Z}{r}\right] 1s\, d\tau - \int 1s\left(\frac{3-Z}{r}\right) 1s\, d\tau$$

$$= -\frac{Z^2}{2} - (3-Z)\int (1s)^2 \frac{1}{r}\, d\tau$$

$$\left[\text{because } 1s \text{ is the eigenfunction} \left(-\frac{1}{2}\nabla^2 - \frac{Z}{r}\right)\right]$$

Using $1s = \left(\frac{Z^3}{\pi}\right)^{1/2} \exp(-Zr)$, and $d\tau = r^2\, dr \sin\theta\, d\theta\, d\varphi$,

We get $E_{1s}^{Li^{2+}} = -\frac{Z^2}{2} - (3-Z)Z = \frac{Z^2}{2} - 3Z$

Recalling that integrals of the type

$$J_{12} = J_{23} = J_{13} = \frac{5}{8} Z, \text{ we get}$$

$$E_{1s^3}^{Li} = 3 \times \left[\frac{Z^2}{2} - 3Z\right] + 3 \times \frac{5}{8} Z$$

Even if we put Z = 3 (no screening) $E_{1s^3} = -7.875$ a.u. = – 214 eV. The experimental value is – 202.4 eV, which is much higher than the calculated value. By considering the screening effect (*i.e.*, Z < 3), and applying variation method, the calculated energy will be further lowered which is absurd.

Hence, the state $1s^3$ is not possible)].

9.15 Compare Slater type orbitals with hydrogen-like orbitals and mention the points of differences.

[**Hint**: STO: $\psi_{nlM}(r, \theta, \phi) = N r^{n'-1} \exp\left(-\frac{Z' r}{n'}\right) Y_{lM}(\theta, \varphi)$

H-like orbital: $\psi_{nlM}(r, \theta, \phi) = N r^{l} F(r) \exp(-Zr/n)\, Y_{lM}(\theta, \phi)$

The larger the value of Z or Z′, the more rapidly the wave function decreases at large values of r.

Increase in n or n' leads to wave function which gives probability density (ψ^2) extending further from the nucleus.

Unlike H-like atomic orbitals, STO's (*i*) have no radial nodes and (*ii*) are not mutually orthogonal.

9.16 Derive the expression for the average value of r for polyelectronic atom using Slater type orbital. Comment.

[**Hint:**
$$\bar{r} = \frac{\int_0^\infty r^{n'-1}\exp(-Z'r/n')\,\hat{r}\,(r^{n'-1})\exp(-Z'r/n')\,r^2\,dr}{\int_0^\infty \left(r^{n'-1}\exp(-Z'r/n')\right)^2 r^2\,dr}$$

$$= \frac{\int_0^\infty r^{2n'+1}\exp(-2Z'r/n')\,dr}{\int r^{2n'}\exp(-2Z'r/n')\,dr}$$

$$= \frac{\dfrac{(2n'+1)!}{(2Z'/n')^{2n'+2}}}{\dfrac{2n'!}{(2Z'/n')^{2n'+1}}} = \frac{n'(2n'+1)}{2Z'}$$

For $r_{\text{m.p.}}$
$$\frac{d}{dr}\left[r^2 R(r)^2\right] = \frac{d}{dr}\left[r^{2n'}\exp(-2Z'r/n')\right] = 0$$

or
$$\left[2n'r^{2n'-1} - \frac{2Z'}{n'}.r^{2n'}\right]\exp(-2Z'r/n') = 0$$

or
$$r_{\text{m.p.}} = \frac{n'^2}{Z'}$$

Comment: $\bar{r}$ increases with n' and decreases with Z'. The value $r_{\text{m.p.}} < \bar{r}$, but when $n' \geq 1$, $r_{\text{m.p.}} \approx \bar{r}$. (M.P. = most possible)

9.17 Calculate the effective nuclear charge for the 2s electron in Li atom, given that the first ionisation potential is 5.4 eV.

[**Hint:**
$$E_{n'} = -\frac{1}{2}\frac{Z'}{n'^2} \text{ or I.P.} = +\frac{1}{2}\frac{Z'^2}{n'^2} = 13.6\frac{Z'^2}{n'^2}\text{ eV}$$

$$Z' = \left(\frac{\text{I.P.} \times n'^2}{13.6}\right)^{1/2}$$

For 2s electron, $n' = n = 2$

$$Z' = \left(\frac{5.4}{13.6}\right)^{1/2} \times 2 = 1.26$$].

9.18 The effective nuclear charge for the 3s electron in Na atom is 1.9. Calculate the first ionisation potential and compare it with that for H-atom.

[Hint: $$(\text{I.P.})_1 = +\frac{1}{2}\frac{Z'^2}{n'^2} = \frac{1}{2}\times\frac{1.9\times 1.9}{3\times 3}$$

For H, $$(\text{I.P.})_1 = \frac{1}{2}\frac{Z^2}{n^2} = \frac{1}{2}\times\frac{1}{1}$$

Therefore, $$\frac{(\text{I.P.})_{\text{Na}}}{(\text{I.P.})_{\text{H}}} = \frac{Z'^2}{n'^2}\times\frac{n^2}{Z^2} = \frac{1.9\times 1.9\times 1}{3\times 3\times 1} = 0.4$$ **]**.

9.19 Write the ground state configuration and calculate the screening constant and the effective nuclear charge for the following using Slater's rules:

(*i*) $2s$ and $2p$ electrons of C

(*ii*) $2s$ and $2p$ electrons of N

(*iii*) $3s$ and $3p$ electrons of S

(*iv*) $1s$ electron of F.

[Hint: Electronic configuration for C : $1s^2\,2s^2\,2p^2$

For its $2s$ and $2p$ electrons, $S = 3\times 0.35 + 2\times 0.85 = 2.75$

$$Z' = Z - S = 6 - 2.75 = 3.25$$

Electronic configuration for N : $1s^2\,2s^2\,2p^3$,

$$Z' = 7.0 - 3.10 = 3.90$$

Electronic configuration for S : $1s^2\,2s^2\,2p^6\,3s^2\,3p^4$

For the $3s$ or $3p$ electron,

$$S = (5\times 0.35) + (8\times 0.85) + 2\times 1.00 = 10.55$$

$$Z' = 16 - 10.55 = 5.45$$

Electronic configuration for F : $1s^2\,2s^2\,2p^5$

For $1s$ electron, $S = 0.30,\ Z' = 9 - 0.30 = 8.70$].

9.20 Calculate the first ionisation potential for Li atom on the basis of Slater's rules.

[Hint: $(\text{I.P.})_1$ of Li $= E_{\text{Li}^+} - E_{\text{Li}}$

$$E = \sum\left(\frac{1}{2}\frac{Z'^2}{n'^2}\right) \text{ in a.u.}$$

For $1s$ electron in Li, $Z' = 2.7$, for $2s$, $Z' = 1.3$.

Therefore, $$E_{\text{Li}(1s^2\,2s)} = 2\times\left(-\frac{1}{2}\right)\times\left(\frac{2.7}{1}\right)^2 + \left(-\frac{1}{2}\right)\left(\frac{1.3}{2}\right)^2 = -7.5 \text{ a.u.}$$

$$E_{\text{Li}^+(1s^1)} = 2\times\left(-\frac{1}{2}\right)\left(\frac{2.70^2}{1}\right) = -7.29 \text{ a.u.}$$

$$(\text{I.P.}) \text{ for Li} = -7.29 - (-7.5) = 0.21 \text{ a.u.}$$

$$= 0.21\times 27.2 = 5.71 \text{ eV}].$$

9.21 Calculate the first and second ionisation potentials for Be atom on the basis of Slater's rules.

[Hint: $(\text{I.P.})_2 = E_{\text{Be}^+(1s^2\,2s)} - E_{\text{Be}(1s^2\,2s^2)}$

$$14.35 - (14.64) = 0.29 \text{ a.u.} = 7.89 \text{ eV}$$

$$(\text{I.P.})_2 = E_{\text{Be}^{++}(1s^2)} - E_{\text{Be}^+(1s^2\,2s)}$$

$$= \frac{1}{2} \times \left(\frac{2.30}{2}\right)^{1/2} = 0.6450 \text{ a.u.}$$

$$= 17.55 \text{ eV}].$$

9.22 Sketch the radial function for 1s atomic orbitals of He^+ ion and He atom and compare.

[Hint: $$\psi_{1s}^{\text{He+}} = \left(\frac{2^3}{\pi}\right)^{1/2} e^{-2r}$$

$$\psi_{1s}^{\text{He}} = \left(\frac{1.7^3}{\pi}\right)^{1/2} e^{-1.7r}$$

At the same value of r, $\psi_{1s}^{\text{He+}}$ will be lower than ψ_{1s}^{He}].

CHAPTER 10

Theory of Angular Momentum

We have seen (Chapter 6) that angular momentum is an important physical quantity associated with rotational motion. We have also seen (Chapter 7) that for a system with spherically symmetric field, *e.g.*, an electron moving around the nucleus, the wave functions are the eigenfunctions of the square of the angular momentum operator. Spherically symmetric fields are quite common in atomic structure and therefore, angular momentum is a very important physical quantity in the quantum mechanical treatment of atomic structure.

10.1 ANGULAR MOMENTUM—CLASSICAL AND QUANTUM MECHANICAL CONCEPT

Classically, for a particle of mass m rotating around a point O (see Figure 10.1), the angular momentum $(\vec{L})$ is defined as the vector product.

$$(\vec{L}) = \vec{r} \times \vec{p} \qquad \text{...(10.1)}$$

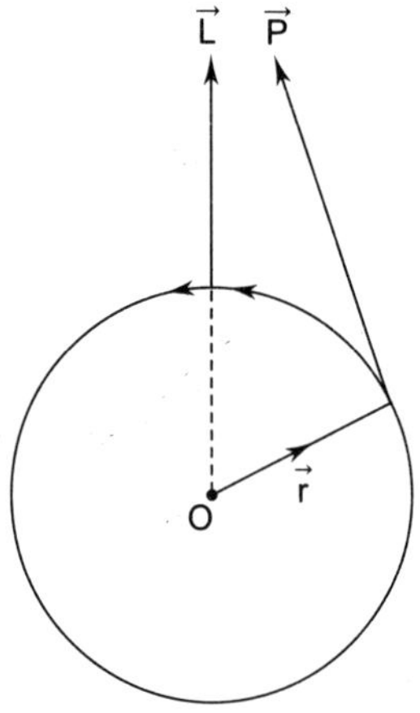

Fig. 10.1 *The angular momentum vector*

where, $\vec{r}$, a vector, is the distance of the particle from O and $\vec{p}$, another vector, is the linear momentum of the particle.

By convention, the vector $\vec{L}$ is directed outwards from O at right angles to the plane of the rotation, *i.e.*, the plane of the vectors $\vec{r}$ and $\vec{p}$.

In cartesian coordinate system, a vector is expressed in terms or unit vectors $\vec{i}, \vec{j}$ and $\vec{k}$, and the cartesian components. Thus,

$$\left.\begin{aligned} \vec{r} &= x\vec{i} + y\vec{j} + z\vec{k} \\ \vec{p} &= p_x\vec{i} + p_y\vec{j} + p_z\vec{k} \\ \text{and} \quad \vec{L} &= L_x\vec{i} + L_y\vec{j} + L_z\vec{k} \end{aligned}\right\} \qquad \dots(10.2)$$

The vector product, Equation (10.1) is usually expressed as a determinant, (Chapter 3; section 3.4.4.2)

$$\vec{L} = \vec{r} \times \vec{p} = \begin{vmatrix} \vec{i} & \vec{j} & \vec{k} \\ x & y & z \\ p_x & p_y & p_z \end{vmatrix}$$

$$= \left(yp_z - zp_y\right)\vec{i} + \left(zp_x - xp_z\right)\vec{j} + \left(xp_y - yp_x\right)\vec{k} \qquad \dots(10.3)$$

Comparing Equations (10.2) and (10.3), we get

$$\left.\begin{aligned} L_x &= yp_z - zp_y \\ L_y &= zp_x - xp_z \\ L_z &= xp_y - yp_x \end{aligned}\right\} \qquad \dots(10.4)$$

Classical mechanics puts no restriction on the magnitude of the angular momentum, and its three components L_x, L_y and L_z can be determined precisely simultaneously. In quantum mechanics, however, simultaneous determination of two physically observable quantities depends on whether the corresponding operators commute. Position and momentum of a particle, for example, cannot be simultaneously determined because their operators do not commute. Most of the conclusions arrived at with respect to angular momentum of microparticles stem from the commuting relations of the operators.

10.1.1 Angular Momentum Operators

By replacing p_x, p_y and p_z in Equation (10.4) by their operators, the operators for L_x, L_y and L_z may be written as,

$$\hat{L}_x = \frac{\hbar}{i}\left[y\frac{\partial}{\partial z} - z\frac{\partial}{\partial y}\right]$$

$$\hat{L}_y = \frac{\hbar}{i}\left[z\frac{\partial}{\partial x} - x\frac{\partial}{\partial z}\right]$$

$$\hat{L}_z = \frac{\hbar}{i}\left[x\frac{\partial}{\partial y} - y\frac{\partial}{\partial x}\right] \qquad \text{... (10.5)}$$

where $\hbar = \dfrac{h}{2\pi}$, a standard rotation.

Now, can L_x, L_y and L_z be precisely specified simultaneously ? For this, let us evaluate the commutators $\left[\hat{L}_x, \hat{L}_y\right], \left[\hat{L}_y, \hat{L}_z\right]$ and $\left[\hat{L}_z, \hat{L}_x\right]$.

$$\left[\hat{L}_x, \hat{L}_y\right] = \hat{L}_x\hat{L}_y - \hat{L}_y\hat{L}_x$$

$$\hat{L}_x\hat{L}_y = \frac{\hbar}{i}\left[y\frac{\partial}{\partial z} - z\frac{\partial}{\partial y}\right]\cdot\frac{\hbar}{i}\left[z\frac{\partial}{\partial x} - x\frac{\partial}{\partial z}\right]$$

$$= -\hbar^2\left[y\frac{\partial}{\partial z}z\frac{\partial}{\partial x} - y\frac{\partial}{\partial z}x\frac{\partial}{\partial z} - z\frac{\partial}{\partial y}z\frac{\partial}{\partial x} + z\frac{\partial}{\partial y}x\frac{\partial}{\partial z}\right]$$

$$= -\hbar^2\left[y\frac{\partial}{\partial x} + yz\frac{\partial^2}{\partial z\,\partial x} - yx\frac{\partial^2}{\partial z^2} - z^2\frac{\partial^2}{\partial y\,\partial x} + zx\frac{\partial^2}{\partial y\,\partial z}\right]$$

$$\left(\text{because terms like } \frac{\partial x}{\partial z} = 0 \text{ and } \frac{\partial z}{\partial z} = 1\right)$$

$$\hat{L}_y\hat{L}_x = -\hbar^2\left[z\frac{\partial}{\partial x} - x\frac{\partial}{\partial z}\right]\cdot\left[y\frac{\partial}{\partial z} - z\frac{\partial}{\partial y}\right]$$

$$= -\hbar^2\left[z\frac{\partial}{\partial x}y\frac{\partial}{\partial z} - z\frac{\partial}{\partial x}z\frac{\partial}{\partial y} - x\frac{\partial}{\partial z}y\frac{\partial}{\partial z} + x\frac{\partial}{\partial z}z\frac{\partial}{\partial y}\right]$$

$$= -\hbar^2\left[zy\frac{\partial^2}{\partial x\,\partial z} - z^2\frac{\partial^2}{\partial x\,\partial y} - xy\frac{\partial^2}{\partial z^2} + x\frac{\partial}{\partial y} + xz\frac{\partial^2}{\partial z\,\partial y}\right]$$

Therefore, $\hat{L}_x\hat{L}_y - \hat{L}_y\hat{L}_x = -\hbar^2\left[y\dfrac{\partial}{\partial x} - x\dfrac{\partial}{\partial y}\right]$

$$= i\hbar\left[i\hbar\left(y\frac{\partial}{\partial x} - x\frac{\partial}{\partial y}\right)\right]$$

$$= i\hbar\left[\frac{\hbar}{i}\left(x\frac{\partial}{\partial y} - y\frac{\partial}{\partial x}\right)\right]$$

$= i\hbar\hat{L}_z$ [Using Equation (10.5)]

or $$[L_x, L_y] = i\hbar \hat{L}_z$$

Similarly, $$[L_y, L_z] = i\hbar \hat{L}_x \qquad \text{...(10.6)}$$

$$[L_z, L_x] = i\hbar \hat{L}_y$$

The relations in Equation (10.6) are noncommutative which means that the three components L_x, L_y and L_z of angular momentum cannot be specifed simultaneously. (see Chapter 3, section 3.1.2 and 3.1.3). If we specify one component the other two become uncertain. By convention, the component L_z is chosen so that L_x and L_y cannot have specific values. However, the z-axis itself is chosen arbitrarily. (But when the atom or molecule is placed in a magnetic or electric field, the direction of the field is chosen as the z-axis.)

The more important thing to know is whether L (the angular momentum itself) and L_z (its z-component) can be specified simultaneously or not; L is given by,

$$L = \left(L_x^2 + L_y^2 + L_z^2\right)^{1/2}$$

so that the operator $\hat{L}$ has to be defined as the square root of another operator. Leaving aside the meaning of the square root of an operator, let us find out whether the operators $\hat{L}^2$ and $\hat{L}_z$ commute.

$$[L^2, L_z] = \left[\left(\hat{L}_x^2 + \hat{L}_y^2 + \hat{L}_z^2\right), \hat{L}_z\right]$$

$$= \left(\hat{L}_x^2 + \hat{L}_y^2 + \hat{L}_z^2\right)\hat{L}_z - \hat{L}_z\left(\hat{L}_x^2 + \hat{L}_y^2 + \hat{L}_z^2\right)$$

$$= \hat{L}_x^2\hat{L}_z + \hat{L}_y^2\hat{L}_z + \hat{L}_z^2\hat{L}_z - \hat{L}_z\hat{L}_x^2 - \hat{L}_z\hat{L}_y^2 - \hat{L}_z\hat{L}_z^2$$

$$= \left(\hat{L}_x^2\hat{L}_z - \hat{L}_z\hat{L}_x^2\right) + \left(\hat{L}_y^2\hat{L}_z - \hat{L}_z\hat{L}_y^2\right) + \left(\hat{L}_z^2\hat{L}_z - \hat{L}_z\hat{L}_z^2\right)$$

$$= \left[\hat{L}_x^2, \hat{L}_z\right] + \left[\hat{L}_y^2, \hat{L}_z\right] + \left[\hat{L}_z^2, \hat{L}_z\right] \qquad \text{...(10.7)}$$

The first term in Equation (10.7) is

$$\left[L_x^2, L_z\right] = \hat{L}_x\hat{L}_x\hat{L}_z - \hat{L}_z\hat{L}_x\hat{L}_x$$

$$= \hat{L}_x\hat{L}_x\hat{L}_z - \hat{L}_x\hat{L}_z\hat{L}_x + \hat{L}_x\hat{L}_z\hat{L}_x - \hat{L}_z\hat{L}_x\hat{L}_x$$

$$= \hat{L}_x\left(\hat{L}_x\hat{L}_z - \hat{L}_z\hat{L}_x\right) + \left(\hat{L}_x\hat{L}_z - \hat{L}_z\hat{L}_x\right)\hat{L}_x$$

$$= \hat{L}_x\left[L_x, L_z\right] + \left[L_x, L_z\right]\hat{L}_x$$

$$= -i\hbar\hat{L}_x\hat{L}_y - i\hbar\hat{L}_y\hat{L}_x \qquad (\because [L_x, L_z] = -[L_z, L_x])$$

$$= -i\hbar\left(\hat{L}_x\hat{L}_y + \hat{L}_y\hat{L}_x\right) \qquad \text{...(10.8)}$$

Similarly, it can be shown that

$$\left[L_y^2, L_z\right] = +i\hbar\left(\hat{L}_x\hat{L}_y + \hat{L}_y\hat{L}_x\right) \quad \text{... (10.9)}$$

and

$$\left[L_z^2, L_z\right] = 0 \quad \text{... (10.10)}$$

By adding Equations (10.8), (10.9) and (10.10), we obtain

$$[L^2, L_z] = 0 \quad \text{... (10.11)}$$

which means that the square of the angular momentum and its z-component can be specified simultaneously.

In the same way, it can be shown that $\hat{L}^2$ commutes with $\hat{L}_x$ and $\hat{L}_y$.

10.1.2 Physical Significance of the Commutation Rules and Quantum Mechanical Definition of Angular Momentum

The commutation relations (Equations (10.6) and (10.11)) mean that the angular momentum L of a rotating microparticle can be represented by a vector of precise length L with one and only one of its components (conventionally L_z) precisely defined. Since the other two components (L_x and L_y) are uncertain, the vector may lie anywhere on the surface of a cone whose axis coincides with the z-axis. In a sense, it would correspond to the vector $\vec{L}$ precessing around the z-axis (Figure 10.2).

The Equations (10.6) and (10.11) constitute a quantum mechanical definition of angular momentum—any vector $\vec{J}$ may be called angular momentum if it satisfies the following relations:

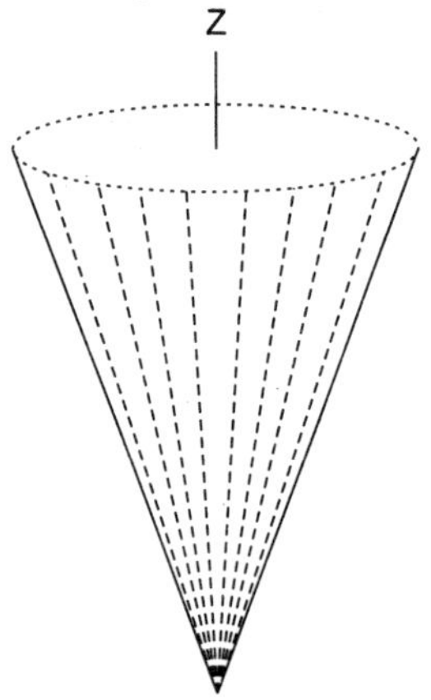

Fig. 10.2 *Cone of location of angular momentum vector*

$$[J_x, J_y] = i\hbar J_z;\ [J_y, J_z] = i\hbar J_x;\ [J_z, J_x] = i\hbar y \quad \text{... (10.12)}$$

$$[J^2, J_k] = 0$$

where $k = x, y$ or z

and

$$J^2 = J_x^2 + J_y^2 + J_z^2 \quad \text{... (10.13)}$$

A rotating system is, therefore, characterised by two operators $\hat{J}^2$ and $\hat{J}_z$. The two operators are commutative and hence can have common eigenfunctions. The eigenvalue equations are

$$\hat{J}^2 \phi_{j,m} = k_j \phi_{j,m} \qquad \text{... (10.14)}$$

$$\hat{J}_z \phi_{j,m} = k_m \phi_{j,m} \qquad \text{... (10.15)}$$

where j and m are quantum numbers to specify the eigenvalues k_j and k_m and together, the eigenfunction $\phi_{j,m}$.

10.1.3 Ladder Operators

Now to find the nature of the eigenvalues and eigenfunctions it is necessary to introduce two new operators $\hat{J}_+$ and $\hat{J}_-$ called "ladder operators" or raising and lowering operators defined as

$$\hat{J}_\pm = \hat{J}_x \pm i\hat{J}_y \qquad \text{... (10.16)}$$

They are so called because, as will be shown later, they have the effect of raising and lowering the eigenvalues k_m, the effect being described by equation

$$\hat{J}_\pm \phi_{j,m} = c_\pm \phi_{j,m\pm 1} \qquad \text{... (10.17)}$$

where the coefficient $c_\pm$ is given by

$$c_\pm = \sqrt{j(j+1) - m(m\pm 1)} \qquad \text{... (10.18)}$$

The importance of ladder operators lies in the fact that they can be used to generate eigenfunctions having the same quantum number j but different quantum number m. For example, if we know the eigenfunction $\phi_{1,0}$ where $j = 1$, $m = 0$ then, using Equations (10.17) and (10.18) we get the eigenfunction $\phi_{1,+1}$ and $\phi_{1,-1}$ as follows:

$$\hat{J}_+ \phi_{1,0} = [1(1+1) - 0(0+1)]^{1/2} \phi_{1,+1}$$

or

$$\phi_{1,+1} = \frac{1}{\sqrt{2}}\left(J_+ \phi_{1,0}\right) \qquad \text{... (10.19)}$$

Similarly,

$$\phi_{1,-1} = \frac{1}{\sqrt{2}}\left(\hat{J}_- \phi_{1,0}\right)$$

These operators commute with $\hat{J}^2$ but not with $\hat{J}_z$, nor among themselves. For example,

$$\left[\hat{J}^2, \hat{J}_+\right] = \left[\hat{J}^2, \left(\hat{J}_x + i\hat{J}_y\right)\right]$$

$$= \hat{J}^2\left(\hat{J}_x + i\hat{J}_y\right) - \left(\hat{J}_x + i\hat{J}_y\right)\hat{J}^2$$

$$= \hat{J}^2\hat{J}_x + i\hat{J}^2\hat{J}_y - \hat{J}_x\hat{J}^2 - i\hat{J}_y\hat{J}^2$$

$$= \left[\hat{J}^2, \hat{J}_x\right] + i\left[\hat{J}^2, \hat{J}_y\right]$$

$$= 0 + 0 = 0$$

Similarly, $\left[\hat{J}^2, \hat{J}_-\right] = 0$

But $\left(\hat{J}_+, \hat{J}_z\right) = \left[\left(\hat{J}_x + i\hat{J}_y\right), \hat{J}_z\right]$

$$= \left[\hat{J}_x, \hat{J}_z\right] + i\left[\hat{J}_y, \hat{J}_z\right]$$

$$= -\, i\hbar\hat{J}_y - \hbar\hat{J}_x$$

$$= -\, \hbar\hat{J}_+ \qquad \text{... (10.20)}$$

Similarly, it can be shown that

$$\left[\hat{J}_-, \hat{J}_z\right] = -\, \hbar\hat{J}_-$$

and $\left[\hat{J}_+, \hat{J}_-\right] = -\, 2\hbar\hat{J}_z$

An alternative and more useful expression for $\hat{J}^2$ can be derived in terms of $\hat{J}_\pm$ as follows:

$$\hat{J}_+\hat{J}_- = \left(\hat{J}_x + i\hat{J}_y\right)\left(\hat{J}_x - i\hat{J}_y\right)$$

$$= \hat{J}_x^2 + \hat{J}_y^2 + i\hat{J}_y\hat{J}_x - i\hat{J}_x\hat{J}_y$$

$$= \hat{J}_x^2 + \hat{J}_y^2 - i\left[\hat{J}_x, \hat{J}_y\right]$$

$$= \hat{J}_x^2 + \hat{J}_y^2 - i\left(i\hbar\hat{J}_z\right)$$

$$= \hat{J}_x^2 + \hat{J}_y^2 + \hbar\hat{J}_z$$

$$= \hat{J}^2 - \hat{J}_z^2 + \hbar\hat{J}_z \qquad \left(\because \hat{J}^2 = \hat{J}_x^2 + \hat{J}_y^2 + \hat{J}_z^2\right)$$

or $$\hat{J}^2 = \hat{J}_+\hat{J}_- + \hat{J}_z^2 - \hbar\hat{J}_z \qquad \text{... (10.21)}$$

Similarly, it can be shown that

$$\hat{J}_-\hat{J}_+ = \hat{J}^2 + \hat{J}_z^2 - \hbar\hat{J}_z$$

giving $$\hat{J}^2 = \hat{J}_-\hat{J}_+ - \hat{J}_z^2 + \hbar\hat{J}_z \qquad \text{... (10.21}a\text{)}$$

We shall find several uses of the Equations (10.20) and (10.21) later.

10.1.4 Eigenvalues of $\hat{J}^2$ and $\hat{J}$

These relations also provide an elegant means of arriving at the eigenvalues of the angular momentum operators $\hat{J}^2$ and $\hat{J}_z$.

Operating both sides of Equation (10.15) by $\hat{J}_z$, we get

$$\hat{J}_z^2 \phi_{j,m} = \hat{J}_z \left(k_m \phi_{j,m}\right) = k_m \hat{J}_z \phi_{j,m} = k_m^2 \phi_{j,m} \qquad \text{... (10.22)}$$

Subtracting Equation (10.22) from Equation (10.14), we get

$$\left(\hat{J}^2 - \hat{J}_z^2\right) \phi_{j,m} = \left(k_j - k_m^2\right) \phi_{j,m} \qquad \text{... (10.23)}$$

or

$$\left(\hat{J}_x^2 + \hat{J}_y^2\right) \phi_{j,m} = \left(k_j - k_m^2\right) \phi_{j,m} \qquad \text{... (10.24)}$$

[because $\hat{J}^2 = \hat{J}_x^2 + \hat{J}_y^2 + \hat{J}_z^2$]

Now, $\left(\hat{J}_x^2 + \hat{J}_y^2\right)$ is the operator for a physical quantity $\left(J_x^2 + J_y^2\right)$ which can never be negative; hence, the eigenvalue $k_j - k_m^2$ in Equation (10.24) must always be positive, that is,

$$k_j \geq k_m^2 \text{ for any value of } k_m \qquad \text{... (10.25)}$$

10.1.4.1 Effect of $J_\pm$

Let us consider the effect of ladder operators now and also see why they are so called. The effect of J_+, for example, on the eigenvalue of $\hat{J}^2$ will be determined as follows:

Since $\hat{J}^2$ commutes with $\hat{J}_+$

$$\hat{J}^2 \hat{J}_+ \phi_{j,m} = \hat{J}_+ \hat{J}^2 \phi_{j,m} = \hat{J}_+ \left(k_j \phi_{j,m}\right) = k_j \left(\hat{J}_+ \phi_{j,m}\right) \qquad \text{... (10.26)}$$

[in view of Equation (10.14)]

This means that $\hat{J}_+ \phi_{j,m}$ is also an eigenfunction of $\hat{J}^2$ with the same eigenvalue (k_j), that is, there is no effect of J_+ on the eigenvalue of $\hat{J}^2$.

Now let us see the effect on k_m. By adding and subtracting $\hat{J}_+ \hat{J}_z$, we get

$$\begin{aligned}
\hat{J}_z \hat{J}_+ \phi_{j,m} &= \left\{\hat{J}_+ \hat{J}_z + \hat{J}_z \hat{J}_+ - \hat{J}_+ \hat{J}_z\right\} \phi_{j,m} \\
&= \left\{\hat{J}_+ \hat{J}_z + \left[\hat{J}_z, \hat{J}_+\right]\right\} \phi_{j,m} \\
&= \left\{\hat{J}_+ \hat{J}_z \phi_{j,m} + \left[\hat{J}_z, \hat{J}_+\right] \phi_{j,m}\right\} \\
&= \hat{J}_+ k_m \phi_{j,m} + \hbar \hat{J}_+ \phi_{j,m}
\end{aligned}$$

by Equations (10.15) and (10.20) as well as the fact that

$$[J_z, J_+] = -[J_+, J_z]$$

$$= J_+ [k_m + \hbar]\, \phi_{j,m} \quad \text{... (10.27)}$$

$$= (k_m + \hbar)\, \hat{J}_+\, \phi_{j,m}$$

$$\therefore \quad [J_z, J_+] = J_z\, J_+\, \phi_{j,m}$$

which means that $(\hat{J}_+ \phi_{j,m})$ is also an eigenfunction of $\hat{J}_z$, but its eigenvalue is raised from k_m to $k_m + \hbar$, *i.e.*, by one atomic unit. The clue to this derivation is that J_+ does not commute with $\hat{J}_z$.

Similarly, it can be shown that $\hat{J}_-$ lowers the eigenvalue of $\hat{J}_z$ from k_m to $k_m - \hbar$, *i.e.*, by one atomic unit but keeps that of $\hat{J}^2$ unaltered, that is,

$$\hat{J}^2 (\hat{J}_- \phi_{j,m}) = k_j (\hat{J}_- \phi_{j,m}) \quad \text{... (10.28)}$$

$$\hat{J}_z (J_- \phi_{j,m}) = (k_m - \hbar)(\hat{J}_- \phi_{j,m}) \quad \text{... (10.29)}$$

It is now easy to show that

$$J_\pm (J_\pm \phi_{j,m}), J_\pm [J_\pm (J_\pm \phi_{j,m})], \ldots \quad \text{... (10.30)}$$

are all eigenfunctions of $\hat{J}_z$ with altered eigenvalues and also of $\hat{J}^2$ with unaltered eigenvalues. Successive applications of the operators $\hat{J}_\pm$ will, therefore, generate a series of eigenfunctions of $\hat{J}_z$ whose eigenvalues constitute the series :

$$k'_m, k'_m + \hbar, k'_m + 2\hbar, \cdots, k''_m - 2\hbar, k''_m - \hbar, k''_m$$

or

$$k'_m, k'_m + 1, k'_m + 2, \cdots, k''_m - 2, k''_m - 1, k''_m \text{ (in atomic units)} \quad \text{... (10.31)}$$

where, for a given value of k_j, k'_m is the lowest and k''_m the highest eigenvalue. The lowest and the highest values of k_m are governed by the condition Equation (10.25), *i.e.*,

$$k_m^2 \le k_j$$

This also shows that the maximum and minimum values are related as,

$$\left.\begin{aligned} k''_m &= k'_m + n\hbar \\ \text{or} \quad k''_m &= k'_m + n \text{ (in a.u.)} \end{aligned}\right\} \quad \text{... (10.32)}$$

where, n is some positive integer.

Now for the maximum value of k_m, *i.e.*, k''_m let $\phi''_{j,m}$ be the eigenfunction ; then, we have the eigenvalue equation,

$$\hat{J}_z \phi_{j,m}'' = k''_m \phi_{j,m}$$

Since k''_m is the upper limit of the eigenvalue, further application of the operator $\hat{J}_+$ will yield zero as the eigenvalue, *i.e.*,

$$\hat{J}_+\phi_{j,m}'' = 0$$

Operating with $\hat{J}_-$, we get

$$\hat{J}_-\hat{J}_+\phi_{j,m}'' = 0$$

or $$\left(\hat{J}_x - i\hat{J}_y\right)\left(\hat{J}_x + i\hat{J}_y\right)\phi_{j,m}'' = 0$$

or $$\left(\hat{J}_x^2 + \hat{J}_y^2 + i\hat{J}_x\hat{J}_y - i\hat{J}_y\hat{J}_x\right)\phi_{j,m}'' = 0$$

or $$\left(\hat{J}^2 - \hat{J}_z^2 + i^2\hbar\hat{J}_z\right)\phi_{j,m}'' = 0$$

or $$\left(k_j - k_m''^2 - \hbar k_m''\right)\phi_{j,m}'' = 0 \text{ (because } k_j'' = k_j)$$

Since $$\phi_{j,m}'' \neq 0, k_j = k_m''\left(k_m'' + \hbar\right) \quad \text{...(10.33)}$$

Similarly, we can show that

$$k_j = k_m'\left(k_m' - \hbar\right) \quad \text{...(10.34)}$$

From Equations (10.33) and (10.34), we get

$$k_j = k_m''\left(k_m'' + \hbar\right) = k_m'\left(k_m' - \hbar\right) \quad \text{...(10.35)}$$

and from Equation (10.32), $\left(k_n' + n\hbar\left[k_m' + (n+1)\hbar\right] = k_m'\left(k_m' - \hbar\right)\right)$

or $$2(n+1)\hbar k_m' + n(n+1)\hbar^2 = 0$$

or $$k_m' = -\frac{n\hbar}{2} = j\hbar\left(\text{where } j = \frac{n}{2}\right) \quad \text{...(10.36)}$$

Similarly, $$k_m'' = +\frac{n\hbar}{2} = +j\hbar \quad \text{...(10.37)}$$

Equations (10.36) and (10.37) show that j must be either a positive integer (0, 1, 2, 3, ...) or a half-integer ($n/2$).

Therefore, Equation (10.35) gives,

$$k_j = j(j+1)\hbar^2 \text{ or } j(j+1) \text{ in a.u.} \quad \text{...(10.38)}$$

and $$k_m = m\hbar \text{ or m (in a.u.)} \quad \text{...(10.39)}$$

where for a given value of j, m can take any of the values in the series

$$j, j-1, j-2, ..., 0, ... -(j-2), -(j-1), -j \quad \text{...(10.40)}$$

making a total of $2j + 1$ values for m.

Equations (10.14) and (10.15) may, thus, be written as

$$\hat{J}^2\phi_{j,m} = \left[j(j+1)\hbar^2\right]\phi_{j,m} \quad \text{...(10.41)}$$

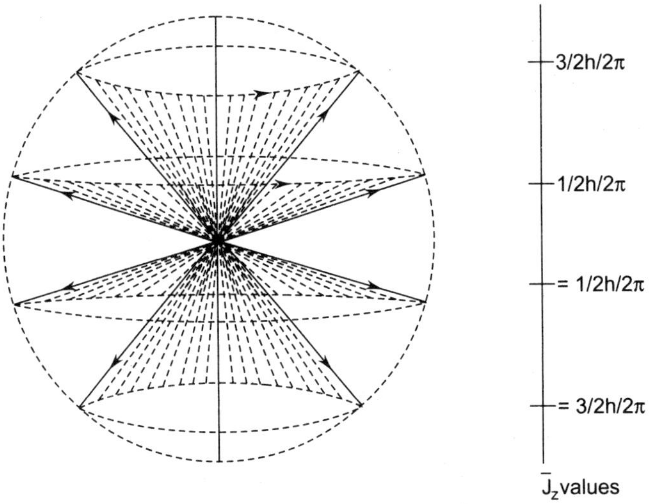

Fig. 10.3 *Location of angular momentum vector for which j = 3/2, the magnitude of the vector $\vec{J}$ is given by the radius, $\sqrt{3/2 \times 5/2}\,\hbar$ of the dashed circle, the vector takes only such orientation that gives the J_z values + 3/2 ħ, + 1/2 ħ, – 1/2 ħ and – 3/2 ħ only.*

and
$$\hat{J}_z \phi_{j,m} = m\hbar\phi_{j,m} \qquad \text{... (10.42)}$$

where m takes any value in the series (Equation (10.40)). For example, for $j = 2$, m can be +2, +1, 0, –1 or –2, and for j = 3/2, m can be 3/2, 1/2, –1/2 or –3/2.

In the physical sense, it may be concluded that the behaviour of the angular momentum vector $\vec{J}$ is governed by the Equations (10.41) and (10.42), that is, the magnitude of $\vec{J}$ is quantised and given by $\sqrt{j(j+1)}\,\hbar$ where j is the angular momentum quantum number. The vector is oriented in space in a manner such that its z-component has the value $m\hbar$, m being the quantum number corresponding to the z-component of $\vec{J}$ (Figure 10.3). This is often termed "space quantisation".

10.1.5 Orbital and Spin Motion

Subatomic particles (electrons, protons, etc.) execute two types of rotational motion—rotation of the particle about a nuclear centre, *i.e.*, orbital motion (see Chapter 7), and rotation about its own axis, *i.e.*, spin motion (see Chapter 9). The angular momentum operators for orbital motion are denoted by $\hat{L}^2$ and $\hat{L}_z$ and those for spin motion by $\hat{S}^2$ and $\hat{S}_z$. The two quantum numbers needed to characterise the eigenfunctions are denoted as l and m_l for orbital motion and s and m_s for spin motion.

For the orbital motion, denoting the eigenfunctions by Y_{l,m_l}, the eigenvalue equations are

$$\hat{L}^2 Y_{l,m_l} = l(l+1)\hbar^2 Y_{l,m_l} \qquad \text{... (10.43)}$$

$$\hat{L}_z Y_{l,m_l} = m_l \hbar Y_{l,m_l} \qquad \text{... (10.44)}$$

where, $$\hat{L}^2 = -\left[\frac{1}{\sin\theta}\frac{\partial}{\partial\theta}\left(\sin\theta\frac{\partial}{\partial\theta}\right) + \frac{1}{\sin^2\theta}\frac{\partial^2}{\partial\varphi^2}\right] \text{ and}$$

$$\hat{L}_z = \frac{h}{2\pi i}\frac{\partial}{\partial\varphi}$$

using spherical coordinates.

For a rotating particle, we have seen earlier (Chapter 6) that the quantum number l must be zero or a positive integer, *i.e.*, $l = 0, 1, 2, 3,...$ and that there are $2l + 1$ values for m_l ranging from $+ l$ to $- l$ including zero.

The values of the orbital angular momentum are then restricted to $\sqrt{l(l+1)}\,\hbar$, and its z-component to $m_l\,\hbar$.

The eigenfunctions Y_{l,m_l} are the spherical harmonics (see Chapter 6) in which the symbol for quantum number M has been changed to m_l

$$Y_{l,m_l} = P_l^{m_l}(\theta)\,F_{m_l}(\varphi) \qquad ...(10.45)$$

where, $P_l^{m_l}(\theta)$ are the associated Legendre functions (see Chapter 7) and $F_{m_l}(\varphi)$ are given as,

$$F_{m_l}(\varphi) = \frac{1}{\sqrt{2\pi}}\exp(im_l\varphi)$$

θ and φ are the spherical angular coordinates. For example, corresponding to $l = 1$, m_l will be +1, 0 or −1, and correspondingly there will be three spherical harmonics, given as

$$\left.\begin{aligned} Y_{1,1} &= N\sin\theta\exp(i\varphi) \\ Y_{1,0} &= N\cos\theta \\ Y_{1,-1} &= N\sin\theta\exp(-i\varphi) \end{aligned}\right\} \qquad ...(10.46)$$

where N is normalisation factor.

For spin motion the eigenvalue equations are

$$\hat{S}^2\,\phi_{s,ms} = s(s+1)\,\hbar^2\,\phi_{s,m_s} \qquad ...(10.47)$$

$$\hat{S}_z\,\phi_{s,ms} = m_s\,\hbar\phi_{s,m_s} \qquad ...(10.48)$$

where, ϕ_{s,m_s} is the spin eigenfunction characterised by the two quantum numbers s and m_s. However, unlike the spherical harmonics, it is not possible to write down an analytical expression for ϕ_{s,m_s}. Studies of atomic spectra reveal that for a single electron, the quantum number s has a single value $\frac{1}{2}$; accordingly, the spin vector has the length $\frac{\sqrt{3}}{2}\hbar$, the z-component being restricted to $m_s\,\hbar$ with $m_s = \pm(1/2)$ (Figure 10.4). For a single electron, therefore, there can be only two possible eigenfunctions $\phi_{\frac{1}{2},\frac{1}{2}}$ and $\phi_{\frac{1}{2},-\frac{1}{2}}$ denoted conventionally as α and β respectively. The Equations (10.47) and (10.48) may accordingly be written as (see also Chapter 9, Section 9.1.4.2)

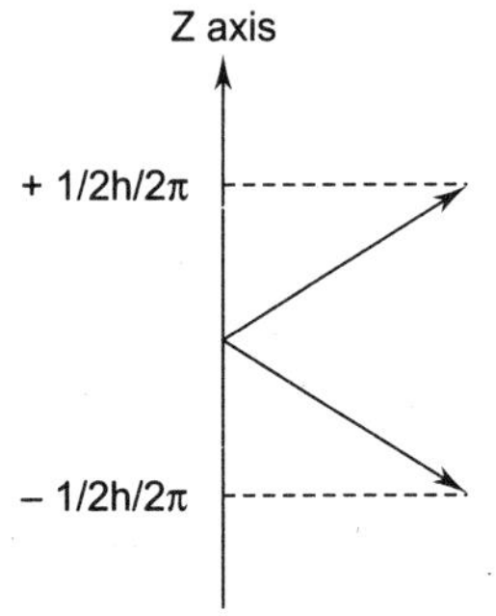

Fig. 10.4 *Allowed directions of the spin angular momentum vector*

$$\hat{S}^2\,\alpha = \frac{3}{4}\hbar^2\,\alpha;\ \hat{S}^2\,\beta = \frac{3}{4}\hbar^2\,\beta \qquad \text{... (10.49)}$$

$$\hat{S}_z\,\alpha = \frac{1}{2}\hbar\alpha;\ \hat{S}_z\,\beta = -\frac{1}{2}\hbar\,\beta \qquad \text{... (10.50)}$$

Since $\hat{S}_x, \hat{S}_y$ and $\hat{S}_z$ do not commute with each other while $\hat{S}^2$ and $\hat{S}_z$ (or $\hat{S}^2$ and $\hat{S}_x$, and so on) do so, the vector $\vec{S}$ and one of its components (usually the S_z) can be specified. A more useful expression for $\hat{S}^2$, as we shall see later, is analogous to Equation (10.21) *i.e.*,

$$\hat{S}^2 = S_{\pm}S_{\mp} + \hat{S}_z^2 - \hat{S}_z\,.$$

10.1.6 Spin Angular Momentum

The raising and lowering operators for spin angular momentum are

$$S_{\pm} = S_x \pm i\,S_y \qquad \text{... (10.51)}$$

and we have, analogous to Equation (10.21)

$$S^2 = S_{\pm}S_{\mp} \pm S_z^2 \mp \hbar S_z \qquad \text{... (10.52)}$$

Since α is the eigenfunction with the highest possible value of m_s, the operator S_+ acting on α will annihalate it, *i.e.*,

$$S_+\alpha = 0 \qquad \text{... (10.53)}$$

Similarly, $\quad S_-\beta = 0 \qquad \text{... (10.54)}$

The effect of S_- on α is to transform it to β

$$S_-\alpha = \hbar\beta \qquad \text{... (10.55)}$$

and likewise, $\quad S_+\beta = \hbar\alpha \qquad \text{... (10.56)}$

Therefore, using the Equations (10.53) to (10.54), we get

$$\left(\hat{S}_+ \pm \hat{S}_-\right)\beta = \hbar\alpha \qquad \text{... (10.57)}$$

Use of Equation (10.51) in (10.57), gives

$$\hat{S}_x\beta = \frac{1}{2}\hbar\alpha, \; S_y\beta = -\frac{1}{2}i\hbar\alpha \qquad \text{... (10.58)}$$

$$S_x\alpha = \frac{1}{2}\hbar\beta, \; S_y\alpha = \frac{1}{2}i\hbar\beta \qquad \text{... (10.59)}$$

The spin operators can be expressed in matrix form (see Chapter 9, Section 9.1.4.3).

10.1.7 Addition of Angular Momenta

When we have two sources of angular momentum $\vec{J}_1$ and $\vec{J}_2$ (for example, $\vec{L}_1$ and $\vec{L}_2$ due to orbital motion of two electrons, or $\vec{L}$ and $\vec{S}$ due to orbital and spin motions of the same electron in an atom) their resultant J and their components are defined as follows:

$$\left.\begin{aligned} \vec{J} &= \vec{J}_1 + \vec{J}_2 \\ J^2 &= J_x^2 + J_y^2 + J_z^2 \\ \text{and} \quad J_k &= J_{1k} + J_{2k}, \; k = x, y \text{ or } z \end{aligned}\right\} \qquad \text{... (10.60)}$$

By investigating the commutation relations of J_k it can be shown that $\vec{J}$ is also angular momentum. For example,

$$\begin{aligned} \left[\hat{J}_x, \hat{J}_y\right] &= \left[\left(\hat{J}_{1x} + \hat{J}_{2x}\right), \left(\hat{J}_{1y} + \hat{J}_{2y}\right)\right] \\ &= \left[\hat{J}_{1x}, \hat{J}_{1y}\right] + \left[\hat{J}_{1x}, \hat{J}_{2y}\right] + \left[\hat{J}_{2x}, \hat{J}_{1y}\right] + \left[\hat{J}_{2x}, \hat{J}_{2y}\right] \\ &= i\hbar\hat{J}_{1z} + 0 + 0 + i\hbar\hat{J}_{2z} \\ &= i\hbar\hat{J}_z \end{aligned}$$

and so on.

Since $\vec{J}_1$ and $\vec{J}_2$ refer to different vectors they will commute as each will affect only the functions of the coordinates of one electron and not the other. For the same electron, $\hat{L}$ and $\hat{S}$ also commute. All components of $\hat{J}_1$ commute with all components of $\hat{J}_2$. Hence the terms involving different coordinates such as $\left[\hat{J}_{1x}, \hat{J}_{2y}\right]$ vanish.

Also,

$$\begin{aligned} \left[\hat{J}^2, \hat{J}_z\right] &= \left[\left(\hat{J}_x^2 + \hat{J}_y^2 + \hat{J}_z^2\right), \left(\hat{J}_{1z} + \hat{J}_{2z}\right)\right] \\ &= \left[\left(\hat{J}_x^2 + \hat{J}_y^2 + \hat{J}_z^2\right), \hat{J}_{1z}\right] + \left[\left(\hat{J}_x^2 + \hat{J}_y^2 + \hat{J}_z^2\right), \hat{J}_{2z}\right] \end{aligned}$$

The term within the first square bracket may be expanded as

$$\left[\left(\hat{J}_x^2 + \hat{J}_y^2 + \hat{J}_z^2\right), \hat{J}_{1z}\right] = \left[\hat{J}_x^2, \hat{J}_{1z}\right] + \left[\hat{J}_y^2, \hat{J}_{1z}\right] + \left[\hat{J}_z^2, \hat{J}_{1z}\right]$$

$$= \left[\left(\hat{J}_{1x} + \hat{J}_{2x}\right)^2, \hat{J}_{1z}\right] + \left[\left(\hat{J}_{1y} + \hat{J}_{2y}\right)^2, \hat{J}_{1z}\right] + \left[\left(\hat{J}_{1z} + \hat{J}_{2z}\right)^2, \hat{J}_{1z}\right]$$

$$= \left[\left(\hat{J}_{1x}^2 + 2\hat{J}_{1x}\hat{J}_{2x} + \hat{J}_{2x}^2\right), \hat{J}_{1z}\right] + \left[\left(\hat{J}_{1y}^2 + 2\hat{J}_{1y}\hat{J}_{2y} + \hat{J}_{2y}^2\right), \hat{J}_{1z}\right]$$

$$+ \left[\left(\hat{J}_{1z}^2 + 2\hat{J}_{1z}\hat{J}_{2z} + \hat{J}_{2z}^2\right), \hat{J}_{1z}\right]$$

$$= \left[\left(\hat{J}_{1x}^2 + \hat{J}_{1y}^2 + \hat{J}_{1z}^2\right), \hat{J}_{1z}\right] + \left[\left(2\hat{J}_{1x}\hat{J}_{2x}\right), \hat{J}_{1z}\right] + \left[\left(2\hat{J}_{1y}\hat{J}_{2y}\right), \hat{J}_{1z}\right]$$

$$+ \left[\left(2\hat{J}_{1z}\hat{J}_{2z}\right), \hat{J}_{1z}\right] + \left[\left(\hat{J}_{2x}^2 + \hat{J}_{2y}^2 + \hat{J}_{2z}^2\right), \hat{J}_{1z}\right]$$

$$= \left[\hat{J}_1^2, \hat{J}_{1z}\right] + 2\left[\hat{J}_{1x}, \hat{J}_{1z}\right]\hat{J}_{2x} + 2\left[\hat{J}_{1y}, \hat{J}_{1z}\right]\hat{J}_{2y} + 2\left[\hat{J}_{1z}, \hat{J}_{1z}\right]\hat{J}_{2z} + \left[\hat{J}_{2z}^2, \hat{J}_{1z}\right]$$

$$= 0 - 2i\hbar\hat{J}_{1y}\hat{J}_{2x} + 2i\hbar\hat{J}_{1x}\hat{J}_{2y} + 0 + 0$$

Similarly, the term in the second bracket

$$= 0 - 2i\hbar\hat{J}_{1x}\hat{J}_{2y} + 2i\hbar\hat{J}_{1y}\hat{J}_{2x} + 0 + 0$$

making $\left[\hat{J}^2, \hat{J}_z\right] = 0$

The operators $\hat{J}^2$ and $\hat{J}_z$ for the resultant angular momentum will, therefore, have common set of eigenfunctions ϕ_{j,m_j}, the eigenvalue equations being similar to Equations (10.14) and (10.15). Here j is quantum number for the resultant angular momentum and m_j for its z-component. j can take integral or half integral positive values $\left(\text{e.g., } 0, \frac{1}{2}, 1, \frac{3}{2}, \text{etc.}\right)$ and for each value of j there will be $2j + 1$ values of m_j ranging from $+j$ to $-j$ decreasing successively by one unit $(j, j-1, j-2, \ldots -j)$. Also, since $\hat{J}^2$ and $\hat{J}_i^2$ $(i = 1, 2)$ commute, the individual quantum numbers j_1 and j_2 can also be specified along with j; but since $\hat{J}^2$ and $\hat{J}_{1z}$ do not commute (see above), m_{j_1} and m_{j_2} cannot be specified with j. Thus for the composite system of two rotating particles, out of the six possible quantum numbers, we can specify only four – either the set $j_1, m_{j_1}, j_2, m_{j_2}$, or the set j, m_j, j_1, j_2 – leaving the remaining two undetermined.

The eigenfunction ϕ_{j,m_j} can be expressed in terms of the individual eigenfunctions of the components as a simple product

$$\phi_{j}, m_j = \phi_{j_1, m_{j_1}} \phi_{j_2, m_{j_2}} \qquad \text{... (10.61)}$$

or as a linear combination of a complete set of such products

$$\phi_{j,m_j} = \sum_{m_{j1},m_{j2}} c\left(m_{j_1}, m_{j_2}\right) \phi_{j_1,m_{j1}} \cdot \phi_{j_2,m_{j2}} \qquad \text{... (10.62)}$$

with all permissible values of m_{j_1} and m_{j_2} subject to the condition $m = m_{j_1} + m_{j_2}$. The summation is overall permissible values of m_{j_1} and m_{j_2}.

10.1.8 Permissible Values of j and m_j in Relation to j_1 and j_2

We have stated earlier that for any value of j there are $2j + 1$ values of m_j ranging from $+ j$ to $- j$ including 0 [Equation (10.40)], and the same is true for j_1 and j_2. Hence denoting the maximum values by *,

$$m_j^* = j,\ m_{j_1}^* = j_1 \text{ and } m_{j_2}^* = j_2 \qquad \text{... (10.63)}$$

Dropping the subscript j in m_j, m_{j_1} and m_{j_2} for simplicity, we have the eigenvalue equation

$$\hat{J}_z \phi_{j,m^*} = \left(\hat{J}_{1z} + \hat{J}_{2z}\right) \phi_{j,m^*} = m^* \phi_{j,m^*} \qquad \text{... (10.64)}$$

In the state corresponding to m^*, m_1^* and m_2^*, the eigenfunction of the composite system is the simple product of the eigenfunctions of the component systems, *i.e.*,

$$\phi_{j,m^*} = \phi_{j_1,m_1^*} \cdot \phi_{j_2,m_2^*} \qquad \text{... (10.65)}$$

That is, $$\hat{J}_z \phi_{j,m^*} = \left(\hat{J}_{1z} + \hat{J}_{2z}\right) \phi_{j_1,m_1^*} \cdot \phi_{j_2,m_2^*} \qquad \text{... (10.66)}$$

or by Equations (10.64) and (10.65)

$$m^*\left(\phi_{j_1,m_1^*} \cdot \phi_{j_2,m_2^*}\right) = \left(m_1^* + m_2^*\right) \phi_{j_1,m_1^*} \cdot \phi_{j_2,m_2^*} \qquad \text{... (10.67)}$$

or $$m^* = m_1^* + m_2^* \qquad \text{... (10.68)}$$

or $$j = j_1 + j_2 \qquad \text{... (10.69)}$$

This (*i.e.*, $j_1 + j_2$) is one value of j. For finding the other values, let us examine the permitted values of m_j. A system with $j = j_1 + j_2$ will have the following $2j + 1$ ($= 2j_1 + 2j_2 + 1$) values of m_j [vide Equation (10.40)] :

$$(j_1 + j_2), (j_1 + j_2 - 1), (j_1 + j_2 - 2), \ldots - (j_1 + j_2) \qquad \text{... (10.70)}$$

In the above series, $m_j = j_1 + j_2$ is obtained in only one way *i.e.*, when $m_1 = j_1$ and $m_2 = j_2$. Another value, *i.e.*, $j_1 + j_2 - 1$ can arise in two ways :

(*i*) $m_1 = j_1$, $m_2 = j_2 - 1$, and
(*ii*) $m_1 = j_1 - 1$, $m_2 = j_2$.

One of these two combinations "belongs" to $j = j_1 + j_2$ in the combined system as a whole. However, $j_1 + j_2 - 1$ is the second highest value of m_j ; so, the other combination must belong to the other value of j, *i.e.*, $j = j_1 + j_2 - 1$.

But the system with this value of j has another set of $2j + 1$, *i.e.*, $2(j_1 + j_2 - 1) + 1 = 2j_1 + 2j_2 - 1$ permitted values of m_j.

Similarly, the next lower value of m_j, *i.e.*, $j_1 + j_2 - 2$ can arise from three combinations :

(*i*) $m_1 = j_1$, $m_2 = j_2 - 2$
(*ii*) $m_1 = j_1 - 1$, $m_2 = j_2 - 1$
(*iii*) $m_1 = j_1 - 2$, $m_2 = j_2$

One of these belongs to $j = j_1 + j_2$; another to $j = j_1 + j_2 - 1$, and so the third must arise from $j = j_1 + j_2 - 2$.

The series can thus be continued till j becomes equal to $j_1 - j_2$, provided $j_1 > j_2$ (negative values of j are not permissible). Thus, the possible values of the total angular momentum quantum number constitute the series,

$$j_1 + j_2, j_1 + j_2 - 1, j_1 + j_2 - 2, \ldots \mid j_1 - j_2 \mid \text{ where } j_1 \geq j_2. \qquad \ldots (10.71)$$

and || stands for the magnitude irrespective of sign. To summarise, the resultant of two angular momenta characterised by quantum numbers j_1 and j_2 is an angular momentum whose quantum number j has values from $j_1 + j_2$ to $\mid j_1 - j_2 \mid$ given by Equation (10.71) decreasing successively by one unit. For example, if $j_1 = 2$ and $j_2 = 3$, then j will be 5, 4, 3, 2 and 1.

This series is known as Clebsch-Gordon series. For every value of j, there will be $2j + 1$ values of m_j.

For an electron in an atom, accordingly, the possible values of the total angular momentum quantum number will be determined from the series,

$$j = l + s, l + s - 1, l + s - 2, \ldots [l - s], \qquad \ldots (10.72)$$

where || stands for the magnitude irrespective of sign. For a p-electron, therefore, for which $l = 1$, $s = \frac{1}{2}$, the possible values of j will be,

$$j = l + s\left(= \frac{3}{2}\right), l + s - 1 = l - s = \frac{1}{2}.$$

$$j = l + s - 2 = -\frac{1}{2} \text{ is not permitted.}$$

[**Exercise 1:** *What are the possible magnitudes of the total angular momentum vector $\vec{J}$ of an electron in an atom ?*

For an electron in an atom, j can be $\frac{1}{2}$ or $\frac{3}{2}$ or $\frac{5}{2}$, and so on. So the magnitudes of $\vec{J}$ will be,

$$\sqrt{j(j+1)} = \frac{\sqrt{3}}{2}, \frac{\sqrt{15}}{2}, \frac{\sqrt{35}}{2} \text{ [... (a.u.) respectively].}$$

[**Exercise 2:** *For a p-electron determine all the values of m_j, and assign them to the various values of j. Derive all the corresponding eigenfunctions ϕ_{j,m_j} as linear combinations of ϕ_{j_1,m_1} and ϕ_{j_2,m_2}.*

Here, $\qquad j_1 = l = 1 \text{ and } j_2 = s = \frac{1}{2}.$

So $\qquad j = j_1 + j_2 = \frac{3}{2}; j_1 - j_2 = \frac{1}{2}$

Corresponding to $j = \frac{3}{2}$, the $2j + 1 = 4$ values of m_j are $\frac{3}{2}, \frac{1}{2}, -\frac{1}{2}$ and $-\frac{3}{2}$; for $j = \frac{1}{2}$, $m_j = \frac{1}{2}, -\frac{1}{2}$.

The corresponding eigenfunctions are

$$\phi_{j,m} = \phi_{3/2,3/2}, \phi_{3/2,1/2}, \phi_{3/2,-1/2}, \phi_{3/2,-3/2}, \phi_{1/2,1/2} \text{ and } \phi_{1/2,-1/2}$$

Since $\phi_{j_1,m_1} = \phi_{1,1}, \phi_{1,0}$ and $\phi_{1,-1}$, and

$$\phi_{j_2,m_2} = \phi_{1/2,1/2}, \text{ and } \phi_{1/2,-1/2}.$$

We have $\phi_{3/2,3/2} = c\left(1, \frac{1}{2}\right) \phi_{1,1} \cdot \phi_{1/2,1/2}$

$$\phi_{3/2,1/2} = c\left(1, -\frac{1}{2}\right) \phi_{1,0} \cdot \phi_{1/2,-1/2} + c\left(0, \frac{1}{2}\right) \phi_{1,0} \cdot \phi_{1/2,1/2}$$

$$\phi_{3/2,-1/2} = c\left(0, -\frac{1}{2}\right) \phi_{1,0} \cdot \phi_{1/2,-1/2} + c\left(-1, \frac{1}{2}\right) \phi_{1,-1} \cdot \phi_{1/2,1/2}$$

and so on].

10.1.9 Coupled and Uncoupled Representations of Angular Momentum

The basic features of the combinations of two angular momenta may thus be summarised as follows :

(*i*) The total angular momentum can be represented as a vector $\vec{J}$ of length $\sqrt{j(j+1)}\,\hbar$ with j, the quantum number, having any of the values permitted by the Clebsch-Gorden series Equation (10.71).

$$j_1 + j_2, j_1 + j_2 - 1, j_1 + j_2 - 2, \ldots \mid j_1 - j_2 \mid \qquad \ldots(10.71)$$

(*ii*) The vector will lie anywhere along the surface of a cone around the z-axis, the component J_z being specified and J_x and J_y remaining unspecified.

(*iii*) The lengths of the contributing vectors $\vec{J}_1$ and $\vec{J}_2$ will have definite values $\sqrt{j_1(j_1+1)}\,\hbar$ and $\sqrt{j_2(j_2+1)}\,\hbar$, respectively, even when $\vec{J}$ has been specified.

(*iv*) The component J_z will have the magnitude $m_j\hbar$, where m_j can have any of the $2j + 1$ values ranging from $+j$ to $-j$.

(*v*) Then we have two choices:

(*a*) We may specify j_1, j_2 and z-components m_{j_1} and m_{j_2} leaving the total quantum number j and m_j undetermined. In the physical sense the vectors $\vec{J}_1$ and $\vec{J}_2$ lie on the surfaces of the two well-defined cones, but the cone (magnitude and direction) of their resultant $\vec{J}$ is not defined at all. This method is called uncoupled representation.

(*b*) Alternatively, we may specify j_1, j_2, j and m_j leaving m_{j_1} and m_{j_2} undetermined except in the special case of $m_{j_1} = j_1$ and $m_{j_2} = j_2$ when $m_j = m_{j_1} + m_{j_2} = j_1 + j_2$. This means that the vector $\vec{J}$ and its component J_z (hence the corresponding cone) are defined ; the cones of the individual vectors $\vec{J}_1$ and $\vec{J}_2$ are also defined but their *z*-components J_{z_1} and J_{z_2}, that make up the component J_z of the total momentum $\vec{J}$, remain indefinite. This is coupled representation.

We explain these features by taking the example of a system of two particles each having $s = \frac{1}{2}$ (*e.g.*, electron or proton). For each particle, $s = \frac{1}{2}$, $m_s = \pm\frac{1}{2}$. Thus,

$$j_1 = s_1 = \frac{1}{2}, j_2 = s_2 = \frac{1}{2}$$

$$m_{j_1} = m_{s_1} = \pm\frac{1}{2}; m_{j_2} = m_{s_2} = \pm\frac{1}{2},$$

The eigenfunctions of $\hat{S}^2$ and $\hat{S}_z$ are

$$\alpha\left(s = \frac{1}{2}, m_S = \frac{1}{2}\right) \text{ and } \beta\left(s = \frac{1}{2}, m_S = -\frac{1}{2}\right)$$

for each particle. The eigenfunctions of the total system (both particles together) are,

$$\alpha_1\alpha_2\left(s_1 = \frac{1}{2}, m_{S_1} = \frac{1}{2}, s_2 = \frac{1}{2}, m_{S_2} = \frac{1}{2}\right)$$

$$\alpha_1\beta_2\left(s_1 = \frac{1}{2}, m_{S_1} = \frac{1}{2}, s_2 = \frac{1}{2}, m_{S_2} = -\frac{1}{2}\right)$$

$$\beta_1\alpha_2\left(s_1 = \frac{1}{2}, m_{S_1} = -\frac{1}{2}, s_2 = \frac{1}{2}, m_{S_2} = \frac{1}{2}\right)$$

and

$$\beta_1\beta_2\left(s_1 = \frac{1}{2}, m_{S_1} = -\frac{1}{2}, s_2 = \frac{1}{2}, m_{S_2} = -\frac{1}{2}\right)$$

In such a representation (uncoupled) the individual momenta $\vec{S}_1$ and $\vec{S}_2$ will lie on definite cones and the total momentum $\vec{S}$ will remain undetermined.

On the other hand, if we determine the total spin angular momentum $(\vec{S})$ (coupled representation) it can take the following possible values:

$$S = \frac{1}{2} + \frac{1}{2} = 1, \text{ and } S = \frac{1}{2} - \frac{1}{2} = 0$$

With S = 0, there will be only one permissible value of its *z*-component (M_S), which is zero. This is called the singlet state and is represented by the quantum numbers

$$j_1 (= s_1) = \frac{1}{2}, j_2 = (= s_2) = \frac{1}{2}, j (= S) = 0, m_j (= m_S) = 0$$

It is not possible to specify which particle has $m_s = \frac{1}{2}$ and which has $m_s = -\frac{1}{2}$. Similarly, with S = 1, M_S has three values, viz., 1, 0, and – 1. This is the triplet state represented by three sets of quantum numbers j_1, j_2, j, m_j which are

$$\left(\frac{1}{2}, \frac{1}{2}, 1, 1\right), \left(\frac{1}{2}, \frac{1}{2}, 1, 0\right) \text{ and } \left(\frac{1}{2}, \frac{1}{2}, 1, -1\right).$$

10.2 ANGULAR MOMENTUM IN MANY-ELECTRON ATOMS

Each electron in an atom executes two types of rotatory motion—orbital and spin. The total orbital and spin angular momenta are given as the vector sum of the individual momenta,

$$\vec{L} = \sum_i \vec{L}_i \text{ and } \vec{S} = \sum_i \vec{S}_i \qquad \text{... (10.73)}$$

Although the operators for individual orbital angular momentum $\hat{L}_i$ do not commute with the atomic Hamiltonian, it can be shown that the operator for total angular momentum, $\hat{L}^2$, does. Therefore, the operators $\hat{H}$ and $\hat{L}^2$ as also $\hat{L}_z$ have common eigenfunctions,

$$\left.\begin{aligned} \hat{H}\psi &= E\psi \\ \hat{L}^2 \psi &= L(L+1)\,\hbar^2 \psi \\ \hat{L}_z \psi &= M_L\,\hbar\psi \end{aligned}\right\} \qquad \text{... (10.74)}$$

The eigenvalue L (L + 1) $\hbar^2$ represents the square of the magnitude of the total orbital angular momentum which is quantised, L being the quantum number, with 2L + 1 values of its *z*-component M_L. The permissible values of L are given by the Clebsh-Gordon series Equation (10.71). Each value of L is denoted by a code letter (in capital)—S, P, D, F, ... according as L = 0, 1, 2, 3, ... analogous to lower case letters, *s, p, d, f*, ... denoting l = 0, 1, 2, 3, ... for individual orbital angular momentum. The quantum numbers L and M_L are important parameters to characterize the state of an atom.

Similarly, the total spin angular momentum operators $\hat{S}^2$ and $\hat{S}_z$ commute with atomic Hamiltonian $\hat{H}$ and, therefore, have common eigenfunction ψ,

$$\left.\begin{aligned} \hat{S}^2 \psi &= S(S+1)\,\hbar\psi \\ \hat{S}_z \psi &= M_s\,\hbar\psi \end{aligned}\right\} \qquad \text{... (10.75)}$$

S is the total spin quantum number having 2S + 1 values of M_s, the *z*-component.

Consider an electron *i.e.*, configuration 2*s* 2*p*. The quantum numbers for individual orbital angular momenta of the two electrons are l_1 = 0 for (2*s*) and l_2 = 1 (for 2*p*). The total orbital angular momentum quantum number is 1 only (L = 0 + 1 = 1 and | 0 – 1 | = 1) that is, it corresponds to P state. The individual spin quantum numbers are $s_1 = s_2 = \frac{1}{2}$. The total spin quantum numbers S are $\frac{1}{2}+\frac{1}{2}=1$ and $\frac{1}{2}-\frac{1}{2}=0$. Corresponding to S = 0, $M_s = 0$ (singlet), while for S = 1, $M_s = +1$, 0 and –1 (triplet).

10.2.1 Atomic States, Atomic Terms and Term Symbol

In an atom, a single electronic configuration can have a number of representative wave functions. (Chapter 9, section 9.1.4). Each wave function may be said to correspond to an atomic state. The He 1*s* 2*s* (excited) configuration has four zero-order wave functions, one corresponding to S = 0 (singlet) and three to S = 1 (triplet) [Chapter 9, Equations (9.49) to (9.52)]. The triplet wave functions have lower energy than the singlet.

Now, consider the 1*s* 2*p* configuration for which L = 1 and S = 0 and 1. The zero-order wave functions will be similar to those in Equation (9.49) to (9.52) except that 2*s* are replaced by 2*p*. But there are three 2*p* orbitals $2p_x$, $2p_y$ and $2p_z$. Substitution of 2*s* in Equation (9.49) by these will lead to three different zero-order wave functions all having the same energy. Similarly, substitution of 2*s* in Equations (9.50), (9.51) and (9.52) will lead to nine different wave functions all having the same energy which will be different from that of the previous three. Each of the 3 + 9 = 12 electronic wave functions is an atomic state.

Thus the different atomic states arising from a given electron configuration can be grouped into sets according to their energy value. The atomic states in one set have not only the same energy (E) but also the same L and S values ; they differ only in M_L values. Such a set of atomic states is called an atomic term, or simply term. For a definite value of L and S there are 2L + 1 values of M_L and 2S + 1 values of M_S respectively. Since the electronic energy does not depend on M_L or M_S, for a fixed value of L and S there are, in general, (2L + 1) (2S + 1) atomic states in an atomic term (in the 1*s* 2*p* configuration above we have a term consisting of 3 × 1 = 3 and another of 3 × 3 = 9 atomic states).

Each term is given a symbol—the term symbol—by writing 2S + 1 values as a left superscript on the code letter corresponding to the value of L; for example, for L = 1, and S = 1, the term symbol is $\mathbf{^{2S+1}L} = {}^3P$. The value of 2S + 1 is called 'spin multiplicity'.

Exercise : *Find the terms and term symbols for the configuration $1s^2\ 2s^2\ 2p\ 3d$.*

For the 1*s* and 2*s* electrons, l = 0 and hence L = 0, *i.e.*, they do not contribute towards total orbital angular momentum. For the 2*p* and 3*d*, $l_1 = 1$ and $l_2 = 2$ respectively; therefore, L = 1 + 2 = 3, 1 + 2 – 1 = 2 and | 1 – 2 | = 1 these values correspond to F, D and P states respectively. As regards spin, for the $1s^2$ $\left(s=\frac{1}{2}\right)$ the total S = 1 and 0. But the individual m_s values are $+\frac{1}{2}$ and $-\frac{1}{2}$ (according to Pauli principle) and therefore the only M_S value in $m_{s_1}+m_{s_2}=0$. This means that the only acceptable value of S is 0. Similarly, the spins of the 2*s* electrons add up to zero. The 2*p* and 3*d* electrons have the S-value $\frac{1}{2}+\frac{1}{2}=1$ and $\frac{1}{2}-\frac{1}{2}=0$ and the Pauli principle does not restrict the values of m_s for the single electron in each. Thus even though the 1*s* and 2*s* electrons do not make any contribution, the total S-values are 1 and 0 and the spin multiplicity 2S + 1 = 3 and 1 respectively.

Accordingly, we have six terms as follows: ^3F, ^1F, ^3D, ^1D, ^3P and ^1P with degeneracies, (2l + 1) . (2S + 1) = 21, 7, 15, 5, 9 and 3 respectively.

10.2.2 Derivation of Terms and Term Symbols

In a polyelectronic atom, electrons in completely filled orbitals (in accordance with Pauli principle) do not make any contribution towards total orbital or total spin angular momentum. This can be seen as follows. Consider a filled shell $2p^6$ where we have two electrons with $m_l = +1$, two with $m_l = -1$ and two with $m_l = 0$. The total $M_L = \sum_{i=1}^{b} m_{l_i} = 0$. Since no other value of M_L is possible this corresponds to L = 0, therefore the angular momentum is zero. Similarly, the spin angular momentum of one electrons is $+\frac{1}{2}$ and the other is $-\frac{1}{2}$ in each of the three $2p$ atomic orbitals, and their sum, $M_s = \sum_i m_{s_i} = 0$. For reason similar to above S is 0. Thus for a configuration like $1s^2\ 2s^2\ 2p\ 3d$, only the p and d electrons need be considered.

For the sake of calculation of L and S, the electrons have to be divided into two classes—equivalent and non-equivalent. Two electrons (1 and 2) are equivalent if their quantum numbers $n_1 = n_2$ and $l_1 = l_2$, *e.g.*, in $2p^2$. For non-equivalent electrons $n_1 \neq n_2$ or $l_1 \neq l_2$ or both, *e.g.*, in $2s\ 2p$ ($n_1 = n_2 = 2$, $l_1 = 0$, $l_2 = 1$).

For non-equivalent electrons calculation of L and S is straight forward. Take, for example, the excited state of carbon, $1s^2\ 2s^2\ 2p\ 3p$. The $1s^2\ 2s^2$ electrons do not contribute towards total L or S. For the $2p$ and $3p$ electrons, $S = s_1 + s_2 = 1$ and $s_1 - s_2 = 0$; $L = l_1 + l_2 = 1 + 1 = 2$, $l_1 + l_2 - 1 = 1$ and $|\ l_1 - l_2\ | = 0$. The terms $\mathbf{2S + 1}_L$ are, accordingly, ^1D (for L = 2, S = 0), ^3D (for L = 2, S = 1) ^1P (for L = 1, S = 0), ^3P (for L = 1, S = 1), ^1S (for L = 0, S = 0) and ^3S (for L = 0, S = 1).

The calculation for equivalent electrons, however, is not that simple. Here the Pauli principle and the indistinguishability of the electrons eliminate many of the terms. Consider, for example, the ground state configuration of carbon, $1s^2\ 2s^2\ 2p^2$. The electrons in $1s$ and $2s$ need not be considered. For the $2p^2$ electrons ($n_1 = n_2 = 2$ and $l_1 = l_2 = 1$), the m_l values for each can be +1, 0, or –1, and m_s is $+\frac{1}{2}$ or $-\frac{1}{2}$. If $m_{l_1} = m_{l_2}$, $m_{s_1} \neq m_{s_2}$ and vice-versa. Similarly, if $m_{s_1} = m_{s_2}$, we have the following sets of values of m_{l_1} and m_{l_2}

$$m_{l_1} = 1,\ m_{l_2} = 0 \text{ or } -1$$

$$m_{l_1} = 0,\ m_{l_2} = 1 \text{ or } -1$$

$$m_{l_1} = -1,\ m_{l_2} = 0 \text{ or } 1$$

Since electrons are indistinguishable, the arrangement $m_{l_1} = 1$, $m_{l_2} = 0$ is the same $m_{l_1} = 0$, $m_{l_2} = 1$; $m_{l_1} = 1$, $m_{l_2} = -1$ is the same as $m_{l_1} = -1$, $m_{l_2} = 1$; $m_{l_1} = -1$, $m_{l_2} = 0$ is the same as $m_{l_1} = 0$, $m_{l_2} = -1$. So we have to deal with only three pairs of values of m_l instead of six. Thus while combination of $(m_{l_1}, m_{l_2}, m_{s_1} \text{ and } m_{s_2})$ like $\left(1, 1, \frac{1}{2}, \frac{1}{2}\right)$ is forbidden by Pauli principle, combinations in which $m_{l_1} = m_{l_2}$ and $m_{s_1} \neq m_{s_2}$, like $\left(1, 1, \frac{1}{2}, -\frac{1}{2}\right)$ and $\left(1, 1, -\frac{1}{2}, \frac{1}{2}\right)$ are the same because the two electrons in the same orbital merely interchange their spins. Also, $\left(1, 0, \frac{1}{2}, -\frac{1}{2}\right)$ and $\left(0, 1, -\frac{1}{2}, \frac{1}{2}\right)$ in which the electrons interchange both m_l and m_s values are the same because the electrons are indistinguishable. But combinations like $\left(1, 0, \frac{1}{2}, -\frac{1}{2}\right)$ and $\left(1, 0, -\frac{1}{2}, \frac{1}{2}\right)$ in which only one pair of quantum numbers is interchanged are not identical.

Now bearing in mind the basic rule that

$$M_L = m_{l_1} + m_{l_2} \text{ and } M_S = m_{s_1} + m_{s_2},$$

the various possible combinations (microstates) of $m_{l_1}, m_{l_2}, m_{s_1}$ and m_{s_2} along with the values of M_L and M_S for the $2p^2$ electrons can be obtained. We can see that there are fifteen such combinations, as shown in Table 10.1. Let us distinguish each combination through a symbol 1, 2, 3, ... etc., as indicated in the table in its last column.

TABLE 10.1 Various M_L and M_S Values for $2p^2$ Electrons

m_{l_1}	m_{l_2}	m_{s_1}	m_{s_2}	M_L $(m_{l_1} + m_{l_2})$	M_S $(m_{s_1} + m_{s_2})$	*Combination No.*
+ 1	+ 1	+ 1/2	– 1/2	+ 2	0	(1)
+ 1	0	+ 1/2	+ 1/2	+ 1	+ 1	(2)
+ 1	0	+ 1/2	– 1/2	+ 1	0	(3)
+ 1	0	– 1/2	+ 1/2	+ 1	0	(4)
+ 1	0	– 1/2	– 1/2	+ 1	– 1	(5)
+ 1	– 1	+ 1/2	+ 1/2	0	+ 1	(6)
+ 1	– 1	+ 1/2	– 1/2	0	0	(7)
+ 1	– 1	– 1/2	+ 1/2	0	0	(8)
+ 1	– 1	– 1/2	– 1/2	0	– 1	(9)
0	0	+ 1/2	– 1/2	0	0	(10)
0	– 1	+ 1/2	+ 1/2	– 1	+ 1	(11)
0	– 1	+ 1/2	– 1/2	– 1	0	(12)
0	– 1	– 1/2	+ 1/2	– 1	0	(13)
0	– 1	– 1/2	– 1/2	– 1	– 1	(14)
– 1	– 1	+ 1/2	– 1/2	– 2	0	(15)

It may be noted that each row in the table stands for a slater determinantal wave function which when expanded contains terms for all possible electron interchanges among the spin-orbitals.

We see that the maximum value of M_L is + 2, which is associated with $M_S = 0$. $M_L = +2$ is one of the z-components of L = 2, the other components being $M_L = +1, 0, -1$ and -2. In Table 10.2, we see that $M_S = 0$ is associated with $M_L = +2$ in combination (1) and with $M_L = -2$ in combination (15) only ; but it is associated with other components ($M_L = +1, 0, -1$) in more than one combinations; for example, the pair $M_L = +1$, $M_S = 0$ occurs in (3) and (4). We can select any one of these two as belonging to + 1-component of L = 2 (the other combination will correspond to the + 1-component of L = 1). Thus, let us select (3), (7) and (12). Now since L = 2 and $M_S = 0$ (so that S = 0), the state must be singlet (^1D), which corresponds to combinations (1), (3), (7), (12) and (15). Further, since L = 2, S = 0, J must be 2, so that the complete term symbol is $^1D_2$. (see Section 10.2).

In the ten remaining combinations the largest M_L (+ 1) is associated with $M_S = +1$ in (2). Since $M_L = +1$ is a component of L = 1 and $M_S = +1$ is a component of S = 1, the combination (2) must be a component of ^3P. Combinations (4), (5), (6), (8), (10), (11), (13) and (14) of $M_L = +1, 0, -1$ and $M_S = +1, 0, -1$ will also belong to the same ^3P term since these M_L and M_S values are components of L = 1 and S = 1, respectively. But for L = 1, S = 1, the values of J are 2, 1 and 0; so there are ultimately three components of ^3P, viz., $^3P_2$, $^3P_1$ and $^3P_0$.

There remains finally only one combination (10), for which $M_L = 0$, $M_S = 0$. These are z-components of L = 0 and S = 0, respectively, so this corresponds to $^1S_0$ state.

We thus arrive at the following five terms (different energy states) for the two equivalent $2p^2$ electrons, viz., $^1D_2$, $^3P_2$, $^3P_1$, $^3P_0$ and $^1S_0$.

10.3 SPLITTING OF TERM LEVEL INTO ATOMIC LEVELS

10.3.1 Spin-Orbit Interaction

P. Dirac was able to show, by relativistic treatment of electrons, that the orbital and spin motions in an atom are not completely independent the two interact and the energy of interaction is proportional to the dot product $\vec{L}.\vec{S}$ depending on the relative orientation of the two vectors. Also, the two vectors can be added to give the *total electronic angular momentum vector* $\vec{J}$

$$\vec{L} + \vec{S} = \vec{J} \quad \text{...(10.76)}$$

The operator $\hat{J}$ for the total angular momentum commutes with the atomic Hamiltonian $\vec{H}$ and therefore

$$\hat{J}^2 \psi = J(J+1)\hbar^2 \psi \quad \text{...(10.77)}$$

where J is the total angular momentum quantum number whose values are given by the Clebsch-Gordon series

$$J = L + S, L + S - 1, L + S - 2, \ldots | L \quad S |$$

and ψ is the electronic wave function.

10.3.2 Atomic Levels

If the atomic Hamiltonian is expressed as $\hat{H} = \hat{H}^0 + \hat{H}_{rep}$, $\hat{H}^0$ being the zeroth order Hamiltonian and $\hat{H}_{rep}$ the perturbation operator due to interelectronic repulsions, all states belonging to the same term are degenerate (*i.e.*, have the same energy). If, however, the spin-orbit interaction is included, *i.e.*, $\hat{H} = \hat{H}^0 + \hat{H}_{rep} + \hat{H}_{S-0}$, the terms are split into sublevels differing very slightly in energy. The energy of each sublevel, called *atomic level*, will be determined by its J-value. An atomic level is thus defined as an electronic energy level in an atom having the same L, S and J value. An atomic level is denoted by simply putting the value of J as a right subscript on the term symbol, $\mathbf{2S+1}_{\mathbf{L_j}}$. For 2*s* 2*p* configuration for example, L = 1, S = 1 and 0 ; the terms are ^3P and ^1P and the J values being 2, 1, 0 (1 + 1 = 2, 1 + 1 – 1 = 1 and 1 – 1 = 0) for ^3P and 1 for ^1P (1 + 0 = 1), the atomic levels are $^3P_2$, $^3P_1$, $^3P_0$ and $^1P_1$.

Like other angular momentum vectors, $\vec{J}$ has also its *z*-components, the values of M_j being 2J + 1 (For J = 1, for example, there will be three *z*-components of $\vec{J}$). Those belonging to the same J will have the same energy (2J + 1-fold degenerate). Thus the atomic levels given above are 5-fold degenerate, 3-fold degenerate, non-degenerate and 3-fold degenerate respectively.

In terms of wave function, each of these degenerate states characterized by a definite value of M_j is a Slater determinant.

10.3.3 Spin Multiplicity

The quantity 2S + 1 is called "spin-multiplicity" or simply "multiplicity" of the term. Corresponding to S = 0, $\frac{1}{2}, 1, \frac{3}{2}, 2, \cdots$ the multiplicities are 1 (singlet), 2 (doublet), 3 (triplet), 4 (quadruplet), 5 (quintuplet) .... If L > S the values of J range from L + S to L – S, and the multiplicity gives the number of levels that arise from a given term. If L < S, the values of J range from S + L to and are 2L + 1 in number. If, for example, L = 0 and S = 1, only one value of J (= 1) is possible but the multiplicity is 3.

10.3.4 L-S and *J*-*J* Coupling

The foregoing discussion is based on a scheme in which the vectors of indivdiual orbital angular momenta $(\vec{l}_i)$ of electrons in an atom are added to give the total orbital angular momentum $(\vec{L})$ vector and similarly for the spins, *i.e.*,

$$\vec{L} = \sum_i \vec{L}_i \text{ and } \vec{S} = \sum_i \vec{S}_i$$

Then the vectors $\vec{L}$ and $\vec{S}$ are combined to give the total electronic angular momentum vector $\vec{J}$. This scheme is called L-S coupling or Russell-Saunders coupling. Consider, for example, the configuration $2p\,3p$ having $l_1 = 1$ and $l_2 = 1$ and $s_1 = s_2 = \frac{1}{2}$. The vectors $\vec{l}_1$ and $\vec{l}_2$ can be combined in three possible ways so as give the three values of L viz 2, 1 and 0. Similarly s_1 and s_2 combine vectorially in two different ways to give S = 1 and 0. Then $\vec{L}$ and $\vec{S}$ can combine to give $\vec{J}$ for which J = 3, 2 and 1.

L-S coupling is appropriate for atoms with small atomic number where the spin-orbit interaction is small in comparions to interelectronic repulsion. For atoms with large atomic number the spin-orbit interaction becomes much larger than the interelectronic repulsion. Under such condition the operators for $\vec{L}$ and $\vec{S}$ do not commute with $\hat{H}$ but that for $\vec{J}$ does. In such cases the spin and orbital angular momenta of individual electrons are first combined to give the total angular momentum for indivdiual electrons,

$$\vec{J}_i = \vec{L}_i + \vec{S}_i \quad \text{... (10.78)}$$

and then the $\vec{J}_i's$, are added vectorially to get the total electronic angular momentum vector.

$$\vec{J} = \sum_i \vec{J}_i \quad \text{... (10.79)}$$

this scheme is called *j-j* coupling.

10.3.5 Hund's Rule

We have seen that a single electronic configuration gives rise to a number of atomic states due to repulsion between the electrons. Which of these states will be most stable, *i.e.*, of lowest energy. For this, there is an empirical rule known as the Hund's rule which states

"For terms arising from the same electron configuration, the term which has the largest value of S will lie lowest; if there is more than one term with the largest S, then the one with the largest S and the largest L will lie lowest."

In the carbon ground state configuration $1s^2\,2s^2\,2p^2$, for example, we have three terms: ^3P, ^1D and ^1S. According to Hund's rule ^3P will be the lowest energy state. In a d^2 configuration, where there are five terms: ^3F, ^3P, ^1G, ^1D and ^1S, the terms ^3F and ^3P have the largest S, but F has L = 3, and P has L = 1; therefore, ^3F will be the lowest.

This rule works well with the ground state configuration but may fail for excited ones. Further, the rule gives the lowest term of a configuration but not the remaining terms.

Highest value of S means largest number of parallel spin which tends to keep each other away there by minimizing the Coulombic repulsion between them. Therefore, the term that has larger number of parallel spins will be the lowest.

To determine the lowest term in a configuration with partly filled subshell of orbitals it is not necessary to draw the complete table of the type 10.2. We simply put the electrons in the orbitals so as to give the maximum number of parallel spins. For example, in a d^3 configuration we have

	d_{xy}	d_{yz}	d_{xz}	$d_{x^2-y^2}$	d_{z^2}
m_l:	+ 2	+ 1	0	− 1	− 2

The maximum value of $M_L = \sum_{i=1}^{3} m_{l_i} = +2 + 1 + 0 = 3$. This value must belong to L = 3, *i.e.*, the F-term.

Since the maximum value of $S = \frac{3}{2}$ giving 2S + 1 = 4 Hund's rule say that ^4F will be the lowest energy term.

We have seen earlier that the spin-orbit interaction splits a term into several atomic states, each state being designated by total electronic angular momentum quantum number J. Take the example of excited state of sodium ($1s^2\,2s^2\,2p^6\,3p$). This gives rise to a single term ^2P having two atomic states $^2P_{3/2}$ and $^2P_{1/2}$ corresponding to $J = 1 + \frac{1}{2} = \frac{3}{2}$ and $1 - \frac{1}{2} = \frac{1}{2}$. So there are two excited states of sodium. The lower value of J will be for the lower of the two. This explains the observed fine structure of D-line in the spectrum of sodium. (see Figure 10.5).

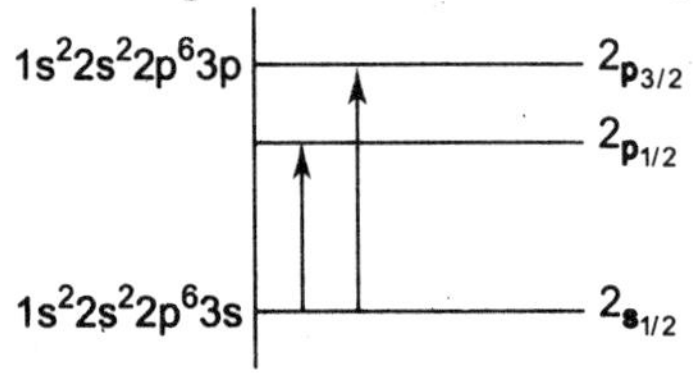

Fig. 10.5 *Fine structure of sodium D-line*

To summarise, as we go on to include the perturbation terms in the atomic Hamiltonian $\hat{H}^0 + \hat{H}_{rep} + \hat{H}_{SO}$ the successive interactions lead to splitting of the energy level. In the case of a 1*s* 2*p* configuration, for example, we have the following Schematic diagram (see Fig. 10.6).

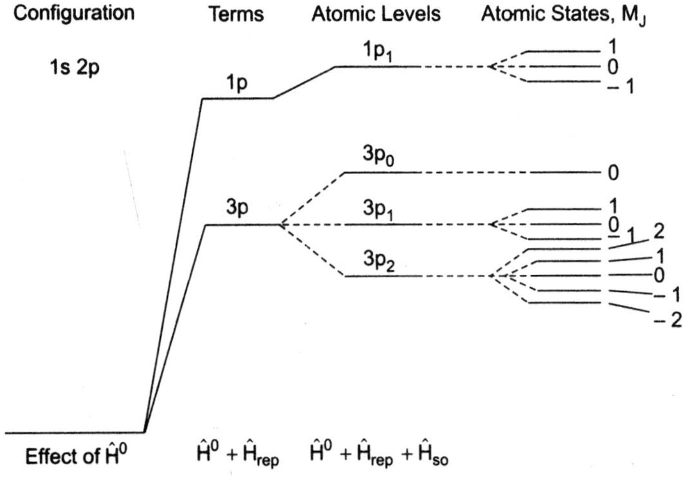

Fig. 10.6 *Splitting of energy due to perturbation by electronic repulsion and spin-orbit interaction*

PROBLEMS

10.1 Give a quantum mechanical definition of angular momentum. Explain its physical significance. [**Hint** : See text].

10.2 Give the commutation relations for the orbital and spin angular momenta L and S, respectively.

Given that the components of L commute with the similar components of S, establish the commutation relations for the total angular momentum J formed by combination of L and S.

[**Hint:** $[L_x, L_y] = i\hbar Lz, \ldots, [S_x, S_y] = i\hbar S_z, \ldots,$

$[L_y, S_x] = 0\ [L_x, S_y] = 0$

$$\vec{J} = \vec{L} + \vec{S}$$

Therefore, $J_x = L_x + S_x ; J_y = L_y + S_y ; J_z = L_z + S_z$

$$[J_x, J_y] = \hat{J}_x\hat{J}_y - \hat{J}_y\hat{J}_x$$

$$= \left(\hat{L}_x + \hat{S}_x\right)\left(\hat{L}_y + \hat{S}_y\right) - \left(\hat{L}_y + \hat{S}_y\right)\left(\hat{L}_x + \hat{S}_x\right)$$

$$= \hat{L}_x\hat{L}_y + \hat{L}_x\hat{S}_y + \hat{S}_x\hat{L}_y + \hat{S}_x\hat{S}_y - \hat{L}_y\hat{L}_x - \hat{L}_y\hat{S}_x - \hat{S}_y\hat{L}_x - \hat{S}_y\hat{S}_x$$

$$= \left(\hat{L}_x\hat{L}_y - \hat{L}_y\hat{L}_x\right) + \left(\hat{S}_x\hat{S}_y - \hat{S}_y\hat{S}_x\right) + \left(\hat{L}_x\hat{S}_y - \hat{S}_y\hat{L}_x\right) + \left(\hat{S}_x\hat{L}_y - \hat{L}_y\hat{S}_x\right)$$

$$= i\hbar\hat{L}_z + i\hbar\hat{S}_z + 0 + 0$$

$$= i\hbar\hat{J}_z$$

Similarly, $[J_y, J_z] = i\hbar\hat{J}_x ; [J_z, J_x] = i\hbar\hat{J}_y$

10.3 Define ladder operators $\hat{L}_{\pm}$. Derive the relations

$$[L^2, L_{\pm}] = 0, [L_z, L_{\pm}] = i\hbar\hat{L}_{\pm} \text{ and}$$

$$[L_+, L_-] = 2\hbar\hat{L}_z$$

[**Hint:** See text].

10.4 Explain that L_+ or L_- is not Hermitian, but $L_+ L_-$ or $L_- L_+$ is.

10.5 What are spherical harmonics? Show that they are eigenfunctions of both $\hat{L}^2$ and $\hat{L}_z$, L being the orbital angular momentum. What are the eigenvalues for each of the two operators?

[**Hint:** Spherical harmonics: $Y_{l,M}(\theta, \varphi) = P(\theta) . F(\varphi)$

$$E = \frac{L^2}{2I} = \frac{l(l+1)h^2}{8\pi^2 I}$$

or $$\frac{\hat{L}^2}{2I} Y_{l,M} = \frac{l(l+1)h^2}{8\pi^2 I} Y_{l,M}$$

or $$\hat{L}^2 Y_{l,M} = l(l+1)\hbar^2 Y_{l,M};\ \hbar = \frac{h}{2\pi};$$

eigenvalue $= l(l+1)\hbar^2$

$$\hat{L}_z Y_{l,M} = \frac{\hbar}{i}\frac{d}{d\varphi}\left[P(\theta).F(\varphi)\right]$$

$$= \frac{\hbar}{i}\frac{d}{d\varphi}\left[P(\theta)\frac{1}{\sqrt{2\pi}}e^{iM\varphi}\right]$$

$$= M\hbar\left[P(\theta).\frac{1}{\sqrt{2\pi}}e^{iM\varphi}\right] = M\hbar\left[P(\theta).F(\varphi)\right]$$

Eigenvalue $= M\hbar, M = 0, \pm 1, \pm 2$].

10.6 How are the spin eigenfunctions expressed? Give the eigenvalues of $\hat{S}^2$ and $\hat{S}_z$.
[**Hint :** See text].

10.7 Do the following pairs of operators commute?

$$\hat{p}_x \text{ and } \hat{p}_y, \hat{p}_x \text{ and } \hat{x}, \hat{p}_x \text{ and } \hat{z},$$

$$\hat{J}_z \text{ and } \hat{J}_y, \hat{J}^2 \text{ and } \hat{J}_y, \hat{J}_z \text{ and } \hat{z}$$

Draw conclusions regarding the possibility of simultaneously observing the corresponding points of physical quantities.

[**Hint:** $$[p_x, x] = \hat{p}_x\hat{x} - \hat{x}\hat{p}_x$$

$$= \frac{h}{2\pi i}\left[\frac{d}{dx}(x) - x\frac{d}{dx}\right]$$

$$= \frac{h}{2\pi i}\left[x\frac{d}{dx} + 1 - x\frac{d}{dx}\right] \neq 0$$

p_x and x cannot be simultaneously observed.

$$[p_x, z] = \hat{p}_x\hat{z} - \hat{z}\hat{p}_x = \frac{h}{2\pi i}\left[\frac{d}{dx}(z) - z\frac{d}{dx}\right]$$

$$= \frac{h}{2\pi i}\left[z\frac{d}{dx} + 0 - z\frac{d}{dx}\right] = 0$$

p_x and z can be observed simultaneously].

10.8 Give the following for an electron in 3*d* orbital:

(*a*) The magnitudes of the vectors $\vec{L}$ and $\vec{S}$.

(*b*) The posible values of the quantum numbers *j* and m_j.

(*c*) The magnitudes of the vectors $\vec{J}$ and their *z*-components.

[Hint:

(*a*) $l = 2,\ s = \frac{1}{2}; \vec{L} = \frac{\sqrt{6}\hbar}{2\pi}; \vec{S} = \frac{\sqrt{3}}{2}\hbar$

(*b*) $j = \frac{5}{2}, \frac{3}{2}, \frac{1}{2}$

(*c*) $\vec{J} = \frac{\sqrt{35}}{2}, \frac{\sqrt{15}}{2}, \frac{\sqrt{3}}{2}$

$$m_j = \frac{5}{2}, \frac{3}{2}, \frac{1}{2}, -\frac{1}{2}, -\frac{3}{2}, -\frac{5}{2} \text{ belong to } j = \frac{5}{2}$$

$$m_j = \frac{3}{2}, \frac{1}{2}, -\frac{1}{2}, -\frac{3}{2} \text{ belong to } j = \frac{3}{2}$$

$$m_j = \frac{1}{2}, -\frac{1}{2} \text{ belong to } j = \frac{1}{2}\Big].$$

10.9 Give the magnitudes of the angular momentum and its possible orientations in space for an electron in 1*s*, 2*p* and 3*d* orbitals.
[Hint : 1*s*, $l = 0$; $L = 0$; $L_z = 0$, *i.e.*, the vector and all its components have zero length, *i.e.*, there is no vector.

$$2p : l = 1, L = \sqrt{2}\hbar \ ; L_z = +\hbar, 0, -\hbar$$

$$3d : l = 2, L = \sqrt{6}\hbar \ ; L_z = +2\hbar + \hbar, 0 - \hbar, -2\hbar].$$

10.10 Show that $Y_{1,0} = \cos\theta$ is an eigenfunction of both $\hat{L}^2$ and $\hat{L}_z$. Give the corresponding eigenvalues and the magnitude and orientations of the angular momentum vector.

[Hint:

$$\hat{L}^2 Y_{1,0} = -\left[\frac{1}{\sin\theta}\frac{\partial}{\partial\theta}\left(\sin\theta\frac{\partial}{\partial\theta}\right) + \frac{1}{\sin^2\theta}\frac{\partial^2}{\partial\varphi^2}\right]\cos\theta$$

$$= 2\cos\theta = 2Y_{1,0}$$

Eigenvalue $= l(l+1) = 2.$

Therefore, $l = 1$

$$L = \sqrt{2}\hbar \ L_z = +\hbar, 0, -\hbar \text{ (3 orientations)}].$$

10.11 Determine the term symbols for a p^3 configuration of nitrogen atom. Arrange the different states in order of increasing energy. How many micro-states exist for this configuration?

TABLE 10.2 Various M_L and M_S Values for the $2p^3$ Configuration

	$M_S = \frac{3}{2}$	$M_S = \frac{1}{2}$	$M_S = -\frac{1}{2}$	$M_S = -\frac{3}{2}$
$M_L = 2$		(abc) (1)	(abd) (1)	
$M_L = 1$		(abe), (acd) (2)	(abf), (bcd) (2)	x
$M_L = 0$	(ace) (1)	(bce), (acf) (ade) (3)	(bcf), (adf) (bde) (3)	(bdf) (1)
$M_L = -1$		(cde), (aef) (2)	(cdf), (bef) (2)	
$M_L = -2$		(cef) (1)	(def) (1)	

[Figures in the parentheses indicate the number of possible combinations. A combination like $\left(1, \frac{1}{2}\right), \left(1 - \frac{1}{2}\right), \left(1, \frac{1}{2}\right)$ with $M_L = 3$ for 3 electrons is not permissible].

[Hint: $n_1 = n_2 = n_3 = 2\,;\, l_1 = l_2 = 1;$

$$s_1 = s_2 = s_3 = \frac{1}{2}$$

For $l = 1, m_l = 1, 0$ and -1 ; for $s = \frac{1}{2}$, $m_S = \pm \frac{1}{2}$

No two electrons can have the same values of both m_l and m_S. Therefore, the different states of the atom can be built up by taking any three of the following (m_l, m_S) combinations :

(*a*) $\left(1, \frac{1}{2}\right)$, (*b*) $\left(1, -\frac{1}{2}\right)$, (*c*) $\left(0, \frac{1}{2}\right)$, (*d*) $\left(0, -\frac{1}{2}\right)$, (*e*) $\left(-1, \frac{1}{2}\right)$, and (*f*) $\left(-1, -\frac{1}{2}\right)$

Values of $M_L = \sum m_{l_i}$ and $M_S = \sum m_{s_i}$ along with the possible combinations are presented in Table 10.2. Pick up the highest value of M_L, *i.e.*, + 2 ; it is a component of L = 2 and is associated with $M_S = \pm \frac{1}{2}$ which are components of $S = \frac{1}{2}$; so it constitutes ^2D term. The other M_L components of L = 2 are + 1, 0, – 1 and – 2. Pick up the combinations of each of these M_L values with $M_S = \pm \frac{1}{2}$; they will all constitute ^2D. Strike out these combinations from the table. The truncated table is shown in Table 10.3.

TABLE 10.3

	$M_S = \frac{3}{2}$	$M_S = \frac{1}{2}$	$M_S = -\frac{1}{2}$	$M_S = -\frac{3}{2}$
$M_L = +1$		1	1	
$M_L = 0$	1	2	2	1
$M_L = -1$		1	1	

The highest M_L value is now + 1 which is a component of L = 1. Its combinations with $\pm\frac{1}{2}$ constitute ^2P term. The other components, viz., 0 and – 1 on combination with $M_S = \pm\frac{1}{2}$ also give rise to ^2P. On striking out one combination from such array, we are left with a table having the single array :

TABLE 10.4

	$M_S = \frac{3}{2}$	$M_S = \frac{1}{2}$	$M_S = -\frac{1}{2}$	$M_S = -\frac{3}{2}$
$M_L = 0$	1	1	1	1

This belongs to L = 0 and $S = \frac{3}{2}$; the highest component of the S, *i.e.*, $M_S = \frac{3}{2}$ has one entry ; this gives the ^4S term.

Values of J : for $\quad {}^4S, L = 0, S = \frac{3}{2}\ ; J = \frac{3}{2}$

$$^2D, L = 2, S = \frac{1}{2}\ ; J = \frac{5}{2}, \frac{3}{2}$$

$$^2P, L = 1, S = \frac{1}{2}\ ; J = \frac{3}{2}, \frac{1}{2}$$

Term symbols in order of increasing energy levels :

$$^4S_{3/2} < {}^2D_{3/2} < {}^2D_{5/2} < {}^2P_{1/2} < {}^2P_{3/2}$$

The combinations are to be decided by the M_J value. Thus, there are the following 20 combinations].

$$^4S_{3/2} : M_J = \frac{3}{2}, \frac{1}{2}, -\frac{1}{2}, -\frac{3}{2}$$

$$^2D_{3/2} : M_J = \frac{3}{2}, \frac{1}{2}, -\frac{1}{2}, -\frac{3}{2}$$

$$^2D_{5/2} : M_J = \frac{5}{2}, \frac{3}{2}, \frac{1}{2}, -\frac{1}{2}, -\frac{3}{2}, -\frac{5}{2}$$

$$^2P_{1/2} : M_J = \frac{1}{2}, -\frac{1}{2}$$

$$^2P_{3/2} : M_J = \frac{3}{2}, \frac{1}{2}, -\frac{1}{2}, -\frac{3}{2}\Big]$$

10.12 Determine the term symbols for np^4, np^5, d^1, d^2, d^3, d^4 and d^5 systems.

[**Hint :** Follow the procedure as shown in 10.12.

p^4 : ^1S, ^1D, ^3P
p^5 : ^2P
d^1 : ^2D
d^2 : ^1S, ^1D, ^1G, ^3P, ^3F

d^3 : ^{2}P (2), ^{2}G, ^{2}F, ^{2}H, ^{4}P, ^{4}F
d^4 : ^{1}S (2), ^{1}D (2), ^{1}F, ^{1}G (2), ^{1}J, ^{3}P (2), ^{3}D
^{3}F (2), ^{3}G, ^{3}H, ^{5}D
d^5 : ^{2}S, ^{2}P, ^{2}D (3), ^{2}F (2), ^{2}G (2), ^{2}H, ^{2}I,
^{4}P, ^{4}D, ^{4}F, ^{4}G, ^{6}S

The numbers in the parentheses indicate the number of terms of the same type obtained from the configuration.]

10.13 Draw the energy level diagrams for ^{3}D and ^{3}P states.

[**Hint:** $^3D : L = 2, S = 1$; therefore, $J = 3, 2, 1$

$^3P : L = 1, S = 1$; therefore, $J = 2, 1, 0$

$^3D_3$ ———— $J = 3$
$^3D_2$ ———— 2
$^3D_1$ ———— 1
$^3P_2$ ———— 2
$^3P_1$ ———— 1
$^3P_0$ ———— 0].

10.14 The p^3 configuration gives rise to the terms ^{2}D, ^{2}P and ^{4}S. Indicate diagrammatically the spliting of these terms due to spin-orbit interaction and due to magnetic field.

10.15 Show that there can be no term symbol like $^3D_0$.

[**Hint:** $2S + 1 = 3, S = 1 ; L = 2$; therefore, $J = 3, 2, 1$ but not 0].

10.16 What are the magnitudes of total orbital, total spin and total angular momenta for the ground state term ^{4}F of vanadium?

[**Hint:** $S = \frac{3}{2}$; $L = 3$

$$J = \frac{4}{2}, \frac{7}{2}, \frac{5}{2}, \frac{3}{2}$$

Magnitudes of $\vec{S} = \frac{\sqrt{15}}{2}\hbar, \vec{L} = \sqrt{12}\,\hbar$

$$\vec{J} = \frac{\sqrt{99}}{2}, \frac{\sqrt{63}}{2}, \frac{\sqrt{35}}{2}, \frac{\sqrt{15}}{2}\Bigg].$$

10.17 A closed shell electronic configuration always gives rise to the ^{1}S term; explain why?

[**Hint:** For any closed shell configuration,

$$L = \sum l_i = 0, S = \sum s_i = 0 \text{ ; therefore, } 2S + 1 = 1$$

For example, for

$$p^6 : L = 1 + 0 - 1 = 0,$$

$$S = \frac{1}{2} - \frac{1}{2} + \frac{1}{2} - \frac{1}{2} + \frac{1}{2} - \frac{1}{2} = 0\Bigg].$$

PART IV

MOLECULAR STRUCTURE AND CHEMICAL BOND

CHAPTER 11

Symmetry, Group Theory and Quantum Chemistry

Symmetry is a very important and fascinating property of molecules. The concepts of symmetry and group theory are important in the study of quantum chemistry because it is possible with their help to find out eigenfunctions and eigenvalues of certain types of molecules without actually solving the Schrödinger equation. A formal treatment of the concepts of symmetry and group theory constitutes the subject matter of this Chapter.

11.1 SYMMETRY OPERATIONS AND SYMMETRY ELEMENTS

We may often say by mere inspection that a particular molecule is unsymmetrical and another symmetrical, and that one molecule is more symmetrical than the other. For example, H_2O molecule is symmetrical, HOCl is not, and BF_3 is more symmetrical than H_2O. However, the concept may be treated in a formal manner in terms of the symmetry "operations' and symmetry "elements". A symmetry operation over a molecule leaves it in an indistinguishable configuration from the starting one. For example, if a molecule of H_2O is rotated through 180° around an axis which bisects the HOH angle, the molecule acquires a configuration (structure II, Fig. 11.1) which is indistinguishable from the original one (structure I, Fig. 11.1).

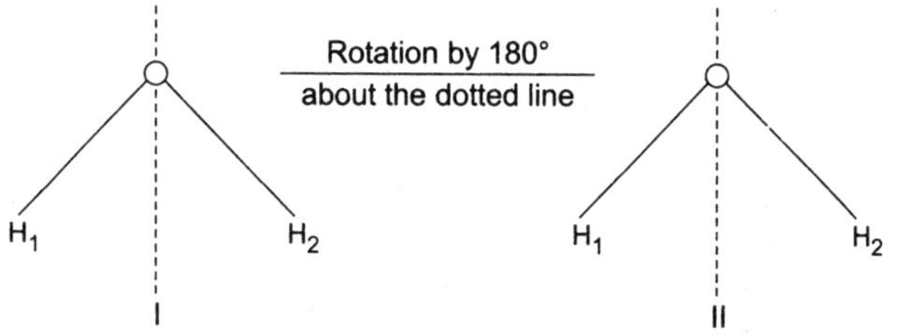

Fig. 11.1 *Rotation and rotational axis in H_2O molecule*

We call the rotation through 180° a symmetry operation and rotation axis (the dotted line) a symmetry element.

Apart from rotation around an axis, the other symmetry operations that are possible for different molecules include reflection planes, improper rotations, inversion, etc. There are altogether five different types of symmetry operations and symmetry elements as listed in Table 11.1. The symmetry of a molecule is described by listing all the symmetry elements present in it.

TABLE 11.1 Symmetry Elements and Operations

	Operation	*Element*	*Symbol*
1.	To leave the molecule as such	Identity	E
2.	Rotation about an axis through $\frac{2\pi}{n}$ angle, n being 1, 2, 3, ...	n-fold "proper" axis of rotation	C_n
3.	Reflection in a plane	Plane of symmetry	σ
4.	Inversion through a point	Centre of inversion	i
5.	Rotation about an axis through $\frac{2\pi}{n}$ angle followed by reflection in a plane perpendicular to that axis	n-fold "improper" axis of rotation	S_n

11.1.1 Proper Rotation

A simple rotation of the type described for H_2O molecule is called the proper rotation and the axis of rotation is denoted by the symbol C. In H_2O molecule the rotation axis described above is called C_2 axis since the molecule is rotated by $2\pi/2$. In some molecules (more symmetrical) there may be several axes of rotation. In BF_3, for example, there is a C_3 axis perpendicular to the molecular plane and passing through the atom B (Fig. 11.2).

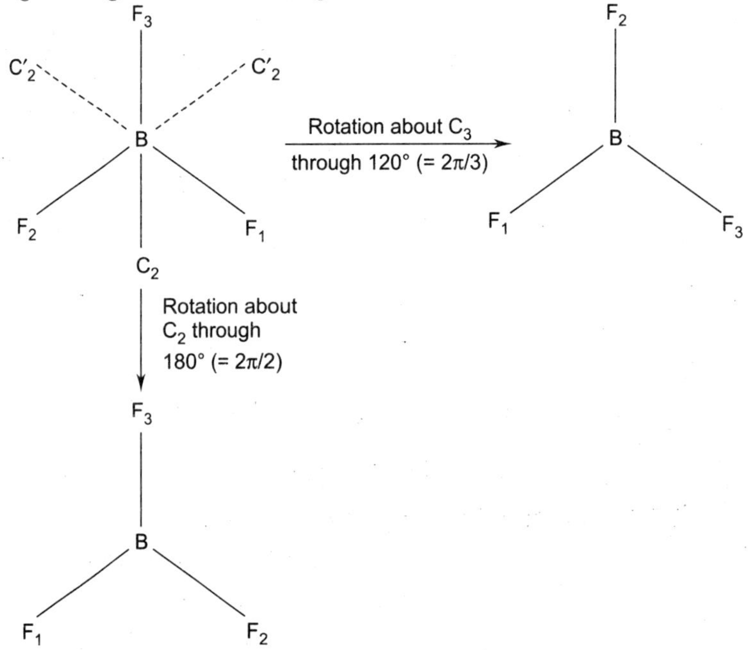

Fig. 11.2 *Rotational axes of symmetry in* BF_3 *molecule*

Besides, there are three C_2 axes. The axis C_n with the highest value of n is taken as the principal axis; for example, the C_3 axis in BF_3 is the principal axis.

11.1.2 Reflection

A reflection plane is a symmetry element that acts as a mirror and makes one half of the molecule the mirror image of the other half. In every flat molecule the molecular plane is a reflection plane, denoted by symbol σ. In H_2O, we notice two reflection planes (see Fig. 11.3)—a molecular plane σ (xz) and a perpendicular plane σ (yz) bisecting the HOH angle. Both these planes contain the C_2-axis of rotation, which is also the principal axis. Symmetry planes containing the principal axis are called vertical planes, σ_v, denoted as σ_v and σ_v'. If a vertical plane bisects the angle between two C_2-axes in a molecule it is called a dihedral plane, σ_d. In BF_3, there are three σ_d planes.

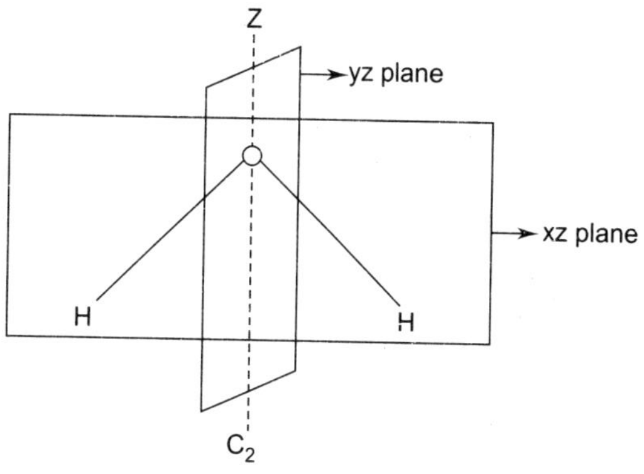

Fig. 11.3 *Symmetry planes in H_2O molecule*

A molecular plane of symmetry perpendicular to the principal axis of rotation is a horizontal plane, σ_h. In H_2O, there is no σ_h; in BF_3 there is one.

11.1.3 Inversion

If a point exists in the centre of a molecule such that identical atoms are found on either side at equal distances from it, the central point is called the centre of inversion, i. In H_2O and BF_3 molecules there is no i; in C_2H_4 molecule there is one (see Fig. 11.4).

11.1.4 Improper Rotation

If a rotation of a molecule about an axis through an angle $\frac{2\pi}{n}$ (n = integer) followed by reflection along the plane perpendicular to it leaves the molecule in an indistinguishable configuration, it is called an improper rotation, S_n. In the molecules considered so far, there is no such axis. Consider the staggered and eclipsed conformations of ethane (Fig. 11.5).

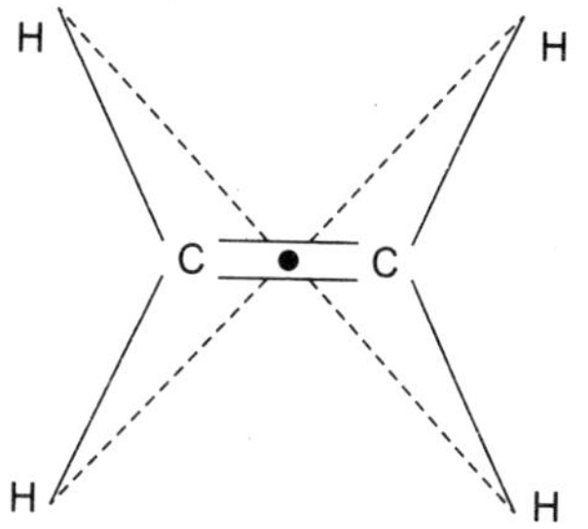

Fig. 11.4 *Inversion centre in C_2H_4 molecule*

It can be seen that both conformations have a C_3 axis of proper rotation coincident with the C—C bond axis. The eclipsed form has σ_h but no i. Rotation through 120° about the C—C bond followed by reflection along σ_h perpendicular to this axis constitutes the S_3 axis of improper rotation. On the other hand, the staggered form has i but no σ_h. Rotation through 60° about the C—C axis followed by reflection along the plane perpendicular to the C—C axis constitute the S_6 axis, even though the molecule has no C_6 axis.

If a molecule has a plane of symmetry σ_h perpendicular to a proper axis of rotation C_2, C_4 or C_6, the axis naturally becomes S_2, S_4 and S_6 respectively. An S_2 axis is equivalent to i.

11.1.5 Identity

If a sequence of symmetry operations brings the molecule back to its original configuration, the net operation is called identity operation, E. For example, two successive rotations about the C_2-axis in H_2O are equivalent to identity; this fact is expressed as $C_2^2 = E$. Also, $\sigma_v^2 = E$, $\sigma_v'^2 = E$.

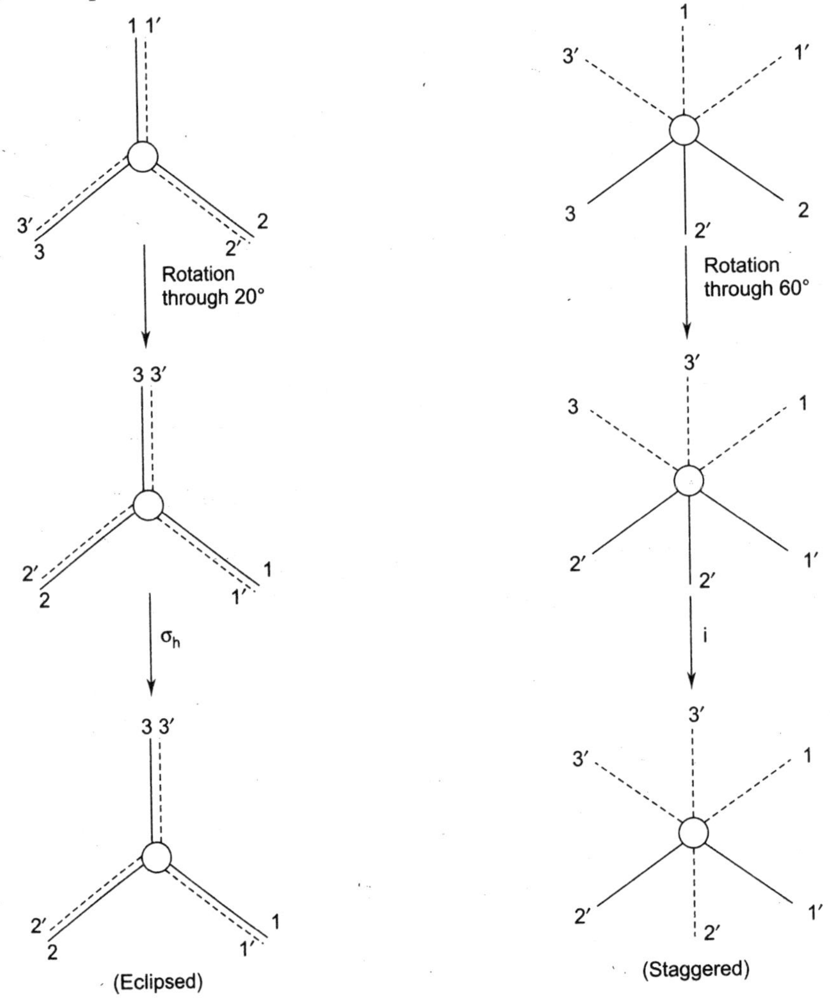

Fig. 11.5 *Eclipsed and staggered conformations of C_2H_6. The circle O at the centre is the projection of C—C bond, numbers 1, 1′etc. denote the H atoms*

In BF_3, $$C_3^3 = E,\ C_2^2 = E,\ C_2'^2 = E,\ C_2''^2 = E,\ \sigma_d^2 = E, \text{etc.} \quad \text{... (11.1)}$$

The identity operation leaves the molecule unchanged and it appears as if no operation has been performed. This operation sounds trivial, but in group theory it has great significance. It is obvious that even the most unsymmetrical molecule has at least one operation E.

Each of the elements E, σ and i generates only one operation because two successive i or σ operations bring back the molecule to its original configuration.

$$\sigma^2 = E, i^2 = E \quad \text{... (11.2)}$$

But C_n and S_n (with $n > 2$) elements can generate a number of operations. For example, element C_3 generates operations C_3^1 and C_3^2. In some cases two or three successive operations produce the same effect as a single different operation. For example, the element C_6 in benzene (hexagonal planar) generates the sequence of operations $C_6^1, C_6^2, C_6^3, C_6^4, C_6^5$ and C_6^6 (= E). But benzene has also C_3- and C_2-axes collinear with the C_6-axis so that,

$$C_6^2 = C_3^1, C_6^3 = C_2^1, C_6^4 = C_3^2 \qquad \text{... (11.3)}$$

By convention, the operation C_6^1 and C_6^5, which are unique, are considered to be generated by the axis C_6 and others by the axes C_3 and C_2.

Similarly, an S_6 axis when present in a molecule as in the case of staggered conformation of C_2H_6, generates the operation $S_6^1, S_6^2, S_6^3, S_6^4, S_6^5$ and S_6^6. But the C—C axis, which is the S_6-axis, is also the C_3-axis in this molecule and it can be seen that,

$$S_6^2 = C_3^1, S_6^3 = i, S_6^4 = C_3^2 \text{ and } S_6^6 = E \qquad \text{... (11.4)}$$

Only S_6^1 and S_6^5 are unique operations.

If can be verified that, in general, $S_n^{n/2} = i$ and $S_n^n = E$ if n is even and $n/2$ is odd. In other words, if in a molecule there is an S_n-axis with n even and $\frac{n}{2}$ odd (as in the above case or in benzene), the existence of an inversion centre i is implied, though the converse is not necessarily true.

But this is not true if n is odd; here $S_n^n \neq E$ and $S_n^{2n} = E$. The important thing to note is that a molecule having an S_n axis with n odd has also a C_n-axis and also a σ plane. The improper rotation may then appear trivial but is still important from group theoretical considerations. For example, in BF_3 molecule we have S_3, C_3 and σ_h elements. If we carry out the sequence of improper rotations $S_3^1, S_3^2, S_3^3, \ldots$, we can see the following effects:

$$S_3^1 = C_3^1 + \sigma_h, S_3^2 = C_3^2, S_3^3 = \sigma_h, S_3^4 = C_3^1.$$

$$S_3^5 = C_3^2 + \sigma_h \text{ and } S_3^6 = C_3^3 = E$$

Here only S_3^1 and S_3^5 are unique operations ; others are generated also by C_3 or σ_h.

11.1.6 Total Symmetry of a Molecule

The symmetry of a molecule can be determined by listing all the symmetry elements present in it. For the examples considered so far, we have the following lists of symmetry elements:

H_2O : E, C_2, σ_v (*yz*), σ_v' (*xz*)

BF_3 : E, C_3, S_3, $3C_2$, σ_h, 3 σ_d

C_2H_4 : E_s C_2, σ_h, i

C_6H_6 : E, C_6, C_3, C_2, $3C_2'$, $3C_2''$, i, S_6, S_3, σ_h, σ_4, $3\sigma_d$

Listing of the symmetry elements clearly requires a prior knowledge of the geometry of the molecule. In benzene, for example, the symmetry elements can be identified as follows (Fig. 11.6).

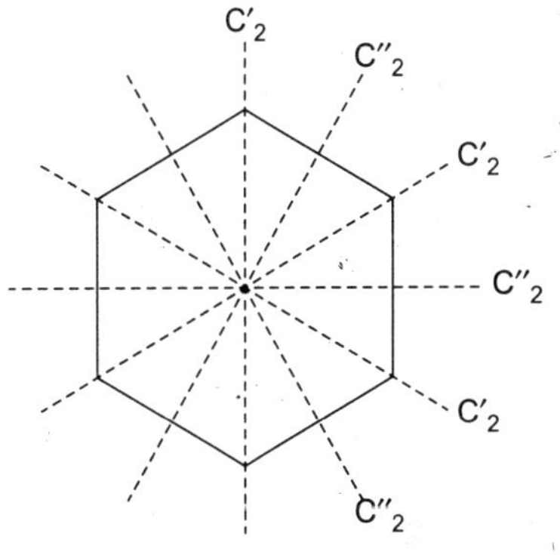

Fig. 11.6 *Symmetry elements in benzene molecule*

C_6, C_3, C_2, S_6 and S_3 are all collinear and vertical to the molecular plane σ_h, C_2' bisects the C—C—C angles on opposite sides. C_2'' bisects the C—C bonds on opposite sides, σ_v' and σ_d' (not shown in the figure) contain the C_2'-and C_2''-axes respectively. i is at the centre of the hexagonal ring.

It should be clear now as to why we say that benzene is more symmetrical than H_2O, BF_3 or C_2H_4.

[**Exercise:** List the symmetry elements in the following molecules.

NH_3 (pyramidal), trans-dichloroethylene (planar) cis-dichloroethylene, Co $(NH_3)_4Cl_2$ ($4NH_3$ and Co in one plane), XeF_4 (square planar).

NH_3 : E, C_3, $3\sigma_v$

trans-dichloroethylene: E, C_2, σ_v, σ_v'

cis-dichloroethylene: E, C_2, σ_v, σ_v'

Co $(NH_3)_4Cl_2$: E, C_4, C_2, S_4, i, $2C_2', 2C_2'', \sigma_h, 2\sigma_v, 2\sigma_v'$].

11.1.7 Combination of Operations

We have seen that the effect of performing C_6^1 operation twice is the same as that of performing C_3^1 once. We express this fact by the relation $C_6^1, C_6^1 = C_6^2 = C_3^1$. Now it will be seen that for any molecule possessing more than one symmetry element if two symmetry operations are performed one after the other, the result is the same as that obtained on performing one single operation. In other words, two operations over a molecule may be "combined" to get a third operation. For example, in H_2O if the operation C_2 is followed by the operation σ_v the result is the same as that of the single operation σ_v' (Fig. 11.7). In writing such equations the convention is to write the sequence of operations from right to left. A combination like $C_2\ \sigma_v\ \sigma_v'$ means operation, σ_v' followed by σ_v followed by C_2.

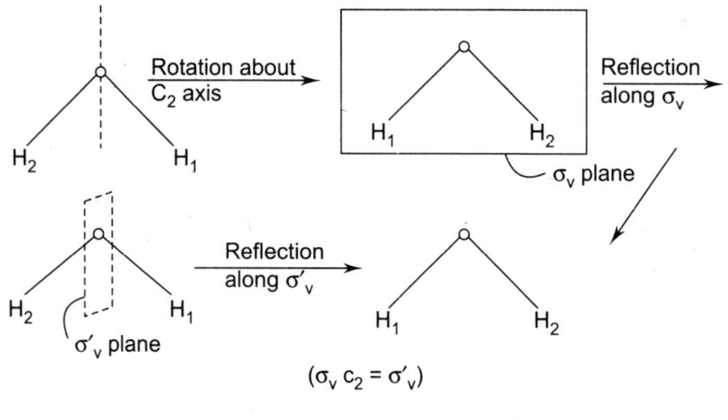

Fig. 11.7 *Combination of two operations*

11.2 GROUP THEORY

The relationships among the symmetry elements can be treated very elegantly in terms of the concepts of group theory. It is very important to note that the "set of symmetry operations" of a molecule constitutes a "mathematical group". A group in mathematics consists of a set of members (which may be numbers or matrices) which obey the following four rules as given below.

1. The "combination" of any two members A and B results in a third member C, which also belongs to the same group. The order of combination is very important as AB is not necessarily equal to BA. If AB = BA the members A and B are said to be commutative.
2. There must be a member E in the group such that
$$AE = EA = A, BE = EB = B, \text{etc.} \quad ...(11.5)$$
The member E is called identity.
3. When more than two members of a group combine, they do so in an associative manner, *i.e.*,
$$(AB)\,C = A\,(BC) \quad ...(11.6)$$
4. Every member A must have its inverse (or reciprocal) A^{-1}, which is also a member of the group, *i.e.*,
$$AA^{-1} = A^{-1}\,A = E \quad ...(11.7)$$

In group theory each member of a group is called "element", but here we shall avoid using this term as it may be confused with the elements of symmetry.

As noted earlier, in the symmetry group of a molecule, a symmetry operation (R) and not a symmetry element, is a member of the group.

We can test these rules in the case of the "group" of symmetry operations in water molecule:

1. Rule 1 is followed as $\sigma_v\,C_2 = \sigma'_v$, $\quad C_2\,\sigma'_v = \sigma_v$, etc.
2. The group has identity operation E as a member of the group,
$$EC_2 = C_2\,E = C_2, \quad E\,\sigma_v = \sigma_v\,E = \sigma_v, \text{etc.}$$
3. Operations are performed associatively as,
$$\sigma'_v\,(\sigma_v\,C_2) = (\sigma'_v\,\sigma_v)\,C_2, \text{etc.}$$
4. Every operation in the group has its inverse; for example,
$$C_2^{-1}\,C_2 = E$$

where C_2 is clockwise rotation and C_2^{-1} is anticlockwise rotation. similarly, $\sigma_v\,\sigma_v^{-1} = E$, etc.

H_2O molecule provides a very simple example. Let us take the case of BF_3. The following symmetry operations are possible in BF_3 molecule:

$$E, C_3^1, C_3^2\left(=C_3^{-1}\right), C_2, C'_2, C''_2, \sigma_h, \sigma_d, \sigma'_d, \sigma''_d.$$

1. Rule 1 is followed as $\sigma_v\,C_3^1 = C'_2$, $C'_3\,\sigma_v = C''_2$

   (Here $\sigma_v\,C_3^1 \neq C_3^1\,\sigma_v$)
2. There is identity, E, in the group.
3. Associative law of combination is followed,
$$C_3^1\left(\sigma_v\,C_2\right) = \left(C_3^1\,\sigma_v\right)C_2$$
4. Every operation has its inverse,
$$C_3^1\,C_3^{-1} = E, \text{where } C_3^{-1} = C_3^2.$$

11.3 SYMMETRY POINT GROUPS

The group of symmetry operations of a molecule is called "point group". Several molecules may have the same set of operations. For example, the following molecules have the same set of operations, *viz.*, E, C_2, σ_v, σ_v', and hence, belong to the same point group.

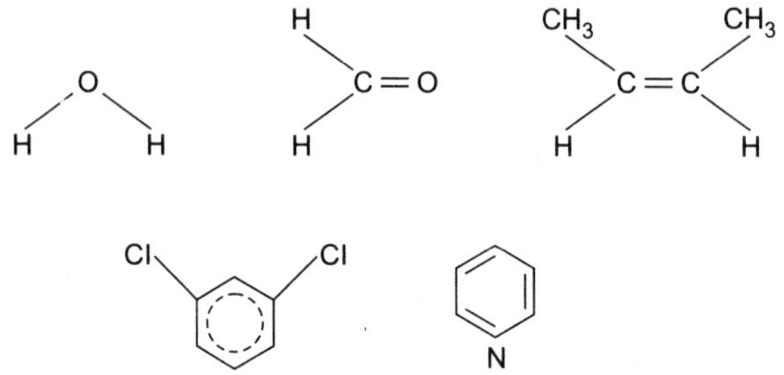

Molecules can thus be classified according to their symmetry point groups. Such a classification has several advantages and, as will be evident later, it is the first step towards reducing the labour involved in the calculation of wave functions and energies of molecules.

Each point group is assigned a symbol; for example, the flat molecules mentioned just above belong to the point group C_{2v}. The method of assigning such symbols for molecules is described below.

The method does not involve the listing of all symmetry operations for the molecule, it involves only looking for certain key symmetry elements. A key symmetry operation is the rotation around an axis. The symbols for most of the point groups can be grouped on the basis of principal axis of rotation as C_{nv}, C_{nh}, D_{nh}, D_{nd} where $n \geq 2$. The number n indicates the order of the principal axis. This axis defines the vertical direction. if the n-fold principal axis is accompanied by n two-fold axes at right angles to it the letter D is used in the symbol for the point group otherwise the letter used is C.

If a σ_h plane is present, the small letter h is used (C_{nh} or D_{nh}). If n σ_v planes are present without σ_h, the symbol used is C_{nv}. If n σ_d planes are present, the symbol is D_{nh} (in case σ_h is present) or D_{nd} (if σ_h is absent). If no symmetry plane is present, the small letter is dropped.

Thus H_2O belongs to C_{2v}, trans-dichloroethylene belongs to C_{2h}, BF_3 belongs to D_{3h}, C_2 H_6 (staggered) belongs to D_{3d} and so on.

If there is an S_{2n}-axis collinear with a C_n-axis and there is no reflection plane σ, the symbol S_{2n} is used for the point group.

In addition to the above mentioned groups, whose symbols are determined by the principal axis of rotation, we have some special groups. These are:

(*i*) C_1, in which no symmetry element is present except E, *e.g.*, the molecule CH_2 Cl Br, (tetrahedral)

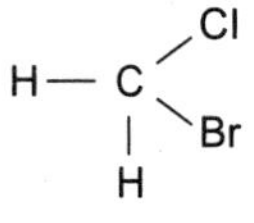

(*ii*) C_s, in which no symmetry element is present except the molecular plane, *e.g.*, the molecule HOCl,

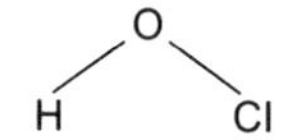

(*iii*) C_i, in which no symmetry element is present except *i* *i.e.*, the molecule $C_2F_2Cl_2Br_2$.

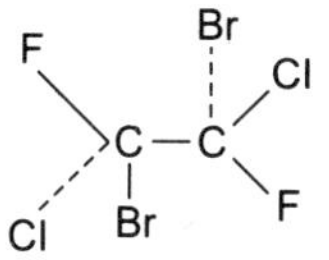

Atoms F and C connected by continuous lines (–) are in one plane; atoms connected to C by broken lines (– – –) are below this plane and those connected by thick lines are above it.

(*iv*) $C_{\infty v}$, a linear, molecule having C_n with $n = \infty$ and σ_v but no σ_h, *e.g.*, S = C = O.

(*v*) $D_{\infty h}$, any linear molecule having C_n with $n = \infty$ and a σ_h plane, *e.g.*, O = C = O.

(*vi*) T_d, a molecule having tetrahedral symmetry, *e.g.*, CH_4.

(*vii*) T_h, a molecule having tetrahedral symmetry with *i*.

(*viii*) O_h, a molecule having octahedral symmetry, *e.g.*, Co $[(NH_3)_6]^{2+}$.

(*ix*) I_h, a molecule having dodecahedral or icosahedral symmetry.

The procedure indicated in the Flow Chart (11.1) as shown on next page, may be of help in determining the point group symbol for a molecule.

11.4 MULTIPLICATION TABLES

Corresponding to a single point group, numerous combinations of symmetry operations are possible. For example, consider the trans-dichloroethylene molecule.

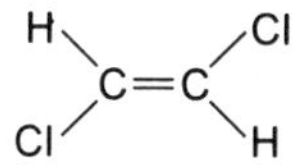

It belongs to the point group C_{2h} (operations : E, C_2, σ_h and *i*). It is easily seen that $C_2 C_2 = C_2^2 = E$; $C_2 \sigma_h = i$; $\sigma_h i = C_2$ and so on. All such combinations are better represented by a multiplication table in which all combinations of type AB are shown by writing the operations A at the left of each row and B at the head of each column (see Table 11.2) and AB means operation B followed by A.

TABLE 11.2 Multiplication Table for C_{2h} Point Group

C_{2h}	E	C_2	σ_h	i
E	E	C_2	σ_h	i
C_2	C_2	E	i	σ_h
σ_h	σ_h	i	E	C_2
i	i	σ_h	C_2	E

Chart 11.1 *Procedure for finding point groups*

1. Examine for special groups : $C_{\infty v}$, $D_{\infty h}$, T_d, O_h and I_h.
2. If no special group is present, look for a C_n-axis (principal).

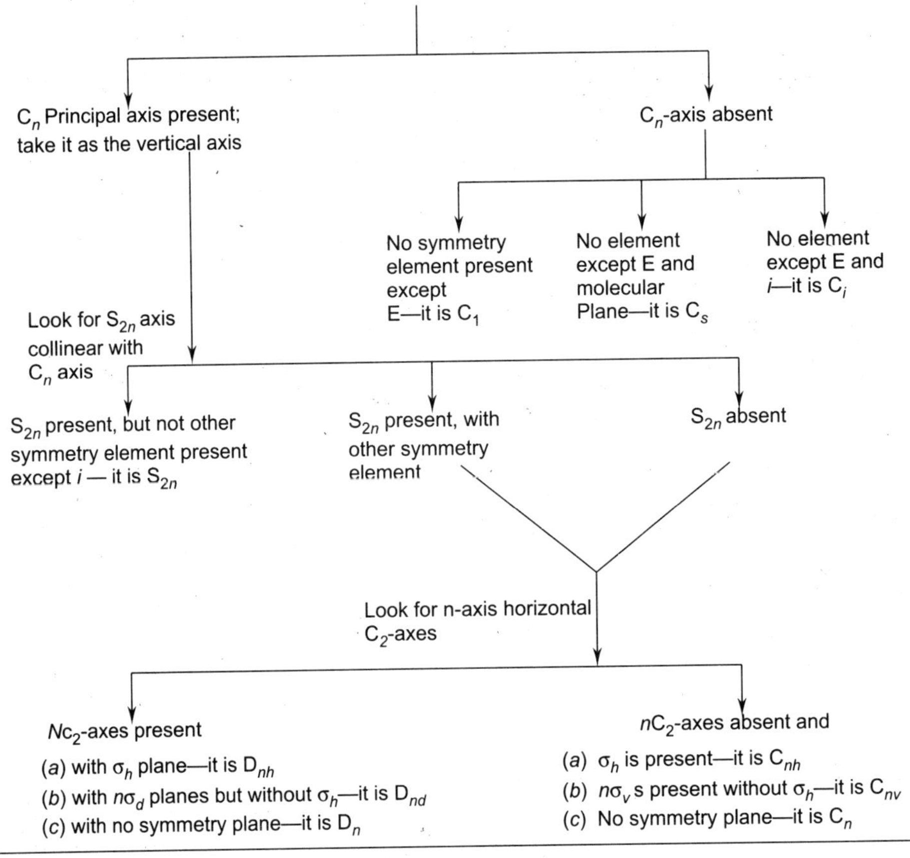

Table 11.2 has 4 rows and 4 columns involving a total of 16 combinations. For a group having more symmetry operations, the table will be larger. For example, NH_3 (pyramidal with N-atom at the apex) belongs to C_{3v} point group ($E, C_3^1, C_3^2, \sigma_v, \sigma_v'$ and σ_v'' ; see Fig. 11.8 where the molecule is viewed downward from the N-atom; the three H-atoms form an equilateral triangle base).

It is easy to see that $\sigma_v' \sigma_v = C_3^2, \sigma_v, \sigma_v' = C_3$ and so on.

The multiplication table for the C_{3v} group is as follows:

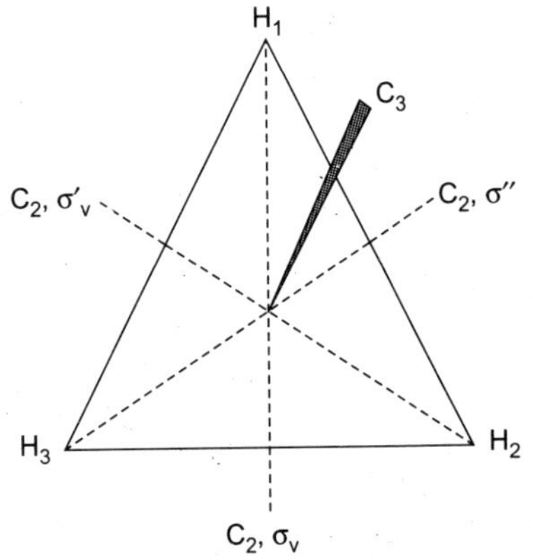

Fig. 11.8 *Symmetry operations in NH_3 molecule ; C_3 is perpendicular to the H_1 H_2 H_3 triangle; dotted lines are the C_2 axes as well as the bases of vertical planes*

TABLE 11.3 Multiplication Table for C_{3v} Point Group

C_{3v}	E	C_3	C_3^2	σ_v	σ_v'	σ_v''
E	E	C_3	C_3^2	σ_v	σ_v'	σ_v''
C_3	C_3	C_3^2	E	σ_v''	σ_v	σ_v'
C_3^2	C_3^2	E	C_3	σ_v'	σ_v''	σ_v
σ_v	σ_v	σ_v'	σ_v''	E	C_3	C_3^2
σ_v'	σ_v'	σ_v''	σ_v	C_3^2	E	C_3
σ_v''	σ_v''	σ_v	σ_v'	C_3	C_3^2	E

11.4.1 Similarity of Symmetry Operations

It can be said on the basis of common sense that in the C_{3v} point group the operations C_3 and C_3^2 are similar, though not identical, as are σ_v, σ_v' and σ_v''. According to group theory, similar members of a group obey the following rule:

"If two members A and B are similar, then

$$A = R^{-1} BR \qquad \text{... (11.8)}$$

where R is any member of the group including A or B itself."

This rule is called the rule of similarity transformation. This is applicable to the symmetry point groups. Take, for example, $B = C_3^1$ and $R = \sigma_v$, then also $R^{-1} = \sigma_v$. By Equation (11.8),

$$A = \sigma_v C_3^1 \sigma_v = \sigma_v \sigma_v'' = C_3^2 \qquad \text{... (11.9)}$$

Letting $B = C_3^1$, we can use any operation R of the C_{3v} group and see that the formula (11.8) leads to either C_3^2 or C_3^1, that is, C_3^1 and C_3^2 are similar. In group theoretical language they belong to the same "class".

We can likewise show that σ_v, σ_v' and σ_v'' belong to the same class. The point C_{3v} has three classes of operations E, C_3 and σ_v.

It is not, however, always necessary to carry out the whole process of similarity transformation to know the number of classes in a group. More often it is possible to do so by mere inspection. For example,

$$C_{2h} : E, C_2, \sigma_h, i = 4 \text{ classes}$$

$$C_{2v} : E, C_2, \sigma_v, \sigma_v' = 4 \text{ classes}$$

$$D_{3h} : E, C_3, C_3^2, C_2, C_2', C_2'', \sigma_h, S_3, S_3^5, \sigma_v, \sigma_v', \sigma_v''$$

or

$$E, 2C_3, 3C_2, \sigma_h, 2S_3, 3\sigma_v = 6 \text{ classes.}$$

11.5 REPRESENTATION OF GROUPS

Each symmetry operation in a point group can be represented by a number or, more generally, by a matrix of numbers. A set of numbers (or matrices) will be a true representation of the group in question if any two of these numbers (or matrices), representing two operations, on being multiplied give another number (or matrix) which represents another operation of the group. A representation is denoted by Γ.

A trivial but very important representation is produced for any group on assigning a number 1 or a unit matrix of any dimension to each operation R. For example, for the C_{2h} group,

$$C_{2h} : E \quad C_2 \quad \sigma_h \quad i$$

$$\Gamma_1 : 1 \quad 1 \quad 1 \quad 1 \qquad \text{... (11.10)}$$

or,

$$\Gamma_1' : \begin{bmatrix} 1 & 0 \\ 0 & 1 \end{bmatrix} \begin{bmatrix} 1 & 0 \\ 0 & 1 \end{bmatrix} \begin{bmatrix} 1 & 0 \\ 0 & 1 \end{bmatrix} \begin{bmatrix} 1 & 0 \\ 0 & 1 \end{bmatrix} \qquad \text{... (11.11)}$$

is a representation because as $C_2 \, \sigma_h = i$, so $1 \times 1 = 1$.

or

$$\begin{bmatrix} 1 & 0 \\ 0 & 1 \end{bmatrix} \begin{bmatrix} 1 & 0 \\ 0 & 1 \end{bmatrix} = \begin{bmatrix} 1 & 0 \\ 0 & 1 \end{bmatrix}.$$

There are non-trivial representation too. For example,

$$C_{2h} : E \quad C_2 \quad \sigma_h \quad i$$

$$\Gamma_2 : 1 \quad -1 \quad -1 \quad 1 \qquad \text{... (11.12)}$$

in Γ_2, for example, $C_2 \, \sigma_h = i$ is paralleled by $(-1)(-1) = 1$.

We can have non-trivial matrix representation too; for example,

$$\begin{matrix} & E & C_2 & \sigma_h & i \\ \Gamma_2' : & \begin{bmatrix} 1 & 0 \\ 0 & 1 \end{bmatrix} & \begin{bmatrix} -1 & 0 \\ 0 & 1 \end{bmatrix} & \begin{bmatrix} 1 & 0 \\ 0 & -1 \end{bmatrix} & \begin{bmatrix} -1 & 0 \\ 0 & -1 \end{bmatrix} \end{matrix} \qquad \text{... (11.13)}$$

These are diagonal matrices. The diagonal numbers in Equation (11.13) constitute two sets Γ_3 and Γ_4

$$\Gamma_3 : 1 \quad -1 \quad 1 \quad -1 \ldots$$

and

$$\Gamma_4 : 1 \quad 1 \quad -1 \quad -1 \ldots$$

so that we can write

$$\Gamma_2 = \Gamma_3 + \Gamma_4 \qquad \text{... (11.14)}$$

[**Exercise:** Verify that Γ_2' faithfully represents the C_{2h} point group].

11.5.1 Reducible and Irreducible Representations

It should be clear that any number of such diagonal matrix representations of larger sizes can be constructed with ± 1 as the diagonal numbers. Each of these representations can, however, be decomposed into the component one-dimensional representations (Γ_1 to Γ_4). Therefore, the former are "reducible" and the latter, which cannot be decomposed, are "irreducible" representations of the C_{2h} point group.

For many groups, matrices are constructed that cannot be reduced to diagonal form. They may, however, be reduced to block-diagonal form. An example, in C_{3v} point group is the matrix corresponding to C_3, which is,

$$\Gamma(C_3) = \begin{bmatrix} [1] & 0 & 0 & 0 \\ 0 & [1] & 0 & 0 \\ 0 & 0 & [-1/2 & \sqrt{3}/2] \\ 0 & 0 & [-\sqrt{3}/2 & -1/2] \end{bmatrix} \quad \text{... (11.15)}$$

The above matrix consists of three blocks of submatrices—two are 1×1, and one is 2×2 as indicated. It is obvious that the complete matrix representation is "reducible" to three smaller "irreducible' representations, two of which consist of numbers ± 1 and the third consists of 2×2 matrix.

Yet, we may have multidimensional reducible representations that are not even in block-diagonal form but can be diagonalised through matrix manipulations. Block diagonalisation can be carried out by similarity transformation [Equation (11.8)]. This converts the original set of matrices into another set which too represents the same group. For example, consider a 3-dimensional molecule of the type.

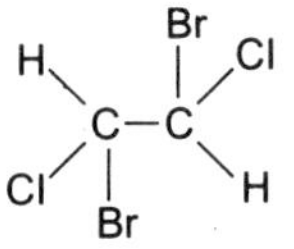

The molecule has only two symmetry operations E and i, and hence, belongs to the point group C_i (see the Chart 11.1). A reducible representation for this group is,

$$\begin{array}{ccc} & E & i \\ \Gamma: & \begin{pmatrix} 1 & 0 \\ 0 & 1 \end{pmatrix} & \begin{pmatrix} 0 & 1 \\ 1 & 0 \end{pmatrix} \end{array}$$

[The method of constructing a reducible representation will be described shortly]. We see that the matrix for E is in diagonal form but that for i is not. Similarly transformation by any matrix R will not affect E as,

$$R^{-1} ER = R^{-1} R = E \qquad \text{[by Equations (11.5) and (11.7)]}$$

So we look for a matrix R which will diagonalise the matrix for i. The process is often very tedious and we shall see later that we have better and easier means to reduce a matrix into the diagonal form. However, for the present, let

$$R = \begin{pmatrix} \frac{1}{\sqrt{2}} & -\frac{1}{\sqrt{2}} \\ \frac{1}{\sqrt{2}} & \frac{1}{\sqrt{2}} \end{pmatrix} \text{ so that } R^{-1} = \begin{pmatrix} \frac{1}{\sqrt{2}} & \frac{1}{\sqrt{2}} \\ -\frac{1}{\sqrt{2}} & \frac{1}{\sqrt{2}} \end{pmatrix}$$

[To find the inverse of a matrix, see Appendix 3]. Then by Equation (11.8),

$$A = R^{-1}\, iR = \begin{pmatrix} \frac{1}{\sqrt{2}} & \frac{1}{\sqrt{2}} \\ -\frac{1}{\sqrt{2}} & \frac{1}{\sqrt{2}} \end{pmatrix} \begin{pmatrix} 0 & 1 \\ 1 & 0 \end{pmatrix} \begin{pmatrix} \frac{1}{\sqrt{2}} & -\frac{1}{\sqrt{2}} \\ \frac{1}{\sqrt{2}} & \frac{1}{\sqrt{2}} \end{pmatrix}$$

$$= \begin{pmatrix} 1 & 0 \\ 0 & -1 \end{pmatrix} \qquad \text{...(11.16)}$$

The resulting matrix Equation (11.16) is in the diagonal form; the submatrices occurring along the diagonal are 1 and –1. The new representation Γ′ (shown below) for the C_i group,

$$\Gamma' : \overset{E}{\begin{pmatrix} 1 & 0 \\ 0 & 1 \end{pmatrix}} \quad \overset{i}{\begin{pmatrix} 1 & 0 \\ 0 & -1 \end{pmatrix}}$$

actually consists of the following two one-dimensional representations:

TABLE 11.4 Representation of the C_i Group

C_i	E	i
Γ_1	1	1
Γ_2	1	−1

When it is not possible to diagonalise or block-diagonalise the matrices, they are called "irreducible". One-dimensional representations are obviously irreducible. In fact, when a reducible matrix is diagonalised or block-diagonalised, each block along the diagonal is an irreducible matrix. The 2 × 2 submatrix in Equation (11.15) is irreducible.

11.5.2 Generating an Irreducible Representation

We have been discussing representations of a point group but have not yet discussed how to find them. For this, we require to know what effect a symmetry operation produces on the set of coordinates (x, y, z) of a point, or a function of coordinates, which we call "basis" of representation.

11.5.2.1 Cartesian Coordinates as Bases

Consider a molecule belonging to C_{2h} point group and concentrate on the effect of the four symmetry operations E, C_2, σ_h and i on the coordinates of atom 1 (Fig. 11.9).

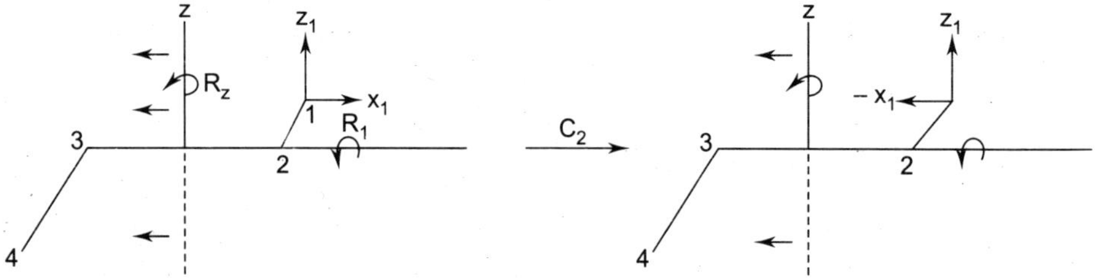

Fig. 11.9 *Effect of symmetry operations on the coordinates of atoms; only x and z-axes have been shown in the figure: y-axis lies in the plane of the molecule*

Let z-axis be the C_2 axis of symmetry which is perpendicular to the molecular plane; then the effect on z coordinate of the atom 1 can be expressed as,

$$E(z) = z, C_2(z) = z, \sigma_h(z) = -z, i(z) = -z.$$

That is, the z-coordinate is symmetric with respect to E and C_2 but antisymmetric with respect to σ_h and i. This generates the following representation,

E	C_2	σ_h	i	Basis
1	1	– 1	– 1	(z)

Similarly, the effect on the x and y-coordinates of the same atom 1 can be seen to be as follows:

$$E(x) = x, C_2(x) = -x, \sigma_h(x) = x, i(x) = -x$$

$$E(y) = y, C_2(y) = -y, \sigma_h(y) = y, i(y) = -y$$

Accordingly, both x and y generate the same representation,

E	C_2	σ_h	i	Basis
1	– 1	1	– 1	(x or y)

11.5.2.2 Wave Functions as Bases

Functions of coordinates—wave functions or orbitals—can also be used as bases, and herein lies the importance of group theory to quantum chemistry.

Consider, for example, the effect of the operations of the C_{2h} point group on s and p atomic orbitals.

s atomic orbitals are functions of the radial distance r only, and r is given by

$$r = (x^2 + y^2 + z^2)^{1/2}$$

x, y, or z may or may not change sign after a symmetry operation but x^2, y^2 and z^2 must not. Hence, the effect of any operation R will be,

$$R(r) = R[(x^2 + y^2 + z^2)^{1/2}] = (x^2 + y^2 + z^2)^{1/2} = r$$

That is, $$E(r) = r, C_2(r) = r, \sigma_h(r) = r, i(r) = r \quad ...(11.17)$$

In fact any function of r is unaffected by any symmetry operation. In other words, the s atomic orbital generates a "totally symmetric" representation,

C_{2h}	E	C_2	σ_h	i	Basis
	1	1	1	1	s

p-atomic orbitals are given as,

$$2p_x = Nr \sin\theta \cos\varphi \, e^{-r/2} = Nxf(r)$$

$$2p_y = Nr \sin\theta \sin\varphi \, e^{-r/2} = Nyf(r)$$

$$2p_z = Nr \cos\theta \, e^{-r/2} = Nzf(r)$$

N, the normalisation factor, and $f(r)$ will remain unaffected by symmetry operations. So the p_x, p_y and p_z orbtials will transform just as x, y and z do, *i.e.*,

$$E(p_x) = p_x, C_2(p_x) = -p_x, \sigma_h(p_x) = p_x, i(p_x) = -p_x \quad ...(11.18)$$

The effect on p_y is the same. The effect on p_z is as follows:

$$E(p_z) = p_z, C_2(p_z) = p_z, \sigma_h(p_z) = -p_z, i(p_z) = -p_z \quad ...(11.19)$$

So the orbitals p_x, p_y and p_z generate the following representations of the C_{2h} point group.

C_{2h}	E	C_2	σ_h	i	Basis
	1	−1	1	−1	$(p_x \text{ or } p_y)$
	1	1	−1	−1	(p_z)

Exercise: Use the five 3*d* atomic orbitals as bases to generate representations of the C_{2h} and C_{2v} point groups.

$$d_{xz} = Nf(r)\,xz$$

$$E\,(xz) = xz,\ C_2\,(xz) = (-x)\,z = -(xz)$$

$$\sigma_h\,(xz) = x\,(-z) = -(xz),\ i\,(xz) = (-x)\,(-z) = xz$$

This leads to,

C_{2h}	E	C_2	σ_h	i	Basis
	1	−1	−1	1	xz or d_{xz}

and so on.

11.5.2.3 Rotational Coordinates as Bases

Rotations R_x, R_y and R_z around the three cartesian axes can also act as bases. This basis set can be conveniently understood by using curved arrows, *e.g.*, an arrow around *x*-axis to represent R_x, etc. (Fig. 11.9). It requires a little imagination to see the effects of E, C_2, σ_h and i on the curved arrows. If you stand before a plane mirror and rotate your finger around the vertical (*z*) axis, the direction of rotation of the image in the mirror is unchanged; but if you rotate it around the horizontal (*x*) axis, the direction of rotation in the mirror is reversed.

The effects of E, C_2, σ_h and i on R_x, R_y and R_z can be seen to be as follows:

$$E\,(R_x) = R_x,\ C_2\,(R_x) = -R_x,\ \sigma_h\,(R_x) = -R_x,\ i\,(R_x) = R_x$$

$$E\,(R_y) = R_y,\ C_2\,(R_y) = -R_y,\ \sigma_h\,(R_y) = -R_y,\ i\,(R_y) = R_y$$

$$E\,(R_z) = R_z,\ C_2\,(R_z) = R_z,\ \sigma_h\,(R_z) = R_z,\ i\,(R_z) = R_z \quad \ldots (11.20)$$

The following representations are generated accordingly:

C_{2h}	E	C_2	σ_h	i	Basis
	1	1	1	1	(R_z)
	1	−1	−1	1	(R_x, R_y)

We have thus generated a total of four representations for the C_{2h} group, which are shown in Table 11.5.

TABLE 11.5 Representation of C_{2h} Group

C_{2h}	E	C_2	σ_h	i	*Basis*
Γ_1	1	1	1	1	R_z
Γ_2	1	−1	−1	1	R_x, R_y
Γ_3	1	−1	1	−1	x, y, p_x, p_y
Γ_4	1	1	−1	−1	z, p_z

The following important features of these representations are to be noted:

(*i*) A single coordinate is sufficient to act as a basis for a single representation.

(*ii*) Each representation is irreducible, consisting of the numbers ±1 (or the 1 × 1 matrices).

(*iii*) The numbers ±1 actually represent the 'characters' of transformation of the coordinates under the symmetry operations, *e.g.*,

$$C_2\,(z) = z \text{ and } C_2\,(x) = -x$$

mean that z is symmetric and x antisymmetric to transformation under the operation C_2.

(*iv*) A total of only four irreducible representations can be generated for C_{2h} group.

(*v*) There is one representation (Γ_1) which is symmetric to transformation under all operations (*i.e.*, totally symmetric).

Irreducible representations of dimensions greater than one are generated for groups having the principal axis C_n with $n > 2$. The C_n axis is taken as the z-axis (vertical) and the rotation considered in xy-plane. A rotation about C_n axis leaves the z-coordinate of a point unchanged (symmetric) but the x and y-coordinates are neither unchanged nor just reversed in sign, rather the effect is a mixing of the two coordinates. For example, for a molecule belonging to C_{4v} point group (Fig. 11.10), C_4 is the principal axis.

The symmetry operations of C_{4v} group are E, C_4, C_4^3, $C_2\left(=C_4^2\right)$, σ_v, σ_v', σ_d and σ_d' (σ_v is the xz-plane, σ_v' the yz-plane, and σ_d and σ_d' planes are as indicated in Fig. 11.10.

The effects of a clockwise rotation C_4^1 around the three axes are,

$$C_4^1\,(z) = z;\; C_4^1\,(x) = -y;\; C_4^1\,(y) = x$$

The character of transformation of z is + 1, but there is no simple number to represent those of x and y. The only way to represent their transformations is to use a matrix as follows:

$$C_4^1\begin{bmatrix} x \\ y \end{bmatrix} = \begin{bmatrix} -y \\ x \end{bmatrix}.$$

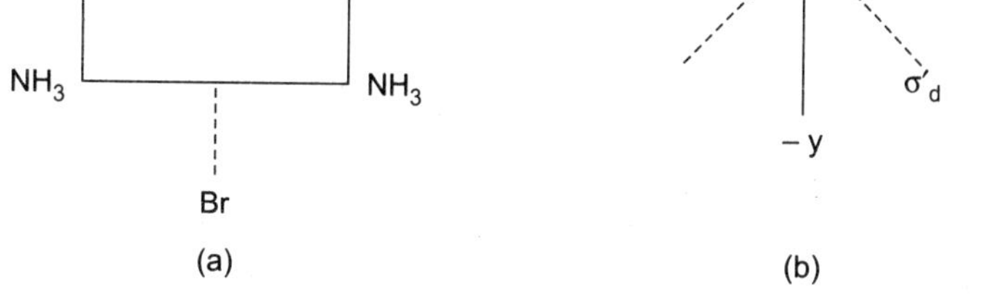

Fig. 11.10 *(a) The Co-NH_3 complex with C_{4v} symmetry*
(b) The coordinates x and y in the molecule

Also, $$\begin{bmatrix} 0 & -1 \\ 1 & 0 \end{bmatrix}\begin{bmatrix} x \\ y \end{bmatrix} = \begin{bmatrix} -y \\ x \end{bmatrix}$$

Therefore, the corresponding matrix of transformation is

$$C_1^4 : \begin{bmatrix} 0 & -1 \\ 1 & 0 \end{bmatrix} \qquad \text{... (11.21)}$$

The matrices for other operations of the group may likewise be derived as follows:

$$C_4^3 \begin{bmatrix} x \\ y \end{bmatrix} = \begin{bmatrix} y \\ -x \end{bmatrix} = \begin{bmatrix} 0 & 1 \\ -1 & 0 \end{bmatrix}\begin{bmatrix} x \\ y \end{bmatrix} \qquad \text{... (11.22)}$$

$$C_2 \begin{bmatrix} x \\ y \end{bmatrix} = \begin{bmatrix} -x \\ -y \end{bmatrix} = \begin{bmatrix} -1 & 0 \\ 0 & -1 \end{bmatrix}\begin{bmatrix} x \\ y \end{bmatrix} \qquad \text{... (11.23)}$$

$$\sigma_v\,(xz) \begin{bmatrix} x \\ y \end{bmatrix} = \begin{bmatrix} x \\ -y \end{bmatrix} = \begin{bmatrix} 1 & 0 \\ 0 & -1 \end{bmatrix}\begin{bmatrix} x \\ y \end{bmatrix} \qquad \text{... (11.24)}$$

$$\sigma_v'\,(yz) \begin{bmatrix} x \\ y \end{bmatrix} = \begin{bmatrix} -x \\ y \end{bmatrix} = \begin{bmatrix} -1 & 0 \\ 0 & 1 \end{bmatrix}\begin{bmatrix} x \\ y \end{bmatrix} \qquad \text{... (11.25)}$$

$$\sigma_d \begin{bmatrix} x \\ y \end{bmatrix} = \begin{bmatrix} y \\ x \end{bmatrix} = \begin{bmatrix} 0 & 1 \\ 1 & 0 \end{bmatrix}\begin{bmatrix} x \\ y \end{bmatrix} \qquad \text{... (11.26)}$$

$$\sigma_d' \begin{bmatrix} x \\ y \end{bmatrix} = \begin{bmatrix} -y \\ -x \end{bmatrix} = \begin{bmatrix} 0 & -1 \\ -1 & 0 \end{bmatrix}\begin{bmatrix} x \\ y \end{bmatrix} \qquad \text{... (11.27)}$$

None of these operations alters the z-axis. The representations generated for C_{4v} point group are accordingly as shown below:

C_{4v}	E	C_4^1	C_4^3	C_2	$\sigma_v\,(xz)$	$\sigma_v'\,(yz)$	σ_d	σ_d'	Basis
Γ_1	1	1	1	1	1	1	1	1	z
Γ_2	$\begin{bmatrix} 1 & 0 \\ 0 & 1 \end{bmatrix}$,	$\begin{bmatrix} 0 & -1 \\ 1 & 0 \end{bmatrix}$,	$\begin{bmatrix} 0 & 1 \\ -1 & 0 \end{bmatrix}$,	$\begin{bmatrix} -1 & 0 \\ 0 & -1 \end{bmatrix}$,	$\begin{bmatrix} 1 & 0 \\ 0 & -1 \end{bmatrix}$,	$\begin{bmatrix} -1 & 0 \\ 0 & 1 \end{bmatrix}$,	$\begin{bmatrix} 0 & 1 \\ 1 & 0 \end{bmatrix}$,	$\begin{bmatrix} 0 & -1 \\ -1 & 0 \end{bmatrix}$	(x, y)

In general, the transformation of the coordinates x and y under a symmetry operation is represented as,

$$x_2 = ax_1 + by_1 \qquad \text{... (11.28)}$$
$$y_2 = cx_1 + dy_1$$

or $$\begin{bmatrix} x_2 \\ y_2 \end{bmatrix} = \begin{bmatrix} a & b \\ c & d \end{bmatrix}\begin{bmatrix} x_1 \\ y_1 \end{bmatrix} \qquad \text{... (11.29)}$$

[see Appendix 3]

where x_1 and y_1 are old coordinates and x_2 and y_2 are new coordinates.

A little application of trigonometry will show that any clockwise rotation through an angle θ transforms the coordinates (x_1, y_1) to the new coordinates (x_2, y_2) through the relations

$$x_2 = x_1 \cos\theta + y_1 \sin\theta$$

$$y_2 = -x_1 \sin\theta + y_1 \cos\theta \qquad \text{...(11.30)}$$

Equation (11.30) can be expressed in matrix form as,

$$\begin{bmatrix} x_2 \\ y_2 \end{bmatrix} = \begin{bmatrix} \cos\theta & \sin\theta \\ -\sin\theta & \cos\theta \end{bmatrix} \begin{bmatrix} x_1 \\ y_1 \end{bmatrix} \text{ (see Chapter 3, section 3.3)} \qquad \text{...(11.31)}$$

Similarly, anticlockwise rotation leads to,

$$\begin{bmatrix} x_2 \\ y_2 \end{bmatrix} = \begin{bmatrix} \cos\theta & -\sin\theta \\ \sin\theta & \cos\theta \end{bmatrix} \begin{bmatrix} x_1 \\ y_1 \end{bmatrix} \qquad \text{...(11.32)}$$

The 2×2 matrix in Equation (11.31) represents C_n^1 operation while that in Equation (11.32) represents C_n^{-1}. In NH_3 (C_{3v} group), for example, the different operations are E, C_3^1, C_3^2, σ_v, σ_v' and σ_v''. None of the operations alters the z-coordinate of any atom; so z forms a basis for a totally symmetric representation.

C_{3v}	E	C_3^1	C_3^2	σ_v	σ_v'	σ_v''	Basis
Γ_1	1	1	1	1	1	1	z

Putting $\theta = 120°$ in Equation (11.31) and (11.32), we get the corresponding matrices for C_3^1 and C_3^2 with x and y-coordinates taken together as basis,

$$C_3^1 = \begin{vmatrix} -\frac{1}{2} & \frac{\sqrt{3}}{2} \\ -\frac{\sqrt{3}}{2} & -\frac{1}{2} \end{vmatrix}, \quad C_3^2 = C_3^{-1} = \begin{vmatrix} -\frac{1}{2} & -\frac{\sqrt{3}}{2} \\ \frac{\sqrt{3}}{2} & -\frac{1}{2} \end{vmatrix} \qquad \text{...(11.33)}$$

The operation σ_v (along the plane passing through H_1) (see Fig. 11.8) leads to interchange of the coordinates of H_2 and H_3, which reverses the sign of x and leaves y unaltered. Hence,

$$\sigma_v \begin{bmatrix} x \\ y \end{bmatrix} = \begin{bmatrix} -x \\ y \end{bmatrix} = \begin{bmatrix} -1 & 0 \\ 0 & 1 \end{bmatrix} \begin{bmatrix} x \\ y \end{bmatrix} \qquad \text{...(11.34)}$$

The matrices for the other two reflection σ_v' and σ_v'' may be obtained from the table of multiplications from which

$$\sigma_v' = C_3^2 \sigma_v \text{ and } \sigma_v'' = C_3 \sigma_v$$

Using the matrices for σ_v, C_3 and C_3^2 and the rules of matrix multiplication we have

$$\sigma_v' = \begin{bmatrix} -\frac{1}{2} & -\frac{\sqrt{3}}{2} \\ \frac{\sqrt{3}}{2} & -\frac{1}{2} \end{bmatrix} \begin{bmatrix} -1 & 0 \\ 0 & 1 \end{bmatrix} = \begin{bmatrix} \frac{1}{2} & -\frac{\sqrt{3}}{2} \\ -\frac{\sqrt{3}}{2} & -\frac{1}{2} \end{bmatrix}$$

$$\sigma_v'' = \begin{bmatrix} -\frac{1}{2} & \frac{\sqrt{3}}{2} \\ -\frac{\sqrt{3}}{2} & -\frac{1}{2} \end{bmatrix} \begin{bmatrix} -1 & 0 \\ 0 & 1 \end{bmatrix} = \begin{bmatrix} \frac{1}{2} & \frac{\sqrt{3}}{2} \\ \frac{\sqrt{3}}{2} & -\frac{1}{2} \end{bmatrix}$$

The complete representation of the group, taking x and y together as basis (which is through 2×2 matrices) may be given as,

C_{3v}	E	C_3^1	C_3^2	σ_v	σ_v'	σ_v''	Basis
Γ_2	$\begin{bmatrix} 1 & 0 \\ 0 & 1 \end{bmatrix}$,	$\begin{bmatrix} -\frac{1}{2} & \frac{\sqrt{3}}{2} \\ -\frac{\sqrt{3}}{2} & -\frac{1}{2} \end{bmatrix}$,	$\begin{bmatrix} -\frac{1}{2} & -\frac{\sqrt{3}}{2} \\ \frac{\sqrt{3}}{2} & -\frac{1}{2} \end{bmatrix}$,	$\begin{bmatrix} -1 & 0 \\ 0 & 1 \end{bmatrix}$	$\begin{bmatrix} \frac{1}{2} & -\frac{\sqrt{3}}{2} \\ -\frac{\sqrt{3}}{2} & -\frac{1}{2} \end{bmatrix}$,	$\begin{bmatrix} \frac{1}{2} & \frac{\sqrt{3}}{2} \\ \frac{\sqrt{3}}{2} & -\frac{1}{2} \end{bmatrix}$	(x, y)

Further representation can be generated by taking the rotational coordinate R_z as the basis. Under E, C_3^1 and $C_3^2 = \left(C_3^{-1}\right)$, the direction of R_z is unaltered, but under σ_v, σ_v' and σ_v'' it is reversed (Fig. 11.11).

Accordingly, R_z generates a one-dimensional representation as follows:

C_{3v}	E	C_3^1	C_3^2	σ_v	σ_v'	σ_v''	Basis
Γ_3	1	1	1	−1	−1	−1	R_z

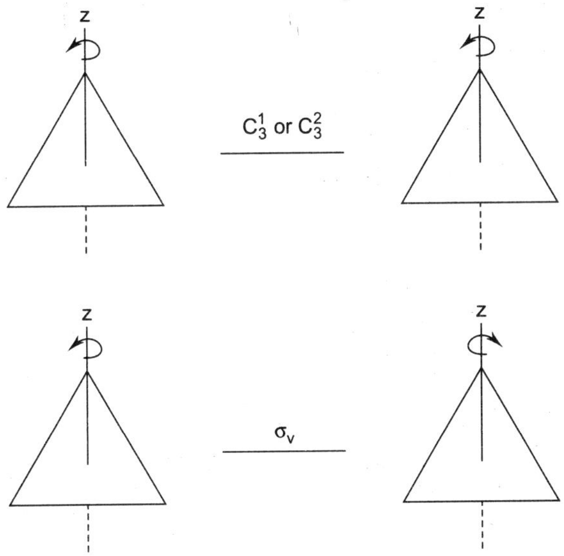

Fig. 11.11 *Effect of symmetry operations on R_z*

No new representation is generated by R_x or R_y.

Thus, Γ_1, Γ_2 and Γ_3 are the three irreducible representations of the C_{3v} point group.

11.5.3 Generating a Reducible Representation

We have seen that irreducible representations are generated for a point group by using a single coordinate (as in C_{2h} group) or a pair of coordinates x and y (as in C_{3v}, C_{4v}, etc.) as the basis. If we use the set of all the coordinates of an atom, we generate a representation consisting of larger matrices which are reducible to small irreducible matrices. For example, take the case of C_{2h} group. Using x, y, z collectively as a basis, written as 3×1 matrix, we get,

$$E\begin{bmatrix} x \\ y \\ z \end{bmatrix} = \begin{bmatrix} x \\ y \\ z \end{bmatrix} = \begin{bmatrix} 1 & 0 & 0 \\ 0 & 1 & 0 \\ 0 & 0 & 1 \end{bmatrix}\begin{bmatrix} x \\ y \\ z \end{bmatrix}$$

$$C_2\begin{bmatrix} x \\ y \\ z \end{bmatrix} = \begin{bmatrix} -x \\ -y \\ z \end{bmatrix} = \begin{bmatrix} -1 & 0 & 0 \\ 0 & -1 & 0 \\ 0 & 0 & 1 \end{bmatrix}\begin{bmatrix} x \\ y \\ z \end{bmatrix}$$

$$\sigma_h\begin{bmatrix} x \\ y \\ z \end{bmatrix} = \begin{bmatrix} x \\ y \\ -z \end{bmatrix} = \begin{bmatrix} 1 & 0 & 0 \\ 0 & 1 & 0 \\ 0 & 0 & -1 \end{bmatrix}\begin{bmatrix} x \\ y \\ z \end{bmatrix}$$

$$i\begin{bmatrix} x \\ y \\ z \end{bmatrix} = \begin{bmatrix} -x \\ -y \\ -z \end{bmatrix} = \begin{bmatrix} -1 & 0 & 0 \\ 0 & -1 & 0 \\ 0 & 0 & -1 \end{bmatrix}\begin{bmatrix} x \\ y \\ z \end{bmatrix} \quad \text{...(11.35)}$$

A three dimensional representation Γ' for C_{2h} group is generated accordingly. However, in Γ' all the 3-dimensional matrices are diagonal and each is reducible to three 1×1 matrices. By inspection, it can be seen that,

$$\Gamma' = 2\Gamma_3 + \Gamma_4 \qquad \text{... (11.36)}$$

where Γ_3 and Γ_4 are irreducible representations of C_{2h} as given in Table 11.5.

Similarly, for C_{3v} group, if we use the set of the four coordinates x, y, z and R_z together as the basis, we generate a 4-dimensional reducible representation of the type:

$$\begin{array}{cccc} & E & C_3^1 & C_3^2 \\ \Gamma_r : & \begin{bmatrix} 1 & 0 & 0 & 0 \\ 0 & & 0 & 0 \\ 0 & 1 & 1 & 0 \\ 0 & 0 & 0 & 1 \end{bmatrix} & \begin{bmatrix} 1 & 0 & 0 & 0 \\ 0 & 1 & 0 & 0 \\ 0 & 0 & -1/2 & \sqrt{3/2} \\ 0 & 0 & -\sqrt{3/2} & -1/2 \end{bmatrix} & \begin{bmatrix} 1 & 0 & 0 & 0 \\ 0 & 1 & 0 & 0 \\ 0 & 0 & -1/2 & -\sqrt{3/2} \\ 0 & 0 & \sqrt{3/2} & -1/2 \end{bmatrix} \end{array}$$

$$\begin{array}{ccc} \sigma_v & \sigma_v' & \sigma_v'' \\ \begin{bmatrix} 1 & 0 & 0 & 0 \\ 0 & -1 & 0 & 0 \\ 0 & 0 & -1 & 0 \\ 0 & 0 & 0 & 1 \end{bmatrix} & \begin{bmatrix} 1 & 0 & 0 & 0 \\ 0 & -1 & 0 & 0 \\ 0 & 0 & 1/2 & -\sqrt{3/2} \\ 0 & 0 & -\sqrt{3/2} & -1/2 \end{bmatrix} & \begin{bmatrix} 1 & 0 & 0 & 0 \\ 0 & -1 & 0 & 0 \\ 0 & 0 & 1/2 & \sqrt{3/2} \\ 0 & 0 & \sqrt{3/2} & -1/2 \end{bmatrix} \end{array}$$

which is reducible as

$$\Gamma_r = \Gamma_1 + \Gamma_2 + \Gamma_3. \qquad \text{... (11.37)}$$

11.5.4 Characters of Representation

It would be more convenient to represent the symmetry operations by simple numbers rather than matrices. The numbers ± 1 in the representation Table 11.5 represent the "characters" of transformation of the basis coordinates. Matrices also have their characters denoted by the letter χ. The character χ of a matrix is defined as the sum of its diagonal elements. If the matrix is diagonal, *i.e.*, reducible like Equation (11.38).

$$\Gamma(R) = \begin{bmatrix} \Gamma_1(R) & 0 & 0 & 0 \\ 0 & \Gamma_2(R) & 0 & 0 \\ 0 & 0 & \Gamma_3(R) & 0 \\ 0 & 0 & 0 & \Gamma_4(R) \end{bmatrix} \qquad \text{... (11.38)}$$

it is obvious that its character is,

$$\chi(R) = \chi_1(R) + \chi_2(R) + \chi_3(R) + \chi_4(R) \qquad \text{... (11.39)}$$

But the most significant thing is that a non-diagonal matrix can be diagonalised by similarity transformation without altering its character.* It is, therefore, possible to represent symmetry operations through their characters.

* For the proof of this statement the reader is referred to *Chemical Applications of Group Theory* by F.A. Cotton, (Academic Press, N.Y.), 1963, P. 77.

Thus, the 2 × 2 matrices constituting the representation Γ_2 of C_{3v} point group can be better represented as,

C	E	C_3^1	C_3^2	σ_v	σ_v'	σ_v''	Basis
Γ_2	2	−1	−1	0	0	0	(x, y)

The advantage of using characters in the case of reducible non-diagonal matrices is that it is not necessary at all to carry out the diagonalisation of the matrices, which is a very tedious process. Thus, for example, a reducible representation Γ_r of C_{3v} point group with x, y, z and R_z as basis can be written as,

C_{3v}	E	C_3^1	C_3^2	σ_v	σ_v'	σ_v''	Basis
Γ_r	4	1	1	0	0	0	(x, y, z, R_z)

Exercise: Use three 2p atomic orbitals of N-atom in NH_3 to determine the character of a reducible representation of C_{3v} group.

$$E\begin{bmatrix} p_x \\ p_y \\ p_z \end{bmatrix} = \begin{bmatrix} 1 & 0 & 0 \\ 0 & 1 & 0 \\ 0 & 0 & 1 \end{bmatrix}\begin{bmatrix} p_x \\ p_y \\ p_z \end{bmatrix}, \chi(E) = 3$$

Similarly, $\chi(C_3^1) = \chi(C_3^2) = 0; \chi(\sigma_v) = \chi(\sigma_v') = \chi(\sigma_v'') = 1$

Finally,

	E	C_3^1	C_3^2	σ	σ'	σ''
Γ_r:	3	0	0	1	1	1

11.5.5 Labelling the Representations

Instead of using the symbol Γ, it is cutomary to use letters A, B, E, F, etc., to label the irreducible representation.

The letters A and B are reserved for one-dimensional representations, E for 2-dimensional, F for 3-dimensional, etc. The character of the identity operation (E) is equal to the dimension of the representation. (The reader should be cautious of the use of letter E as E is also used for identity).

A totally symmetric representation is given the symbol A_1. But if the point group contains the operation i, the total symmetry is inicated by A_{1g}.

If in the one-dimensional representation $\chi(C_n) = +1$, the representation is A and if $\chi(C_n) = -1$, it is B.

The subscript 1 or 2 is attached to the labels A and B to denote whether $\chi(\sigma_v) = +1$ or -1 respectively; σ_v may be any symmetry plane containing C_n.

To indicate in a representation whether $\chi(\sigma_h) = +1$ or -1, a single prime (′) or a double prime (″) is used.

The subscript g or u is used according to whether $\chi(i) = +1$ or -1 respectively.

11.5.6 Character Tables

A more compact and self-explanatory representation table, called "character table" can thus be drawn for every point group. Operations belonging to the same class (*e.g.*, C_3^1 and C_3^2 in C_{3v} group) have the same character; they are put under the same column. As examples, the tables for C_{3v} and C_{2h} point groups are given below (Tables 11.6 and 11.7).

TABLE 11.6 Character Table for C_{3v} Group

C_{3v}	E	$2C_3$	$3\sigma_v$	*Basis*
A_1	1	1	1	z or p_z
A_2	1	1	−1	R_z
E	2	−1	0	(x, y) or (p_x, p_y)

TABLE 11.7 Character Table for C_{2h} Group

C_{2h}	E	C_2	σ_h	i	*Basis*
A_g	1	1	1	1	R_z
A_u	1	1	−1	−1	z, p_z
B_u	1	−1	1	−1	x or y, p_x or p_y
B_g	1	−1	−1	1	R_x, R_y

Character table for every point group may be found in any book on applications of group theory to chemistry.

11.6 IMPORTANT THEOREMS REGARDING IRREDUCIBLE REPRESENTATIONS

Inspection of character tables reveals some very important general features of irreducible representations. These are:

1. The number of irreducible representations in a group is equal to the number of classes in it; C_{2h} has four and C_{3v} has three representations.
2. One of the representations is totally symmetric; for example, A_1 in C_{3v} and A_g in C_{2h}.
3. The dimension (l_i) of a representation Γ_i is determined by χ (E); for example, the E-representation in C_{3v} has $\chi(E) = l_i = 2$; all representations in C_{2h} have $\chi(E) = l_i = 1$.
4. $$\sum_i l_i^2 = \sum_i \chi(E)^2 = h \qquad \text{... (11.40)}$$

   where h is the total number of symmetry operations in the group. In C_{3v} point group,

   $$l_1^2 + l_2^2 + l_3^2 = 1^2 + 1^2 + 2^2 = 6$$

5. The set of the corresponding numbers Γ_i^{mn} (R) of each matrix (m = row number and n = column number) in a representation Γ_i, when written in a row or a column, represents a vector in h-dimensional space. This is called a representation vector. For example, in C_{3v} group the representation A_1 and A_2 provide one vector each,

   $$\underset{A_1}{[1, 1, 1, 1, 1, 1]}, \quad \underset{A_2}{[1, 1, 1, -1, -1, -1]}$$

and the E-representation provides 4 vectors like,

$$\left[0, \frac{\sqrt{3}}{2}, -\frac{\sqrt{3}}{2}, 0, -\frac{\sqrt{3}}{2}, \frac{\sqrt{3}}{2}\right] \text{(using } \Gamma_2^{12} \text{ of each matrix)}$$

(It is easy to visualise a vector in 2- or 3-dimensionsal space but not in a 6-dimensional space as in the above case. It is better to follow only the rules of vectors mathematically rather than to construct models of vectors in such a hyperspace).

6. The characters χ_i (R) of matrices in an irreducible representation Γ_i also constitute a vector—the character vector. For a one-dimensional representation, the representation and character vectors are the same, but in a multidimensional representation, the number of the former is l_i^2 while that of the latter is only one. The character vectors in C_{3v} group are:

$$A_1 : [1, 1, 1, 1, 1, 1]$$

$$A_2 : [1, 1, 1, -1, -1, -1]$$

$$E : [2, -1, -1, 0, 0, 0,].$$

7. All the representation of character vectors are orthogonal and normalised, *i.e.*,

$$\sum_R \chi_i(R) \cdot \chi_j(R) = 0 \text{ for } i \neq j$$

$$= h \text{ for } i = j \qquad \text{... (11.41)}$$

For example, the representation vectors of A_1 and A_2 in C_{3v} are orthogonal as,

$$[1, 1, 1, 1, 1, 1] \cdot \begin{bmatrix} 1 \\ 1 \\ 1 \\ -1 \\ -1 \\ -1 \end{bmatrix} = 0$$

A_2 is orthogonal to all four representation vectors in E, as

$$[1, 1, 1, -1, -1, -1] \cdot \begin{bmatrix} 0 \\ \frac{\sqrt{3}}{2} \\ -\frac{\sqrt{3}}{2} \\ -0 \\ -\frac{\sqrt{3}}{2} \\ \frac{\sqrt{3}}{2} \end{bmatrix} = 0 + \frac{\sqrt{3}}{2} - \frac{\sqrt{3}}{2} - 0 + \frac{\sqrt{3}}{2} - \frac{\sqrt{3}}{2} = 0$$

and so on.

Similarly, the characters of A_2 and E, for example, are orthogonal as,

$$[1, 1, 1, -1, -1, -1] \cdot \begin{bmatrix} 2 \\ -1 \\ -1 \\ 0 \\ 0 \\ 0 \end{bmatrix} = 2 - 1 - 1 - 0 - 0 - 0 = 0$$

The above generalisations can be used to derive the irreducible representations of any point group. For example, in C_{4v} group (operation E, $2C_4$, C_2, $2\sigma_v$, $2\sigma_d$) there are five classes, so by rule 1, there will be five representations.

Since $h = 8$, by rule 4,

$$l_1^2 + l_2^2 + l_3^2 + l_4^2 + l_5^2 = 8$$

which leads to $l_1 = l_2 = l_3 = l_4 = 1$, and $l_5 = 2$.

By rule 2,

C_{4v}	E	$2C_4$	C_2	$2\sigma_v$	$2\sigma_d$
Γ_1	1	1	1	1	$1 \cdots A_1$

In Γ_1 to Γ_4, since $l_i = 1, \chi(E) = 1$ (rule 3).

Rule 7 (orthogonality) requires that four of the characters be +1 and the other four –1. Thus, following are the possibilities:

C_{4v}	E	$2C_4$	C_2	$2\sigma_v$	$2\sigma_d$
Γ_2:	1	1	1	-1	$-1 \cdots A_2$
Γ_3:	1	-1	1	1	$-1 \cdots B_1$
Γ_4:	1	-1	1	-1	$1 \cdots B_2$

As regards Γ_5, the rule 7 (normalisation) requires that

$$\chi(E)^2 + 2\chi(C_4)^2 + \chi(C_2)^2 + 2\chi(\sigma_v)^2 + 2\chi(\sigma_d)^2 = 8$$

Since $\chi(E) = 2$,

$$2\chi(C_4)^2 + \chi(C_2)^2 + 2\chi(\sigma_v)^2 + 2\chi(\sigma_d)^2 = 4$$

The possible solutions are

$\chi(E)$	$2\chi(C_4)$	$\chi(C_2)$	$2\chi(\sigma_v)$	$2\chi(\sigma_d)$
2	± 1	0	± 1	0
2	0	0	± 1	± 1
2	± 1	0	0	0
2	0	-2	0	0

Of these, only the last set is orthogonal to other representations.

Hence,

C_{4v}	$\chi(E)$	$2\chi(C_4)$	$\chi(C_2)$	$2\chi(\sigma_v)$	$2\chi(\sigma_d)$
Γ_5	2	0	-2	0	$0 \cdots E$

11.6.1 Resolution of Reducible Representation to Symmetry Types

Most applications of group theory to chemistry involve finding the reducible representation for the molecular symmetry group and then resolving it to its irreducible components (also called symmetry types). A reducible matrix representation is generated by using a set of coordinates or orbitals as basis. However, for determining the characters of a reducible representation we need not work out the matrices but may use the following rule as a labour saving device : "If a symmetry operation leaves a member of the basis set as such, or transforms it into its negative it contributes + 1 or – 1, respectively, towards the character of the matrix corresponding to that operation, and if it shifts the position of the basis the contribution is zero". Consider, for example, the H_2O molecule (C_{2v} point group). Let us select the two 1*s* atomic orbitals (s_1 and s_2) of the two H atoms for our basis set and examine the effects of the symmetry operations on the set.

$E(s_1, s_2) = (s_1, s_2)$; both orbitals remain as such; hence, each member contributes + 1; $\chi(E) = +2$

$C_2(s_1, s_2) = (s_2, s_1)$; orbitals exchange their positions, hence, each contributes 0; $\chi(C_2) = 0$

$\sigma_{yz}(s_1, s_2) = (s_2, s_1)$; orbitals exchange positions ; $\chi(\sigma_{yz}) = 0$ (C_2 is assumed to be the *z*-axis)

$\sigma_{xz}(s_1, s_2) = (s_1, s_2)$; orbitals remain as such ; $\chi(\sigma_{xz}) = +2$

This generates a reducible representation,

C_{2v}	E	C_2	σ_{yz}	σ_{xz}	Basis
Γ_2	2	0	0	2	(s_1, s_2)

(These characters do not, however, faithfully represent the group in the manner the irreducible characters do as $E \times \sigma_{xz} = \sigma_{xz}$ whereas $2 \times 2 = 4$. Yet, we loosely call such a set of characters a reducible representation.)

Such a set of characters can be easily resolved by inspection into sets of "characters of irreducible representation of that group" for example,

C_{2v}	E	C_2	σ_{yz}	σ_{xz}
A_1	1	1	1	1
B_2	1	-1	-1	1
Γ_r	2	0	0	2

which means $\Gamma_r = A_1 + B_2$ ... (11.42)

We could, however, select the three 2*p* orbitals of oxygen as our basis. Then,

$E(p_x, p_y, p_z) = (p_x, p_y, p_z)$; the orbitals remain unshifted; therefore, $\chi(E) = +3$

$C_2(p_x, p_y, p_z) = (-p_x, -p_y, p_z)$; which p_x and p_y are transformed into their negatives the p_z (coinciding with the C_2-axis) remains unshifted; $\chi(C_2) = -1$

$\sigma_{yz}\ (p_x, p_y, p_z) = (-p_x, p_y, p_z)$; p_x is inverted while p_y and p_z remain unshifted; $\chi\ (\sigma_{yz}) = +1$
$\sigma_{yz}\ (p_x, p_y, p_z) = (p_x, -p_y, p_z)$; only p_y is inverted; $\chi\ (\sigma_{xz}) = +1$

This generates another reducible representation

C_{2v}	E	C_2	σ_{yz}	σ_{xz}	Basis
Γ_r	3	−1	1	1	(p_x, p_y, p_z)

which can be resolved as

A_1 :	1	1	1	1
B_1 :	1	−1	1	−1
B_2 :	1	−1	−1	1
$\Gamma_r = A_1 + B_1 + B_2$:	3	−1	1	1

... (11.43)

Similarly, for NH_3 molecule, we may use the 1*s* atomic orbitals of the three H atoms as bases to generate a reducible representation and find the component irreducible representations in it.

Point group : C_{3v}

$$E\,(s_1, s_2, s_3) = (s_1, s_2, s_3)\,; \qquad \chi\,(E) = +3$$

$$C_3^1\ (s_1, s_2, s_3) = (s_3, s_1, s_2)\,; \qquad \chi\left(C_3^1\right) = 0$$

$$C_3^2\ (s_1, s_2, s_3) = (s_2, s_3, s_1)\,; \qquad \chi\left(C_3^2\right) = 0$$

$$\sigma_v\,(s_1, s_2, s_3) = (s_1, s_2, s_3)\,; \qquad \chi\,(\sigma_v) = 1$$

$$\sigma_v'\ (s_1, s_2, s_3) = (s_3, s_2, s_1)\,; \qquad \chi\left(\sigma_v'\right) = 1$$

$$\sigma_v''\ (s_1, s_2, s_3) = (s_2, s_1, s_3)\,; \qquad \chi\left(\sigma_v''\right) = 1$$

This generates the following reducible representation:

$C3_v$	E	$2C_3$	$3\sigma_v$	Basis
Γ_r	3	0	1	(s_1, s_2, s_3)

The character table for the C_{3v} point group is as follows:

C_{3v}	E	$2C_3$	$3\sigma_v$	Basis
A_1	1	1	1	(z)
A_2	1	1	−1	R_z
E	2	−1	0	(x, y)

Thus Γ_r is seen to be resolved as

$$\Gamma_r = A_1 + E \qquad \text{... (11.44)}$$

In these examples, the resolution of Γ_r could be done by mere inspection. Many examples are far too complex and we must have a formula for resolution. Such a formula is given below without derivation.

$$a_i = \frac{1}{h} \sum_{\text{all classes}} \chi(\text{R})\, \chi_i(\text{R}) \,.\, n \qquad \text{...(11.45)}$$

Here a_i is the number of irreducible representations (symmetry types) of one kind i in Γ_r, h is the total number of symmetry operations in the symmetry group, χ (R) is the character of the operation R in the reducible representation. χ_i (R) is the character of the same operation R in the irreducible representation i and n is number of the operations R in one class.

Equation (11.45) may now be used to reduce the Γ_r as follows,

	E	$2C_3$	$3\sigma_v$	Basis
Γ_r:	3	0	1	(s_1, s_2, s_3)

$$a_{A_1} = \frac{1}{6}\left[(3\times1\times1)+(0\times1\times2)+(1\times1\times3)\right] = 1$$

$$a_{A_2} = \frac{1}{6}\left[(3\times1\times1)+(0\times1\times2)+(1\times-1\times3)\right] = 0$$

$$a_E = \frac{1}{6}\left[(3\times2\times1)+(0\times-1\times2)+(1\times0\times3)\right] = 1$$

or $\qquad \Gamma_r = A_1 + E,$

which is the same as Equation (11.44).

[**Exercise :** *Apply Equation (11.45) to reduce the following reducible representations of the C_{3v} group,*

Γ_r: 5 2 −1

$(\Gamma_r = A_1 + 2A_2 + E)$].

11.6.2 Symmetry Adapted Linear Combination Functions

But in Equation (11.44) which of the s orbitals belongs to A_1 and which to E ? This cannot be decided by inspection of the character table as all s orbitals are totally symmetric. So we need another technique which may convert the members of the set (s_1, s_2, s_3) into another equivalent set of functions whose one member belongs to A_1 and two members together belong to E type. Such functions, which are constructed by taking suitable linear combinations of the members of the basis set, are called "symmetry adapted linear combination (SALC)" functions. Further, the SALC's must be orthogonal as the irreducible representations themselves are orthogonal to each other.

There is another magic formula for this task which we give here without proof. A SALC ψ_i belonging to an irreducible representation Γ_i is given as,

$$\psi_i = \left[\frac{l_i}{h} \sum_{\text{R}} \chi_i(\text{R}) \,.\, \text{R}\right] \phi_j \qquad \text{...(11.46)}$$

where the expression within the square brackets is called "Projection Operator, P_i", ϕ_j is one of the members of the basis set used for generating the reducible representation, χ_i (R) is the character of the matrix for the operation R in the irreducible representation Γ_i whose dimension is l_i, and h is the order of the group.

In the present example of NH_3, choose any one member s_1 of the basis set and apply Equation (11.46) to get the SALC ψ_{A_1} belonging to A_1 as follows:

$$\psi_{A_1} = \frac{1}{6}\left[1 \times Es_1 + 1 \times C_3^1 s_1 + 1 \times C_3^2 s_1 + 1 \times \sigma_v s_1 + 1 \times \sigma_v' s_1 + 1 \times \sigma_v'' s_1\right]$$

$$= \frac{1}{6}\left[s_1 + s_2 + s_3 + s_1 + s_2 + s_3\right]$$

$$= \frac{1}{3}\left(s_1 + s_2 + s_3\right)$$

To normalise the function introduce a factor f; then

$$\int \psi_{A_1}^2 \, d\tau = \int \frac{f^2}{9}\left(s_1 + s_2 + s_3\right)^2 d\tau = 1, \text{or } \frac{f^2}{9} \times 3 = 1$$

($\because$ the orbitals are normalised. Hence $f = \sqrt{3}$, and

$$\psi_{A_1} = \frac{1}{\sqrt{3}}\left(s_1 + s_2 + s_3\right) \quad \text{... (11.47)}$$

There will be two SALC's with respect to representation E, ψ_{E_1} and ψ_{E_2}.

$$\psi_{E_1} = \frac{1}{6}\left[2 \times Es_1 - 1 \times C_3^1 s_1 - 1 \times C_3^2 s_1 + 0 \times \sigma_v s_1 + 0 \times \sigma_v' s_1 + 0 \times \sigma_v'' s_1\right]$$

$$= \frac{1}{6}\left[2s_1 - s_2 - s_3\right] \quad \text{... (11.48)}$$

For getting ψ_{E_2}, we make use of the two conditions : (*i*) ψ_{E_2}, must be orthogonal to ψ_{E_1}, and (*ii*) any symmetry operation, say C_3^1, of the group converts ψ_{E_1} into a linear combination of ψ_{E_1} and ψ_{E_2}, *i.e.*,

$$R\,\psi_{E_1} = a\psi_{E_1} + b\psi_{E_2} \quad \text{... (11.49)}$$

Let $R = C_3^1$

$$C_3^1\,\psi_{E_1} = a\psi_{E_1} + b\psi_{E_2} \quad \text{... (11.49 a)}$$

where the values of a and b are to be determined,

$$\left(\text{Recall that } C_3^1 p_x = -\frac{1}{2} p_x - \frac{\sqrt{3}}{2} p_y\right)$$

The effect of C_3^1 on y_{E_1}, for example, is

$$C_3^1\,\psi_{E_1} = C_3^1 \frac{1}{6}\left(2s_1 - s_2 - s_3\right) \text{ by Equation (11.48)}$$

$$= \frac{1}{6}\left(2C_3^1\, s_1 - C_3^1\, s_2 - C_3^1\, s_3\right)$$

$$= \frac{1}{6}\left(2s_2 - s_3 - s_1\right) \qquad \text{... (11.50)}$$

The function (11.50) will be a linear combination of the type Equation (11.49*a*). Multiplying both sides of Equation (11.49*a*) by ψ_{E_1} and integrating, we get

$$\int \left(C_3^1\, \psi_{E_1}\right) \psi_{E_1}\, d\tau = a \int \psi_{E_1}^2\, d\tau + b \int \psi_{E_2}\, \psi_{E_1}\, d\tau$$

$$= a \int \psi_{E_1}^2\, d\tau \qquad \text{[because } \psi_{E_1} \text{ and } \psi_{E_2} \text{ must be orthogonal]}$$

or

$$a = \frac{\int \left(C_3^1\, \psi_{E_1}\right) \psi_{E_1}\, d\tau}{\int \psi_{E_1}^2\, d\tau} \qquad \text{... (11.51)}$$

Substituting Equations (11.50) and (11.48) in Equation (11.51), we get

$$a = \frac{\int \frac{1}{6}\left(2s_2 - s_3 - s_1\right) \frac{1}{6}\left(2s_1 - s_2 - s_3\right) d\tau}{\int \frac{1}{36}\left(2s_1 - s_2 - s_3\right)^2 d\tau} \qquad \text{... (11.52)}$$

On expanding the numerator and denominator in Equation (11.52), since

$$\int s_1\, s_2\, d\tau = \int s_2\, s_3\, d\tau = \int s_1\, s_3\, d\tau = 0$$

s_1, s_2, s_3 belonging to the three different H atoms are widely separated and hence orthogonal) and

$$\int s_1^2\, d\tau = \int s_2^2\, d\tau = \int s_3^2\, d\tau = 1 \text{ (by normalisation)}$$

we get the simplified form of Equation (11.52),

$$a = \frac{-\frac{1}{12}}{\frac{1}{6}} = -\frac{1}{2} \qquad \text{... (11.53)}$$

From Equation [11.49 *a*], $b\, \psi_{E_2} = \left(C_3^1\, \psi_{E_1}\right) - a\psi_{E_1}$

$$= \frac{1}{6}\left(2s_2 - s_3 - s_1\right) - \left(-\frac{1}{2}\right)\frac{1}{6}\left(2s_1 - s_2 - s_3\right)$$

$$= \frac{1}{4}\left(s_2 - s_3\right) \qquad \text{... (11.54)}$$

or $$\psi_{E_2} = \frac{1}{4b}(s_2 - s_3) \qquad \text{... (11.55)}$$

The expressions (11.48) and (11.55) represent the two SALC's belonging to the representation E. These are not normalised. Using the appropriate normalisation factors, we get

$$\psi_{E_1} = \frac{1}{\sqrt{6}}(2s_1 - s_2 - s_3) \qquad \text{... (11.56)}$$

and $$\psi_{E_2} = \frac{1}{\sqrt{2}}(s_2 - s_3) \qquad \text{... (11.57)}$$

[For example, $$\int \psi_{E_2}^2\, d\tau = \int \left[\frac{f}{4b}(s_2 - s_3)\right]^2 d\tau = 1$$

or $$\int \frac{f^2}{16b^2}(s_2 - s_3)^2\, d\tau = \frac{f^2}{16b^2}\left[\int s_2^2\, d\tau + \int s_3^2\, d\tau - 2\int s_2\, s_3\, d\tau\right] = 1$$

or $$\frac{f^2}{16b^2} \times 2 = 1, \text{ or } f = \sqrt{8}\, b$$

or $$\psi_{E_2} = \left[\frac{\sqrt{8}b}{4b}(s_2 - s_3) = \frac{1}{\sqrt{2}}(s_2 - s_3)\right].$$

11.6.3 Product Representations and Product Bases

We have another very important theorem about "product representation". If two functions f_i and f_j form bases of representations Γ_a and Γ_b, then their quadratic products like $f_i f_j$, f_i^2, f_j^2 etc., will be bases of representations in which the characters χ (R) will be equal to the product of the characters of the representations based on individual functions. Thus, the character table of C_{3v} point group gives rise to product representations like:

C_{3v}		E	$2C_3$	3σ	Basis
$E \times E = E^2$	:	(2×2)	(-1×-1)	(0×0)	(x^2, y^2, xy, yx)
	or	4	1	0	
$A_1 \times E = E$	:	(1×2)	(1×-1)	(1×0)	(xz, yz)
	or	2	-1	0	

Use of formula Equation (11.45) reduces E^2 as,

$$E^2 = A_1 + A_2 + E \qquad \text{... (11.58)}$$

and $A_1 \times E = E$ is irreducible.

Exercise 1: *Determine the product representation for C_{3v} group with quadratic products of x, y and z as the basis. Reduce it to its components.*

C_{3v}	E	$2C_3$	$3\sigma_v$	Basis
Γ_1:	3	0	1	(x, y, z)
Γ_2:	9	0	1	$(x^2, y^2, z^2, xy, yx, xz, zx, yz, zy)$

$$\Gamma_2 = 2A_1 + A_2 + 3E$$

Exercise 2: *Use the character table for C_{2h} group to find the product representation with product bases xy, yz, xz, x^2, y^2 and z^2.*

C_{2h}	E	C_2	σ_h	1	Basis
$B_u \times B_u = A_g$	1	1	1	1	x^2, y^2, xy, yx
$A_u \times A_u = A_g$	1	1	1	1	x^2
$A_u \times B_u = B_g$	1	−1	−1	1	xz, yz

For every group, table of product representation can be constructed; such tables are often of great use. For C_{2h} group, for example,

C_{2h}	A_g	A_u	B_u	B_g
A_g	A_g	A_u	B_u	B_g
A_u	A_u	A_g	B_g	B_u
B_u	B_u	B_g	A_g	A_u
B_g	B_g	B_u	A_u	A_g

that is, $g \times g = g, \quad u \times u = g, \quad g \times u = u \times g = u.$

11.7 PROBLEM OF INTEGRALS

In molecular quantum chemistry, very often, one is faced with the problem of evaluating an integral that is not easy to work out. Group theory enables one to see that in many cases the integral vanishes under certain conditions of symmetry. The rule is:

"The integral of a function or a product of functions must be zero unless the integrand belongs to or contains the totally symmetric representation of the point group to which the molecule under consideration belongs."

A product of two functions under integration can belong to totally symmetric representation (A_1, A_g, etc.) only if both the functions individually belong to the same irreducible representation. As we have seen earlier for C_{2h} group, for example, the functions of x or y individually form the basis of the same representation B_u. In such a situation,

$$\int f(x) \, . \, f(y) \, d\tau \neq 0$$

as $B_u \times B_u = A_g$.

In molecular orbital theory, we shall come across integrals like

$$\int \phi_i \hat{H} \phi_j \, d\tau .$$

The Hamiltonian $\hat{H}$ is the operator for total energy, which is unaffected by a symmetry operator (*i.e.*, symmetric). So, for the integral to be non-zero the orbitals ϕ_i and ϕ_j must belong to the same irreducible representation.

Thus, we have another very useful theorem : "An energy integral

$$\int \phi_i \hat{H} \phi_j \, d\tau$$

can be non-zero only if ϕ_i and ϕ_j belong to the same irreducible representation (symmetry type) of the group to which the molecule belongs."

11.7.1 Applications to Quantum Chemistry

Principles of symmetry and group theory find applications in several areas of quantum chemistry like chemical bonding, molecular spectroscopy, ligand field theory, crystal field theory, etc. The procedure in all these cases involves (*i*) generating a reducible representation Γ_r of the symmetry group to which the molecule belongs using a set of atomic orbitals as basis, (*ii*) resolving the Γ_r to irreducible representations (Γ_i's) using Equation (11.45), and (*iii*) constructing SALC's corresponding to the Γ_i's of the group.

In the present text we concentrate on the applications of symmetry to chemical bonding, which will be described in the next two chapters, specially with respect to construction of molecular orbitals and hybrid orbitals.

PROBLEMS

11.1 For each of the following molecules (*a*) list the symmetry elements and the symmetry operations, and (*b*) determine the symmetry point group:

C_2H_4, CH_4, C_6H_6, napthalene, *cis*-dichloroethylene, trans dichloro-ethylene CO_3^{2-} (planar), isomeric trichlorobenzenes.

[**Hint:** D_{2h}, T_d, D_{6h}, D_{2h}, C_{2v}, C_{2h}, C_{2v}, for (1 : 2 : 3 isomer), c_s (for 1 : 2 : 4 isomer), D_{3h} (for 1 : 3 : 5 isomer)].

11.2 For the H_2O molecule, carry out the following:

(*a*) Determine all the symmetry operations and set up a multiplication table; ascertain that this constitutes a group.

(*b*) Use the coordinates x, y, z and R_z as bases to set up a character table for the group; treat the line bisecting the < HOH angle as the z-axis and that perpendicular to it as the y-axis.

(*c*) Use the 1*s* atomic orbitals of the two H atoms to generate a representation of the symmetry group of the molecule.

(*d*) Reduce the representation to its irreducible components.

(*e*) Find the symmetry combinations of these atomic orbitals that can appear in the molecular orbitals of the water molecule.

[**Hint :** (*a*) C_{2v} : E, C_2 (z), σ (yz), σ (xz).

$$C_2^2 = E, \text{etc.}$$

$$\begin{bmatrix} -1 & 0 & 0 & 0 \\ 0 & -1 & 0 & 0 \\ 0 & 0 & 1 & 0 \\ 0 & 0 & 0 & 1 \end{bmatrix}\begin{bmatrix} -1 & 0 & 0 & 0 \\ 0 & -1 & 0 & 0 \\ 0 & 0 & 1 & 0 \\ 0 & 0 & 0 & 1 \end{bmatrix} = \begin{bmatrix} 1 & 0 & 0 & 0 \\ 0 & 1 & 0 & 0 \\ 0 & 0 & 1 & 0 \\ 0 & 0 & 0 & 1 \end{bmatrix}$$

and so on.

(*b*) Character table:

C_{2v}	E	$C_2(z)$	$\sigma(yz)$	$\sigma(xz)$	Basis
A_1	1	1	1	1	z
A_2	1	1	-1	-1	R_z
B_1	1	-1	1	-1	x, R_y
B_2	1	-1	-1	1	y, R_z

(*c*) $E(s_1, s_2) = (s_1, s_2)\ \chi(E) = 2$, etc.

C_{2v}	E	C_2	$\sigma(yz)$	$\sigma(xz)$	Basis
Γ_r :	2	0	0	2	(s_1, s_2)

(*d*) $\Gamma_r = A_1 + B_1$

(*e*) $A_1 = \dfrac{1}{2}(s_1 + s_2)$; $B_1 = \dfrac{1}{2}(s_1 - s_2)$].

11.3 The molecule of formaldehyde is planar with

$$< HCH = < HCO = 120°$$

(*a*) list the symmetry operations for this molecule, and

(*b*) use the valence atomic orbitals to form the symmetry adapted molecular orbitals, grouping them by symmetry types.

[**Hint :** (*a*) C_{2v}

(*b*) use Equations (11.45) and (11.46) of the text].

11.4 List the symmetry operations of the molecule C_2H_4 (planar). Treat the C—C bond axis as the *z*-axis and consider the effect of the symmetry operations on the six *p*-atomic orbitals located at C-atoms. Give the matrices of the 6-dimensional reducible representation of the symmetry group generated by the six atomic orbitals. Reduce this representation to irreducible representations.

11.5 For the octahedral chlorobromotetramine complex of Co (III) carry out the following:

(*a*) Find the symmetry elements and identify the point group.

(*b*) Derive the irreducible representations using $x, y, z, x^2 - y^2, xy$ and R_z as basis; check up all the representations by the formula $\sum l_i^2 = h$. Set up the character table.

(*c*) Use the 1*s* atomic orbitals of the H atoms to generate a reducible representation and determine the symmetry types.

(*d*) Determine the symmetry adapted orbitals that contain 2*s* atomic orbitals of the N-atom.

[**Hint :** See Figure 11.12.

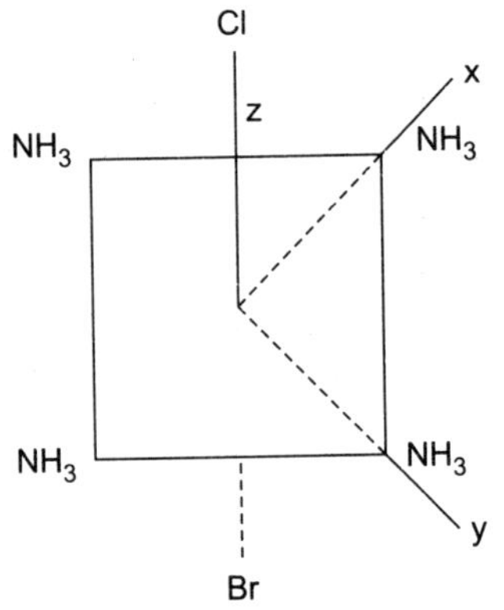

Fig. 11.12 *Structure of Co^{II} $(NH_3)_4$ Cl Br complex*

(*a*) C_{4v} (E, $2C_4$ (z), C_2 (z) ; $2\sigma_v$ (passing through NH_3 on opposite corners, $2\sigma_d$ (bisecting N-N bonds on opposite sides).

(*b*) E (z) = z, C_4 (z) = z, C_2 (z) = z, σ_v (z) = z, σ_d (z) = z

$$\chi = 1 \quad \chi = 1 \quad \chi = 1 \quad \chi = 1 \quad \chi = 1 \ldots A_1$$

$$E\begin{pmatrix} x \\ y \end{pmatrix} = \begin{pmatrix} x \\ y \end{pmatrix}, C_4\begin{pmatrix} x \\ y \end{pmatrix} = \begin{pmatrix} y \\ -x \end{pmatrix}, C_2\begin{pmatrix} x \\ y \end{pmatrix} = \begin{pmatrix} -x \\ -y \end{pmatrix}, \sigma_v\begin{pmatrix} x \\ y \end{pmatrix} - \begin{pmatrix} x \\ -y \end{pmatrix}, \sigma_d = \begin{pmatrix} x \\ y \end{pmatrix} = \begin{pmatrix} y \\ x \end{pmatrix}$$

$$E = \begin{pmatrix} 1 & 0 \\ 0 & 1 \end{pmatrix}, C_4 = \begin{pmatrix} 0 & 1 \\ -1 & 0 \end{pmatrix}, C_2 = \begin{pmatrix} -1 & 0 \\ 0 & -1 \end{pmatrix},$$

$$\chi = 2 \qquad \chi = 0 \qquad \chi = -2$$

$$\sigma_v = \begin{pmatrix} 1 & 0 \\ 0 & -1 \end{pmatrix}, \sigma_d = \begin{pmatrix} 0 & 1 \\ 1 & 0 \end{pmatrix}$$

$$\chi = 0 \qquad \chi = 0$$

This is two-dimensional, hence, it is E representation.

$$E(x^2 - y^2) = (x^2 - y^2), C_4(x^2 - y^2) = -(x^2 - y^2),$$

$$\chi = 1 \qquad \chi = -1$$

$$C_2(x^2 - y^2) = (x^2 - y^2), \sigma_v(x^2 - y^2) = (x^2 - y^2),$$

$$\chi = 1 \qquad \chi = 1$$

$$\sigma_d(x^2 - y^2) = -(x^2 - y^2)$$

$$\chi = -1 \quad \ldots B_1$$

Similarly, the basis xy leads to

$$1 \quad -1 \quad 1 \quad -1 \quad 1 \cdots B_2$$

and R_z leads to

$$1 \quad 1 \quad 1 \quad 1 \quad -1 \cdots A_2$$

The character table is:

C_{4v}	E	$2C_4$	C_2	$2\sigma_v$	$2\sigma_d$	Basis
A_1	1	1	1	1	1	z
A_2	1	1	1	−1	−1	R_z
B_1	1	−1	1	−1	−1	$x^2 - y^2$
B_2	1	−1	1	−1	1	xy
E	2	0	−2	0	0	(x, y)

$$\sum l_i^2 = 1^2 + 1^2 + 1^2 + 1^2 + 2^2 = 8 = h$$

(*c*)

C_{4v}	E	$2C_4$	C_2	$2\sigma_v$	$2\sigma_d$	Basis
Γ_4:	4	0	0	2	0	$(1s_1, 1s_2, 1s_3, 1s_4)$

(*d*) Use Equation (11.46) to obtain

$$\psi(A_1) = 2s_1 + 2s_2 + 2s_3 + 2s_4$$

$$\psi(B_1) = 2s_1 - 2s_2 + 2s_3 - 2s_4$$

$$\left.\begin{aligned}\psi(E_{1A}) &= 2s_1 - 2s_3\\ \psi(E_{1B}) &= 2s_2 - 2s_4\end{aligned}\right\} \text{ or } \left\{\begin{aligned}&2s_1 + 2s_2 - 2s_3 - 2s_4\\ &2s_1 - 2s_2 - 2s_3 + 2s_4\end{aligned}\right.$$

11.6 A symmetry point group consists of the following operations:
E, $2C_3$, $3C_2$, σ_h, $2S_3$ and $3\sigma_v$.
(*a*) Assign the symbol for the group.
(*b*) What is the order of the group ?
(*c*) How many classes are in the group ?
(*d*) How many irreducible representations are possible ?
(*e*) What is the dimension of each group ?

[Hint : (*a*) D_{3h}, (*b*) $h = 12$, (*c*) $g = 6$, (*d*) Γ_1 to Γ_6, (*e*) $l_1^2 + l_2^2 + l_3^2 + l_4^2 + l_5^2 + l_6^2 = 12$
Therefore, $l_1 = l_2 = l_3 = l_4 = 1$; $l_5 = l_6 = 2$].

11.7 D_5 has four classes and the order of the group is 10.
(*a*) How many irreducible representations are possible ?
(*b*) What is the dimension of each ?
[Hint: (*a*) 4; (*b*) $l_1 = l_2 = 1$; $l_3 = l_4 = 2$].

11.8 A group has the following irreducible representations:
A_1, A_2, B_1, B_2, E_1, E_2.
(*a*) What is the order of the group ?
(*b*) How many classes are in the group ?

[Hint: (*a*) $2l_i^2 = 8$; (*b*) $g = 6$].

CHAPTER 12

Theory of Chemical Bonding (Diatomic Molecules)

In the heart of chemistry lies the question as to how atoms are held together in molecules, or, put in other words, what makes a molecule stable, why the total energy of atoms is lowered when they combine, etc. We shall seek answers to ths basic question in the present Chapter.

From the point of view of chemical bonding, it is not the kinetic energy (translational, rotational, vibrational, etc.), but the potential energy of a molecule which is of interest. Potential energy of a molecule is the sum of its electronic energy (due to nuclear-electronic attractions and inter-electronic repulsions) and nuclear energy (due to inter-nuclear repulsions). For a diatomic molecule, the potential energy, which depends on internuclear distance R, can be conveniently plotted against R. For the normal state of the molecule the potential energy curve (Fig. 12.1) exhibits a minimum at a particular value of R, which is the equilibrium internuclear distance or bond distance (R_e).

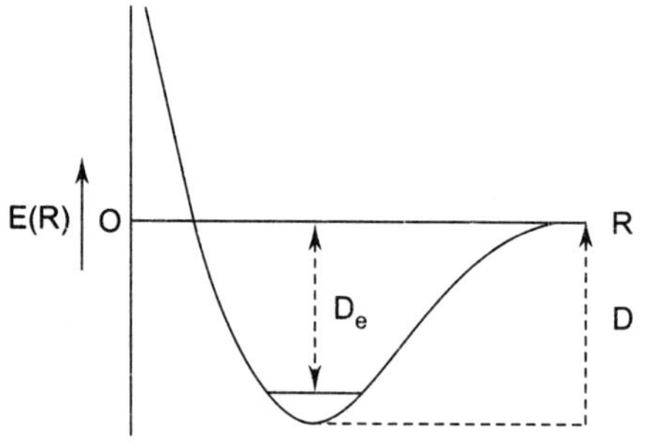

Fig. 12.1 *Potential energy curve of a diatomic molecule*

The depth of the minimum (D) represents the energy required to dissociate the molecule into atoms. However, the observed dissociation energy (D_e) is D minus the zero point vibrational energy (even at the absolute zero of temperature the molecule executes vibration).

12.1 TREATMENT OF MOLECULES–THE BORN OPPENHEIMER APPROXIMATION

For calculating the electronic energy we need to solve the electronic Schrödinger equation. The complete Schrödinger equation covers both the nuclear and electronic motions. For a system of n nuclei and p electrons, whose coordinates are collectively denoted as R and r, respectively, the Hamiltonian is given by the equation,

$$\hat{H} = -\sum_{i=1}^{n} \frac{h^2}{8\pi^2 M_i} \nabla_i^2 - \sum_{j=1}^{p} \frac{h^2}{8\pi^2 m} \nabla_j^2 + V(r, R) \quad \text{... (12.1)}$$

and the potential energy V (r, R) is given by,

$$V(r, R) = -\sum_{k=1}^{n}\sum_{j=1}^{p} \frac{Z_k e^2}{r_{jk}} + \sum_{m<j} \frac{e^2}{r_{mj}} + \sum_{k<l} \frac{Z_k Z_l e^2}{R_{kl}} \quad \text{... (12.2)}$$

In Equations (12.1) and (12.2), M_i is the mass of the ith nucleus, m that of an electron, subscript j is for the jth electron Z_k is the atomic number of the kth nucleus, r_{jk} is the distance of the jth electron from the kth nucleus, r_{mj} is the distance betwen the mth and jth electrons and R_{kl} is the distance between the kth and the lth nuclei. The first term in Equation (12.1) represents the nuclear kinetic energy operator $\hat{T}_N$ while the second and third terms together make up the "electronic Hamiltonian operator", $\hat{H}_e$, *i.e.*,

$$\hat{H} = \hat{T}_N (R) + \hat{H}_e (r, R) \quad \text{... (12.3)}$$

The electronic operator describes the motion of the electrons for fixed positions of nuclei, that is, it depends on the positions (and not on momenta) of the nuclei. The Schrödinger equation of the molecule is,

$$\hat{H}\Psi = E_T \Psi, \text{T stands for total} \quad \text{... (12.4)}$$

To separate the part of Schrödinger equation due to electronic motion, Max Born and J. Robert Oppenheimer assumed that since the nuclei are several thousand times heavier than electrons, the former may be assumed to be stationary when the latter move. So the electronic wave function can be obtained by solving the electronic equation for some fixed positions of the nuclei. Each choice of nuclear coordinates (R) will lead to a different potential energy and, hence a different electronic Schrödinger equation. Thus, while the "electronic wave function, ψ_e" will depend on r as well as R, the "nuclear wave function, ψ_N" will depend on R only. We can assume that the complete wave function Ψ in Equation (12.4) can be written as,

$$\Psi = \psi_e (r, R) \,.\, \psi_N (R) \quad \text{... (12.5)}$$

Substituting Equation (12.1) for $\hat{H}$ and Equation (12.5) for Ψ in Equation (12.4), we get

$$\left[-\sum_{i=1}^{n} \frac{h^2}{8\pi^2 M_i} \nabla_i^2 - \sum_{j=1}^{p} \frac{h^2}{8\pi^2 m} \nabla_j^2 + V(r, R)\right] \psi_e (r, R) \,.\, \psi_N (R) = E_T \psi_e (r, R) \,.\, \psi_N (R) \quad \text{... (12.6)}$$

On carrying out the partial differentiations,

$$\nabla_i^2 \psi_e (r, R) \,.\, \psi_N (R) = \vec{\nabla}_i \,.\, \vec{\nabla}_i \psi_e (r, R) \,.\, \psi_N (R)$$

$$= \vec{\nabla}_i \left[\psi_N(R)\,\vec{\nabla}_i \psi_e(r,R) + \psi_e(r,R)\,\vec{\nabla}_i \psi_N(R)\right]$$

$$= \psi_N(R)\,\nabla_i^2 \psi_e(r,R) + \vec{\Delta}_i \psi_e(r,R)\,.\,\vec{\nabla}_i \psi_N(R) + \psi_e(r,R)\,\nabla_i^2 \psi_N(R)$$

$$+ \ \vec{\Delta}_i \psi_N(R)\,\vec{\Delta}_i\,.\,\psi_e(r,R)$$

$$= \psi_N(R)\,\nabla_i^2 \psi_e(r,R) + \psi_e(r,R)\,\nabla_i^2 \psi_N(R) + 2\vec{\nabla}_i \psi_e(r,R)\,.\,\vec{\nabla}_i \psi_N(R)$$

Here we have used the relations

$$\nabla_i^2 = \vec{\nabla}_i\,.\,\vec{\nabla}_i, \text{ where the vector operator } \vec{\nabla}_i \text{ is given as}$$

$$\vec{\nabla}_i = \vec{i}\frac{\partial}{\partial x} + \vec{j}\frac{\partial}{\partial y} + \vec{k}\frac{\partial}{\partial z}.$$

$\vec{i}$, $\vec{j}$ and $\vec{k}$ are unit vectors. The operators $\vec{\nabla}_i$ and ∇_i^2 refer to differentiations with respect to R only. Since ∇_j^2 does not operate on ψ_N (R),

$$\nabla_j^2 \psi_e(r,R)\,.\,\psi_N(R) = \psi_N(R)\,.\,\nabla_j^2 \psi_e(r,R).$$

Thus the Equation (12.6) becomes

$$\left[-\sum_{i=1}^{n}\frac{h^2}{8\pi^2 M_i}\left[\psi_N(R)\,\nabla_i^2 \psi_e(r,R) + \psi_e(r,R)\,\nabla_i^2 \psi_N(R) + 2\vec{\nabla}_i \psi_e(r,R)\,.\,\vec{\nabla}_i \psi_N(R)\right]\right]$$

$$-\sum_{j=1}^{p}\frac{h^2}{8\pi^2 m}\,.\,\psi_N(R)\,\nabla_j^2 \psi_e(r,R) + V(r,R)\,\psi_e(r,R)\,\psi_N(R)$$

$$= E_T\,\psi_e(r,R)\,\psi_N(r) \qquad \ldots (12.7)$$

Now the approximation is made that since nuclear motions are very slow changes in electronic wave function ψ_e (*r*, R) due to changes in R are negligible, *i.e.*, the first and third terms in Equation (12.7) may be neglected.

Then $-\sum_{i=1}^{n}\frac{h^2}{8\pi^2 M_i}\psi_e(r,R)\,\nabla_i^2 \psi_N(R) - \sum_{j=1}^{p}\frac{h^2}{8\pi^2 m}\psi_N(R)\,\nabla_j^2 \psi_e(r,R) + V(r,R)\,\psi_e(r,R)\,.\,\psi_N(R)$

$$= E_T\,\psi_e(r,R)\,.\,\psi_N(R) \qquad \ldots (12.8)$$

Dividing both sides of Equation (12.8) by ψ_e (*r*, R) . ψ_N (R) and rearranging,

$$\sum_{i=1}^{n}\frac{h^2}{8\pi^2 M_i}\frac{\nabla_i^2 \psi_N(R)}{\psi_N(R)} + E_T = -\sum_{j=1}^{p}\frac{h^2}{8\pi^2 m}\nabla_j^2\frac{\psi_e(r,R)}{\psi_e(r,R)} + V(r,R)$$

$$= \text{constant, E (R) (say)} \qquad \ldots (12.9)$$

Equation (12.9) leads to two separate equations,

$$-\sum_{i=1}^{n} \frac{h^2}{8\pi^2 M_i} \nabla_i^2 \psi_N (R) + E(R)\, \psi_N (R) = E_T\, \psi_N (R) \qquad ...(12.10)$$

or $$\left[\hat{T}_N + E(R)\right] \psi_N (R) = E_T\, \psi_N (R)$$

or $$\hat{H}_N (R)\, \psi_N (R) = E_T\, \psi_N (R) \qquad ...(12.11)$$

This is nuclear Schrödinger equation in which $\hat{T}_N = -\sum_{i=1}^{n} \frac{h^2}{8\pi^2 M_i} \nabla_i^2$ is kinetic energy operator and E (R) is potential energy operator, together making $\hat{H}_N$ the nuclear Hamiltonian.

Similarly, $$-\sum_{j=1}^{r'} \frac{h^2}{8\pi^2 m} \nabla_j^2 \psi_e (r, R) + V(r, R)\, \psi_e (r, R) = E (R)\, \psi_e (r, R)$$

or $$\left[\hat{T}_e + V(r, R)\right] \psi_e (r, R) = E (R)\, \psi_e (r, R)$$

or $$\hat{H}_e\, \psi_e (r, R) = E (R)\, \psi_e (r, R) \qquad ...(12.12)$$

This is electronic Schrödinger equation.

Solution of Equation (12.12) gives the electronic energy E (R) and the wave function ψ_e (*r*, R) for a particular value of R. A plot of E (R) for various values of R yields the potential energy curve (Fig. 12.1).

The eigenvalue E (R) of Equation (12.12) is the potential energy for the nuclear motion [Equation (12.10)], E_T being the total energy.

For the determination of bond dissociation energy and the wave function that describe a bond, only Equation (12.12) is of relevance. Henceforth, we shall write simply $\hat{H}, \psi$ and E for $\hat{H}_e, \psi_e (r, R)$ and E (R) respectively.

Early attempts to calculate the electronic wave functions (ψ) and energies (E) were confined to simple system like H_2^+, H_2, etc., but success so achieved provided basis for extension of the approaches to bigger molecules. Such calculations led to the emergence of two very important theories of bonding: **(*i*) Molecular orbital (MO) theory and (*ii*) Valence bond (VB) theory.** These will be elaborated in the present Chapter with respect to bonding in diatomic molecules. Extension to polyatomic molecules will be the subject matter of the next Chapter.

12.2 THE MOLECULAR ORBITAL THEORY

The Born Oppenheimer approximation enables one to treat a molecule like an atom with the difference that the particles constituting potential field for each electron in the molecule include more than one nucleus. Direct solution of the Equation (12.12) for Ψ is not easy, so approximations have to be made. The chief approximation is the 'orbital approximation' as in the case of polyelectronic atoms, *i.e.*, Schrödinger equation for each electron in the molecule has to be solved separately to get the wave function ψ_i for every electron i. The ψ_i's are called 'molecular orbitals' (MO). The complete wave function Ψ is then given as the antisymmetrised product of all the molecular orbitals,

$$\Psi = N \mid \psi_1 (1)\, \bar{\psi}_1 (2)\, \psi_2 (3)\, \bar{\psi}_2 (4) \ldots (\psi_{n/2} - 1)(n-1)\, \psi_{n/2} (1) \mid \quad \ldots (12.13)$$

where, for example, $\psi_1 (1) = \psi_1 (1)\, \alpha (1)$ and $\bar{\psi}_1 (2) = \psi_1 (2)\, \beta (2)$, and so on. Since each MO can accommodate two electrons with opposite spins, only $\frac{n}{2}$ MOs are needed for n electrons. The MOs are occupied by the electrons following all the rules of occupancy (aufbau, Pauli, and Hund rules). Thus the MOs serve as basis of electronic structure of the molecules as a.o's do for atoms.

12.2.1 The LCAO Approximation

The Schrödinger equation for a single electron i in a diatomic molecule AB is

$$\hat{H}(i)\, \psi_i = E_i\, \psi_i \quad \ldots (12.14)$$

where ψ_i is the MO and E_i the MO energy of the electron and the Hamiltonian $\hat{H}(i)$ in atomic units is

$$\hat{H}(i) = -\frac{1}{2}\nabla_i^2 - \frac{Z_A}{r_{iA}} - \frac{Z_B}{r_{iB}} + \sum_{j>i} \frac{1}{r_{ij}} + \frac{Z_A Z_B}{R} \quad \ldots (12.15)$$

The first term in Equation (12.15) represents kinetic energy operator of the electron i, second and third terms the coulombic attraction of i with nuclei A and B, fourth term the coulombic repulsion of i by all the other electrons, Z_A and Z_B are effective nuclear charges of A and B respectively, r_i is the distance of the electron from the nucleus, r_{ij} is the distance of i from any other electron j, and R is the internuclear distance.

The Equation (12.14), with the Hamiltonian operator (12.15), is not easy to solve because of the interelectronic repulsion terms. Approximations are made chief of which is to take a trial function ψ_i (MO) as a linear combination (l.c.) of all atomic orbitals (a.o.) of the atoms constituting the molecule and use the variation method to determine the minimum energy E_i. Also, self consistent field method (Chapter 9) is used to determine the best possible MOs, *i.e.*, those which give the lowest value of the total energy E of the molecule. The corresponding electronic wave function Ψ of the molecule (Equation 12.13) then represents the bonded state of the molecule.

Each LCAO MO ψ_i is given as

$$\psi_i = a_{i1}\, \phi_1 + a_{i2}\, \phi_2 + \ldots = \sum_{p=1}^{n} a_{ip}\, \phi_p \quad \ldots (12.16)$$

where n is the number of *ao's* combined, a_{ip}'s are the coefficients of the a.o.'s in the l.c. in the MO ψ_i. The a.o.'s are also called 'basis functions'. There is no restriction to the number of basis functions to be used; in fact, larger the basis better the result. However, in practical calculations the basis set is kept finite. If one basis function (atomic orbital) is used for each electron, the set is called 'minimal basis set'.

12.3 THE HYDROGEN MOLECULE ION

There is only one molecular system—the H_2^+ ion for which Schrödinger equation has been solved exactly. In the theory of molecular electronic structure, therefore, H_2^+ has the same status as H-atom in atomic structure; both are 1-electron systems. The Schrödinger equation for H-atom is solved by separating it in spherical coordinates with nucleus at the centre while the equation for H_2^+ is separated in elliptical coordinates with the two nuclei at the two foci of the ellipse. As the wave functions of the H-atom are atomic orbitals, those of the H_2^+ ion are called 'molecular orbitals'.

However, results obtained on using elliptical coordinates for H_2^+ lead to little physical significance from the point of view of bonding. Hence, rather than worrying about exact wave function, it is more convenient to follow the approximate procedure of using a trial wave function of the type described in the earlier section.

12.3.1 The LCAO MO Wave Function of H_2^+ Ion (Ground State)

The trial LCAO MO wave function of H_2^+ with a minimal basis in the ground state is

$$\psi = a_1\, 1s_A + a_2\, 1s_B \qquad \text{...(12.17)}$$

where $1s_A$ and $1s_B$ are the a.o.'s centred around H atoms A and B. These a.o.'s (hydrogen like) are given (in atomic units) as

$$1s_A = \frac{1}{\sqrt{\pi}} e^{-r_A}, \text{ and } 1s_B = \frac{1}{\sqrt{\pi}} e^{-r_B} \qquad \text{...(12.18)}$$

where r_A and r_B are the distances of the electron from the nuclei A and B respectively (Fig. 12.2). From the symmetry point of view the only MOs that can be constructed are

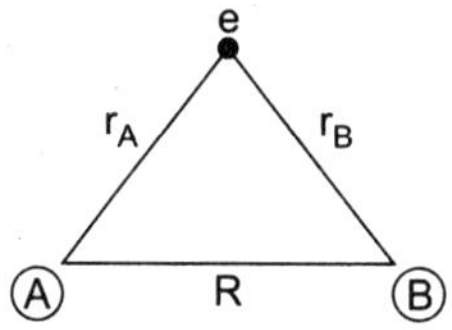

Fig. 12.2

$$\psi_1 = N_1\,(1s_A + 1s_B) \qquad \text{...(12.19)}$$

and

$$\psi_2 = N_2\,(1s_A - 1s_B) \qquad \text{...(12.20)}$$

where N_1 and N_2 are normalisation factors. However, we shall determine the MOs with appropriate normalisation factors in a formal way in a later section.

12.3.2 The Ground State Electronic Energy (Orbital Energy)

For the H_2^+, a 1-electron system, the electronic energy in the ground state is same as orbital energy. The orbital energy (E_i) is given as

$$E_i = \frac{\int \psi^* \hat{H} \psi \, dT}{\int \psi^* \psi \, dT} \qquad \text{... (12.21)}$$

$$= \frac{\int (a_1 1s_A + a_2 1s_B) \hat{H} (a_1 1s_A + a_2 1s_B) \, dT}{\int (a_1 1s_A + a_2 1s_B)^2 \, dT} \qquad (\psi \text{ being real})$$

where $\hat{H}$ (in atomic units) is

$$\hat{H} = -\frac{1}{2}\nabla^2 - \frac{1}{r_A} - \frac{1}{r_B} + \frac{1}{R}$$

Variation treatment $\left(\frac{\partial E}{\partial a_1} = \frac{\partial E}{\partial a_2} = 0\right)$ leads to the secular equations

$$\left.\begin{aligned} a_1 (H_{AA} - ES_{AA}) + a_2 (H_{AB} - ES_{AB}) = 0 \\ a_1 (H_{BA} - ES_{BA}) + a_2 (H_{BB} - ES_{BB}) = 0 \end{aligned}\right\} \qquad \text{... (12.22)}$$

where

$$H_{AA} = \int 1s_A \hat{H} 1s_A \, d\tau, \quad H_{BB} = \int 1s_B \hat{H} 1s_B \, d\tau$$

$$H_{AB} = \int 1s_A \hat{H} 1s_B \, d\tau, \quad H_{BA} = \int 1s_B \hat{H} 1s_A \, d\tau$$

$$S_{AA} = \int 1s_A . 1s_A \, d\tau, \quad S_{BB} = \int 1s_B . 1s_B \, d\tau$$

$$S_{AB} = \int 1s_A \, 1s_B \, d\tau, \quad S_{BA} = \int 1s_B \, 1s_A \, d\tau$$

The Equation (12.22) can have non-trivial solution (*i.e.*, a_1 and $a_2 \neq 0$) only if the secular determinant,

$$\begin{vmatrix} H_{AA} - ES_{AA} & H_{AB} - ES_{AB} \\ H_{BA} - ES_{BA} & H_{BB} - ES_{BB} \end{vmatrix} = 0 \qquad \text{... (12.23)}$$

The Equation (12.23) can be simplified as follows. Since the two H-atoms in H_2^+ are alike, $H_{AA} = H_{BB}$; the operator $\hat{H}$ being Hermitian, $H_{AB} = H_{BA}$; 1s atomic orbitals are already normalised so that $S_{AA} = S_{BB} = 1$, and $S_{AB} = S_{BA} = S$ (say). Then Equation (12.23) becomes

$$\begin{vmatrix} H_{AA} - E & H_{AB} - ES \\ H_{AB} - ES & H_{AA} - E \end{vmatrix} = 0 \qquad \text{... (12.24)}$$

On expanding the determinant, we get

$$(H_{AA} - E)^2 = (H_{AB} - ES)^2$$

or

$$H_{AA} - E = \pm (H_{AB} - ES) \qquad \text{... (12.25)}$$

The two values for E corresponding to the – and + signs on the right hand side of Equation (12.25) are given, respectively, as

$$E_1 = \frac{H_{AA} + H_{AB}}{1+S} \quad \text{... (12.26)}$$

and $$E_2 = \frac{H_{AA} - H_{AB}}{1-S} \quad \text{... (12.27)}$$

Thus, the calculation of E_1 and E_2 requires evaluation of the integrals H_{AA}, H_{AB} and S. Writing explicitly for the Hamiltonian, [*i.e.*, Equation (12.21)], we get

$$H_{AA} = \int 1s_A \left(-\frac{1}{2}\nabla^2 - \frac{1}{r_A}\right) 1s_A\, d\tau - \int 1s_A \cdot \frac{1}{r_B} 1s_A\, d\tau + \int 1s_A \cdot \frac{1}{R} \cdot 1s_A\, d\tau$$

... (12.28)

Taking the operator within the brackets in the first integral of Equation (12.28) as the Hamiltonian of an H-atom and $1s_A$ and $1s_B$ are the orbitals of the two H-atoms,

$$\int 1s_A \left(-\frac{1}{2}\nabla^2 - \frac{1}{r_A}\right) 1s_A\, d\tau = \int 1s_A \cdot E_H\, 1s_A\, d\tau = E_H$$ (because $1s_A$ is normalised).

E_H is the energy of a single H-atom. In the second integral (with 2 nuclear centres) $\frac{1}{r_B}$ is the operator for the energy (in a.u.) of attraction between the electron and the nucleus B at a distance of r_B; so, the integral gives the potential energy of coulombic attraction (say j) between the electron and that nucleus, *i.e.*,

$$j = \int 1s_A \frac{1}{r_B} 1s_A\, d\tau \quad \text{... (12.29)}$$

The 3rd integral $\int 1s_A \cdot \frac{1}{R} \cdot 1s_A\, d\tau = \frac{1}{R}\int 1s_A \cdot 1s_A\, d\tau = \frac{1}{R}$ (for a fixed value of R) ... (12.30)

is the energy of repulsion between the two nuclei at a distance R from each other.

Thus, $$H_{AA} = E_H - j + \frac{1}{R} \quad \text{... (12.31)}$$

Similarly, $$H_{AB} = \int 1s_A\, \hat{H}\, 1s_B\, d\tau = E_H \cdot S - k + \frac{S}{R} \quad \text{... (12.32)}$$

where $$k = \int 1s_A \cdot \frac{1}{r_A} \cdot 1s_B\, d\tau \quad \text{... (12.33)}$$

Substituting the value of H_{AA} and H_{AB} from Equations (12.31) and (12.32) into Equations (12.26) and (12.27) for E_1 and E_2 and rearranging, we get

$$E_1 = E_H - \frac{j+k}{1+S} + \frac{1}{R} \quad \text{... (12.34)}$$

$$E_2 = E_H - \frac{j-k}{1-S} + \frac{1}{R} \quad \text{... (12.35)}$$

The evaluation of E_1, therefore, requires evaluation of the three integrals *j*, *k* and S. The results of evaluation (details of which are avoided here) are as follows:

$$j = \frac{1}{R}\left[1-(1+R)\,e^{-2R}\right] \qquad \text{... (12.36)}$$

$$k = (1 + R)\,e^{-R} \qquad \text{... (12.37)}$$

$$S = \left(1 + R + \frac{R^2}{3}\right)e^{-R} \qquad \text{... (12.38)}$$

Equations (12.34) to (12.38) can thus be used to calculate the values of E_1 and E_2 for any value of R in a straight forward manner. The results of such calculations for several values of R, relative to the energy of H-atom (*i.e.*, E_H taken as zero) are presented in Table 12.1.

TABLE 12.1 Energy of H_2^+ for Various Values of R

R (a.u.)	E_1 (a.u.)*	E_2 (a.u.)*
0.5	1.079	2.35
1.0	0.212	1.019
1.5	0.005	0.572
2.0	– 0.054	0.338
2.5	– 0.065	0.208
3.0	– 0.059	0.132
3.5	– 0.048	0.085
4.0	– 0.038	0.055
4.5	– 0.028	0.037
5.0	– 0.019	0.023

* These values of E_1 are with respect to E_H taken as zero; each will decrease by 0.5 atomic unit if E_H (= –0.5 a.u.) is added to it.

The values of E_1 may be plotted against R as shown in Figures 12.13 (*a*), (*b*).

These calculations and plottings bring forth certain very interesting features that are discussed below:

For any value of R, E_1 is less than E_2. Beyond a certain value of R, E_1 becomes negative (*i.e.*, $< E_H$), but E_2 is always greater than E_H, *i.e.*, it is always positive.

The curve for E_1 shows a minimum corresponding to R = 2.5 a.u. where E_1 = – 0.065 a.u. but that for E_2 decreases continuously with increase in R, always remaining above the E_H line.

This means that in the ground state, the energy of H_2^+ is 0.065 a.u. less than that of H + H^+ separated infinitely; this value (0.065 a.u. = 1.77 eV), therefore, represents the dissociation energy (D_e) of H_2^+. Similarly, the position of minimum, *i.e.*, R = 2.5 a.u. = 1.32 Å represents the equilibrium bond length (R_e) in H_2^+.

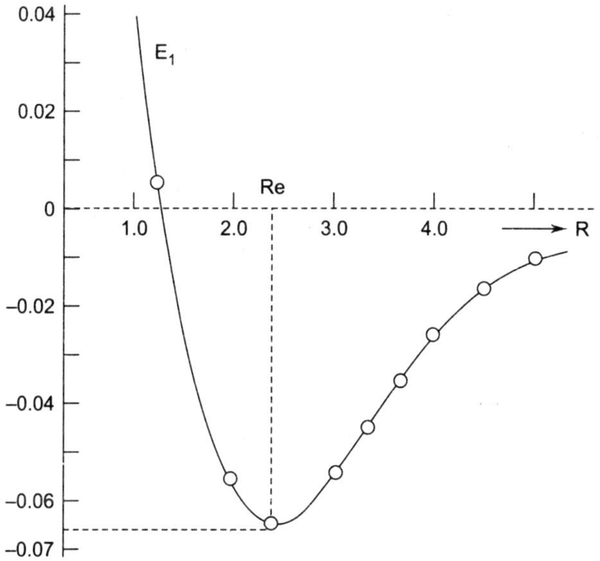

Fig. 12.3 (*a*)

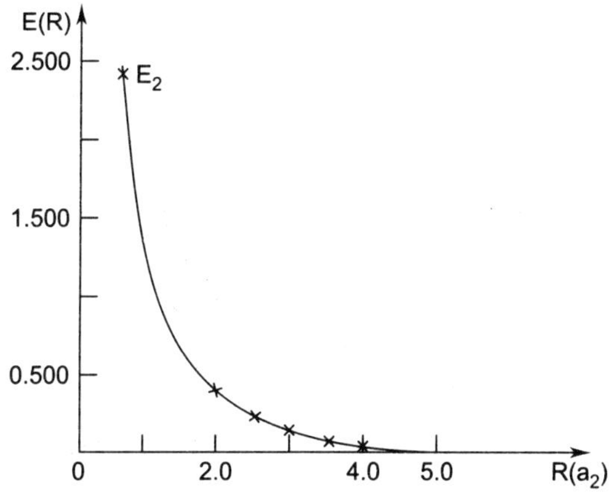

Fig. 12.3 (*b*)

The experimentally observed values of dissociation energy and bond length are 2.8 eV and 1.06 Å, respectively. The agreement is crude but the model used too is a crude one. There is, however, enough scope for improvements.

One improvement, which is due to C.A. Coulson, is to modify the 1s basis functions. When H-atom and H^+ are infinitely separated, the 1s exponential function is $\frac{1}{\sqrt{\pi}} e^{-r}$. On the other hand, if they are fused together the exponential function is $\sqrt{\frac{8}{\pi}} e^{-2r}$. Therefore, at intermediate distances, as in H_2^+, it should be $\sqrt{\frac{Z'^3}{\pi}} . e^{-Z'r}$ where Z', a variable parameter, lies between 1 and 2.

The exact value of Z′ was determined by minimization of energy, *i.e.*, by setting $\frac{dE}{dZ'} = 0$. On calculation, it was found that Z′ = 1.24 and dissociation energy (D_e) = 2.25 eV.

Further improvement was made by B.N. Dickinson who argued that an H-atom in a molecule cannot have the spherical electronic charge distribution as in an isolated atom; the charge distribution is polarised on molecule formation. Therefore, the basis functions to be used must have some *p*-character with *p*-orbitals oriented along the line joining the nuclei. Accordingly, the better trial LCAO-MO function should be,

$$\psi = [1s_A + \lambda\, 2p_{zA}] + [1s_B + \lambda\, 2p_{zB}] \qquad \text{... (12.39)}$$

where λ is another variable parameter. The parameters (Z′ and Z″) to be used in the exponential parts of the 1*s* and 2*p* functions are different. The values of λ, Z′ and Z″ are determined by setting,

$$\frac{\partial E}{\partial \lambda} = \frac{\partial E}{\partial Z'} = \frac{\partial E}{\partial Z''} = 0$$

On calculation, it is found that λ = 0.145, Z′ = 1.247, Z″ = 2.868 and D_e = 2.65 eV.

12.3.3 The LCAO Coefficients and the Orthonormal Molecular Orbitals (MOs)

Let us now denote the E_1 and E_2 by E_+ and E_- respectively which correspond to the + and – signs in the Equations (12.26) and (12.27) and replace E by E_+ or E_- in the secular Equation (12.22) to find the values of a_1 and a_2. With E_+, for example,

$$a_1 (H_{AA} - E_+) + a_2 (H_{AB} - E_+ S) = 0$$
$$a_1 (H_{AB} - E_+ S) + a_2 (H_{AA} - E_+) = 0 \qquad \text{... (12.40)}$$

where we have used the relations,

$$H_{AA} = H_{BB},\ H_{BA} = H_{AB},\ S_{AB} = S_{BA} = S \text{ and } S_{AA} = S_{BB} = 1.$$

Substituting the value of E_+ from 12.26 in 12.40, we get

$$a_1 \left[H_{AA} - \left(\frac{H_{AA} + H_{AB}}{1+S} \right) \right] + a_2 \left[H_{AB} - \left(\frac{H_{AA} + H_{AB}}{1+S} \right) S \right] = 0$$

or $$a_1 [H_{AA} (1+S) - (H_{AA} + H_{AB})] + a_2 [H_{AB} (1+S) - (H_{AA} + H_{AB}) S] = 0$$

or $$a_1 [H_{AA} S - H_{AB}] + a_2 [H_{AB} - H_{AA} S] = 0$$

or $$a_1 - a_2 = 0, \text{ or } a_1 = a_2 \qquad \text{... (12.41)}$$

By the condition of normalisation,

$$\int \psi^2\, d\tau = \int (a_1\, 1s_A + a_2\, 1s_B)^2\, d\tau = 1$$

or $$a_1^2 \int 1s_A^2\, d\tau + a_2^2 \int 1s_B^2\, d\tau + 2a_1 a_2 \int 1s_A\, 1s_B\, d\tau = 1$$

or $$a_1^2 + a_2^2 + 2a_1 a_2 S = 1 \qquad \text{(since } 1s_A \text{ and } 1s_B \text{ are normalised)}$$

or $$2a_1^2 + 2a_1^2 S = 1 \qquad \text{(because } a_1 = a_2)$$

or $$a_1 = \frac{1}{\sqrt{2(1+S)}} = a_2 \quad ...(12.42)$$

Thus, the normalised MO for H_2^+ corresponding to $E = E_+$ is

$$\psi_+ = \frac{1}{\sqrt{2(1+S)}} [1s_A + 1s_B] \quad ...(12.43)$$

Similarly, using $E = E_-$ in Equation (12.22), we shall find that $a_1 = -a_2$ which gives,

$$\psi_- = \frac{1}{\sqrt{2(1-S)}} [1s_A - 1s_B] \quad ...(12.44)$$

It is another normalised MO for H_2^+.

It is easy to see that the two MOs ψ_+ and ψ_- are orthogonal, as

$$\int (1s_A + 1s_B)(1s_A - 1s_B)\, d\tau = \int 1s_A^2\, d\tau - \int 1s_B^2\, d\tau = 1 - 1 = 0.$$

Thus, we find that the linear combination of the two atomic orbitals $1s_A$ and $1s_B$ has given two orthonormal MOs for the H_2^+ system similar to orthonormal AOs in H-atom. More MOs can be generated for H_2^+ if we include more basis functions (2*p*, etc.) in Equation (12.17).

12.3.4 Electron Density and Bonding in H_2^+

By definition, ψ^2 represents probability density of finding the electron, or the electron density, which varies from position to position in the molecule. For the two energy states $E_\pm$,

$$\psi_+^2 = \frac{1}{2(1+S)}\left[1s_A^2 + 1s_B^2 + 2(1s_A\, 1s_B)\right] \quad ...(12.45)$$

$$\psi_-^2 = \frac{1}{2(1-S)}\left[1s_A^2 + 1s_B^2 - 2(1s_A\, 1s_B)\right] \quad ...(12.46)$$

The first and second terms in Equations (12.45) and (12.46) represent spherical electron cloud around the nuclei while the third term.

$$2(1s_A\, 1s_B) \approx 2\exp(-(r_A + r_B)),$$

represents a cloud that is elliptical in shape.

Analysis of the variation of electron density $(\psi_\pm^2)$ along the internuclear axis provides explanation for the stability of the H_2^+ ion. In the absence of bonding, the average electron density would be given by $\frac{1}{2}(1s_A^2 + 1s_B^2)$. In the bonded state E_+, the electron density ψ_+^2 has three component functions $N^2\, 1s_A^2$, $N^2\, 1s_B^2$ and $2N^2\, 1s_A \cdot 1s_B$, where N, the normalisation factor, is

$\frac{1}{\sqrt{2(1+S)}}$. In between the nuclei where $1s_A = 1s_B$, ψ_+^2 will be $4N^2\ 1s_A^2$ [by Equation (12.45)], which amounts to increase in electron density by $(4N^2 - 1)\ 1s_A^2$, a positive quantity (see Fig. 12.4). This means that the MO ψ_+ has the effect of concentrating the electron density between the two nuclei. Due to attraction of the electron by both the nuclei there is lowering of the potential energy. Thus increased electron density is responsible for the stability (or bonding) in H_2^+. Accordingly, ψ_+ is called the "bonding MO".

Exercise : Given S = 0.46, calculate the increase in electron density between the two H nuclei in H_2^+ ion.

Ans. $0.37\ 1s_A^2$.

The MO ψ_-, on the other hand, has the opposite effect, it reduces the electron density between the nuclei to zero [Equation (12.46)]; it is called "antibonding MO" (see Fig. 12.4) where the difference between ψ_+ and ψ_- is seen to be due to an internuclear nodal point in ψ_-).

The force that holds the two nuclei together is the resultant of the coulombic repulsion between the two nuclei and attraction of the electron by the two nuclei. This leads to a minimum in E_+ at R_e = 1.32 Å. Calculations show that at this value of R, the nuclear repulsion energy is largely compensated by coulombic attraction energy $\frac{j}{1+S}$ [vide Equation (12.34)]. The decrease in energy of the H_2^+ ion relative to that of $H + H^+$ is then essentially due to the energy $\frac{k}{1+S}$ which represents the energy of attraction of the "overlap electron cloud $1s_A \cdot 1s_B$" localised between the two nuclei. In other words, bonding is due to overlap of atomic orbitals and exchange of the electron between the orbitals.

In the energy state E_-, the electron distribution changes and the negative charge is withdrawn from the region between the nuclei. This raises the energy level.

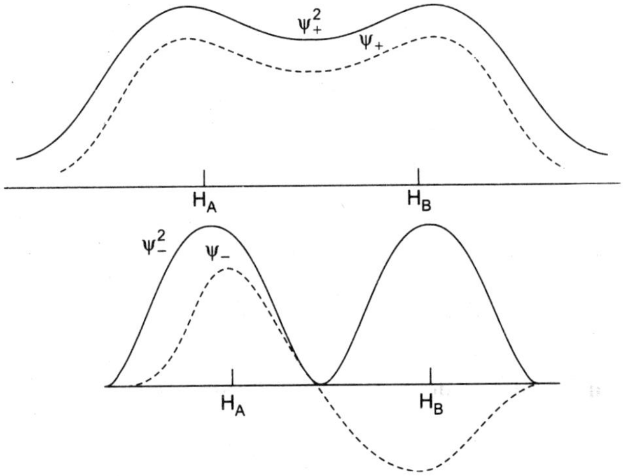

Fig. 12.4 *Plots of $\psi_\pm$ and $\psi_\pm^2$ against the internuclear distance in H_2^+*

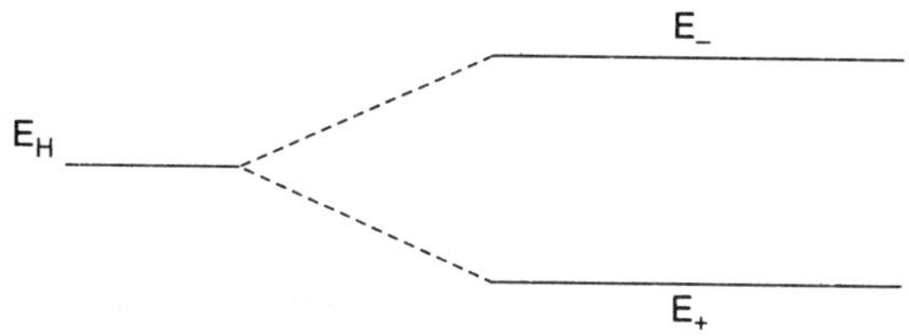

Fig. 12.5 *Energy levels of the MOs ψ_+ and ψ_-*

The splitting of the energy levels resulting from the linear combination of the $1s_A$ and $1s_B$ atomic orbitals may be represented diagrammatically as shown in Fig. 12.5.

12.3.5 Physical Representation

The two MOs, ψ_+ and ψ_-, can be displayed pictorially in more than one way. One way is to plot the value of ψ_+ or ψ_+^2 along the internuclear axis. Another approach is to sketch a three-dimensional surface of constant ψ or ψ^2 containing about 90–95% of the wave function or the electronic charge respectively. These sketches are shown in Figures 12.6 (*a*) and (*b*).

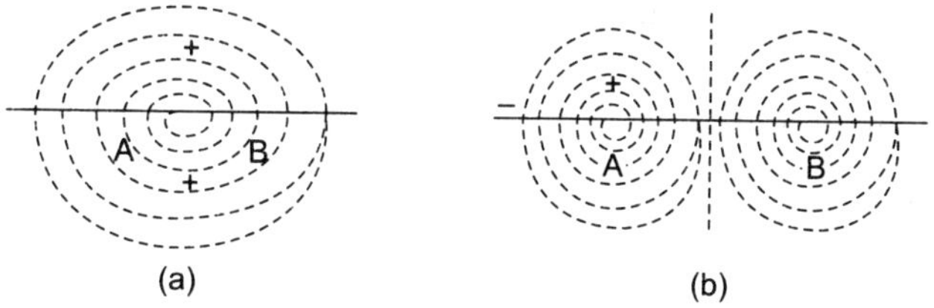

Fig. 12.6

The antibonding MO ψ_- is characterised by the presence of a nodal point in Fig. 12.4 and a nodal plane in Fig. 12.6 (*b*).

12.3.6 Symmetry of the MOs – σ and σ* Orbitals

Both ψ_+ and ψ_- MOs are symmetric with respect to rotation around the internuclear axis A-B as well as reflection across the vertical plane containing the same axis (Fig. 12.6). In such cases we say that the orbitals are cylindrically symmetrical, such MOs are denoted as σ (bonding) and σ^* (antibonding), respectively.

With respect to the centre of inversion (Fig. 12.7) existing just midway between the two nuclei. The σ-MO is symmetric (the function does not change sign across the point), while the σ^* orbital is antisymmetric. Following the notation described in Chapter 11 the MOs symmetric and anti-symmetric with respect to inversion are distinguished by the subscript *g* (gerade) and *u* (ungerade), respectively. Thus, σ is σ_g and σ^* is σ_u^* (or simply σ_u).

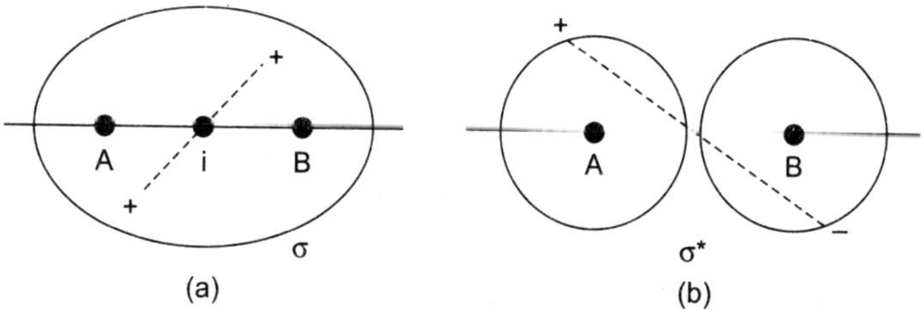

Fig. 12.7

The LCAO-MO (σ_g) thus provides a simple and convenient, though crude, model for the chemical bond and we have considered the simple example of H_2^+ ion in terms of this model. The bond in H_2^+ is formed by increased electron density due to overlap of electron clouds $1s_A$ and $1s_B$ between the two nuclei. In other one-electron systems where Z > 1, the integrals *j* and *k* will be too small compared to nuclear repulsion term $\left(\frac{Z^2 e^2}{R}\right)$ to effect binding. Thus, for example, He^{2+} H is not stable. However, in a molecule with more electrons there are more attraction terms to stabilise it. In all such cases of diatomic molecules, the LCAO-MOs of the type discussed above serve as satisfactory basis to build up the molecular wave function.

12.4 MOLECULAR ORBITAL THEORY OF H_2 MOLECULE

12.4.1 The Ground State

We model the structure of H_2 molecule by adding one electron to the H_2^+ ion. Accordingly, the ground state of H_2 is represented by a wave function Ψ which is antisymmetric product of two σ_g MOs of H_2^+,

$$\Psi = [\sigma_g(1)\,\sigma_g(2)]\cdot\frac{1}{\sqrt{2}}\left[\alpha(1)\,\beta(2)-\alpha(2)\,\beta(1)\right] \qquad \text{... (12.47)}$$

where 1 and 2 refer to the two electrons, $\frac{1}{\sqrt{2}}$ is the normalisation factor of the antisymmetric spin function and the σ_g's are given as

$$\sigma_g(i) = \frac{1}{\sqrt{2+2S}}\left[1s_A(i)+1s_B(i)\right], i = 1, 2, \ldots \qquad \text{... (12.48)}$$

Expressed as a Slater determinant,

$$\Psi = \frac{1}{\sqrt{2}}\begin{vmatrix} \sigma_g(1) & \bar{\sigma}_g(1) \\ \sigma_g(2) & \bar{\sigma}_g(2) \end{vmatrix} \qquad \text{... (12.49)}$$

where, as usual, the bar over σ_g denotes β spin and the lack of it α spin.

We see that, the two electrons have the same MO (σ_g) but different spins (α, β)—often called 'paired' spins; the molecule has the configuration $1\sigma_g^2$.

Eigenfunctions of the spin operators: It is not difficult to see that the antisymmetric spin function in Equation (12.47) is eigenfunction of spin operators $\hat{S}^2$ and $\hat{S}_z$. Since

$$\hat{S}_z = \hat{S}_{1z} + \hat{S}_{2z}$$ (see Chapter 9, Section 9.1.4.4)

$$\hat{S}_z \chi(s) = \left(\hat{S}_{1z} + \hat{S}_{2z}\right)\chi(s) = \hat{S}_{1z}\chi(s) + \hat{S}_{2z}\chi(s)$$

where $\chi(s) = \alpha(1)\beta(2) - \alpha(2)\beta(1)$ and s within the small brackets is the hypothetical spin coordinate.

$$\hat{S}_{1z}\chi(s) = \hat{S}_{1z}[\alpha(1)\beta(2) - \alpha(2)\beta(1)]$$

$$= \beta(2) . \hat{S}_{1z}\alpha(1) - \alpha(2) . \hat{S}_{1z}\beta(1)$$

$$= \frac{1}{2}\alpha(1)\beta(2) + \frac{1}{2}\alpha(2)\beta(1) \quad \text{...(12.50)}$$

in view of the fact that $\hat{S}_z\ \alpha = \frac{1}{2}\ \alpha$, $\hat{S}_z\ \beta = -\frac{1}{2}\ \beta$, and the operator $\hat{S}_{1z}$ acts on electron 1 only (see Chapter 10). Similarly,

$$\hat{S}_{2z}\chi(s) = -\frac{1}{2}\alpha(1)\beta(2) - \frac{1}{2}\alpha(2)\beta(1) \quad \text{...(12.51)}$$

Therefore $\quad \hat{S}_z\chi(s) = 0$; the eigenvalue $(M_s) = 0$.

The eigenvalue of $\hat{S}^2$ is derived through the relation

$$\hat{S}^2 = \hat{S}_+\hat{S}_- + \hat{S}_z^2 - S_z \quad \text{(see Chapter 10)}$$

and the relation $\quad \hat{S}_\pm = \hat{S}_{1\pm} + S_{2\pm}$

Thus $\quad \hat{S}_+\hat{S}_-\chi(s) = \left(\hat{S}_{1+} + \hat{S}_{2+}\right)\left(S_{1-} + S_{2-}\right)\chi(s)$

Since $\quad \hat{S}_z\chi(s) = \hat{S}_z^2\chi(s) = 0$

$$\hat{S}^2(\chi(s)) = \hat{S}_+\hat{S}_-\chi(s) = \left(\hat{S}_{1+} + \hat{S}_{2+}\right)\left(S_{1-} + S_{2-}\right)\chi(s) \quad \text{...(12.52)}$$

The operator $\hat{S}_{1\pm}$ operates on electron 1 and $\hat{S}_{2\pm}$ on electron 2 only; operating with $\hat{S}_-$ first and using the relation

$$\hat{S}_-\alpha = \beta, \text{ and } \hat{S}_-\ \beta = 0 \quad \text{(see Chapter 10)}$$

$$\hat{S}_-\chi(s) = \left(\hat{S}_{1-} + \hat{S}_{2-}\right)\left[\alpha(1)\beta(2) - \alpha(2)\beta(1)\right]$$

$$= \beta_1\beta_2 - 0 - 0 - \beta_2\beta_1 = 0$$

i.e., $\quad \hat{S}_+\hat{S}_-\chi(s) = S_+(0) = 0 \quad$ ...(12.53)

Thus the eigenvalue S, of $\hat{S}^2$ – 0. This gives the spin multiplicity (2S + 1) = 1 (singlet), and the antisymmetric wave function of H_2 molecule in the ground state of ${}^1\Psi$. Further, the molecule belongs to the $D_{\infty h}$ point group, and the atomic orbitals $1s_A$ and $1s_B$ used as basis are symmetric to rotation as well as the centre of inversion (i) which lies at the middle of the internuclear axis. Therefore, the MOs σ_g (1) and σ_g (2) belong to the irreducible representation Σ_g^+ of the group. Accordingly, the molecule is said to be in the $^1\Sigma_g^+$ (singlet sigma gee) state.

12.4.2 Graphical Representation

The wave function $^1\Psi_1$ (the subscript 1 denoting the ground state of the molecule) can be represented graphically through their spatial part θ_1,

$$\theta_1 = \sigma_g(1)\,\sigma_g(2) \qquad \text{(ground state } ^1\Psi_1\text{)} \quad \text{... (12.54)}$$

A two-dimensional representation can be best shown by contour maps by taking the distances of the electrons along the internuclear axis AB as two coordinates x and y. The contours denote the locations of equal values of θ. The Fig. (12.8) shows such a plot for the ground state spatial function θ_1.

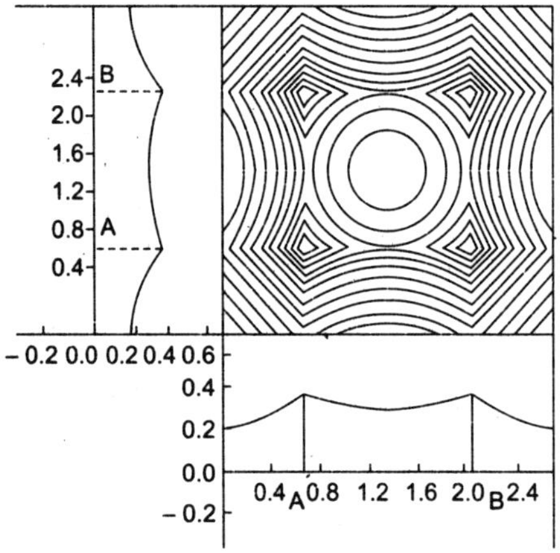

Fig. 12.8 *Contour map* indicating the variation of θ_1 with distances of the two electrons along AB.*

It may be noted that there are four points of maximum and equal value of θ which correspond to situations where both electrons are near nucleus A or both are near B, one is near A and the other near B.

12.4.3 Electron Density

The physical quantity of use is θ_1^2 which gives probability (electron) density. In the H_2 molecule, the probability of finding simultaneously electron 1 in the volume element $d\tau_1$ and electron 2 in $d\tau_2$ of space is defined by $|\Psi(1,2)|^2\, d\tau_1\, d\tau_2$. But the probability density (ρ_1) of a single electron, say 1, at any point is obtained by adding the probabilities of the other electron 2 at all locations. This amounts to

$$\rho_1 = \int |\Psi(1,2)|^2\, d\tau_2$$

* J Chem. Education, Vol. 48, 1971.

$$= \int \left| \sigma_g(1)\,\sigma_g(2) \right|^2 dV_2 \,.\, \int \frac{1}{\sqrt{2}} \left[\alpha(1)\,\beta(2) - \alpha(2)\,\beta(1) \right]^2 ds_1\, ds_2$$

where dV_2 (spatial coordinates) and ds_1 and ds_2 (spin coordinates) have been separated. This leads to

$$\rho_1 = \left| \sigma_g(1) \right|^2 . \int \left| \sigma_g(2) \right|^2 dV_2 \qquad \text{... (12.55)}$$

as the normalised spin function on integration gives 1.

[In systems with more than two electrons such factoring is not possible as we have only two spin eigenfunctions α and β, and the determinant like

$$\begin{vmatrix} \alpha(1) & \beta(1) & \alpha(1) \\ \alpha(2) & \beta(2) & \alpha(2) \\ \alpha(3) & \beta(3) & \alpha(3) \end{vmatrix}$$

with two identical columns cannot exist].

Using Equation (12.48) for σ_g (1) and σ_g (2),

$$\rho_1 = \frac{\left[1s_A(1) + 1s_B(1)\right]^2}{(2+2S)^2} . \int \left[1s_A(2) + 1s_B(2)\right]^2 dV_2$$

$$= \frac{1s_A(1)^2 + 1s_B(1)^2 + 2\,1s_A(1) . 1s_B(1)}{2+2S} \qquad \text{... (12.56)}$$

$$\left[\because \int 1s_A(2)^2\, dV_2 = \int 1s_B(2)^2\, dV_2 = 1 \text{ and } \int 1s_A(2) . 1s_B(2)\, dV_2 = S \right]$$

Similarly, for electron 2,

$$\rho_2 = \frac{1s_A(2)^2 + 1s_B(2)^2 + 2\,1s_A(2) . 1s_B(2)}{2+2S} \qquad \text{... (12.57)}$$

Since electrons do not carry labels,

$$\rho_1 = \rho_2 = \frac{1s_A^2 + 1s_B^2 + 2\,1s_A . 1s_B}{2+2S} \qquad \text{... (12.58)}$$

and the total electron density is

$$\rho = \rho_1 + \rho_2 = \frac{1s_A^2 + 1s_B^2 + 2\,1s_A . 1s_B}{1+S} \qquad \text{... (12.59)}$$

The electron probability density could best be represented as a three-dimensional plot with θ_1^2 as the *z*-coordinate. However, on a two-dimensional graph paper, the best representation that can be is through contour maps of θ_1^2 *vs* pairs of distances of the electrons from the nuclei as in Fig. (12.8). Such plots indicate that the electrons in $\hat{H}_2$ molecule are as likely to be found near the same nuclei (ionic state) as near different nuclei (covalent state). This is very unlikely as the molecule is known to be strongly covalently bonded. Obviously, there is a snag.

12.4.4 Energy and Bond Length in the Ground State

The total energy E of H_2 molecule in the ground state with normalised wave function ${}^1\Psi_1$ can be given by

$$E = \int {}^1\Psi \hat{H} \, {}^1\Psi \, d\tau \quad \text{... (12.60)}$$

where $\hat{H}$ is the complete electronic Hamiltonian operator (in atomic units) given by

$$\hat{H} = -\frac{1}{2}\nabla_1^2 - \frac{1}{2}\nabla_2^2 - \frac{1}{r_{A1}} - \frac{1}{r_{B1}} - \frac{1}{r_{A2}} - \frac{1}{r_{B2}} + \frac{1}{r_{12}} + \frac{1}{R} \quad \text{... (12.61)}$$

where 1 and 2 refer to the two electrons, r's refer to the distance of the electrons from the nuclei A and B, r_{12} is the interelectronic distance and R the internuclear distance [see Fig. (12.9)]. Equation (12.61) may be written in brief as

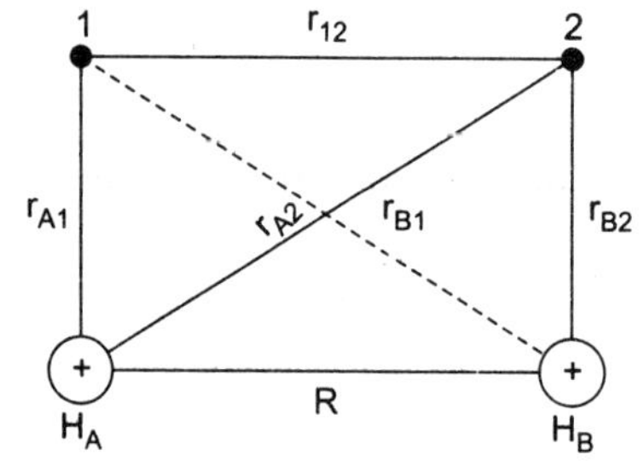

Fig. 12.9 *Coordinates in H_2 molecule*

$$\hat{H} = \hat{H}(1) + \hat{H}(2) + \frac{1}{r_{12}} + \frac{1}{R} \quad \text{... (12.62)}$$

where $$\hat{H}(i) = -\frac{1}{2}\nabla_i^2 - \frac{1}{r_{Ai}} - \frac{1}{r_{Bi}} \quad (i = 1, 2) \quad \text{... (12.63)}$$

which may be taken as the electronic Hamiltonian of two separate H_2^+ ions, and together constitute the 'core' Hamiltonian.

During electronic motion, R and hence $\frac{1}{R}$, is considered stationary (Born Oppenheimer approximation, so it is usual to calculate the electronic energy (E_e) for different values of R to which the nuclear repulsion energy for those values of R is added and the total energy E_T plotted against R. The minimum in the curve represents the bond energy and the bond length of H_2.

For the integration of Equation (12.60) spin part is factored out and integrated separately to 1 (see Chapter 9). This reduces the integral to

$$E_e = \iint \sigma_g(1)\,\sigma_g(2)\left[\hat{H}(1) + \hat{H}(2) + \frac{1}{r_{12}}\right]\sigma_g(1)\,\sigma_g(2)\, dV_1\, dV_2$$

$$= \int \sigma_g(1)\,\hat{H}(1)\,dV_1 . \int \sigma_g(2)^2\,dV_2 + \int \sigma_g(2)\,\hat{H}(2)\,\sigma_g(2)\,dV_2$$

$$\int \sigma_g(1)^2\,dV_1 + \iint \sigma_g(1)\,\sigma_g(2)\,\frac{1}{r_{12}}\,\sigma_g(1)\,\sigma_g(2)\,dV_1\,dV_2$$

$$= \int \sigma_g(1)\,\hat{H}\,\sigma_g(1)\,dV_1 + \int \sigma_g(2)\,\hat{H}(2)\,\sigma_g(2)\,dV_2 +$$

$$\iint \sigma_g(1)^2 . \frac{1}{r_{12}}\,\sigma_g(2)^2\,dV_1\,dV_2 \qquad \text{... (12.64)}$$

This simplification has been made in view of the fact that (*i*) $\hat{H}(1)$ and $\hat{H}(2)$ operate on electrons 1 and 2 respectively separately, (*ii*) σ_g's are normalised, and (*iii*) the operator $\frac{1}{r_{12}}$ is a multiplier operating on both electrons and the integral is inseparable.

The first two integrals in Equation (12.64) give the energies corresponding to the 'core' (E^0) and the third is the coulombic repulsion (J) of the two electrons, *i.e.*,

$$E_e = 2E^0 + J \qquad \text{... (12.65)}$$

In terms of integrals involving the basis functions (atomic orbitals),

$$E^0 = \int \frac{1}{2+2S}\left[1s_A(1) + 1s_B(1)\right]\hat{H}(1)\left[1s_A(1) + 1s_B(1)\right]dV_1$$

$$= \frac{1}{2+2S}\left[H_{AA} + H_{AB} + H_{BA} + H_{BB}\right] \qquad \text{... (12.66)}$$

where $\hat{H}$ (1) being Hermitian, and $1s_A$ and $1s_B$ being identical, the integrals

$$H_{AA} = H_{BB} = \int 1s_A(1)\,\hat{H}(1)\,1s_A\,d\tau_1$$

$$H_{AB} = H_{BA} = \int 1s_A(1)\,\hat{H}\,1s_B(1)\,d\tau$$

and $\quad S = \int 1s_A . 1s_B\,d\tau$

Using Equation (12.63) for $\hat{H}(1)$

$$H_{AA} = \int 1s_A(1)\left[-\frac{1}{2}\nabla_1^2 - \frac{1}{r_{A1}} - \frac{1}{r_{B1}}\right]1s_A(1)\,d\tau_1$$

$$= \int 1s_A(1)\left(-\frac{1}{2}\nabla_1^2\right)1s_A(1)\,d\tau_1 \qquad \text{.... (1-centre kinetic energy)}$$

$$+ \int 1s_A(1)\left(-\frac{1}{r_{A1}}\right)1s_A(1)\,d\tau_1 \qquad \text{... (1-centre coulombic energy of attraction)}$$

$$+ \int 1s_A(1)\left(-\frac{1}{r_{B1}}\right)1s_B(1)\,d\tau_1 \qquad \text{... (2-centre coulombic attraction energy)}$$

Similarly,

$$H_{AB} = \int 1s_A(1)\left[-\frac{1}{2}\nabla_1^2 - \frac{1}{r_{A1}} - \frac{1}{r_{B1}}\right]1s_B(1)\,d\tau_1$$

$$= \int 1s_A(1)\left(-\frac{1}{2}\nabla_1^2\right)1s_B(1)\,d\tau_1 \quad \text{... (2-centre kinetic energy)}$$

$$+ \int 1s_A(1)\left(-\frac{1}{r_{A1}}\right)1s_B(1)\,d\tau_1 \quad \text{... (2-centre coulombic attraction energy, } V_{AB}^{A})$$

$$+ \int 1s_A(1)\left(-\frac{1}{r_{B1}}\right)1s_B(1)\,d\tau_1 \quad \text{... (2-centre coulombic attraction energy, } V_{AB}^{B})$$

and

$$J = \iint\left[1s_A(1) + 1s_B(1)\right]\frac{1}{r_{12}}\left[1s_A(2) + 1s_B(2)\right]d\tau_1\,d\tau_2$$

... (coulombic repulsion energy)

On expanding, this integral (J) gives 16 integrals of the type $\iint\left(ij\frac{1}{r_{12}}kl\right)d\tau_1\,d\tau_2$, where i and j can be $1s_A(1)$ or $1s_B(1)$ and k and l can be $1s_A(2)$ or $1s_B(2)$. Following the convention adopted for 2-electron integrals of this type (see Chapter 9), they may be written as (ij/kl) and only the subscripts of the atomic orbitals are used. Then, since $\frac{1}{r_{12}}$ is a multiplier we have the following equalities

$$(AA/BB) = (BB/AA)$$
$$(AA/AB) = (AA/BA) = (AB/AA) = (BA/AA)$$
$$(BB/AB) = (BB/BA) = (BA/BB) = (AB/BB), \text{ and}$$

by symmetry,

$$(AA/AA) = (BB/BB$$
$$(AA/AB) = (BB/BA)$$

This reduces the integral J (Equation 12.66) to

$$J = \frac{1}{2(1+S)^2}\left[(AA/AA) + (AA/BB) + 2(AB/AB) + 4(AA/AB)\right] \quad \text{... (12.67)}$$

Most of these integrals are evaluated numerically (analytical expressions for some of them may be found in the article by Dewar and Koleman, J. Chem. Ed. 1971, 48, 494). The results may be used to calculate the ground state electronic energy (E_e) of H_2 for various values of R. When plotted the curve shows a minimum at R = 0.84 A and E_e = – 2.68 eV (experimental values are R = 0.74 A and E_e = –4.78 eV respectively), the –ve sign indicating the stability with respect to two separate H-atoms. The value with +ve sign would be the dissociation energy (D_e). The total energy E of the molecule is

$$E_T = E_e + \frac{1}{R}$$

The calculation is on the right track but the agreement is not fair, the treatment needs improvement.

12.4.5 Excited States of H_2

With two basis functions ($1s_A$ and $1s_B$) two MOs σ_g and σ_u are generated. In H_2, the two electrons can occupy them in the following six ways (Fig. 12.10).

σ_u	—	↑	↓	↓	↑	↑↓
σ_g	↑↓	↑	↓	↑	↓	—
	${}^1\Psi_1$	${}^3\Psi_2$	${}^3\Psi_3$	Ψ_4	Ψ_5	${}^1\Psi_6$
	(G.S.)	E.S.				

↑ = α spin, ↓ = β spin, G.S. = ground state, E.S. = excited.

Fig. 12.10

Each of the above configurations is represented by a slater determinant,

1. $${}^1\Psi_1 = \left\| \sigma_g(1)\bar{\sigma}_g(2) \right\| = \sigma_g(1)\,\sigma_g(2)\,.\,\frac{1}{\sqrt{2}}\left[\alpha(1)\beta(2) - \alpha(2)\beta(1)\right]$$

2. $${}^3\Psi_2 = \left\| \sigma_g(1)\sigma_u(2) \right\| = \frac{1}{\sqrt{2}}\left[\sigma_g(1)\sigma_u(2) - \sigma_g(2)\sigma_u(1)\right]\alpha(1)\alpha(2)$$

3. $${}^3\Psi_3 = \left\| \bar{\sigma}_g(1)\bar{\sigma}_u(2) \right\| = \frac{1}{\sqrt{2}}\left[\sigma_g(1)\sigma_u(2) - \sigma_g(2)\sigma_u(1)\right]\beta(1)\beta(2)$$

4. $$\Psi_4 = \left\| \sigma_g(1)\bar{\sigma}_u(2) \right\| = \frac{1}{\sqrt{2}}\left[\sigma_g(1)\alpha(1)\sigma_u(2)\beta(2) - \sigma_g(2)\alpha(2)\sigma_u(1)\beta(1)\right]$$

5. $$\Psi_5 = \left\| \bar{\sigma}_g(1)\sigma_u(2) \right\| = \frac{1}{\sqrt{2}}\left[\sigma_g(1)\beta(1)\sigma_u(2)\alpha(2) - \sigma_u(1)\alpha(1)\sigma_g(2)\beta(2)\right]$$

6. $${}^1\Psi_6 = \left\| \sigma_u(1)\bar{\sigma}_u(2) \right\| = \sigma_u(1)\,\sigma_u(2)\,.\,\frac{1}{\sqrt{2}}\left[\alpha(1)\beta(2) - \alpha(2)\beta(1)\right]$$

where $\frac{1}{\sqrt{2}}$ is the normalisation factor and the determinants have been written in short hand form with diagonal elements only.

Four of these functions ${}^1\Psi_1$, ${}^3\Psi_2$, ${}^3\Psi_3$ and ${}^1\Psi_6$ can be factored into spatial and spin parts and can be shown to be eigenfunctions of the spin operators $\hat{S}^2$ and $\hat{S}_z$. Therefore, these determinants can serve as representations of H_2. ${}^1\Psi_1$ has already been shown to be so in Section 12.4.1. Proceeding in the same manner for Ψ_2 and Ψ_3,

$$\hat{S}_z\left[\alpha(1)\,\alpha(2)\right] = \alpha(1)\,\alpha(2);\ \hat{S}_z\left[\beta(1)\,\beta(2)\right] = -\beta(1)\,\beta(2)$$

and $$\hat{S}^2\,[\alpha(1)\,\alpha(2)] = 2\,\alpha(1)\,\alpha(2);\ \hat{S}^2\,[\beta(1)\,\beta(2)] = 2\,\beta(1)\,\beta(2)$$

That is, the eigenvalue S (S + 1) of $\hat{S}^2 = 2$, or S = 1 and the multiplicity 2S + 1 = 3 (triplet). Thus Ψ_2 and Ψ_3 are ${}^3\Psi_2$ and ${}^3\Psi_3$. The functions Ψ_4 and $\bar{\Psi}_5$ are eigenfunctions of $\hat{S}_z$ but not of $\hat{S}^2$. However, we can construct their linear combinations which are eigenfunctions of both

$${}^3\Psi_4 = \frac{1}{\sqrt{2}}(\Psi_4 - \Psi_5) = \frac{1}{\sqrt{2}}\left[\sigma_g(1)\,\sigma_u(2) - \sigma_g(2)\,\sigma_u(1)\right]\times\frac{1}{\sqrt{2}}\left[\alpha(1)\,\beta(2) + \alpha(2)\,\beta(1)\right]$$

(S = 1, 2S + 1 = 3)

and $${}^1\Psi_5 = \frac{1}{\sqrt{2}}(\Psi_4 + \Psi_5) = \frac{1}{\sqrt{2}}\left[\sigma_g(1)\,\sigma_u(2) + \sigma_u(1)\,\sigma_g(2)\right]\times\frac{1}{\sqrt{2}}\left[\alpha(1)\,\beta(2) - \alpha(2)\,\beta(1)\right]$$

(S = 0, 2S + 1 = 1)

Similarly, Ψ_6 is ${}^1\Psi_6$.

(Readers should convince themselves by carrying out the derivations themselves.)

These six states of the H_2 molecule (one ground and five excited states) belong to Σ_g^+ or Σ_u^+ irreducible representations of the symmetry point group $D \propto h$ classified as

$$\Sigma_g^+ : {}^1\Psi_1, {}^1\Psi_6$$

$$\Sigma_u^+ : {}^3\Psi_2, {}^3\Psi_3, {}^3\Psi_4, {}^1\Psi_5.$$

12.4.6 Electronic Energy of the Excited States

The electronic energy of an excited state can be determined by the same procedure as described for ${}^1\Psi_1$ in section (12.4.4). Of the five excited states of H_2, three are triplets $\left({}^3\Psi_2, {}^3\Psi_3 \text{ and } {}^3\Psi_4\right)$ and two are singlets $\left({}^1\Psi_5 \text{ and } {}^1\Psi_6\right)$.

${}^3\Psi_2, {}^3\psi_3, \Psi_4$: The spatial wave function corresponding to these states is

$$\theta_2 = \frac{1}{\sqrt{2}}\left[\sigma_g(1)\,\sigma_u(2) - \sigma_g(2)\,\sigma_u(1)\right]$$

Therefore,
$$E_e = \iint \frac{1}{\sqrt{2}}\left[\sigma_g(1)\,\sigma_u(2) - \sigma_g(2)\,\sigma_u(1)\right]\left[\hat{H}(1) + \hat{H}(2) + \frac{1}{r_{12}}\right]$$
$$\frac{1}{\sqrt{2}}\left[\sigma_g(1)\,\sigma_u(2) - \sigma_g(2)\,\sigma_u(1)\right] dV_1\, dV_2 \qquad \text{... (12.68)}$$

On expanding the integral (12.68) and using (12.48) for σ_g and σ_u along with orthonormality of σ_g and σ_u, we finally obtain

$$E_e = \frac{H_{AA} + H_{AB}}{1+S} + \frac{H_{AA} - H_{AB}}{1-S} + J_{\sigma_g\sigma_u} - K_{\sigma_g\sigma_u} \qquad \text{... (12.69)}$$

where H_{AA}, H_{AB} and S have been defined earlier (Section 12.4.4),

$$J_{\sigma_g\sigma_u}\text{ (Coulombic repulsion energy)} = \iint \sigma_g(1)^2\, \sigma_u(2)^2 \cdot \frac{1}{r_{12}}\, dV_1\, dV_2$$

$$= \frac{1}{2\left(1-S^2\right)}\left[(AA/AA) + (AA/BB) - 2\,(AB/AB)\right]$$

and $$K_{\sigma_g\sigma_u}\text{ (Exchange energy)} = \iint \sigma_g(1)\,\sigma_u(2)\frac{1}{r_{12}}\,\sigma_u(1)\,\sigma_g(2)\, dV_1\, dV_2$$

$$= \frac{1}{2\left(1-S^2\right)}\left[(AA/AA) - (AA/BB)\right]$$

$^1\Psi_5$ (Singly excited state) : The spatial wave function is

$$\theta_3 = \frac{1}{\sqrt{2}}\left[\sigma_g(1)\,\sigma_u(2) + \sigma_g(2)\,\sigma_u(1)\right]$$

$$E_e = \frac{H_{AA} + H_{AB}}{1+S} + \frac{H_{AA} - H_{AB}}{1-S} + J_{\sigma_g\sigma_u} + K_{\sigma_g\sigma_u} \qquad \text{... (12.70)}$$

$^1\Psi_6$ (Double excited state) : $\theta_4 = \sigma_u(1)\,\sigma_u(2)$

$$E_e = \frac{2\left(H_{AA} - H_{AB}\right)}{1-S} + J_{\sigma_u\sigma_u} \qquad \text{... (12.71)}$$

where $$J_{\sigma_u\sigma_u} = \iint \sigma_u(1)^2\, \sigma_u(2)^2 \cdot \frac{1}{r_{12}}\, dV_1\, dV_2$$

$$= \frac{1}{2\,(1-S)^2}\left[(AA/AA) + (AA/BB) + (AB/AB)\right]$$

(Readers should convince themselves by making all these derivations themselves).

12.4.7 Shortcomings of the Simple MO Theory

The calculated value of electronic energy (E_e) in the ground state is obtained as expectation value of the Hamiltonian using the spatial wave function

$$\theta_1 = \sigma_g(1)\,\sigma_g(2)$$

$$= \frac{1}{2(1+S)}\left[1s_A(1) + 1s_B(1)\right]\left[1s_A(2) + 1s_B(2)\right]$$

$$= \frac{1}{2(1+S)}\left[1s_A(1)\,1s_A(2) + 1s_B(1)\,1s_B(2) + 1s_A(1)\,1s_B(2) + 1s_A(2)\,1s_B(1)\right] \quad \text{... (12.72)}$$

where the atomic orbital used is hydrogen like (Z = 1),

$$1s_A(1) = \frac{1}{\sqrt{\pi}}\,e^{-r_{A1}}$$

and similarly for the other a.o. In Equation (12.72) the first and second terms within the square bracket denote the situation where both electrons are near the nucleus A or near B which correspond to the ionic structures $H_A^- \, H_B^+$ and $H_A^+ \, H_B^-$ respectively. The third and fourth terms together represent a hybrid of covalent structures $H_A(1) - H_B(2)$ and $H_A(2) - H_B(1)$, the two electrons shared equally between the two nuclei. In other words the simple MO treatment predicts an equal contribution of ionic and covalent structures. For a molecule like H_2 this is highly unlikely and is possibly the reason for such a large divergence of the calculated value from the observed value of E_e.

The model for the calculation is a crude one. Coulson replaced the hydrogen like a.o. (Z = 1) by

$$1s = \frac{\xi^{3/2}}{\sqrt{\pi}}\,e^{-\xi r}$$

where ξ, the effective nuclear charge, is a variable parameter, and used variation method to obtain the values of E_e = 3.49 eV and R = 0.732 A with ξ = 1.197 (Rev. Mod. Phys. 1960, 32, 211). Hartree-Fock SCF calculation led to a further, though slight, improvement (R = 0.733 A, E_e = 3.64 eV). This led to the consideration that something very significant is missing in the HFSCF calculation.

12.4.8 Configuration Interaction

An obvious snag in the above treatment is the failure to take into consideration the "electron correlation" that is, the tendency of the two electrons in H_2 molecule to remain apart. (see Chapter 9 also). Further improvement in the calculation may therefore be expected by including "configuration interaction (C.I.) in the wave function, that is, by taking a wave function (Θ) as a linear combination of the wave functions (Ψ_m) corresponding to different configurations of the electrons in the molecule (see Chapter 9)

$$\Theta = \sum_m a_m \Psi_m \quad \text{... (12.73)}$$

This leads, on variation treatment, to a set of linear secular equations and a secular determinant which, on solution, give the energies (E_m) corresponding to each configuration wave function (CSF).

But there are two conditions for the wave functions to enter into linear combination:

(*i*) They must belong to the same irreducible representations, of the symmetry point group ($D \propto h$) to which the molecule belongs failing which the off-diagonal elements of the secular determinant will vanish and there will be no combination, and (*ii*) The configurations entering into combination must have the same spin multiplicity otherwise the integrals will vanish on account of spin orthogonality. For example, let

$$^1\Psi = \theta_m\,[\alpha(1)\,\beta(2) - \alpha(2)\,\beta(1)], \text{ and } ^3\Psi = \theta_n\,[(\alpha(1)\,\alpha(2)]$$

where θ_m and θ_n are spatial functions. Then,

$$\int {}^1\Psi\,\hat{H}\,{}^3\Psi\,d\tau = \iint \theta_m \hat{H}\,\theta_n\,dV_m\,dV_n \,.\iint \left[\alpha(1)\beta(2) - \alpha(2)\beta(1)\right] \times \left[\alpha(1)\alpha(2)\right] ds_1\,ds_2$$

$$= \iint \theta_m\,\hat{H}\,\theta_n\,dV_m\,dV_n \,.\int \alpha(1)^2\,ds_1 \,.\int \alpha(2)^2\,ds_2 \,.\int \alpha(1)\,\beta(1)\,ds_1$$

$$\int \alpha(2)\,\beta(2)\,ds$$

$$= 0$$

In the case of H_2 we have six configuration wave functions: ${}^1\Psi_1$, ${}^3\Psi_2$, ${}^3\Psi_3$, ${}^3\psi_4$, ${}^1\Psi_5$ and ${}^1\Psi_6$ (Section 12.4.5). Of these only the ${}^1\Psi_1$ and ${}^1\Psi_6$ have the same spin multiplicity (singlet) and belong to the same irreducible representation Σ_g^+; the singlet ${}^1\Psi_5$ together with ${}^3\Psi_2$, ${}^3\Psi_3$ and ${}^3\Psi_4$ belong to Σ_u^+ and hence cannot mix with ${}^1\Psi_1$ and ${}^1\Psi_6$. Accordingly, the C.I. wave function for H_2 molecule is

$$\Theta = a_1\,{}^1\Psi_6 + a_6\,{}^1\Psi_6 \qquad \text{... (12.74)}$$

This leads to a secular determinant which gives the two energy states E_I and E_{II} of H_2.

$$\begin{vmatrix} H_{11} - E & H_{16} \\ H_{61} & H_{66} - E \end{vmatrix} = 0 \qquad \text{... (12.75)}$$

where
$$H_{11} = \int {}^1\Psi_1\,\hat{H}\,{}^1\Psi_1\,d\tau\,, H_{66} = \int {}^1\Psi_6\,\hat{H}\,{}^1\Psi_6\,d\tau\,,$$

$$H_{16} = \int {}^1\Psi_1\,\hat{H}\,{}^1\Psi_6\,d\tau = H_{66}\text{; the integrals}$$

$$S_{11} = \int {}^1\Psi_1 \,.\, {}^1\Psi_1\,d\tau = 1 = S_{66} \text{ and } S_{16} = \int {}^1\Psi_1 \,.\, \Psi_6\,d\tau = 0 = S_{66}$$

due to orthonormality of ${}^1\Psi_1$ and ${}^1\Psi_6$.

The elements H_{11} and H_{66} of the determinant (12.75) are equal to the energies of the corresponding configuration, *i.e.*, E_1 and E_6, while

$$H_{16} = \int {}^1\Psi_1\,\hat{H}\,\Psi_6\,d\tau$$

$$= \int \sigma_g(1)\,\sigma_g(2)\left[\hat{H}(1) + \hat{H}(2) + \frac{1}{r_{12}}\right]\sigma_u(1)\,\sigma_u(2)\,dV_1\,dV_2$$

$$= \int \sigma_g(1)\,\hat{H}(1)\,\sigma_u(1)\,dV_1 \int \sigma_g(2)\,\sigma_u(2)\,dV_2 + \int \sigma_g(2)\,\hat{H}(2)\,\sigma_u(2)\,dV_2$$

$$\int \sigma_g(1)\sigma_u(1)dV_1 + \iint \sigma_g(1)\sigma_u(1)\frac{1}{r_{12}}\sigma_g(2)\sigma_u(2)\,dV_1\,dV_2$$

$$= 0 + 0 + K.$$

The first two integrals vanish due to orthonormality of σ_g and σ_u while K is defined as,

$$K = \frac{1}{2\left(1 - S^2\right)}\,[(AA/AA) - (AA/BB)]$$

The coefficients a_1 and a_6 in Equation (12.74) are obtained from the secular equations

$$a_1\,(H_{11} - E) + a_6\,H_{16} = 0$$

$$a_1\,H_{16} + a_6\,(H_{66} - E) = 0 \qquad \text{... (12.76)}$$

Finally, the ground state energy (E_I) of H_2 can be evaluated by evaluating the integrals E_1, E_6 and K for various values of R and plotted. With hydrogen like atomic orbitals, Dewar and Koleman found the minimum in the curve at R = 0.88 A and E_e = 3.24 eV. But with optimised value of ξ = 1.19 using SCF method with configuration interaction Weinbaum (1963) found R_e = 0.757 A and E_e = 4.03 eV. Hagstrom (Rev. Mod. Phys. 1963, **33,** 624) using 33 configuration functions got the values of R = 0.75 A and E_e = 4.71 eV, very close to the true value of E_e = 4.75 eV.

12.5 VALENCE BOND THEORY

The valence bond (VB) theory is nearer to the classical Lewis concept of electron pair bond to which it provides a quantum mechanical interpretation. In VB theory, bond formation occurs by overlap of atomic orbitals as in MO theory. However, in VB theory, unlike in MO theory, no new orbital is formed; electrons are still supposed to be present in atomic orbitals, but it is not certain which orbital is occupied by which electron because electrons cannot be distinguished from each other. So, the wave function has to be such that it allows the presence of an electron in either of the overlapping atomic orbitals.

We elaborate these principles with respect to the two systems considered earlier, H_2^+ and H_2. Later, we shall extend the discussion to diatomic molecules in general.

12.5.1 Hydrogen Molecule Ion, H_2^+

The VB treatment begins with writing down the structure of the molecule. We may write the structure of H_2^+ as $H_A - H_B^+$ (or $H_A\,.\,H_B^+$) or $H_A^+ - H_B$ (or $H_A^+\,.\,H_B$) assuming that the single electron lies in the atomic orbital $1s_A$ or $1s_B$ respectively. Assuming structure $H_A\ H_B^+$, if the internuclear distance (R) is very large, ground state wave function of the system may be approximated to

$$\psi_1 = 1s_A = \frac{1}{\sqrt{\pi}} \exp\left(-r_A\right) \text{ (in a.u.)} \qquad \text{... (12.77)}$$

Thus, for large bonding distance, we could use Equation (12.77) as an approximate trial function for calculating the energy of H_2^+. In that case,

$$E = \int 1s_A \, \hat{H} \, 1s_A \, d\tau = H_{AA} \text{ (say)} \qquad \text{... (12.78)}$$

(1*s* atomic orbital is normalised)

where $\hat{H}$, the Hamiltonian, is given by Equation (12.21),

$$\hat{H} = -\frac{1}{2}\nabla^2 - \frac{1}{r_A} - \frac{1}{r_B} + \frac{1}{R} \text{ (in a.u.)} \qquad \text{... (12.79)}$$

or

$$\hat{H} = \hat{H}_A - \frac{1}{r_B} + \frac{1}{R} \qquad \text{... (12.80)}$$

where

$$\hat{H}_A = -\frac{1}{2}\nabla^2 - \frac{1}{r_A}$$

is the Hamiltonian for the isolated atom H_A.

Thus,

$$H_{AA} = \int 1s_A \, H_A \, 1s_A \, d\tau - \int 1s_A \left(\frac{1}{r_B}\right) 1s_A \, d\tau + 1s_A \left(\frac{1}{R}\right) 1s_A \, d\tau$$

$$= E_H - j + \frac{1}{R} \qquad \text{... (12.81)}$$

E_H is the energy of the isolated H-atom and 1/R the internuclear repulsion energy (in a.u.).

The integral $j = \int 1s_A \left(\frac{1}{r_B}\right) 1s_A \, d\tau$ [Equation (12.29)] represents the coulombic energy of attraction between the electron in the $1s_A$ orbital and the nucleus B, which on evaluation gives

$$j = \frac{1}{R}\left[1 - (1 + R)\, e^{-2R}\right]$$

Therefore

$$E = H_{AA} = E_H + \left(1 + \frac{1}{R}\right) e^{-2R} \qquad \text{... (12.82)}$$

The value of E is greater than that of E_H for all values of R.

Certainly, this cannot represent the bonding situation.

Now the VB theory says that the appropriate trial function should be a linear combination of $1s_A$ and $1s_B$, *i.e.*,

$$\psi_{VB} = a_1 \, 1s_A + a_2 \, 1s_B \qquad \text{... (12.83)}$$

where values of a_1 and a_2 are determined by the variation method.

This makes ψ_{VB} the same as ψ_{MO} for H_2^+ system. The variation treatment will lead to the two energy levels:

$$E_{\pm} = \frac{H_{AA} \pm H_{AB}}{1 \pm S} \qquad \text{... (12.84)}$$

and the normalised wave function,

$$\psi_{\pm} = \frac{1}{\sqrt{2 \pm 2S}} [1s_A \pm 1s_B] \qquad \text{... (12.85)}$$

where H_{AA}, H_{AB} and S are as defined earlier.

H_{AB} is given as, $H_{AB} = E_H\, S - k + S/R$ [see Equation (12.32)] and k is defined as [Equation (12.33)]

$$k = \int 1s_A \left(1/r_B\right) 1s_B \, d\tau$$

In VB terminology, however, the signs + and – in Equations (12.84) and (12.85) refer to the "symmetric" and "antisymmetric" states with respect to the exchange of electron between the orbitals $1s_A$ and $1s_B$ as against the terms bonding and antibonding states used in MO theory.

12.5.1.1 Nature of Bonding

In terms of the VB theory the single structure $H_A . H_+$ or $H_A^+ . H_B$ yields the energy of H_2^+ always greater than that of isolated atoms H_A and H_B^+ or H_A^+ and H_B, respectively. The two structures considered together lead to lowering of energy and, hence, to bonding. The difference between the two situations lies simply in the "exchange" of electron's position between H_A and H_B.

The VB theory, therefore, stipulates that it is the electron's exchange of position between the orbitals $1s_A$ and $1s_B$ that is responsible for bonding in H_2^+. In MO theory it is the presence of an electron in a bonding MO which is responsible for bonding.

12.5.2 Heitler-London Theory of H_2 Molecule

For VB theory the case of H_2^+ is trivial. The theory developed by W. Heitler and F. London in 1927 for H_2 molecule was the first attempt to provide a quantum mechanical basis for the electron-pair bond. It initiated the process of development of more comprehensive theories of bonding, accordingly, the year 1927 is regarded as the date of birth of quantum chemistry.

12.5.2.1 The Wave Function

The wave function for two non-bonded H-atoms would be

$$\phi_1 = 1s_A (1)\, 1s_B (2) \qquad \text{... (12.86)}$$

where A and B are refer to the two atoms and 1 and 2 to the two electrons. This wave function presumes electron 1 to be associated with A and 2 with B.

Heitler and London argued that since the electrons do not carry labels an equally good wave function would be

$$\phi_2 = 1s_A(2)\, 1s_B(1) \quad \text{...(12.87)}$$

Then in the bonded (perturbed) state the appropriate trial wave function should be a linear combination (l.c.) of the two,

$$\psi = a_1 \phi_1 + a_2 \phi_2 = a_1\, 1s_A(1)\, 1s_B(2) + a_2\, 1s_A(2)\, 1s_B(1) \quad \text{...(12.88)}$$

where a_1 and a_2 are the l.c. coefficients.

Variation treatment leads to two simultaneous linear equations:

$$a_1 (H_{11} - E) + a_2 (H_{12} - S^2E) = 0$$

$$a_1 (H_{21} - S^2E) + a_2 (H_{22} - E) = 0 \quad \text{...(12.89)}$$

and the corresponding secular determinant

$$\begin{vmatrix} H_{11} - E & H_{12} - S^2E \\ H_{21} - S^2E & H_{22} - E \end{vmatrix} = 0 \quad \text{...(12.90)}$$

where $$H_{11} = \int \phi_1 \hat{H} \phi_1 \, d\tau, \quad H_{22} = \int \phi_2 \hat{H} \phi_2 \, d\tau$$

$$H_{12} = H_{21} \text{ or } \int \phi_1 \hat{H} \phi_2 \, d\tau = \int \phi_2 \hat{H} \phi_1 \, d\tau$$

$$S = \int 1s_A(1)\, 1s_B(1)\, d\tau_1 = \int 1s_A(2)\, 1s_B(2)\, d\tau_2;$$

$$S^2 = \int \phi_1 \phi_2 \, d\tau, \text{and } E = \text{energy}.$$

S is called overlap integral.

On solving, the 2 × 2 determinant yields two values of E – E_+ (lower energy) and E_- (higher energy),

$$E_+ = \frac{H_{11} + H_{12}}{2 + 2S^2}\ ;\ E_- = \frac{H_{11} - H_{12}}{2 - 2S^2} \quad \text{...(12.91)}$$

Here + correspond to the – signs in the numerator of the above equations.

Substituting value of $E_\pm$ for E in the linear Equation (12.89) and solving for a_1 and a_2 we find

$$a_1 = a_2 \text{ corresponding to } E_+$$

Similarly, $$a_1 = -a_2 \text{ corresponding to } E_-.$$

By normalisation (1s orbitals are real),

$$\int \psi^2 \, d\tau = \iint \left[a_1\, 1s_A(1)\, 1s_B(2) + a_2\, 1s_A(2)\, 1s_B(1)\right]^2 d\tau_1\, d\tau_2 = 1$$

We obtain

$$a_1^2 + a_2^2 + 2a_1 a_2 S^2 = 1$$

or $$a_1 = a_2 = \frac{1}{\sqrt{2\left(1 + S^2\right)}} \text{ corresponding to } E_+.$$

Similarly, corresponding to E_{-}, $a_1 = -a_2 = \dfrac{1}{\sqrt{2(1-S^2)}}$. Accordingly, we have the two orbital functions

$$\psi_{+} = \frac{1}{\sqrt{2(1+S^2)}}\left[1s_A(1)\,1s_B(2) + 1s_A(2)\,1s_B(1)\right] \quad \text{...(12.92)}$$

and

$$\psi_{-} = \frac{1}{\sqrt{2(1-S^2)}}\left[1s_A(1)\,1s_B(2) - 1s_A(2)\,1s_B(1)\right] \quad \text{...(12.93)}$$

where + and – refer to "symmetric" and "antisymmetric" orbital wave function with respect to electron exchange.

Since the complete wave function has to be antisymmetric, the symmetric orbital part must have antisymmetric spin part, *i.e.*,

$$^1\Psi_1 = \frac{1}{\sqrt{2+2S^2}}\left[1s_A(1)1s_B(2) + 1s_A(2)1s_B(1)\right].\frac{1}{\sqrt{2}}\left[\alpha(1)\beta(2) - \alpha(2)\beta(1)\right] \quad \text{...(12.94)}$$

This spin function is eigenfunction of $\hat{S}^2$ with eigenvalue S (S + 1) = 0, or S = 0; therefore, the spin multiplicity is 1 (2S + 1 = 1) and the state is 'singlet'.

The antisymmetric orbital will have symmetric spin function of which there are three (S = 1); accordingly, there are three antisymmetric wave functions,

$$^3\Psi_2 = \frac{1}{\sqrt{2-2S^2}}\left[1s_A(1)\,1s_B(2) - 1s_A(2)\,1s_B(1)\right]\left[\alpha(1)\,\alpha(2)\right] \quad \text{...(12.95)}$$

$$^3\Psi_3 = \frac{1}{\sqrt{2-2S^2}}\left[1s_A(1)\,1s_B(2) - 1s_A(2)\,1s_B(1)\right].\left[\beta(1)\,\beta(2)\right] \quad \text{...(12.96)}$$

$$^3\Psi_4 = \frac{1}{\sqrt{2-2S^2}}\left[1s_A(1)\,1s_B(2) - 1s_A(2)\,1s_B(1)\right].\frac{1}{\sqrt{2}}\left[\alpha(1)\,\beta(2) + \alpha(2)\,\beta(1)\right] \quad \text{...(12.97)}$$

These spin functions are eigenfunctions of $\hat{S}^2$ with eigenvalue corresponding to S = 1; the multiplicity is, therefore three and the state is 'triplet'.

12.5.2.2 Evaluation of Energy E_{+}

The energy can be evaluated by evaluating the integrals H_{11}, H_{12} and S.

$$H_{11} = \int \phi_1\,\hat{H}\,\phi_1\,d\tau$$

where $\hat{H}$ (Hamiltonian operator) atomic units is given by

$$\hat{H} = -\frac{1}{2}\nabla_1^2 - \frac{1}{2}\nabla_2^2 - \frac{1}{r_{A1}} - \frac{1}{r_{A2}} - \frac{1}{r_{B1}} - \frac{1}{r_{B2}} + \frac{1}{r_{12}} + \frac{1}{R}$$

(Reference to Equation 12.61 and Fig. 12.9)

or
$$\hat{H} = \hat{H}_{A1} + \hat{H}_{B2} + \left(-\frac{1}{r_{A2}} - \frac{1}{r_{B1}} + \frac{1}{r_{12}} + \frac{1}{R}\right)$$

where $\hat{H}_{A1} = -\frac{1}{2}\nabla_1^2 - \frac{1}{r_{A1}}$ and $H_{B2} = -\frac{1}{2}\nabla_1^2 - \frac{1}{r_{B2}}$ are the Hamiltonians for electrons 1 and 2 in isolated H-atoms A and B respectively, and the terms within bracket constitute the perturbation $(\hat{H}')$ operator in the bonded atoms.

Since 1*s* orbitals are real and normalised and the operator H_{A1} acts on electron 1 only while H_{B2} on electron-2,

$$\int \phi_1 \hat{H}_{A1} \phi_1 \, d\tau_1 = \int 1s_A(1)\, \hat{H}_{A1}\, 1s_A(1) = E_{H_A}$$

(energy of the H-atom A)

Similarly,
$$H_{22} = \int \phi_2 \hat{H}_{B2} \phi_2 \, d\tau_2 = E_{H_B}$$

and
$$E_{H_A} = E_{H_B} = -\frac{1}{2} \text{ a.u.}$$

$$\int \phi_1 H' \phi_1 \, d\tau = \iint 1s_A(1)\, 1s_B(2)\left(-\frac{1}{r_{B1}}\right) 1s_A(1)\, 1s_B(2)\, d\tau_1\, d\tau_2$$

$$+ \iint 1s_A(1)\, 1s_B(2)\left(-\frac{1}{r_{A2}}\right) 1s_A(1)\, 1s_B(2)\, d\tau_1\, d\tau_2$$

$$+ \iint 1s_A(1)\, 1s_B(2)\left(\frac{1}{r_{12}}\right) 1s_A(1)\, 1s_B(2)\, d\tau_1\, d\tau_2$$

$$+ \iint 1s_A(1)\, 1s_B(2)\left(\frac{1}{R}\right) 1s_A(1)\, 1s_B(2)\, d\tau_1\, d\tau_2$$

$$= \int 1s_A(1)\left(-\frac{1}{r_{B1}}\right) 1s_A(1)\, d\tau_1 + \int 1s_B(2)\left(-\frac{1}{r_{A2}}\right) 1s_B(2)\, d\tau_2$$

$$+ \iint 1s_A(1)\, 1s_B(2)\left(\frac{1}{r_{12}}\right) 1s_A(1)\, 1s_B(2)\, d\tau_1\, d\tau_2 + \frac{1}{R}$$

$$\left(\because \int \phi_1 \left(\frac{1}{R}\right) \phi_1 \, d\tau_1 = \frac{1}{R}\int \phi_1 \phi_1 \, d\tau_1 = \frac{1}{R}\right)$$

The first two integrals are 2-centre, 1-electron coulombic attraction energy and are equal (say j) while the third is a 2-centre, 2-electron repulsion energy (say j') so that $(j' - 2j)$ is the net coulombic energy (J). Thus,

$$H_{11} = 2E_H + (j' - 2j) + \frac{1}{R} = 2E_H + J + \frac{1}{R} \quad \text{... (12.98)}$$

The value of J depends on internuclear distance R.

Proceeding in the same manner,

$$H_{12} = \int \phi_1 \hat{H} \phi_2 \, d\tau$$

$$= 2E_H S^2 + \int 1s_A(1)\left[-\frac{1}{r_{A1}}\right]1s_B(1)\, d\tau_1 + \int 1s_B(2)\left[-\frac{1}{r_{B2}}\right]1s_A(2)\, d\tau_2$$

$$+ \iint 1s_A(1)\, 1s_B(2)\left[\frac{1}{r_{12}}\right]1s_A(2)\, 1s_B(1)\, d\tau_1\, d\tau_2$$

$$+ \frac{1}{R}\int 1s_A(1)\, 1s_B(1)\, d\tau_1 \,.\int 1s_A(2)\,.\, 1s_B(2)\, d\tau_2$$

$$\int 1s_A(1)\left[-\frac{1}{r_{A1}}\right]1s_B(1)\, d\tau = \int 1s_B(2)\left[-\frac{1}{r_{B2}}\right]1s_A(2)\, d\tau_2$$

$= K$ (say) (2-centre 1-electron exchange integral)

$$\int 1s_A(1)\, 1s_B(2)\left[\frac{1}{r_{12}}\right]1s_A(2)\, 1s_B(1)\, d\tau_1\, d\tau_2 = k' \text{ (say)}$$

(2-centre 2-electron exchange integral)

Therefore, $$H_{12} = 2E_H S^2 + k' - 2kS + \frac{S}{R}$$

$$= 2E_H S^2 + K + \frac{S}{R} \quad \text{... (12.99)}$$

where $K = k' - 2kS$ is the net exchange energy.

This type of energy has no classical counterpart and is the outcome of quantum mechanical treatment.

Substituting for H_{11} and H_{12} in Equation (12.91), we have, after rearrangement,

$$E_+ = 2E_H + \frac{J + K}{1 + S^2} + \frac{1}{R} \quad \text{... (12.100)}$$

$$E_- = 2E_H + \frac{J - K}{1 - S^2} + \frac{1}{R} \quad \text{... (12.101)}$$

These equations provide the total potential energy of the H_2 molecule in the ground and excited states. First two terms on the right constitute electrostatic energies and the third term is the nuclear repulsion energy. $2E_H$, the energy of two H atoms is equal to –1 a.u., the integrals J, K and S are evaluated by numerical method (analytical expressions are long exercises not needed here).

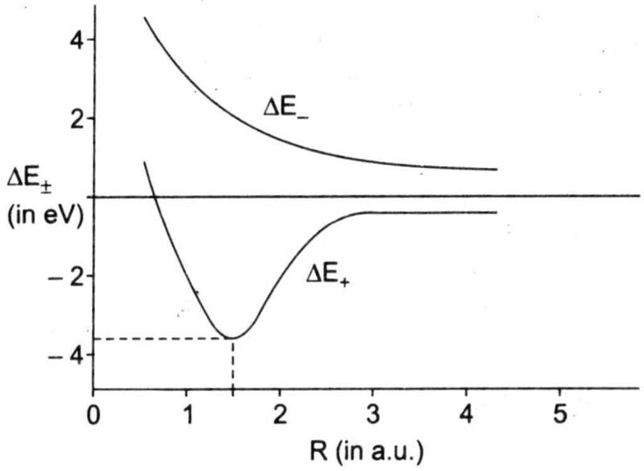

Fig. 12.11 *PE curve for H_2*

12.5.2.3 Stability of the bond in H_2

Relative to $2E_H$,
$$\Delta E_{\pm} = \frac{J \pm K}{1 \pm S^2} \quad \text{...(12.102)}$$

Both J and K are found to be negative of which K is more negative than J. Therefore, ΔE_+ is negative $\left(E_{H_2} < 2E_H\right)$ for all values of R and represents stable state, while ΔE_- is positive $\left(E_{H_2} > 2E_H\right)$ representing repulsive state. Fig. (12.11) shows plots of both ΔE_+ and ΔE_- against R. The ΔE_+ plot shows that two H-atoms attract each other as they approach, passes through a state of minimum energy and begin to repel when they are very close. The plot for ΔE_- never shows minimum.

The minimum in the ΔE_+ curve corresponds to the bond dissociation energy (D_e) of 0.116 a.u. (3.15 eV) and equilibrium bond distance of 1.166 a.u. (0.87 A or 0.087 nm).

Figure (12.12) shows individual plots of J and K against R. One can see that it is K_1 the exchange integral that contributes most to the stability of the H_2 molecule. Since exchange integral appears as a result of electron exchange—a quantum mechanical phenomenon one can say that the existence of chemical bond in H_2 molecule is quantum mechanical effect.

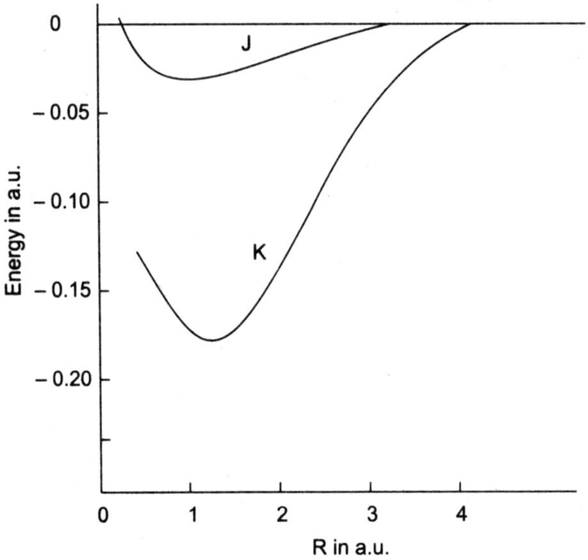

Fig. 12.12 *Plots of J and K as functions of R*

12.5.2.4 Electron Density Distribution

The electron density due to the symmetric and antisymmetric wave functions is given by the equation

$$\psi_{\pm}^2 = \frac{1}{2 \pm 2S^2} [1s_A(1)^2 1s_B(2)^2 + 1s_A(2)^2 1s_B(1)^2 \pm 2\{1s_A(1)\, 1s_B(2)\,.\, 1s_A(2)\, 1s_B(1)\}] \quad \text{... (12.103)}$$

The density of one electron is obtained by integrating Equation (12.103) over the coordinates of the other electron so that,

$$\left.\begin{aligned}
\rho(1) &= \int_2 \psi_{\pm}^2 (1,2)\, d\tau \\
&= \frac{1}{2 \pm 2S^2}\left[1s_A(1)^2 \int 1s_B(2)^2\, dV_2 + 1s_B(1)^2 \int 1s_A(2)^2\, dV_2 \right.\\
&\qquad \left. \pm 2\, 1s_A(1)\, 1s_B(1) \int 1s_A(2)\,.\, 1s_B(2)\, dV_2\right] \\
&= \frac{1}{2 \pm 2S^2}\left[1s_A(1)^2 + 1s_B(1)^2 \pm 2S\, 1s_A(1)\, 1s_B(1)\right] \\
\rho(2) &= \int_1 \psi_{\pm}^2 (1,2)\, d\tau = \frac{1}{2 \pm 2S^2}\left[1s_A(2)^2 + 1s_B(2)^2 \pm 2S\, 1s_A(2)\, 1s_B(2)\right]
\end{aligned}\right\} \quad \text{... (12.104)}$$

The total electron density

$$\rho_{VB} = \rho(1) + \rho(2)$$

$$= \frac{1}{1 \pm S^2}\left[1s_A^2 + 1s_B^2 \pm 2S\, 1s_A\, 1s_B\right] \qquad \dots (12.105)$$

(Since the electrons have no labels, $\rho_1 = \rho_2$).
(see Problem Q. 12.27 also).
Comparing with the

$$\rho_{MO} = \frac{1}{1 \pm S}\left[1s_A(1)^2 + 1s_B(1)^2 \pm 2\, 1s_A(1)\, 1s_B(1)\right]$$

we see that at the mid-point of the bond $\rho_{MO} > \rho_{VB}$. This means that the MO function piles up more negative charge between the nuclei than the VB function.

If the electron density contours are drawn for the symmetric and antisymmetric states, it is seen that in the former case there is a concentration of electron cloud between the nuclei which corresponds to attraction or formation of bond [Fig. 12.13 (*a*)] ; in the latter case the electron cloud is away from the space between the nuclei corresponding to the repulsion and existence of a nodal place in the middle [Fig. 12.13 (*b*)].

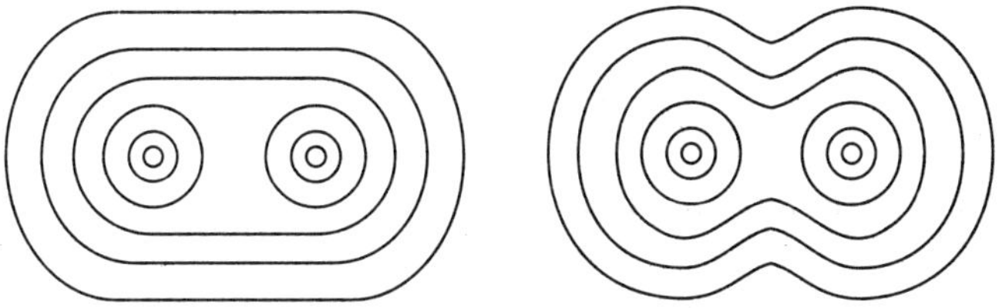

Fig. 12.13 *Electron density contour for the (a) symmetric (bonding) state in H_2; (b) antisymmetric (repulsive) state in H_2*

12.5.2.5 Antisymmetry of the Molecular Wave Function and the Nature of the Bonding

Energy and electron density calculations show that the bonding between the two H-atoms results as the symmetric wave function increases the electron density in the internuclear region. But what is the nature of the bond in the physical sense and what determines the valency of the atoms? In the VB theory we seek to find the answer in the complete wave function (orbital and spin combined) of the molecule which, according to Pauli's principle, must be antisymmetric. The antisymmetric wave function will be the product of symmetric orbital function with antisymmetric spin combination or *vice versa*.

Again, we how the following four possible combinations:

$$\left.\begin{array}{ll} {}^1\Psi_g = \psi_+ \frac{1}{\sqrt{2}}[\alpha(1)\beta(2) - \alpha(2)\beta(1)] & (i) \\ {}^3\Psi_e = \psi_-[\alpha(1)\alpha(2)] & (ii) \\ {}^3\Psi_e = \psi_-[\beta(1)\beta(2)] & (iii) \\ {}^3\Psi_e = \psi_- \frac{1}{\sqrt{2}}[\alpha(1)\beta(2) + \alpha(2)\beta(1)] & (iv) \end{array}\right\} \qquad \dots (12.106)$$

The superscripts 1 and 3 in Ψ indicate singlet and triplet states, respectively, and the subscripts g and e indicate ground and excited states, respectively.

In Equations (12.106), only (*i*) corresponds to the ground state of the molecule, which is singlet $\left({}^1\bar{\Psi}_g\right)$. The functions (*ii*) to (*iv*) correspond to the excited triplet states $\left({}^3\Psi_e\right)$. The former has total spin S = 0 with M_s = 0 and the latter has S = 1 with M_S = +1, 0 and –1.

The antisymmetric ${}^1\Psi_g$ wave function of the H_2 molecule that corresponds to the bonding situation, has the explicit form

$$ {}^1\Psi_g = \frac{1}{\sqrt{2+2S^2}} [\{1s_A(1)\,1s_B(2) + 1s_A(2)\,1s_B(1)]\,.\,\frac{1}{\sqrt{2}}\,[\alpha(1)\,\beta(2) - \alpha(2)\,\beta(1)] \quad \text{... (12.107)} $$

This on expansion and rearrangement, becomes

$$ {}^1\Psi_g = \frac{1}{2\sqrt{1+S^2}} [\{1s_A(1)\,\alpha(1)\,1s_B(2)\,\beta(2) - 1s_A(2)\,\alpha(2)\,1s_B(1)\,\beta(1)\} $$

$$ - 1s_A(1)\,\beta(1)\,1s_B(2)\,\alpha(2) + 1s_A(2)\,\beta(2)\,1s_B(1)\,\alpha(1)] \quad \text{... (12.108)} $$

It can be expressed in the determinant form as,

$$ {}^1\Psi_g = \frac{1}{2\sqrt{1+S^2}} \left[\begin{vmatrix} 1s_A(1)\,\alpha(1) & 1s_B(1)\,\beta(1) \\ 1s_A(2)\,\alpha(2) & 1s_B(2)\,\beta(2) \end{vmatrix} - \begin{vmatrix} 1s_A(1)\,\beta(1) & 1s_B(1)\,\alpha(1) \\ 1s_A(2)\,\beta(2) & 1s_B(2)\,\alpha(2) \end{vmatrix} \right] \quad \text{... (12.109)} $$

or in contracted form,

$$ {}^1\Psi_g = \frac{1}{2\sqrt{1+S^2}} [\,|\,1s_A(1)\,\bar{1}s_B(2)\,| - |\,\bar{1}s_A(1)\,1s_B(2)\,|\,] \quad \text{... (12.110)} $$

So the VB wave function of H_2 molecule reduces to the difference of two determinants, called Slater determinants. The first determinant corresponds to the configuration $H_{A^\alpha}\,H_{B^\beta}$ in which the electron 1 or 2 associated with the atom H_A has α spin and that with H_B has β spin. The second determinant corresponds to the configuration $H_{A^\beta}\,H_{B^\alpha}$. The difference between two configurations is only of an exchange of spin between H_A and H_B. Therefore, Equation (12.110) may be written as,

$$ \Psi_{VB} = \psi\left(H_{A^\alpha}\,H_{B^\beta}\right) - \psi\left(H_{A^\beta}\,H_{B^\alpha}\right) \quad \text{... (12.111)} $$

If the electrons on both H_A and H_B have identical spin, say $H_{A^\alpha}\,H_{B^\alpha}$, an exchange of spin would lead to

$$ \Psi_{VB} = \psi\left(H_{A^\alpha}\,H_{B^\alpha}\right) - \psi\left(H_{A^\alpha}\,H_{B^\alpha}\right) = 0 $$

This means that "the covalent bond in H_2 is formed as a result of exchange of electrons with opposite spins, α (↑) and β (↓), between the two atomic centres".

The exchange of spins is often referred to as pairing (↑↓) of spins. For forming a covalent bond an atom must have an orbital with an unpaired electron and the valency of the atom will be equal to the number of the unpaired electrons.

12.5.2.6 Shortcomings of the Heitler-London Treatment

The simple Heitler-London valence bond treatment of H_2 molecule described above gives a value (3.15 eV) of dissociation energy which is much lower than the experimental value (4.75 eV). But then it suffers from a number of defects which needs refinement. The wave function (12.92) is built up from hydrogen 1*s* orbitals with nuclear charge (Z) one in the exponent, one should straightforward allow the orbital exponent to vary instead of fixing it at unity as it is likely that during bond formation the nuclear charge may alter. If one chooses Z to minimise the energy then one finds that the optimum value of Z = 1.166, ΔE_+ (or D_e) = 0.139 a.u. (3.80 eV) and R_e = 1.39 a.u. (0.76 A).

Further, the simple treatment does not consider the situation when both electrons are near the same nucleus A or B, *i.e.*, it ignores the ionic structures. In corporating ionic contribution a better wave function would be a linear combination

$$\psi = a_1 [1s_A(1)\, 1s_B(2) + 1s_A(2)\, 1s_B(1)] + a_2 [1s_A(1)\, 1s_A(2) + 1s_B(1)\, 1s_B(2)]$$

$$= a_1\, \psi_{\text{covalent}} + a_2\, \psi_{\text{ionic}} \qquad \text{... (12.112)}$$

Weinbaum (1933) used this type of wave function to find that with Z = 1, D_e = 3.23 eV and R_e = 0.88 A and with Z = 1.166 (optimum), D_e = 4.03 eV and R_e = 0.76 A. He also found that with Z = 1, $\frac{a_2}{a_1} = 0.18$ at the bond distance implying $(0.18)^2 = 0.0324$ or 3.24% ionic character, (see section 12.6.2.1). However, this value will change drastically when Z = 1.166 is used.

Accordingly, the bond in H_2 molecule may be viewed as largely covalent with some ionic character and the molecule is a hybrid of three structures.

$$H_A - H_B \leftrightarrow H_A^- \; H_B^+ \leftrightarrow H_A^+ \leftrightarrow H_B^-$$

Further improvement is possible if we do not use simple 1*s* orbitals. As a result of bond formation, the electron distributions in each hydrogen atom do not remain spherical. If the bond axis is taken as the *z*-axis, then a better orbital will be a hybrid of 1*s* and $2p_z$ a.o.'s, *i.e.*,

$$\phi = a_1\, 1s + a_2\, 2p_z$$

instead of 1*s*.

12.5.2.7 Resonance

The idea of introducing ionic terms in valence bond wave function provides quantum mechanical illustration to the idea of 'resonance' in classical chemistry. If we can write two or more possible electronic structures for a molecule then the wave function (Ψ) of that molecule will be a linear combination of the wave functions of the individual structures (ψ_i)

$$\Psi = a_1\, \psi_1 + a_2\, \psi_2 + \ldots. \qquad \text{... (12.113)}$$

The true structure is said to be a 'resonance' of all such structures. The numerical values of the coefficients a_i in the linear combination obtained by variation method, give us the indication of the relative importance of the various structures.

12.6 DIATOMIC MOLECULES IN GENERAL

12.6.1 LCAO-MO Treatment of Diatomic Molecules

The type of molecular orbital discussed in the case of H_2 molecule can serve as the basis for a simple model of the electronic structure of other diatomic molecules and their bonding. For H_2, the ground state configuration is σ_g^2 and the molecular wave function including spin is the determinant

$$\Psi = \left| \sigma_g (1) \bar{\sigma}_g (2) \right|$$

where
$$\sigma_g = \frac{1}{\sqrt{2(1+S)}} \left[1s_A + 1s_B \right]$$

is an MO. For molecules with more electrons, more MOs are needed, each MO being formed by linear combination of atomic orbitals (AOs). But electrons are present is several AOs of the combining atoms. Which AOs of the atoms will enter into effective combination ? While a rigorous treatment will involve self consistent field method involving all AOs of all atoms (see Chapter 13) the following three considerations may act as our guide for an approximate and a qualitative prediction of the combining of atomic orbitals.

(*i*) The AOs of only matching symmetry with respect to the bond axis can combine.

(*ii*) The AOs of only matching energy can combine.

(*iii*) The AOs that can overlap can combine.

This is understood from the LCAO theory. The linear combination of atomic orbitals ϕ_A and ϕ_B from atoms A and B leads to the secular determinant

$$\begin{vmatrix} \alpha_A - E & \beta - ES \\ \beta - ES & \alpha_B - E \end{vmatrix} = 0 \qquad \text{... (12.114)}$$

where $\alpha_A = \int \phi_A \hat{H} \phi_A \, d\tau$, $\alpha_B = \int \phi_B \hat{H} \phi_B \, d\tau$ and $\beta = \int \phi_A \hat{H} \phi_B \, d\tau = \int \phi_B \hat{H} \phi_A \, d\tau$; E is energy of an MO generated, S is overlap integral and $\hat{H}$ is Hamiltonian operator.

As regards condition (*i*) (symmetry match), if ϕ_A and ϕ_B do not have same symmetry with respect to internuclear axis then both integrals S and β vanish (see Chapter 11). This reduces the determinant to $\alpha_A - E = 0$ and $\alpha_B - E = 0$, *i.e.*, $\alpha_A = \alpha_B = E$ and hence no combination.

Condition (*ii*) is met by a consideration of the polynomial equation obtained from the determinant,

$$(1 - S^2) E + [2\beta S - (\alpha_A + \alpha_B)] E + (\alpha_A \alpha_B - \beta)^2 = 0$$

A satisfactory approximation is to consider $S^2 <<1$ and $2\beta S << (\alpha_A + \alpha_B)$; then the resulting quadratic equation has the following two roots

$$E_{\pm} = \frac{(\alpha_A + \alpha_B) \pm \left[(\alpha_A - \alpha_B)^2 + 4\beta^2 \right]^{\frac{1}{2}}}{2} \qquad \text{... (12.115)}$$

If $\alpha_A \approx \alpha_B = \alpha$, then $E_{\pm} = \alpha \pm \beta$, that is two MOs are formed one of which has lower energy $\alpha + \beta$ and the other has higher energy $\alpha - \beta$.

If $\alpha_A \neq \alpha_B$ and $\alpha_A > \alpha_B$, then

$$E_{\pm} = \frac{(\alpha_A + \alpha_B)}{2} \pm \frac{(\alpha_A - \alpha_B)}{2}\left[1 + \frac{4\beta^2}{(\alpha_A - \alpha_B)^2}\right]^{\frac{1}{2}} \quad \text{... (12.116)}$$

Using the expansion

$$(1+x)^{1/2} = 1 + \frac{x}{2} - \frac{x^2}{8} + \cdots$$

$$E_{\pm} = \frac{(\alpha_A + \alpha_B)}{2} \pm \frac{(\alpha_A - \alpha_B)}{2}\left[1 + \frac{2\beta^2}{(\alpha_A - \alpha_B)^2} - \frac{2\beta^4}{(\alpha_A - \alpha_B)^4} + \cdots\right]$$

Assume $\beta^2 < (\alpha_A - \alpha_B)^2$ and neglect the terms beyond the second in the expansion, then

$$E_{\pm} = \frac{\alpha_A + \alpha_B}{2} \pm \frac{\alpha_A - \alpha_B}{2} \pm \frac{\beta^2}{(\alpha_A - \alpha_B)}$$

or

$$E_{+} = \alpha_A + \frac{\beta^2}{\alpha_A - \alpha_B} \quad \text{... (12.117)}$$

and

$$E_{-} = \alpha_B - \frac{\beta^2}{\alpha_A - \alpha_B} \quad \text{... (12.118)}$$

If $\alpha_A - \alpha_B$ is large $\frac{\beta^2}{\alpha_A - \alpha_B}$ will be negligible and then $E_+ \approx \alpha_A$, and $E_- \approx \alpha_B$, that is no effective combination.

Now consider a molecule AB with the atoms A and B having the atomic orbitals (ϕ) 1*s*, 2*s*, $2p_x$, $2p_y$, etc. Let the bond axis A—B be the *z*-axis and let the *x*-axis be perpendicular to the plane of the paper (Fig. 12.14). Qualitative MO theory predicts that not all the AOs of A can combine with all the AO's of B. Atomic orbital 1*s* of A cannot combine with 2*s* or 2*p* of B because of the energy mismatch. The 2*s* of A can combine with 2*s* of B; similarly, $2p_z$ of A and B, which are oriented along the *z*-axis, can combine, but $2p_z$ of A cannot combine with $2p_y$ or $2p_x$ of B and *vice versa* because of symmetry mismatch ($2p_z$ is symmetric while $2p_y$ and $2p_x$ are antisymmetric with respect to rotation about the axis A-B). For the same reasons, $2p_y$ can combine with $2p_y$ and $2p_x$ with $2p_x$ but not with others. However, the 2*s* AO of A can combine not only with 2*s* but also with $2p_z$ AO of the atom B provided their energies match because both the AOs are symmetric with respect to the axis AB. The 2*s* of A cannot combine with $2p_y$ or $2p_x$ of B.

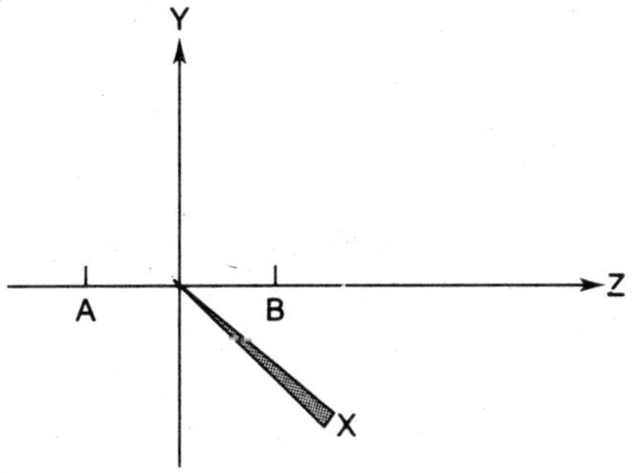

Fig. 12.14 *Axes in the diatomic molecule AB, x-axis is perpendicular to the z_y plane*

The following linear combinations of AOs are thus possible:

$$\psi_{(2s)} = a_1\ 2s_A + a_2\ 2s_B \qquad ...(12.119)$$

$$\psi_{(2pz)} = a_1\ 2p_{z_A} + a_2\ 2p_{z_B} \qquad ...(12.120)$$

$$\psi_{(2py)} = a_1\ 2p_{y_A} + a_2\ 2p_{y_B} \qquad ...(12.121)$$

$$\psi_{(2px)} = a_1\ 2p_{x_A} + a_2\ 2p_{x_B} \qquad ...(12.122)$$

Each of these combinations yields two MOs—a bonding and an antibonding. So, from the four AOs of each atom under consideration eight MOs are generated, four of which are bonding and four antibonding. Under conditions of energy match, ψ_{2s} and ψ_{2pz} [Equations (12.119) and (12.120)] can mix and the resulting MOs can be expressed, in general, as

$$\psi = a_1\ 2s_A + a_2\ 2s_B + a_3\ 2p_{z_A} + a_4\ 2p_{z_B} \qquad ...(12.123)$$

Such a linear combination of four AOs will lead to four secular equations and a 4 × 4 secular determinant. The solution of the determinant will give four possible energy levels and, hence, four MOs two of which will be bonding and two antibonding.

The determination of the expressions for the MOs involves determination of the coefficients $a_1, a_2, ...$ of the linear combinations. For this, the secular equations have to be solved. However, for homonuclear molecules certain simplifying features, based on symmetry, may be mentioned. If the atoms A and B are identical,

$$a_1 = \pm\ a_2 = \frac{1}{\sqrt{2(1 \pm S)}} \qquad ...(12.124)$$

in the MOs given by Equations (12.119) to (12.122) ; the + sign is for the bonding and – sign for the antibonding MO. In the MOs given by Equation (12.123), symmetry requires that $a_1 = \pm a_2$ and $a_3 = \pm a_4$.

12.6.1.1 Angular Momentum: σ and π MOs

The MOs of a diatomic molecule can be designated in terms of symmetry and angular momentum symbols in a manner similar to that for atomic orbitals. It may be remembered that atomic orbitals are designated by two angular momentum quantum numbers l and M, l representing the orbital angular momentum (L) of the electron and M its z-component (L_z). But, whereas in the case of atom there are $2l + 1$ orientations of the z-axis, in the case of a diatomic molecule the z-axis is fixed, being the internuclear axis. The MOs of a diatomic molecule can, therefore, be distinguished from each other by the component of the angular momentum along this axis. This is given by $\frac{\Lambda h}{2\pi}$, where $\Lambda = 0, \pm 1, \pm 2, ...$ is the quantum number analogous to M, and not l, of atomic orbitals, and the MOs may be regarded as eigenfunctions of the operator $\hat{L}_z$.

The MOs can then be labelled as σ, π, δ ... for $\Lambda = 0, \pm 1, \pm 2, ...$ respectively, just as AOs are labelled as $s, p, d, ...$ corresponding to $l = 0, 1, 2, ...$

Except for $\Lambda = 0$, the MOs are doubly degenerate. The MOs [Equations (12.119), (12.120) and (12.123)] formed from σ and p_z AOs (M = 0) have $\Lambda = 0$ and are accordingly the σ MOs.

Here an immediate difficulty arises. The eigenfunctions of $\hat{L}_z$, except for $\Lambda = 0$, involve imaginary functions exp $(i \Lambda \varphi)$, where φ is the angle of L with the internuclear axis. No real picture can be drawn of them. The difficulty can, however, be resolved by taking linear combination of the degenerate pairs. For example, the π_+ and π_- corresponding to $\Lambda = +1$ and -1, respectively, may be combined to get two real π functions. The resulting functions are no longer eigenfunctions of $\hat{L}_z$ and the significance of the quantum number Λ is lost, but they are still denoted as π functions. This is analogous to forming real p_x and p_y AOs from the complex p_{+1} and p_{-1} functions. One of the two real π-functions is then considered to be the linear combination of $2p_{x_A}$ and $2p_{x_B}$ [the ψ $(2p_x)$ in Equation (12.122) and the other of $2p_{y_A}$ and $2p_{y_B}$ ψ $(2p_y)$ in Equation (12.121)]. These may, therefore, be designated as π_x and π_y, respectively. The negative combinations lead to π_x^* and π_y^*.

Further distinctions among the MOs may be made by utilising their symmetries with respect to inversion centre of the molecule. In homonuclear molecules (A_2 or B_2) the inversion centre lies in the middle point of the internuclear axis. The bonding σ MOs are σ_g (symmetric) and the antibonding are σ_u (antisymmetric) (see also the MOs of H_2).

For homonuclear diatomic molecules, in general (*e.g.*, A_2), for which $| a_1 | = | a_2 |$, the σ MOs formed by the (+) combinations, viz.,

$$(2s_A)_1 + (2s_A)_2 \text{ and } \left(2p_{z_{A1}}\right) + \left(2p_{z_{A2}}\right)$$

are σ_g's; the corresponding (–) combinations give σ_u MOs. The π MOs, on the other hand, resulting from the (+) combinations *e.g.*, $(2p_x)_{A1} + (2p_x)_{A2}$, etc., are π_u and the (–) combinations, *e.g.*, $(2p_x)_{A1} - (2p_x)_{A2}$ are π_g. This is clear from Fig. 12.15.

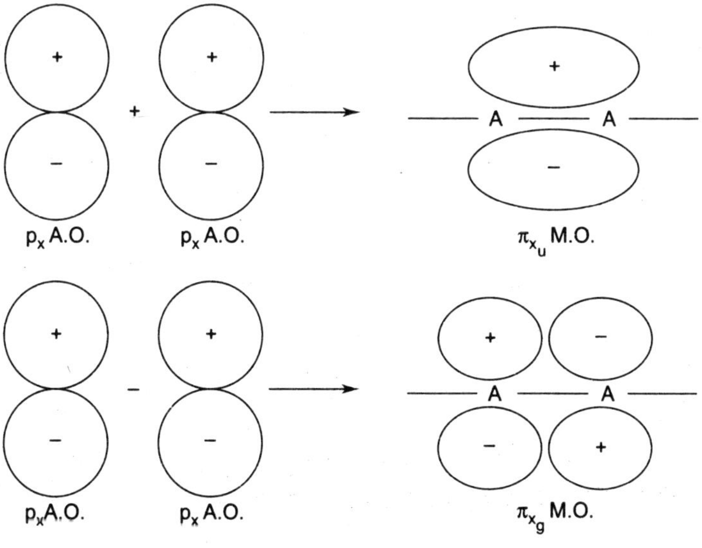

Fig. 12.15 *π_{x_u} and π_{x_g} MOs formed from p_x AOs of two A atoms; analogous π_{y_u} and π_{y_g} MOs are formed from p_y AOs. The π_x and π_y are oriented at right angles to each other*

12.6.1.2 Order of MO Energy Levels

From one 2s and three 2p atomic orbitals of each of the two combining atoms, eight MOs are formed—two σ_g's, two σ_u's, $\pi_{x_u}, \pi_{y_u}, \pi_{x_g}$ and π_{y_g}. The energies of these MOs which for homonuclear molecules are given roughly by Equation (12.125), ultimately depend on (*i*) the type of AOs from which they are built up, and (*ii*) the extent of overlap between these AOs

$$E_{\pm} = \frac{H_{11} \pm H_{12}}{1 \pm S} \qquad \text{... (12.125)}$$

Calculations show that the exchange integral H_{12}, which stablises a molecule, runs parallel to the overlap integral S. Thus the σ MO, $1s_A + 1s_B$ will have much lower energy than another σ MO, $2s_A + 2s_B$, simply because 1s AO has much lower energy than 2s. Similarly, σ MO of $2s_A + 2s_B$ type will have lower energy than the σ MO of $2p_{z_A} + 2p_{z_B}$ type as, except for H, 2s AO has lower energy than 2p. Generally, π MOs have greater energy than the σ MOs due to weaker overlap between two $2p_x$ or two $2p_y$ AOs. As p_x and p_y AOs are degenerate, the π_{x_u} and π_{y_u} MOs are degenerate too and so are π_{x_g} and π_{y_g}. The antibonding MOs have higher energy than the corresponding bonding MOs.

The MOs can now be labelled are arranged in order of their increasing energies. The modern system is to number the MOs of a particular type (*e.g.*, σ_g) consecutively beginning with the lowest energy MO, *e.g.*, $1\sigma_g$, $2\sigma_g$, $3\sigma_g$, etc.; and then $1\sigma_u$, $2\sigma_u$, $3\sigma_u$, etc. Similarly, we have the π set—$1\pi_u$, $2\pi_u$, ... and $1\pi_g$, $2\pi_g$ ... There are some anomalies, which have to be pointed out. Experimentally, it is found that among the homonuclear diatomic molecules of the first row elements, the $1\pi_u$ orbital is lower in energy than $3\sigma_u$ for Li_2 to N_2; to O_2 and F_2, the reverse is true. This may be explained as follows:

When the 2s AO is much lower in energy than 2p (as in O, F) no interaction is possible between the two and the σ MOs are given by Equations (12.119) and (12.120) (Fig. 12.16). But when 2s is not much lower than 2p (as in Li, Be, B, C, N), the s and p_z AOs mix and the σ MOs are given by Equation (12.123). Such an interaction between the s and p_z AOs depresses the first two σ MOs ($2\sigma_g$ and $2\sigma_u$) and raises the next two σ MOs ($3\sigma_g$ and $3\sigma_u$) to such an extent as to make the π_u's lower in energy than the $3\sigma_g$ (see Fig. 12.17).

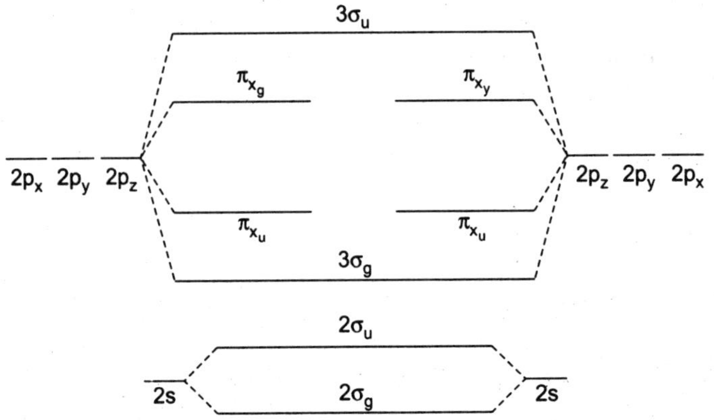

Fig. 12.16

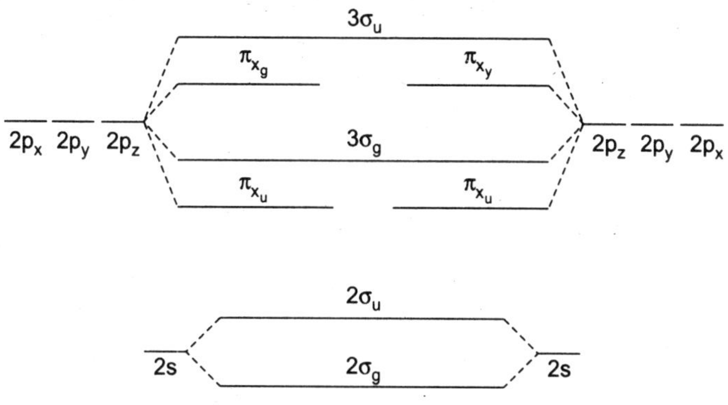

Fig. 12.17

In heteronuclear diatomic molecules (AB), there is no inversion centre; so the MOs cannot be labelled as *g* or *u*, and they are just numbered directly making distinctions of σ and π (see Fig. 12.18).

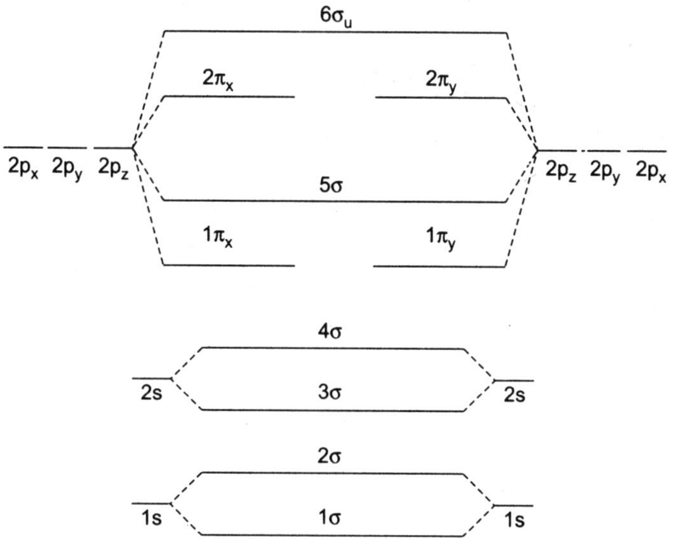

Fig. 12.18

12.6.1.3 Complete Wave Functions of the Molecules

MOs are just one-electron eigenfunctions of molecules. In molecules having more than one electron, the complete wave function representing a bond is the antisymmetrised product of the MO wave functions written as a single determinant for H_2 for example (for the ground state), it is

$$\Psi_{\text{H-H}} = \left| 1\sigma_g(1) \cdot 1\bar{\sigma}_g(2) \right| \qquad \text{... (12.126)}$$

We can write MO wave functions for any diatomic molecule in the likewise manner. For Li_2, for example, the wave function may be written as (ignoring the $1\sigma_g$ and $1\sigma_u$ elements which do not contribute significantly towards bonding),

$$\Psi_{\text{Li-Li}} = \left| 2\sigma_g(5) \cdot 2\bar{\sigma}_g(6) \right| \qquad \text{... (12.127)}$$

For N_2, it is written as

$$\Psi_{N\equiv N} = \left|1\pi_{x_u}(9).1\bar{\pi}_{x_u}(10).1\pi_{y_u}(11).1\bar{\pi}_{y_u}(12).3\sigma_g(13).3\bar{\sigma}_g(14)\right| \quad ...(12.128)$$

where the low lying σ electrons have not been considered and normalisation factor has not been included. For O_2, the wave function is,

$$\Psi_{O=O} = \left|3\sigma_g(9).3\bar{\sigma}_g(10).1\pi_{x_u}(11).1\bar{\pi}_{x_u}(12).1\pi_{y_u}(13).1\bar{\pi}_{y_u}(14).1\pi_{x_g}(15).1\pi_{y_g}(16)\right| \quad ...(12.129)$$

12.6.1.4 Electronic Structure and Bonds

We can now use the rules of building up of electronic configuration for molecules as in the case of atoms. We have to place pairs of electrons with opposite spins in the MOs, starting with the lowest energy MO and going up, adhering to the principles of Pauli and Hund, until all the electrons are accounted for. The electronic configurations for some homonuclear and heteronuclear diatomic molecules are given below.

Homonuclear molecules

H_2 (2 electrons): $1\sigma_g^2$

Li_2 (6 electrons): $1\sigma_g^2\, 1\sigma_u^2\, 2\sigma_g^2$

B_2 (10 electrons):

$1\sigma_g^2\, 1\sigma_u^2\, 2\sigma_g^2\, 2\sigma_u^2\, 1\pi_{x_u}\, 1\pi_{y_u}$

C_2 (12 electrons): $[Be_2]\; 1\pi_{x_u}^2\, 1\pi_{y_u}^2$

N_2 (14 electrons): $[Be_2]\; 1\pi_{x_u}^2\, 1\pi_{y_u}^2\, 3\sigma_g^2$

O_2 (16 electrons):

$[Be_2].3\sigma_g^2\, 1\pi_{x_u}^2\, 1\pi_{y_u}^2\, 1\pi_{x_g}\, 1\pi_{y_g}$

and so on, where

$[Be_2] = 1\sigma_g^2\, 1\sigma_u^2\, 2\sigma_g^2\, 2\sigma_u^2$

Heteronuclear molecules

CO (14 electrons):

$1\sigma^2\, 2\sigma^2\, 3\sigma^2\, 4\sigma^2\, 1\pi_x^2\, 1\pi_y^2\, 5\sigma^2$

NO (15 electrons): [CO] $2\pi_x$

This arrangement reveals the number of bonds as well as some molecular properties. A pair of electrons in a bonding MO contributes a single bond, a pair in an antibonding MO cancels it. Thus, the MO theory predicts that molecules like $He_2\left(1\sigma_g^2\, 1\sigma_u^2\right)$, $Ne_2\left(1\pi_u^4\, 3\sigma_g^2\, 1\pi_g^4\, 3\sigma_u^2\right)$ cannot be stable.* Molecules of N_2, O_2 and F_2 have triple, double and single bonds, respectively.

More generally, the "bond order" for homonuclear diatomic molecules is defined as 1/2 × (number of bonding electrons—number of antibonding electrons). Thus, H_2 and Li_2 have bond orders of 1.0; H_2^+ has a bond order of 0.5, He_2 has zero, O_2 has two, N_2 has 3, and so on. Greater the bond order, more are the bonds and stabler is the molecule. We find that N_2 is indeed the most stable of the diatomic molecules.

* However, the Ne_2 molecule has been shown to have some stability (dissociation energy = 50 cm^{-1}). Simple MO theory does not account for this.

This arrangement also explains some important properties of these molecules. For B_2 and O_2, there are unpaired electrons in π_u and π_g MOs respectively. This predicts paramagnetic property for these molecules, and we know that these are actually highly paramagnetic. This fact cannot be explained in terms of the valence bond theory.

The CO molecule has a bond order of 3, which means a triple bond similar to that in N_2. So this is a very stable molecule. NO has a bond order of 2.5. This also means a very strong bond, but NO^+ has one electron less in one of the π_g's, so it is more stable than NO. Further, the single unpaired electron in π_g MO of NO explains why it is paramagnetic.

12.6.1.5 Electronic States and Term Symbols

As in the case of atoms (see Chapter 10), the net orbital angular momentum, denoted as Λ in diatomic molecules, about the z-axis (the internuclear axis) can be used to derive the electronic state and term symbols for diatomic molecules. Whereas the electrons in an atom having net orbital angular momentum (L) equal to 0, 1, 2, 3, ... units are said to be in S, P, D, F, ... states, respectively, the electrons in diatomic molecules having $\Lambda = 0, 1, 2, 3, \ldots$ units are said to be in $\Sigma, \Pi, \Delta, \Phi, \ldots$ states, respectively. The overall symmetry of the state is governed by the symmetries of the MO's occupied by the electrons, the rule being $g \times g = g$, $u \times u = g$ and $g \times u = u$. Finally, the spin multiplicity (2S + 1) is determined by the Hund's rule.

In the ground state of H_2, for example, both electrons are in $1\sigma_g$ MO; therefore, the overall symmetry is $g \times g = g$. The σ electrons, like s electrons in AOs, do not contribute anything towards the orbital angular momentum, *i.e.*, $\Lambda = 0$; this corresponds to the Σ state. Since both electrons are paired, the total spin S = 0 and the multiplicity is 1 (singlet). The ground state of H_2, is, therefore, the ${}^1\Sigma_g$ (singlet sigma gee) state.

In the excited state of H_2, having the configuration $1\sigma_g\ 1\sigma_u$, (symmetry $g \times u = u$). The spins may be parallel (S = 1) or antiparallel (S = 0). Accordingly, the excited state may either be ${}^1\Sigma_u$ or ${}^3\Sigma_u$.

We can consider a few more examples. In N_2, all electrons are paired (S = 0, singlet); net symmetry is g; contribution from σ-electrons towards orbital angular momentum is zero; the two π MOs (π_+ and π_- have angular momenta in opposite directions about the nuclear axis, and since they are fully occupied, their net contribution is also zero; thus $\Lambda = 0$, which corresponds to the symbol Σ. The electronic state is ${}^1\Sigma_g$.

Configuration of O_2 gives rise to a number of terms depending on how the two electrons occupy the π_g (*i.e.*, π^*) MO. If both enter the same π_g (*i.e.*, π^*) MO, the net angular momentum will be $\pm \dfrac{2h}{2\pi}$; then the term symbol is Δ ($\Lambda = 2$). In such a case the spins will be paired (S = 0) and the symmetry will be g; so the electronic state is ${}^1\Delta_g$. If, however, one of the electrons enters π_x^* and the other π_y^*, the total contribution towards angular momentum will be zero (as in N_2) and the term will be Σ. The two electrons in π_x^* and π_y^* may have opposite (S = 0) or identical (S = 1) spins which lead to ${}^1\Sigma$ and ${}^3\Sigma$ states, respectively. The symmetry will be $g \times g = g$. Since electrons in different orbitals will suffer less interaction as compared with that in the same orbital, the Σ term will have lower energy than the Δ term; and if we apply the Hund's rule of maximum multiplicity, we should expect the triplet state to lie below the singlet. Thus, we can predict that the ground state of O_2 is $^3\Sigma_g$ which is confirmed experimentally by spectroscopy. Similarly, the ground state of F_2 is $^1\Sigma_g$.

12.6.2 VB Treatment of Diatomic Molecules

VB treatment is the quantum mechanical version of the chemical ideas of Lewis. A covalent bond can be formed between two atoms A and B, as in H_2, through overlap of singly occupied atomic orbitals ϕ_A and ϕ_B and exchange of α and β spins. Each pairing scheme gives a VB structure. The bond is described by a VB wave function of the H.L. (Heitler-London) type, written usually as antisymmetrised product of atomic wave functions including spins (spin-orbitals). The wave function is expressed as a difference of two Slater determinants. For electrons 1 and 2 occupying the orbitals ϕ_A and ϕ_B, respectively, the two normalised determinants are,

$$\psi_1 = \frac{1}{\sqrt{2}}\begin{vmatrix} \phi_A(1) & \bar{\phi}_B(1) \\ \phi_A(2) & \bar{\phi}_B(2) \end{vmatrix}$$

and

$$\psi_2 = \frac{1}{\sqrt{2}}\begin{vmatrix} \bar{\phi}_A(1) & \phi_B(1) \\ \bar{\phi}_A(2) & \phi_B(2) \end{vmatrix} \qquad \text{... (12.130)}$$

or, written in a contracted form (diagonal elements only).

$$\psi_1 = \frac{1}{\sqrt{2}}\left| \phi_A(1)\,\bar{\phi}_B(2) \right|, \text{ and } \psi_2 = \frac{1}{\sqrt{2}}\left| \bar{\phi}_A(1)\,\phi_B(2) \right| \qquad \text{... (12.131)}$$

where bar over ϕ indicates β-spin and no bar α-spin. The difference between ψ_1 and ψ_2 lies in the exchange of spin; in ψ_1 spin α is always associated with ϕ_A and β with ϕ_B, while in ψ_2 the position is just reversed. A linear combination of the two determinants.

$$\Psi = a_1\psi_1 + a_2\psi_2 \qquad \text{... (12.132)}$$

which is an eigenfunction of the spin operators $\hat{S}_z$ and $\hat{S}^2$ is called "bond eigenfunction." Variational calculation leads to,

$$\Psi = \frac{1}{\sqrt{2+2S^2}}\left[\frac{1}{\sqrt{2}}\left|\phi_A(1)\,\bar{\phi}_B(2)\right| - \frac{1}{\sqrt{2}}\left|\bar{\phi}_A(1)\,\phi_B(2)\right|\right] \qquad \text{... (12.133)}$$

Functions of the type (12.133) are known as Heitler-London (HL) or valence bond wave functions. Here $S^2 = \int \psi_1 \psi_2 \, d\tau$. The function corresponds to the singlet spin state as it contains the antisymmetric spin function

$$\frac{1}{\sqrt{2}}\left[\alpha(1)\,\beta(2) - \alpha(2)\,\beta(1)\right]$$

having $S = 0$ and $M_S = 0$; this is also equivalent to "pairing" of the spins.

If one or both of the atomic orbitals ϕ_A and ϕ_B are doubly occupied, exchange of spins is not possible without violating Pauli's principle (it will not produce a new determinant). If the two AOs have zero overlap integral, say due to symmetry, bonding will not occur as the exchange integral will be zero. If each of the combining atoms has more than one singly occupied orbital, overlap will occur individually between pairs of orbitals following the rules of symmetry; this will lead to multiple bonding.

Consider for example, the formation of a bond between two helium atoms A and B. Helium has the electronic configuration 1*s* (1) $\overline{1s}$ (2) (or He : $\overset{\alpha}{\beta}$). For bonding, the two He atoms must exchange spins. Exchange of α-spin of an electron in one He atom with α-spin in the other does not lead to any new configuration. On the other hand, if α-spin is exchanged with β it puts two electrons of the same spin in one orbital, which is not permissible by Pauli's principle. So no bonding is possible between two He atoms.

Bonding in He_2 is not possible by MO theory too, as the number of bonding electrons equals that of the antibonding electrons.

Similarly, in He, H the two electrons of $1s_{He}$ orbital are paired while in the $1s_H$ orbital there is one electron whose spin may be α or β. Accordingly, assuming α-spin in the $1s_H$ orbital, we have the configuration He^{α}_{β}, $^{\alpha}$H. The ionic structure $He^{+}\,\overset{\alpha}{\underset{\beta}{}}\!\overset{\alpha}{}\!:H^-$ is not likely because of the very large ionisation potential of He.

Corresponding to the covalent configuration, we have the determinant

$$\psi_1 = \frac{1}{\sqrt{3!}} \begin{vmatrix} 1s_{He}(1) & \overline{1s}_{He}(1) & 1s_H(1) \\ 1s_{He}(2) & \overline{1s}_{He}(2) & 1s_H(2) \\ 1s_{He}(3) & \overline{1s}_{He}(3) & 1s_H(3) \end{vmatrix} \quad \text{... (12.134)}$$

Now if the spin α in $1s_H$ is exchanged with spin α in $1s_{He}$, no new determinant is produced. If, on the other hand, it is exchanged with spin β in $1s_{He}$, the resulting determinant is,

$$\psi_2 = \frac{1}{\sqrt{3!}} \begin{vmatrix} 1s_{He}(1) & 1s_{He}(1) & \overline{1s}_H(1) \\ 1s_{He}(2) & 1s_{He}(2) & \overline{1s}_H(2) \\ 1s_{He}(3) & 1s_{He}(3) & \overline{1s}_H(3) \end{vmatrix} \quad \text{... (12.135)}$$

This determinant has two identical columns and is, therefore, equal to zero (Pauli's principle). Thus, in terms of VB theory, since the $1s_{He}$ orbital has two electrons already paired, bonding is not possible between He and H.

In terms of the MO theory, combination of $1s_{He}$ and $1s_H$ orbitals is not possible because of energy mismatch.

Consider the F_2 molecule. The ground state configuration of an F atom is $1s^2\,2s^2\,2p^5$, one of *p* orbitals being available for bonding with the corresponding *p* orbital of the other atom. If the internuclear axis is taken as the *z*-axis, the overlap will occur between the two p_z AOs and the bond eigenfunction will be,

$$\psi = \frac{1}{\sqrt{2+2S^2}} \left[\left| p_{z_A}(1)\, \bar{p}_{z_B}(2) \right| - \left| \bar{p}_{z_A}(1)\, p_{z_B}(2) \right| \right] \quad \text{... (12.136)}$$

Pictorially, it can be represented as shown in Fig. 12.19.

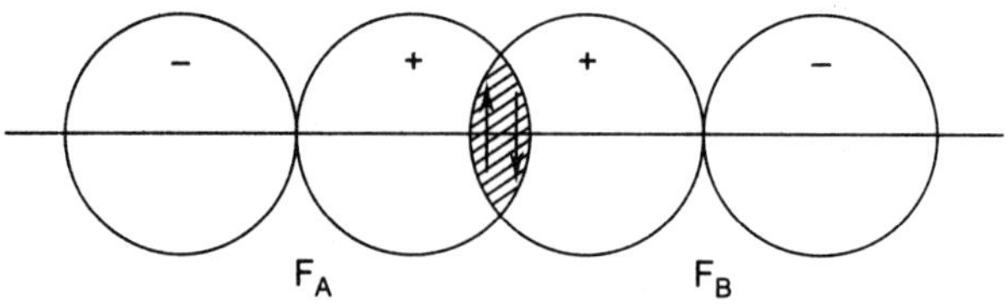

Fig. 12.19 *Overlap of the p_z atomic orbitals in F_2*

For the calculation of energy, the spin part of Equation (12.136) is of no significance and the function,

$$\psi_{VB} = \frac{1}{\sqrt{2+2S^2}}\left[p_{z_A}(1)\,p_{z_B}(2) + p_{z_B}(1)\,p_{z_A}(2)\right] \quad ...(12.137)$$

can be used for the singlet ground state. The calculated value will be approximate. We can improve the result by adding ionic function

$$\left(p_{z_A}(1)\,p_{z_A}(2) + p_{z_B}(1)\,p_{z_B}(2)\right)$$

to the Heitler-London type function Equation (12.137) with a variable parameter. Further improvement can be made by introducing determinants due to inner orbitals containing unshared pairs of electrons. We can see that our efforts to improve the result will bring more and more mathematical complexity.

Calculations become much more tedious when multiple bonds are formed. Take the example of N_2 ($1s^2\ 2s^2\ 2p^3$). Each of the three $2p$-electrons in one N atom is available for bonding with corresponding $2p$-electrons of the other N atom. If the internuclear axis is taken to be the z-axis, the $p_z - p_z$ overlap will give a σ-bond, $p_y - p_y$ a π-bond and $p_x - p_x$ another π-bond giving a triple (≡) bond consistent with the Lewis Structure : N ≡ N. Here again the notations σ, π, etc. are derived from the $|M|$ values of the p-orbitals constituting the bonds.

$$\psi_\sigma = \left|p_{z_A}(1)\,\bar{p}_{z_B}(2)\right| - \left|\bar{p}_{z_A}(1)\,p_{z_B}(2)\right|$$

$$\psi_{\pi_x} = \left|p_{x_A}(3)\,\bar{p}_{x_B}(4)\right| - \left|\bar{p}_{x_A}(3)\,p_{x_B}(4)\right|$$

$$\psi_{\pi_y} = \left|p_{y_A}(5)\,p_{y_B}(6)\right| - \left|\bar{p}_{y_A}(5)\,p_{y_B}(6)\right| \quad ...(12.138)$$

where the normalisation factors have been omitted.

The molecular wavefunction (ignoring the 1s and 2s electrons, which do not participate in bonding) is,

$$\Psi_{N_2}^{VB} = \left[\left|p_{z_A}(1)\,\bar{p}_{z_B}(2)\right| - \left|\bar{p}_{z_A}(1)\,p_{z_B}(2)\right|\right] \times \left[\left|p_{x_A}(3)\,\bar{p}_{x_B}(4)\right|\right.$$

$$\left. - \left|\bar{p}_{x_A}(3)\,p_{x_B}(4)\right|\right] \times \left[\left|p_{y_A}(5)\,\bar{p}_{y_B}(6)\right| - \left|\bar{p}_{y_A}(5)\,p_{y_B}(6)\right|\right] \quad ...(12.139)$$

To allow exchange of electrons between, say, the orbital p_z and p_x, we have to multiply the three factors in Equation (12.139) and write out the expression for $\Psi_{N_2}^{VB}$ in full. Carrying out the multiplication in the usual algebraic manner (*i.e.*, treating each term in Equation (12.139) as an algebraic term) and arranging the resulting product terms as determinants, we find an expression for $\Psi_{N_2}^{VB}$ as a linear combination of eight 6×6 determinants as given below,

$$\Psi = |z_A\, \bar{z}_B\, x_A\, \bar{x}_B\, y_A\, \bar{y}_B| - |z_A\, \bar{z}_B\, \bar{x}_A\, x_B\, y_A\, \bar{y}_B| - |\bar{z}_A\, z_B\, x_A\, \bar{x}_B\, y_A\, \bar{y}_B| + |\bar{z}_A\, z_B\, \bar{x}_A\, x_B\, y_A\, \bar{y}_B|$$
$$- |z_A\, \bar{z}_B\, x_A\, \bar{x}_B\, \bar{y}_A\, y_B| + |z_A\, \bar{z}_B\, \bar{x}_A\, x_B\, \bar{y}_A\, y_B| + |\bar{z}_A\, z_B\, x_A\, \bar{x}_B\, \bar{y}_A\, y_B| - |\bar{z}_A\, z_B\, \bar{x}_A\, x_B\, \bar{y}_A\, y_B| \quad \text{... (12.140)}$$

where, for the sake of neatness of the expression, only the subscripts have been used to denote the orbitals and the numbers 1, 2, ... have been dropped. This function is antisymmetric as it changes sign when the spins α and β associated with any bonding pair of orbitals are exchanged. For each single exchange of spins in the first term the sign changes from +1 to −1. This is consistent with the Heitler-London theory.

If there are Ψ electron pair bonds, we shall need 2^n determinants to describe the function.

We may now compare the Ψ^{VB} with the corresponding MO wave function (a single determinant) for N_2, which has the electronic configuration $1\pi_{x_u}^2\, 1\pi_{y_u}^2\, 3\sigma_g^2$,

$$\Psi_{N_2}^{MO} = \left| 1\pi_{x_u} . 1\bar{\pi}_{x_u} . 1\pi_{y_u} . 1\bar{\pi}_{y_u} . 3\sigma_g . 3\bar{\sigma}_g \right| \quad \text{... (12.141)}$$

We can likewise consider the VB wave function for O_2 molecule. The electronic configuration ($1s^2\, 2s^2\, 2p^4$) of an O atom suggests that two bonds can be formed—the pair of electrons in the two p_z AOs of each atom form σ bond having lower energy, and the pair in the p_y AOs form π bond. The remaining four electrons remain in the two p_x AOs as lone pairs. Then the bond eigenfunction can be written as,

$$\psi_\sigma = \left| p_{z_A}(1)\, \bar{p}_{z_B}(2) \right| - \left| \bar{p}_{z_A}(1)\, p_{z_B}(2) \right|$$

$$\psi_\pi = \left| p_{y_A}(3)\, \bar{p}_{y_B}(4) \right| - \left| \bar{p}_{y_A}(3)\, p_{y_B}(4) \right| \quad \text{... (12.142)}$$

The complete antisymmetric molecular wave function of O_2, $\Psi_{O_2}^{VB}$, is a product of ψ_σ and ψ_π.

It is interesting to compare this function with the single determinantal MO wave function for O_2 molecule, which is

$$\Psi_{O_2}^{MO} = \left| 3\sigma_g\, 3\bar{\sigma}_g\, 1\pi_{x_u}\, 1\bar{\pi}_{x_u}\, 1\pi_{y_u}\, 1\bar{\pi}_{y_u}\, 1\pi_{x_g}\, 1\pi_{x_g} \right| \quad \text{... (12.143)}$$

The VB functions (12.142) have all the electrons paired and, therefore, correspond to a singlet ground state; the ground state is, however, known to be triplet. Further, the wave function does not explain the paramagnetic properties of the molecule. The MO function (12.143), on the other hand, provides a satisfactory explanation for both these properties.

12.6.2.1 Ionic Contributions

Heitler-London wave functions do not adequately account for the bond energy unless amended by adding ionic contributions. The total wave function for a molecule A – B is then given by,

$$\psi = a\psi(A - B) + b\psi(A^+ B^-) + c\psi(A^- B^+) \quad \text{... (12.144)}$$

where ψ (A – B) is given by Equation (12.133), and

$$\psi(A^+B^-) = \left| \phi_B \bar{\phi}_B \right|, \psi(A^-B^+) = \left| \phi_A \bar{\phi}_A \right|$$

The terms a, b and c in Equation (12.144) are the weighing coefficients determined by variation method. The relative contributions of the three structures are in the ratio $a^2 : b^2 : c^2$. For homonuclear molecules, $b = c$, and for hetero-nuclear molecules that are highly polar, one of the two ionic structures does not contribute significantly.

In HF, for example, we have a 1s electron of H and a 2p electron of F available for bonding. Ignoring the other four 2p electrons of F, which are nonbonding, we may write the bond eigenfunction as,

$$\psi_{H-F} = a\left[\left| 1s_H(1)\, 2\bar{p}_F(2) \right| - \left| 1\bar{s}_H(1)\, 2p_F(2) \right|\right] + b\left[\left| 2p_F(1)\, 2\bar{p}_F(2) \right|\right] + c\left[\left| 1s_H(1)\, 1\bar{s}_H(2) \right|\right] \quad \text{... (12.145)}$$

The last two terms represent the ionic structures $H^+ F^-$ and $H^- F^+$, respectively. However, F is known to be far more electronegative than H ; accordingly, the probability that the two electrons are in 1s AO of H is far less than the probability that they are in 2p AO of F. Therefore, the last term in Equation (12.145) may be ignored without loss of accuracy.

Similarly, the bond between Li ($1s^2\, 2s$) and H (1s) in LiH can be described by,

$$\psi_{Li-H} = a\left[\left| 2s_{Li}(1)\, 1\bar{s}_H(2) \right| - \left| 2\bar{s}_{Li}(1)\, 1s_H(2) \right|\right] + b\left| 1s_H(1)\, 1\bar{s}_H(2) \right| + c\left| 2s_{Li}(1)\, 2\bar{s}_{Li}(2) \right| \quad \text{... (12.146)}$$

Since Li has much less ionisation potential than H, the structure $Li^+ H^-$ is much more probable than $Li^- H^+$.

For a highly polar molecule AB in general with B more electronegative than A.

$$\psi = a\psi(A - B) + b\psi(A^+B^-) \quad \text{... (12.147)}$$

If the overlap integral

$$S = \int \psi(A - B) \cdot \psi(A^+ B^-)\, d\tau$$

is very small, and the functions ψ (A – B) and ψ ($A^+ B^-$) are separately normalised, then it is necessary that $a^2 + b^2 = 1$. The quantities a^2 and b^2 represent the relative covalent and ionic contributions, respectively, (the fractional covalent and ionic characters) to the bond A – B. If we put $\frac{b}{a} = \lambda$, the normalised wave function can be written as

$$\Psi = N[\psi(A - B) + \lambda\psi(A^+B^-)],$$
$$N = \text{normalisation factor.} \quad \text{... (12.148)}$$

and the percentage ionic character (ρ) can be calculated by the formula

$$\rho = \frac{100\lambda^2}{1 + \lambda^2}.$$

12.7 COMPARISON OF MO AND VB THEORIES

We have two parallel theories of bonding and molecular structure, each of which has its own merits and demerits.

In the VB theory, the electronic structure of a molecule is described in terms of atomic orbitals as in the case of atomic structure; in MO theory it is done in terms of new orbitals, the molecular orbitals, which are linear combinations of atomic orbitals.

The ground state of H_2 in either theory corresponds to a symmetric spatial wave function which in MO treatment is

$$\psi^{MO} = [1s_A(1) + 1s_B(1)]\,[1s_A(2) + 1s_B(2)]$$

and in VB treatment $\psi^{VB} = [1s_A(1)\,1s_B(2) + 1s_B(1)\,1s_A(2)]$

The overall antisymmetry of the molecular wave function, as required by Pauli's principle, is ensured through the antisymmetric spin combination $[\alpha(1)\,\beta(2) - \alpha(2)\,\beta(1)]$, which leads to singlet state.

In both the theories emphasis is laid on the overlap of atomic orbitals and the cause of bonding is shown to be displacement of electron density into the internuclear region. But MO treatment puts greater electron density between the nuclei than the VB treatment. The stabilisation of the molecule, according to either theory, is attributed to exchange integral, *i.e.*, lowering of energy by exchange (or sharing) of electrons between two atomic orbitals. In MO theory the exchange integral is

$$\int \phi_A\, \hat{H}\, \phi_B\, d\tau,$$

which refers to the exchange of one electron between two AO's ϕ_A and ϕ_B and which implies an interaction or "coupling" between the two orbitals. In VB theory the exchange integral

$$\int \phi_A(1)\,\phi_B(2)\,\hat{H}\,\phi_B(1)\,\phi_A(2)\,d\tau$$

refers to the exchange of a pair of electrons between the two atomic orbitals. In this way while the VB theory retains the concept of "electron pair bond" between two atoms, it is lost in MO theory, there being a continuous electron density distribution over the whole molecule with no localisation of the electron pair so that the bond is not identifiable.

The typical VB function for a bond in homonuclear molecule, like H_2, in ground state is the Heitler-London (H-L) function

$$\psi^{VB} = \phi_A(1)\,\phi_B(2) + \phi_B(1)\,\phi_A(2)$$

while the corresponding MO function is

$$\psi^{MO} = [\phi_A(1) + \phi_B(1)]\,[\phi_A(2) + \phi_B(2)]$$

$$= \phi_A(1)\,\phi_B(2) + \phi_B(1)\,\phi_A(2) + \phi_A(1)\,\phi_A(2) + \phi_B(1)\,\phi_B(2)$$

The first two terms in ψ^{MO} correspond to the H-L wave function and the next two terms represent ionic bonds $H_{A^-}\,H_{B^+}$ and $H_{A^+}\,H_{B^-}$, *i.e.*, ψ^{MO} is an equal mixture of covalent and ionic wave functions. ψ^{VB} completely ignores the ionic function. In the other words, according to VB theory, if one electron of H_2 is in the orbital $1s_A$, the other must be in $1s_B$ and there is no chance of both electrons being in the same orbital $1s_A$ or $1s_B$. This is called complete "charge correlation"—the tendency of an electron to resist the presence of another electron in its orbital. The MO theory underestimates charge correlation, *i.e.*, if one electron is in orbital $1s_A$ the other electron may be in either $1s_A$ or $1s_B$.

The two functions ψ^{VB} and ψ^{MO} as described have different implications. While the VB theory predicts the dissociation of H_2 like $H_2 = H + H$, the MO theory predicts two reactions

$H_2 = H + H$, and $H_2 = H^+ + H^-$ of equal probability. This prediction from ψ^{MO} is in poor agreement with the chemical experience as the dissociation of ground state H_2 into ions is much less probable.

The VB calculations using H-L wave functions yield a dissociation energy of 3.14 eV for H_2 ; the MO calculations give a value of 2.68 eV. Both the values are far below the experimental value of 4.75 eV.

Thus, the two wave functions ψ^{MO} and ψ^{VB} represent two extremes of the situation. Which is closer to the truth ? For small values of internuclear distance R, when there are greater chances of finding the two electrons in one orbital, MO theory applies better. For larger values of R, VB treatment seems more adequate.

Efforts have been made to improve both VB and MO treatments. VB treatment has been improved by the use of "ion-covalent resonance" which means adding ionic function to the H-L function; for H_2 molecule, it is expressed as,

$$\psi^{VB} = \psi(H-H) + \lambda\,[\psi(H^+H^-) + \psi(H^-H^+)] \qquad \text{... (12.149)}$$

Variation calculation leads to $\lambda = \frac{1}{6}$ or $\lambda^2 = \frac{1}{36}$, which means nearly 3% ionic contribution to the bond. MO treatment has been improved by including "configuration interaction", which means taking a linear combination of the functions corresponding to different electronic configurations having the same symmetry. In H_2, for example, the ground state configuration is $\sigma_g(1)\ \bar{\sigma}_g(2)$ and the doubly excited state is $\sigma_u(1)\ \bar{\sigma}_u(2)$. Both have singlet state with overall symmetry $^1\Sigma_g^+$. Therefore, a better wave function is the linear combination of the two $^1\Sigma_g^+$ functions *i.e.*,

$$\psi^{MO} = a_1 \left| \sigma_g(1)\bar{\sigma}_g(2) \right| + a_2 \left| \sigma_u(1)\bar{\sigma}_u(2) \right| \qquad \text{... (12.150)}$$

where a_1 and a_2 are in a mixing parameters.

Both the wave functions can be further improved by using effective nuclear charge $Z^* = 1.193$ in place of $Z = 1$ in the exponent of the 1*s* orbitals.

MO theory provides a more convenient explanation for electronic transition in molecules as compared to the VB theory.

In recent years MO theory has gained more popularity compared with the VB theory on account of mathematical simplicity. For large molecules, VB treatment involves an unmanageably large number of determinants, but MO treatment is comparatively less tedious and it is easy to programme it on computers.

PROBLEMS

12.1 Apply the linear variation method to H_2^+ using a trial function,

$$\psi = a_1\phi_A + a_2\phi_B,$$

where $$\phi_A = \frac{1}{\sqrt{m}}\exp(-r_A) \text{ and } \phi_B = \frac{1}{\sqrt{\pi}}\exp(-r_B),$$

to obtain approximate eigenfunctions and eigenvalues for the ground and first excited states.
[**Hint :** See text].

12.2 Find the expression for the expectation value of the Hamiltonian for H_2 in terms of atomic integrals.
[**Hint :** See text].

12.3 The He_2^+ ion has the configuration $1\sigma_g^2\ 1\sigma_u$. Find the total energy of this system in terms of integrals J and K.
[**Hint :** Let the energies of $1\sigma_g$ and $1\sigma_u$ be E_1 and E_2.

$$E = 2E_1 + E_2 + J_{11} + 2J_{12} - K_{12}$$

where
$$J_{11} = \int 1\sigma_g(1)\, 1\sigma_g(2) \frac{1}{r_{12}} 1\sigma_g(1)\, 1\sigma_g(2)\, d\tau$$

$$J_{12} = \int 1\sigma_g(1)\, 1\sigma_u(2) \frac{1}{r_{12}} 1\sigma_g(1)\, 1\sigma_u(2)\, d\tau$$

and
$$K_{12} = \int 1\sigma_g(1)\, 1\sigma_u(2) \frac{1}{r_{12}} 1\sigma_g(2)\, 1\sigma_u(1)\, d\tau$$

for further treatment see the text].

12.4 For a one-electron homonuclear diatomic molecule the values of some relevant integrals are given below:

$$\int \phi_A\, \hat{H}\, \phi_A\, d\tau = -2\text{ a.u.}, \int \phi_B\, \hat{H}\, \phi_B\, d\tau = -2\text{ a.u.}$$

$$\int \phi_A\, \hat{H}\, \phi_B\, d\tau = -1\text{ a.u.}, \int \phi_A\, \phi_B\, d\tau = 0.25$$

where ϕ_A and ϕ_B are the normalised set of basis functions for an LCAO wave function. Find the upper bound for the electronic energy of this system and also the corresponding normalised wave function.

[**Hint :** $\begin{vmatrix} -2-E & -1-0.25\,E \\ -1-0.25\,E & -2-E \end{vmatrix} = 0$

or $0.9375\,E^2 + 3.5\,E + 3 = 0$

or
$$E = -2.4\text{ a.u. and } -1.33\text{ a.u.}$$

$$C_1(-2+2.4) + C_2(-1+2.4\times 0.25) = 0$$

or
$$0.4\,C_1 - 0.4\,C_2 = 0 \text{ or } C_1 = C_2$$

$$C_1^2 + C_2^2 = 1\text{; therefore, } C_1 = C_2 = \frac{1}{\sqrt{2}}$$

$$\psi_+ = \frac{1}{\sqrt{2}}(\phi_A + \phi_B)].$$

12.5 For a one-electron heteronuclear diatomic molecule the values of some relevant integrals are given below:

$$\int \phi_A \hat{H} \phi_A \, d\tau = -2 \text{ a.u.}; \int \phi_B \hat{H} \phi_B \, d\tau = -1 \text{ a.u.}$$

$$\int \phi_A \hat{H} \phi_B \, d\tau = -0.5 \text{ a.u.}, \int \phi_A \phi_B \, d\tau = \frac{1}{3} \text{ a.u.}$$

where ϕ_A and ϕ_B are the normalised basis functions for an LCAO wave function. Find the lowest energy that can be computed from the LCAO wave function $\psi = C_1 \phi_A + C_2 \phi_B$. Find the normalised wave function.

[**Hint:** $E_{min} = -2.03$ a.u.

$\psi = 0.984\, \phi_A - 0.174\, \phi_B$].

12.6 Show that at $R = \infty$, the wave functions ψ_+ and ψ_- for H_2^+ can describe a state wherein the electron is in a $1s_A$ AO on atom A or on atom B.

[**Hint:** At $R = \infty$, ψ_+ and ψ_- are degenerate and can, therefore, be mixed.

$\psi_+ + \psi_- = 1s_A + 1s_B + 1s_A - 1s_B = 21s_A$ (when electron is on atom A)

$\psi_+ - \psi_- = 1s_A + 1s_B - 1s_A + 1s_B = 21s_B$

(when the electron is on atom B)].

12.7 Give the determinantal form of the wave function for H_2 in ground state.

$$\left[\textbf{Hint}: \psi = \frac{1}{\sqrt{2}} \left| 1\sigma_g(1)\, 1\bar{\sigma}_g(2) \right| \right].$$

12.8 The two lowest electronic states of H_2 can be understood in terms of the MO theory using spatial functions of the form,

$$\psi_{\pm} = \frac{1}{\sqrt{2(1 \pm S)}} [1s_A \pm 1s_B]$$

Construct all possible two-electron functions which are anti-symmetric with respect to electron exchange.

[**Hint :** There are six possible ways to arrange the electrons in keeping with the Pauli principles:

ψ_-	—	↑	↓	↑	↓	↑↓
ψ_+	↑↓	↑	↑	↓	↓	—
	ψ_1	ψ_2	ψ_3	ψ_4	ψ_5	ψ_6
$M_s =$	0	1	0	0	−1	0

$$\psi_1 = |\psi_+ \bar{\psi}_+| = \frac{1}{\sqrt{2}} [\psi_+(1)\, \psi_+(2)][\alpha(1)\beta(2) - \alpha(2)\beta(1)]$$

$$\psi_2 = |\psi_+ \psi_-| = \frac{1}{\sqrt{2}}[\psi_+(1)\psi_-(2) - \psi_-(1)\psi_+(2)][\alpha(1)\alpha(2)]$$

$$\psi_3 = |\psi_+ \bar{\psi}_-| = \frac{1}{\sqrt{2}}[\psi_+(1)\psi_-(2)\alpha(1)\beta(2) - \psi_-(1)\psi_+(2)\alpha(2)\beta(1)]$$

$$\psi_4 = |\bar{\psi}_+ \psi_-| = \frac{1}{\sqrt{2}}[\psi_+(1)\psi_-(2)\beta(1)\alpha(2) - \psi_-(1)\psi_+(2)\alpha(1)\beta(2)]$$

$$\psi_5 = |\bar{\psi}_+ \bar{\psi}_-| = \frac{1}{\sqrt{2}}[\psi_+(1)\psi_-(2) - \psi_-(1)\psi_+(2)][\beta(1)\beta(2)]$$

$$\psi_6 = |\psi_- \bar{\psi}_-| = \frac{1}{\sqrt{2}}[\psi_-(1)\psi_-(2)][\alpha(1)\beta(2) - \alpha(2)\beta(1)].$$

12.9 Give the molecular wave functions in terms of AO wave function for HCI and CO.
[**Hint:** HCl $\psi(1.2) = [C_1 1s_H(1) + C_2 3p_{z(C_1)}(1)][C_1 1s_H(2) + C_2 3p_{z(C_1)}(2)]$

$$= C_1^2 [1s_H(1) 1s_H(2)] + C_2^2 [3p_{z(C_1)}(1) 3p_{z(C_1)}(2)] + C_1 C_2 [1s_H(1) 3p_{z(C_1)}(2) + 1s_H(2) 3p_{z(C_1)}(1)]]$$

12.10 Show that the two MO's of H_2 given by

$$\psi_\pm = \frac{1}{\sqrt{2(1 \pm S)}}\{1s_A \pm 1s_B\}$$

are orthogonal.

$$\left[\textbf{Hint: } \int \psi_+ \psi_- \, d\tau = \frac{1}{2(1-S^2)} \int \left\{1s_{A^2}\, d\tau - \int 1s_{B^2}\, d\tau\right\} = 0\right].$$

12.11 Given the following MO's:

$$\psi_1 = \frac{1}{\sqrt{2}}(\phi_1 + \phi_2)$$

$$\psi_2 = \frac{1}{\sqrt{2}}(\phi_1 - \phi_2)$$

$$\psi_3 = \frac{1}{\sqrt{3}}(\phi_1 + \phi_2 + \phi_3)$$

$$\psi_4 = \frac{1}{2}(\phi_1 - 2\phi_2 + \phi_3)$$

where ϕ_i^1's are orthonormal set of basis functions. Examine if the MO's are orthonormal.

[**Hint:** $$\int \psi_1^2 \, d\tau = \frac{1}{2}\left\{\int \phi_{1^2}\, d\tau + \int \phi_{2^2}\, d\tau + 2\int \phi_1 \phi_2 \, d\tau = 1\right.$$

$$\int \psi_{4^2}\, d\tau = \frac{1}{4}\left\{\int \phi_{1^2}\, d\tau + 4\int \phi_{2^2}\, d\tau + \int \phi_{3^2}\, d\tau - 4\int \phi_1 \phi_2 \, d\tau\right.$$

$$- 4\int \phi_2 \phi_3 \, d\tau + 2\int \phi_1 \phi_3 \, d\tau = \frac{3}{2}\int \psi_1 \psi_2 \, d\tau = 0\Big].$$

12.12 Consider the one electron He – H^{++} ion system.

(*i*) Write the Hamiltonian (Born-Oppenheimer approximation) for the electronic energy in atomic units.

(*ii*) Calculate the electronic energies for the lowest energy state of this system in the (*a*) separated atom limit, and (*b*) united atom limit.

[**Hint:** $$\hat{H} = -\frac{1}{2}\nabla^2 - \frac{1}{r_H} - \frac{2}{r_{He}}$$

(*a*) $$E_{el} = E_{H^+} + E_{He^+}(1s) = 0 + \left(-\frac{2^2}{2\times 1}\right) = -2 \text{ a.u.}$$

(*b*) $$E_{el} = E_{Li^{++}}(1s) = -\frac{3^2}{2\times 1} = -4.5 \text{ a.u.}\Big].$$

12.13 Explain that in MO theory ionic bond is a limiting case of covalent bond.
[**Hint:** For a molecule AB]

$$\psi_{MO} = C_A \phi_A + C_B \phi_B$$

If $C_A >> C_B$, $\psi_{MO} \approx \phi_A$, a non-bonding MO. If now we place the two valence electrons in ϕ_A we have only the ions A^- and B^+ which will be held together by coulombic attraction only].

12.14 Calculate the expectation value of the Hamiltonian for H_2^+ using the ground state wave function of H atom. Can this be used as a possible trial function to explain the stability of the one-electron H_2^+ system ? Explain. Given, the integral.

$$\frac{1}{\pi}\int \exp(-2r_A)\cdot\frac{1}{r_B}\cdot r_{A^2}\, dr_A \cdot \sin\theta \, d\theta \, d\phi$$

$$= \frac{1}{R}\left[1 - (1+R)\, e^{-2R}\right]$$

R being the internuclear distance.

[**Hint:** $$E_{H_2^+} = \int 1s_A \left[-\frac{1}{2}\nabla^2 - \frac{1}{r_A} - \frac{1}{r_B}\right] 1s_A \, d\tau$$

$$= \int 1s_A \left(-\frac{1}{2}\nabla^2 - \frac{1}{r_A}\right) 1s_A \, d\tau - \int 1s_A \cdot \frac{1}{r_B} 1s_A \, d\tau$$

$$= E_H - \frac{1}{\pi}\int \exp(-2r_A)\frac{1}{r_B} \cdot r_{A^2} \cdot dr_A \cdot \sin\theta\, d\theta\, d\phi$$

$$= -\frac{1}{2} - \frac{1}{R}\left[1-(1+R)e^{-2R}\right] \text{ (in a.u.)}$$

When $R \to \infty$, $\quad E_{H_2^+} = E_H = -\frac{1}{2}$ a.u.

When R is very small, $e^{-2R} \approx 1 - 2R$; then,

$$(1 + R)\, e^{-2R} \approx 1 - R - 2R^2, \text{ and}$$

$$E_{H_2^+} \approx E_H - (1 + 2R) \approx -\frac{1}{2} + 1 = +\frac{1}{2} \text{ a.u.}$$

At an intermediate value of R, addition of the internuclear repulsion energy $\frac{1}{R}$ gives the total,

$$E_{H_2^+} = -\frac{1}{2} + \left(1 + \frac{1}{R}\right)e^{-2R}$$

Calculated energy for various of R, when plotted against R, does not show a minimum indicating no stability; in fact, it is never less than $-\frac{1}{2}$ a.u., the energy of an H-atom. So 1*s* not a good trial function.]

12.15 (*a*) Give expression for H_2^+ electron density using

$$\psi_+ = \text{(bonding MO)} = \frac{1}{\sqrt{2(1+S)}}\{1s_A + 1s_B\}, \text{and}$$

$$S = \left(1 + R + \frac{R^2}{3}\right)e^{-R}.$$

(*b*) Calculate the values of electron density (e.d.) for R = 2 a.u. at each nucleus, at the mid-point between the nuclei and at a point one-fourth of the distance from one nucleus to the other. Plot the e.d. as a function of distance along the internuclear axis.

(*c*) Compare the values of the e.d. with the average of the e.d.'s of two 1*s* atomic orbitals centred at the two nuclei.

(*d*) Calculate the e.d.'s corresponding to an electron in ψ_- (antibonding MO) at the same points as given in (*a*) along the internuclear axis. Compare the results with the average of the e.d.'s of two 1*s* atomic orbitals.

[Hint: (*a*) $\quad \psi_+^2 = \frac{1}{2(1+S)}\left\{1s_{A^2} + 1s_{B^2} + 2(1s_A \cdot 1s_B)\right\}$

(*b*) At $\quad R = 2 \text{ a.u.}, S = \frac{13}{3}e^{-2}\,;\, 1s = \frac{1}{\sqrt{\pi}}e^{-r}$

At the nuclei ($r = 0$), e.d. $= \frac{1}{\pi}$ ($\because$ at the nucleus A $1s_B^2$ is negligible and *vice versa*)

At the mid-point ($r_A = r_B = 1$).

$$\psi_+^2 \text{ (e.d.)} = \frac{1}{2\left(1+\frac{13}{3}e^{-2}\right)}\left\{\frac{1}{\pi}.e^{-2}+\frac{1}{\pi}.e^{-2}+\frac{2}{\pi}.e^{-2}\right\}$$

$$= \frac{1}{2\left(1+\frac{13}{3}.e^{-2}\right)} \times \frac{4}{\pi}.e^{-2}$$

Now use a calculator to evaluate ψ_+^2. Similarly, carry out the calculation for $r_A = \frac{R}{4}$ and $r_B = \frac{3R}{4}$; calculate ψ_+^2 for various values of r_A and r_B (*i.e.*, along the internuclear axis R) and plot these.

(*c*) Average of the e.d.'s of two 1*s* AOs at the two nuclei

$$= \left.\frac{1s_{A^2} + 1s_{B^2}}{2} = \frac{1}{\pi}\right].$$

12.16 A homonuclear diatomic molecule has the ground state molecular orbital configuration:

$$1\sigma_g^2\ 1\sigma_u^2\ 2\sigma_g^2\ 2\sigma_u^2\ 1\pi_u^4\ 3\sigma_g^2\ 1\pi_g^2$$

(*i*) What is the net number of bonding electrons?

(*ii*) What will be the spin multiplicity for the ground state?

(*iii*) What would be the effect on the dissociation energy of the molecule of the ionisation from the

(*a*) $1\pi_g$ M.O. (*b*) $3\sigma_g$ M.O.?

(*iv*) What would be the spin multiplicity of the resulting molecule ion if one electron goes-out of the $1\pi_g$ level ?

[**Hint :** (*i*) 4, (*ii*) triplet, (*iii*) (*a*)) stabilised *i.e.*, dissociation energy is increased, (*iii*) (*b*)) destablished, (*iv*) doublet].

12.17 Calculate the bond orders for the following molecule ions and compare the strengths of the bonds with those of the parent neutral molecules:

$$NO^+,\ He_{2^+},\ Be_{2^+},\ Be_{2^-},\ F_{2^+},\ F_{2^-},\ CO^+,\ CO^-$$

Ionisation occurs from the highest occupied MO.

[**Hint :** $NO^+ : 1\sigma_2^2\ 2\sigma^{2^*}\ 3\sigma^{2^*}\ 4\sigma^2\ 1\pi^4\ 5\sigma^2$, B.O. $= \frac{6-0}{2} = 3$

$$NO : 1\sigma^2\ 2\sigma^{2^*}\ 3\sigma^{2^*}\ 4\sigma^2\ 1\pi^4\ 5\sigma_2^2\ \pi^*, \text{ B.O.} = \left.\frac{6-1}{2} = 2.5\right].$$

12.18 Predict the ground state configuration of

$$C_2, C_{2^+}, C_{2^-}, N_{2^+}, N_{2^-}, O_2, O_{2^+}, CO, NO \text{ and } NO^+.$$

Decide which terms can arise in each case and suggest which is lowest.

[**Hint :** C_2 : $1\sigma_g^2\, 1\sigma_u^2\, 2\sigma_g^2\, 2\sigma_u^2\, 1\pi_g^4$ (without spin correlation)

This gives rise to ${}^1\Sigma_g$.

C_2 : $1\sigma_g^2\, 1\sigma_u^2\, 2\sigma_g^2\, 2\sigma_u^2\, 1\pi_u^3\, 3\sigma_g^1$ (with spin correlation)

This gives rise to ${}^3\pi_u$.

(The second configuration can be justified by the facts that (*i*) the difference between $1\pi_u$ and $3\sigma_g$ is not very large. (*ii*) the disadvantage of entering the higher energy $3\sigma_g$ MO is offset by the lessening of the electron-electron repulsion in the $1\pi_u$ MO, and (*iii*) spin correlation helps to stabilise it. Similarly for other molecules].

12.19 Calculate the energy of the atomic orbitals involved in the bonding of H and F atoms in HF molecule using screening rules. On the basis of the energies what would be the polarity of the HF molecules? Would HCl be more polar than HF on this basis ?

[**Hint:**

$$F : Z^* = Z - 5 \times 0.85 = 9 - 4.25 = 4.75$$

$$Cl ; Z^* = Z - 5 \times 0.85 = 17 - 4.25 = 12.75$$

$$E_F = -\frac{1}{2} \times \frac{4.75^2}{4} = -2.82 \text{ a.u.}$$

$$E_{Cl} = -\frac{1}{2} \times \frac{12.75}{9} = -9.02 \text{ a.u.}$$

In $C_H\ (1s_H) + C_F\ (2p_{zF})$, because $E_F < E_H$, $C_F > C_H$; hence,

$$\overset{\delta^+}{H}-\overset{\delta^-}{F} \text{ is polar.}$$

Since $E_{Cl} < E_F$, $C_{Cl} >> C_H$: hence, HCl will be much more polar than HF].

12.20 On the basis of the MO theory predict the stability of He-H and Li-H. What will be the nature of polarity in Li-H?

[**Hint:** He-H: From screening rules,

$$Z^* = 2 - 0.35 = 1.65$$

$$E_{He}(1s) = -\frac{1}{2} \times 1.65^2 = -1.36 \text{ a.u.}$$

$$E_H(1s) = -0.5 \text{ a.u.}$$

Difference = 0.86 a.u. = 23 eV, which is very large; therefore, there is no effective combination.

$$\text{Li-H: } E_{Li}(1s) = -\frac{1}{2} \times 3^2 = -4.5 \text{ a.u.} << E_H$$

For Li (2*s*) AO, $Z^* = 3 - 3 \times 0.85 = 1.3$

$$E_{Li}(2s) = -\frac{1}{2}\times\frac{1.3^2}{2} = -0.21 \text{ a.u.}$$

Difference with $E_H(1s) = 0.29$ a.u. = 87.89 eV, which is not very large; therefore, combination is possible between $2s_{Li}$ and $1s_H$.

$$\psi \text{ Li-H} = C_{Li}\, 2s_{Li} + C_H\, 1s_H \text{ (bonding MO)}$$

There is a total of 4 electrons, of which two are in $1s_{Li}$ and two in $\psi_{Li\text{-}H}$, since

$$E_{1s_H} (= -0.5 \text{ a.u.}) < E_{2s\,Li} (= -0.21 \text{ a.u.})$$

$C_H > C_{Li}$, *i.e.*, the MO formulation puts more electron density on the H side than on the Li side of the molecule; therefore,

$$\text{Li-H is } \overset{\delta^+}{\text{Li}}-\overset{\delta^-}{\text{H}} \text{].}$$

12.21 Compare the MO and VB theories of bonding.
[**Hint :** See the text].

12.22 Write the normalised antisymmetric VB wave functions for $H^+ H^-$ and $H^- H^+$ using 1*s* AO's of the H-atoms.

$$\left[\textbf{Hint}: H_{A^+}\, H_{B^-} : \frac{1}{\sqrt{2}} . 1s_B(1)\, 1s_B(2) \{\alpha(1)\beta(2) - \alpha(2)\beta(1)\}\right].$$

12.23 Write the ground state VB wave functions for Li-F, and Cl-F molecule including ionic structures.
[**Hint :** Using 2*s* (Li) and $2p_z$ (F) atomic orbitals, we can write

$$\psi_{Li\text{-}F} = 2s(1)\, 2p_z(2) + 2s(2)\, 2p_z(1)] + \lambda\, [2p_z(1)\, 2p_z(2)]$$

Since F is much more electronegative than Li, the contribution of 2*s* (1) 2*s* (2) negligible].

12.24 Write the Slater determinantal wave function for Cl_2.
[**Hint :** Use the $2p_z$ AO of each Cl atom].

12.25 Using the expressions given in the text for J, K and S, calculate (*i*) $\frac{J}{S^2}$, (*ii*) $\frac{J \pm K}{1 \pm S^2}$ for H_2 for the values of R = 0, 0.5, 1.0, 1.5, 2.0 and 2.5 atomic units. Plot them against R and comment. Use a calculator.

12.26 Give the resonance structures for

$$NO, NO_2\ NO_3^-, CO_3^-, CH_3COOH, CH_3COO^-$$

explaining which structures are more probable or equally probable.

12.27 Use the Heitler-London wave function of H_2 to show that the electron density between the nuclei increases by an amount

$$2S . 1s_A\, 1s_B - S^2 \left(1s_{A^2} + 1s_{B^2}\right)$$

in the bonding state and decreases by the same amount in the non-bonding state.
[**Hint:** Refer to Equation (12.105);

$$\rho = \frac{1}{1 \pm S^2}\left[1s_{A^2} + 1s_{B^2} \pm 2S . 1s_A\, 1s_B\right]$$

change in e.d. between the nuclei

$$= \frac{1}{1 \pm S^2}\left[1s_{A^2} + 1s_{B^2} \pm 2S \, . \, 1s_A \, 1s_B\right] - \left[1s_{A^2} + 1s_{B^2}\right]$$

$$= \frac{\pm 2S \, . \, 1s_A \, 1s_B - S^2\left[1s_{A^2} + 1s_{B^2}\right]}{1 \pm S^2}$$

$$= \pm 2S \, . \, 1s_A \, 1s_B - S^2\left[1s_{A^2} + 1s_{B^2}\right], \text{assuming } S^2 << 1].$$

12.28 The VB wave function of HCl is given by

$$\psi = N\,(\psi_{H-Cl} + \lambda \; \psi_{H^+Cl^-}).$$

Calculate the percentage ionic character of the molecule, given the dipole moment (μ) = 1.03 D and bond length R = 1.27 Å. Assume that

(*i*) ψ_{H-Cl} and $\psi_{H^+Cl^-}$ are orthonormal and

(*ii*) covalent part is non-polar (μ = 0).

[Hint: $N = \frac{1}{\sqrt{1+\lambda^2}}$;

$$\mu = e\hat{r} = \int \psi \hat{\mu} \psi \, d\tau \text{, and \% ionic character, } \rho = \frac{100\lambda^2}{1+\lambda^2}$$

$$\mu = \int \psi \hat{\mu} \psi \, d\tau$$

$$= \frac{1}{1+\lambda^2}\left[\int \psi_{H-Cl} \hat{\mu} \psi_{H-Cl} \, d\tau + \lambda^2 \int \psi_{H^+Cl^-} \hat{\mu} \psi_{H^+Cl^-} \, d\tau + 2\lambda \int \psi_{H-Cl} \hat{\mu} \psi_{H^+Cl^-} \, d\tau\right]$$

$$= \frac{1}{1+\lambda^2}\left[0 + \lambda^2 \int \psi_{H^+Cl^-} \hat{\mu} \psi_{H^+Cl^-} \, d\tau + 0\right]$$

[Using assumptions (*i*) and (*ii*)]

Also, $\hat{\mu} = e\,\hat{R}$

Therefore, $$\mu = \frac{\lambda^2}{1+\lambda^2}\int \psi_{H^+Cl^-} (eR)\, \psi_{H^+Cl^-} \, d\tau = \frac{\lambda^2}{1+\lambda^2}\cdot(eR) = 1.03 \text{ D}$$

$e = 4.8 \times 10^{-10}$ e.s.u., R = 1.27 Å, therefore eR = 6.10 D

$$\% \text{ ionic character} = \frac{100\lambda^2}{1+\lambda^2} = \frac{1.03}{6.10} = 17\Bigg].$$

CHAPTER 13

Theory of Chemical Bonding (Polyatomic Molecules)

The ideas introduced during the discussion of chemical bonding in diatomic molecules (*e.g.*, overlap of atomic orbitals, pairing of spins, classification of orbitals and bonds into σ and π, etc.) form a basis of treatment of bonding in polyatomic molecules too. However, in diatomic molecules the orbitals are distinguished by their angular momenta around the internuclear axis (σ MO has no angular momentum, π has 1 unit, etc.); in polyatomic molecules the orbitals are distinguished by their spatial characteristics; a π orbital has a nodal plane containing the bond axis while a σ orbital does not have it. Thus, the π MO in ethylene is similar to the π MO in O_2. A bond (σ or π) in VB theory is not described in terms of a single valence structure, but by a resonance of several structures.

Due to increased numbers of electrons and atomic orbitals involved in bonding, the calculations become much more complicated in the case of polyatomic molecules. Schemes of simplifications and further approximations used in both MO and VB theories for simple polyatomic molecules will be outlined in the following sections.

13.1 MOLECULAR ORBITAL THEORY

13.1.1 General

In this text the quantum mechanical treatment of polyatomic molecules will be confined to 'closed shell' systems only (*i.e.*, those with all electrons paired ($\alpha\beta$) in molecular orbitals. The wave function (antisymmetric) in such systems with n electrons is a single Slater determinant which in abbreviated form (diagonal elements only) is

$$\Psi = \frac{1}{\sqrt{n!}}\left| \psi_1(1)\,\bar{\psi}_1(2)\,\psi_2(3)\,\bar{\psi}_2(4)\cdots\cdots\psi_{\frac{n}{2}}(n-1)\,\psi_{\frac{n}{2}}(n)\right| \quad \text{... (13.1)}$$

where, say, $\psi_i\,(k-1)$ and $\bar{\psi}_i\,(k)$ are spin molecular orbitals (MO) of electrons numbering $k-1$ and k with spins α and β respectively, and $\frac{1}{\sqrt{n!}}$ is the normalisation factor. The Schrödinger equation is

$$\hat{H}\,\bar{\Psi} = E\,\bar{\Psi} \qquad \text{... (13.2)}$$

where $\hat{H}$ is the Hamiltonian operator and E is total electronic energy of the molecule. The energy is determined as the expectation value,

$$E = \int \bar{\Psi}^* \,\hat{H}\,\bar{\Psi}\, d\tau \qquad \text{... (13.3)}$$

as $\bar{\Psi}$ is normalised. The operator $\hat{H}$ is

$$\hat{H} = \sum_{i=1}^{n} \hat{H}^0\,(i) + \hat{G} \qquad \text{... (13.4)}$$

where 1-electron operator $\hat{H}^0\,(i)$ is given as

$$\hat{H}^0\,(i) = -\frac{1}{2}\nabla_i^2 - \sum_{p=1} \frac{Z_p}{r_{pi}} \ \text{(in atomic units)} \qquad \text{... (13.5)}$$

and 2-electron operator $\hat{G}$ is

$$\hat{G} = \sum_{i}^{n} \sum_{<\, j}^{n} \frac{1}{r_{ij}} \ \text{(in atomic units)} \qquad \text{... (13.6)}$$

$\hat{H}^0$ (i) is the operator for electron i in the field of N nuclei with charges z_p and r_{pi} is the distance of the electron i from the nucleus p. $\hat{G}$ is the operator for interelectronic repulsion energy.

$\hat{H}^0\,(i)$ is also called 'core energy operator'.

The total electronic energy is thus partitioned into (1) sum of 1-electron core energies and (2) average sum of electronic repulsion energies between each pair of electrons 1 and 2. It is the latter which, on account of 2-electron coordinates (r_{ij}) has posed challenge in the evaluation of E. It is convenient to determine the energy through individual MOs energies by appropriate formulae. Further, the MOs have to be optimal in the sense that any change in any ψ_i to $\psi_i + \delta\psi_i$ will not change the energy, *i.e.*, $\delta E = 0$.

13.1.2 MOs, MO Energies and Total Energy

Calculations of MOs and MO energies may be classified as

(*a*) Ab Initio method.
(*b*) Semiempirical method.
(*c*) Empirical method.

All calculations are more or less approximate. The success of any calculation can be judged by nearness of the result to the experimental value. Ab initio (meaning calculation from the beginning) uses the Hamiltonian and seeks approximate solution without taking recourse to experimental data except for some basic quantities like bond distance etc. Semiempirical methods attempt at the solution of the Schrödinger equation by using empirical quantities for some integrals. Empirical methods do not solve Schrödinger equation and use empirical data for integrals.

13.2 AB INITIO METHOD–HARTREE-FOCK SCF METHOD

Ab initio method is Hartree-Fock SCF (Self Consistent Field) method. To meet the antisymmetry requirement of the wave function Fock, using the calculus of variation, replaced the operator $\frac{1}{r_{ij}}$ by two new operators 'coulomb $(\hat{J})$' and 'exchange $(\hat{K})$', in the Hamiltonian operator. The resulting "Fock operator" for electron 1 is

$$\hat{F}\ (1) = \hat{H}^0\ (1) + \sum_{j=1}^{n/2} \left(2\hat{J}_j\ (1) - \hat{K}_j\ (1)\right) \qquad \text{... (13.7)}$$

(See Chapter 9, Section 9.4)

(Derivation is lengthy, interested readers are referred to "Semi-empirical Methods of Quantum Chemistry" by J. Sadlej, John Wiley and Sons, Pages 18–22). The operators $\hat{J}$ and $\hat{K}$ for a pair of electrons 1 and 2 in MOs ψ_i and ψ_j are defined as,

$$\hat{J}_j\ (1)\ \psi_i\ (1) = \left[\int \psi_j^*\ (2) \frac{1}{r_{12}}\ \psi_j\ (2)\ d\tau_2\right] \psi_i\ (1) \qquad \text{... (13.8)}$$

$$\hat{K}_j\ (1)\ \psi_i\ (1) = \left[\int \psi_j^*\ (2) \frac{1}{r_{12}}\ \psi_i\ (2)\ d\tau_2\right] \psi_j\ (1) \qquad \text{... (13.9)}$$

Note that Equation (13.8) is an eigenvalue equation while Equation (13.9) is not. The operator $\hat{K}_j$ exchanges the electrons 1 and 2 between the MOs ψ_i and ψ_j.

The Orbital Energy: We thus arrive at the "pseudo-Schrödinger equation" for electron 1 (13.10) as

$$\hat{F}\ (1)\ \psi_i\ (1) = E_i\ (1)\ \psi_i\ (1) \qquad \text{... (13.10)}$$

where E_i (1) is called the orbital energy of electron 1 in the MO ψ_i. The orbital energy is, however, calculated as the expectation value of the $\hat{F}$-operator over the molecular orbital; thus, if ψ_i is normalised

$$E_i\ (1) = \int \psi_i^*\ (1)\ \hat{F}\ (1)\ \psi_i\ (1)\ d\tau_1$$

$$= \int \psi_i^*\ (1)\ \hat{H}^0\ (1)\ \psi_i\ (1)\ d\tau_1 + \int \psi_i^*\ (1) \sum_{j=1}^{n/2} \left(2\hat{J}_j\ (1) - \hat{K}_j\ (1)\right) \psi_i\ (1)\ d\tau_1$$

$$= H_{ii}^0\ (1) + \sum_{i}^{n/2} \underset{<}{\ } \sum_{j}^{n/2} \left(2J_{ij} - K_{ij}\right) \qquad \text{... (13.11)}$$

where H_{ii}^0 (1) (or E_i^0 (1)) is the core energy for electron 1; J_{ij} (coulombic repulsion energy) and K_{ij} (exchange energy) between electrons 1 and 2 in ψ_i and ψ_j are given by

$$J_{ij} = \iint \psi_i^*(1)\, \psi_j^*(2) \frac{1}{r_{12}} \psi_j(2)\, \psi_i(1)\, d\tau_1\, d\tau_2 \qquad \text{...(13.12)}$$

$$K_{ij} = \iint \psi_i^*(1)\, \psi_j^*(2) \frac{1}{r_{12}} \psi_i(2)\, \psi_j(1)\, d\tau_1\, d\tau_2 \qquad \text{...(13.13)}$$

(double indices *ij* have been used for energy and single *j* is for operators). Summation on the right side of (13.11) extends over all MOs and represents the net average energy of all interelectronic interactions. If $i = j$, then J_{ii} is the same as K_{ii} (no exchange) and $2J_{ii} - K_{ii} = J_{ii}$. The factor 2 appears in J_{ij} because repulsion occurs between two electrons in ψ_i and two in ψ_j; K_{ij}, on the other hand, denotes exchange of single electrons in ψ_i and ψ_j whose spins match.

Total Electronic Energy: The total electronic energy (E) of the molecule is not equal to the sum of all orbital energies $\left(\sum_i E_i\right)$. This is because while counting the MOs in the summation term one must remember that J_{ij} is the same as J_{ji} and K_{ij} same as K_{ji}. To avoid this double counting one has to subtract an amount $\sum_j^{n/2}\sum_i^{n/2}\left(2J_{ji} - K_{ji}\right)$ from the sum of orbital energies, *i.e.*,

$$E = 2\sum_{i=1}^{n/2} E_i - \sum_{j<i}^{n/2}\sum^{n/2}\left(2J_{ji} - K_{ji}\right)$$

$$= \left[2\sum_{i=1}^{n/2} E_i^0 + 2\sum_i^{n/2}\sum_j^{n/2}\left(2J_{ij} - K_{ij}\right)\right] - \sum_{j<}^{n/2}\sum_i^{n/2}\left(2J_{ji} - K_{ji}\right)$$

$$= 2\sum_{i=1}^{n/2} E_i^0 + \sum_{i<j}^{n/2}\sum^{n/2}\left(2J_{ij} - K_{ij}\right) \qquad \text{...(13.14)}$$

The factor 2 appears in $\sum_{i=1}^{n/2} E_i$ because there are two electrons in each MO ψ_i.

Equations (13.11) and (13.14) provide the expressions of HF-orbital energy and total electronic energy of a molecule respectively. The 1-electron HF Equation (13.10) much simpler than the initial many electron Schrödinger Equation (13.2). Yet to obtain the set of optimal MOs by solving these integro differential equations is a very cumbersome process.

13.2.1 The Roothan Equations

Roothan (1951) used the LCAO approximation for MOs to obtain algebraic equations from the HF integro differential equations. This made the MO determination somewhat easy. An unknown molecular orbital ψ_i is a linear combination of known basic functions (atomic orbitals) ϕ_v,

$$\psi_i = \sum_{\nu} a_{i\nu}\, \phi_\nu \qquad \text{... (13.15)}$$

where $a_{i\nu}$ is the LCAO coefficient for ϕ_ν in MO ψ_i. (Henceforth the Greek indices will be used for the atomic orbitals and Latin indices for MOs).

The HF Equation (13.10) under LCAO approximation becomes

$$\hat{F}(1) \sum_{\nu} a_{i\nu}\, \phi_\nu(1) = E_i \sum_{\nu} a_{i\nu}\, \phi_\nu(1) \qquad \text{... (13.16)}$$

Multiplying both sides of (13.16) by another basis function ϕ_μ^* and integrating over the coordinates of electron 1.

$$\sum_{\nu} a_{i\nu} \int \phi_\mu^*(1)\, \hat{F}(1)\, \phi_\nu(1)\, d\tau_1 = E_i \sum_{\nu} a_{i\nu} \int \phi_\mu^*(1)\, \phi_\nu(1)\, d\tau_1$$

On rearranging, $\sum_{\nu} a_{i\nu} \left(F_{\mu\nu} - E_i S_{\mu\nu}\right) = 0$ ... (13.17)

where $$F_{\mu\nu} = \int \phi_\mu^*(1)\, \hat{F}(1)\, \phi_\nu(1)\, d\tau_1,$$

and $$S_{\mu\nu} = \int \phi_\mu^*(1)\, \phi_\nu(1)\, d\tau_1$$

Equation (13.17) represents a set of ν secular equations for the different values of ν which are called "Roothan equations".

The corresponding secular determinant is

$$\left\| F_{\mu\nu} - E_i S_{\mu\nu} \right\| = 0 \qquad \text{... (13.18)}$$

which gives ν roots for E_i. The two index quantities $F_{\mu\nu}$ and $S_{\mu\nu}$ are the matrix elements of the Fock operator (matrix) and overlap matrix respectively. Writing the operator $\hat{F}$ in full,

$$F_{\mu\nu} = \int \phi_\mu^*(1) \left[\hat{H}^0(1) + \sum_{j=1}^{n/2} \left(2\hat{J}_j(1) - \hat{K}_j(1)\right) \right] \phi_\nu(1)\, d\tau_1 \qquad \text{... (13.19)}$$

There are three integrals in Equation (13.19): I_1, I_2 and I_3.

$$I_1 = \int \phi_\mu^*(1)\, \hat{H}^0(1)\, \phi_\nu(1)\, d\tau_1 = \hat{H}^0_{\mu\nu} \text{ (Standard notation)}$$

$$I_2 = \int \phi_\mu^*(1)\, \hat{J}_j(1)\, \phi_\nu(1)\, d\tau_1 = \int \phi_\mu^*(1) \left[\int \psi_j^*(2) \frac{1}{r_{12}} \psi_j(2)\, d\tau_2 \right] \phi_\nu(1)\, d\tau_1$$

... (by 13.8)

$$I_3 = \int \phi_\mu^*(1)\, \hat{K}_j\, \phi_\nu(1)\, d\tau_1 = \int \phi_\mu^*(1) \left[\int \psi_j^*(2) \frac{1}{r_{12}} \phi_\nu(2)\, d\tau_2 \right] \psi_j(1)\, d\tau_1$$

... (by 13.9)

where ψ_j (2) is another MO containing electron 2 and ψ_j^* (2) its complex conjugate. Let

$$\psi_j(2) = \sum_{\sigma} a_{j\sigma}\,\phi_\sigma(2)\,,\text{ and } \psi_j^*(2) = \sum_{\lambda} a_{j\lambda}^*\,\phi_\lambda^*(2)$$

This gives, after rearrangement

$$I_2 = \iint \sum_{\lambda}\sum_{\sigma} a_{j\lambda}^*\,a_{j\sigma}\,\phi_\mu^*(1)\,\phi_\nu(1)\frac{1}{r_{12}}\,\phi_\lambda^*(2)\,\phi_\sigma(2)\,d\tau_1\,d\tau_2 \quad \text{... (13.20)}$$

$$= \sum_{\lambda}\sum_{\sigma} a_{j\lambda}^*\,a_{j\sigma}\,(\mu\nu/\lambda\sigma) \quad \text{... (13.21)}$$

(using the standard short hand notation for 2-electron double integrals in which the basic functions are indicated by their indices, electron 1 remains on the left and electron 2 on the right side of a slash which stands for the operator $\frac{1}{r_{12}}$).

Proceeding in the same way

$$I_3 = \sum_{\lambda,\ \sigma}\sum a_{j\lambda}^*\,a_{j\sigma}\,(\mu\sigma/\lambda\nu) \quad \text{... (13.22)}$$

Further, if we define

$$P_{\lambda\sigma} = 2\sum_{j=1}^{n/2} a_{j\lambda}^*\,a_{j\sigma} \quad \text{... (13.23)}$$

Then,

$$F_{\mu\nu} = H_{\mu\nu}^0 + \sum_{\lambda,\sigma}\sum P_{\lambda\sigma}\left[(\mu\nu/\lambda\sigma) - \frac{1}{2}(\mu\sigma/\lambda\nu)\right] \quad \text{... (13.24)}$$

$$= H_{\mu\nu}^0 + G_{\mu\nu} \quad \text{... (13.25)}$$

These are matrix elements of 'Fock matrix' in terms of the basis functions.

$H_{\mu\nu}^0$, another two-index quantity, is also a matrix element of the 'core Hamiltonian operator', which is also a matrix. Likewise the quantity $P_{\lambda\sigma}$ is also a matrix element of what is called 'charge density matrix'.

13.2.2 Charge Density Matrix and Chemical Binding

The electronic charge density at a position r due to two electrons in an MO ψ_i may be defined as

$$\rho(r) = 2\sum_{i}^{\text{occ}} \psi_i^*\,\psi_i$$

$$= 2\sum\sum c_{\mu i}^*\,c_{\nu i}\,\phi_\mu(r)\,\phi_\nu(r)$$

$$= \sum_{\mu, r} P_{\mu r} \, \phi_\mu(r) \, \phi_\nu(r) \text{ (by definition of } P_{\mu\nu})$$

The total charge is

$$\int \rho(r)\, dr = \sum_{\mu,\nu} P_{\mu\nu} \int \phi_\mu(r)\, \phi_\nu(r)\, dr = \sum_{\mu,\nu} P_{\mu\nu}\, S_{\mu\nu} = n$$

where n is the total number of electrons in the molecule. This provides a convenient interpretation of the contributions of the electronic charge in terms of basis orbitals of the constituent atoms. The quantity $\sum P_{\mu\nu} S_{\mu\nu}$ may be considered the electronic population of the atomic overlap, the diagonal terms $P_{\mu\mu} S_{\mu\mu}$ denote the net charge residing in the orbital ϕ_μ and off-diagonal terms $P_{\mu\nu}$ $S_{\mu\nu}$ with ϕ_μ and ϕ_ν centred on different atoms give indication of the chemical bonding.

13.2.3 MOs of H_2O–An Example

The molecular orbitals of H_2O can be formed by linear combination of all atomic orbitals of oxygen and hydrogen which provide a minimal basis set of 7 atomic orbitals $1s^0$, $2s^0$, $2p_x^0, 2p_y^0, 2p_z^0, 1s_A^H$ and $1s_B^H$, the superscripts 0 and H denoting oxygen and hydrogen respectively and A and B refer to the two hydrogen atoms. The linear combination leads to a 7×7 secular determinant solution of which does not seem to be easy. However, if a molecule has symmetry, group theory provides a powerful means to simplify. Since the Hamiltonian $(\hat{H})$ is invariant under any symmetry operation, the MOs that are formed must belong to some irreducible representation (symmetry type) of the symmetry group to which the molecule belongs. This leads to factorisation (symmetry factorisation) of the determinant into smaller size determinants the number of which is equal to the number of the symmetry types of the MOs.

H_2O belongs to C_{2v} point group. The character table of this group has four irreducible representations A_1, A_2, B_1 and B_2. Each MO must belong to any of these types. For MOs and a.o.'s, however, the lower case alphabets a_1, a_2, b_1 and b_2 will be used keeping the upper case (A, B, ...) for the total wave function.

Let the molecular plane be the xy-plane and the y-axis the C_2-axis of rotation (see Fig. 13.1).

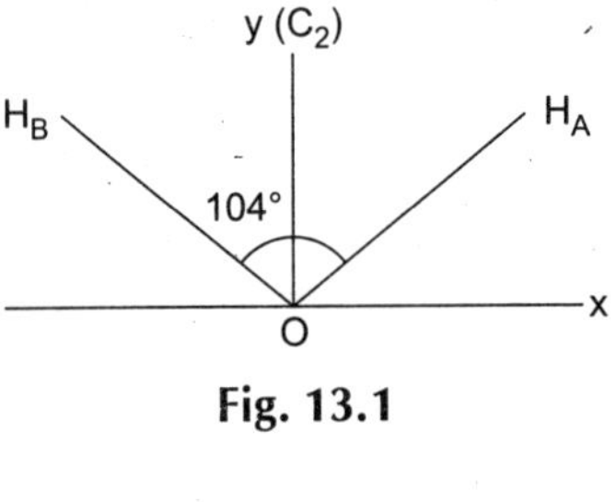

Fig. 13.1

The character table of C_{2v} group shows that the atomic orbitals $1s^0$, $2s^0$ and $2p_y^0$ belong to symmetry type a_1, $2p_x^0$ to b_2 and $2p_z^0$ to b_1. The AOs $1s_A$ and $1s_B$ of the two H atoms (the superscript H henceforth will remain dropped) are neither symmetric nor antisymmetric to C_2 or σ' (yz), and therefore, belong to none of these symmetry types; they just interchange their positions in these operations. But if we take their linear combination, the function $1s_A + 1s_B$ will be symmetric and $1s_A - 1s_B$ antisymmetric to C_2 and σ' (yz); for example

$$C_2\,(1s_A + 1s_B) = 1s_B + 1s_A = (1s_A + 1s_B)$$

$$C_2\,(1s_A - 1s_B) = 1s_B - 1s_A = -\,(1s_A - 1s_B)$$

Then $1s_A + 1s_B$ belongs to a_1 and $1s_A - 1s_B$ to b_2. These are called "symmetry adapted orbitals" or simply "symmetry orbitals" (SO).

Now we arrange the symmetry orbitals of H_2O as follows:

$$1s^0\,(\phi_1),\,2s^0\,(\phi_2),\;2p_y^0\,(\phi_3),\,(1s_A + 1s_B)\,(\phi_4)\;a_1$$

$$2p_x^0\,(\phi_5),\,(1s_A - 1s_B)\,(\phi_6)\;b_2$$

$$2p_z^0\,(\phi_7)\;b_1$$

There is no orbital of the type a_2.

Now consider the SOs (ϕ_r's) rather than the AOs as the basis function in the linear combination

$$\psi = a_1\,\phi_1 + a_2\,\phi_2 + \ldots + a_7\,\phi_7$$

The 7 × 7 determinantal equation is $|\,F_{ij} - ES_{ij}\,| = 0$ where

$$F_{ij} = \int \phi_i\,\hat{F}\,\phi_j\,d\tau\,,\,S_{ij} = \int \phi_i\,\phi_j\,d\tau$$

and

$$S_{ii} = \int \phi_i^2\,d\tau$$

$\hat{F}$ is the Fock operator as defined earlier. If ϕ_i and ϕ_j do not belong to the same symmetry type and all ϕ's are normalised, then

$$F_{ij} \text{ and } S_{ij} = 0 \text{ and } S_{ii} = 1$$

This reduces the 7 × 7 determinant to three blocks of smaller determinants as shown below:

$$\begin{vmatrix} & a_1 & & & & b_2 & b_1 \\ F_{11}-E & F_{12} & F_{13} & F_{14} & 0 & 0 & 0 \\ F_{21} & F_{22}-E & F_{23} & F_{24} & 0 & 0 & 0 \\ F_{31} & F_{32} & F_{33}-E & F_{34} & 0 & 0 & 0 \\ F_{41} & F_{42} & F_{43} & F_{44}-E & 0 & 0 & 0 \\ 0 & 0 & 0 & 0 & 0 & 0 & F_{77}-E \\ 0 & 0 & 0 & 0 & F_{55}-E & F_{56} & 0 \\ 0 & 0 & 0 & 0 & F_{65} & F_{66} & 0 \end{vmatrix} = 0 \qquad \ldots (13.26)$$

which means each of the three small determinants is equal to zero. It is easier to work with smaller determinants.

Correspondingly, the Roothan's simultaneous equations also break up into three sets of simultaneous equations—4 equations containing matrix elements involving symmetry orbitals of

a_1 type, two involving those of b_2 and one of b_1 type. Accordingly, the 7 lowest energy LCAO MOs of water will be grouped into four MOs of a_1, two of b_2 and one of b_1 symmetry as follows:

$$\left.\begin{aligned} \psi_1(a_1) &= a_{11}\,\phi_1 + a_{12}\,\phi_2 + a_{13}\,\phi_3 + a_{14}\,\phi_4 \\ \psi_2(a_1) &= a_{21}\,\phi_1 + a_{22}\,\phi_2 + a_{23}\,\phi_3 + a_{24}\,\phi_4 \\ \psi_3(a_1) &= a_{31}\,\phi_1 + a_{32}\,\phi_2 + a_{33}\,\phi_3 + a_{34}\,\phi_4 \\ \psi_4(a_1) &= a_{41}\,\phi_1 + a_{42}\,\phi_2 + a_{43}\,\phi_3 + a_{44}\,\phi_4 \end{aligned}\right\} \quad \ldots (13.27)$$

$$\left.\begin{aligned} \psi_5(b_2) &= a_{55}\,\phi_5 + a_{56}\,\phi_6 \\ \psi_6(b_2) &= a_{65}\,\phi_5 + a_{66}\,\phi_6 \\ \psi_7(b_1) &= \phi_7 \end{aligned}\right\}$$

where i in the coefficients a_{ij}, denotes the number in the MO (ψ) and j denotes the number in the SO (ϕ).

Pitzer and Merrifield (J. Chem. Phys. 1970, 52, 4782), writing the STOs for the atomic orbitals in explicit forms with optimised values of the orbital coefficients

$$(\xi_{1s^H} = 1.27,\ \xi_{1s^0} = 7.66,\ \xi_{2s^0} = 2.25 \text{ and } \xi_{2s^0} = 2.21)$$

calculated the MOs and their energies (details of which involve repeated SCF iterations and are avoided here) and obtained the MOs in the following order of energy:

$$1a_1 < 2a_1 < 1b_2 < 3a_1 < 1b_1$$

Nature of the MOs: The bonding, antibonding and non-bonding character of an MO is determined by the degree of overlap (S_{ij}) between the AOs of the combining atoms and the consequent electron density build-up.

ψ_1 ($1a_1$): The atomic orbital $1s^0$ lies so low in energy with respect to the others that it does not effectively overlap with any other, therefore,

$$\psi_1(1a_1) \approx 1s^0$$

is the lowest energy non-bonding MO.

ψ_2 ($2a_1$): Calculations of Pitzer and Merifield reveal that (*i*) coefficient of ϕ_1 ($1s^0$) is negligible and negative and (*ii*) those of ϕ_2, ϕ_3 and ϕ_4 are substantial and positive. Hence the hybridized (mixed) $2s^0$ and $2p_y^0$ orbital has positive overlap with 1s AOs of the H atoms and the MO

$$\psi_2(2a_1) \approx a_{22}(2s^0) + a_{23}(2p_y^0) + a_{24}(1s_A + 1s_B)$$

leads to a build-up of electron density in the negative y-direction in the region around oxygen and H atoms. Therefore, ψ_2 ($2a_1$) is a bonding MO [see Fig. 13.2 (*a*)].

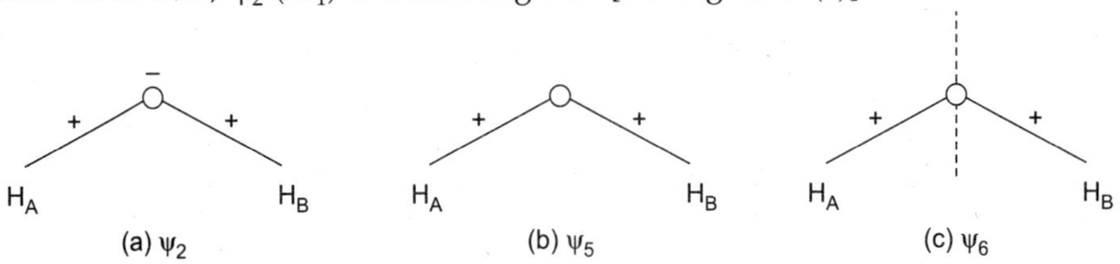

Fig. 13.2 *MOs of H_2O; the dotted vertical line in (c) shows the nodal plane*

$\psi_3\ (3a_1)$: Pitzer and Merifield found negative coefficients for ϕ_1 and ϕ_2 but positive coefficients for ϕ_3 and ϕ_4

$$\psi_3\ (3a_1) = -a_{31}\ (1s^0) - a_{32}\ (2s^0) + a_{33}\ (2p_y^0) + a_{34}\ (1s_A + 1s_B)$$

The positive overlap of $2p_y^0$ and $(1s_A + 1s_B)$ is almost cancelled by the negative overlap of $2s^0$ and $(1s_A + 1s_B)$ making the $\psi_3\ (3a_1)$ a non-bonding MO. The $1s^0$ does not overlap with any other because of the reasons given above.

$\psi_4\ (4a_1)$: The coefficient of ϕ_1, ϕ_2 and ϕ_3 are positive while that of ϕ_4 is negative, *i.e.*,

$$\psi_4\ (4a_1) = a_{41}\ (1s^0) + a_{42}\ (2s^0) + a_{43}\ \left(2s_y^0\right) - a_{44}\ (1s_A + 1s_B)$$

The overlap of $2s^0$ as well as $2s_y^0$ with $(1s_A + 1s_B)$ are both negative; hence the MO $\psi_4\ (4a_1)$ is antibonding.

$\psi_5\ (1b_1)$: The coefficient of both ϕ_5 and ϕ_6 are positive, therefore

$$\psi_5\ (1b_2) = a_{55}\ \left(2p_x^0\right) + a_{56}\ (1s_A + 1s_B)$$

is bonding with a build-up of electron density in the region around the oxygen and the two H atoms [see Fig. 13.2 (*b*)].

$\psi_6\ (1b_2)$: The MO is

$$\psi_6\ (1b_2) = a_{65}\ \left(2p_x^0\right) - a_{66}\ (1s_A + 1s_B)$$

due to the negative overlap between $2p_x^0$ and $(1s_A + 1s_B)$ the MO is strongly antibonding [see Fig. 13.2 (*c*)].

$\psi_7\ (1b_1)$: The a.o. $2p_z^0$ (ϕ_7) remains isolated and therefore

$$\psi_7\ (1b_1) = 2p_z^0$$

is a non-bonding MO.

Electron Occupancy and the Energy Level Diagram: Each MO can accommodate two electrons of opposite spin (α, β). The 10 electrons of H_2O can be accommodated in five MOs—$2a_1$ and $1b_2$ (bonding), $1a_1$, $3a_1$ and $1b_1$ (non-bonding) in the increasing order of energy (Fig. 13.3). Accordingly, the electronic configuration is $\left(1a_1^2\ 2a_1^2\ 1b_2^2\ 3a_1^2\ 1b_1^2\right)$ and the corresponding wave function is a 10×10 determinant

$$\Psi\ (1, 2, ..., 10) = \text{N} \left|\ 1a_1 1\bar{a}_1\ 2a_1\ 2\bar{a}_1\ 1b_2\ 1\bar{b}_2\ 3a\ 3\bar{a}_1\ 1b_1\ 1\bar{b}_1\ \right|$$

(The bar over an MO indicates β spin and the absence of a bar α-spin); N = normalization factor. Since each MO is doubly occupied, the ground state is a closed shell system having the symmetry $^1\text{A}_1$.

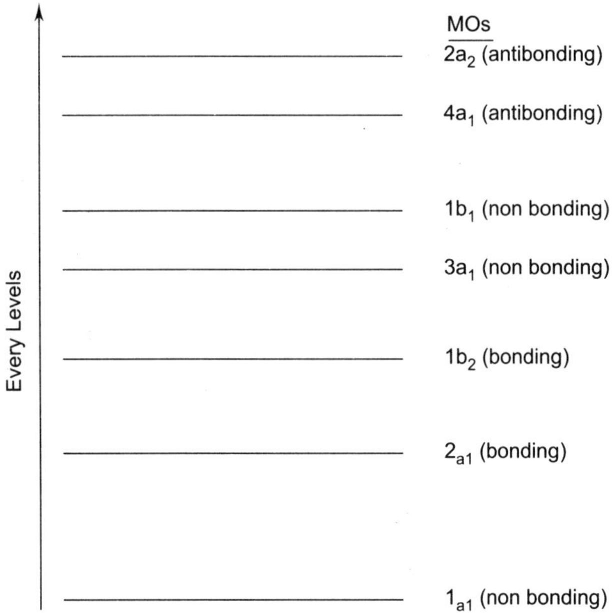

Fig. 13.3 *Energy level diagram of the MOs of H_2O*

13.2.4 Configuration Interaction

With 7 basis a.o.'s used in H_2O, we have two antibonding MOs ($4a_1$ and $2b_2$) which are unoccupied. A larger basis set would provide more unoccupied (virtual) MOs. These virtual MOs can be used to construct configurations other than the ground state. The wave functions (determinants) corresponding to these configurations can be combined linearly to obtain better wave function (linear combination of determinants) that would lead to lower electronic energy of H_2O. The choice of such configurations is, however, restricted by (*i*) considerations of symmetry and (*ii*) complexity of calculations due to appearance of a larger number of integrals over the basis functions when the integrals like H_{ij} and S_{ij} (*i* and *j* referring to the determinants) are expanded. In the case of H_2O, for example, a wave function corresponding to a singly excited state, may be

$$\Psi(1, 2, ..., 10) = \left| 1a_1\ 1\bar{a}_1\ 2a_1\ 2\bar{a}_1\ 1b_2\ 1\bar{b}_2\ 3a\ 3\bar{a}_1\ 1b_1\ 4a_1 \right| \qquad ...(13.28)$$

Denoting the ground state wave function by D_1 and the excited state by D_2 and taking the linear combination configuration interaction (C.I.) wave function as

$$\Psi_{CI} = c_1 D_1 + c_2 D_2 \qquad ...(13.29)$$

the secular determinant will involve interaction terms like

$$H_{12} = \int D_1 \hat{H} D_2\, d\tau \text{ and } S_{12} = \int D_1 D_2\, d\tau$$

The ground state configuration is a closed shell system and hence belongs to the totally symmetric $^1A_1$ state while the excited configuration may be $^1B_1$ or $^3B_1$ depending on the spin of the electron undergoing transition. The two wave functions D_1 and D_2 being of different symmetries, the integrals H_{12} and S_{12} will be zero which means no contribution of D_2. The doubly excited configuration like

$$D_3 = \left| 1a_1\ 1\bar{a}_1\ 2a\ 2\bar{a}_1\ 1b_2\ 1\bar{b}_2\ 3a\ 3\bar{a}_1\ 4a_1\ 4\bar{a}_1 \right| \quad \text{... (13.30)}$$

(in which the two b_1 electrons undergo transition to $4a_1$) has $^1A_1$ symmetry. Therefore, the configuration of D_1 and D_3 can linearly combine.

Further, the singly excited configuration

$$D_4 = \left| 1a_1\ 1\bar{a}_1\ 2a_1\ 2\bar{a}_1\ 1b_2\ 1\bar{b}_2\ 3a\ 1b_1\ 1\bar{b}_1\ 4a_1 \right| \quad \text{... (13.31)}$$

(in which an electron from $3a_1$ undergoes transition to $4a_1$) has A_1 symmetry but it can be $^1A_1$ or $^3A_1$ of which only $^1A_1$ is allowed for configuration interaction on spin consideration.

The total electronic energy of H_2O has been calculated and found to be – 76.431 a.u. which includes the C.I. contribution of – 0.364 a.u.

13.2.5 Equivalent and Localised MOs

Such an MO treatment assumes complete delocalisation of electrons over the whole molecule and does not seem to be consistent with the classical ideas of electron pair bond. If the molecule loses an electron, the latter is supposed to come out not from one bond but from the molecule as a whole; in other words, each MO loses some electron density. We know, on the other hand, that H_2O has two equivalent O—H bonds. The bond properties in H_2O are so characteristic of separate OH entities that even if one of the H atoms is replaced by a substituent, say CH_3, the bond length, energy, I.R. stretching frequency, etc., of the O—H bond are not much affected. How are we to explain this?

To explain these bond properties of a molecule. Lennard-Jones, Hall and Pople introduced the ideas of "localised" and "equivalent" MOs. The naivest approach to explain these ideas in the case of water is to consider the oxygen atom at the origin of the xy coordinate system with the lines from the centre to the two hydrogen atoms, H_A and H_B, making angles of 45° with the x and y-axes. (Fig. 13.4).

This, however, gives a bond angle of 90° for H_2O which, we know, is not correct; the experimental value is 104.5°. But to emphasise the physical ideas involved in the concepts of localised and equivalent MOs we shall use the simple $2p_x^0$ and $2p_y^0$ valence orbitals of oxygen for overlap with the $1s$ orbitals of hydrogen.

To achieve maximum overlap we have to direct the $2p$ orbitals of oxygen towards the $1s$ orbitals of H. This would amount to rotating the $2p_x$ and $2p_y$ orbitals anticlockwise through 45° and would lead to new $2p$ orbitals

$$2p_1 = \frac{1}{\sqrt{2}}\left(2p_x^0 + 2p_y^0\right)$$

$$2p_2 = \frac{1}{\sqrt{2}}\left(-2p_x^0 + 2p_y^0\right)$$

the factor $\frac{1}{\sqrt{2}}$ being introduced to normalise the new orbitals.

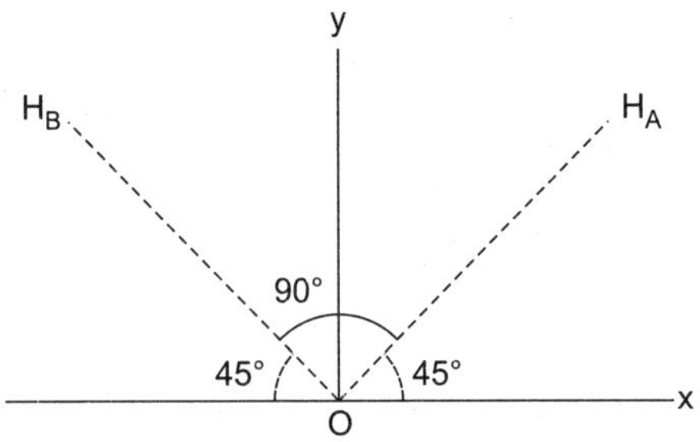

Fig. 13.4 *Coordinate system for H_2O*

The linear combination of the 1*s* orbitals of H and 2*p* orbitals of oxygen then gives the following two σ (bonding) MOs [Fig. 13.2 (*a*) and (*b*)].

$$\left.\begin{aligned}\sigma_1 &= 1s_A + 2p_1 = 1s_A + \frac{1}{\sqrt{2}}\left(2p_x^0 + 2p_y^0\right)\\ \sigma_2 &= 1s_A + 2p_2 = 1s_B + \frac{1}{\sqrt{2}}\left(-2p_x^0 + 2p_y^0\right)\end{aligned}\right\} \quad \text{... (13.32)}$$

where the normalisation factor has not been included. The negative combination gives σ^* (antibonding) MOs.

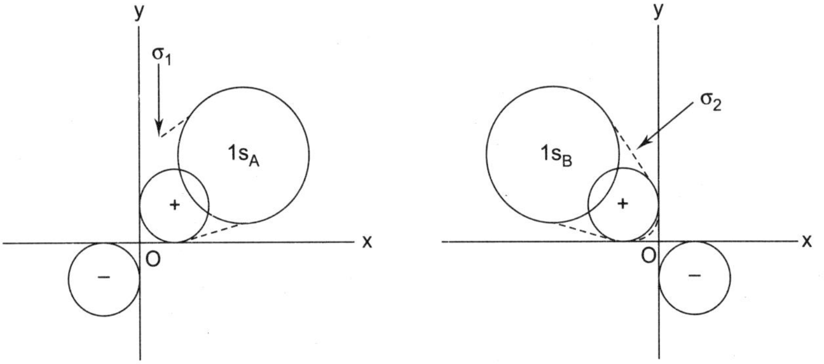

Fig. 13.5 *The σ_1 and σ_2 MOs of water*

The σ_1 and σ_2 MOs with a pair of electrons in each represent the two localised OH bonds (the LMOs) of the H_2O molecule. They are equivalent as they can be transformed into one another under a symmetry operation of the molecule.

$$C_2\,\sigma_1 = C_2\left[1s_A + \frac{1}{\sqrt{2}}\left(2p_x + 2p_y\right)\right] = 1s_A + \frac{1}{\sqrt{2}}\left(-2p_x + 2p_y\right) = \sigma_2$$

and *vice versa*. This leaves a lone pair of electrons in $2s^0$ and another pair in $2p_z^0$ orbital of the oxygen.

A better approach, and one that is more consistent with the experimental bond angle is to consider that the orbitals which combine with the orbitals of H are not $2p_1$ and $2p_2$ but hybrids (h_1 and h_2) of $2S^0$, $2p_z^0$ and $2p_y^0$ of Oxygen, subject to their being equivalent:

$$h_1 = a_1\,(2S^0) + b_1\left(2p_x^0\right) + c_1\left(2p_y^0\right)$$

$$h_2 = a_2\,(2S^0) + b_2\left(2p_x^0\right) + c_2\left(2p_y^0\right)$$

The $2p_z^0$ being perpendicular to the xy-plane does not contribute to these hybrids. For the h_1 and h_2 to be equivalent under the symmetry operations C_2 and σ_{yz},

$$a_1 = a_2 = a;\ b_1 = -b_1 = b;\ c_1 = c_2 = c$$

Then a^2, b^2 and c^2 represent the relative contributions of $2S^0$, $2p_x^0$ and $2p_y^0$ in the hybrids.

Now, the two localised and equivalent σ (bonding) MOs (LMOs), apart from their normalisation factors, representing the two OH bonds in H_2O are

$$\sigma_1 = 1s_A + h_1 = 1s_A + a\,(2s) + b\,(2p_x) + c\,(2p_y) \quad \text{...(13.33)}$$

$$\sigma_2 = 1s_B + h_2 = 1s_B + a\,(2s) - b\,(2p_x) + c\,(2p_y)$$

These are degenerate MOs. The negative combination gives the corresponding degenerate pair of σ^* (antibonding MOs).

There are two more hybrids h_3 and h_4 to accommodate the two lone pairs; these are orthogonal but not equivalent to h_1 and h_2.

Thus we have the following hierchy of LMO energy levels of water.

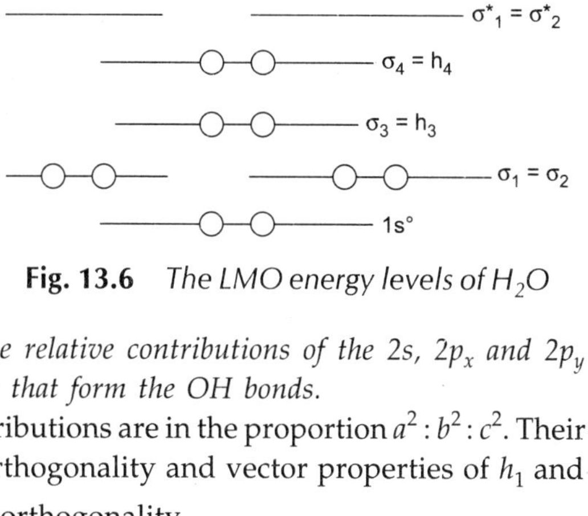

Fig. 13.6 *The LMO energy levels of H_2O*

Exercise: *Determine the relative contributions of the 2s, $2p_x$ and $2p_y$ orbitals in the two hybrid orbitals h_1 and h_2 of oxygen that form the OH bonds.*

Ans : The relative contributions are in the proportion $a^2 : b^2 : c^2$. Their values can be determined from the normalisation, orthogonality and vector properties of h_1 and h_2.

By normalisation and orthogonality,

$$a^2 + b^2 + c^2 = 1 \quad \text{...}(i)$$

$$a^2 - b^2 + c^2 = 0 \quad \text{...}(ii)$$

As regards vector properties, the direction of the vectors are determined from the 2p and not the 2s orbitals. Accordingly, the required vectors are

$$\vec{V}_1 = (b, c) \text{ and } \vec{V}_2 = (-b, c)$$

The scalar product of $\vec{V}_1$ and $\vec{V}_2$ is given as

$$\vec{V}_1 \cdot \vec{V}_2 = (b)(-b) + (c)(c) = -b^2 + c^2 \quad \text{...}(iii)$$

and also,

$$\vec{V}_1 \cdot \vec{V}_2 = |V_1| \cdot |V_2| \cdot \cos\theta \quad \text{...}(iv)$$

Here $\theta = 104.5°$; $|v_1| = |v_2| = \sqrt{b^2 + c^2}$ are the norms of the two vectors;

Hence

$$\vec{V}_1 \cdot \vec{V}_2 = (b^2 + c^2)(-0.25) \quad \text{...}(v)$$

From Equations (*iii*) and (*v*), we have

$$-b^2 + c^2 = -0.25\,(b^2 + c^2) \qquad \text{... }(vi)$$

From Equations (*i*), (*ii*) and (*vi*), we have

$$-a^2 = -0.25\,(1 - a^2), \text{ or } a^2 = 0.2$$

From Equations (*i*) and (*ii*), $b^2 = 0.5$; hence $c^2 = 0.3$.

The relative contributions are 20%, 50% and 30%].

It is important to note that while the delocalised MOs (DMOs) belong to definite symmetry types the equivalent and localised MOs (LMOs) do not. However, the two sets of MOs are not independent of each other; one can be transformed into the other by appropriate linear combinations. For example, the LMOs σ_1 and σ_2 of water can be formed by appropriate linear combination of the DMOs ψ_2 ($3A_1$) and ψ_3 ($1B_2$),

$$\left.\begin{aligned} \sigma_1 &= m\,\psi_2\,(3A_1) + n\,\psi_3\,(1B_2) \\ \sigma_2 &= m\,\psi_2\,(3A_1) - n\,\psi_3\,(1B_2) \end{aligned}\right\} \qquad \text{... (13.33a)}$$

where the coefficients m and n are to be determined. The equivalence of σ_1 and σ_2 can be demonstrated as follows:

$$C_2\,\sigma_1 = C_2\,[m\,\psi_2\,(3A_1) + n\,\psi_3\,(1B_2)] = m\,\psi_2\,(3A_1) - n\,\psi_3\,(1B_2)$$

and *vice versa*.

13.2.6 Matrix Form of the Roothan Equations

Roothan equations are customarily expressed in matrix form. We write the secular Equation (13.17) as

$$\sum_{\nu} F_{\mu\nu}\, a_{\nu i} = \sum_{\nu} S_{\mu\nu}\, a_{\nu i}\, E_i \qquad \text{... (13.34)}$$

The two-index quantities $F_{\mu\nu}$, $S_{\mu\nu}$ and $a_{\nu i}$ are the elements of square matrices [F], [S] and [A] respectively. E_i may be written as E_{mi}, an element of diagonal matrix, where $E_{mi} = \delta_{mi}\, E_i$ *i.e.*, $E_{mi} = E_i$ when $m = i$ and 0 when $m \neq i$. The order of each matrix is the number of basis orbitals used.

By the rules of matrix multiplication (see Chapter 3) the left hand side of (13.34) is the (μ, i)th element (*i.e.*, in the μth row and ith column) of the product of [F] and [A]. In the case of 3 × 3 matrices, for example, where

$$[F] = \begin{bmatrix} F_{11} & F_{12} & F_{13} \\ F_{21} & F_{22} & F_{23} \\ F_{31} & F_{32} & F_{33} \end{bmatrix} \text{ and } [A] = \begin{bmatrix} a_{11} & a_{12} & a_{13} \\ a_{21} & a_{22} & a_{23} \\ a_{31} & a_{32} & a_{33} \end{bmatrix}$$

$$[F]\,[A] = \begin{bmatrix} \sum_{\nu=1}^{3} F_{1\nu}\, a_{\nu 1} & \sum_{\nu=1}^{3} F_{1\nu}\, a_{\nu 2} & \sum_{\nu=1}^{3} F_{1\nu}\, a_{\nu 3} \\ \sum_{\nu=1}^{3} F_{2\nu}\, a_{\nu 1} & \sum_{\nu=1}^{3} F_{2\nu}\, a_{\nu 2} & \sum_{\nu=1}^{3} F_{2\nu}\, a_{\nu 3} \\ \sum_{\nu=1}^{3} F_{3\nu}\, a_{\nu 1} & \sum_{\nu=1}^{3} F_{3\nu}\, a_{\nu 2} & \sum_{\nu=1}^{3} F_{3\nu}\, a_{\nu 3} \end{bmatrix}$$

where, for example,

$$\sum_{\nu=1}^{3} F_{2\nu}\, a_{\nu 3} = F_{21}\, a_{13} + F_{22}\, a_{23} + F_{23}\, a_{33}$$

By the same rule, $\sum a_{\nu i}\, E_i$ is the (ν, i)th element of the product of [A] and [E] $\left(\sum (AE)_{\nu, i} = \sum a_{\nu i}\, \delta_{mi}\, E_i = \sum a_{\nu i}\, E_i\right)$. Then the right hand side of (13.34) becomes the (μ, i)th element of the product of [S] and [AE]. Thus (μ, i)th element of the product matrix [F] [A] is equal to the (μ, i) the element of the product matrix [S] [A] [E], therefore the Equation (13.26) may be written in matrix form as

$$[F]\,[A] = [S]\,[A]\,[E] \qquad \dots (13.35)$$

The Equation (13.35) is, however, not an eigenvalue equation if the basis orbitals are not orthogonal. Non-orthogonal functions can be made orthogonal by Schmidt or some other procedure without altering the eigenvalue. With orthogonal bases (ϕ'_ν) in which $S'_{\mu\nu} = 0$ for $\mu \neq \nu$, the Equation (13.35) becomes an eigenvalue equation

$$[F']\,[A'] = [A']\,[E] \qquad \dots (13.36)$$

in which $F'_{\mu\nu} = \int \phi'_\mu\, F\, \phi'_\nu\, d\tau$, and A′ is the matrix of coefficients that relate the MOs to the orthonormal basis orbitals.

In this eigenvalue equation [A′] and [E] are the matrices of the eigenvectors and eigenvalues respectively. Each column of [A′] is an eigenvector and the orbital energies E_i are the eigenvalues of the Fock Matrix [F], there being as many such eigenvectors and eigenvalues as the number of bases.

Iteration : In the Hartree-Fock-Roothan (HFR) calculations we see that the operator $\hat{F}$ depends on the MOs and, therefore, on the linear combination coefficients ($a_{i\nu}$) which we have to determine. Therefore we have to take to iterative procedure.

First, make an appropriate choice of orthogonal basic functions (if they are not orthogonal, make them so by an orthogonalisation procedure). Then calculate the matrix elements $H^0_{\mu\nu}$ and the integrals $\mu\nu/\lambda\sigma$. Make an initial guess of the linear combination (l.c.) coefficients and calculate the elements $P_{\lambda\sigma}$. Use these quantities to calculate the Fock matrix elements $F_{\mu\nu}$. Solve the secular determinant (13.18) for the eigenvalues E_i and the Equations (13.17) for the l.c. coefficients which will be different from the initially guessed coefficients. Use these new coefficients and recalculate $F_{\mu\nu}$ to get still other values of the coefficients. Go on reiterating till the values converge and use the final values to construct the MOs.

Alternatively, we adopt the matrix diagonalisation method. If the matrix [A] has an inverse we can multiply each side of the eigenvalue Equation (13.28) by $[A]^{-1}$ on the left to get

$$[A]^{-1}\,[F]\,[A] = [A]^{-1}\,[A]\,[E] = [E] \qquad \dots (13.37)$$

(multiplication must be done from the same side, left or right, of the equation). So the problem of finding the eigenvalues and eigenvectors of the matrix [F] reduces to finding an unitary or orthogonal matrix $[A]^+$ which can diagonalise the $[A]^+$ [F] [A] matrix. Then the elements of this diagonal matrix will give the eigenvalues and the columns will be the eigenvectors. We start with an initial guess of l.c. coefficients and construct [A] and [F] matrices. Then find a unitary matrix such that the product matrix $[F]_1 = [A]_1^+ [F][A]$ has 0 in place of the largest off diagonal element of the matrix [F]. Then construct another matrix $[A]_2$ such that $[A]_2 [F]_1 [A]_2 = [A]_2 [A]_1 [F] [A]_1 [A]_2$ has 0 in place of the largest off diagonal element of $[F]_1$. Go on repeating the process till all off diagonal elements of [F] become negligibly small. Then the diagonal elements of the final matrix ... $[A]_3 [A]_2 [A]_1 [F] [A]_1 [A]_2 [A]_3$ ... will be the eigenvalues and the columns the eigenvectors of the original matrix [F].

For large size matrices as it often occurs in quantum chemistry the matrix diagonalisation method is preferably chosen.

13.3 SEMI EMPIRICAL METHODS

Evaluating large number of integrals is the main bottleneck in the HFR method. Even in a small molecule like methane with a minimal basis set of nine functions one has to encounter 1035 two-electron integrals with 1-, 2-, 3- and 4- centred integrals. Hence semiempirical methods with drastic approximations and use of empirical quantities for some integrals have been developed.

13.3.1 Valence Electrons

In the first place, all inner shell electrons are ignored (for example, only 2*s*, $2p_x$, $2p_y$ and $2p_z$ atomic orbitals in C, N and O are considered). This is effected by replacing the nuclear charge Z_p by effective nuclear charge Z'_p in the "core Hamiltonian operator", *i.e.*,

$$H^c(1) = -\frac{1}{2}\nabla_1^2 - \sum_p \frac{Z'_p}{r_{p_1}} \qquad \text{... (13.38)}$$

which now represents the energy of the valence electron 1 in the field of atomic nuclei and the inner shell electrons. The Fock operator becomes

$$\hat{F}(1) = \hat{H}^c(1) + \sum_{j=1}^{n/2} \left(2\hat{J}_j(1) - \hat{K}_j \cdot (1)\right) \qquad \text{... (13.39)}$$

where *n* is the number of electrons in $\frac{n}{2}$ molecular orbitals.

13.3.2 Zero Differential Overlap (ZDO)

Further simplification is made by assuming that any product of atomic orbitals (ϕ) within an integral is zero if they are different, *i.e.*,

$$\phi_{\mu_A} \cdot \phi_{\nu_B} = \delta_{\mu_A \nu_B} \begin{cases} = 1 \text{ for } \mu_A = \nu_B \\ = 0 \text{ for } \mu_A \neq \nu_B \end{cases} \qquad \text{... (13.40)}$$

Here μ and ν refer to atomic orbitals and A and B are atomic centres. This approximation applies to both overlap and 2-electron integrals. The general form of these integrals are

Overlap integral: $$S_{\mu_A \nu_B} = \int \phi^*_{\mu_A} \phi_{\nu_B} \, d\tau \qquad \text{... (13.41)}$$

2-Electron integral: $$(\mu_A \, \nu_B / \lambda_C \, \sigma_D) = \int \phi^*_{\mu_A}(1) \, \phi^*_{\nu_B}(1) \frac{1}{r_{12}} \phi_{\lambda_C}(2) \, \phi_{\sigma_D}(2) \, d\tau_1 \, d\tau_2 \qquad \text{... (13.42)}$$

A, B, C and D are atomic centres (2-electron integrals cannot have more than four atomic centres).

The ZDO approximation eliminates all 3- and 4- centred integrals and allows one to work with only 1- and 2- centred integrals.

Even these are simplified further by some more drastic approximations which may be classified into three main categories as follows:

1. **NDDO** (Neglect of Diatomic Differential Overlap): In this scheme all overlap integrals in which $\mu_A \neq \nu_B$, and all 2-electron integrals in which A ≠ B and C ≠ D are taken as zero. This amounts to taking all atomic orbitals as orthonormal and allowing integrals of the type $(\mu_A \, \nu_A / \lambda_C \, \sigma_C)$.
2. **INDO** (Intermediate Neglect of Differential Overlap):

   Here again $S_{\mu_A \nu_B} = 0$ if $\mu_A \neq \nu_B$, and

   $$(\mu_A \, \nu_B / \lambda_C \, \sigma_D) = 0 \text{ if } \mu_A \neq \nu_B \text{ and } \lambda_C \neq \sigma_D.$$

   This amounts to allowing only 2-centred coulombic and 1-centred non-coulombic (exchange) integrals of the type

   $$(\mu_A \, \mu_A / \lambda_C \, \lambda_C) \qquad \text{(coulombic)}$$

   $$(\mu_A \, \mu_A / \lambda_A \, \lambda_A) \qquad \text{(non-coulombic)}$$
3. **CNDO** (Complete Neglect of Differential Overlap): In this scheme $S_{\mu_A \nu_B} = 0$ if $\mu_A \neq \nu_B$ and $(\mu_A \, \nu_B / \lambda_C \, \sigma_D) = 0$ if $A \neq B, C \neq D, \mu \neq \nu$ and $\lambda \neq \sigma$. This amounts to retaining only diagonal $S_{\mu_A \mu_A}$ elements and 2- and 1- centred coulombic integrals $(\mu_A \, \mu_A / \mu_A \, \mu_A)$, $(\mu_A \, \mu_A / \mu_B \, \mu_B)$ and $(\mu_A \, \mu_A / \nu_B \, \nu_B)$. It is seen that INDO is the reduced form of NDDO and CNDO is further reduction of INDO. The CNDO method which is most approximate, and which is commonly used will be discussed briefly.

13.3.3 The HFR Equation under CNDO Scheme

The evaluation of HFR matrix elements, $F_{\mu\nu}$, under this scheme involve (*i*) core Hamiltonian matrix elements, $H^c_{\mu\nu}$, and (*ii*) coulombic repulsion integrals mentioned above. It is further assumed that the results of integration (energy etc.) are independent of the type of atomic orbitals and depend only on the nature of atoms involved. This means that the results are invariant to simple transformation of the basis functions such as rotation of axes or replacing the *s* and *p*-orbitals by their hybrids. This has been discussed in detail by Popple, Santry and Segal (1965) who gave this scheme. This is called 'condition of invariance' of the basis functions. This gives

$$(\mu_A \mu_A / \mu_A \mu_A) = \gamma_{AA} \text{ (all orbitals } \mu \text{ on atom A)}$$

$$(\mu_A \mu_A / \mu_B \mu_B) = \gamma_{AB} \text{ (all orbitals } \mu \text{ on A and B)}$$

$$(\mu_A \mu_A / \nu_B \nu_B) = \gamma_{AB} \text{ (all } \mu \text{ on A and all } \nu \text{ on B)}$$

γ_{AB}, for example, represents an average electronic repulsion between any electron on A and any electron on B. This is a fairly drastic approximation because some 1-centred integrals like $(2s_A\ 2p_{z_A} / 2s_A\ 2p_{z_A})$ are also ignored.

13.3.3.1 Hamiltonian Matrix Elements

The core operator may be written as

$$H^c(1) = -\frac{1}{2}\nabla_1^2 - V_A(1) - \sum V_B(1) \quad \text{... (13.43)}$$

where, for example, $V_A(1) = \dfrac{Z_A}{r_{A_1}}$.

The matrix element $H_{\mu\nu}^c$ is

$$H_{\mu\nu}^c = \left(\mu_A \left| -\frac{1}{2}\nabla_1^2 - V_A(1) \right| \nu_A\right) - \sum_{B \neq A} (\mu_A | V_B(1) | \nu_A)$$

$$= u_{\mu_A \nu_A} - \sum_{B \neq A} (\mu_A | V_B(1) | \nu_A) \quad \text{... (13.44)}$$

where $u_{\mu_A \nu_A} = \left(\mu_A \left| -\frac{1}{2}\nabla_1^2 - V_A(1) \right| \nu_A\right)$

$$= \int \phi_{\mu_A}(1) \left[-\frac{1}{2}\nabla_1^2 - V_A(1)\right] \phi_\nu(1)\, d\tau_1$$

If the atomic orbitals are pure (like s, p_x etc., *i.e.*, non-hybrid) but of different symmetry, then the integral $u_{\mu_A \nu_A} = 0$ and only $u_{\mu_A \mu_A}$ will remain. Thus,

$$H_{\mu_A \mu_A}^c = u_{\mu_A \mu_A} - \sum_{B \neq A} \mu_A | V_B | \mu_A, \text{ for } \mu_A = \nu_A \quad \text{... (13.45)}$$

$$H_{\mu_A \nu_A}^c = u_{\mu_A \nu_A} - \sum_{B \neq A} (\mu_A | V_B | \nu_A), \text{ for } \mu_A \neq \nu_A \quad \text{... (13.46)}$$

The ZDO approximation is applied to integrals $(\mu_A | V_B(1) | \nu_A)$ also by which the integral is zero if $\mu_A \neq \nu_A$. This gives,

$$H^{c}_{\mu_A \nu_A} = -\sum_{B \neq A} \left(\mu_A \mid V_B(1) \mid \mu_A\right). \qquad \text{... (13.47)}$$

To satisfy the invariance condition it is also assumed that the integrals are independent of the type of atomic orbitals and depend only on the nature of the atoms A and B; this means

$$\left(\mu_A \mid V_B(1) \mid \mu_A\right) = V_{AB}$$

The matrix elements of the type $H^{c}_{\mu_A \nu_B}$ for $\mu_A \neq \nu_B$ are treated as 2-centred empirical quantities $\beta_{\mu_A \nu_B}$, *i.e.*,

$$\beta_{\mu_A \nu_B} = \left(\mu_A \left| -\frac{1}{2}\nabla_1^2 - V_A(1) - \sum_{B \neq A} V_B(1) \right| \nu_B\right).$$

Finally, we have three types of Fock matrix elements $F_{\mu_A \mu_A}$, $F_{\mu_A \nu_A}$ and $F_{\mu_A \nu_B}$. These are given as

$$F_{\mu_A \mu_A} = u_{\mu_A \mu_A} - \sum_{B \neq A} V_{AB} + \sum_{A} P_{\mu_A \mu_A}\left[\left(\mu_A \mu_A / \mu_A \mu_A\right) - \frac{1}{2}\left(\mu_A \mu_A / \mu_A \mu_A\right)\right] + \sum_{B \neq A} P_{\mu_B \mu_B}\left(\mu_A \mu_A / \mu_B \mu_B\right)$$

$$= u_{\mu_A \mu_A} + P_{AA}\,\gamma_{AA} - \frac{1}{2} P_{\mu_A \mu_A}\,\gamma_{AA} + \sum_{B \neq A}\left(P_{BB}\,\gamma_{AB} - V_{AB}\right) \qquad \text{... (13.48)}$$

where $P_{AA} = \sum_{A} P_{\mu_A \mu_A}$ (all μ on A)

and $P_{BB} = \sum_{B \neq A} P_{\mu_B \mu_B}$ (all μ on all B other than A).

Similarly, $$F_{\mu_A \nu_A} = u_{\mu_A \nu_A} - \frac{1}{2} P_{\mu_A \nu_A}\,\gamma_{AA}, \text{ for } \mu \neq \nu \qquad \text{... (13.49)}$$

and $$F_{\mu_A \nu_B} = \beta_{\mu_A \nu_B} - \frac{1}{2} P_{\mu_A \nu_B}\,\gamma_{AB}, \text{ for } B \neq A \qquad \text{... (13.50)}$$

If the basis consists of non-hybridised atomic orbitals then $u_{\mu_A \nu_A} = 0$

Thus we see that under the CNDO scheme the HFR matrix elements require the evaluation of five types of integrals:

$$u_{\mu_A \mu_A},\ \beta_{\mu_A \nu_B},\ \gamma_{AA},\ \gamma_{AB} \text{ and } V_{AB}.$$

Summarising, the total molecular electronic energy by Hartree-Fock-Roothan method is given by

$$E = 2\sum_i H_{ii}^0 + \sum_i \sum_j \left(2J_{ij} - K_{ij}\right) \quad \text{... (13.51)}$$

where $$H_{ii}^0 = \int \psi_i^* (1)\, \hat{H}^0 (1)\, \psi_i (1)\, d\tau_1$$

On expanding the integrals H_{ij}^0, J_{ij} and K_{ij} in terms of the basis functions $\phi\nu$, we obtain

$$E = \frac{1}{2}\sum_{\mu,\nu} P_{\mu\nu}\left(H_{\mu\nu}^0 + F_{\mu\nu}\right) \quad \text{... (13.52)}$$

Under the CNDO scheme this takes the form

$$E = \frac{1}{2}\sum_{\mu,\nu} P_{\mu\nu}\left(H_{\mu\nu}^c + F_{\mu\nu}\right) \quad \text{... (13.53)}$$

where H^0 has been replaced by H^c and μ, ν refer to valence electrons only.

The total molecular energy (including nuclear repulsion) is given by

$$E_+ = E + \sum_{A<B}\sum \frac{Z_A Z_B}{R_{AB}} \quad \text{... (13.54)}$$

where R_{AB} is the internuclear separation distance.

A further improvement, CNDO/2, which differs from the above scheme in some details is now widely used. (For a brilliant exposition of the method with an example of LiH the reader is referred to J. Sadlej, "Semi Empirical Methods in Quantum Chemistry", John Wiley & Sons, Page 118).

13.4 CHOICE OF BASIS FUNCTIONS

The calculation of molecular integrals is the most cumbersome step in the solution of the HFR equations. The numerical difficulties depend largely on the choice of the basis set of functions $\{\phi_\nu\}$. In principle, for high accuracy, a complete (infinite) basis set should be used. In practice, however a finite basis set of reasonable dimension is used. The functions are generally so chosen as to create least difficulty in integration.

Within a naive model, we can consider electrons in MOs arising from atomic orbitals of atoms constituting the molecule. The MOs are then the 'linear combination of atomic orbitals'.

Several type of basis functions have been proposed two of which are popular : (*i*) STO and (*ii*) Gaussian.

13.4.1 STO Basis

Atomic orbitals to be used for high accuracy in calculations should be a linear combination of several slater type functions (see Chapter 9). However, at the minimum, one may choose a set of Slater type orbitals (STO), one for each of the occupied orbitals. Such a set is called 'minimal basis set'. For example, in H_2O molecule, the minimal basis set consists of five STOs for $1s$, $2s$, $2p_x$, $2p_y$ and $2p_z$ of oxygen and two $1s$ STOs for the two H atoms.

Double Zeta (DZ) Basis : If each atomic orbital is taken as a linear combination of two STOs differing in effective nuclear charge (orbital exponent ξ), we have a 'double zeta basis set' (DZ).

The set will contain double the number of basis functions of the minimal set (*e.g.*, 14 in case of H_2O) and will give better atomic orbitals.

Double Zeta Plus Polarisation (DZP): On molecule formation atomic orbitals of a free atom get distorted (polarised towards bonds). Allowance for this is made by including STOs which have characters of *p* atomic orbitals.

13.4.2 Gaussian Basis

Boys (1950) proposed the use of Gaussian type function in place of STO. A Gaussian function at a point centred around atom A is defined as

$$\chi_G = N\, x_A^p\, y_A^q\, z_A^r\, e^{-\alpha r_A^2}$$

where N is normalisation constant ; *x*, *y*, and *z* are cartesian coordinates of the point ; *p*, *q* and *r* are small positive integers including zero; α is a variable parameter and r_A is the radial distance of the point from the nucleus of A. The product $(x^p\, y^q\, z^r)$ represents the angular part of the orbital; for example, if $p = q = r = 0$, the Gaussian function $Ne^{-\alpha r_A^2}$ is of *s*-type; if $p = 1$ and $q = r = 0$, the function $N\, x\, e^{-\alpha r_A^2}$ will be of p_x type and similarly for p_y and p_z; if $p + q = 2$ and $r = 0$, we have d_{xy} type and so on. Functions of the type $d_{x^2-y^2}$ and d_{z^2} can be formed by taking suitable linear combinations, for example $\left(x_A^2 - y_A^2\right)e^{-\alpha r_A^2}$ represents $d_{x^2-y^2}$ orbital.

s atomic orbital is represented by a linear combination of several Gaussian functions (GF) with different values of α; a p_x orbital by a linear combination of GFs like $x\, e^{-\alpha r_A^2}$. Due to the exponential factor like $e^{-\alpha r^2}$, as against $e^{-\varepsilon r}$ in STO, a GF does not have the desired cusp near the nucleus, *i.e.*, the function remains constant within a certain small distance near the nucleus and, therefore, is not a very good representation of an atomic orbital. But the advantage with the Gaussian basis set is that the product of two GFs at points A and B is also a GF at point C somewhere on the line joining A and B; this reduces a 4-centred electron repulsion integral to a 2-centred integral,

$$\iint G_A(1)\, G_B(1)\, \frac{1}{r_{12}}\, G_C(2)\, G_D(2)\, d\tau_1\, d\tau_2$$

$$= \iint G_e(1)\, \frac{1}{r_{12}}\, G_f(2)\, d\tau_1\, d\tau_2$$

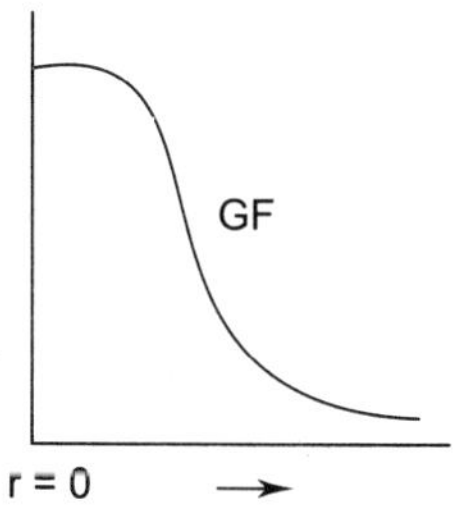

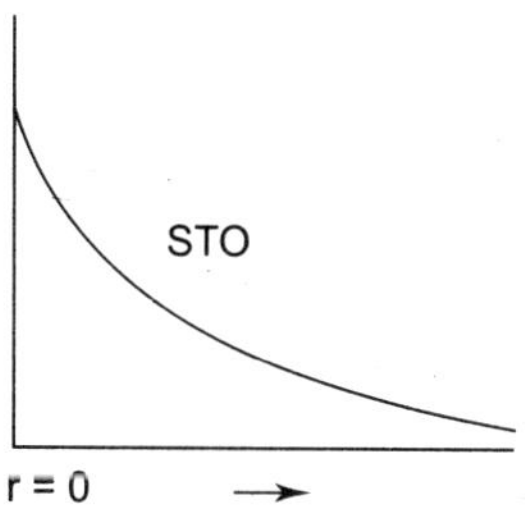

Further, to reduce the number of variable coefficients in the linear combination, one forms small groups of GFs with fixed coefficients

$$\chi_i = \sum a_{ik}\,\lambda_k$$

where λ_k's are groups of the same type of GFs, *i.e.*, have the same p, q, r values-centred on the same atom but have different α values. The χ_i's are then called 'contracted GF'. By using contracted GFs as basis functions only a few coefficients of GFs are to be determined in a SCF calculation.

13.5 EMPIRICAL METHOD: THE HÜCKEL MOLECULAR ORBITAL (HMO) THEORY

This is empirical method specially popular for planar organic compounds containing conjugated carbon chain, linear as well as cyclic, for example, butadiene, benzene, etc. where we have localised σ (C—C) and σ (C—H) MOs and delocalised π MOs that encompass all nuclear centres involved in conjugation. In benzene, for example, we have six equivalent σ (C—C) and six σ (C—H) MOs which accommodate 24 of the valence electrons. The remaining six electrons are housed in a network of three bonding π MOs, there being three more π MOs that are antibonding. Each π MO encompasses all six carbon atoms. The delocalised π MOs differ in their symmetry and nodal characteristics as will be discussed in a later section.

This is the simplest of all MO treatments which goes by the name Hückel Molecular Orbital (HMO) theory and is based on the following assumptions:

1. It is first assumed that π-electrons in a conjugated molecule do not interact with σ-electrons. The HMO theory applies to π-electrons only.
2. It is further assumed that the total π-electron wave function, Ψ_π, is a single product of one-electron functions called (the Hückel MOs) and not a determinant. The total energy of the π-electrons is then the sum of the one electron (HMO) energies. For a system of n π-electrons in the ground state, (with n even)

$$\Psi_\pi = \psi_1(1)\,\bar{\psi}_1(2)\,\psi_2(3)\,\bar{\psi}_2(4)\cdots\psi_{n/2}(n-1)\,\bar{\psi}_{n/2}(n) \qquad \text{... (13.55)}$$

where ψ_i is the ith HMO and

$$E_\pi = (n_1 E_1 + n_2 E_2 + ... + n_n E_n) \qquad \text{... (13.56)}$$

where E_i is the energy of a single electron in ψ_i; the factors n_i may be 1 or 2 or 0 depending upon whether the HMO ψ_i is singly or doubly occupied or unoccupied.

Each ψ is supposed to be an approximate solution of a one-electron Schrödinger equation,

$$\hat{H}(i)\,\psi_i = E_i\,\psi_i \qquad \text{... (13.57)}$$

though the Hamiltonian $\hat{H}(i)$ is not specified and the equation is not solved.

3. Each HMO (ψ_i) is taken as a linear combination of the carbon $2p_z$ AOs, taking molecular plane as the xy-plane.

$$\psi_i = a_{i1}\,p_1 + a_{i2}\,p_2 + ... + a_{in}\,p_n = \sum_{r=1}^{n} a_{ir}\,p_r \qquad \text{... (13.58)}$$

where p_r is the $2p_z$ AO of the rth carbon atom and a_{ir} is the coefficient of the rth AO in the ith HMO.

4. The energy of the HMO is calculated by the formula.

$$E_i = \frac{\int \psi_i \hat{H} \psi_i \, d\tau}{\int \psi_i^2 \, d\tau} \quad \text{... (13.59)}$$

assuming ψ_i to be real.

5. Variation treatment leads to n secular equations of the type (see Chapter 8)

$$\begin{aligned} a_1 (H_{11} - ES_{11}) + a_2 (H_{12} - ES_{12}) + \ldots + a_n (H_{1n} - ES_{1n}) &= 0 \\ a_1 (H_{21} - ES_{21}) + a_2 (H_{22} - ES_{22}) + \ldots + a_n (H_{2n} - ES_{2n}) &= 0 \\ \ldots \quad \ldots \quad \ldots \quad \ldots \quad \ldots \quad \ldots \quad \ldots & \\ \ldots \quad \ldots \quad \ldots \quad \ldots \quad \ldots \quad \ldots \quad \ldots & \\ \ldots \quad \ldots \quad \ldots \quad \ldots \quad \ldots \quad \ldots \quad \ldots & \\ a_1 (H_{n1} - ES_{n1}) + a_2 (H_{n2} - ES_{n2}) + \ldots + a_n (H_{nn} - ES_{nn}) &= 0 \end{aligned} \quad \text{... (13.60)}$$

The corresponding nth order secular determinant is,

$$\begin{vmatrix} H_{11} - ES_{11} & H_{12} - ES_{12} & \cdots & H_{1n} - ES_{1n} \\ H_{21} - ES_{21} & H_{22} - ES_{22} & \cdots & H_{2n} - ES_{2n} \\ \cdots \quad \cdots & \cdots \quad \cdots & & \cdots \quad \cdots \\ \cdots \quad \cdots & \cdots \quad \cdots & & \cdots \quad \cdots \\ H_{n1} - ES_{n1} & H_{n2} - ES_{n2} & \cdots & H_{nn} - ES_{nn} \end{vmatrix} = 0 \quad \text{... (13.61)}$$

where $H_{ij} = \int p_i \hat{H} p_j \, d\tau$ and $S_{ij} = \int p_i \, p_j \, d\tau$

and the integrals are over the space coordinates of a single electron.

6. At this stage, E. Hückel introduced some more drastic approximations.

(*a*) All integrals of the type H_{rr}, which represent the average energy of an electron in the atomic orbital p_r, are assumed to be equal, *i.e.*,

$$H_{11} = H_{22} = \ldots\ldots.. = \alpha \text{ (say)} \quad \text{... (13.62)}$$

(*b*) All integrals of the type H_{rs} representing energy of interaction between two AOs p_r and p_s are identical and given the symbol β if the atoms r and s are just "neighbours" (*i.e.*, directly bonded).

$$H_{12} = H_{23} = H_{34} = \ldots\ldots.. = \beta \text{ (say)} \quad \text{... (13.63)}$$

For atoms r and s that are not directly bonded (non-neighbours) $H_{rs} = 0$:

(*c*) Values of α and β are used as experimental data.

(*d*) Integrals of the type S_{rr} (S_{11}, S_{22} etc.) are equal to 1:

(*e*) Integrals of the type S_{rs} are assumed to be zero. (This may not be correct as actual evaluation of the integrals S_{rs} involving p_r and p_s gives a value of about 0.3, which is far from zero. This assumption is drastic but it does not produce any substantial change in the conclusion that would be otherwise derived, and it simplifies the mathematical procedure considerably).

Thus for a linear conjugated chain the secular determinantal Equation (13.61) assumes the form,

$$\begin{vmatrix} \alpha - E & \beta & 0 & & 0 & \cdots\cdots & 0 \\ \beta & \alpha - E & \beta & & 0 & \cdots\cdots & 0 \\ 0 & \beta & \alpha - E & \beta & 0 & \cdots\cdots & 0 \\ \cdots\cdots & \cdots\cdots & \cdots\cdots & \cdots\cdots & \cdots\cdots & \cdots\cdots & \cdots\cdots \\ \cdots\cdots & \cdots\cdots & \cdots\cdots & \cdots\cdots & \cdots\cdots & \cdots\cdots & \cdots\cdots \\ 0 & 0 & 0 & 0 & \beta & \cdots\cdots & \alpha - E \end{vmatrix} = 0 \quad \text{... (13.64)}$$

(*f*) The Equation (13.63) can be made still simpler if we put $\dfrac{\alpha - E}{\beta} = x$.

$$\text{This gives} \begin{vmatrix} x & 1 & 0 & 0 & & & \cdots & & 0 \\ 1 & x & 1 & 0 & & & \cdots & & 0 \\ 0 & 1 & x & 1 & & 0 & \cdots & & 0 \\ \cdots & \cdots & \cdots & \cdots & \cdots & \cdots & \cdots & \cdots & \cdots \\ \cdots & \cdots & \cdots & \cdots & \cdots & \cdots & \cdots & \cdots & \cdots \\ 0 & 0 & 0 & 0 & \cdots & 0 & \cdots & 1 & x \end{vmatrix} = 0 \quad \text{... (13.65)}$$

This determinant reveals some interesting features. It is seen that x appears on the principal diagonal. The number 1 appears in position where the indices r and s correspond to bonded carbon atoms (*e.g.* H_{12}, H_{21}, H_{23}, etc.) and 0 appears where they are not bonded (*e.g.*, H_{13}, H_{14}, etc.).

This generalisation enables one to write the Hückel determinant for an unsaturated conjugated hydrocarbon by looking at the structure of the molecule. The determinant may be constructed easily by the following procedure:

(*i*) sketch the framework of the hydrocarbon indicating the carbon atoms;

(*ii*) number the carbon atoms 1, 2, 3, ... n;

(*iii*) fill the $n \times n$ determinant with x's on the principal diagonal, 1 in positions where row-column indices correspond to neighbours and zero everywhere else; and

(*iv*) check that the determinant is symmetric with respect to reflection through the principal diagonal.

The following two examples of butadiene and benzene will serve to explain the procedure. The skeletal framework of the molecules is shown below along with numbering of the carbon atoms.

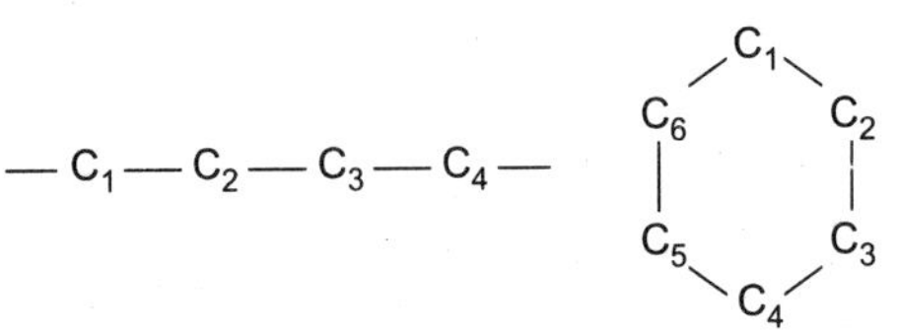

Butadiene (C_4H_6) (I)   Benzene (C_6H_6) (II)

The 4×4 determinant (I) in the first case and the 6×6 determinant (II) in second case will be obtained by following the step.

	1	2	3	4
1	x	1	0	0
2	1	x	1	0
3	0	1	x	1
4	0	0	1	x

(I)

	1	2	3	4	5	6
1	x	1	0	0	0	1
2	1	x	1	0	0	0
3	0	1	x	1	0	0
4	0	0	1	x	1	0
5	0	0	0	1	x	1
6	1	0	0	0	1	x

(II)

(Hückel determinants for butadiene and benzene)

7. *The HMO Energy Levels:* On expanding the $n \times n$ determinant, one obtains a polynomial of nth degree in x which has n real roots $x_1, x_2, ..., x_n$. Since $x = (\alpha - E)/\beta$, a root x_j leads to an energy E_j of the jth MO.

$$E_j = \alpha - x_j \beta \quad \text{... (13.66)}$$

There will be n energy levels corresponding to n HMOs, each being expressed in terms of α and β. Since α represents the energy of a p-electron bound to a carbon atom in the molecule, it is negative relative to a free electron. Similarly, β represents the energy of an electron in a bond and is negative. Thus,

(*i*) for the negative root ($x_j < 0$), $E_j < \alpha$; it corresponds to the "bonding level";

(*ii*) for positive root; ($x_j > 0$), $E_j > \alpha$; it corresponds to "antibonding level"; and

(*iii*) when n is odd, there occurs a root $x_j = 0$, and for $x_j = 0$, $E_j = \alpha$; it corresponds to "non-bonding level".

8. *The Coefficients:* By inserting the values of E, one by one, in the n simultaneous secular equations, the relative values of the HMO coefficients $a_1, a_2, ..., a_n$ are obtained. To get their absolute values, another equation, reflecting the condition of normalisation, has to be used.

$$\int \psi^2 \, d\tau = 1$$

or
$$\int (a_1 p_1 + a_2 p_2 + \cdots + a_n p_n)^2 \, d\tau = 1$$

or
$$a_1^2 + a_2^2 + \cdots + a_n^2 = 1$$

because the functions $p_1, p_2, ..., p_n$ are normalised and the integrals

$$\int p_r \, p_s \, d\tau = S_{rs} = 0$$

For each value of E, we shall obtain a set of coefficients constituting an HMO.

For a conjugated system of n carbon atoms there will be n HMOs. The π-electrons of the molecule will fill up the HMOs in order of increasing energy, with two electrons of opposite spins being accommodated in an HMO.

13.5.1 Application to Simple π-Systems

13.5.1.1 Ethylene

The skeletal framework of ethylene is $C_1 - C_2$. The π MO (HMO) may be written as,

$$\psi = a_1 p_1 + a_2 p_2 \qquad \text{... (13.67)}$$

where p_1 and p_2 are the p_z AOs associated with the carbon atoms C_1 and C_2, treating the molecular plane as the xy plane. For this system, the Hückel determinant equation is,

$$\begin{vmatrix} \alpha - E & \beta \\ \beta & \alpha - E \end{vmatrix} = 0$$

or

$$\begin{vmatrix} x & 1 \\ 1 & x \end{vmatrix} = 0 \qquad \text{... (13.68)}$$

where

$$x = \frac{\alpha - E}{\beta}$$

or

$$x^2 - 1 = 0,$$

or

$$x = \pm 1$$

Corresponding to $x = -1$ and $+1$, the two HMO energies are,

$$E_1 = \alpha + \beta$$

$$E_2 = \alpha - \beta$$

respectively E_1, which is less than α (since β is negative), is the bonding and E_2 the antibonding energy level (Fig. 13.7).

The π-Bond Energy: In the ground state, the two π electrons of ethylene are in the lower energy level (E_1) with a total energy $E_\pi = 2(\alpha + \beta)$. In the absence of bonding, the total energy of the two electrons lying in the two p_z AOs would be 2α. Therefore,

$$2(\alpha + \beta) - 2\alpha = 2\beta$$

gives the π bond energy in ethylene.

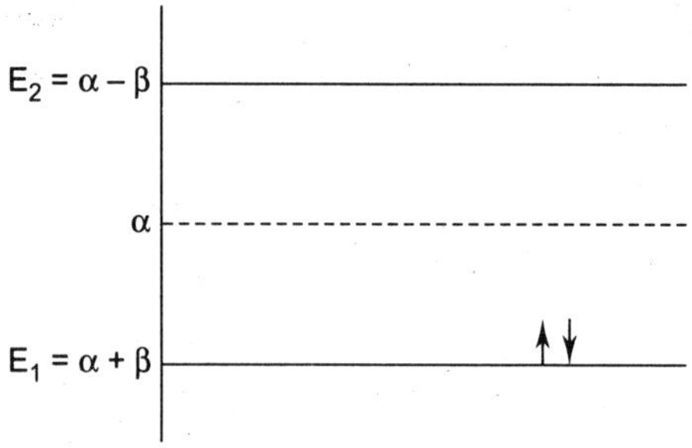

Fig. 13.7 *The two HMO levels of ethylene*

The Coefficients and the HMO Functions: The secular equations are,

$$\left.\begin{aligned} a_1(\alpha - E) + a_2\beta &= 0 \\ a_1\beta + a_2(\alpha - E) &= 0 \end{aligned}\right\}$$

or

$$\left.\begin{aligned} a_1 x + a_2 &= 0 \\ a_1 + a_2 x &= 0 \end{aligned}\right\}$$

For the bonding level ($x = -1$), $-a_1 + a_2 = 0$ or $a_1 = a_2$

and $a_1^2 + a_2^2 = 1$ (by normalisation condition).

Hence, $a_1 = a_2 = \frac{1}{\sqrt{2}}$, and

$$\psi_1 = \frac{1}{\sqrt{2}}(p_1 + p_2) \quad \text{... (13.69)}$$

Similarly, for the antibonding level ($x = +1$)

$$a_1 = -a_2 = \frac{1}{\sqrt{2}}$$

and

$$\psi_2 = \frac{1}{\sqrt{2}}(p_1 - p_2) \quad \text{... (13.70)}$$

Physical Representations: The two HMOs may be represented in the following two ways:

(*i*) *Graphical Representation.* The HMO function ψ_1 and ψ_2 may be plotted against various distances along a fixed direction *i.e.*, along the $C_1 - C_2$ axis (Fig. 13.8). The function ψ_1 increases continuously till it is maximum near C_1, beyond which it decreases. Around C_2, where the function p_2 dominates, ψ_1 increases again, reaches a maximum and then falls off continuously with a concentration of π electron density between C_1 and C_2. The function ψ_2 changes sign in the middle of the $C_1 - C_2$ axis—the point being called "node", or the radial node.

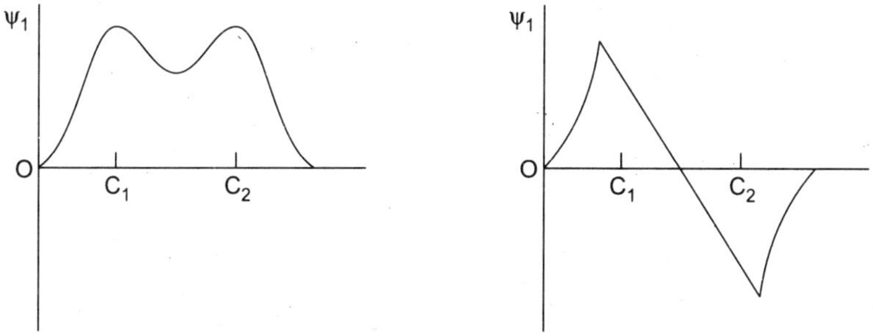

Fig. 13.8 *The two HMO functions of ethylene; ψ_2 has a node between C_1 and C_2*

(*ii*) *Three Dimensional Shapes:* The shapes of HMOs may be derived from three-dimensional plots, *i.e.*, along different directions. These may be represented as in Fig. 13.9 in a manner similar to the MOs of H_2.

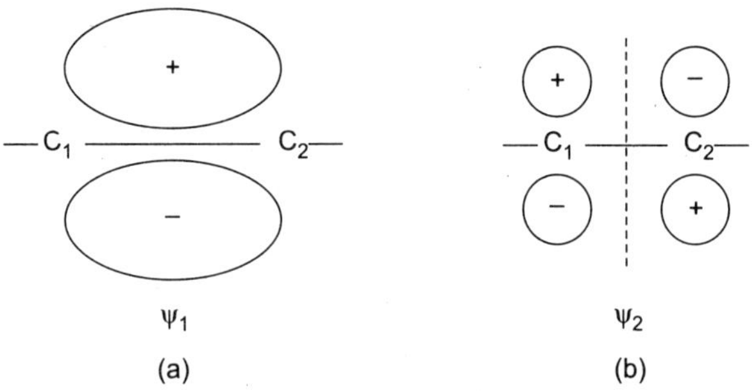

Fig. 13.9 *The bonding (a) and antibonding (b) π MOs (HMOs) of ethylene; the + and – signs represent the signs of the functions ψ_1 and ψ_2*

Each function changes sign along $C_1 - C_2$ axis. The plane containing this axis is the nodal plane. The presence of such a nodal plane is characteristic of all π-orbitals. The orbital ψ_1 is 'ungerade' (π_u) and ψ_2 'gerade' (π_g) as the latter has centre of inversion. The π-electron configuration in the ground state is, therefore, π_u^2.

13.5.1.2 The Allyl System ($C_1 - C_2 - C_3$)

The HMOs for the allyl system have the general expression

$$\psi = a_1 p_1 + a_2 p_2 + a_3 p_3 \qquad \text{... (13.71)}$$

and the Hückel determinant is,

$$\begin{vmatrix} x & 1 & 0 \\ 1 & x & 1 \\ 0 & 1 & x \end{vmatrix} = 0$$

The corresponding polynomial is,

$$x^3 - 2x = 0$$

whose roots are $x = 0$ (consistent with n being odd), $+\sqrt{2}$ and $-\sqrt{2}$. The allowed π-energy levels are, therefore,

$$\left.\begin{aligned} E_1 &= \alpha + \sqrt{2}\beta \\ E_2 &= \alpha \\ E_3 &= \alpha - \sqrt{2}\beta \end{aligned}\right\} \qquad \text{... (13.72)}$$

with $E_1 < E_2 < E_3$.

We have three allyl systems: Allyl carbonium ion (2π electrons), allyl radical (3π electrons) and allyl carbanion (4π electrons).

The arrangement of the π-electrons and their total π-energies are indicated in Fig. (13.10).

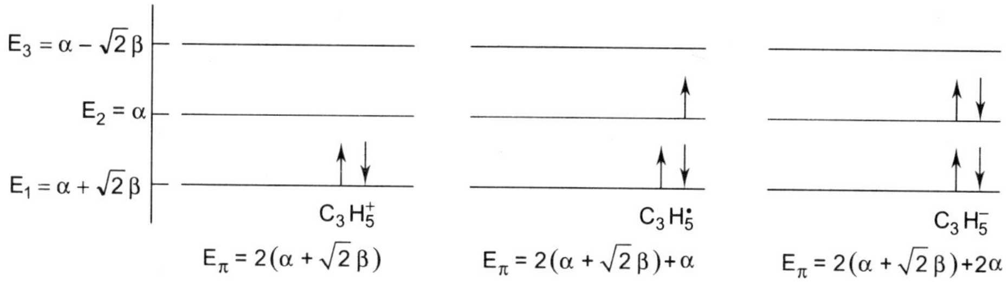

Fig. 13.10 *π-HMO energy levels for the three allyl systems*

π-Bond and Delocalisation Energies: The π-bond energies for the three allyl systems are identical

$$\left.\begin{aligned} E_\pi\left(C_3\,H_5^+\right) &= \left[2\left(\alpha+\sqrt{2}\,\beta\right)\right]-2\alpha = 2\sqrt{2}\,\beta \\ E_\pi\left(C_3\,H_5^\bullet\right) &= \left[2\left(\alpha+\sqrt{2}\,\beta\right)+\alpha\right]-3\alpha = 2\sqrt{2}\,\beta \\ E_\pi\left(C_3\,H_5^-\right) &= \left[2\left(\alpha+\sqrt{2}\,\beta\right)+2\alpha\right]-4\alpha = 2\sqrt{2}\,\beta \end{aligned}\right\} \quad \text{...(13.73)}$$

The π-bond energies given above are due to the delocalised structures. The energies due to localised structures arising from just one ethylenic bond in each case *i.e.*, C═C—C would be 2β. The difference $2\sqrt{2}\,\beta - 2\beta = 0.828\,\beta$ (which is negative) is, therefore, the decrease in energy due to delocalisation of the π-electrons—the "delocalisation energy". The delocalised allyl structures correspond to greater stability than the localised (classical) structures by an amount 0.828β.

The delocalisation energy in all the three allyl systems is the same. This is because in the delocalised structure the additional electrons, *i.e.*, those in addition to the electrons present in ψ_1, are housed in the non-bonding HMO ψ_2, having the same energy (α) as that of the isolated p_z AO in the case of the localised structures.

The HMO Coefficients: The secular equations for the allyl system are

$$\left.\begin{aligned} a_1 x + a_2 &= 0 \\ a_1 + a_2 x + a_3 &= 0 \\ a_2 + a_3 x &= 0 \end{aligned}\right\} \quad \text{where } x = \frac{\alpha - E}{\beta}$$

For $\quad x = -\sqrt{2}$ (bonding level),

$$-\sqrt{2}\,a_1 + a_2 = 0, \text{ or } a_2 = \sqrt{2}\,a_1$$

and $\quad a_2 - \sqrt{2}\,a_3 = 0, a_2 = \sqrt{2}\,a_3$

therefore, $\quad a_1 = a_3$

From normalisation condition, $a_1^2 + a_2^2 + a_3^2 = 1$, one finds $a_1 = a_3 = \frac{1}{2}$, and $a_2 = \frac{\sqrt{2}}{2}$.

Thus, ψ_1 (bonding HMO) $= \frac{1}{2} p_1 + \frac{\sqrt{2}}{2} p_2 + \frac{1}{2} p_3$ ... (13.74)

Similar procedure for $x = 0$ (non-bonding level), leads to $a_1 = \frac{1}{\sqrt{2}}$, $a_2 = 0$ and $a_3 = -\frac{1}{\sqrt{2}}$

and for $x = +\sqrt{2}$ (antibonding level) to, $a_1 = a_2 = \frac{1}{2}$, $a_2 = -\frac{\sqrt{2}}{2}$.

Thus, ψ_2 (non-bonding HMO) $= \frac{1}{\sqrt{2}}(p_1 - p_3)$, ... (13.75)

and ψ_3 (antibonding HMO) $= \frac{1}{2} p_1 - \frac{\sqrt{2}}{2} p_2 + \frac{1}{2} p_3$ ... (13.76)

Physical Representation: (*i*) Graphical pictures. Plots of ψ_1, ψ_2 and ψ_3 against various points along the $C_1 - C_2 - C_3$ axis in the molecule are shown in Fig. 13.11.

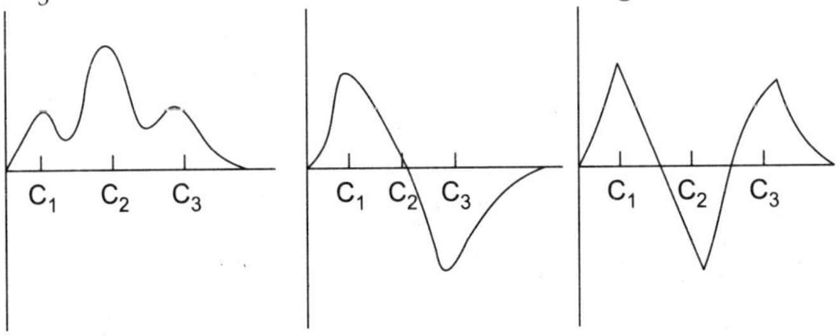

Fig. 13.11 *Graphical plots of the three HMOs in the allyl system*

With respect to the point at C_2, the functions ψ_1 and ψ_3 are seen to be symmetric while ψ_2 is antisymmetric. Increasing number of nodes in the functions appear with increasing energy levels—in case of ψ_1 there is no node; in the cases of ψ_2 and ψ_3 there are one and two nodes respectively.

Three Dimensional Shapes: These may be derived from the plots of ψ_1, ψ_2 and ψ_3 in various directions sections of which are shown below:

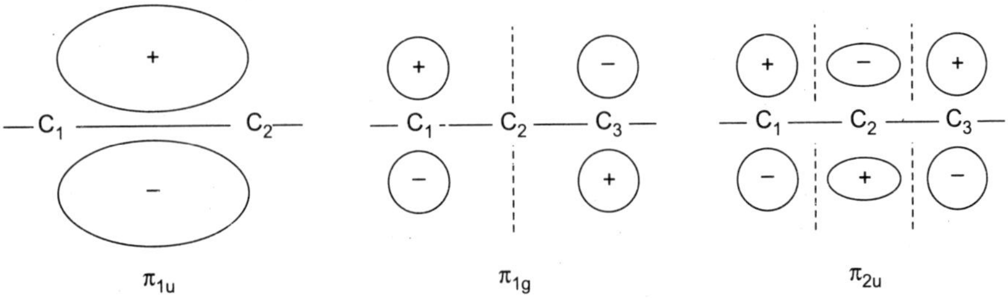

Fig. 13.12 *Sections of three-dimensional shapes of the HMOs of allyl systems; dotted lines indicate bases of the nodal planes*

The three allyl system may be represented by the configurations: $\pi_u^2, \pi_u^2\,\pi_g$ and $\pi_u^2\,\pi_g^2$ respectively.

13.5.1.3 Butadiene ($C_1 - C_2 - C_3 - C_4$)

There are four $2p_z$ AOs to be combined and four π-electrons in the molecule. The HMOs are of the form

$$\psi = a_1 p_1 + a_2 p_2 + a_3 p_3 + a_4 p_4 \qquad \text{... (13.77)}$$

and the secular determinant is,

$$\begin{vmatrix} x & 1 & 0 & 0 \\ 1 & x & 1 & 0 \\ 0 & 1 & x & 1 \\ 0 & 0 & 1 & x \end{vmatrix} = 0$$

On expansion, the fourth degree polynomial,

$$x^4 - 3x^2 + 1 = 0$$

indicates that there will be 4 roots and hence four energy levels. The equation can be solved easily by putting

$$y = x^2, \text{ then}$$
$$y^2 - 3y + 1 = 0$$

which has the following two roots:

$$y_1 = \frac{3+\sqrt{5}}{2} = \frac{1+5+2\sqrt{5}}{4} = \left(\frac{1+\sqrt{5}}{2}\right)^2$$

$$y_2 = \frac{3-\sqrt{5}}{2} = \frac{1+5-2\sqrt{5}}{4} = \left(\frac{1-\sqrt{5}}{2}\right)^2.$$

The four roots can thus be obtained as

$$x = \pm\sqrt{y},$$

i.e.,

$$x_1, x_2 = \pm\sqrt{y_1} = \pm\left(\frac{1+\sqrt{5}}{2}\right) = \pm 1.618$$

$$x_3, x_4 = \pm\sqrt{y_2} = \pm\left(\frac{1-\sqrt{5}}{2}\right) = \pm 0.618$$

The ground state electronic distribution of the four π-electrons is shown in Fig. 13.13.

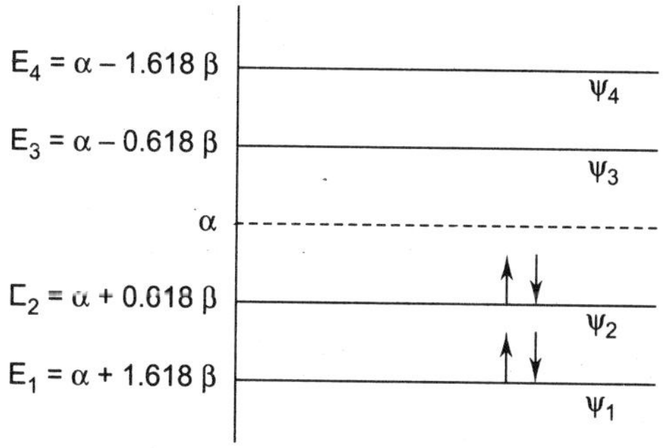

Fig. 13.13 *HMO levels in butadiene*

Thus, the total energy is,

$$\left.\begin{aligned} E_\pi &= 2\,(\alpha + 1.618\,\beta) + 2\,(\alpha + 0.618\,\beta) = 4\,\alpha + 4.48\,\beta \\ \pi\text{-bond energy} \quad &= (4\,\alpha + 4.48\,\beta) - 4\,\alpha = 4.48\,\beta \\ \text{and delocalisation energy} \quad &= (4\,\alpha + 4.48\,\beta) - 2 \times 2\,(\alpha + \beta) = 0.48\,\beta \end{aligned}\right\} \quad \text{... (13.78)}$$

Localised structure:	Delocalised structure:
C=C—C=C	C—C—C—C (with dashed line above)
$2\,(\alpha + \beta) + 2\,(\alpha + \beta)$	$2\,\alpha + 0.48\,\beta$

The HMO Coefficients: In terms of x, the secular equations are,

$$\left.\begin{aligned} a_1\,x + a_2 &= 0 \\ a_1 + a_2\,x + a_3 &= 0 \\ a_2 + a_3\,x + a_4 &= 0 \\ a_3 + a_4\,x &= 0 \end{aligned}\right\}$$

Using $x = -1.618$, corresponding to the lowest energy HMO ψ_1, the normalisation condition:

$$a_1^2 + a_2^2 + a_3^2 + a_4^2 = 1$$

one finds that

$$a_1 = a_4 = 0.372, \text{ and } a_2 = a_3 = 0.602$$

Thus,
$$\psi_1 = 0.372\,p_1 + 0.602\,p_2 + 0.602\,p_3 + 0.372\,p_4$$

Similarly, the coefficients for ψ_2, ψ_3 and ψ_4 can be found by using the value $x = -0.618$, $+0.618$ and 1.618 respectively. The four HMOs of butadiene are thus found to be as follows:

$$\left.\begin{aligned} \psi_1 &= 0.372\,p_1 + 0.602\,p_2 + 0.602\,p_3 + 0.372\,p_4 \\ \psi_2 &= 0.602\,p_1 + 0.372\,p_2 - 0.372\,p_3 - 0.602\,p_4 \\ \psi_3 &= 0.602\,p_1 - 0.372\,p_2 - 0.372\,p_3 + 0.602\,p_4 \\ \psi_4 &= 0.372\,p_1 - 0.602\,p_2 + 0.602\,p_3 - 0.372\,p_4 \end{aligned}\right\} \quad \text{... (13.79)}$$

The graphical plots of these HMOs along the C_1, ..., C_4 axis and the sections of the three-dimensional shapes are shown in Figs. 13.14 and 13.15 respectively.

Consistent with the expression (13.79), ψ_1 has no node, ψ_2 has one, ψ_3 has two, and ψ_4 has three, along the bond axis.

The ground state configuration of butadiene may be written as $\pi_{1u^2}\,\pi_{1g^2}$.

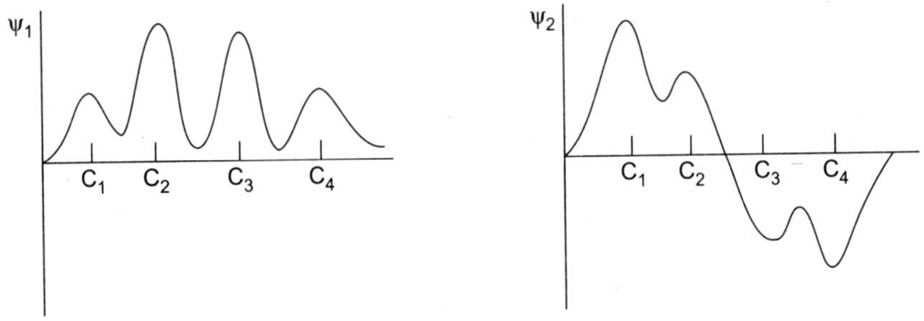

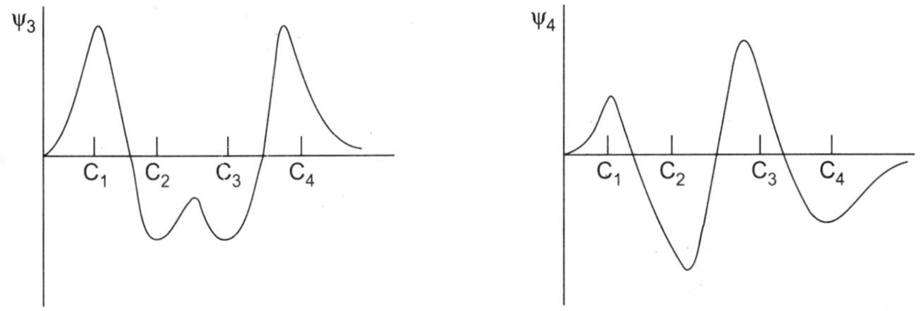

Fig. 13.14 *Graphical sketches of the four HMOs of butadiene along the bond axis*

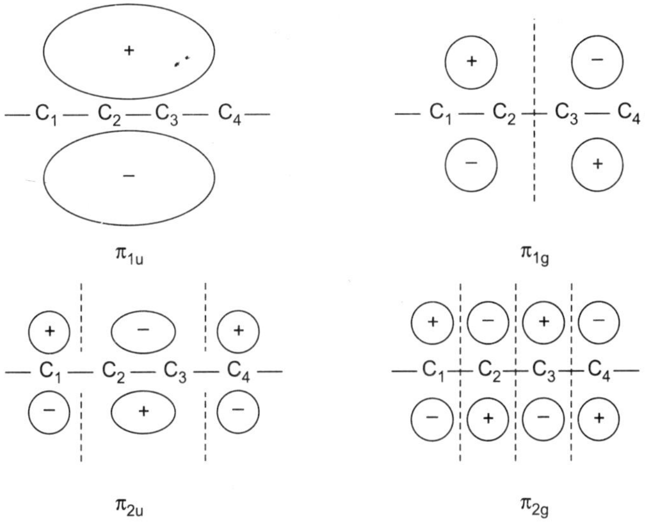

Fig. 13.15 *Sections of the HMOs along a vertical plane*

13.5.1.4 Cyclopropenyl System

The skeletal framework for this molecule is as shown below.

The HMO function for this system is

$$\psi = a_1 p_1 + a_2 p_2 + a_3 p_3 \quad \text{...(13.80)}$$

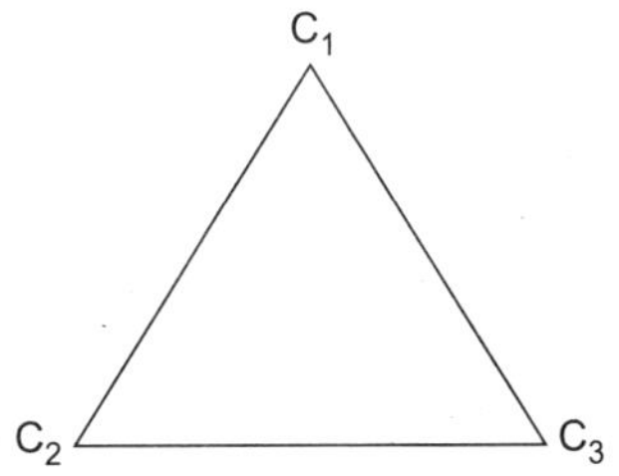

The secular determinant in the case also is of third order; however, C_1 and C_3 here are neighbours, so

$$H_{12} = H_{21} = H_{13} = H_{31} = H_{23} = H_{32} = \beta$$

$$\text{In terms of } x, \begin{vmatrix} x & 1 & 1 \\ 1 & x & 1 \\ 1 & 1 & x \end{vmatrix} = 0$$

It has to be noted here that for all cyclic π systems the element 1 will appear in the HMO determinant at the positions $1 \times n$ as well as $n \times 1$ simply because the p_z AOs 1 and n are neighbours.

The determinant leads to the polynomial equation

$$x^3 - 3x + 2 = 0$$

or
$$(x + 2)(x^2 - 2x + 1) = 0$$

The roots of equation are

$$x_1 = -2, x_2 = 1 \text{ and } x_3 = 1$$

The three corresponding π-energy levels are,

$$E_1 = \alpha + 2\beta, E_2 = E_3 = \alpha - \beta \quad \text{... (13.81)}$$

Thus, two of the levels (E_2 and E_3) are degenerate.

The ground state π-electron distribution in the three HMOs of the cyclopropenyl carbonium ion, radical and the carbanion is shown in Fig. 13.16.

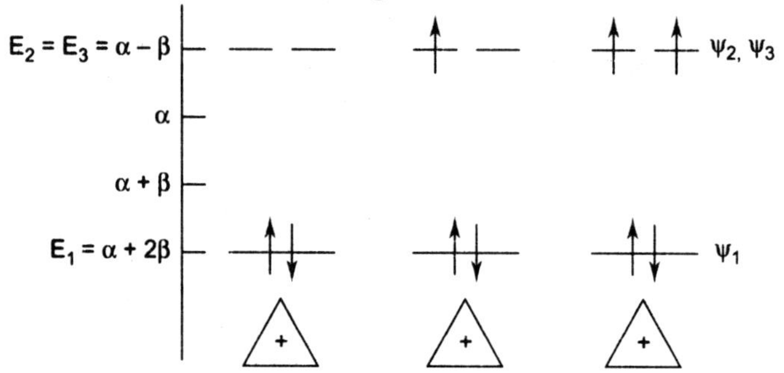

Fig. 13.16 *π-Electron distribution in the cyclopropenyl systems*

The total energy E_π, and the delocalisation energy (D.E.) for the three systems (Fig. 13.16) are:

Cyclopropenyl carbonium ion

$$E_\pi = 2(\alpha + 2\beta)$$

$$\text{D.E.} = 2(\alpha + 2\beta) - 2(\alpha + \beta) = 2\beta$$

Cyclopropenyl radical:

$$E_\pi = 2(\alpha + 2\beta) + (\alpha - \beta) = 3\alpha + 3\beta$$

$$\text{D.E.} = (3\alpha + 3\beta) - (2\alpha + 2\beta) - \alpha = \beta$$

Cyclopropenyl carbanion:

$$E_\pi = 2(\alpha + 2\beta) + 2(\alpha - \beta) = 4\alpha + 2\beta$$

$$\text{D.E.} = (4\alpha + 2\beta) - (2\alpha + 2\beta) - 2\alpha = 0$$

This leads to the prediction that in the cyclopropenyl system, the carbonium ion will be more stable than the radical or the carbanion.

The HMO Coefficients: *In terms of x, the secular equations for the cyclopropenyl are,*

$$\left.\begin{aligned} a_1x + a_2 + a_3 &= 0 \\ a_1 + a_2x + a_3 &= 0 \\ a_1 + a_2 + a_3x &= 0 \end{aligned}\right\} \quad \text{...(13.82)}$$

For $x = -2$, we have

$$\left.\begin{aligned} -2a_1 + a_2 + a_3 &= 0 \\ a_1 - 2a_2 + a_3 &= 0 \\ a_1 + a_2 - 2a_3 &= 0 \end{aligned}\right\} \quad \text{...(13.83)}$$

The three equations and the normalisation condition

$$a_1^2 + a_2^2 + a_3^2 = 1$$

give $$a_1 = a_2 = a_3 = \frac{1}{\sqrt{3}} \quad \text{...(13.84)}$$

Thus, $$\psi_1 = \frac{1}{\sqrt{3}}(p_1 + p_2 + p_3) \quad \text{...(13.85)}$$

For $x = 1$, we have from Equation (13.82),

$$\left.\begin{aligned} a_1 + a_2 + a_3 &= 0 \\ a_1 + a_2 + a_3 &= 0 \\ a_1 + a_2 + a_3 &= 0 \end{aligned}\right\} \quad \text{...(13.86)}$$

The values of the coefficients cannot be found by these equations alone. However, corresponding to $x = 1$, the energy levels (the MOs ψ_2 and ψ_3) are degenerate. In the case of degenerate orbitals the MO methods do not allow us to determine the coefficients uniquely. We are free to choose any values for a_1, a_2 and a_3 provided only that they satisfy the conditions of normalisation and orthogonality, as well as the relationship Equation (13.86).

One simple way to satisfy the three conditions is to set one of the coefficients equal to zero. Let $a_2 = 0$; then

or $$a_1 + a_3 = 0 \quad a_3 = -a_1$$

From normalisation condition, $a_1^2 + 0 + a_1^2 = 1$

$$a_1 = \frac{1}{\sqrt{2}} \text{ and } a_3 = -\frac{1}{\sqrt{2}}$$

Thus, one possible expression for ψ_2 is

$$\psi_2 = \frac{1}{\sqrt{2}}(p_1 - p_3) \quad \text{...(13.87)}$$

Having chosen ψ_2, we are no longer free to choose the coefficients for ψ_3 arbitrarily. The coefficients for ψ_3 have to be such that ψ_3 becomes orthogonal to ψ_1 and ψ_2,

$$\int \psi_1 \psi_3 \, d\tau = 0 \qquad \text{... (13.88)}$$

$$\int \psi_2 \psi_3 \, d\tau = 0 \qquad \text{... (13.89)}$$

Taking the second relationship, for example, we get

$$\int \frac{1}{\sqrt{2}} (p_1 - p_3)(a_1 p_1 + a_2 p_2 + a_3 p_3) d\tau = 0$$

or
$$\int \frac{1}{\sqrt{2}} a_1 p_1^2 \, d\tau + \int \frac{1}{\sqrt{2}} a_2 p_1 p_2 \, d\tau + \int \frac{1}{\sqrt{2}} a_3 p_1 p_3 \, d\tau$$

$$- \int \frac{1}{\sqrt{2}} a_1 p_3 p_1 \, d\tau - \int \frac{1}{\sqrt{2}} a_2 p_3 p_2 \, d\tau - \int \frac{1}{\sqrt{2}} a_3 p_3^2 \, d\tau = 0$$

or
$$\frac{1}{\sqrt{2}} a_1 - \frac{1}{\sqrt{2}} a_3 = 0 \text{ or } a_1 = a_3 \quad \left[\begin{aligned} \text{because} \int p_r \, p_s \, d\tau &= 0 \text{ for } r \neq s \\ &= 1 \text{ for } r = s \end{aligned}\right]$$

But
$$a_1 + a_2 + a_3 = 0$$

$$2a_1 + a_2 = 0$$

or
$$a_2 = -2a_1$$

From normalisation condition, $a_1 = \frac{1}{\sqrt{6}}$; $a_2 = -\frac{2}{\sqrt{6}}$; $a_3 = \frac{1}{\sqrt{6}}$

Therefore,
$$\psi_3 = \frac{1}{\sqrt{6}} p_1 - \frac{2}{\sqrt{6}} p_2 + \frac{1}{\sqrt{6}} p_3 \qquad \text{... (13.90)}$$

Any linear combinations of the degenerate MOs, which satisfy the orthogonality and normalisation conditions, will be equally valid MOs.

Physical Representation

A convenient method to represent the HMOs in such a cyclic system is through circles drawn at the carbon centres. The spotted circles represent the positive lobes and open circles the negative lobes of the $2p_z$ AOs entering into linear combination. If the plane of the ring which lies in the plane of the paper be taken as the *xy* plane and the orbitals are viewed from above, only one of the two lobes of a $2p_z$ AO participating in the linear combination will be visible to the observer. The radii of the circles may be made to be proportional to the magnitudes of the LCAO coefficients (Fig. 13.17). The broken lines inside the triangle represent the bases of the nodal planes.

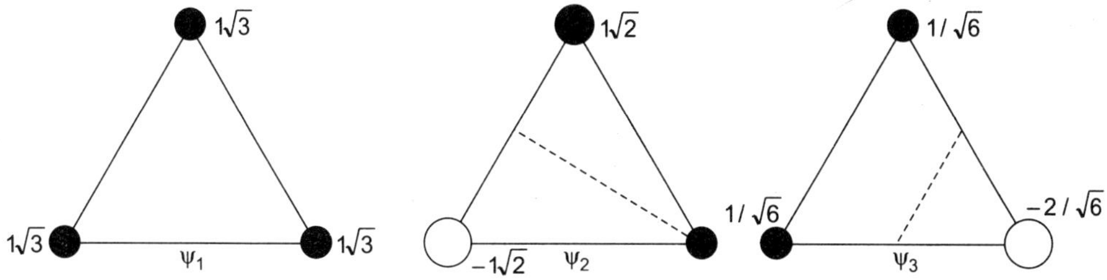

Fig. 13.17

13.5.1.5 Cyclobutadiene

The HMOs are of the form

$$\psi = a_1 p_1 + a_2 p_2 + a_3 p_3 + a_4 p_4 \qquad \text{... (13.91)}$$

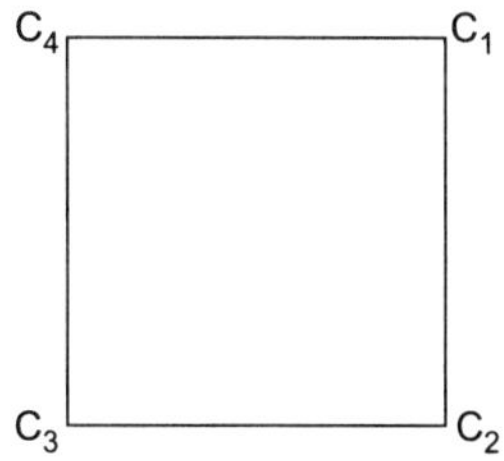

Since $H_{14} = H_{41} = \beta$, the secular determinant, in terms of x is

$$\begin{vmatrix} x & 1 & 0 & 1 \\ 1 & x & 1 & 0 \\ 0 & 1 & x & 1 \\ 1 & 0 & 1 & x \end{vmatrix} = 0 \qquad \text{... (13.92)}$$

On expansion this gives the polynomial,

$$x^4 - 4x^2 = 0$$

with the following four roots,

$$x_1 = -2, x_2 = 0, x_3 = 0, x = +2 \qquad \text{... (13.93)}$$

and the energy levels

$$E_1 = \alpha + 2\beta, E_2 = E_3 = \alpha, E_4 = \alpha - 2\beta \qquad \text{... (13.94)}$$

This again indicates two doubly degenerate non-bonding levels.

The ground state electronic distribution and the π-electronic energy are shown in Fig. 13.18.

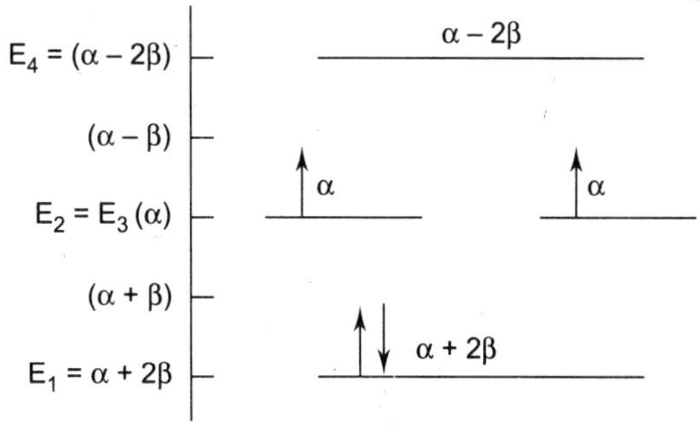

Fig. 13.18 *HMO energy levels in cyclobutadiene*

$$E_\pi = 2(\alpha + 2\beta) + \alpha + \alpha = 4\alpha + 4\beta \quad \text{... (13.95)}$$

Delocalisation Energy: *For the localised structure.*

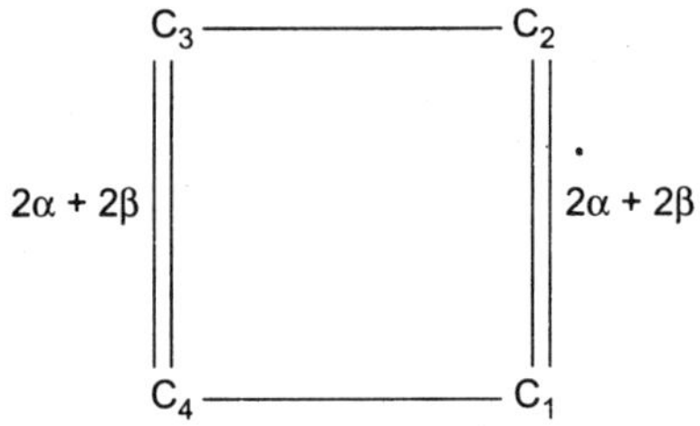

$$E_\pi = 4\alpha + 4\beta$$

Therefore, the delocalisation energy = (4α + 4β) – (4α + 4β) = 0, *i.e.*, there is no additional stability in the molecule by delocalisation. (The ring is small and is therefore, under severe strain. Since the strain is not compensated by delocalisation the molecule is unstable and difficult to synthesis).

HMO Coefficients: The secular equations are,

$$\left.\begin{aligned} a_1x + a_2 + a_4 &= 0 \\ a_1 + a_2x + a_3 &= 0 \\ a_2 + a_3x + a_4 &= 0 \\ a_1 + a_3 + a_4x &= 0 \end{aligned}\right\} \quad \text{... (13.96)}$$

For $x = -2,$

$$-2a_1 + a_2 + a_4 = 0 \quad \text{... (13.97)}$$

$$a_1 - 2a_2 + a_3 = 0 \quad \text{... (13.98)}$$

$$a_2 - 2a_3 + a_4 = 0 \quad \text{... (13.99)}$$

$$a_1 + a_3 - 2a_4 = 0 \quad \text{... (13.100)}$$

Such a set of equations can be solved by the method of elimination. Coefficient a_2 can be eliminated by multiplying Equation (13.97) by 2 and adding Equation (13.98) to it; this gives

$$-3a_1 + a_3 + 2a_4 = 0 \quad \text{... (13.101)}$$

Subtraction of Equation (13.99) from Equation (13.97) gives

$$-2a_1 + 2a_3 = 0, \text{ so that } a_1 = a_3 \quad \text{... (13.102)}$$

To eliminate a_3, we multiply Equation (13.100) by 2 and then subtract it from Equation (13.102) which gives,

$$-4a_1 + 4a_4 = 0 \text{ that is, } a_1 = a_4 \quad \text{... (13.103)}$$

We eliminate a_4 from Equation (13.97) by multiplying it by 4 and subtracting Equation (13.103) from it; this gives,

$$-4a_1 + 4a_2 = 0 \text{ or } a_1 = a_2 \quad \text{... (13.104)}$$

From the condition of normalisation, $a_1^2 + a_2^2 + a_3^2 + a_4^2 = 1$

and Equations (13.102), (13.103) and (13.104), $4a_1^2 = 1$

or

$$a_1 = a_2 = a_3 = a_4 = \frac{1}{2} \quad \text{... (13.105)}$$

Hence $$\psi_1 = \frac{1}{2}(p_1 + p_2 + p_3 + p_4) \quad \text{...(13.106)}$$

(Such a process can be extended and applied to systems of any size).

For $x = 0$ (corresponding to the degenerate HMOs (ψ_2 and ψ_3), the set of Equations (13.97) to (13.100) reduces to

$$\left.\begin{aligned} a_2 + a_4 &= 0 \\ a_1 + a_3 &= 0 \\ a_2 + a_4 &= 0 \\ a_1 + a_3 &= 0 \end{aligned}\right\} \quad \text{...(13.107)}$$

Here again we may choose any value for one of the coefficients and use the orthogonality and normalisation conditions. Let $a_2 = 0$; then from Equation (13.107) $a_1 = -a_3$ and $a_4 = 0$, and the relation

$$a_1^2 + 0 + a_3^2 + 0 = 1$$

$$2a_1^2 = 1, \text{ or } a_1 = \frac{1}{\sqrt{2}}\ ; a_3 = -\frac{1}{\sqrt{2}}$$

Hence $$\psi_2 = \frac{1}{\sqrt{2}}(p_1 - p_3) \quad \text{...(13.108)}$$

The coefficients for ψ_3 will be determined by the orthogonality condition.

$$\int \psi_2\, \psi_3\, d\tau = 0$$

or $$\int \frac{1}{\sqrt{2}}(p_1 - p_3)(a_1\, p_1 + a_2\, p_2 + a_3\, p_3 + a_4\, p_4)\, d\tau = 0$$

or $$\int \frac{1}{\sqrt{2}} a_1\, p_1^2\, d\tau + \int \frac{1}{\sqrt{2}} a_2\, p_1\, p_2\, d\tau + \int \frac{1}{\sqrt{2}} a_3\, p_1\, p_3\, d\tau + \int \frac{1}{\sqrt{2}} a_4\, p_1\, p_4\, d\tau$$

$$- \int \frac{1}{\sqrt{2}} a_1\, p_3\, p_1\, d\tau - \int \frac{1}{\sqrt{2}} a_2\, p_3\, p_2\, d\tau - \int \frac{1}{\sqrt{2}} a_3\, p_3^2\, d\tau - \int \frac{1}{\sqrt{2}} a_4\, p_3\, p_4\, d\tau = 0$$

or $$\frac{1}{\sqrt{2}} a_1 - \frac{1}{\sqrt{2}} a_3 = 0\ ; a_1 = a_3$$

But $$a_1 + a_3 = 0 \quad \text{...(13.107)}$$

Therefore, $a_1 = a_3 = 0$, and since $a_2 + a_4 = 0$, $a_2 = -a_4$, and $0 + a_2^2 + 0 + a_4^2 = 1$

$$2a_2^2 = 1, \text{ or } a_2 = \frac{1}{\sqrt{2}} = -a_4$$

Hence $$\psi_3 = \frac{1}{\sqrt{2}}(p_2 - p_4) \quad \text{...(13.109)}$$

or $x = +2$ (which corresponds to ψ_4) using the method of elimination (as in case of ψ_1), we get

$$a_1 = \frac{1}{2}, a_2 = -\frac{1}{2}, a_3 = \frac{1}{2}, a_4 = -\frac{1}{2}$$

so that $$\psi_4 = \frac{1}{2}\left(p_1 - p_2 + p_3 - p_4\right) \quad \text{... (13.110)}$$

The HMOs of cyclobutadiene may be represented as in Fig. 13.19.

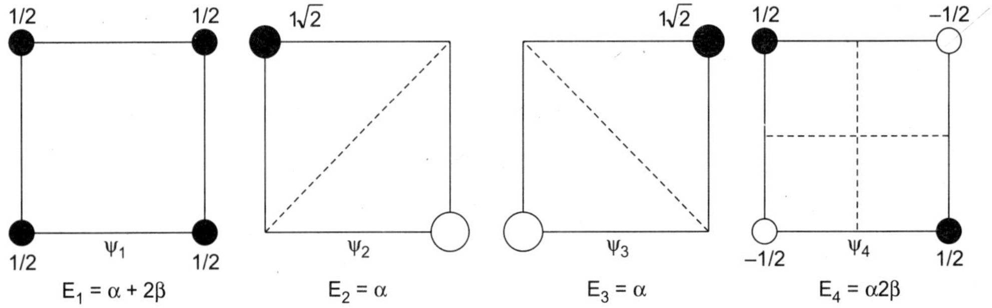

Fig. 13.19 *Nodes in HMOs of cyclobutadiene*

In going around the ring, the HMO ψ_1 shows no node, ψ_2 has nodes at C_2 and C_4, ψ_3 has nodes at C_1 and C_3 and ψ_4 has nodes between each pair of adjacent carbon atoms.

13.5.2 Use of Symmetry

The method outlined so far for finding the HMOs and the energy levels can, in principle, be used for any conjugated molecule. But with increasing number of carbon atoms, the calculations will become more and more tedious. However, if a molecule possesses some elements of symmetry, the calculations can be simplified by making some guesses. The principles of group theory can be used to factorise the secular determinant of high order into those of smaller orders. We can examine, for example, the simple case of butadiene first, which has a 4 × 4 secular determinant and whose solutions we know.

13.5.2.1 Butadiene

The *cis*-butadiene belongs to C_{2v} point group and the *trans* isomer to C_{2h} point group.

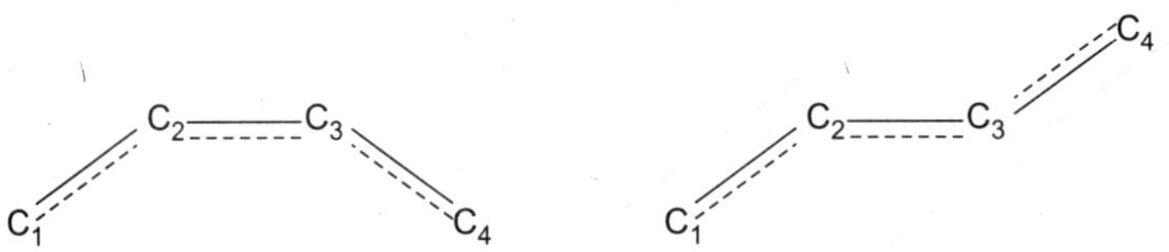

(C_{2v}) (C_{2v})

However, in either case the HMOs and the secular equations are of the same form as Equation (13.77). Taking the case of *trans* isomer (C_{2h}), the following reducible representation may be constructed (see Chapter 11),

C_{2h} :	E	C_2	i	σ	Basis
Γ_r :	4	0	0	4	(p_1, p_2, p_3, p_4)

By Equation (11.45), it reduces as

$$\Gamma_r = 2A_u + 2B_g \quad \text{... (13.111)}$$

This means that there will be two categories of SALCs for the system, distinguished by their symmetry types A_u and B_g. Using Equation (11.46) and one of the p AOs say p_1, for ψ_i, we may construct one of the two SALCs of A_u type as follows:

$$\psi(A_u) = \frac{1}{4}\left[\chi(E)\,.\,Ep_1 + \chi(C_2)\,C_2\,p_1 + \chi(i)\,ip_1 + \chi(\sigma_h)\,\sigma_h\,p_1\right]$$

$$= \frac{1}{4}\left[E\,p_1 + C_2\,p_1 - ip_1 - \sigma_h\,p_1\right] \qquad \text{(using the character table of } C_{2h})$$

$$= \frac{1}{4}\left[p_1 + p_4 - (-p_4) - (-p_1)\right]$$

$$= \frac{1}{2}\left[p_1 + p_4\right] = \phi_1 \text{ (say)} \qquad \text{... (13.112)}$$

For the other SALC of A_u, we use p_2 in Equation (11.46) and obtain.

$$\psi'(A_u) = \frac{1}{2}(p_2 + p_3) = \phi_2 \text{ (say)} \qquad \text{... (13.113)}$$

Similarly, using p_1 and p_2 in Equation (11.46) we obtain the SALCs of B_g type,

$$\psi(B_g) = \frac{1}{2}(p_1 - p_4) = \phi_3 \qquad \text{... (13.114)}$$

$$\psi(B_g) = \frac{1}{2}(p_2 - p_3) = \phi_4 \qquad \text{... (13.115)}$$

(Use of p_3 and p_4 in Equation (11.46) will generate the same set of SALCs).

The linear combination of functions ϕ_1, ϕ_2, ϕ_3 and ϕ_4 will lead to the secular determinant

$$\begin{vmatrix} H_{11} - S_{11}\,E & H_{12} - S_{12}\,E & H_{13} - S_{13}\,E & H_{14} - S_{14}\,E \\ H_{21} - S_{21}\,E & H_{22} - S_{22}\,E & H_{23} - S_{23}\,E & H_{24} - S_{24}\,E \\ H_{31} - S_{31}\,E & H_{32} - S_{32}\,E & H_{33} - S_{33}\,E & H_{34} - S_{34}\,E \\ H_{41} - S_{41}\,E & H_{42} - S_{42}\,E & H_{43} - S_{43}\,E & H_{44} - S_{44}\,E \end{vmatrix} = 0 \qquad \text{... (13.116)}$$

where $$H_{ij} = \int \phi_i\,\hat{H}\,\phi_j\,d\tau \text{ and } S_{ij} = \int \phi_i\,\phi_j\,d\tau$$

Integrals will be zero if the functions ϕ_i and ϕ_j belong to different symmetry type. This sets

$$H_{13} = H_{31} = H_{14} = H_{41} = H_{23} = H_{32} = H_{24} = H_{42} = 0$$

$$S_{13} = S_{31} = S_{14} = S_{41} = S_{23} = S_{32} = S_{24} = S_{42} = 0$$

[For example, $$H_{13} = \int \phi_1\,\hat{H}\,\phi_3 = \frac{1}{4}\int (p_1 + p_4)\,\hat{H}\,(p_1 - p_4)\,d\tau$$

$$= \frac{1}{4}\left[\int p_1\,\hat{H}\,p_1\,d\tau + \int p_4\,\hat{H}\,p_1\,d\tau - \int p_1\,\hat{H}\,p_4\,d\tau - \int p_4\,\hat{H}\,p_4\,d\tau\right] = 0$$

The determinant takes the form,

$$\begin{vmatrix} H_{11} - S_{11}\,E & H_{12} - S_{12}\,E & 0 & 0 \\ H_{21} - S_{21}\,E & H_{22} - S_{22}\,E & 0 & 0 \\ 0 & 0 & H_{33} - S_{33}\,E & H_{34} - S_{34}\,E \\ 0 & 0 & H_{43} - S_{43}\,E & H_{44} - S_{44}\,E \end{vmatrix} = 0 \qquad \text{... (13.117)}$$

which is block-diagonalised or symmetry-factored. The Equation (13.117) can be satisfied only if each block is equal to zero;

$$\underset{(A_u)}{\begin{vmatrix} H_{11} - S_{11}E & H_{12} - S_{12}E \\ H_{21} - S_{21}E & H_{22} - S_{22}E \end{vmatrix}} = 0, \quad \underset{(B_g)}{\begin{vmatrix} H_{33} - S_{33}E & H_{34} - S_{34}E \\ H_{43} - S_{43}E & H_{44} - S_{44}E \end{vmatrix}} = 0 \qquad \text{... (13.118)}$$

Thus, instead of the 4×4 determinant, we get two 2×2 determinants which is easier to work with. In terms of Hückel parameters α and β, we get

$$H_{11} = H_{33} = \frac{1}{2}\alpha \; H_{12} = H_{21} = H_{34} = H_{43} = \frac{1}{2}\beta$$

$$H_{22} = \frac{1}{2}(\alpha + \beta) \text{ and } H_{44} = \frac{1}{2}(\alpha - \beta)$$

[For example, $H_{11} = \int \phi_1 \hat{H} \phi_1 \, d\tau$

$$= \frac{1}{4}\int (p_1 + p_4)\hat{H}(p_1 + p_4)\, d\tau$$

$$= \frac{1}{4}\left[\int p_1 \hat{H} p_1 \, d\tau + \int p_1 \hat{H} p_4 \, d\tau + \int p_4 \hat{H} p_1 \, d\tau + \int p_4 \hat{H} p_4 \, d\tau\right]$$

$$= \frac{1}{4}[\alpha + 0 + 0 + \alpha] = \frac{1}{2}\alpha\Big].$$

The integrals $S_{ii} = \frac{1}{2}$ and $S_{ij} = 0$

The Equation (13.118) may be written as,

$$\underset{(A_u)}{\begin{vmatrix} \frac{1}{2}(\alpha - E) & \frac{1}{2}\beta \\ \frac{1}{2}\beta & \frac{1}{2}(\alpha + \beta - E) \end{vmatrix}} = 0 \text{ and } \underset{(B_g)}{\begin{vmatrix} \frac{1}{2}(\alpha - E) & \frac{1}{2}\beta \\ \frac{1}{2}\beta & \frac{1}{2}(\alpha - \beta - E) \end{vmatrix}} = 0 \qquad \text{... (13.119)}$$

or putting $\frac{\alpha - E}{\beta} = x$, we get ... (13.120)

$$\underset{(A_u)}{\begin{vmatrix} x & 1 \\ 1 & x+1 \end{vmatrix}} = 0 \text{ and } \underset{(B_g)}{\begin{vmatrix} x & 1 \\ 1 & x-1 \end{vmatrix}} = 0 \qquad \text{... (13.121)}$$

On expanding, the determinant belonging to A_u gives,

$$x^2 + x - 1 = 0 \text{ or } x = -\frac{1 \pm \sqrt{5}}{x} = -1.618 \text{ and } 0.618$$

The other determinant (B_g) gives,

$$x^2 - x - 1 = 0, \text{ or } x = \frac{1 \pm \sqrt{5}}{2} = 1.618 \text{ and } -0.618$$

Using these values of x in Equation (13.120), we obtain the four energy levels as

$$E_1 = \alpha + 1.618\,\beta \ldots (A_u)$$
$$E_2 = \alpha + 0.618\,\beta \ldots (B_g)$$
$$E_3 = \alpha - 0.618\,\beta \ldots (A_u)$$
$$E_4 = \alpha - 1.618\,\beta \ldots (B_g) \qquad \ldots (13.122)$$

where $E_1 < E_2 < E_3 < E_4$.

We have seen earlier that SALCs of same symmetry type may be combined, so the HMOs are,

$$\psi = a_i\,\phi_i + a_j\,\phi_j \qquad \ldots (13.123)$$

We thus need to determine only two coefficients instead of four. Use of symmetry properties has simplified our job.

Corresponding to A_u symmetry, the HMO is,

$$\psi = a_1\,\phi_1 + a_2\,\phi_2 = \frac{1}{2}a_1\,(p_1 + p_4) + \frac{1}{2}a_2\,(p_2 + p_3) \qquad \ldots (13.124)$$

The corresponding secular equations are,

$$\left.\begin{aligned} a_1\,(H_{11} - E\,S_{11}) + a_2\,(H_{12} - E\,S_{12}) = 0 \\ a_1\,(H_{21} - E\,S_{21}) + a_2\,(H_{22} - E\,S_{22}) = 0 \end{aligned}\right\} \qquad \ldots (13.125)$$

$$\left.\begin{aligned} \frac{1}{2}a_1\,(\alpha - E) + \frac{1}{2}a_2\,\beta = 0 \\ \frac{1}{2}a_1\,\beta + a_2\,(\alpha + \beta - E) = 0 \end{aligned}\right\} \qquad \ldots (13.126)$$

or

$$a_1\,x + a_2 = 0 \qquad \ldots (13.127)$$

or

$$a_1 + a_2\,(x + 1) = 0 \qquad \ldots (13.128)$$

Two values of x viz., -1.618 and $+0.618$, are obtained from the determinant of A_u type. For $x = -1.618$, which corresponds to the lowest energy, Equation (13.127) gives

$$a_2 = 1.618\,a_1 \qquad \ldots (13.129)$$

From normalisation condition,

$$\int \psi^2\,d\tau = \int (a_1\,\varphi_1 + a_2\,\phi_2)^2\,d\tau = 1$$

or

$$\frac{1}{4}\left[\int a_1^2\,(p_1 + p_4)^2\,d\tau + \int a_2^2\,(p_2 + p_3)^2\,d\tau = 1\right]$$

or

$$a_1^2 + a_2^2 = 2 \qquad \ldots (13.130)$$

From Equations (13.129) and (13.130), $a_1 = 0.744$, $a_2 = 1.204$.

The corresponding HMO, ψ_1, is

$$\psi_1 = 0.744\ \phi_1 + 1.204\ \phi_2$$

$$= 0.372\ p_1 + 0.602\ p_2 + 0.602\ p_3 + 0.372\ p_4 \quad \text{... (13.131)}$$

[in view of Equations (13.112) and (13.113)].

The other value of x (= +0.618), similarly, yields another HMO of the same symmetry (A_u); but since this corresponds to the energy E_3, we shall number it as ψ_3;

$$\psi_3 = 0.602\ p_1 - 0.372\ p_2 - 0.372\ p_3 + 0.602\ p_4 \quad \text{... (13.132)}$$

Using SALCs of B_g type (ϕ_3 and ϕ_4) we likewise construct the HMOs of the B_g symmetry which are,

$$\psi_2 = 0.602\ p_1 + 0.372\ p_2 - 0.372\ p_3 - 0.602\ p_4 \quad \text{... (13.133)}$$

$$\psi_4 = 0.372\ p_1 - 0.602\ p_2 + 0.602\ p_3 - 0.372\ p_4 \quad \text{... (13.134)}$$

corresponding to the energy levels E_2 and E_4 respectively.

Each HMO can accommodate two electrons so that the group theory notation for the ground state configuration of the π electrons is $A_u^2\ B_g^2$.

13.5.2.2 Benzene

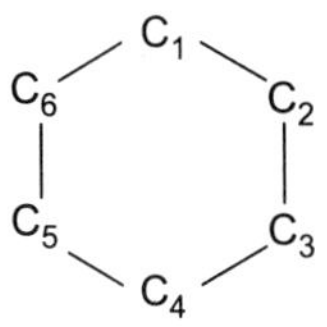

The HMO wave function for benzene is

$$\psi = a_1 p_1 + a_2 p_2 + a_3 p_3 + a_4 p_4 + a_5 p_5 + a_6 p_6 \quad \text{... (13.135)}$$

and the secular equations in terms of x are,

$$\left.\begin{aligned} a_1 x + a_2 + a_6 &= 0 \\ a_1 + a_2 x + a_3 &= 0 \\ a_2 + a_3 x + a_4 &= 0 \\ a_3 + a_4 x + a_5 &= 0 \\ a_4 + a_5 x + a_6 &= 0 \\ a_1 + a_5 + a_6 x &= 0 \end{aligned}\right\} \quad \text{... (13.136)}$$

The corresponding determinant is,

$$\begin{vmatrix} x & 1 & 0 & 0 & 0 & 1 \\ 1 & x & 1 & 0 & 0 & 0 \\ 0 & 1 & x & 1 & 0 & 0 \\ 0 & 0 & 1 & x & 1 & 0 \\ 0 & 0 & 0 & 1 & x & 1 \\ 1 & 0 & 0 & 0 & 1 & x \end{vmatrix} = 0 \quad \text{... (13.137)}$$

The determinant can be expanded into the polynomial,

$$x^6 - 6x^4 + 9x^2 - 4 = 0 \qquad \text{... (13.138)}$$

which can be factorised as,

$$(x+2)(x-2)(x^2-1)^2 = 0 \qquad \text{... (13.139)}$$

The equation leads to the following six roots and correspondingly six energy levels:

x_j	E_j	j	
$x_1 = -2$	$E_1 = \alpha + 2\beta$	1	— Lowest bonding HMO
$x_2 = -1$	$E_2 = \alpha + \beta$	2	— Doubly degenerate bonding HMOs
$x_3 = -1$	$E_3 = \alpha + \beta$	3	
$x_4 = +1$	$E_4 = \alpha - \beta$	4	— Doubly degenerate antibonding HMOs
$x_5 = +1$	$E_5 = \alpha - \beta$	5	
$x_6 = +2$	$E_6 = \alpha - 2\beta$	6	— Highest antibonding HMO

In this case, the expansion of determinant Equation (13.137) into the polynomial Equation (13.138) as also the determination of the coefficients a_i is a very lengthy and tedious procedure. But the symmetry of the molecule may be used to determine the energy levels directly from the determinant without actually solving it.

Benzene belongs to D_{6h} point group, which has 24 symmetry operations, viz.,

$$E,\ C_6^1,\ C_6^2 = C_3^1,\ C_6^3 = C_2,\ C_6^4 = C_3^2,\ C_6^5,\ 3C_{2'},\ 3C_2'',\ i,$$

$$S_6^1,\ S_6^2 = S_3^1,\ S_6^5,\ S_6^4 = S_3^2,\ \sigma_h,\ 3\sigma_d,\ 3\sigma_v.$$

The C_2' axes and σ_v's pass through opposite carbon atoms while the C_2'' and σ_d's bisect the opposite sides of the hexagon (Fig. 13.21).

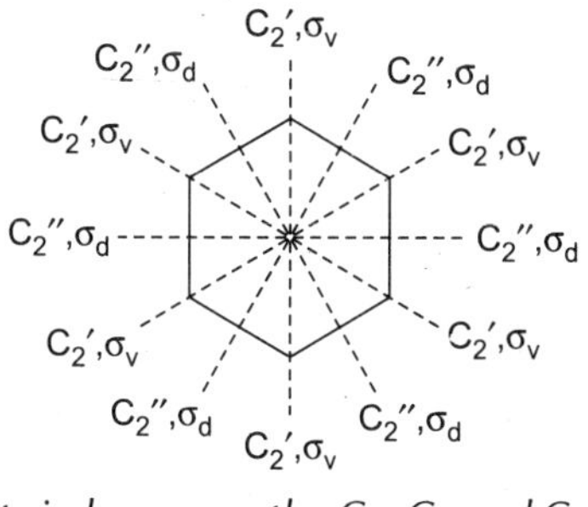

Fig. 13.20 *Symmetry elements in benzene; the C_6, C_3 and C_2, S_6 and S_3 are all collinear and perpendicular to the molecular plane; the dotted lines are C_2', C_2'' axes as well as bases of the σ_v and σ_d planes respectively the centre of the hexagon is i*

Let the molecule be in the xy-plane and the centre of the ring at the origin. Using the set of the six p_z AOs of the six C atoms as the basis, we have

D_{6h}	E	$2C_6$	$2C_3$	C_2	$3C_2'$	$3C_2''$	i	$2S_3$	$2S_6$	σ_h	$3\sigma_v$	$3\sigma_d$	Basis
Γ_r	6	0	0	0	−2	0	0	0	0	−6	2	0	$p_1 \cdots p_6$

[Rotation about the z-axis and reflection along σ_d planes shift all the p AOs contributing zero to the characters; reflection along σ_v planes leaves two p AOs unshifted; therefore, $\chi(\sigma_v) = 2$; reflection along σ_h inverts all and rotation about C_2' inverts only two of the AOs thus contributing – 6 and –2 towards the characters respectively].

Use of formula (11.45) leads to

$$\Gamma_r = A_{2u} + B_{2g} + E_{1g} + E_{2u} \quad \text{... (13.140)}$$

Six SALCs have to be constructed—one each for A_{2u} and B_{2g}, and two each for E_{1g} and E_{2u} symmetry types (E-representations, being two-dimensional, require doubly degenerate wave functions.)

Use of the formula (11.46) and reference to the character table of point group D_{6h} involves cumbersome work. However, since all the HMOs, like the p_z AOs of which they are made, change sign at the molecular plane, it will be sufficient for the present purpose to confine ourselves to only those operations which do not involve the sign change, for example,

$$E,\ C_6^1,\ C_3^1,\ C_3^2,\ C_2,\ C_6^5\ \sigma_v \text{ and } \sigma_d$$

In other words, we may look at the sub-group C_{6v} only of the complete symmetry group D_{6h}.

The representation for C_{6v} sub-group with the same basis set would be,

C_{6v}	E	$2C_6$	$2C_3$	C_2	$3\sigma_v$	$3\sigma_d$	Basis
Γ_r :	6	0	0	0	2	0	$(p_1 - p_6)$

This reduces as $\Gamma_r = A_1 + B_1 + E_1 + E_2$ ... (13.141)

Reference to the character table [Table (13.1)] and the use of the formula (11.46) with the atomic orbital p_1 leads to the following SALCs:

TABLE 13.1 Character Table for C_{6v} Group

C_{6v}	E	$2C_6$	$2C_3$	C_2	$3\sigma_v$	$3\sigma_d$	Basis
A_1	1	1	1	1	1	1	(z)
A_2	1	1	1	1	−1	−1	
B_1	1	−1	1	−1	1	−1	
B_2	1	−1	1	−1	−1	1	
E_1	2	1	−1	−1	0	0	(x, y)
E_2	2	−1	−1	2	0	0	

$$\psi(A_1) = \frac{1}{12}\Big[E\,p_1 + C_6^1\,p_1 + C_6^5\,p_1 + C_3^1\,p_1 + C_3^2\,p_1 + C_2\,p_1 + \sigma_v\,p_1 + \sigma_v'\,p_1 + \sigma_v''\,p_1 + \sigma_d{}'\,p_1 + \sigma_{d'}'\,p_1 + \sigma_{d'}''\,p_1\Big]$$

$$= \frac{1}{6}\big[p_1 + p_2 + p_3 + p_4 + p_5 + p_6\big] \quad \text{... (13.142)}$$

Similarly,

$$\psi(B_1) = \frac{1}{6}\big[p_1 - p_2 + p_3 - p_4 + p_5 - p_6\big] \quad \text{... (13.143)}$$

One of the two HMOs belonging to E_1, is

$$\psi(E_{1A}) = \frac{1}{12}\left[2p_1 + p_2 - p_3 - 2p_4 - p_5 + p_6\right] \quad \text{... (13.144)}$$

and that belonging to E_2 is

$$\psi(E_{2A}) = \frac{1}{12}\left[2p_1 - p_2 - p_6 - p_3 - p_5 + 2p_4\right] \quad \text{... (13.145)}$$

The partners of ψ (E_{1A}) and ψ (E_{2A}), which are ψ (E_{1B}) and ψ (E_{2B}) respevtively, may be obtained using the principle of linear combination. By the linear combination principle,

$$R\psi(E_{1A}) = a\,\psi(E_{1A}) + b\,\psi(E_{1B}) \quad \text{... (13.146)}$$

ψ (E_{1A}) is already known, and we have to find ψ (E_{1B}). Multiplying Equation (13.146) by ψ (E_{1A}) and integrating, we get

$$\int \psi(E_{1A})\,R\,\psi(E_{1A})\,d\tau = a\int \psi(E_{1A})^2\,d\tau \qquad \text{[because } \psi(E_{1A}) \text{ and } \psi(E_{1B}) \text{ are orthogonal]}$$

or

$$a = \frac{\int \psi(E_{1A})\,R\,\psi(E_{1A})\,d\tau}{\int \psi(E_{1A})^2\,d\tau} \quad \text{... (13.147)}$$

(assuming ψ's to be real)

From Equation (13.146),

$$b\,\psi(E_{1B}) = R\,\psi(E_{1A}) - a\,\psi(E_{1A})$$

$$= R\,\psi(E_{1A}) - \frac{\int \psi(E_{1A})\,R\,\psi(E_{1A})\,d\tau}{\int \psi(E_{1A})^2\,d\tau}\cdot\psi(E_{1A}) \quad \text{... (13.148)}$$

Let R be the operation C_6^1, for example; then,

$$C_6^1\,\psi(E_{1A}) = \frac{1}{12}\left(2p_2 + p_3 + p_1 - p_4 - p_6 - 2p_5\right)$$

and

$$\int \psi(E_{1A})\,C_6^1\,\psi(E_{1A})\,d\tau = \frac{1}{144}\int\left(2p_1 + p_2 + p_6 - p_3 - p_5 - 2p_4\right)\left(2p_2 + p_3 + p_1 - p_4 - p_6 - 2p_5\right)d\tau$$

$$= \frac{1}{144}\left(2 + 2 - 1 + 2 + 2 - 1\right) = \frac{6}{144}$$

(in view of the orthogonality of the *p*-orbitals)

Also,

$$\int \psi(E_{1A})^2\,d\tau = \frac{1}{144}\left(4 + 1 + 1 + 1 + 1 + 4\right) = \frac{12}{144}$$

Therefore, by Equation (13.148),

$$b\,\psi(E_{1B}) = \frac{1}{12}\left(2p_2 + p_3 + p_1 - p_4 - p_6 - 2p_5\right) - \frac{6}{144}\times\frac{144}{12}\times\frac{1}{12}\left(2p_1 + p_2 + p_6 - p_3 - p_5 - 2p_4\right)$$

$$= \frac{1}{8}(p_2 + p_3 - p_5 - p_6) \quad \text{... (13.149)}$$

The factor $\frac{1}{8}$ as well as the coefficient b in Equation (13.149) can be incorporated in the normalisation factor and, hence, they are presently dropped; then

$$\psi(E_{1B}) = N(p_2 + p_3 - p_5 - p_6) \quad \text{... (13.150)}$$

By a similar procedure,

$$\psi(E_{2B}) = N'(p_2 - p_3 + p_5 - p_6) \quad \text{... (13.151)}$$

The normalised SALCs are listed below:

$$\left.\begin{aligned}
\psi(A_1) &= \frac{1}{\sqrt{6}}(p_1 + p_2 + p_3 + p_4 + p_5 + p_6) \\
\psi(B_1) &= \frac{1}{\sqrt{6}}(p_1 - p_2 + p_3 - p_4 + p_5 - p_6) \\
\psi(E_{1A}) &= \frac{1}{\sqrt{12}}(2p_1 + p_2 - p_3 - 2p_4 - p_5 + p_6)
\end{aligned}\right\}$$

$$\left.\begin{aligned}
\psi(E_{1B}) &= \frac{1}{2}(p_2 + p_3 - p_5 - p_6) \\
\psi(E_{2A}) &= \frac{1}{\sqrt{12}}(2p_1 - p_2 - p_3 + 2p_4 - p_5 - p_6) \\
\psi(E_{2B}) &= \frac{1}{2}(p_2 - p_3 + p_5 - p_6)
\end{aligned}\right\} \quad \text{... (13.152)}$$

The secular determinant obtained using the SALCs in place of the component p AOs take the form,

$$\begin{vmatrix}
H_{A_1A_1} - ES_{A_1A_1} & H_{A_1B_1} - ES_{A_1B_1} & \cdots & H_{A_1E_{2B}} - ES_{A_1E_{2B}} \\
H_{B_1A_1} - ES_{B_1A_1} & H_{B_1B_1} - ES_{B_1B_1} & \cdots & H_{B_1E_{2B}} - ES_{B_1E_{2B}} \\
\vdots & & & \\
E_{E_{2B}A_1} - ES_{E_{2B}A_1} & & \cdots & H_{E_{2B}E_{2B}} - ES_{E_{2B}E_{2B}}
\end{vmatrix} = 0 \quad \text{... (13.153)}$$

Now we use the following two symmetry-based rules for evaluating the integrals:

$$H_{ij} = \int \psi_i \hat{H} \psi_j \, d\tau = 0$$

if ψ_i and ψ_j do no belong to the same symmetry type:

and $$\int p_i \hat{H} p_j \, d\tau = 0$$

unless $i = j$, when it is α, or unless i and j are neighbours when it is β. By orthonormality of p AOs, Also

$$\int p_i \, p_j \, d\tau = 1 \text{ if } i = j, \text{ and } 0 \text{ if } i \neq j.$$

All the off-diagonal elements in the determinant, therefore vanish. Even the integrals, in which the SALCs belong to the same symmetry but are orthogonal to each other, vanish; for example,

$$H_{E_{1A}\,E_{1B}} = \int \psi(E_{1A})\hat{H}\,\psi(E_{1B})\,d\tau$$

$$= \frac{1}{2\sqrt{12}}\int (2p_1 + p_2 - p_3 - 2p_4 - p_5 + p_6) \times \hat{H}\,(p_2 + p_3 - p_5 - p_6)\,d\tau$$

$$= \frac{1}{2\sqrt{12}}(2\beta - 2\beta + \alpha + \beta - \beta - \alpha - 2\beta + 2\beta + \alpha + \beta - \beta - \alpha) = 0$$

The elements along the diagonal are evaluated as follows:

$$H_{A_1\,A_1} = \int \psi(A_1)\hat{H}\,\psi(A_1)\,d\tau$$

$$= \frac{1}{6}\int (p_1 + p_2 + p_3 + p_4 + p_5 + p_6)\hat{H}\,(p_1 + p_2 + p_3 + p_4 + p_5 + p_6)\,d\tau$$

$$= \alpha + 2\beta \qquad \text{... (13.154)}$$

$$H_{B_1\,B_1} = \int \psi(B_1)\hat{H}\,\psi(B_1)\,d\tau$$

$$= \frac{1}{6}\int (p_1 - p_2 + p_3 - p_4 + p_5 - p_6)\hat{H}\,(p_1 - p_2 + p_3 - p_4 + p_5 - p_6)\,d\tau$$

$$= \alpha - 2\beta \qquad \text{... (13.155)}$$

$$H_{E_{1A}\,E_{1A}} = \int \psi(E_{1A})\hat{H}\,\psi(E_{1A})\,d\tau = \alpha + \beta \qquad \text{... (13.156)}$$

$$H_{E_{1B}\,E_{1B}} = \int \psi(E_{1B})\hat{H}\,\psi(E_{1B})\,d\tau = \alpha + \beta \qquad \text{... (13.157)}$$

$$H_{E_{2A}\,E_{2A}} = \int \psi(E_{2A})\hat{H}\,\psi(E_{2A})\,d\tau = \alpha - \beta \qquad \text{... (13.158)}$$

$$H_{E_{2B}\,E_{2B}} = \int \psi(E_{2B})\hat{H}\,\psi(E_{2B})\,d\tau = \alpha - \beta \qquad \text{... (13.159)}$$

$$S_{ii} = \int \psi_i \, \psi_i \, d\tau = 1$$

and $$S_{ij} = \int \psi_i \, \psi_j \, d\tau = 0$$

where ψ_i and ψ_j are the SALCs.

The diagonalised determinant is

$$\begin{array}{c} A_1 \\ B_1 \\ E_{1A} \\ E_{1B} \\ E_{2A} \\ E_{2B} \end{array} \begin{vmatrix} (\alpha+2\beta-E) & 0 & 0 & 0 & 0 & 0 \\ 0 & (\alpha-2\beta-E) & 0 & 0 & 0 & 0 \\ 0 & 0 & (\alpha+\beta-E) & 0 & 0 & 0 \\ 0 & 0 & 0 & (\alpha+\beta-E) & 0 & 0 \\ 0 & 0 & 0 & 0 & (\alpha-\beta-E) & 0 \\ 0 & 0 & 0 & 0 & 0 & (\alpha-\beta-E) \end{vmatrix} = 0$$

... (13.160)

Such a determinant is solved trivially as each element along the diagonal will be zero; thus,

$$\left.\begin{aligned} E(A_1) &= \alpha + 2\beta \\ E(B_1) &= \alpha - 2\beta \\ E(E_{1A}) = E(E_{1B}) &= \alpha + \beta \\ E(E_{2A}) = E(E_{2B}) &= \alpha - \beta \end{aligned}\right\} \quad \text{... (13.161)}$$

Since α and β are both negative, the six energy levels in increasing order can be arranged as in Fig. 13.21.

It can be easily seen that the SALCs themselves are the HMOs and no further exercise is needed. This solution has become possible because the determinant has been diagonalised into blocks of 1×1 determinants.

It is interesting to note that the π-MOs (HMOs) and the corresponding π-energies of benzene could be determined directly from the inspection of the SALCs and without going through the secular equations. This is possible because of the high (hexagonal) symmetry of the molecule.

The π-electron configuration of benzene in the ground state (g.s.) may thus be denoted as $A_1^2\ E_1^4$ as the MOs of B_1 and E_2 type have higher energies. It is now necessary to point out that the symmetry types A_1, B_1, E_1 and E_2 of the C_{6v} group become A_{1u}, E_{1g}, E_{1g} and E_{2u} respectively in the D_{6h} group. So when the full symmetry group of the molecule is considered the g.s. configuration is $A_{1u}^2\ E_{1g}^4$.

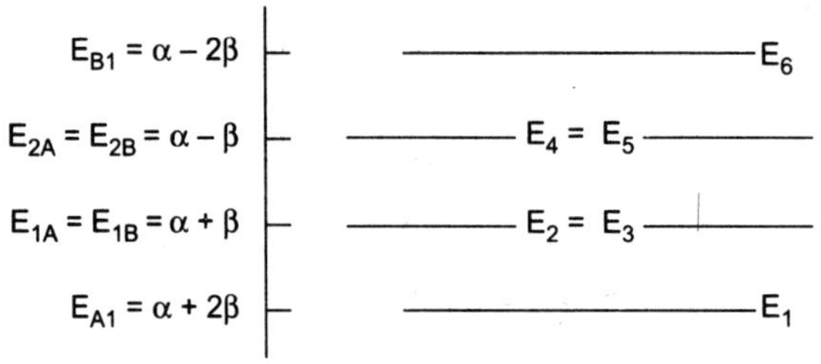

Fig. 13.21 *HMO energy levels of benzene*

Graphical Representation of the HMOs: A very convenient way to represent the HMOs of benzene and their nodal characteristics is as shown in Fig. 13.22. Here the HMOs are also numbered ψ_1 to ψ_6 so as to correspond to the order of the energy levels shown in Fig. 13.21.

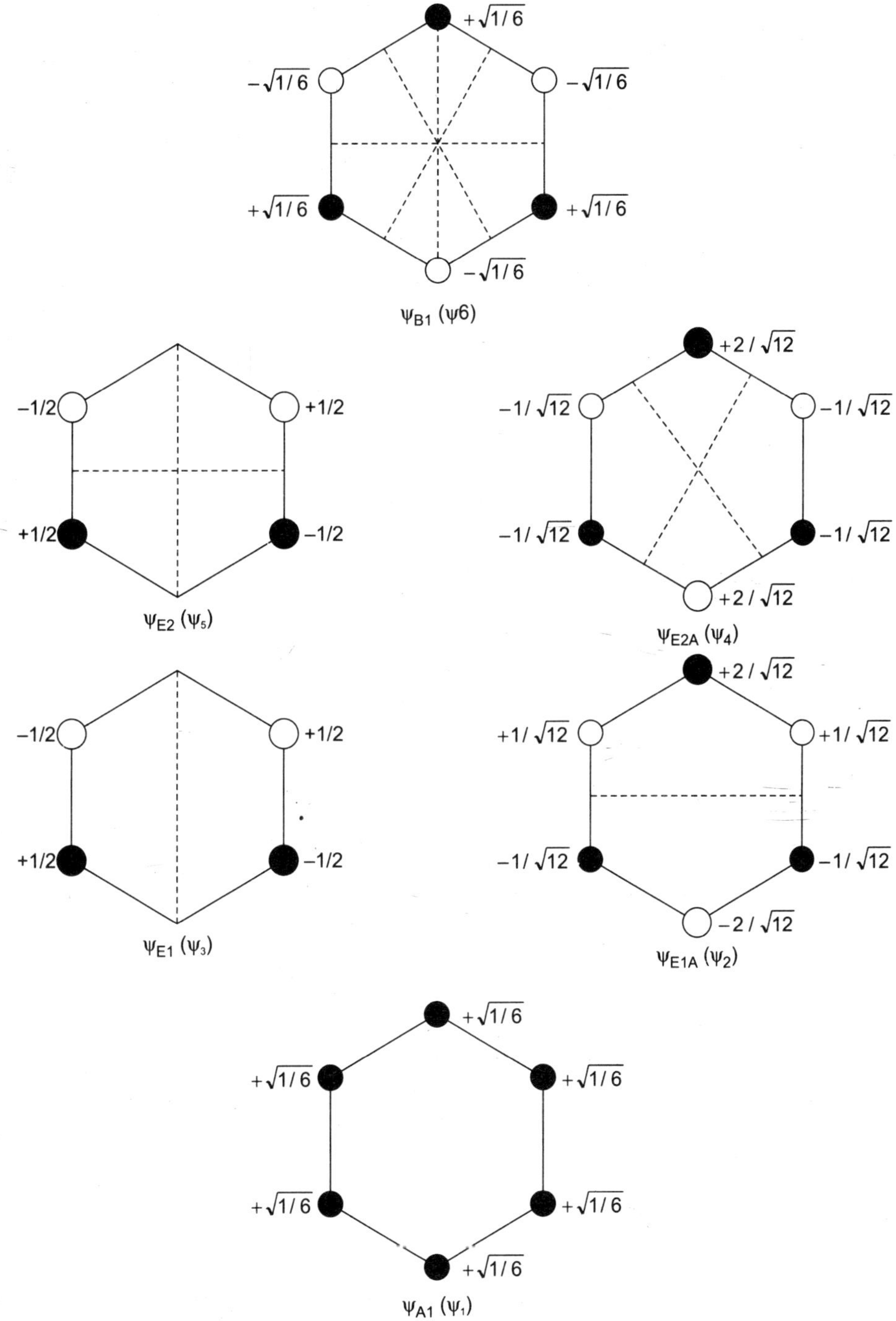

Fig. 13.22 *Graphical representation of the HMOs of benzene*

If, in these figures, xy plane is taken as the molecular plane (plane of the paper) and the orbitals are viewed from above it, only one of the two lobes of the $2p_z$ AOs participating in the linear combination, will be visible to the observer. The spotted circles represent the positive lobes and open circles the negative lobes. The magnitudes of the coefficients of the AOs in the linear combination (also given beside the circles) are reflected in the radii of the circles. The dashed lines in the hexagonal rings represent the bases of the nodal planes.

13.5.3 Physical Significance of the HMO Coefficients—Electron Density

The probability that an electron will be found in a small volume element $d\tau$ is $\psi^2\, d\tau$ where ψ is the normalised real wave function; for a LCAO-HMO function

$$\psi = \sum_r a_r\, p_r \qquad \text{... (13.162)}$$

$$\int \psi^2\, d\tau = \int\left(\sum_r a_r\, p_r\right)^2 d\tau$$

$$= \int \sum_r a_r^2\, p_r^2\, d\tau + \int \sum_r \sum_{r \neq s} a_r\, a_s\, p_r\, p_s\, d\tau \qquad \text{... (13.163)}$$

Since the overlap integral, $S = \int p_r\, p_s\, d\tau = 0$ for $r \neq s$ Equation (13.163) becomes,

$$\int \psi^2\, d\tau = \int \sum a_r^2\, p_r^2\, d\tau$$

$$= \sum_r a_r^2 \int p_r^2\, d\tau = \sum_r a_r^2 \qquad \text{... (13.164)}$$

as the p_z atomic orbitals are normalised,

Thus, in the LCAO-HMO approximation a_r^2 represents the probability of, or electron density due to, one electron at the atom r. But there may be several electrons distributed in a number of HMOs. The total electron density q_r at an atom r is, therefore, the sum of electron densities contributed by different electrons in each HMO

$$q_r = \sum n_j\, a_{jr}^2 \qquad \text{... (13.165)}$$

where a_{jr} is the coefficient of the atom r in the jth HMO, and n_j is the number of electrons in that HMO; the value of n_j can be 0, 1 or 2 (Pauli's principle). The sum is taken over all the HMOs. The following examples will serve to clarify the situation.

13.5.3.1 Ethylene

$$\psi_1 = \frac{1}{\sqrt{2}}(p_1 + p_2) \qquad \text{... (13.166)}$$

$$\psi_2 = \frac{1}{\sqrt{2}}(p_1 - p_2)$$

We have the two π-electrons in ψ_1. The electron density (e.d.) due to one π-electron

at carbon atom 1, $$a_1^2 = \left(\frac{1}{\sqrt{2}}\right)^2 = \frac{1}{2}$$

at carbon atom2, $$a_2^2 = \left(\frac{1}{\sqrt{2}}\right)^2 = \frac{1}{2}$$

Since we have two π-electrons in ψ_1, the total e.d. at C_1 and C_2 each is $2 \times \frac{1}{2} = 1$.

13.5.3.2 Allyl System

Allyl Carbonium: Both π-electrons are in ψ_1, which is

$$\psi_1 = \frac{1}{2} p_1 + \frac{\sqrt{2}}{2} p_2 + \frac{1}{2} p_3$$

The e.d. at the three carbon atoms due to a single electron will be,

$$\left(\frac{1}{2}\right)^2 = \frac{1}{4} \text{ at } C_1, \left(\frac{\sqrt{2}}{2}\right)^2 = \frac{1}{2} \text{ at } C_2, \left(\frac{1}{2}\right)^2 = \frac{1}{4} \text{ at } C_3$$

The total e.d. due to the two electrons will be,

$$q_1 = 2 \times \frac{1}{4} = \frac{1}{2} \text{ at } C_1;\ q_2 = 2 \times \frac{1}{2} = 1 \text{ at } C_2;\ q_3 = 2 \times \frac{1}{4} = \frac{1}{2} \text{ at } C_3$$

The e.d. at the middle carbon (C_2) is greatest.

Allyl Radical: Here we have two π-electrons in ψ_1 and one in ψ_2;

$$\psi_1 = \frac{1}{2} p_1 + \frac{\sqrt{2}}{2} p_2 + \frac{1}{2} p_3$$

$$\psi_2 = \frac{1}{\sqrt{2}} p_1 - \frac{1}{\sqrt{2}} p_3$$

Therefore, the total e.d. at each position is as follows:

at C_1, $q_1 = 2 \times \left(\frac{1}{2}\right)^2$ due to the two electrons in $\psi_1 + 1 \times \left(\frac{1}{\sqrt{2}}\right)^2$ due to one electron in $\psi_2 = 1.0$

at C_2, $q_2 = 2 \times \left(\frac{\sqrt{2}}{2}\right)^2 + 0 = 1.0$ [because $a_2 = 0$ for ψ_2], at C_3, $q_3 = 2 \times \left(\frac{1}{2}\right)^2 + 1 \times \left(\frac{1}{\sqrt{2}}\right)^2 = 1.0$

Thus, the e.d. at each carbon atom is the same.

Allyl Carbanion: It has two π-electrons in ψ_1 and two in ψ_2. Therefore,

$$q_1 = 2\times\left(\frac{1}{2}\right)^2 + 2\times\left(\frac{1}{\sqrt{2}}\right)^2 = 1.5 \text{ at } C_1;$$

$$q_2 = 2\times\left(\frac{\sqrt{2}}{2}\right)^2 + 0 = 1.0 \text{ at } C_2;$$

$$q_3 = 2\times\left(\frac{1}{2}\right)^2 + 2\times\left(\frac{1}{\sqrt{2}}\right)^2 = 1.5 \text{ at } C_3.$$

13.5.3.3 Cyclopropenyl System

The three HMOs are

$$\psi_1 = \frac{1}{\sqrt{3}}p_1 + \frac{1}{\sqrt{3}}p_2 + \frac{1}{\sqrt{3}}p_3$$

$$\psi_2 = \frac{1}{\sqrt{2}}p_1 - \frac{1}{\sqrt{2}}p_3$$

$$\psi_3 = \frac{1}{\sqrt{6}}p_1 - \frac{2}{\sqrt{6}}p_2 + \frac{1}{\sqrt{6}}p_3$$

For the carbonium ion, we have two π-electrons in ψ_1, and none in ψ_2 and ψ_3. Hence,

at $$C_1, q_1 = 2\times\left(\frac{1}{\sqrt{3}}\right)^2 = \frac{2}{3}$$

at $$C_2, q_2 = 2\times\left(\frac{1}{\sqrt{3}}\right)^2 = \frac{2}{3}$$

at $$C_3, q_3 = 2\times\left(\frac{1}{\sqrt{3}}\right)^2 = \frac{2}{3}$$

For the carbanion, we have two π-electrons in ψ_1, one in ψ_2 and one in ψ_3 (as ψ_2 and ψ_3 are degenerate). Hence,

at $$C_1, q_1 = 2\times\left(\frac{1}{\sqrt{3}}\right)^2 + 1\times\left(\frac{1}{\sqrt{2}}\right)^2 + 1\times\left(\frac{1}{\sqrt{6}}\right)^2 = \frac{4}{3}$$

at $$C_2, q_2 = 2\times\left(\frac{1}{\sqrt{3}}\right)^2 + 0 + 1\times\left(-\frac{2}{\sqrt{6}}\right)^2 = \frac{4}{3}$$

at $$C_3, q_3 = 2\times\left(\frac{1}{\sqrt{3}}\right)^2 + 1\times\left(-\frac{1}{\sqrt{2}}\right)^2 + 1\times\left(\frac{1}{\sqrt{6}}\right)^2 = \frac{4}{3}$$

In cyclopropenyl radical, two π-electrons are in ψ_1 and the third electron may be placed in either ψ_2 or ψ_3 (degenerate). In such a case, the e.d. is calculated by assuming that half of the available electron is in each of the degenerate MOs, ψ_2 and ψ_3. This procedure leads to

$$q_1 = 2\times\left(\frac{1}{\sqrt{3}}\right)^2 + \frac{1}{2}\times\left(\frac{1}{\sqrt{2}}\right)^2 + \frac{1}{2}\times\left(\frac{1}{\sqrt{6}}\right)^2 = 1.0$$

$$q_2 = 2\times\left(\frac{1}{\sqrt{3}}\right)^2 + 0 + \frac{1}{2}\times\left(-\frac{2}{\sqrt{6}}\right)^2 = 1.0$$

$$q_3 = 2\times\left(\frac{1}{\sqrt{3}}\right)^2 + \frac{1}{2}\times\left(-\frac{1}{\sqrt{2}}\right)^2 + \frac{1}{2}\times\left(\frac{1}{\sqrt{6}}\right)^2 = 1.0$$

(**Note:** The calculation may be checked by determining the sum of the e.d.'s over all the atoms which ust equal the total number of π-electrons).

Exercise: *Calculate the e.d. at each carbon atom in butadiene molecule in the ground state.*

In the ground state there are two π-electrons in ψ_1 and two in ψ_2. Hence, the total e.d.'s at the four carbon atoms are as follows:

at $C_1, q_1 = 2\times(0.372)^2 + 2\times(0.602)^2 = 1.0$

at $C_2, q_2 = 2\times(0.602)^2 + 2\times(0.372)^2 = 1.0$

at $C_3, q_3 = 2\times(0.602)^2 + 2\times(-0.372)^2 = 1.0$

at $C_4, q_4 = 2\times(0.372)^2 + 2\times(-0.602)^2 = 1.0$

Total e.d. = 4.0, in agreement with the fact that there are 4π-electrons in the molecule.

13.5.4 Charge Density

In a π-system, a neutral carbon is associated with an electron density of 1.00 and the net charge density is defined as

$$\xi_r = 1 - q_r \qquad \text{... (13.167)}$$

For example, in ethylene,

ξ_1 at $C_1 = 1.0 - 1.0 = 0$

ξ_2 at $C_2 = 1.0 = 1.0 = 0$

In allyl cation $(C—C—C)^+$

ξ at $C_1 = 1.0 - 0.5 = 0.5$

ξ_2 at $C_2 = 1.0 - 1.0 = 0$

ξ_3 at $C_3 = 1.0 - 0.5 = 0.5$

Thus, in ethylene each carbon atom is neutral whereas in allyl cation the positive charge is distributed equally among the terminal carbon atoms and the central carbon is neutral. In the same way it can be shown that in the allyl radical, each carbon is neutral; in allyl anion the additional electron distributes its charge between the two terminal carbon atoms without affecting the central carbon atom.

Exercise: *Calculate the charge density at each carbon in (i) cyclopropenyl cation and anion, (ii) butadiene and (iii) benzene.*

(*i*) For cyclopropenyl cation, charge density at each carbon = $1-\frac{2}{3}=\frac{1}{3}$.

Similarly, for the anion, charge density at each carbon is $-\frac{1}{3}$. The charge is distributed among the three carbon atoms equally.

(*ii*) Butadiene: $\xi_i = 1 - q_i = 1 - 1 = 0$

(*iii*) Benzene: Using the coefficients of HMOs, we get

$$q_i = 1.0 \text{ and } \xi_i = 1 - q_i = 1 - 1 = 0].$$

13.5.5 π-Bond Order

The HMO coefficients can be used to calculate the π-electron distribution in the bonds too. A very important quantity, called π-bond order, p_{rs}, representing the degree of π-bonding between adjacent carbon atoms r and s was first introduced by Coulson in 1939; it is defined as,

$$p_{rs} = \sum_{\substack{\text{all}\\ \text{electrons}}} p_{rs}^{j} = \sum_{j} n_j\, a_{jr}\, a_{js} \qquad \text{... (13.168)}$$

$$p_{rs}^{j} = n\, j a_{jr}\, a_{js} \qquad \text{... (13.169)}$$

in which n_j is the number of electrons in the jth HMO. For example, in allyl carbonium ion, where we have the two π-electrons in ψ_1,

$$\psi_1 = \frac{1}{2}p_1 + \frac{\sqrt{2}}{2}p_2 + \frac{1}{2}p_3$$

the π-bond order between the atoms C_1 and C_2 is

$$p_{12} = 2\times\frac{1}{2}\times\frac{\sqrt{2}}{2} = \frac{\sqrt{2}}{2} = 0.707$$

and that between C_2 and C_3 is,

$$p_{23} = 2\times\frac{\sqrt{2}}{2}\times\frac{1}{2} = \frac{\sqrt{2}}{2} = 0.707$$

In the allyl radical, two electrons are in ψ_1 and one in ψ_2.

$$\psi_2 = \frac{1}{\sqrt{2}}p_1 - \frac{1}{\sqrt{2}}p_3$$

Hence,

$$p_{12} = \left(2\times\frac{\sqrt{2}}{2}\times\frac{1}{2}\right)+\left(1+\frac{1}{\sqrt{2}}\times 0\right) = 0.707 \qquad [\text{coefficient } a_2 = 0 \text{ in } \psi_2.]$$

$$p_{23} = \left(2\times\frac{\sqrt{2}}{2}\times\frac{1}{2}\right)+\left(1\times 0\times\frac{-1}{\sqrt{2}}\right) = 0.707$$

Similarly, for the carbanion, $p_{12} = p_{23} = 0.707$.

The calculation shows that the bond between C_1 and C_2 as also that between C_2 and C_3 is not fully double bond; rather there is π-bond character in each to the extent to 70.7%. Larger the coefficients, greater will be the π-bond order. If one of the coefficients is large and the other small, it will imply that the electrons are chiefly located around one of the nuclei, and not between them. If one of coefficients a_r or a_s is zero, it will indicate node at the atom and p_{rs} will be zero in conformity with a nonbonding situation. If the coefficients a_r and a_s are of opposite signs, it will indicate a node between the atoms r and s and a negative π-bond order, in agreement with an antibonding situation.

Exercise: *Calculate the π-bond orders in ground and excited states between the adjacent carbon atoms in butadience. Comment over the result.*

Ground State of Butadiene: Only the first two HMOs ψ_1 and ψ_2 will be used in the present calculations.

$$p_{12} = 2 \times (0.372 \times 0.602) + 2 \times (0.602 \times 0.372) = 0.896$$

$$p_{23} = 2 \times (0.602 \times 0.602) + 2 \times (0.372 \times - 0.372) = 0.448$$

$$p_{34} = 2 \times (0.602 \times 0.372) + 2 \times (- 0.372 \times - 0.602) = 0.896$$

The calculations show that:

(*i*) $0 < p_{rs} < 1.0$, meaning that each of the three bonds is neither a full double bond nor a single bond; all have partial double bond character.

(*ii*) $p_{12} = p_{34} > p_{23}$, meaning that the terminal bonds $C_1—C_2$ and $C_3—C_4$ have more double bond character (are more tightly bonded) than the central bond $C_2—C_3$).

(*iii*) The terminal bonds $C_1—C_2$ and $C_3—C_4$ should be shorter than the central bond $C_2—C_3$, but longer than the olefinic (C=C) bond.

Excited State of Butadiene: The three HMOs ψ_1, ψ_2 and ψ_3 are to be used with only one electron distributed in ψ_2 and ψ_3.

$$p_{12} = 2 \times (0.372 \times 0.602) + 1 \times (0.602 \times 0.372) + 1 \times (0.602 \times - 0.372) = 0.448$$

$$p_{23} = 2 \times (0.602 \times 0.602) + 1 \times (0.372 \times - 0.602) + 1 \times (- 0.372 \times - 0.372) = 0.724$$

$$p_{34} = 2 \times (0.602 \times 0.372) + 1 \times (- 0.372 \times - 0.602) + 1 \times (- 0.372 \times 0.602) = 0.448$$

The calculations show that the double bond character of the central bond ($C_2—C_3$) is increased and that of the terminal bonds decreased in the excited state of butadiene. This may lead to the following *cis-trans* equilibrium in the excited state of butadiene.

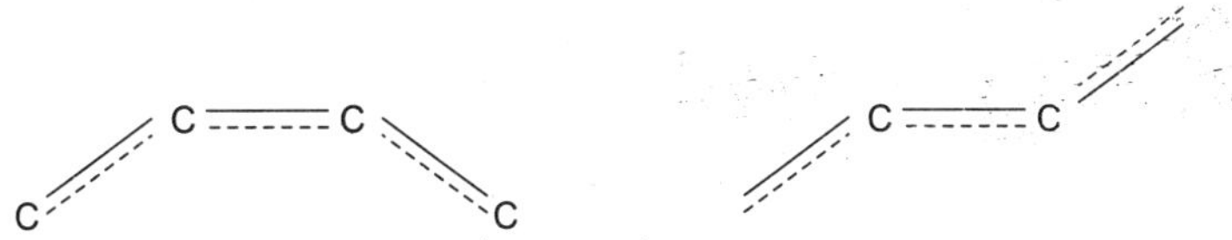

Cis Trans

Exercise: *Using the following HMOs calculate the π-bond orders between the adjacent C-atoms in the ground state of benzene: comment.*

$$\psi_1 = \frac{1}{\sqrt{6}}\left(p_1 + p_2 + p_3 + p_4 + p_5 + p_6\right)$$

$$\psi_2 = \frac{1}{2}\left(p_1 + p_2 - p_4 - p_5\right)$$

$$\psi_3 = \frac{1}{\sqrt{12}}(p_1 - p_2 - 2p_3 - p_4 + p_5 + 2p_6)$$

$$p_{12} = 2\times\left(\frac{1}{\sqrt{6}}\times\frac{1}{\sqrt{6}}\right)+2\times\left(\frac{1}{2}\times\frac{1}{2}\right)+2\left(\frac{1}{\sqrt{12}}\times-\frac{1}{\sqrt{12}}\right)=\frac{2}{3}$$

$$p_{23} = 2\times\left(\frac{1}{\sqrt{6}}\times\frac{1}{\sqrt{6}}\right)+2\times\left(\frac{1}{2}\times 0\right)+2\times\left(\frac{1}{\sqrt{12}}\times-\frac{2}{\sqrt{12}}\right)=\frac{2}{3}$$

Similarly, $p_{34} = p_{45} = p_{56} = p_{61} = \dfrac{2}{3}$.

This shows that (*i*) all the six C—C bonds in benzene are equivalent, and (*ii*) the bonds are not true double bonds. The conclusions are supported by experimentally observed bond length (1.39 Å) in benzene which is intermediate between that of a single (1.54 A) and a double (1.33 A) bond.

Bond Orders and Bond Lengths: Calculated bond orders may be used to predict approximate bond length of a C—C bond and estimate its double bond character. A π-bond order of 1.0 would mean 100% double bond with a bond length of 1.33 Å, while an order of say 2/3 would mean only 66.6% double character with a C—C bond length intermediate between a single (1.54 Å) and a double bond (1.33 Å). Caution, however, must be exercised in any correlation of bond order with bond length as the bond length is also affected by the hybridisation of the carbon atoms involved [For hybidisation principle, see the later part of this chapter. Increasing the amount of *s*-character in a hybrid orbital shortens σ-bond. Thus an $sp^2 - sp^2$ σ-bond is shorter than an $sp^3 - sp^3$ σ-bond].

13.5.6 Free Valence

The concept of free valence at a carbon atom is used as an index to indicate the ease of attack by free radicals at that carbon. It gives a measure of the reactivity; in a molecule that position will be most reactive which has the largest free valence.

The free valence, F_r, at an atom r is defined as

$$F_r = N_{max} - N_r \qquad \text{... (13.170)}$$

where N_{max} is the maximum possible π-bonding that a carbon atom is capable of, and N_r is the actual amount of π-bonding that it exhibits in the molecule. The amount of π bonding is taken as the sum of all the π-bond orders involving that atom.

To determine the value of N_{max}, as an example, the central carbon atom in trimethylenemethane is considered. This atom is involved in π-bonding to the maximum extent. Each C—C bond in this system has a π-bond order of $\dfrac{1}{\sqrt{3}}$ so that the total π-bond order associated with the central carbon is $\sqrt{3}$. Hence, the free valence at any atom may be defined as

$$F_r = \sqrt{3} - N_r \qquad \text{... (13.171)}$$

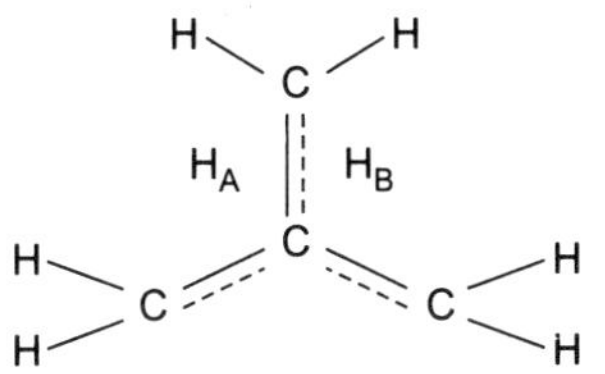

In ethylene, for example, the free valence at carbon atom 1 or 2 is,

$$F_1 = F_2 = \sqrt{3} - 1 = 0.732$$

In butadiene, (C_1—C_2—C_3—C_4),

$$F_1 = F_4 = \sqrt{3} - 0.896 = 0.836$$

For the carbon atom 2, the extent of π-bonding is,

$$p_{12} + p_{23} = 0.896 + 0.448 = 1.344 = N_2$$

and for carbon 3 it is,

$$p_{23} + p_{34} = 0.448 + 0.896 = 1.344 = N_3$$

Hence, $$F_2 = F_3 = \sqrt{3} - 1.344 = 0.388$$

Clearly, C_2 and C_3 are much more deeply engaged in bonding than C_1 and C_4 and have a smaller free valence. This explains why the terminal carbon atoms are more reactive in butadiene.

In benzene, all the six positions are equivalent. Each carbon atom is joined to two others by partial double bonds. For carbon atom 1, for example, the total π-bond order = $p_{12} + p_{16} = \frac{4}{3}$.

Therefore,

$$F_1 = \sqrt{3} - \frac{4}{3} = 0.4.$$

Free valence may be taken as a quantitative analogue of Thiele's partial valency. From MO calculations, it turns out that free radicals have generally values of F_r equal to or greater than 1.0; values of 0.8 are associated with terminal carbon in a chain, values around 0.4 are observed for aromatic carbon atoms and very small values for internal atoms.

The usual way of representing free valence is by an arrow diverging from the atom with the numerical value of F_r written at its head, e.g., in butadiene.

$$\begin{array}{ccccccc} H_2C & = & CH & — & CH & = & CH_2 \\ \downarrow & & \downarrow & & \downarrow & & \downarrow \\ 0.836 & & 0.388 & & 0.388 & & 0.836 \end{array}$$

The complete molecular diagram giving charge density near the atom, bond orders along the bonds and free valence at the head of the arrows diverging from atoms may be shown as follows for benzene.

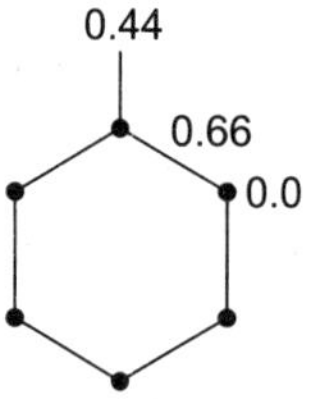

Here the charge density at each carbon atom is 0, the π-bond order for each bond in 0.66 and the free valence of each C is 0.44.

13.6 THE EXTENDED HÜCKEL THEORY

The HMO theory is applicable to planar conjugated π-systems only. An extension to this empirical method was made by Hoffmann in which both σ and π-electrons are considered and which can be used for both planar and non-planar molecules. This has come to be known as *extended Hückel theory (EHT)*. Both HMO and EH methods begin with the approximation that the complete Hamiltonian is sum of 1-electron Hamiltonians, $\hat{H} = \sum_i \hat{H}(i)$, but the Hamiltonian is not specified. Therefore the Schrödinger equation $\hat{H}(i)\,\psi_i = E\psi_i$ is not solved. The complete electronic wave function Ψ is a simple product of 1-electron wave functions (*i.e.*, Molecular orbitals ψ_i), and the total electronic energy E is the sum of 1-electron molecular orbital energies E_i).

The molecular orbtials are linear combination of atomic orbitals ϕ_r containing valence electrons only (inner shell electrons are ignored)

$$\psi_i = \sum_r a_{ir}\,\phi_r$$

The atomic orbitals are of Slater type (STO).

Linear variation method leads to secular equations

$$\sum\left[a_{ir}\left(H_{rs} - E_i\,S_{rs}\right)\right] = 0$$

and the secular determinant

$$\det\left|H_{rs} - E_i\,S_{rs}\right| = 0$$

where a_{ir} = ceofficient of the STO ϕ_r in the MO ψ_i

$$H_{rs} = \int \phi_r\,\hat{H}(i)\,\phi_s\,d\tau,\ S_{rs} = \int \phi_r\,\phi_s\,d\tau \text{ and } E_i = \text{energy of the MO } \psi_i$$

All this is similar to the HMO theory. The difference lies in that now all valence atomic orbitals will be taken into the linear combination (only the inner shell orbitals will be ignored); in addition, all overlap integrals are evaluated formulas for which are readily available. As regard the integrals H_{rs}, since the Hamiltonian is not specified, the off diagonal elements remain unevaluated: the diagonal elements

$$H_{rr} = \int \phi_r \hat{H}(i) \phi_r \, d\tau$$

look like an integral representing the average energy of an electron in the atomic orbital ϕ_r centred on the atom r in the molecule. Therefore, H_{rr} is taken as the orbital energy of the atomic orbital ϕ_r which is equal to the ionization potential (with opposite sign) of the atom in its valence state (VSIP). Tables of ionization potentials are available (see C.E. Moore, Nat. Bur. Std. (U.S.)) J., Hinze and H.H. Jaffe: J.A., Chem. Soc. 1962, 84, 540). The V.S.I.P.'s for different states of carbon, sp^3, sp^2 and sp are different. This difference, however, is ignored and an average value of all the three V.S.I.P.'s is taken.

The off diagonal elements H_{rs} is determined by an approximate formula

$$H_{rs} = \frac{1}{2} KS_{rs} \left(H_{rr} + H_{ss}\right)$$

where K is a number to be adjusted between 1 and 3 (different values of K have been used for different cases). Since both H_{rr} and H_{ss} are negative H_{rs} is also – ve if S_{rs} is positive. If $S_{rs} = 0$, there will be no off diagonal element (HMO theory).

Once the H_{rs} and S_{rs} are known, the linear combination coefficients a_{ir} are obtained by solving the secular equation. This is done on a computer.

No iteration is needed because H_{rs} does not depend on a_{is}.

From the orbital energies are determined the total energy, $E = \sum E(i)$ and from the MOs ψ_i known, the electronic wave function, Ψ is written as the Slater determinant.

An example, CH_4 : The basis set here consists of $2s$, $2p_x$, $2p_y$, $2p_z$ of C and four $1s_H$ of four H atoms a, b, c, d all STOs. The ξ values are determined from Slater's rules (1.625 for carbon and 1.0 for H atomic orbitals). The STOs are

$$\begin{array}{ll} 1.\ \chi_{2s} = N_1 re^{-1.625r} & 5.\ N_5\ \chi_{1s_{H_a}} \\ 2.\ \chi_{2P_x} = N_2 re^{-1.625r} \sin\theta \cos\varphi & 6.\ N_6\ \chi_{1s_{H_b}} \\ 3.\ \chi_{2P_y} = N_3 re^{-1.625r} \sin\theta \sin\varphi & 7.\ N_7\ \chi_{1s_{H_c}} \\ 4.\ \chi_{2P_z} = N_4 re^{1.625}\ r\cos\theta & 8.\ N_8\ \chi_{1s_{H_d}} \end{array} \left.\vphantom{\begin{array}{l}1\\2\\3\\4\end{array}}\right\} = Ne^{-\xi r}$$

(N's are normalization factors). Taking the tetrahedral bond angles and C—H bond distances of 1.1A we can know the relative positions of the atoms. This enables one to calculate the overlap integrals. This is done on a computer for which standard programmes are available. It is easy to see that 8 integrals of the type S_{ii} are equal to one, because of normalization; integrals of the type S_{rs} involving $2s$ and $2p_x$, $2p_y$ or $2p_z$ will be zero due to orthogonality of the angular parts; those involving $1s_H$ centred on the nodal plane of $2p$ will also be zero. This makes 18 of the S_{rs}'s zero. Overlap of $2s$ of carbon with $1s$ of each H will be equal. Overlap of $2p_x$ of C with $1s_a$ of H_a is large and positive, but with $1s_b$, $1s_c$ and $1s_d$ of H atoms will be small and negative. Overlap between every pair of H AOs is the same.

As regards energy integrals the diagonal elements H_{rr} are:

$$H_{11} = \int 2s_c \, \hat{H} \, 2s_c \, d\tau = -\text{V.S.I.P. of C} = -0.7144 \text{ a.u. } (-19.44 \text{ eV})$$

$$H_{22} = H_{33} = H_{44} = \int 2p_c \, \hat{H} \, 2p_c \, d\tau = -0.3921 \text{ a.u. } (-10.67 \text{ eV})$$

$$H_{55} = H_{66} = H_{77} = \int 1s_H \, \hat{H} \, 1s_H \, d\tau = -0.5 \text{ a.u. } (-13.60 \text{ eV})$$

With these values and the formula given above, the off diagonal elements H_{rs} can be easily calculated. Using the Hoffmann's value of K = 1.75 with all necessary data known, the MOs and MO energies of CH_4 have been calculated and are given below:

$\psi_1 = 0.5842\,(2s) + 0.1858\,(1s_a) + 0.1858\,(1s_b) + 0.1858\,(1s_c) + 0.1858\,(1s_d)$;

$E_1 = -0.8519$ a.u.

$\psi_2 = 0.5313\,(2p_x) + 0.0021\,(2p_y) + 0.0007\,(2p_z) + 0.5547\,(1s_a) - 0.1828\,(1s_b) - 0.1853\,(1s_c) - 0.1865\,(1s_d)$;

$E_2 = -0.5487$ a.u.

$\psi_3 = -0.0021\,(2p_x) + 0.5313\,(2p_y) + 0.0021\,(2p_z) - 0.0022\,(1s_a) + 0.5237\,(1s_b) - 0.2589\,(1s_c) - 0.2626\,(1s_d)$;

$E_3 = -0.5487$ a.u.

$\psi_4 = -0.0007\,(2p_x) - 0.0021\,(2p_y) + 0.5313\,(2p_z) - 0.0007\,(1s_a) - 0.0019\,(1s_b) + 0.4542\,(1s_c) - 0.4516\,(1s_d)$;

$E_4 = -0.5487$ a.u.

$\psi_5 = -0.0112\,(2p_x) + 1.1573\,(2p_y) + 0.0176\,(2p_z) + 0.0105\,(1s_a) - 1.0260\,(1s_b) + 0.4943\,(1s_c) + 0.5213\,(1s_d)$;

$E_5 = 0.2068$ a.u.

$\psi_6 = -0.0137\,(2p_x) - 0.0178\,(2p_y) + 1.1572\,(2p_z) + 0.0128\,(1s_a) + 0.0114\,(1s_b) - 0.8977\,(1s_c) + 0.8734\,(1s_d)$;

$E_6 = 0.2068$ a.u.

$\psi_7 = 1.1573\,(2p_x) + 0.0110\,(2p_y) + 0.0139\,(2p_z) - 1.0846\,(1s_a) + 0.3518\,(1s_b) + 0.3558\,(1s_c) + 0.3770\,(1s_d)$;

$E_7 = 0.2068$ a.u.

$\psi_8 = 1.6795\,(2p_x) - 0.6916\,(1s_a) - 0.6916\,(1s_b) - 0.6916\,(1s_c) - 0.6916\,(1s_d)$;

$E_8 = 1.1904$ a.u.

The MO energy level diagram with electron occupancy is given below:

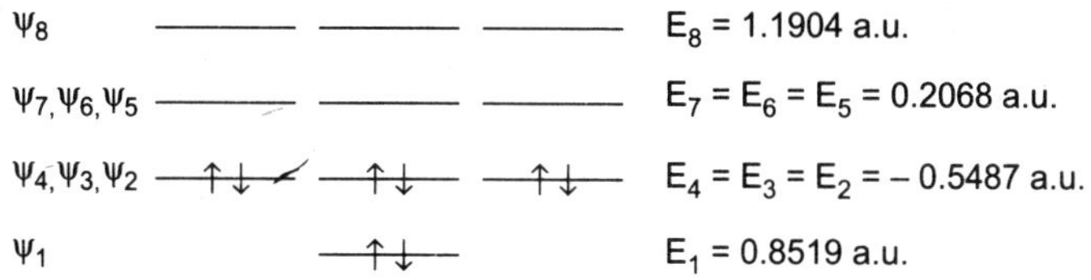

The lowest and the highest energy MOs are non-degenerate, and there are two sets of triply degenerate MOs—three bonding and three antibonding.

The lowest energy non-degenerate bonding MO ψ_1 can be pictured on the basis of the contributing AOs as follows:

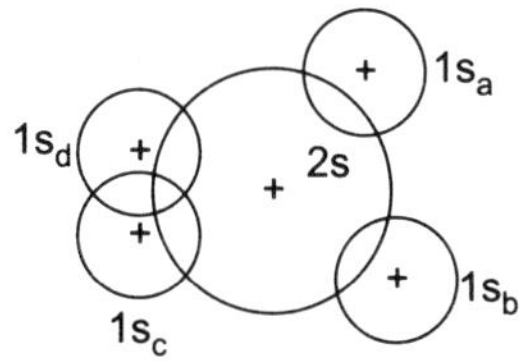

Fig. 13.23 *ψ_1: no contribution of $2p_x$, $2p_y$ or $2p_z$ of C; 1s AOs of H do overlap among themselves but the overlap is not shown for neatness of the diagram*

The 8-electron molecular wave function of methane is accordingly

$$\Psi = \left| \psi_1(1)\, \bar{\psi}_1(2)\, \psi_2(3)\, \bar{\psi}_2(4)\, \psi_3(5)\, \bar{\psi}_3(6)\, \psi_4(7)\, \bar{\psi}_4(8) \right|$$

13.7 VALENCE BOND THEORY

For every system studied by MO theory, there exists an alternative, *viz.*, the Valence Bond (VB) theory. It is just an extension of the Heitler-London treatment of H_2 molecule described in Chapter 12, according to which the covalent bonding occurs by electron exchanges in the available spin orbitals and pairing of spins. With increase in the number of atomic orbitals and electrons, however, the number of possible exchanges increases so rapidly that it becomes too tedious a task, even for very small molecules, to do the variational calculation without simplifications. Slater provided an elegant scheme of simplifying the long and cumbersome expressions of the wave function to neat and manageable forms through the use of appropriate symbolisms. Pauling extended it further by suggesting simplified methods of calculating the energies which otherwise would be very difficult to calculate. Therefore, the VB theory of polyatomic molecules goes by the name Heitler-London-Slater-Pauling (HLSP) theory of covalent bond.

In qualitative terms the HLSP theory may be stated as follows:

(*i*) a single covalent bond is formed by overlap of atomic orbitals and pairing of electron spins from different atoms, or, in other words by exchange of two electrons of opposite spins between two atomic orbitals.

(*ii*) The paired electrons tend to remain localised in the region between the two nuclei that are bonded.

(*iii*) The direction of the bond is that in which the overlap of the orbitals is maximum.

(*iv*) Of the two orbitals in an atom, the one which can overlap more with the orbital of another atom will form the stronger bonds with that atom.

13.7.1 Slater's Method

In Slater's VB method, (*i*) the atomic orbitals are first used to construct normalised antisymmetric wave functions, or Slater determinants, corresponding to various spin configurations (or spin states); these are eigenfunctions of the spin operator $\hat{S}_z$ with definite eigenvalues M_S, (*ii*) The Slater determinants are then suitably combined linearly to give antisymmetric eigenfunctions of the other spin operator $\hat{S}^2$ which have eigenvalues S (S + 1), S being the total spin number. These are called "*bond eigenfunctions*". To accomplish this all possible structures are written by dividing the molecule into pairs of atoms and drawing a bond between atoms with opposite spin (α, β) in each pair; this is called "spin pairing". Each bond eigenfunction then corresponds to a particular structure and hence is also called "structure eigenfunction". Each bond in the structure is represented by an antisymmetric combination of the two spins, αβ – βα, which has $M_S = 0$ and S = 0; the symmetric combination αβ + βα having $M_S = 0$ and S = 1 corresponds to no bond.

In case there is an odd number of electrons, one of them will remain unpaired with spin α or β.

In the simplest 2-electron system of H_2 discussed in chapter 12, there are two spin configuration

$$\overset{\alpha}{H_A} \text{——} \overset{\beta}{H_B} \qquad \overset{\beta}{H_A} \text{——} \overset{\alpha}{H_B}$$

and correspondingly two Slater determinants each with $M_S = 0$,

$$\psi_1 = \frac{1}{\sqrt{2}} \begin{vmatrix} (A\,\alpha)_1 & (B\,\beta)_1 \\ (A\,\alpha)_2 & (B\,\beta)_2 \end{vmatrix} \text{ and}$$

$$\psi_2 = \frac{1}{\sqrt{2}} \begin{vmatrix} (A\,\beta)_1 & (B\,\alpha)_1 \\ (A\,\beta)_2 & (B\,\alpha)_2 \end{vmatrix} \qquad \text{... (13.172)}$$

where $(A\,\alpha)_1$, for example, means the atomic orbital of the atom H_A containing electron 1 with spin α; $\frac{1}{\sqrt{2}}$ is normalisation factor ignoring the overlap integral.

There is only one structure

$$A - B \text{ or } A \uparrow \downarrow B$$

The total wave function of the molecule is the antisymmetric linear combination of ψ_1 and ψ_2. The wave function with symmetric orbital and antisymmetric spin combination, α (1) β (2) – β (1) α (2), (M_S = 0, S = 0) is the bond eigenfunction ψ_{A-B} and belongs to the singlet state (2S + 1 = 1); on the other hand, the wave function with antisymmetric orbital and symmetric spin combination, α (1) β (2) + β (1) α (2) (M_S = 0, S = 1) is a no bond eigenfunction $\psi_{A,\,B}$ and belongs to the triplet state (2S + 1 = 3) of the molecule.

Three-electron System: For electrons in 3 atomic orbitals A, B and C of a molecule there are $2^3 = 8$ spin states as below:

	ABC	ABC	ABC	ABC	ABC	ABC	ABC	ABC	
	α α α	α α β	α β α	β α α	α β β	β α β	β β α	β β β	
M_S	$\frac{3}{2}$	$\frac{1}{2}$	$\frac{1}{2}$	$\frac{1}{2}$	$-\frac{1}{2}$	$-\frac{1}{2}$	$-\frac{1}{2}$	$-\frac{3}{2}$	... (13.173)
	(1)	(2)	(3)	(4)	(5)	(6)	(7)	(8)	

and hence 8 Slater determinants which way be constructed as follows:

Consider the spin state (3) *i.e.*, α β α for the arrangement (123) of the electrons, *i.e.*, electron 1 in atomic orbital A with spin α, 2 in B with spin β and 3 in C with α. The wave function is

$$\phi_1 = (A\,\alpha)_1\,.\,(B\,\beta)_2\,(C\,\alpha)_3 \qquad \text{... (13.174)}$$

Similarly, for the other arrangement (213)

$$\phi_2 = (A\,\alpha)_2\,(B\,\beta)_1\,(C\,\alpha)_3 \qquad \text{... (13.175)}$$

and there are 3! = 6 such wave functions due to permutations of three electrons. The antisymmetric linear combination of all the six wave functions which obeys Pauli principle is the Slater function

$$\psi = \frac{1}{\sqrt{3!}}\,[(A\,\alpha)_1\,(B\,\beta)_2\,(C\,\alpha)_3 - (A\,\alpha)_2\,(B\,\beta)_1\,(C\,\alpha)_3 + (A\,\alpha)_2\,(B\,\beta)_3\,(C\,\alpha)_1$$

$$- (A\,\alpha)_3\,(B\,\beta)_2\,(C\,\alpha)_1 + (A\,\alpha)_3\,(B\,\beta)_1\,(C\,\alpha)_2 - (A\,\alpha)_1\,(B\,\beta)_3\,(C\,\alpha)_2]$$

$$= \frac{1}{\sqrt{3!}}\sum(-1)^p\,\hat{p}\,(A\,\alpha)_1\,(B\,\beta)_2\,(C\,\alpha)_3 \qquad \text{... (13.176)}$$

where $\hat{p}$ is the permutation operator and p is the number of exchanges such that $(-1)^p = -1$ if p is odd and + 1 if it is even.

or

$$\psi = \frac{1}{\sqrt{3!}}\begin{vmatrix} (A\,\alpha)_1 & (B\,\beta)_1 & (C\,\alpha)_1 \\ (A\,\alpha)_2 & (B\,\beta)_2 & (C\,\alpha)_2 \\ (A\,\alpha)_3 & (B\,\beta)_3 & (C\,\alpha)_3 \end{vmatrix} \qquad \text{... (13.177)}$$

is the Slater determinant corresponding to $M_S = \frac{1}{2}$. There will be three such determinants having $M_S = \frac{1}{2}$, three having $M_S = -\frac{1}{2}$, one having $M_S = \frac{3}{2}$ and one having $M_S = -\frac{3}{2}$; there will be no determinant with $M_S = 0$ and hence none with S = 0, which means that there will be no singlet state wave function.

To derive the bond eigenfunctions we write the following three possible structures

$$\underset{\text{I}}{A\,\dot{B}\text{—}C} \qquad \underset{\text{II}}{A\text{—}B\,C} \qquad \underset{\text{III}}{\overset{\frown}{ABC}}$$

In structure I, the bond B—C corresponds to the pairing of spins of electrons 2 and 3 which can be derived from the spin states 2 (α α β) and 3 (α β α) and also from the states 6 (β α β) and 7 (β β α). The required antisymmetric spin combinations are:

α (1) [α (2) β (3) – β (2) α (3)] and β (1) [α (2) β (3) – β (2) α (3)]

$$\left(M_S = \frac{1}{2}\right) \left(M_S = -\frac{1}{2}\right) \qquad \text{... (13.178)}$$

The two functions differ in the spin of the unpaired electron 1. Both represent the bond and since the total spin (S) in either is $\frac{1}{2}$ they together constitute doublet bond eigenfunction (2S + 1 = 2). The spatial part of the bond eigenfunction is the same for all and has the form A (1) B (2) C (3) or any of its 6 permutations. Hence the complete bond eigenfunction in compact form is

$${}^2\psi_{B-C} = \frac{1}{\sqrt{2}}(\psi_2 - \psi_3) = N\sum \hat{P}\phi\alpha(1).[\alpha(2)\beta(3) - \beta(2)\alpha(3)]$$

or

$${}^2\psi_{B-C} = \frac{1}{\sqrt{2}}(\psi_6 - \psi_7) = N\sum \hat{P}\phi\beta(1).[\alpha(2)\beta(3) - \beta(2)\alpha(3)] \qquad \text{... (13.179)}$$

where $\phi = \frac{1}{\sqrt{3}}$ A (1) B (2) C (3), and N is the factor introduced to normalise the linear combination.

Similarly, the bond eigenfunction for A – B in structure (II) is,

$${}^2\psi_{A-B} = \frac{1}{\sqrt{2}}(\psi_3 - \psi_4) \text{ or } \frac{1}{\sqrt{2}}(\psi_5 - \psi_6)$$

or

$$= \frac{1}{\sqrt{2}}\sum \hat{P}\phi[\alpha(1)\beta(2) - \beta(1)\alpha(2)]\alpha(3) \qquad \text{... (13.180)}$$

and

$$= \frac{1}{\sqrt{2}}\sum \hat{P}\phi[\alpha(1)\beta(2) - \beta(1)\alpha(2)]\beta(3) \qquad \text{... (13.181)}$$

Corresponding to Scheme (III), the bond eigenfunction could be written as,

$${}^2\psi_{A-C} = \frac{1}{\sqrt{2}}(\psi_2 - \psi_4)$$

or

$${}^2\psi_{A-C} = \frac{1}{\sqrt{2}}(\psi_5 - \psi_7)$$

But

$$\psi_2 - \psi_4 = (\psi_2 - \psi_3) + (\psi_3 - \psi_4)$$

or

$$\psi_{A-C} = \psi_{B-C} + \psi_{A-B} \qquad \text{... (13.182)}$$

In other words, ψ_{AC} is made of ψ_{AB} and ψ_{BC} and hence, is not independent, and we have only two independent covalent structures for the system under discussion.

Four-electron System: For the 4-electron system in four atomic orbitals A, B, C and D there are 4 ! = 24 permutations in spin-orbitals like (Aα), (Bα), (Cβ) etc., and 2^4 = 16 spin states like αααα, αβαβ etc. Accordingly, there are 16 Slater wave functions, one for each spin configuration. However, for bond formation, the spins must be paired. This reduces the spin states to six only, *viz.*

	ABCD	ABCD	ABCD	ABCD	ABCD	ABCD	
	αβαβ	ααββ	αββα	βααβ	βαβα	ββαα	... (13.183)
M_S	0	0	0	0	0	0	
	(1)	(2)	(3)	(4)	(5)	(6)	

The pairing of electrons and the covalent bonds may then be indicated in the following three ways only.

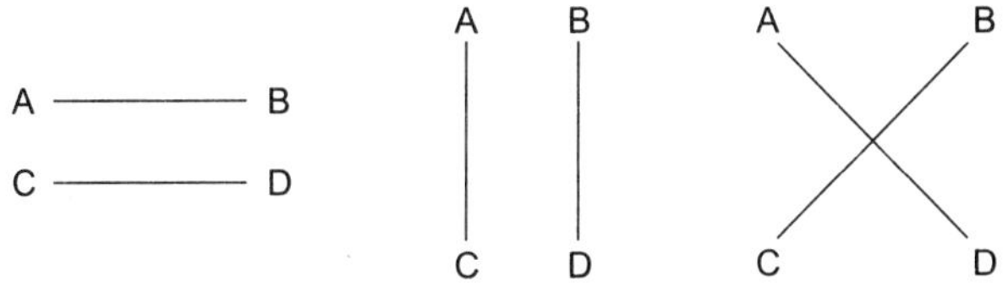

I II III

For the structure I, the bond eigenfunction can be derived from the spin states 1, 3, 4 and 5: for the structure II, it can be derived from spin states 2, 3, 4 and 6. Thus,

$$\psi_{A-B,C-D} = N(\psi_1 - \psi_3 - \psi_4 + \psi_5) \quad \text{... (13.184)}$$

where N is the normalisation factor for the linear combination, and the function ψ_1, for example, is

$$\psi_1 = \frac{1}{\sqrt{4!}} \sum_P (-1)^P \hat{P} (A\alpha)_1 (B\beta)_2 (C\alpha)_3 (D\beta)_4$$

and the sign changes on each single exchange of spins or in compact form

$$\psi_1 = \frac{1}{\sqrt{4!}} \sum_P (-1)^{\hat{P}} \hat{P} A\bar{B}C\bar{D} \quad \text{... (13.185)}$$

Therefore, the bond eigenfunction for structure I is

$$\psi_{A-B,C-D} = N \left[\frac{1}{\sqrt{4!}} \sum (-1)^{\hat{P}} \hat{P}\, ABCD\, (\alpha\beta\alpha\beta - \alpha\beta\beta\alpha - \beta\alpha\alpha\beta + \beta\alpha\beta\alpha) \right]$$

... (13.186)

Similarly, for the structure II, the bond eigenfunction is

$$\psi_{A-C,B-D} = N \left[\frac{1}{\sqrt{4!}} \sum (-1)^P \hat{P}\, ABCD\, (\alpha\alpha\beta\beta - \alpha\beta\beta\alpha - \beta\alpha\alpha\beta + \beta\beta\alpha\alpha) \right]$$

... (13.187)

while structure III is not independent.

The value of N is obtained by normalisation of spin combinations only

$$N^2 (\alpha\beta\alpha\beta - \alpha\beta\beta\alpha - \beta\alpha\alpha\beta + \beta\alpha\beta\alpha)^2 = 1$$

or

$$N^2 (1 + 1 + 1 + 1 + 0 + 0 + ...) = 1,$$

or $$N = \frac{1}{\sqrt{4}} \text{ or } \frac{1}{\sqrt{2^2}}$$

These bond eigenfunctions belongs to the eigenvalue S (S + 1) = 0, or S = 0 and hence belong to singlet state.

The above bond eigenfunctions apply, to a molecule having two bonds. For a molecule having 3 bonds, $N = \frac{1}{\sqrt{2^3}}$, and for the general case of a molecule with n bonds it is $\frac{1}{\sqrt{2^n}}$. Thus, for a polyatomic molecule containing n bonds formed by $2n$ atomic orbitals and $2n$ electrons, the bond eigenfunction corresponding to a single structure in which pairing occurs between A and B, C and D, etc. is,

$$\psi_{A-B, C-D, ...} = \frac{1}{\sqrt{2^n}} \sum_R (-1)^R \hat{R} \frac{1}{\sqrt{2n!}} \sum_P (-1)^P \hat{P} A(1) \bar{B}(2) C(3) \bar{D}(4) \quad ...(13.188)$$

Here $\hat{R}$ is the operator for exchanging the electron spins in bonded orbitals, $\hat{P}$ is the permutation operator for electron rearrangements in the orbitals, R and P denote the number of exchanges of the spins and the electrons respectively; $(-1)^R$ or $(-1)^P$ is + 1 when R or P is even and – 1 when they are odd.

13.7.2 Canonical Structures

The independent covalent structures discussed earlier are called "canonical structures". In the three- and four-electron systems I and II are the canonical structures, G. Rumer suggested the following rule for arriving at the canonical structures for a polyatomic molecule; If the atomic orbitals A, B, C... are denoted by points around a circle (which has no relation to the shape of the molecule) and the points are connected in pairs by lines, the structures formed in which the lines do not cross each other are the canonical structures. The number of canonical structures formed from $2n$ orbitals and $2n$ electrons is given by the formula,

$$N = \frac{(2n)!}{n!(n+1)!} \quad ...(13.189)$$

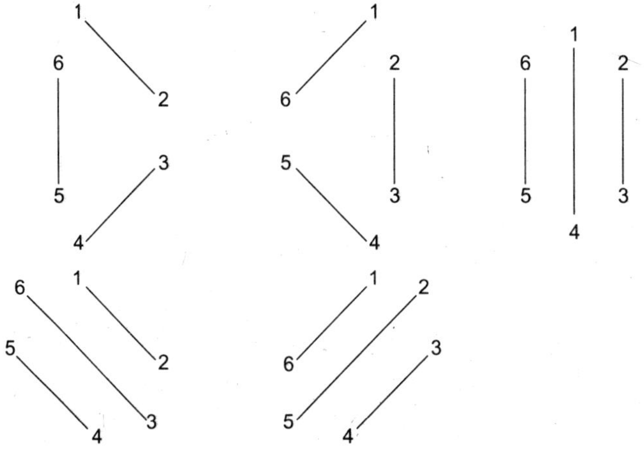

Fig. 13.24 *Canonical structures of benzene*

A typical example is that of benzene in which, taking the p-orbitals forming π-bonds only into consideration, we may write $2n = 6$ and hence $N = 5$. The five canonical structures as shown in Fig. 13.24.

Structures I and II are the well-known Kekule structures, and III, IV and V are the Dewar structures.

13.7.3 Ionic Structures

Slater's extension of Heitler-London treatment leads to canonical covalent structures only. It excludes the possibility that two electrons may be found in a single orbital leading to ionic structures. For the ABC system, the following ionic structures are possible,

$$\underset{(i)}{A^+ B^- - C,} \quad \underset{(ii)}{A^- B^+ - C,} \quad \underset{(iii)}{A^- B^+ C,} \quad \underset{(iv)}{A - B^- C^+,} \quad \underset{(v)}{A^+ BC^-,} \quad \underset{(vi)}{A^- BC^+}$$

The spin-orbital function for the structures may be derived from the configuration,

$$\begin{bmatrix} A & B & C \\ (\alpha\beta) & \alpha & \end{bmatrix} \begin{bmatrix} A & B & C \\ (\alpha\beta) & \alpha & \end{bmatrix} \begin{bmatrix} A & B & C \\ \alpha & (\alpha\beta) & \end{bmatrix} \begin{bmatrix} A & B & C \\ & \alpha & (\alpha\beta) \end{bmatrix} \begin{bmatrix} A & B & C \\ \alpha & (\alpha\beta) & \end{bmatrix} \begin{bmatrix} A & B & C \\ (\alpha\beta) & & \alpha \end{bmatrix}$$

The unpaired electron can equally well be β. Configuration like,

$$\begin{matrix} A & B & C \\ & (\alpha\alpha) & \beta \end{matrix}$$

in which two electrons of the same spin are in the same orbital are not permitted, and there is no point in interchanging α and β in the same orbital.

13.7.4 Bond Eigenfunctions of H_2O

We may consider these principles with respect to bonding in H_2O. The $2s$ and one of the $2p$ (say $2p_x$) atomic orbitals in H_2O have paired electrons. We have $2p_y$ and $2p_z$ and $1s_A$ and $1s_B$ orbitals of the two H atoms available for bonding. If the electrons are attached to the orbitals in the order $1s_A$ (1) $2p_y$ (2) $1s_B$ (3) $2p_z$ (4), there are three possible schemes of pairing.

$$\underset{(I)}{(1 \uparrow\downarrow 2) \;\&\; (3 \uparrow\downarrow 4),} \quad \underset{(II)}{(1 \uparrow\downarrow 3) \text{ and } (2 \uparrow\downarrow 4)} \text{ and } \underset{(III)}{(1 \uparrow\downarrow 4) \;\&\; (2 \uparrow\downarrow 3)}$$

These correspond to the following structures:

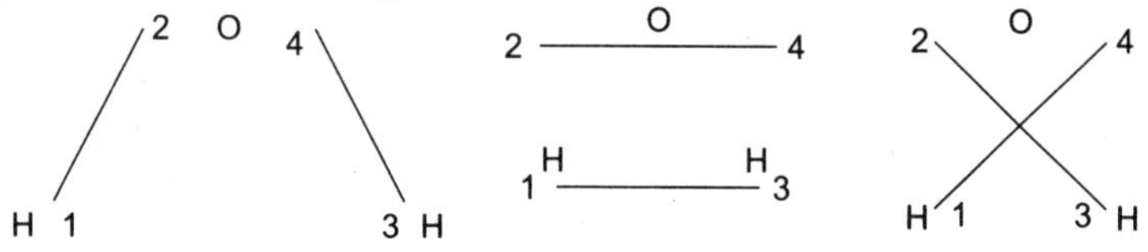

Fig. 13.25 *Canonical structures of H_2O*

where the spin pairing between, say, electrons 1 and 2 is indicated as 1—2. It can be seen that only I and II are canonical structures.

The possible spin states that may be involved in electron pairing are given by (13.183) where,

$$A = 1s_A,\ B = 2p_y,\ C = 1s_B \text{ and } D = 2p_z$$

Then the bond eigenfunction ψ_I corresponding to the structure (I) is obtained by taking linear combination of the functions ψ_1, ψ_3, ψ_5 and ψ_6 corresponding to the spin states, 1, 3, 5 and 6, respectively. The function ψ_1, for example, will be given as

$$\psi_1 = \frac{1}{\sqrt{4!}} \sum (-1)^P \hat{P} \left[1s_A\, 2\bar{p}_y\, 1s_B\, 2\bar{p}_z\right] \qquad \text{... (13.190)}$$

Thus,

$$\psi_I = \frac{1}{\sqrt{2^2}} \sum_R (-1)^R \hat{R} \frac{1}{\sqrt{4!}} \sum_P (-1)^P \hat{P} \left(1s_A\, \overline{2p}_y\, 1s_B\, \overline{2p}_z\right) \qquad \text{... (13.191)}$$

When expanded in terms of determinants,

$$\psi_I = \frac{1}{2} \cdot \frac{1}{\sqrt{24}} \Big[\left|1s_A\, 2\bar{p}_y\, 1s_B\, 2\bar{p}_z\right| - \left|1\bar{s}_A\, 2p_y\, 1s_B\, 2\bar{p}_z\right|$$

$$- \left|1s_A\, 2\bar{p}_y\, 1\bar{s}_B\, 2p_z\right| + \left|1\bar{s}_A\, 2p_y\, 1\bar{s}_B\, 2p_z\right|\Big] \qquad \text{... (13.192)}$$

where each determinant is represented through its diagonal elements only. Similarly, for the structure (II), in which pairing occurs between $1s_A$ and $1s_B$, and $2p_y$ and $2p_z$,

$$\psi_{II} = \frac{1}{2} \frac{1}{\sqrt{24}} \sum (-1)^R \hat{R} \sum (-1)^P \hat{P} \left(1s_A\, 2p_y\, 1\bar{s}_B\, \overline{2p}_z\right) \qquad \text{... (13.193)}$$

which also expands into a linear sum of four determinants. The structure (III) is not independent of I and II.

Thus, we see that in H_2O which has two bonds only, the bond eigenfunction contains four 4×4 determinants. Each determinant expands into $4\,! = 24$ terms so that there are altogether 96 product terms in a single bond wave function. With increase in the number of bonds in a molecule the number of determinants and the product terms increases very rapidly.

The structures (I) and (II) are purely covalent (canonical). The following six ionic structures are also possible.

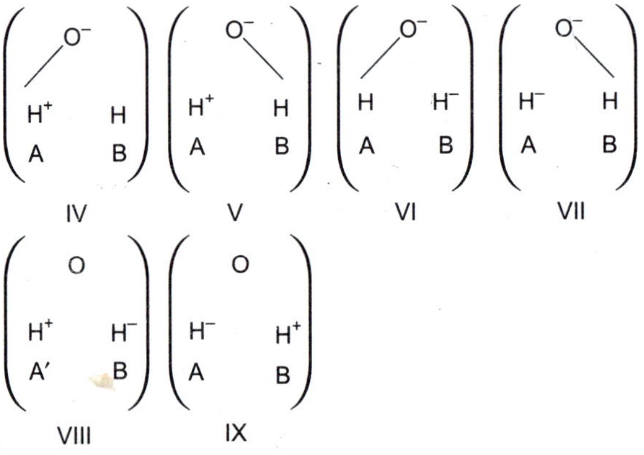

Inclusion of the corresponding ionic wave functions can improve the results of calculation but it will also make the calculation complicated.

13.7.5 Resonance

The theory of resonance which is widely used by chemists is in fact a qualitative extension of the VB theory. The chief characteristics of the VB theory is that the true state of a molecule is a "resonance hybrid" of all the possible canonical and ionic structures and, accordingly, the true wave functions. Ψ, is a linear combination of the functions representing the structure, *i.e.*,

$$\Psi = a_1 \psi_I + a_2 \psi_{II} + a_3 \psi_{III} + ...$$

Each of these structures, however are not equally stable and does not necessarily make an equal contribution to the state of the molecule. The weight of each structure in the wave function ψ is proportional to a_i^2. However, the bond eigenfunctions are not mutually orthogonal, hence the electron density is not equal to the sum of probability densities of the different structures and, in an empirical treatment chemical experience is used to decide which of them are likely to be significant. For example, in H_2O the structure (II) with a long H—H bond will be much less stable than (I); the ionic structures (IV) and (V) are equivalent and are far more stable than the structures (VI) and (VII) in which the electronegative oxygen atom becomes the positive and hydrogen the negative charge, or the structures (VIII) and (IX) in which the positive and negative charges are separated far apart.

If E_I, E_{II}, E_{III} ... are the energies of the structures (I), (II), (III), ... respectively, the true energy of the molecule (E) is lower than that of any of the individual structures (resonance stabilisation). The difference between E and the lowest of the energies due to individual structures is the "resonance energy".

Calculation of the energy and the resonance energy of a molecule and the coefficients of the linear combination are the main tasks in the quanitative VB treatment of a molecule.

13.7.6 Calculation of Energy

Coming back to the system ABC, and confining to the two canonical structures (I) and (II) only, we find that the true wave function is,

$$\Psi = a_1 \psi_I + a_2 \psi_{II} \qquad ...(13.194)$$

Using the variation function (13.194) to calculate the energy (E) of the system, we obtain the secular determinant

$$\begin{vmatrix} H_{II} - ES_{II} & H_{I\,II} - ES_{I\,II} \\ H_{II\,I} - ES_{II\,I} & H_{II\,II} - ES_{II\,II} \end{vmatrix} \qquad ...(13.195)$$

where
$$H_{II} = \int \psi_I \hat{H} \psi_I \, d\tau;$$

$$H_{I\,II} = \int \psi_I \hat{H} \psi_{II} \, d\tau,$$

$$S_{I\,II} = \int \psi_I \psi_{II} \, d\tau, \text{etc.}$$

where the bond eigenfunctions ψ_I and ψ_{II} are expressed in terms of the Slater functions ψ_2, ψ_3, ψ_4 ... [having the form of Equation 13.176 or 13.177. The elements H_{II}, $H_{II\,II}$, etc., are expanded in terms of the integrals H_{ij} (i = 2, 3, 4, etc.) and $H_{ij} = \int \psi_i \hat{H} \psi_j \, d\tau$.

The evaluation of these integrals can be simplified by utilising the orthonormality property of the spin eigenfunctions α and β.

Consider, for example, the integral

$$H_{23} = \int \psi_2 \hat{H} \psi_3 \, d\tau$$

$$= \frac{1}{3!}\int \Sigma(-1)^P \hat{P}_1(A\alpha)_1(B\alpha)_2(C\beta)_3 \times \hat{H}\Sigma(-1)^P \hat{P}_2(A\alpha\}_1(B\beta\}_2(C\alpha)_3 d\tau \quad \text{... (13.196)}$$

where $\hat{P}_1$ and $\hat{P}_2$ are the permutation operators. One of the summations (that on the left of $\hat{H}$) in the expression (13.196) can be transformed into a single product because all terms within this summation lead to the sme result on integration. For example, one of the terms will be as below.

$$\frac{1}{3!}\int (A\alpha)_1 (B\alpha)_2 (C\beta)_3 \hat{H}(A\alpha)_1 (B\beta)_2 (C\alpha)_3 - (A\alpha)_2 (B\beta)_1 (C\alpha)_3$$

$$+ (A\alpha)_2 (B\beta)_3 (C\alpha)_1 - (A\alpha)_3 (B\beta)_2 (C\alpha)_3 + (A\alpha)_3 (B\beta)_1 (C\alpha)_2$$

$$- (A\alpha)_1 (B\beta)_3 (C\alpha)_2] \, d\tau \quad \text{... (13.197)}$$

This integral is a sum of six integrals many of which vanish due to spin orthogonality; for example, the first term is

$$\int (A\alpha)_1 (B\alpha)_2 (C\beta)_3 \hat{H}(A\alpha)_1 (B\beta)_2 (C\alpha)_3 \, d\tau$$

$$= \int A(1) B(2) C(3) \hat{H} A(1) B(2) C(3) \, d\tau . \int \alpha(1)^2 \, d\tau_1$$

$$\int \alpha(2) \beta(2) \, d\tau_2 . \int \beta(3) \alpha(3) . d\tau_3 = 0 \quad \text{... (13.198)}$$

Only those integrals survive in which the spin of each electron on the left and right of $\hat{H}$ match, and on working out, the expression (13.197) assumes the form

$$\frac{1}{3!}\left[-\int A(1) B(2) C(3) \hat{H} A(1) B(3) C(2) \, d\tau + \int A(1) B(2) C(3) \hat{H} A(2) B(3) C(1) \, d\tau\right]$$

... (13.199)

The integrals in Equation (13.199) may be called exchange integrals. In the first, electrons 2 and 3 exchange the orbitals B and C while in the second all three exchange their orbitals. The former is single exchange and the latter double exchange integral. Now arrange the electrons with their orbitals on the right of $\hat{H}$ in the same order as on the left within the integrals, and then drop the number 1, 2 and 3, the expression (13.199) becomes

$$\frac{1}{3!}\left[-\int ABC \, \hat{H} \, ACB \, d\tau + \int ABC \, \hat{H} \, CAB \, d\tau\right] \quad \text{... (13.200)}$$

Slater simplified the expression still further by (*i*) ignoring multiple exchange integrals in comparison to single exchange integral, (*ii*) denoting the integral through brackets ( ), dropping $\hat{H}$ and indicating only the orbitals involved in exchange. The expression (13.200) thus assumes the simple form

$$-\frac{1}{3!}\left(ABC/\hat{H}/ACB\right) \quad \text{... (13.201)}$$

or

$$-\frac{1}{3!}(BC) \quad \text{... (13.202)}$$

The same result (13.200) will be obtained if we use any of the 3 ! permutations of the left of $\hat{H}$ in Equation (13.196) so that the integral Equation (13.197) becomes

$$H_{23} = -3! \times \frac{1}{3!} (BC) = -(BC) \qquad \text{... (13.203)}$$

In the expression for H_{ii}, one of the integrals will be invariably $(ABC \mid \hat{H} \mid ABC)$. This is known as the "coulomb integral" as it represents the coulombic repulsion between the electron clouds due to A^2, B^2 and C^2. Let it be denoted as Q. Then, we can write down all the elements H_{ij}, required to evaluate the matrix elements $H_{I\,I}$, etc., in the secular determinant as follows :

$$H_{22} = Q - (AB)$$
$$H_{33} = Q - (AC)$$
$$H_{44} = Q - (BC)$$
$$H_{23} = -(BC)$$
$$H_{24} = -(AC)$$
$$H_{34} = -(AB) \qquad \text{... (13.204)}$$

The expressions for S_{ij} will also be like Equation (13.201), except that $\hat{H}$ will be absent. Thus,

$$H_{I\,I} = \int \psi_I \hat{H} \psi_I \, d\tau = \frac{1}{2}(\psi_2 - \psi_3)\hat{H}(\psi_2 - \psi_3)\, d\tau$$

$$= \frac{1}{2}(H_{22} + H_{33} - 2H_{23})$$

$$= Q + (BC) - \frac{1}{2}(AB) - \frac{1}{2}(AC) \qquad \text{... (13.205)}$$

$$H_{II\,II} = Q + (AB) - \frac{1}{2}(AC) - \frac{1}{2}(BC) \qquad \text{... (13.206)}$$

$$H_{I\,II} = H_{II\,I} = (AC) - \frac{1}{2}(Q + BC + AB) \qquad \text{... (13.207)}$$

$$S_{I\,I} = \frac{1}{2}\int (\psi_2 - \psi_3)^2 \, d\tau = \frac{1}{2}(S_{22} + S_{33} - 2S_{23})$$

$$= \frac{1}{2}(1 + 1 - 0) = 1$$

$S_{II\,II} = 1$ and $S_{I\,II} = 0$.

13.7.7 Pauling's Method of Evaluating Energy

With increasing number of electrons and atomic orbitals, there will be many more exchange integrals due to various pairs of atoms. The determination of the coefficients of the integrals is usually very tedious. Pauling proposed a very simple and convenient method for this. It involves writing down of the possible canonical structures and superimposing of two bond structures keeping the arrangement of the atoms, containing all the bonds of the structures, as before. For example, in a four electron system we have two canonical structures,

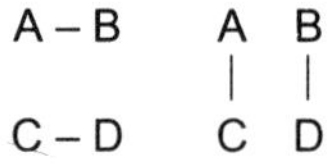

I II ... (13.208)

where A, B, C and D are the atomic orbitals used in bonding. In H_2O, for example, these may be $1s_A$, $2p_y$, $1s_B$ and $2p_z$, respectively, as mentioned earlier. If structure (I) is superimposed on itself an arrangement L is formed; if (II) is superimposed on itself M is formed and if (I) and (II) are superimposed N is formed Equation (13.210).

L (I + I) M (II + II) N (I + II) ... (13.209)

The superpositions lead to arrangements in which atoms are joined by "double lines" (L and M) or by a "polygon" (N). Pauling named these as "islands"; each island is formed by even number of bonds. A separate island is formed as an isolated part of the structure which is not connected to other parts.

If ψ_I and ψ_{II} represent the structures (I) and (II) respectively, the superpositions L, M and N may be treated, according to Pauling, as equivalent to taking the matrix elements of the secular determinant, $H_{I\,I}$, $H_{II\,II}$ and $H_{I\,II}$ respectively, where, for example,

$$H_{I\,II} = \int \psi_I \hat{H} \psi_{II} \, d\tau$$

The matrix elements, we have seen, can be expanded in terms of coulomb and exchange integrals. The coefficients (γ) of these integrals may be obtained by the following rules.*

For the coulomb integral (Q),

$$\gamma = \frac{1}{2^{n-i}} \qquad \text{... (13.210)}$$

where n is the number of bonds and i is the number of islands. In the arrangement L where $i = 2$ and $n = 2$,

$$\gamma = \frac{1}{2^{2-2}} = 1.$$

Similarly, in M ($i = 2$, $n = 2$), $\gamma = 1$ and in N ($i = 1$, $n = 2$), $\gamma = \frac{1}{2}$.

For the exchange integrals (single exchange only).

$$\gamma = \frac{f}{2^{n-i}} \qquad \text{... (13.211)}$$

*For derivation, see Pauling, J. *Chem Phys.*, 1 (1933) 280.

The value of f is determined by the following rules:

(*i*) If in a structure the atoms involved in an exchange integral are in different islands, $f = -\frac{1}{2}$.

Thus, $f = -\frac{1}{2}$ for the integrals (AC), (AD), (BC) and (BD) in L, and for (AB), (AD), (BC) and (CD) in M. For each of these,

$$\gamma = \frac{-\frac{1}{2}}{2^{2-2}} = -\frac{1}{2}.$$

(*ii*) If in a structure the atoms involved in an exchange belong to the same island and are separated by odd number of bonds, $f = +1$.

For (AB) and (CD) in L, $f = +1$, and $\gamma = +1$, for (AC) and (BD) in M $f = +1$ and $\gamma = +1$, and for (AB), (BD), (CD) and (AC) in N, $f = +1$ and $\gamma = -\frac{1}{2}$.

(*iii*) If in a structure the atoms involved in an exchange belong to the same island and are separated by even number of bonds, $f = -2$.

For (AD) and (BC) in N, $f = -2$ and $\gamma = \frac{-2}{2^{2-1}} = -1$.

Thus, we have

$$H_{II} = Q + (AB) + (CD) - \frac{1}{2}[(AC) + (AD) + (BC) + (BD)] \quad ...(13.212)$$

$$H_{II\,II} = Q + (AC) + (BD) - \frac{1}{2}[(AB) + (AD) + (BC) + (CD)] \quad ...(13.213)$$

$$H_{I\,II} = \frac{1}{2}Q - (AD) - (BC) + \frac{1}{2}[(AB) + (AC) + (CD) + (BD)] \quad ...(13.214)$$

The expressions (13.212) and (13.213) for H_{II} and $H_{II\,II}$ represent the energies of the structures (I) and (II) respectively. They can be generalised, that is, for any single VB structure of a molecule, the energy can be given by

$$E = Q + \sum_{(i,j)} J_{ij} - \frac{1}{2}\sum_{(mn)} J_{mn} \quad ...(13.215)$$

where Q is the coulomb energy representing the integral $(ABC\cdots|\hat{H}|ABC\cdots)$, J_{ij} is the exchange energy for a bonded pair of orbitals i and j, J_{mn} is the exchange energy for a non-bonded pair of orbitals m and n, and the summations extend over all bonded (i, j) and non-bonded $(m\ n)$ pairs.

13.7.8 Perfect Pairing Approximation

In many cases, an approximation is made that the molecule can be represented by a single covalent (VB) structure. This is perfect pairing approximation, in which it is assumed that all orbitals are linked in pairs, and the overlap between the atomic orbitals is zero. The energy of the structure is given by Equation (13.215). The H_2O molecule, for example, may be represented by a single covalent structure where energy is given by,

$$E_{H_2O} = Q + J_{1s_A, 2p_y} + J_{1s_B, 2p_z} - \frac{1}{2}\left[J_{1s_A 1s_B} + J_{2p_y 2p_z} + J_{1s_B 2p_y} + J_{1s_A 2p_z}\right].$$

13.7.9 Application to Conjugated π-Systems

The approximation of perfect pairing breaks down in the case of π-systems. The HLSP theory provides a method for the treatment of the π-systems, which is parallel to the HMO method discussed earlier. The π-bond in ethylene, which has only one canonical structure is like a π-bond in O_2 and can be treated in the manner similar to that of a σ-bond in H_2, replacing the 1*s* orbitals of H_2 by the $2p_z$. In the empirical approach, with overlap integral (S) taken as zero, the energy is determined in terms of coulomb and exchange energies obtained from experiment.

We consider below two typical cases, *viz.*, allyl and butadiene systems.

Allyl System: $(C_A - C_B - C_C)$

Denoting the three p_z atomic orbitals of the three carbon atoms involved in π-bond formation by A, B and C, we can represent the allyl system by the following two canonical structures;

$$\underset{\text{I}}{\text{AB} - \text{C}} \quad \text{and} \quad \underset{\text{II}}{\text{A} - \text{BC}}$$

The corresponding total wave function and the secular equation are,

$$\Psi = a_1 \psi_{\text{I}} + a_2 \psi_{\text{II}} \qquad \text{... (13.216)}$$

$$\begin{vmatrix} H_{\text{II}} - ES_{\text{II}} & H_{\text{I II}} - ES_{\text{I II}} \\ H_{\text{I II}} - ES_{\text{I II}} & H_{\text{II II}} - ES_{\text{II II}} \end{vmatrix} = 0 \qquad \text{... (13.217)}$$

As described earlier in the case of 3-electron system, the bond eigenfunctions are given by Equations (13.179) and (13.180),

$$\psi_{\text{I}} = \frac{1}{\sqrt{2}}(\psi_2 - \psi_3)$$

$$\psi_{\text{II}} = \frac{1}{\sqrt{2}}(\psi_3 - \psi_4)$$

where, ψ_2, ψ_3 and ψ_4 are normalised Slater functions given as

$$\psi_2 = \frac{1}{\sqrt{3!}}\sum(-1)^p\, \hat{P}\, A(1)\, B(2)\, \bar{C}(3)$$

$$\psi_3 = \frac{1}{\sqrt{3!}}\sum(-1)^p\, \hat{P}\, A(1)\, \bar{B}(2)\, C(3) \qquad \text{... (13.218)}$$

$$\psi_4 = \frac{1}{\sqrt{3!}}\sum(-1)^p\, \hat{P}\, \bar{A}(1)\, B(2)\, C(3)$$

and $\frac{1}{\sqrt{2}}$ is the normalisation factor for the antisymmetric spin functions. The matrix elements $H_{\text{I I}}$, $H_{\text{II II}}$ and $H_{\text{I II}}$ are given by Equations (13.205), (13.206) and (13.207) respectively.

$$H_{I\,I} = Q + (BC) - \frac{1}{2}(AB) - \frac{1}{2}(AC) \qquad ...(13.205)$$

$$H_{II\,II} = Q + (AB) - \frac{1}{2}(AC) - \frac{1}{2}(BC) \qquad ...(13.206)$$

$$H_{I\,II} = (AC) - \frac{1}{2}[Q + (BC) + (AB)] \qquad ...(13.207)$$

Since ψ_2, ψ_3 and ψ_4 are normalised,

$$S_{I\,I} = \frac{1}{2}\int(\psi_2 - \psi_3)^2\, d\tau = \frac{1}{2}\left[\int\psi_2^2\, d\tau + \int\psi_3^2\, d\tau - \int\psi_2\,\psi_3\, d\tau\right] = 1$$

The last term vanishes due to spin orthogonality. Similarly, $S_{II\,II} = 1$. But

$$S_{I\,II} = S_{II\,I} = \frac{1}{2}\int(\psi_2 - \psi_3)(\psi_3 - \psi_4)\, d\tau$$

$$= \frac{1}{2}\left[\int\psi_2\,\psi_3\, d\tau - \int\psi_2\,\psi_4\, d\tau - \int\psi_3^2\, d\tau + \int\psi_3\,\psi_4\, d\tau\right] = -\frac{1}{2}$$

Exchange integrals involving adajcent atoms are taken to be equal and those involving non-adjacent atoms are assumed to be zero; thus

$$(AB) = (BC) = \alpha \text{ (say)},$$

and $$(AC) = 0$$

Therefore, $$H_{I\,I} = H_{II\,II} = Q + \frac{\alpha}{2};$$

$$H_{I\,II} = -\frac{Q}{2} - \alpha$$

Substituting in Equation (13.217)

$$\begin{vmatrix} Q + \frac{\alpha}{2} - E & -\frac{Q}{2} - \alpha - \frac{1}{2}E \\ -\frac{1}{2}Q - \alpha - \frac{1}{2}E & \frac{Q}{2} + \alpha - E \end{vmatrix} = 0 \qquad ...(13.219)$$

On expanding the determinant,

$$\left(Q + \frac{\alpha}{2} - E\right)^2 = \left[-\left(\frac{Q}{2} + \alpha + \frac{1}{2}E\right)\right]^2$$

or $$Q + \frac{\alpha}{2} - E = \mp\left(\frac{Q}{2} + \alpha + \frac{1}{2}E\right)$$

This yield two solutions,

$$E_1 = (Q + \alpha) \text{ and } E_2 = (Q - \alpha) \qquad ...(13.220)$$

These solutions correspond to two energy states; α being negative, $E_1 < E_2$.

Thus, there are two bond structures for allyl system, C—C═C (I) and C═C—C (II), which have energies $H_{I\,I}$ and $H_{II\,II}$ respectively. Since $H_{II} = H_{II\,II}$, it is concluded that the two structures are equally probable. The resonance stabilisation energy is

$$E_1 - H_{I\,I} = (Q + \alpha) - \left(Q + \frac{\alpha}{2}\right) = \frac{\alpha}{2} \qquad \text{... (13.221)}$$

Substituting the value of E_1 for E in the secular equation,

$$a_1 (H_{I\,I} - E_1) + a_2 (H_{I\,II} - E_1 S_{I\,II}) = 0$$

we can find that $\quad a_1 + a_2 = 0$ or $a_1 = -a_2$

Normalization leads to $a_1 = \dfrac{1}{\sqrt{2}}$

Since the 3-electron system with states $\alpha\alpha\beta$ or $\alpha\beta\alpha$ has spin (S) = $\dfrac{1}{2}$ the total wave function is doublet

$$^2\Psi_1 = \frac{1}{\sqrt{2}}(\psi_I - \psi_{II}) \qquad \text{... (13.222)}$$

Similarly, for the higher energy state E_2

$$^2\Psi_2 = \frac{1}{\sqrt{2}}(\psi_I + \psi_{II}) \qquad \text{... (13.223)}$$

Butadiene: ($C_A = C_B - C_C = C_D$)
Butadiene has two canonical structures (I) and (II),

```
A – B     A   B
          |   |
C – D     C   D
  I        II
```

A line in these structures represents the coupling of the spin functions of two π-electrons. The corresponding "bond structures" are,

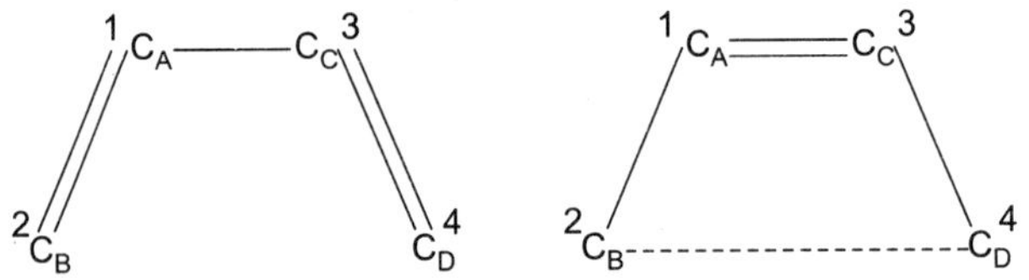

The four π-electron system has the following six possible spin configurations and correspondingly six Slater functions (ϕ_i) with $M_S = 0$ represent the ground state bonding.

	A	B	C	D
ϕ_1	α	α	β	β
ϕ_2	α	β	α	β
ϕ_3	β	α	α	β
ϕ_4	α	β	β	α
ϕ_5	β	α	β	α
ϕ_6	β	β	α	α

The Slater function ϕ_1, for example, is

$$\phi_1 = \frac{1}{\sqrt{4!}}\left| A\,B\,\bar{C}\,\bar{D} \right| \text{ or } \frac{1}{\sqrt{4!}}\Sigma(-1)^p\,\hat{P}\,A\,B\,\bar{C}\,\bar{D} \qquad \text{... (13.224)}$$

where | | denotes determinant with diagonal elements and $A\,B\,\bar{C}\bar{D}$ means A (1) B (2) $\bar{C}(3)\,\bar{D}(4)$. The antisymmetric spin combination (χ) to represent the bonds A – B and C – D (structure I) is constructed through the spin configurations 2, 3, 4 and 5 only,

$$\chi_{AB,CD} = \frac{1}{\sqrt{2}}\left[\alpha(1)\beta(2) - \beta(1)\alpha(2)\right]\frac{1}{\sqrt{2}}\left[\alpha(3)\beta(4) - \beta(3)\alpha(4)\right]$$

$$= \frac{1}{2}\left[\alpha(1)\beta(2)\alpha(3)\beta(4) - \alpha(1)\beta(2)\beta(3)\alpha(4) - \beta(1)\alpha(2)\alpha(3)\beta(4) + \beta(1)\alpha(2)\beta(3)\alpha(4)\right]$$

or simply

$$= \frac{1}{2}\left[\alpha\beta\alpha\beta - \alpha\beta\beta\alpha - \beta\alpha\alpha\beta + \beta\alpha\beta\alpha\right] \qquad \text{... (13.225)}$$

The corresponding bond eigenfunction (or structure eigenfunction) is

$$\psi_I = \frac{1}{2}\left[\phi_2 - \phi_3 - \phi_4 + \phi_5\right] \qquad \text{... (13.226)}$$

Similarly for the structure II,

$$\chi_{AD,BC} = \frac{1}{2}\left[\alpha\alpha\beta\beta - \alpha\beta\alpha\beta - \beta\alpha\beta\alpha + \beta\beta\alpha\alpha\right] \qquad \text{... (13.227)}$$

and

$$\psi_{II} = \frac{1}{2}\left[\phi_1 - \phi_2 - \phi_5 + \phi_6\right] \qquad \text{... (13.228)}$$

The total wave function Ψ of the molecule is a resonance hybrid (linear combination) of ψ_I and ψ_{II},

$$\Psi = a_1\,\psi_I + a_2\,\psi_{II} \qquad \text{... (13.229)}$$

Variation treatment leads to the following two secular equations

$$a_1(H_{II} - ES_{II}) + a_2(H_{I\,II} - ES_{I\,II}) = 0 \qquad \text{... (13.230)}$$

$$a_1(H_{II\,I} - ES_{II\,I}) + a_2(H_{II\,II} - ES_{II\,II}) = 0$$

and a 2 × 2 secular determinant

$$\begin{vmatrix} H_{I\,I} - ES_{I\,I} & H_{I\,II} - ES_{I\,II} \\ H_{II\,I} - ES_{II\,I} & H_{II\,II} - ES_{II\,II} \end{vmatrix} = 0 \qquad \text{... (13.231)}$$

where the matrix elements are defined as

$$H_{I\,I} = \int \psi_I\,\hat{H}\,\psi_I\,d\tau = \frac{1}{4}\int(\phi_2 - \phi_3 - \phi_4 + \phi_5)\,\hat{H}\,(\phi_2 - \phi_3 - \phi_4 + \phi_5)\,d\tau$$

$$H_{II\,II} = \int \psi_{II}\,\hat{H}\,\psi_{II}\,d\tau = \frac{1}{4}\int(\phi_1 - \phi_2 - \phi_5 + \phi_6)\,\hat{H}\,(\phi_1 - \phi_2 - \phi_5 + \phi_6)\,d\tau$$

$$H_{I\,II} = \int \psi_I\,\hat{H}\,\psi_{II}\,d\tau = \frac{1}{4}\int(\phi_2 - \phi_3 - \phi_4 + \phi_5)\,\hat{H}\,(\phi_1 - \phi_2 - \phi_5 + \phi_6)\,d\tau$$

Each of these integrals, on expansion, is a sum of 16 integrals, or matrix elements of $\hat{H}$, of the type $\int \phi_i \, \hat{H} \, \phi_j \, d\tau$ where i and j can be 1, 2, 3, ..., 6.

$$S_{I\,I} = \int \psi_I \cdot \psi_I \, d\tau = \frac{1}{4} \int (\phi_2 - \phi_3 - \phi_4 + \phi_5)^2 \, d\tau$$

$$S_{II\,II} = \frac{1}{4} \int (\phi_1 - \phi_2 - \phi_5 + \phi_6)^2 \, d\tau$$

and

$$S_{I\,II} = S_{II\,I} = \frac{1}{4} \int (\phi_2 - \phi_3 - \phi_4 + \phi_5)(\phi_1 - \phi_2 - \phi_5 + \phi_6) \, d\tau$$

Evaluating the Matrix Elements: When written in full, a matrix element H_{12}, for example, is

$$H_{12} = \int \phi_1 \, \hat{H} \, \phi_2 \, d\tau = \frac{1}{4!} \int \Sigma (-1)^p \, \hat{P} \, A \, B \, \bar{C} \, \bar{D} \, \hat{H} \, \Sigma (-1)^p \, \hat{P} \, A \, \bar{B} \, C \, \bar{D} \, d\tau \qquad \text{... (13.232)}$$

Each of the summations (one on left and the other on right of $\hat{H}$) expands into 4 ! = 24 terms. However, we can replace the summation on the left by one single term, say ABCD and then multiply by 24, such that

$$H_{12} = \frac{1}{4!} \times 24 \int A \, B \, \bar{C} \, \bar{D} \, \hat{H} \, \Sigma (-1)^p \, \hat{P} \, A \, \bar{B} \, C \, \bar{D} \, d\tau$$

Even this integral will expand into 24 integral terms but many of them will vanish due to spin orthogonality; only those will survive in which the spins of each electron on either side match. This reduces H_{12} to

$$\begin{aligned} H_{12} = &- \int A(1) \, B(2) \, \bar{C}(3) \, \bar{D}(4) \, \hat{H} \, A(1) \, \bar{B}(3) \, C(2) \, \bar{D}(4) \, d\tau \\ &+ \int A(1) \, B(2) \, \bar{C}(3) \, \bar{D}(4) \, \hat{H} \, A(1) \, \bar{B}(4) \, C(2) \, \bar{D}(3) \, d\tau \\ &+ \int A(1) \, B(2) \, \bar{C}(3) \, \bar{D}(4) \, \hat{H} \, A(2) \, \bar{B}(3) \, C(1) \, \bar{D}(4) \, d\tau \\ &- \int A(1) \, B(2) \, \bar{C}(3) \, \bar{D}(4) \, \hat{H} \, A(2) \, \bar{B}(4) \, C(1) \, \bar{D}(3) \, d\tau \end{aligned} \qquad \text{... (13.233)}$$

Except the first, all are multiple exchange integrals which are assumed negligible compared to the former, then

$$\begin{aligned} H_{12} &= - \int A(1) \, B(2) \, \bar{C}(3) \, \bar{D}(4) \, \hat{H} \, A(1) \, \bar{B}(3) \, C(2) \, \bar{D}(4) \, d\tau \\ &= - \int A(1) \, B(2) \, \bar{C}(3) \, \bar{D}(4) \, \hat{H} \, A(1) \, C(2) \, \bar{B}(3) \, \bar{D}(4) \, d\tau \\ &= - \int ABCD \, \hat{H} \, ACBD \, d\tau \, . \int (\alpha\alpha\beta\beta)(\alpha\alpha\beta\beta) \, ds \\ &= - \int ABCD \, \hat{H} \, ACBD \, d\tau \end{aligned}$$

which involves an exchange of electrons between orbitals B and C only, and which, under convention, is abbreviated to

$$H_{12} = -(BC) \qquad \ldots (13.234)$$

The matrix elements like H_{ii} involve both exchange and coulomb integrals (Q); for example,

$$H_{11} = \int A(1)\,B(2)\,\bar{C}(3)\,\bar{D}(4)\,\hat{H}\,\Sigma(-1)^p\,\hat{P}\,A(1)\,B(2)\,\bar{C}(3)\,\bar{D}(4)\,d\tau$$

$$= \int ABCD\,\hat{H}\,ABCD\,d\tau - \int ABCD\,\hat{H}\,ABDC\,d\tau - \int ABCD\,\hat{H}\,BACD\,d\tau$$

$$= Q - (CD) - (AB) \qquad \ldots (13.235)$$

and so on for other matrix elements H_{ij}. Further approximation, in which:

(*i*) exchange integrals involving adjacent C atoms are all equal and

(*ii*) exchange integrals involving nonadjacent atoms are all zero, gives

$$(AB) = (AC) = (CD) = a \text{ (say), and}$$

$$(BC) = (BD) = (AD) = 0.$$

This makes $H_{I\,I} = Q + \frac{3}{2}\alpha$, $H_{II\,II} = Q$ and $H_{I\,II} = \frac{1}{2}Q + \frac{3}{2}\alpha$. Since Slater functions are all normalised. $S_{II} = S_{II\,II} = 1$; but $S_{I\,II} = \frac{1}{2}$ because of spin orthonormality. Thus, the secular determinant Equation (13.231) for the π-electron is

$$\begin{vmatrix} Q + \frac{3}{2}\alpha - E & \frac{1}{2}Q + \frac{3}{2}\alpha - \frac{1}{2}E \\ \frac{1}{2}Q + \frac{3}{2}\alpha - \frac{1}{2}E & Q - E \end{vmatrix} = 0 \qquad \ldots (13.236)$$

The solutions are,

$$E_1 = Q + \sqrt{3}\,\alpha = Q + 1.732\,\alpha \qquad \ldots (13.237)$$

$$E_2 = Q - \sqrt{3}\,\alpha = Q - 1.732\,\alpha \qquad \ldots (13.238)$$

Since α is negative representing attraction E_1 is lower than E_2. Thus, there are two states of butadiene which correspond to two different sets of values of a_1 and a_2 in Equation (13.229), representing different contributions of structures (I) and (II).

The resonance stabilisation (energy)

$$= E_1 - H_{I\,I}$$

$$= (Q + 1.732\,\alpha) - \left(Q + \frac{3}{2}\alpha\right) = 0.232\,\alpha.$$

To find the values of a_1 and a_2, substitute the values of $E_1 = Q + \sqrt{3}\,\alpha$ in one of the secular equations.

$$a_1(H_{11} - E_1) + a_2(H_{I\,II} - E_I S_{I\,II}) = 0$$

or $$a_1\left[\left(Q+\frac{3}{2}\alpha\right)-\left(Q+\sqrt{3}\,\alpha\right)\right\}+a_2\left[\left(\frac{Q}{2}+\frac{3}{2}\alpha\right)-\left(Q+\sqrt{3}\,\alpha\right)\frac{1}{2}\right]=0$$

or $a_1\,[-0.23\,\alpha]+a_2\,[0.63\,\alpha]=0$

or $$a_1=\frac{0.63}{0.23}\,a_2$$

By normalisation,

$$a_1^2+a_2^2+2a_1\,a_2\,S_{\mathrm{I\,II}}=1$$

Since $$S_{\mathrm{I\,II}}=\frac{1}{2},$$

$$\left(\frac{0.63}{0.23}\,a_2\right)^2+a_2^2+\left(\frac{0.63}{0.23}\right)a_2^2=1$$

or $$a_2^2=0.089 \text{ and } a_2=0.298;\text{ then } a_1=0.816 \text{ and } a_1^2=0.667.$$

To check up we see that

$$a_1^2+a_2^2+2a_1\,a_2\,S=0.667+0.089+0.243=0.99\approx 1$$

The ground state singlet (S = 0) wave function of butadiene is, therefore

$$^1\Psi_1=0.816\,\psi_{\mathrm{I}}+0.298\,\psi_{\mathrm{II}} \qquad \text{... (13.239)}$$

Use of the other eigenvalue $E_2 = Q - \sqrt{3}\,\alpha$ which corresponds to the excited state of the molecule and the second secular equation

$$a_1\left(\frac{1}{2}Q+\frac{3}{2}\alpha-\frac{1}{2}E_2\right)+a_2\left(Q-E_2\right)=0$$

leads to the excited state singlet (S = 0) wave function

$$^1\Psi_2=0.816\,\psi_{\mathrm{I}}-1.115\,\psi_{\mathrm{II}} \qquad \text{... (13.240)}$$

There are other states of the molecule arising from other spin configurations. Three of them are triplets (S = 1) and one is quintet (S = 2). The six energy levels may be arranged in increasing order as given in Fig. 13.26

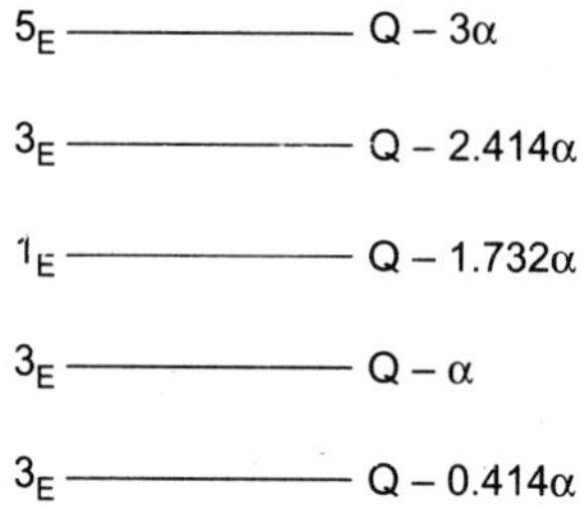

Fig. 13.26 *Energy levels of butadiene*

13.8 SHAPE OF MOLECULES

The HLSP theory has been applied to many other chemical problems, for example, we can say why H_2O is angular, CH_4 is tetrahedral, C_2H_4 is planar, etc. The localised covalent bonds, and the criterion of maximum overlap of atomic orbitals can account for the bond directions; hence, the theory is also known as theory of "directed bonds". For understanding this one has to look at the directional characteristic of the orbitals used for bonding—the atomic orbitals. For bond directions in a molecule only the angular parts of the orbitals are of significance. For example, an *s*-orbital which has no angular part can overlap with another *s*-orbital in any direction, but it can overlap with a *p*-orbital only when it approaches along the axis of the latter. So we say that *p*-orbitals have directional property while *s*-orbitals have not.

To understand the geometry of a molecule in simplest terms one has to look at the atomic orbitals of the central atom and see their orientations in space. For bond formation, the atoms to be bonded must approach each other along directions that lead to maximum overlap of orbitals in each bond. For example, in oxygen atom, with electronic configuration

$$1s^2\, 2s^2\, 2p_x^2\, 2p_y\, 2p_z,$$

the overlap and pairing of $2p_y$ orbital of O atom with $1s$ orbital of one H atom, and of $2p_z$ with $1s$ of another H atom will lead to two O—H bonds which may be predicted to form an angle of 90° since the two *p*-orbitals are mutually perpendicular to each other. Similarly in NH_3, N atom ($1s^2\, 2s^2\, 2p_x\, 2p_y\, 2p_z$) could form three mutually perpendicular N—H bonds.

However, the bond angles in H_2O and NH_3 are not 90° but 104.5° and 107° respectively. The situation is irreconcilable in the case of C ($1s^2\, 2s^2\, 2p_x\, 2p_z$) which forms CH_4 where not only the bond angles are 109° (tetrahedral) but also the four C—H bonds are equivalent.

13.8.1 Principle of Hybridisation

An explanation for these experimental facts can be provided if we assume that instead of the pure $2p$ orbitals of the central atom a combination of $2s$ and $2p$ orbitals is involved in overlap and bond formation. Such a linear combination of the orbitals of the same atom is called "hybridisation". The combination of n atomic orbitals generates n hybrid orbitals of an atom. It can be shown that the hybrid orbitals have better directional properties and can form stronger bonds. We explain it with respect to hybrid orbitals of sp, sp^2 and sp^3 types, *i.e.*, those formed by combination of an *s*-orbital with one, two and three *p*-orbitals, respectively. The important consideration is that the hybrid orbitals are not only orthogonal but also equivalent, which means that a symmetry operation of the molecule can transform one hybrid orbital into another. The hybrid orbitals can form equivalent bonds.

13.8.1.1 s-p Hybridisation

The combination of a *s*- and *p*-orbital giving two hybrid orbitals ψ_1 and ψ_2, may be expressed as

$$\psi_1 = a_1 s + b_1 p$$

$$\psi_2 = a_2 s + b_2 p \qquad \text{...(13.241)}$$

The values of the linear combination coefficients a_1, b_1, a_2 and b_2 may be determined by the following considerations: (*i*) ψ_1 and ψ_2 are normalised, (*ii*) ψ_1 and ψ_2 are orthogonal, and (*iii*) ψ_1 and ψ_2 are equivalent

By (*i*) $$a_1^2 + b_1^2 = 1 \quad \text{... (13.242)}$$

and $$a_2^2 + b_2^2 = 1 \quad \text{... (13.243)}$$

and by (*ii*), $$a_1 a_2 + b_1 b_2 = 0 \quad \text{... (13.244)}$$

Since the *s*-atomic orbital is spherically symmetrical and the two hybrid orbitals ψ_1 and ψ_2 are equivalent, the share of *s* functions is equal in both ψ_1 and ψ_2, *i.e.*,

$$a_1^2 = a_2^2 = \frac{1}{2}, \text{ or } a_1 = a_2 = \frac{1}{\sqrt{2}}$$

Then from Equation (13.242)

$$b_1^2 = \frac{1}{2} \text{ or } b_1 = \frac{1}{\sqrt{2}},$$

so that $$\psi_1 = \frac{1}{\sqrt{2}}(s + p) \quad \text{... (13.245)}$$

Further, from Equation (13.244)

$$\frac{1}{2} + \frac{1}{\sqrt{2}} b_2 = 0, \text{ or } b_2 = -\frac{1}{\sqrt{2}}$$

Therefore, $$\psi_2 = \frac{1}{\sqrt{2}}(s - p) \quad \text{... (13.246)}$$

The directional characteristic of ψ_1 and ψ_2 can be determined as follows:

Using the normalised angular functions P (θ) F (φ) for 2*s* and 2*p* orbitals, and choosing $2p_z$, for example, as the 2*p* orbital, we get the two *sp* hybrid orbitals as,

$$\psi_1 = \frac{1}{\sqrt{2}}\left[\frac{1}{\sqrt{4\pi}} + \sqrt{\frac{3}{4\pi}} \cos\theta\right]$$

and $$\psi_2 = \frac{1}{\sqrt{2}}\left(\frac{1}{\sqrt{4\pi}} - \sqrt{\frac{3}{4\pi}} \cos\theta\right)$$

Taking out the factor $\frac{1}{\sqrt{4\pi}}$, we get the functions which determine the directions of the two hybrid orbitals.

$$f_1 = \frac{1}{\sqrt{2}}\left(1 + \sqrt{3}\cos\theta\right)$$

and $$f_2 = \frac{1}{\sqrt{2}}\left(1 - \sqrt{3}\cos\theta\right) \quad \text{... (13.247)}$$

Functions f_1 and f_2 are maximum for $\theta = 0$ (*i.e.*, in the $+z$-direction) and $\theta = \pi$ (*i.e.*, in the $-z$-direction), respectively. The value of the maximum in either case in $\frac{1+\sqrt{3}}{\sqrt{2}} = 1.932$, which is greater than that for the pure 2*s* orbital ($f = 1$) or a 2*p* orbital ($f = \sqrt{3} = 1.732$). While the simple p_z orbital is directed along both $+z$ and $-z$-directions, an *sp* hybrid orbital is directed towards only either $+z$ or $-z$, the angle between the two being 180°. The polar plots of f_1 and f_2 for various values of θ are shown in Fig. 13.27.

The *sp* hybrid orbitals may be invoked to account for the linear structure of acetylene (Fig. 13.28).

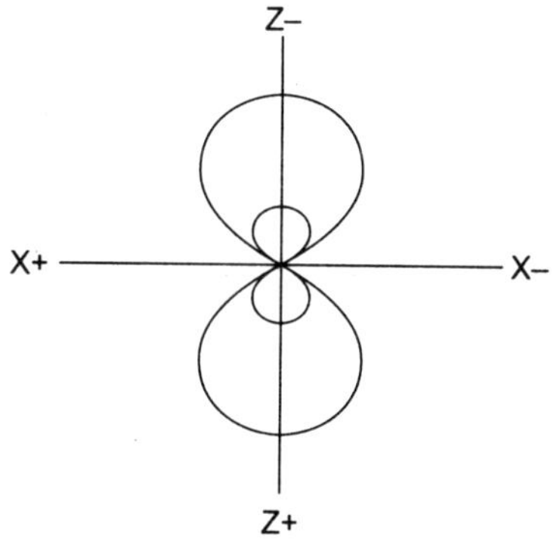

Fig. 13.27 *Polar plots of sp hybrid orbitals*

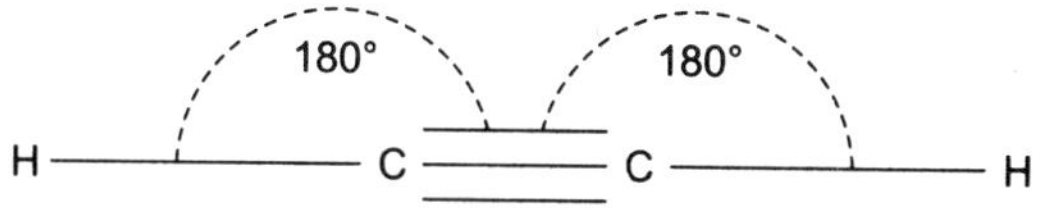

Fig. 13.28 *Shape of acetylene*

13.8.1.2 The sp^2 Hybridisation

The three sp^2 hybrid orbitals formed by combination of an *s*-orbital with two *p*-orbitals are expressed as,

$$\psi_i = a_i s + b_i p_x + c_i p_y \qquad \text{... (13.248)}$$

where $\qquad i = 1, 2, 3$

The coefficients a_i, b_i and c_i ($i = 1, 2, 3$) can be determined as follows:

Since the three hybrids are equivalent, the single *s*-orbital is considered to divide itself equally among them, *i.e.*,

$$a_1^2 = a_2^2 = a_3^2 = \frac{1}{3} \text{ or } a_1 = a_2 = a_3 = \frac{1}{\sqrt{3}}$$

One of the three hybrids, say ψ_1, may be assigned any direction; let it be the x-axis. Then, there will be no contribution from p_y, *i.e.*, $c_1 = 0$. The normalisation condition requires that

$$a_1^2 + b_1^2 + c_1^2 = 1 \text{ or } a_1^2 + b_1^2 = 1$$

or $$\frac{1}{3} + b_1^2 = 1 \text{ or } b_1 = \sqrt{\frac{2}{3}}$$

Thus, $$\psi_1 = \frac{1}{\sqrt{3}} s + \sqrt{\frac{2}{3}} p_x \quad \text{... (13.249)}$$

By orthogonality of ψ_1 and ψ_2,

$$a_1 a_2 + b_1 b_2 + c_1 c_2 = 0$$

or $$\frac{1}{3} + \sqrt{\frac{2}{3}} b_2 = 0, \text{ or } b_2 = -\frac{1}{\sqrt{6}}$$

and by normalisation of ψ_2

$$a_2^2 + b_2^2 + c_2^2 = 1$$

or $$\frac{1}{3} + \frac{1}{6} + c_2^2 = 1, \text{ or } c_2 = \frac{1}{\sqrt{2}}$$

Thus, $$\psi_2 = \frac{1}{\sqrt{3}} s - \frac{1}{\sqrt{6}} p_x + \frac{1}{\sqrt{2}} p_y \quad \text{... (13.250)}$$

Similarly, by orthogonality of ψ_1 and ψ_3,

$$a_1 a_3 + b_1 b_3 + c_1 c_3 = 0$$

and by orthogonality of ψ_2 and ψ_3,

$$a_2 a_3 + b_2 b_3 + c_2 c_3 = 0$$

or $$\frac{1}{3} + \frac{1}{6} + \frac{1}{\sqrt{2}} c_3 = 0 \text{ or, } c_3 = -\frac{1}{\sqrt{2}}$$

Thus, $$\psi_3 = \frac{1}{\sqrt{3}} s - \frac{1}{\sqrt{6}} p_x - \frac{1}{\sqrt{2}} p_y \quad \text{... (13.251)}$$

Substituting the angular parts of the 2s, 2p_x and p_y atomic orbitals and taking out the common factor $\frac{1}{\sqrt{4\pi}}$ we obtain the three functions defining the directional properties of the hybrid orbitals

$$f_1 = \frac{1}{\sqrt{3}} + \sqrt{2} \sin\theta \cos\varphi \quad \text{... (13.252)}$$

$$f_2 = \frac{1}{\sqrt{3}} - \frac{1}{\sqrt{2}} \sin\theta \cos\varphi + \sqrt{\frac{3}{2}} \sin\theta \sin\varphi \quad \text{... (13.253)}$$

$$f_3 = \frac{1}{\sqrt{3}} - \frac{1}{\sqrt{2}} \sin\theta \cos\varphi - \sqrt{\frac{3}{2}} \sin\theta \sin\varphi \quad \text{... (13.254)}$$

If two of the hybridisation functions f_1 and f_2 indicate directions in the xy-plane, for which $\theta = 90°$ or $\sin\theta = 1$ the Equations (13.252) and (13.253)

$$f_1 = \frac{1}{\sqrt{3}} + \sqrt{2}\cos\varphi \qquad \text{... (13.255)}$$

$$f_2 = \frac{1}{\sqrt{3}} - \frac{1}{\sqrt{2}}\cos\varphi + \sqrt{\frac{3}{2}}\sin\varphi \qquad \text{... (13.256)}$$

The maximum value of f_1 will be,

$$f_1 = \frac{1}{\sqrt{3}} + \sqrt{2} = 1.992$$

which points towards x-axis ($\varphi = 0$). The direction for the f_2 can be determined as follows:

Let $\cos\varphi = x$, then

$$f_2 = \frac{1}{\sqrt{3}} - \frac{1}{\sqrt{2}}x + \sqrt{\frac{3}{2}}\left(1 - x^2\right)^{1/2}$$

Maximum f_2 can be found by differentiating f_2 with respect to x and equating it to zero. This leads to the equation,

$$-\frac{1}{\sqrt{2}} - \sqrt{\frac{3}{2}}\,x\left(1 - x^2\right)^{-1/2} = 0$$

or
$$\sqrt{\frac{3}{2}} \cdot \frac{\cos\varphi}{\sin\varphi} = -\frac{1}{\sqrt{2}}$$

or
$$\tan\varphi = -\sqrt{3}\text{, or } \varphi = 120°$$

The value of the maximum will be

$$f_2 = \frac{1}{\sqrt{3}} - \frac{1}{\sqrt{2}} \times \left(-\frac{1}{2}\right) + \sqrt{\frac{3}{2}} \cdot \frac{\sqrt{3}}{2}$$

$$= \frac{1}{\sqrt{3}} + \frac{1}{2\sqrt{2}} + \frac{3}{2\sqrt{2}} = 1.992$$

Thus, a hybrid f_2 which is equivalent to f_1 is found to be at an angle of 120° with respect to the latter.

It is easy to see that the same value, *i.e.*, 1992, is obtained for f_3 when $\theta = 90°$ and $\varphi = 240$. We, thus, have three equivalent sp^2 hybrid orbitals that form angles of 120° with each other in the xy-plane.

The symmetry equivalence of the three hybrids follows directly from the diagram. It can also be demonstrated mathematically as follows. Treating, for example, the x-axis as a C_2 axis of rotation,

$$C_2\,\psi_2 = C_2\left(\frac{1}{\sqrt{3}}s - \frac{1}{\sqrt{6}}p_x + \frac{1}{\sqrt{2}}p_y\right)$$

$$= \frac{1}{\sqrt{3}} s - \frac{1}{\sqrt{6}} p_x - \frac{1}{\sqrt{2}} p_y = \psi_3$$

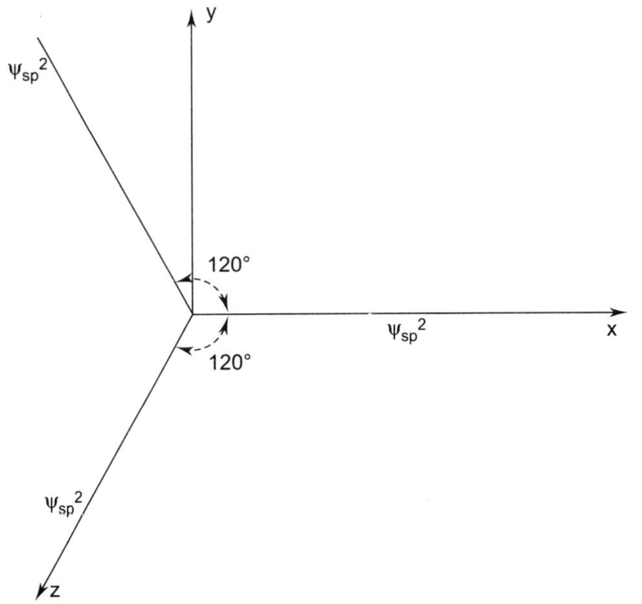

Fig. 13.29 *Orientation of the three sp^2 hybrid orbitals in xy-plane*

Similarly, $$C_3^1\, \psi_1 = C_3^1 \left(\frac{1}{\sqrt{3}} s + \sqrt{\frac{2}{3}}\, p_x \right)$$

$$= \frac{1}{\sqrt{3}} s + \sqrt{\frac{2}{3}} \left(\cos 120\, p_x + \sin 120\, p_y \right)$$

$$= \frac{1}{\sqrt{3}} s - \frac{1}{\sqrt{6}} p_x + \frac{1}{\sqrt{2}} p_y = \psi_2.$$

Example of such a hybridisation may be found in BF_3, which has been found experimentally to have a planar structure with FBF angle = 120°. The sp^2 hybrids are also used to describe the carbon atoms in olefinic or aromatic compounds, which are planar and where bond angles are 120°. With sp^2 hybridisation, there remains a pure *p*-orbitals on each C atom, These *p*-orbitals combine to form π bond in the molecule.

13.8.1.3 sp^3 Hybridisation

Now consider the linear combination (hybridisation) of an *s*-orbital and all the three *p*-orbitals having the same value of the principal quantum number *n* belonging to the same atom. This may be written in a general form as

$$\psi_i \left(\psi_{sp^3} \right) = a_i\, s + b_i\, p_x + c_i\, p_y + d_i\, p_z \qquad \text{... (13.257)}$$

where $i = 1, 2, 3$ or 4.

Applying the condition of normalisation and orthogonality, *i.e.*,

$$\int \psi_i^2 \, d\tau = 1 \text{ and } \int \psi_i \, \psi_k \, d\tau = 0,$$

we obtain, $a_i^2 + b_i^2 + c_i^2 + d_i^2 = 1$ ... (13.258)

and $a_i a_k + b_i b_k + c_i c_k + d_i d_k = 0$ ... (13.259)

where i and k may be 1, 2, 3 or 4 but $i \neq k$.

Since the four hybrid orbitals that are formed equivalent, the single *s*-orbital divides equally among the four hybrids so that

$$a_1^2 = a_2^2 = a_3^2 = a_4^2 = \frac{1}{4}$$

or, $$a_1 = a_2 = a_3 = a_4 = \frac{1}{2}$$

Then the conditions Equations (13.258) and (13.259) lead to,

$$b_i^2 + c_i^2 + d_i^2 = \frac{3}{4} \quad \text{... (13.260)}$$

$$b_i b_k + c_i c_k + d_i d_k = -\frac{1}{4} \quad \text{... (13.261)}$$

respectively.

The first of the four hybrids can be chosen arbitrarily to lie in any direction; let it be along the *x*-axis. Along this direction, $c_1 = d_1 = 0$, so that $b_1 = \frac{\sqrt{3}}{2}$ [from Equation (13.260)].

Thus, $$\psi_1 = \frac{1}{2} s + \frac{\sqrt{3}}{2} p_x \quad \text{... (13.262)}$$

With respect to ψ_1, the directions of ψ_2, ψ_3 and ψ_4 have to be determined. Let the plane constituted by the axes of ψ_1 and ψ_2 be the *xz*-plane. The coefficients of ψ_2 are determined as follows. a_3 is already known to be $\frac{1}{2}$. Since along the *xy* plane, the orbital p_y has no contribution, $c_2 = 0$ and since $d_1 = 0$, $b_2 = -\frac{1}{2\sqrt{3}}$ by Equation (13.261) and $d_2 = \sqrt{\frac{2}{3}}$ by Equation (13.260).

Thus, $$\psi_2 = \frac{1}{2} s - \frac{1}{2\sqrt{3}} p_x + \sqrt{\frac{2}{3}} p_z \quad \text{... (13.263)}$$

In view of the orthogonality of ψ_1 and ψ_3, Equation (13.262) and (13.259) leads to

$$b_3 = -\frac{1}{2\sqrt{3}}$$

(since c_1 and d_1 are zero), and because of orthogonality of ψ_2 and ψ_3,

$$d_3 = -\frac{1}{\sqrt{6}}\left(c_2 = 0\right),$$

Then Equation (13.260) leads to

$$c_3 = \frac{1}{\sqrt{2}}$$

Thus,

$$\psi_3 = \frac{1}{2}s - \frac{1}{2\sqrt{3}}p_x + \frac{1}{\sqrt{2}}p_y - \frac{1}{\sqrt{6}}p_z \quad \text{... (13.264)}$$

Similarly, by the orthogonality relations of ψ_1 and ψ_4, ψ_2 and ψ_4 the coefficients ψ_3 and ψ_4, can be derived as

$$b_4 = -\frac{1}{2\sqrt{3}},\ d_4 = -\frac{1}{\sqrt{6}} \text{ and } c_4 = -\frac{1}{\sqrt{2}}$$

so that

$$\psi_4 = \frac{1}{2}s - \frac{1}{2\sqrt{3}}p_x - \frac{1}{\sqrt{2}}p_y - \frac{1}{\sqrt{6}}p_z \quad \text{... (13.265)}$$

We have thus found the analytical expression for the four hybrid orbitals ψ_1 to ψ_4. It must be pointed out, however, that these are not unique. If we consider the ψ_1 to lie along ψ or the z-axis, the expressions will change. But what remain unaltered are the relative directions and the maximum value of the ψ_1. These may be derived as follows:

The maximum value of ψ_1 may be obtained by substituting the maximum values of the angular parts of s and p_x in Equation (13.262)

$$\psi_1 = \frac{1}{2}\cdot\frac{1}{\sqrt{4\pi}} + \frac{\sqrt{3}}{2}\sqrt{\frac{3}{4\pi}}\sin\theta\cos\varphi \quad \text{(ignoring the radial parts)}$$

$$= \frac{1}{\sqrt{4\pi}}\left[\frac{1}{2} + \frac{3}{2}\sin\theta\cos\varphi\right]$$

or, dividing both sides by $\frac{1}{\sqrt{4\pi}}$, we have

$$f_1 = \frac{1}{2} + \frac{3}{2}\sin\theta\cos\varphi \quad \text{... (13.266)}$$

Along x-axis, $\varphi = 0$ and $\theta = 90°$, so that $f_1 = 2.0$, which is the maximum value.

With respect to ψ_1 along the x-axis, the direction of ψ_2 which lies in the xz-plane can be derived as follows:

$$\psi_2 = \frac{1}{2}s - \frac{1}{2\sqrt{3}}p_x + \sqrt{\frac{2}{3}}p_z$$

or in terms of the function f,

$$f_2 = \frac{1}{2} - \frac{1}{2\sqrt{3}} \sqrt{3} \sin\theta \cos\varphi + \sqrt{\frac{2}{3}} \sqrt{3} \cos\theta$$

In the *xz*-plane, $\varphi = 0$ or 180°. The value $\varphi = 0$ determines the positive lobe of the p_x orbital, so $\varphi = 180°$ will determine its negative lobe which contributes to ψ_2. Then

$$f_2 = \frac{1}{2} + \frac{1}{2} \sin\theta + \sqrt{2} \cos\theta \quad \text{... (13.267)}$$

Differentiating Equation (13.272) with respect of θ and equating to zero, we get

$$\frac{df_2}{d\theta} = \frac{1}{2} \cos\theta - \sqrt{2} \sin\theta = 0$$

or $$\tan\theta = \frac{1}{2\sqrt{2}} \text{ or } \theta = 19°\,28' \quad \text{(from the mathematical tables)}$$

Therefore, the direction of the orbital ψ_2 lying in the *xz*-plane is such that it makes an angle of 19° 28′ with the *z*-axis or an angle of 90 + 19° 28′ = 109° 28′ with ψ_1. Using this value of θ in Equation (13.272), we get

$$f_2 = \frac{1}{2} + \frac{1}{2} \sin 19°\,28' + \sqrt{2} \cos 19°\,28'$$

$$= \frac{1}{2} + \frac{1}{2} \times \frac{1}{3} + \sqrt{2}\sqrt{\frac{8}{9}} = 2.0$$

Similarly, we can show that ψ_3 and ψ_4 too make angles of 109° 28′ with ψ_1 and ψ_2 and with each other, and that all the four hybrid orbitals have the same maximum value (2.0). This angle corresponds to the tetrahedral angle. Accordingly, sp^3 hybridisation leads to four equivalent tetrahedrally oriented orbitals. If an atom uses sp^3 hybridised orbitals for forming bonds, these bonds will be directed towards the vertices of a tetrahedron with the atom at its centre. The typical example of tetrahedral bonding is CH_4.

13.8.1.4 Hybridisation in H_2O

The concept of hybridisation can be generalised to explain the existence of bond angles other than 180°, 120° and 109°. The two conditions common to all hybridisation schemes are: (*i*) the hybrid orbitals are mutually orthogonal, and (*ii*) the hybrid orbitals pointing along the similar bond directions are equivalent.

Consider, for example, the formation of hybrid orbitals in H_2O. The H—O—H bond angle may be predicted by finding the directions in which the two equivalent and mutually orthogonal hybrids have maximum strengths. For convenience, let one of the hybrids (ψ_1) lie along the *z*-axis and the other (ψ_2) in the *xz*-plane (the molecular plane) at an angle θ, which is also the bond angle, (see Fig. 13.30). Then,

$$\psi_1 = as + b_1 p_z$$

$$\psi_2 = as + b_2 p_z + c_2 p_x \quad \text{... (13.268)}$$

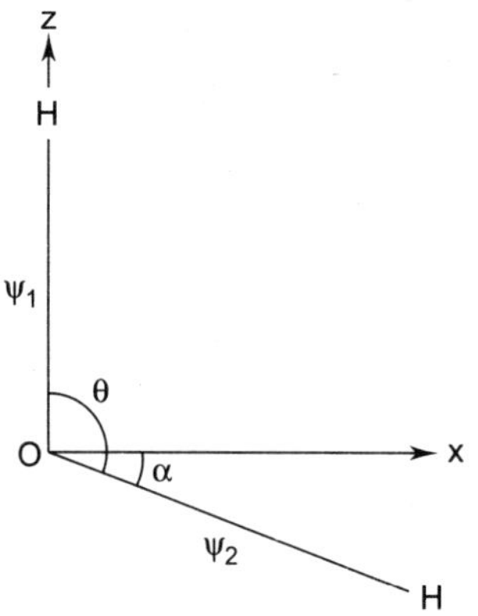

Fig. 13.30 *Hybridisation and bond angle in H_2O*

Each function is normalised; therefore,

$$a^2 + b_1^2 = 1,$$

and $$a^2 + b_2^2 + c_2^2 = 1$$

The two functions are mutually orthogonal; therefore

$$\int \psi_1 \psi_2 \, d\tau = \int (as + b_1 p_z)(as + b_2 p_z + c_2 p_x) \, d\tau = 0$$

or $$a^2 + b_1 b_2 = 0 \qquad \text{... (13.269)}$$

This leads to,

$$b_1 = \sqrt{1 - a^2}$$

$$b_2 = -\frac{a^2}{\sqrt{1 - a^2}}$$

and $$c_2 = \frac{\sqrt{1 - 2a^2}}{\sqrt{1 - a^2}}$$

The direction of the maximum value of ψ_2 can be determined as follows:

$$\psi_2 = a \,.\, R(r) + b_2 R(r) \cos\theta + c_2 R(r) \sin\theta \cos\varphi$$

or $$f_2 = \frac{\psi_2}{R(r)} = \{a + b_2 \cos\theta + c_2 \sin\theta \cos\varphi\}$$

Setting $$\frac{df_2}{d\theta} = -b_2 \sin\theta + c_2 \cos\theta = 0 \qquad (\because \cos\varphi = 1 \text{ along } x\text{-axis})$$

we get, $$\frac{b_2}{c_2} = \frac{\cos\theta}{\sin\theta} = \frac{\cos\theta}{\sin(90^\circ + \alpha)} = \frac{\cos\theta}{\cos\alpha} \text{ (see Fig. 13.30)}$$

That is, b_2 and c_2 are proportional to the cosines of θ and α, respectively, the angles which the hybrid ψ_2 make with z- and x-axes, respectively, in the xz-plane. This gives directly the bond angle θ as,

$$\cos\theta = b_2 = -\frac{a^2}{\sqrt{1-a^2}}$$

Now, $$\psi_1 = as + (1-a^2)^{1/2} p_z \quad \text{... (13.270)}$$

This means that the hybrid orbital ψ_1 (and hence also ψ_2 as they are equivalent) has the s-character given by a^2 and p-character given by $1 - a^2$. As the angle changes from 90° to 180°, the amount of s character (a^2) in hybrid increases from 0 (pure p-orbitals, 90° bond angle) to $\frac{1}{2}$ (sp hybrid, 180° bond angle). For the bond angle of 104.45°, as experimentally observed for H_2O, $a^2 = 0.20$, which means 20% s-character.

The two hybrid orbitals of O atom used for O—H bonding are accordingly,

$$\psi_1 = 0.45s + 0.89\, p_z$$

$$\psi_2 = 0.45s + 0.22\, p_z + 0.86\, p_z \quad \text{... (13.271)}$$

The hybrid orbitals of N in NH_3 can be constructed in a likewise manner. Equation (13.271) does not represent the sp^3 hybrid orbitals though from the preceding discussions it follows clearly that the sp^3 hybrid orbitals form strongest bonds and tetrahedral molecules are the most stable ones. However, stability and shapes of molecules are determined not only by the bond strengths but also by the electrostatic repulsion between the electron pairs. Thus, the repulsion between electron pairs in BeH_2 is minimum when the molecule is linear; for the same reason BF_3 is trigonal planar and CH_4 is tetrahedral. In molecules having lone pair(s) of electrons as in H_2O, NH_3, etc., the lone pairs tend to remain in 2s-orbital as it has lower energy than 2p. Strongest bonds are possible with sp^3 hybrid orbitals.

13.8.1.5 Hybridisation Involving d-Orbitals

We have so far cited examples in which only s-and p-orbitals participate in hybridisation. This satisfactorily explains the geometry of molecules with elements in the first row of periodic table (*e.g.*, O, N, C, B, etc.) as the central atom. For atoms with $n > 3$, d and f orbitals also become important, especially in the case of transition metal complexes. One nd, one $(n + 1)$ s and two $(n + 1)$ p orbitals may combine to form four dsp^2 hybrid orbitals lying in a plane and directed towards the four corners of a square in the xy-plane. The set of four dsp^2 hybrids may be given as

$$\psi_1 = \frac{1}{2}s + \frac{1}{\sqrt{2}}p_x + \frac{1}{2}d_{xy}$$

$$\psi_2 = \frac{1}{2}s - \frac{1}{\sqrt{2}}p_x + \frac{1}{2}d_{xy}$$

$$\psi_3 = \frac{1}{2}s + \frac{1}{\sqrt{2}}p_y - \frac{1}{2}d_{xy}$$

$$\psi_4 = \frac{1}{2}s - \frac{1}{\sqrt{2}}p_y - \frac{1}{2}d_{xy} \quad \text{... (13.272)}$$

Examples of dsp^2 hybridisation are to be found in 4-coordinated square-planar complexes of Cu (II), Ni (II), Pd (II), etc.

Another type of hybridisation is known in which two nd, one $(n + 1)$ s and three $(n + 1)$ p orbitals combine to form six $d^2\,sp^3$ hybrid orbitals directed towards the six corners of an octahedron. These are given as,

$$\psi_1 = \frac{1}{\sqrt{6}} s + \frac{1}{\sqrt{2}} p_z + \frac{1}{\sqrt{3}} d_{z^2}$$

$$\psi_2 = \frac{1}{\sqrt{6}} s - \frac{1}{\sqrt{2}} p_z + \frac{1}{\sqrt{3}} d_{z^2}$$

$$\psi_3 = \frac{1}{\sqrt{6}} s + \frac{1}{\sqrt{2}} p_x - \frac{1}{\sqrt{12}} d_{z^2} + \frac{1}{2} d_{x^2-y^2}$$

$$\psi_4 = \frac{1}{\sqrt{6}} s - \frac{1}{\sqrt{2}} p_x + \frac{1}{\sqrt{12}} d_{z^2} + \frac{1}{2} d_{x^2-y^2}$$

$$\psi_5 = \frac{1}{\sqrt{6}} s - \frac{1}{\sqrt{2}} p_y - \frac{1}{\sqrt{12}} d_{z^2} - \frac{1}{2} d_{x^2-y^2}$$

$$\psi_6 = \frac{1}{\sqrt{6}} s + \frac{1}{\sqrt{2}} p_y - \frac{1}{\sqrt{12}} d_{z^2} - \frac{1}{2} d_{x^2-x^2} \qquad \text{... (13.273)}$$

They form still stronger bonds, examples of which are to be found in 6-coordinated complexes of transition metals. (Readers should check for themselves the normalisation and orthogonality properties of the six hydrid orbitals d^2sp^3;

for example,

$$\int \Psi_1^2 = \frac{1}{6} + \frac{1}{2} + \frac{1}{3} = 1$$

$$\int \Psi_1 \Psi_2 \, dT = \frac{1}{6}\int s^2 \, d\tau - \frac{1}{2}\int p_z^2 \, d\tau + \frac{1}{3}\int d_z^2 \, d\tau = \frac{1}{6} - \frac{1}{2} + \frac{1}{3} = 0$$

13.8.2 Construction of Hybrid Orbitals and Use of Symmetry

We have seen that atomic orbitals of an atom can combine among themselves to form hybrid orbitals, which are more effective in covalent bonding. But which of the atomic orbitals in an atom are to be chosen for hybridisation? Symmetry properties of the molecule again help us in deciding this.

Consider for example, BF_3 molecule which is trigonal planar (Fig. 13.31), belonging to the D_{3h} point group.

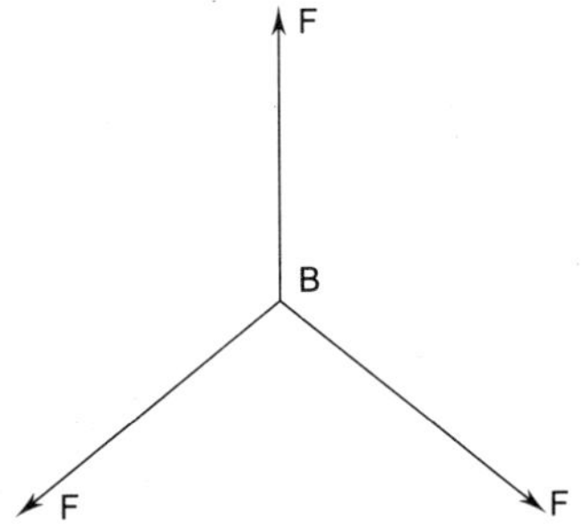

Fig. 13.31 *Trigonal bonds in BF_3 molecule, the B—F bonds are shown as vectors*

The group has the following symmetry operations:

$$E, C_3^1, C_3^2, C_2, C_2', C_2'', \sigma_h, S_3, S_3', \sigma_v, \sigma_v', \sigma_v''$$

Using the three B—F bonds, shown as vectors, as a basis, we can generate a reducible representation of this group in which the characters will be determined by determining the number of vectors that remain unshifted in each symmetry operation. (Hybrid orbitals, having directional characteristics, may be regarded as vectors B $\rightarrow$ F). The effect of various symmetry operators is summarised below:

Operation	*Effect*	*Character*
E	all vectors unshifted	χ (E) = 3
C_3^1, C_3^2	all vectors shifted	χ (C_3) = 0
C_2, C_2', C_2''	one vector unshifted	χ (C_2) = 1
σ_h	all vectors unshifted	χ (σ_h) = 3
S_3, S_3'	all vectors shifted	χ (S_3) = 0
$\sigma_v, \sigma_v', \sigma_v''$	one vector unshifted	χ (σ_v) = 1

Accordingly, the reducible representation is,

D_{3h}	E	$2C_3$	$3C_2$	σ_h	$2S_3$	$3\sigma_v$	Basis
Γ_r	3	0	1	3	0	1	(3 B—F bonds)

The character table for the D_{3h} group is given in Table 13.2.

TABLE 13.2

D_{3h}	E	$2C_3$	$3C_2$	σ_h	$2S_3$	$3\sigma_v$	*Basis*	
A_1'	1	1	1	1	1	1		$x^2 + y^2, z^2$
A_2'	1	1	− 1	1	1	− 1	R_x	
E′	2	− 1	0	2	− 1	0	(x, y)	$(x^2 - y^2, xy)$
A_1''	1	1	1	− 1	− 1	− 1		
A_2''	1	1	− 1	− 1	− 1	1	Z	
E″	2	− 1	0	− 2	1	0	(R_x, R_y)	(xz, yz)

Use of formula (11.46) reduces Γ_r as

$$\Gamma_r = A_1' + E'$$

This means that of the three atomic orbitals that will combine to form the three hybrid orbitals one must belong to A_1' and two to E′ representation. The character table of D_{3h} group shows that the atomic orbitals belonging to A_1' and E′ are as follows:

$$A_1' : s, d_{z^2}$$

$$E' : p_x, p_y, d_{xy}, d_{x^2-y^2}$$

Selecting any three of these orbitals, we get the following possible combinations:

$$(s + p_x + p_y); \left(s + d_{xy} + d_{x^2-y^2}\right);$$

$$\left(d_{z^2} + p_x + p_y\right); \left(d_{z^2} + d_{xy} + d_{x^2-y^2}\right)$$

The three equivalent hybrid orbitals can thus be sp^2, sd^2, dp^2 or d^3. It is not possible to decide on the basis of symmetry considerations alone as to which of these hybrids will be actually used. Energies of the hybrid orbitals may often help in deciding this issue, BF_3 and SO_3 both belong to D_{3h} group. In the former sp^2 hybridisation is more likely as 3*d*-orbitals have higher energy then 2*p*; however, in SO_3 they are lower in energy then 4*p*.

Exercise : *Determine the nature of hybrid orbital in a square planar complex.*

The complex belongs to the point group D_{4h}. With 4 equivalent hybrids as the basis, we have

E	σ_h	$2C_4$	$2S_4$	C_2	i	$2C_2'$	$2\sigma_v$	$2C_2''$	$2\sigma_v''$
$\Gamma_r : 4$	4	0	0	0	0	2	2	0	0

which reduces as

$$\Gamma_r : A_{1g} + B_{1g} + E_{1u}$$

The AOs belonging to these irreducible representations are as follows:

To be used	*Not to be used*
A_{1g} ; s, d_z^2	A_{2u} : p_x
B_{1g} ; $d_{x^2-y^2}$	B_{2g} ; d_{xy}
E_{1u} ; p_x, p_y	E_g ; d_{xy}, d_{yz}

Therefore, the possible combinations for the hybrid orbitals are:

$$s + p_x + p_y + d_{z^2} \ (i.e., sp^2 d), s + p_x + p_y + d_{x^2-y^2} \ (sp^2 d),$$

$$p_x + p_y + d_{z^2} + d_{x^2-y^2} \left(p^2 d^2\right).$$

13.9 COMPARISON OF MO AND VB THEORIES

The VB theory is built around two very important concepts, *viz.*, hybridisation of structure (*i.e.*, resonance) and hybridisation of atomic orbitals. None of the two concepts, however, represents physical reality; they are introduced as necessary mathematical tools to explain experimental facts like bond energy, bond angles, etc., of molecules. This goal is achieved in MO theory by an appropriate linear combination of atomic orbitals which leads to the molecular orbitals. This method is an equally good mathematical concept having no physical reality. MO treatment of a molecule assumes a single structure and is built on the concept of delocalisation of the MOs and electrons. VB treatment, on the other hand, requires several structures for the same molecule, and the equivalent of delocalisation of MOs is to be seen in the resonance of wave functions corresponding to these VB structures.

In VB theory, the bond properties, *e.g.*, bond strengths, bond directions, equivalence of bonds in molecules like NH_3, CH_4, etc., can be understood through the concept of hybridisation of orbitals. The overlap of orbitals yields localised bonds. In MO theory, hybridisation is not essential. Since hybrid orbitals are themselves linear combination of atomic orbitals and an MO encompasses all the nuclei of a molecule, it is immaterial whether an MO is constructed by pure atomic orbitals or hybrid orbitals. However, in certain cases, one may prefer to use hybridisation as a first step and construct MOs by combination of orbitals, atomic or hybrid, obtaining MOs that are good approximation to equivalent MOs. If, for example, in CH_4 an sp^3 hybrid orbital (h_i) is combined with 1s atomic orbital of a hydrogen atom, towards which it is directed, a localised C—H "bond MO" is formed,

$$\psi_i = ah_i + b\,1s$$

which is a good approximation to the equivalent MOs of CH_4. The equivalent MOs are themselves constructed from the delocalised MOs by appropriate linear combinations.

What is achieved in MO theory by the approximation of localised MOs is achieved in VB theory by the approximation of perfect pairing. Thus, in CH_4 most of the bond properties of the molecule can be explained satisfactorily by a single structure in which each of the sp^3 hybrid orbitals is paired with a hydrogen 1s atomic orbital.

Both the concept of localisation of MOs and the perfect pairing scheme of a VB structure suffer complete breakdown in the case of conjugated π-systems. In both the theories one finds the empirical procedure to be more convenient. While in the former case (the HMO method) the procedure involves obtaining experimental parameters like coulomb energy (α) and exchange energy(β); in the latter case (the HLSP method) this involves obtaining resonance energy.

In the ultimate analysis the MO and VB theories are equivalent and lead to almost similar results. They have been used equally well, but with respect to treatment of large molecules, the former theory has gained an edge over the latter.

PROBLEMS

13.1 For LiH molecule,

(*i*) draw the MO level diagram,

(*ii*) write the MO wave function in the determinantal form, and

(*iii*) outline the SCF procedure for calculating the MOs.

[**Hint :** (*i*) $1\sigma \ll 2\sigma < 3\sigma$

(*ii*) $\psi = \left| 1\sigma\, 1\bar{\sigma}\, 2\sigma\, 2\bar{\sigma} \right|$

(*iii*) 1σ (for example) $= a_1\, 1s_{Li} + a_2\, 1s_H + a_3 2s_{Li}$; the A.O. 1s, for example, is

$$\frac{1}{\sqrt{\pi}} \exp(-Z'r),\ Z' = \text{a variable parameter.}$$

Now (*a*) guess some values of *a*'s.

(*b*) Calculate the atomic integrals, for example,

$$H_{11} = \int 1s_{Li}\, \hat{H}\, 1s_{Li}\, d\tau,$$

$$H_{12} = \int 1s_{Li}\, \hat{H}\, 1s_H\, d\tau \text{ etc.,}$$

$$S_{12} = \int 1s_{Li}\, 1s_H\, d\tau, \text{etc.,}$$

and thus find all the matrix elements of the secular determinant. The operator $\hat{H}$ contains the operators $\hat{J}_j$ and $\hat{K}_j$.

(*c*) Solve the determinant to get the E_i's.

(*d*) Use the E_i's in the secular equations to get new *a*'s.

(*e*) Go back to the step (*a*) and repeat the cycle of steps (*a*) to (*d*) with the new *a*'s; still no new set of *a*'s is obtained].

13.2 Write the electronic Hamiltonian for H_2O in its explicit form using atomic units.

$$\left[\textbf{Hint}: \hat{H} = -\frac{1}{2}\sum_{i=1}^{10}\nabla_i^2 - \sum_{i=1}^{10}\left[\frac{1}{(r_{H_1})_i} + \frac{1}{(r_{H_2})_i} + \frac{8}{(r_O)_i}\right] + \frac{1}{2}\sum_{i,j=1}^{10}\frac{1}{r_{ij}}\right].$$

13.3 For BeH_2 molecule write the valence bond eigenfunction under perfect pairing scheme.

[**Hint:** The molecule is linear. Transform the 2*s* and one of the three 2*p* atomic orbitals of Be into two sp hybrid orbitals,

$$h_1 = \frac{1}{\sqrt{2}}(s + p_z),\ h_2 = \frac{1}{\sqrt{2}}(s - p_z)$$

There are two bonds and four electrons; therefore,

$$\psi = \frac{1}{2}\cdot\frac{1}{\sqrt{24}}\left[\left|h_1\bar{1}s_1 h_2\bar{1}s_2\right| - \left|\bar{h}_1 1s_1 h_2\bar{1}s_2\right| - \left|h_1\bar{1}s_1\bar{h}_2 1s_2\right| + \left|\bar{h}_1 1s_1\bar{h}_2 1s_2\right|\right].$$

13.4 Consider the geometry of formaldehyde molecule. List the valence orbitals. Which orbitals combine to form bonding, antibonding and non-bonding molecular orbitals? Which orbitals are filled with electrons? Discuss this in terms of delocalised and localised molecular orbitals.

[**Hint:** HCHO is planar

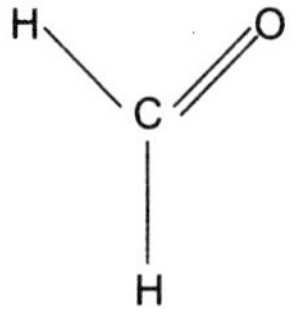

Valence orbitals

C : one 2*s* and three 2*p* AOs, one $2p_z$ AO ⊥ molecular plane.

O : one 2*s* AO and three 2*p* AOs.

2H : one 1*s* AO of each H atom.

Total : 10 AOs and 12 electrons.

Localised MOs

All orbitals of C are utilised; two orbitals (sp^2 and sp_y) are left on O; they are non-bonding MOs n_1 and n_2.

$$\sigma^2(\text{C—H})_1, \sigma^2(\text{C—H})_2\, \sigma^2(\text{CO})\, \pi^2(\text{CO})\, n^2(\text{CO})_1, n^2(\text{CO})_2.$$

Delocalised MOs

With respect to the molecular plane (the *xy*-plane), the two $2p_z$ AOs of C and O change sign (antisymmetric). With respect to the *xz*-plane, the orbitals

$$1s_A + 1s_B\,(a),\quad 2s_C\,(b),\quad 2s_0\,(c),\quad 2p_{xC},\quad (d), 2p_{xO}\,(e).$$

are symmetric and

$$1s_A - 1s_B\,(f),\ 2p_{yC}\,(g),\ 2p_{y0}\,(h)$$

are antisymmetric.

Therefore, the following combinations are possible:

$$2p_{z\,(C)} + 2p_{z\,(O)} \rightarrow \pi \text{ and } \pi^* \qquad \text{(antisymmetric combination)}$$

$$a + b + c + d + e \rightarrow \sigma_1 < \sigma_2 < n_1 < \sigma_2^* < \sigma_1^* \qquad \text{(symmetric combination)}$$

$$f + g + h \rightarrow \sigma_3 < n_2 < \sigma_3^* \qquad \text{(antisymmetric combination)}$$

13.5 Set up the secular determinant for hexatriene electrons in the Hückel approximation. Determine the energies of the HMOs in terms of α and β and calculate delocalisation energy.

[Hint: $\underset{1}{CH_2}=\underset{2}{CH}-\underset{3}{CH}=\underset{4}{CH}-\underset{5}{CH}=\underset{6}{CH_2}$

Follow the procedure laid down for butadiene; the polynomial in x is

$$x^6 - 5x^4 + 6x^2 - 1 = 0$$

$$x = \pm 1.80, \pm 1.25, \pm 0.445$$

$$E_1 = \alpha + 1.80\,\beta \text{ and so on}$$

$$E = 6\alpha + 6.99\beta \text{ and D.E.} = 0.99\beta].$$

13.6 Give the secular equations for fulvene.

According to HMO conventions.

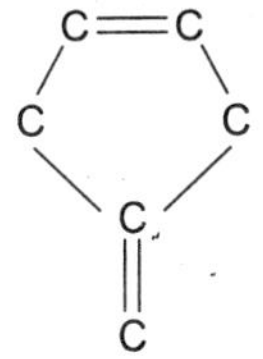

$$a_1(\alpha - E) + a_2\,\beta + a_5\,\beta = 0$$

$$a_1\,\beta + a_2(\alpha - E) + a_3\,\beta = 0$$

$$a_2\,\beta + a_3(\alpha - E) + a_4\,\beta = 0$$

$$a_1\,\beta + a_4\,\beta + a_5(\alpha - E) + a_6\,\beta = 0$$

$$a_5\,\beta + a_6(\alpha - E) = 0].$$

13.7 What are the HMO coefficients and the energy of the π-electrons in the following system?

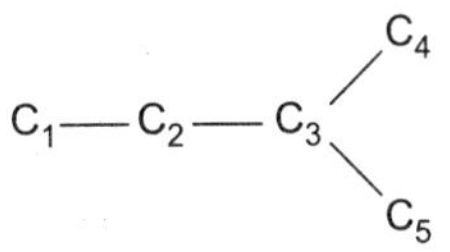

[Hint:

a_1	a_2	a_3	a_4	a_5
$\frac{1}{3}$	$\frac{\sqrt{2}}{3}$	0	$-\frac{1}{3}$	$-\frac{1}{3}$

$$E_\pi = \alpha + 0.544\beta].$$

13.8 Consider a straight chain system of 3 carbon centres and $3p_z$ atomic orbitals. Calculate the HMO energies and coefficients. With two electrons in the system what will be the ground state configuration and bond orders? What about the neutral molecule and negative ion?

[Hint : See the text for allyl system].

13.9 If 1, 3-butadiene were formed by just linking of two $CH_2{=}CH_2$ molecules through a single bond, what would be, the π-electronic energy of the ground state and the bond order?

[Hint: See the text for allyl system].

[Hint: Neglect the integral between the two π-atomic orbitals on the two central carbon atoms,

$$E_\pi = 2 \times 2\,(\alpha + \beta) = 4\,(\alpha + \beta)$$

$$\pi \text{ B.O.} = 1 \text{ for each bond}].$$

13.10 Write the secular determinant for each of the following systems by inspecting the structures:

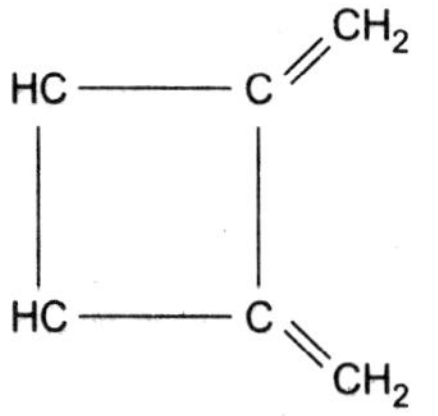

(a)

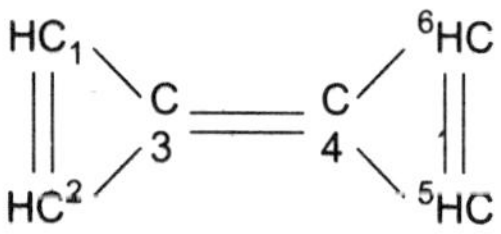

(b)

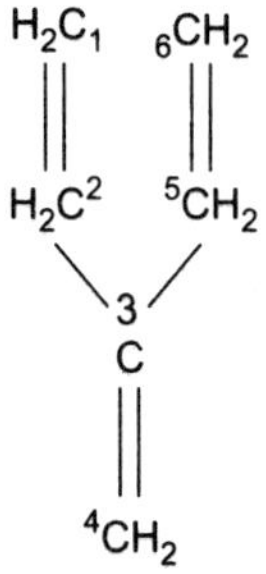

(c)

$CH_3CH_2CH_2CH = Ch_2$

(d)

$H_2C = CHCH_2CH_2CH = CH_2$

(e)

CH = CH

(f)

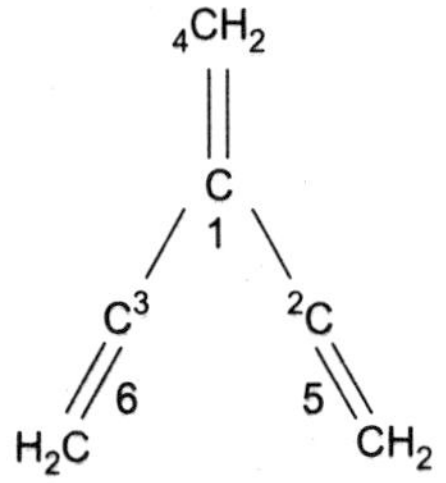

[**Hint** : See the text.

(*a*) $$\begin{vmatrix} x & 1 & 0 & 0 & 0 & 0 \\ 1 & x & 1 & 0 & 1 & 0 \\ 0 & 1 & x & 1 & 0 & 0 \\ 0 & 0 & 1 & x & 0 & 0 \\ & & & & x & \\ & & & & & x \end{vmatrix} = 0$$

(*b*) $$\begin{vmatrix} x & 1 & 1 & 0 & 0 & 0 \\ 1 & x & 1 & 0 & 0 & 0 \\ 1 & 1 & x & 1 & 0 & 0 \\ 0 & 0 & 1 & x & 1 & 1 \\ 0 & 0 & 0 & 1 & x & 1 \\ 0 & 0 & 0 & 1 & 1 & x \end{vmatrix} = 0$$

(*c*) $$\begin{vmatrix} x & 1 & 0 & 0 & 0 & 0 \\ 1 & x & 1 & 0 & 0 & 0 \\ 0 & 1 & x & 1 & 1 & 0 \\ 0 & 0 & 1 & x & 0 & 0 \\ 0 & 0 & 1 & 0 & x & 1 \\ 0 & 0 & 0 & 0 & 1 & x \end{vmatrix} = 0$$

(*d*), (*e*) and (*f*):

$$\begin{vmatrix} x & 1 \\ 1 & x \end{vmatrix} = 0$$

(*g*) $$\begin{vmatrix} x & 1 & 1 & 1 & 0 & 0 \\ 1 & x & 1 & 0 & 1 & 0 \\ 1 & 1 & x & 0 & 0 & 1 \\ 1 & 0 & 0 & x & 0 & 0 \\ 0 & 1 & 0 & 0 & x & 0 \\ 0 & 0 & 1 & 0 & 0 & x \end{vmatrix} = 0$$

13.11 Set up the secular determinant for trimethylenemethane; solve it to obtain the energy levels. Indicate the ground state electronic configuration.

[**Hint:** $$\begin{vmatrix} x & 1 & 1 & 1 \\ 1 & x & 0 & 0 \\ 1 & 0 & x & 0 \\ 1 & 0 & 0 & x \end{vmatrix} = 0$$

or $$x^4 - 3x^2 = 0$$

$$x = -1.732, 0, 0$$

$$E_n = 4\alpha + 3.464\beta].$$

13.12 When butadiene absorbs light of certain frequency, an electron from the highest occupied MO ψ_2 is promoted to the lowest unoccupied MO ψ_3. Which bond is expected to become shorter and which longer? Determine this by calculating the bond orders.

[**Hint:** See text].

13.13 Two MOs of a molecule are:

$$\psi_1 = \frac{1}{\sqrt{3}}(p_1 + p_2 + p_3)$$

$$\psi_2 = \frac{1}{\sqrt{3}}(p_3 + p_4 + p_5)$$

where p's are the orthonormal atomic orbitals. Find by inspection the overlap between the two MOs

$$\left[\textbf{Hint:} \int \psi_1\, \psi_2\, d\tau = \frac{1}{3}\right].$$

13.14 Which of the following HMOs are normalised?

$$\psi_1 = \frac{1}{\sqrt{2}}(p_1 + p_2)$$

$$\psi_2 = \frac{1}{\sqrt{4}}(p_1 - 2p_2 + p_3)^2$$

$$\psi_3 = \frac{1}{\sqrt{3}}(p_1 + p_2 + p_3)$$

Examine if the following linear combination of the HMOs ψ_1 and ψ_2 is normalised,

$$\psi_4 = \frac{1}{\sqrt{2}}(\psi_1 - \psi_3)$$

if not, why not?

[**Hint:**

$$\psi_1 : \ \Sigma a_i^2 = 2 \times \left(\frac{1}{\sqrt{2}}\right)^2 = 1, \text{normalised.}$$

$$\psi_2 : \ \Sigma a_i^2 = \frac{3}{2}, \text{not normalised.}$$

$$\psi_3 : \ \Sigma a_i^2 = 1 ; \text{normalised.}$$

$$\psi_4 : \ \Sigma a_i^2 = 1 - \frac{2}{\sqrt{6}}, \text{not normalised.}$$

ψ_4 : is not normalised because though ψ_1 and ψ_3 are normalised they are not orthogonal.

$$\left.\int \psi_1\, \psi_3\, d\tau = \frac{2}{\sqrt{6}} \neq 0\right].$$

13.15 The following two normalised HMOs of $C_3H_3^+$,

$$\psi_2 = \frac{1}{\sqrt{2}}(p_1 - p_2)$$

$$\psi_3 = \frac{1}{\sqrt{2}}(p_1 - p_3)$$

belong to degenerate energy levels $E_2 = E_3 = \alpha - \beta$. They are not mutually orthogonal. Construct a normalised HMO, $\psi_4 = a_2\,\psi_2 + a_3\,\psi_3$ which is orthogonal to ψ_2 and ψ_3.

[Hint: $$\int \psi_2\,\psi_3\,d\tau = S = \frac{1}{2}$$

$$\int \psi_4^2\,d\tau = \imath_2^2 \int \psi_2^2\,d\tau + a_3^2 \int \psi_3^2\,d\tau + 2a_2\,a_3 \int \psi_2\,\psi_3\,d\tau$$

$$= a_2^2 + a_3^2 + a_2\,a_3.$$

Now, $$\int \psi_4\,\psi_2\,u\,c = 0$$

or $$a_2 \int \psi_2^2\,d\tau + a_3 \int \psi_2\,\psi_3\,d\tau = a_2 + \frac{a_3}{2} = 0$$

$$a_2 = -\frac{a_3}{2}$$

Therefore, $$\frac{a_3^2}{4} + a_3^2 - \frac{a_3^2}{2} = \frac{3}{4}a_3^2 = 1.$$

or $$a_3 = \frac{2}{\sqrt{3}}$$

and $$a_2 = -\frac{2}{\sqrt{3}} \times \frac{1}{2} = -\frac{1}{\sqrt{3}}$$

Therefore, $$\psi_4 = \frac{2}{\sqrt{3}}\psi_3 - \frac{1}{\sqrt{3}}\psi_2$$

$$= \frac{1}{\sqrt{3}} \cdot \frac{1}{\sqrt{2}}\left[2(p_1 - p_3) - (p_1 - p_2)\right]$$

$$= \frac{1}{\sqrt{6}}\left[p_1 + p_2 - 2p_3\right]\Big].$$

13.16 Naphthalene belongs to the point group D_{2h}. Use a sub-group of it to construct the symmetry adapted orbitals (SALCs) with the p_z atomic orbital of each carbon atom as a basis. Determine the π-energy levels and arrange the π MOs in order of increasing energy.

[**Hint :** D_{2h} : E, $C_2(x)$, $C_2(y)$, $C_2(z)$, i, $\sigma_{(xy)}$, (*i.e.*, σ_h), $\sigma_{(yz)}$ and $\sigma_{(xz)}$ (molecular plane is the xy-plane). p_z AOs are inverted by

$$C_2(x), C_2(y), i, \sigma_{(xy)};$$

if these are ignored the molecule reduces to the sub-group C_{2v}. With 10 p_z A.O's as the basis,

C_{2v}	E	$C_2(z)$	$\sigma_{(yz)}$	$\sigma_{(xz)}$
Γ_r	10	0	2	0

$$\Gamma_r = 3A_1 + 2A_2 + 2B_1 + 3B_2$$

Symmetry orbials are [using Equation (11.46)].

$$\psi_1(A_1) = \frac{1}{4}(p_1 + p_4 + p_5 + p_8)$$

$$\psi_2(A_1) = \frac{1}{4}(p_2 + p_3 + p_6 + p_7)$$

$$\psi_3(A_1) = \frac{1}{2}(p_9 + p_{10})$$

$$\psi_1(A_2) = \frac{1}{4}(p_1 - p_4 + p_5 - p_8)$$

$$\psi_2(A_2) = \frac{1}{4}(p_2 - p_3 + p_6 - p_7)$$

$$\psi_1(B_1) = \frac{1}{4}(p_1 + p_4 - p_5 - p_6)$$

$$\psi_2(B_1) = \frac{1}{4}(p_2 + p_3 - p_6 - p_7)$$

$$\psi_1(B_2) = \frac{1}{4}(p_1 - p_4 - p_5 + p_8)$$

$$\psi_2(B_2) = \frac{1}{4}(p_2 - p_3 - p_6 + p_7)$$

$$\psi_3(B_2) = \frac{1}{2}(p_9 - p_{10})$$

The 10 × 10 secular determinant is factorised as

$$A_1: \begin{vmatrix} \alpha - E & \beta & \sqrt{2}\beta \\ \beta & \alpha + \beta - E & 0 \\ \sqrt{2}\beta & 0 & \alpha + \beta - E \end{vmatrix} = 0$$

$$A_2: \begin{vmatrix} \alpha - E & \beta \\ \beta & \alpha - \beta - E \end{vmatrix} = 0 .$$

$$B_1 : \begin{vmatrix} \alpha - E & \beta \\ \beta & \alpha + \beta - E \end{vmatrix} = 0$$

$$B_2 : \begin{vmatrix} \alpha - E & \beta & \sqrt{2}\beta \\ \beta & \alpha - \beta - E & 0 \\ \sqrt{2}\beta & 0 & \alpha - \beta - E \end{vmatrix} = 0$$

$A_1 : (x + 1)(x^2 + 3x - 3) = 0$, or $x = -1, -2.303, +1.303$

$B_1 : (x^2 + x - 1) = 0;$ or $x = -1.618, +0.618$

$A_2 : x^2 - x - 1 = 0;$ or $x = 1.618, -0.618$

$B_2 : (x - 1)(x^2 - x - 3) = 0$

or $$x = +1, +2.303, -1.303 \left(x = \frac{\alpha - E}{\beta}\right)\Big].$$

13.17 Show if it is possible to form six equivalent hybrid orbitals pointing towards the corners of a hexagon using the character table of the point group C_{6v}.

The hexagon is

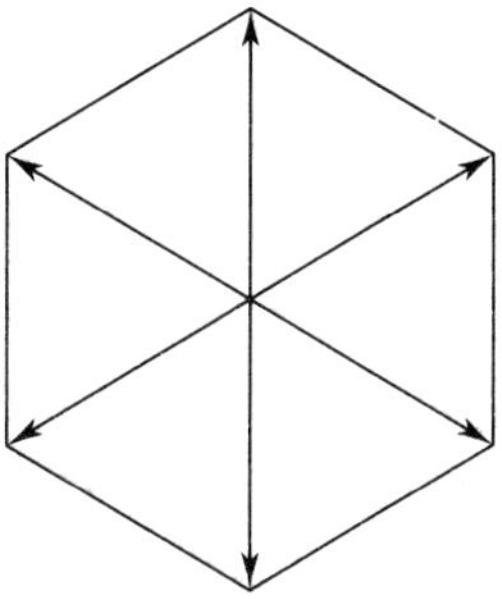

Fig. 13.32

[Hint:

C_{2v}	E	$2C_3$	$2C_6$	C_2	$3\sigma_v$	$3\sigma_v$
Γ_T :	6	0	0	0	2	0

$$\Gamma_r = A_1 + B_1 + E_1 + E_2$$

It can be concluded from the character table that the *s*, *p* and *d* AOs have the following symmetries:

$A_1 : p_z, d_z^2$

$E_1 : p_x, p_y, d_{xz}, d_{yz}$

$E_2 : d_{xy}, d_{x^2-y^2}$

There is no orbital of B_1 symmetry; so it is not possible to form the hybrid orbitals].

13.18 Show that the three sp^2 hybrid orbitals are mutually orthogonal.

13.19 The molecule of HCHO is planar. What hybrid orbitals are constructed on the carbon atom? Which orbitals participate in C—H and C—O bonds?

13.20 Use 2*s* and $2p_z$ atomic orbitals to construct (*i*) two equivalent sp hybrid orbitals, (*ii*) 3 equivalent sp^2 hybrid orbitals and (*iii*) 4 equivalent sp^3 hybrid orbitals. Determine the angle between the hybrid orbitals in each case.

13.21 A hybrid orbitals has 20% *s* and 80% *p*-character. Give the expression for the hybrid orbitals and determine the angle between them.

13.22 Calculate the angular function $f(\theta, \varphi)$ for *sp* and sp^2 hybrid orbitals for the angles $\theta = 0°$, 30°, 60°, 90°, 120°, 150° and 180°, degrees.

13.23 For an sp^3 hybrid orbital directed along the *x*-axis,

$$\psi_{sp^3} = \frac{1}{2}\left(s + \sqrt{3}\, p_x\right)$$

calculate the magnitude of the orbital as a function of position along *x*-axis. Compare it with the magnitudes of the unhybridised *s* and p_x orbitals using the following Slater orbitals:

$$\psi_{2s} = \left[\frac{1}{4!(4\pi)}\left(\frac{Z^*}{a_0}\right)^5\right]^{1/2} re^{-Z^* ri2\, a_0}$$

$$\psi_{2p_x} = \left[\frac{3}{4!(4\pi)}\left(\frac{Z^*}{a_0}\right)^5\right]^{1/2} r \sin\theta \cos\varphi\, e^{-Z^* r/2a_0}$$

For carbon, the effective nuclear charge Z^* is 3.5.

CHAPTER 14

Density Functional Theory

In the Hartree-Fock (HF) method described in earlier Chapter, the equations are solved to obtain spin-orbitals which are then used to construct configuration state functions (CSF). In this method exchange between electrons and correlated motion of electrons of like spins are taken into account. But the correlation due to Coulombic repulsion of all electrons is missing. The method is improved by configuration interaction (CI), and several other modifications for example multi configuration state function (MCSF), Moeller-Plesset perturbation (MP2/MP4), coupled cluster methods etc. not described in this book. All these methods are, however, limited by the difficulties of computation especially when large basis sets are used for accuracy.

An alternative method is provided by "density functional theory (DFT)". The electronic energy (E) in this method is expressed as a 'functional' of electron density and is denoted as E[ρ]. As against a function in which the basic variable is a number, for example $f(x)$ = Sin x is a function of x, in the functional the basic variable is a function and there is a one to one correspondence between the variable and the functional; the expectation value $\left(\bar{E}\right)$ of energy, for example, $\bar{E}[\psi]$ $= \dfrac{\int \psi^* \hat{H} \psi d\tau}{\int \psi^* \psi d\tau}$ is a functional of the wave function Ψ.

The advantage with the DFT method is that the central quantity of interest in it is electron density (ρ) which is a 3-dimensional quantity, in place of wave function (Ψ) which is 3N-dimensional, N being the number of electrons.

The electron density (ρ) is defined, for an N-electron system, by integrating the N-electron distribution function $P(r_1, r_2, ..., r_n)$ over N–1 coordinates as

$$\rho(r_1) = N \int .... \int P(r_1, r_2, ..., r_n) dr_2, dr_3, ..., dr_n \qquad ...(14.1)$$

and represents the number of electrons per unit volume at a point r_1, thus integrating to the total number N,

$$\int \rho(r)\, dr = N \qquad ...(14.2)$$

for the N-electron wave function, the distribution function is given by

$$\rho(r_1, r_2, \ldots, r_n) = |\psi(r_1, r_2, \ldots, r_n)|^2 \quad \text{...(14.3)}$$

An attempt to use the electron density of a system for calculating electronic energy was made by Thomas and Fermi in 1927. They obtained an expression for energy as a functional of electron density without any information about the wave function. They used a uniform electron gas model for the kinetic energy and the electrostatic (Coulombic) potential energy. The results obtained by them were far from accurate because neither exchange nor correlated motion of electrons was considered. No molecular binding could be predicted in this method. Hence the Thomas-Fermi model was considered to be of little quantitative significance in atoms or molecules.

14.1 HOHENBERG-KOHN THEOREMS

In 1964, Hohenberg and Kohn formally justified the use of electron density as the basic variable in determining the electronic energy which became the foundation of modern electron density functional theory. They proposed two theorems:

Theorem 1: There exists, for non-degenerate ground state of a system a one-to-one correspondence between external potential (V_{ext}), wave function (ψ) and electron density (ρ) of the system. Hence there exists a density functional in terms of which the electronic energy (E) can be formulated. From the form of the Schrödinger equation we can see that this energy functional would contain three terms the Kinetic energy T [ρ], the energy of interaction with external potential V_{ext} [ρ] and the energy due to electron-electron interaction V_{ee} [ρ], that is the energy of interaction with external potential

$$E[\rho] = T[\rho] + V_{ext}[\rho] + V_{ee}[\rho] \quad \text{...(14.4)}$$

For atoms and molecules V_{ext} arises from nuclei-electrons attraction; this interaction is trivial given by

$$V_{ext}[\rho] = \int V_{ext} \bullet dr \quad \text{...(14.5)}$$

where V_{ext} is nuclei-electron attraction in atoms and molecules. The kinetic energy functional, T [ρ] and electron-electron interaction energy functional, V_{ee} [ρ], together may be called Hohenberg-Kohn functional, F_{HK} [ρ],

$$F_{HK}[\rho] = T[\rho] + V_{ee}[\rho] \quad \text{...(14.6)}$$

F_{HK} [ρ] is independent of V_{ext} and hence is universal.

If the form of the functional F_{HK} [ρ] were known the electronic energy could be straightway calculated by substituting in the equation (14.4). Unfortunately, explicit form of neither T[P] nor V_{ee} [P] is known. Finding approximations to these is the subject of current research.

The interaction energy V_{ee} contains (*i*) classical caulombic repulsion, or Hartree energy V_H,

$$V_H = \frac{1}{2}\sum_i \sum_j \int\int \psi_i^*(1)\,\psi_j^*(2)\frac{1}{r_{12}}\psi_i(1)\,\psi_j(2)\,dr_1\,dr_2$$

$$= \frac{1}{2}\iint \frac{\rho(1)\rho(2)}{r_{12}} dr_1\, dr_2 \quad ...(14.7)$$

and (*ii*) non-classical interaction arising due to electron exchange and electron correction, V_{nci}.

Theorem 2: The variational principle holds for the minimisation of E [ρ] also, that is, for any arbitrary well behaved electron density ρ(*r*) with

$$\rho \geq 0 \quad \text{and} \quad \int \rho(r)\, dr = N,$$

the energy

$$E[\rho] \geq E_0[\rho_0] \quad ...(14.8)$$

Where E_0 is the true ground state energy and ρ_0 the true density. The minimisation results in the equation

$$\frac{\delta E[\rho]}{\delta \rho} = V_{ext}[\rho] + \frac{\delta F_{HK}[\rho]}{\delta \rho}. \quad ...(14.9)$$

14.2 KOHN-SHAM EQUATIONS

An year after Hohenberg and Kohn proposed their theorems Kohn and Sham proposed a way of approximating the universal functional F_{HK} [ρ]. They separated the kinetic energy functional T [ρ] into the kinetic energy of a hypothetical non-interacting system of electrons T_s [ρ] and an unknown part $T_e[\rho]$ ($T_e[\rho] = T[\rho] - T_s[\rho]$) which contains the correction due to interaction between the electrons in the real system. For the non interacting part the kinetic energy can be known exactly from the 1-practicle Schrodinger equations:

$$T_s = \sum_{i=1}^{N} \int \psi_i \left(-\frac{1}{2}\nabla_i^2\right) \psi_i\, \tau \quad ...(14.10)$$

The functional F_{HK} [ρ] then be expressed as

$$F_{HK}[\rho] = T_s[\rho] + V_H[\rho] + E_{xe}[\rho] \quad ...(14.11)$$

with E_{xc} [ρ], is called exchange-correlation Potential defined as

$$E_{xc}[\rho] = (T[\rho] - T_s[\rho]) + (V_{ee}[\rho] - V_H[\rho]) \quad ...(14.12)$$

that is the functional E_{xc} [P] contains the difference between the kinetic energies of the real system and non-interacting system plus the non-classical part of the electron-electron interaction.

Following this approach the many electron problem is again mapped onto an effective 1-electron problem and all unknown terms are merged into the exchange-correlation part. The 1-particle wave functions (orbitals) can now be determined by solving the 1-particle equations under the constraint to reproduce the density of the real interacting system. This yields the so-called "Kohn-Sham (KS) equations".

$$\left[-\frac{1}{2}\nabla^2 + V_{eff}\left(f\right)\right]\psi_i = E_i\,\psi_i \qquad ...(14.13)$$

where the effective potential V_{eff} (r) contains external potential V_{ext} (r), the classical coulombic potential due to electron-electron repulsion V_H and the exchange-correlation potential V_{xc} (r),

$$V_{eff}(r) = V_{ext}\left(r\right) + \iint \frac{\rho(1)\rho(2)}{r_{12}} dr_1\, dr_2 + V_{xc}\left(r\right) \qquad ...(14.14)$$

The density ρ (r) of the real system can be given in terms of Kohn-Sham orbitals ψ_i,

$$\rho\,(r) = \sum_{i=1}^{N} |\,\psi_i\,(r)\,|^2 \qquad ...(14.15)$$

and the exchange-correlation potential V_{xc} (r) is given by the derivative of the E_{xc} [P] with respect to the density,

$$V_{xc}(r) = \frac{\delta E_{xc}\left[\rho(r)\right]}{\delta\rho(r)} \qquad ...(14.16)$$

If E_{xc} [ρ] is known, V_{xc} $[r]$ is readily obtained.

The Kohn-Sham equation has the same structure as Hartree-Fock equation. Since the effective potential V_{eff} depends on the density ρ itself, the equations have to be solved by self-consistent method. Initially, we guess the electron density ρ (by for example, a superposition of atomic densities, for molecules). By using some approximation for the functional dependence of E_{xc} on ρ we compute V_{xc} as a function of r. The set of K-S equations is then solved to obtain an initial set of K-S orbitals (ψ_i). This set is used to compute an improved ρ by using Equation (14.15). The process is repeated until the ρ and the E_{xc} converge to within certain tolerance. The electronic energy is then calculated from the Equations (14.4) and (14.11).

Since the equations are non-linear, the K-S orbitals are computed numerically. Within this formalism the kinetic energy of the non-interacting system is determined indirectly by using N one-electron wave functions, but still exact. Only the exchange correlation functional E_{xc} [ρ] remains unknown. Finding good approximations of E_{xc} [ρ] is one of the greatest challenges in modern DFT.

14.3 LOCAL DENSITY APPROXIMATION (LDA)

The simplest and the most widely used is the "local density approximation (LDA)". This approximation is based on the assumption that a system of electrons in molecules or atoms is like an electron gas. In the homogeneous electron gas model the electrons move in an infinite region of space with uniform positive charge background to preserve charge neutrality. For an inhomogeneous system it is then assumed that the exchange-correlation energy can be obtained by approximating the density of the inhomogeneous system locally by the density of the homogeneous system of electron gas.

$$E_{xc}^{\mathrm{LDA}}[\rho] = \int \rho(r).\varepsilon_{xc}(\rho(r))dr \qquad \text{...(14.17)}$$

where ε_{xc} (ρ (r)) is the exchange-correlation energy per electron of the homogeneous electron gas. The ε_{xc} (ρ (r)) can be written as the sum of exchange and correlation contributions

$$\varepsilon_{xc}(\rho(r)) = \varepsilon_x(\rho(r)) + \varepsilon_c(\rho(r)) \qquad \text{...(14.18)}$$

The exchange part has been expressed explicitly as

$$\varepsilon_x(\rho(r)) = -\sqrt[\frac{3}{4}]{\frac{3\rho(r)}{\pi}} \qquad \text{...(14.19)}$$

but there is no such explicit expression for the correlation part ε_c (ρ (r)). There are, however, excellent quantum Monte Carlo calculations for the homogeneous electron gas (see, for example, D.M. coparly and B.J. Alder, Phy. Rev. Lett. 1980, Vol. 45, p.566). Although the LDA is a crude approximation it has been used widely and gives good results. To account for the inhomogenity of the electron density a non-local correction involving the gradient of ρ is often added to the exchange correlation energy, which is known as the generalized gradient approximation (GGA) correction.

$$E_{xc}^{\mathrm{GGA}}[\rho] = \int \rho(r)\varepsilon_{xc}(\rho(r)).\nabla\rho(r)\,dr \qquad \text{...(14.20)}$$

where ∇ is vector operator (see Appendix 4).

APPENDICES

Appendix 1

TRANSFORMATION OF SCHRÖDINGER EQUATION FROM CARTESIAN TO POLAR COORDINATES

The basic relations between the Cartesian and Polar coordinates are

$$x = r\cos\varphi,\ y = r\sin\varphi,\ r = (x^2 + y^2)^{1/2}$$

$$\frac{y}{x} = \tan\varphi \qquad \text{... (A1.1)}$$

Therefore,

$$\frac{\partial r}{\partial x} = \frac{1}{2}\cdot\frac{2x}{\left(x^2 + y^2\right)^{1/2}} = \frac{x}{r}$$

Similarly,

$$\frac{\partial r}{\partial y} = \frac{y}{r},\ \frac{\partial\varphi}{\partial x} = -\cos^2\varphi\,\frac{y}{x^2},$$

$$\frac{\partial\varphi}{\partial y} = \cos^2\varphi\cdot\frac{1}{x}$$

Now,

$$\frac{\partial\psi}{\partial x} = \frac{\partial\psi}{\partial r}\cdot\frac{\partial r}{\partial x} + \frac{\partial\psi}{\partial\varphi}\cdot\frac{\partial\varphi}{\partial x}$$

$$= \frac{x}{r}\cdot\frac{\partial\psi}{\partial r} - \cos^2\varphi\cdot\frac{y}{x^2}\cdot\frac{\partial\psi}{\partial\varphi}$$

and

$$\frac{\partial^2\psi}{\partial x^2} = \frac{x^2}{r^2}\cdot\frac{\partial^2\psi}{\partial r^2} + \frac{1}{r}\cdot\frac{\partial\psi}{\partial r} - \frac{x^2}{r^3}\cdot\frac{\partial\psi}{\partial r} - 2\sin\varphi\cdot\cos^2\varphi\cdot\frac{y^2}{x^4}\cdot\frac{\partial\psi}{\partial\varphi}$$

$$+\ 2\cos^2\varphi\,\frac{y}{x^2}\cdot\frac{\partial\psi}{\partial\varphi} + \cos^4\varphi\cdot\frac{y^2}{x^4}\cdot\frac{\partial^2\psi}{\partial\varphi^2}$$

$$= \frac{x^2}{r^2}\cdot\frac{\partial^2\psi}{\partial r^2} + \frac{1}{r}\cdot\frac{\partial\psi}{\partial r} - \frac{x^2}{r^3}\cdot\frac{\partial\psi}{\partial r} - \frac{2\sin^3\varphi}{\cos\varphi}\cdot\frac{1}{r^2}\cdot\frac{\partial\psi}{\partial\varphi}$$

$$+ \frac{2\sin\varphi}{\cos\varphi}\cdot\frac{1}{r^2}\cdot\frac{\partial\psi}{\partial\varphi} + \frac{\sin^2\varphi}{r^2}\cdot\frac{\partial^2\psi}{\partial\varphi^2} \qquad \text{... (A1.2)}$$

Similarly,

$$\frac{\partial^2\psi}{\partial y^2} = \frac{y^2}{r^2}\cdot\frac{\partial^2\psi}{\partial r^2} + \frac{1}{r}\cdot\frac{\partial\psi}{\partial r} - \frac{y^2}{r^3}\cdot\frac{\partial\psi}{\partial r} - \frac{2\sin\varphi\,.\cos^2\varphi}{\cos\varphi}\cdot\frac{1}{r^2}\cdot\frac{\partial\psi}{\partial\varphi} + \frac{\cos^2\varphi}{r^2}\cdot\frac{\partial^2\psi}{\partial\varphi^2} \quad \text{... (A1.3)}$$

Adding Equations (A1.2) and (A1.3), we get

$$\frac{\partial^2\psi}{\partial x^2} + \frac{\partial^2\psi}{\partial y^2} = \frac{\partial^2\psi}{\partial r^2} + \frac{1}{r}\cdot\frac{\partial\psi}{\partial r} + \frac{1}{r^2}\cdot\frac{\partial^2\psi}{\partial\varphi^2} \quad \text{... (A1.4)}$$

For a particle rotating in a circle of fixed radius r,

$$\partial\psi/\partial r = 0$$

Therefore, Equation (A1.4) becomes,

$$\frac{\partial^2\psi}{\partial x^2} + \frac{\partial^2\psi}{\partial y^2} = \frac{1}{r^2}\cdot\frac{\partial^2\psi}{\partial\varphi^2} \quad \text{... (A1.5)}$$

Transformation of the Laplacian or Bel (∇^2) from Cartesian to Spherical Coordinates

$$\nabla^2 = \frac{\partial^2}{\partial x^2} + \frac{\partial^2}{\partial y^2} + \frac{\partial^2}{\partial z^2}$$

For the x-component we have,

$$\frac{\partial\psi}{\partial x} = \frac{\partial\psi}{\partial r}\cdot\frac{\partial r}{\partial x} + \frac{\partial\psi}{\partial\theta}\cdot\frac{\partial\theta}{\partial x} + \frac{\partial\psi}{\partial\varphi}\cdot\frac{\partial\varphi}{\partial x}$$

$$= \psi_r\cdot\frac{\partial r}{\partial x} + \psi_\theta\,\frac{\partial\theta}{\partial x} = \psi_\varphi\cdot\frac{\partial\varphi}{\partial x}$$

and

$$\frac{\partial^2\psi}{\partial x^2} = \left(\frac{\partial\psi_r}{\partial r}\frac{\partial r}{\partial x} + \frac{\partial\psi_r}{\partial\theta}\frac{\partial\theta}{\partial x} + \frac{\partial\psi_r}{\partial\varphi}\frac{\partial\varphi}{\partial x}\right)\frac{\partial r}{\partial x} + \psi_r\frac{\partial^2 r}{\partial x^2}$$

$$+ \left(\frac{\partial\psi_\theta}{\partial r}\frac{\partial r}{\partial x} + \frac{\partial\psi_\theta}{\partial\theta}\frac{\partial\theta}{\partial x} + \frac{\partial\psi_\theta}{\partial\varphi}\frac{\partial\varphi}{\partial x}\right)\frac{\partial\theta}{\partial x} + \psi_\theta\frac{\partial^2\theta}{\partial x^2}$$

$$+ \left(\frac{\partial\psi_\varphi}{\partial r}\frac{\partial r}{\partial x} + \frac{\partial\psi_\varphi}{\partial\theta}\frac{\partial\theta}{\partial x} + \frac{\partial\psi_\varphi}{\partial\varphi}\frac{\partial\varphi}{\partial x}\right)\frac{\partial\varphi}{\partial x} + \psi_\varphi\frac{\partial^2\varphi}{\partial x^2}$$

$$= \frac{\partial^2\psi}{\partial r^2}\left(\frac{\partial r}{\partial x}\right)^2 + \frac{\partial^2\psi}{\partial\theta\,\partial r}\frac{\partial\theta}{\partial x}\frac{\partial r}{\partial x} + \frac{\partial^2\psi}{\partial\varphi\,\partial r}\frac{\partial\varphi}{\partial x}\frac{\partial r}{\partial x}$$

$$+ \frac{\partial\psi}{\partial r}\frac{\partial^2 r}{\partial x^2} + \frac{\partial^2\psi}{\partial r\,\partial\theta}\frac{\partial r}{\partial x}\frac{\partial\theta}{\partial x} + \frac{\partial^2\psi}{\partial\theta^2}\left(\frac{\partial\theta}{\partial x}\right)^2 + \frac{\partial^2\psi}{\partial\varphi\,\partial\theta}\frac{\partial\varphi}{\partial x}\frac{\partial\theta}{\partial x} + \frac{\partial\psi}{\partial\theta}\frac{\partial^2\theta}{\partial x^2}$$

$$+ \frac{\partial^2\psi}{\partial r\,\partial\varphi}\frac{\partial r}{\partial x}\frac{\partial\varphi}{\partial x} + \frac{\partial^2\psi}{\partial\theta\,\partial\varphi}\frac{\partial\theta}{\partial x}\frac{\partial\varphi}{\partial x} + \frac{\partial^2\psi}{\partial\varphi^2}\left(\frac{\partial\varphi}{\partial x}\right)^2 + \frac{\partial\psi}{\partial\varphi}\frac{\partial^2\varphi}{\partial x^2} \quad \text{... (A1.6)}$$

Similar expressions can be obtained for

$$\frac{\partial^2 \psi}{\partial y^2} \text{ and } \frac{\partial^2 \psi}{\partial z^6} \text{ so that}$$

$$\nabla^2 \psi = \frac{\partial^2 \psi}{\partial r^2} \sum_k \left(\frac{\partial r}{\partial k} \right)^2 + \frac{\partial^2 \psi}{\partial \theta} \sum_k \left(\frac{\partial \theta}{\partial k} \right)^2 + \frac{\partial^2 \psi}{\partial \varphi^2} \sum_k \left(\frac{\partial \varphi}{\partial k} \right)^2$$

$$+ 2 \left[\frac{\partial^2}{\partial \theta} \frac{\psi}{\partial r} \sum_k \frac{\partial \theta}{\partial k} \frac{\partial r}{\partial k} + \frac{\partial^2 \psi}{\partial \varphi \, \partial r} \sum_k \frac{\partial \varphi}{\partial k} \frac{\partial r}{\partial k} + \frac{\partial^2 \psi}{\partial \varphi \, \partial \theta} \sum_k \frac{\partial \varphi}{\partial k} \frac{\partial \theta}{\partial k} \right]$$

$$+ \frac{\partial \psi}{\partial r} \sum_k \frac{\partial^2 r}{\partial k^2} + \frac{\partial \psi}{\partial \theta} \sum_k \frac{\partial^2 \theta}{\partial k^2} + \frac{\partial \psi}{\partial \varphi} \sum_k \frac{\partial^2 \varphi}{\partial k^2} \quad \text{... (A1.7)}$$

where $k = x, \ y, \text{ or } z.$

The necessary derivatives are found with the aid of the following relationships:

$$x = r \sin \theta \cos \varphi$$

$$y = r \sin \theta \sin \varphi$$

$$z = r \cos \theta$$

$$r = (x^2 + y^2 + z^2)^{1/2}$$

$$\theta = \cos^{-1} \left(\frac{z}{r} \right)$$

$$\varphi = \tan^{-1} \left(\frac{y}{x} \right)$$

	$\frac{\partial r}{\partial k}$	$\frac{\partial^2 r}{\partial k^2}$	$\frac{\partial \theta}{\partial k}$	$\frac{\partial^2 \theta}{\partial k^2}$	$\frac{\partial \varphi}{\partial k}$	$\frac{\partial^2 \varphi}{\partial k^2}$
when $k = x$	$\frac{x}{r}$	$\frac{y^2 + z^2}{r^3}$	$\frac{1}{r^2} \frac{xz}{\left(x^2 + y^2\right)^{1/3}}$	$\frac{z\left[y^4 - 2x^4 - y^2\left(x^2 - z^2\right)\right]}{r^4 \left(x^2 + y^2\right)^{3/2}}$	$-\frac{y}{x^2 + y^2}$	$\frac{2xy}{\left(x^2 + y^2\right)^2}$
when $k = y$	$\frac{y}{r}$	$\frac{x^2 + z^2}{r^3}$	$\frac{1}{r^2} \frac{y^2}{\left(x^2 + y^2\right)^{1/2}}$	$\frac{z\left[x^4 - 2y^4 - x^2\left(y^2 - z^2\right)\right]}{r^4 \left(x^2 + y^2\right)^{3/2}}$	$\frac{x}{x^2 + y^2}$	$\frac{-2xy}{\left(x^2 + y^2\right)^2}$
when $k = z$	$\frac{z}{r}$	$\frac{x^2 + y^2}{r^3}$	$-\frac{1}{r^2} \sqrt{x^2 + y^2}$	$\frac{2z \sqrt{x^2 + y^2}}{r^4}$	0	0

... (A1.8)

Substitution of Equation (A.1.8) into Equation (A.1.7), gives

$$\nabla^2 \psi = \frac{\partial^2 \psi}{\partial r^2} + \frac{2}{r}\frac{\partial \psi}{\partial r} + \frac{1}{r^2}\frac{\partial^2 \psi}{\partial \theta^2} + \frac{1}{r^2}\cot\theta \frac{\partial \psi}{\partial \theta} + \frac{1}{r^2 \sin^2\theta}\frac{\partial^2 \psi}{\partial \varphi^2} \quad \text{... (A1.9)}$$

Since $$\frac{\partial}{\partial r}\left(r^2 \frac{\partial}{\partial r}\right) = 2r\frac{\partial}{\partial r} + r^2 \frac{\partial^2}{\partial r^2}$$

and $$\frac{\partial}{\partial \theta}\left(\sin\theta \frac{\partial}{\partial \theta}\right) = \cos\theta \frac{\partial}{\partial \theta} + \sin\theta \frac{\partial^2}{\partial \theta^2}$$

we have $$\nabla^2 = \frac{1}{r^2}\frac{\partial}{\partial r}\left(r^2 \frac{\partial}{\partial r}\right) + \frac{1}{r^2 \sin\theta}\frac{\partial}{\partial \theta}\left(\sin\theta \frac{\partial}{\partial \theta}\right) + \frac{1}{r^2 \sin^2\theta}\frac{\partial^2}{\partial \varphi^2} \quad \text{... (A1.10)}$$

Appendix 2

TRANSFORMATION OF ANGULAR MOMENTUM OPERATOR S_z FROM CARTESIAN TO POLAR COORDINATES

$$L_z = xp_y - yp_x$$

$$\hat{L}_z = \frac{h}{2\pi i}\left(x\frac{\partial}{\partial y} - y\frac{\partial}{\partial x}\right)$$

But
$$\frac{\partial}{\partial x} = \left(\frac{\partial r}{\partial x}\right)_y \frac{\partial}{\partial r} + \left(\frac{\partial \varphi}{\partial x}\right)_y \frac{\partial}{\partial \varphi}$$

and
$$\frac{\partial}{\partial y} = \left(\frac{\partial r}{\partial y}\right)_x \frac{\partial}{\partial r} + \left(\frac{\partial \varphi}{\partial y}\right)_x \frac{\partial}{\partial \varphi}.$$

With $r = \sqrt{x^2 + y^2}$, and $\varphi = \tan^{-1}(y/x)$, we have

$$\left(\frac{\partial r}{\partial x}\right)_y = \frac{x}{\sqrt{x^2+y^2}} = \frac{x}{r} = \cos\varphi; \left(\frac{\partial r}{\partial y}\right)_x = \sin\varphi$$

$$\left(\frac{\partial \varphi}{\partial x}\right)_y = -\frac{y}{x^2+y^2} = -\frac{1}{r}\sin\varphi; \left(\frac{\partial \varphi}{\partial y}\right)_x = \frac{1}{r}\cos\varphi$$

On substitution into $\hat{L}_z$ and simplification

$$\hat{L}_z = \frac{h}{2\pi i}\frac{\partial}{\partial \varphi}$$

By definition, $\hat{L}_\pm = \hat{L}_x + i\hat{L}_y$

$$\hat{L}_+ = \hat{L}_x + i\hat{L}_y = \frac{h}{2\pi}\left[\left(i\sin\varphi\frac{\partial}{\partial\theta} + i\cos\varphi\cot\theta\frac{\partial}{\partial\varphi}\right) + \left(\cos\varphi\frac{\partial}{\partial\theta} - \sin\varphi\cot\theta\frac{\partial}{\partial\varphi}\right)\right]$$

$$= \frac{h}{2\pi}\left[(\cos\varphi + i\sin\varphi)\left(\frac{\partial}{\partial\theta} + i\cot\theta\frac{\partial}{\partial\varphi}\right)\right]$$

$$= \frac{h}{2\pi} e^{i\varphi} \left(\frac{\partial}{\partial \theta} + i \cot \theta \frac{\partial}{\partial \varphi} \right)$$

Similarly, we have

$$\hat{L}_- = \hat{L}_x - i \hat{L}_y = \frac{h}{2\pi} e^{-i\varphi} \left(-\frac{\partial}{\partial \theta} + i \cot \theta \frac{\partial}{\partial \varphi} \right)$$

To obtain $\hat{L}^2$, we can use the identity

$$\hat{L}^2 = \hat{L}_x^2 + \hat{L}_y^2 + \hat{L}_z^2 \text{ or } \hat{L}^2 = \hat{L}_+ \hat{L}_- + \hat{L}_z^2 - \hat{L}_z$$

It is more convenient to use the latter. To obtain $\hat{L}_+ \hat{L}_-$, let us inspect the effect on ψ

$$\hat{L}_+ \hat{L}_- \psi = \frac{h^2}{4\pi^2} \left[e^{i\varphi} \left(\frac{\partial}{\partial \theta} + i \cot \theta \frac{\partial}{\partial \varphi} \right) e^{-i\varphi} \left(-\frac{\partial}{\partial \theta} + i \cot \theta \frac{\partial}{\partial \varphi} \right) \right] \psi$$

$$= -\frac{h^2}{4\pi^2} \left[\frac{\partial^2 \psi}{\partial \theta^2} + \cot \theta \frac{\partial \psi}{\partial \theta} + \cot^2 \theta \frac{\partial^2 \psi}{\partial \varphi^2} + i \frac{\partial \psi}{\partial \varphi} \right]$$

$$\hat{L}_z = \frac{h}{2\pi i} \frac{\partial}{\partial \varphi} \text{ and } \hat{L}_z^2 = -\frac{h^2}{4\pi^2} \frac{\partial^2}{\partial \varphi^2}$$

Combining these equations, we obtain

$$\hat{L}^2 = \hat{L}_+ \hat{L}_- + \hat{L}_z^2 - \hat{L}_z$$

$$= -\frac{h^2}{4\pi^2} \left[\frac{\partial^2}{\partial \theta^2} + \cot \theta \frac{\partial}{\partial \theta} + \cot^2 \theta \frac{\partial^2}{\partial \varphi^2} + \frac{\partial^2}{\partial \varphi^2} \right]$$

The identities

$$\frac{1}{\sin \theta} \frac{\partial}{\partial \theta} \sin \theta \frac{\partial \psi}{\partial \theta} = \cot \theta \frac{\partial \psi}{\partial \theta} + \frac{\partial^2 \psi}{\partial \theta^2}, \text{ and}$$

$$\cot^2 \theta + 1 = \frac{1}{\sin^2 \theta}$$

permit $\hat{L}^2$ to be written as

$$\hat{L}^2 = -\frac{h^2}{4\pi^2} \left[\frac{1}{\sin \theta} \frac{\partial}{\partial \theta} \sin \theta \frac{\partial}{\partial \theta} + \frac{1}{\sin^2 \theta} \frac{\partial^2}{\partial \varphi^2} \right].$$

Appendix 3

DETERMINANTS AND MATRICES

DETERMINANTS

A determinant is a number which is calculated by some rules from a set of numbers (called elements) ordered in a square array of rows and columns written between two vertical lines.

A 2 × 2 determinant, for example, is given as

$$D = \begin{vmatrix} a & b \\ c & d \end{vmatrix} = ad - bc \qquad \text{...(A3.1)}$$

Determinants of larger size (higher order) are evaluated as follows. Consider a 4 × 4 determinant.

$$D = \begin{vmatrix} a_{11} & a_{12} & a_{13} & a_{14} \\ a_{21} & a_{22} & a_{23} & a_{24} \\ a_{31} & a_{32} & a_{33} & a_{34} \\ a_{41} & a_{42} & a_{43} & a_{44} \end{vmatrix} \qquad \text{...(A3.2)}$$

in which the elements are indexed such that the first index gives the row number and the second index the column number. Now choose any row, say row 1; then strike out the row 1 and column 1: what remains is a 3 × 3 determinant which is called the "cofactor" of the element a_{11}. The cofactor of a_{11} is denoted as A_{11}. Similarly, determine the cofactors of all the elements in that row.

Multiply every element in that row with its cofactor and take their linear combination as follows:

$$D = a_{11} A_{11} - a_{12} A_{12} + a_{13} A_{13} - a_{14} A_{14} \qquad \text{...(A3.3)}$$

The sign of each term in the linear combination is determined as follows. If the sum of the two indices is even (*e.g.*, a_{11} and a_{13}), the sign is plus (+) and if the sum is odd (*e.g.*, a_{12} and a_{14}), the sign of minus (–).

Go on expanding the determinant in terms of cofactors successively till 2 × 2 determinants are obtained which can be evaluated by (A3.1). The 4 × 4 determinant is expanded into a linear combination of 12 terms involving 2 × 2 determinants. It is clear that for large determinants the number of terms may be unmanageably large.

Some Important Properties of Determinants

1. The determinant can be multiplied by a constant C by multiplying every element in a row or a column by C.

2. If every element in any one row or any one column is zero, the determinant is zero.
3. If any two rows or columns of a determinant D are interchanged the resulting determinant D′ becomes the negative of the first, *i.e.*, D′ = – D.
4. If two rows or columns of a determinant D are identical then D = 0.

Solving Linear Homogeneous Equations Through Determinants

Consider the following set of two homogeneous linear algebraic equations

$$a_1 x + b_1 y = 0 \qquad \text{... (A3.4)}$$

$$a_2 x + b_2 y = 0 \qquad \text{... (A3.5)}$$

Here x and y are unknown and the coefficients a_1, b_1, etc., are known. A non-trivial solution for Equations (A3.4) and (A3.5), can be found as follows:

Multiplying Equation (A3.4) by b_2 and Equation (A3.5) by b_1, we get

$$a_1 b_2 x + b_1 b_2 y = 0 \qquad \text{... (A3.6)}$$

$$a_2 b_1 x + b_1 b_2 y = 0 \qquad \text{... (A3.7)}$$

Subtracting Equation (A3.7) from Equation (A3.6), we get

$$(a_1 b_2 - a_2 b_1)\, x = 0$$

or

$$\begin{vmatrix} a_1 & b_1 \\ a_2 & b_2 \end{vmatrix} x = 0 \qquad \text{... (A3.8)}$$

For x to be non-zero, the determinant in (A.38) must be zero.

Similarly, for y to be non-zero, the corresponding determinant must be zero.

This is a very important result. A set of homogeneous linear equations can have non-trivial solution only if the determinant of the coefficients of the unknown is zero.

MATRICES

A system of $p \times q$ numbers arranged in p rows and q columns is called $p \times q$ (read as p by q) matrix. Each number is called "element" of the matrix.

Consider the following linear homogeneous equations.

$$x - y + 2z = 0 \qquad \text{... (A3.9)}$$

$$3x + y - 3z = 0$$

Here the coefficients of x, y and z-constitute a 2 × 3 matrix which is written as

$$\begin{bmatrix} 1 & -1 & 2 \\ 3 & 1 & -3 \end{bmatrix}$$

Any element in a matrix is located by specifying first its row and next its column. For example, if a matrix [A] is defined as

$$[\text{A}] = \begin{bmatrix} a_{11} & a_{12} & \cdots & a_{1j} & \cdots & a_{1q} \\ a_{21} & a_{22} & \cdots & a_{2j} & \cdots & a_{2q} \\ a_{i1} & a_{i2} & \cdots & a_{ij} & \cdots & a_{iq} \\ a_{p1} & a_{p2} & \cdots & a_{pj} & \cdots & a_{pq} \end{bmatrix} \qquad \text{... (A3.10)}$$

then a_{ij} is one of its elements which occurs in the ith row and jth column.

The elements can be pure or algebraic numbers, real or complex. A matrix can be rectangular ($p \times q$) or square ($p \times p$ or $q \times q$) or one consisting of a single row ($1 \times q$) or single column ($p \times 1$). A row or column-matrix is also called "vector".

Matrix is not the same as determinant. A determinant is essentially a number, whereas a matrix is an array of numbers. The determinants of

$$\begin{vmatrix} 1 & 2 \\ 3 & 4 \end{vmatrix} \text{ and } \begin{vmatrix} 1 & 3 \\ 2 & 4 \end{vmatrix}$$

are the same and equal –2, but the corresponding matrices are different.

Diagonal Matrix

A square matrix is said to be a diagonal matrix if all its non-diagonal elements are zero, for example

$$\begin{bmatrix} 1 & 0 & 0 \\ 0 & 2 & 0 \\ 0 & 0 & 3 \end{bmatrix} \qquad \text{...(A3.11)}$$

Unit Matrix

A diagonal matrix, each of those diagonal element is equal to 1, is called a unit matrix; for example,

$$\begin{bmatrix} 1 & 0 \\ 0 & 1 \end{bmatrix}, \begin{bmatrix} 1 & 0 & 0 \\ 0 & 1 & 0 \\ 0 & 0 & 1 \end{bmatrix}, \begin{bmatrix} 1 & 0 & 0 & 0 \\ 0 & 1 & 0 & 0 \\ 0 & 0 & 1 & 0 \\ 0 & 0 & 0 & 1 \end{bmatrix} \text{etc.}$$

Submatrix

The matrix constituted by the array of elements which remains after some rows or columns, or both, of a matrix are deleted is called a submatrix.

Symmetric Matrix

A square matrix is symmetric if the elements $a_{ij} = a_{ji}$; for example,

$$\begin{bmatrix} 1 & 2 & 3 \\ 2 & 1 & 4 \\ 3 & 4 & 1 \end{bmatrix}. \qquad \text{...(A3.12)}$$

Transpose of a Matrix [A]

The matrix obtained from any given matrix **[A]** by interchanging its rows and columns is called the transpose $\left[\tilde{\mathbf{A}}\right]$ or **[A]**; for example, if

$$[\mathbf{A}] = \begin{bmatrix} 1 & 2 \\ 3 & 4 \end{bmatrix}, \quad [\tilde{\mathrm{A}}] = \begin{bmatrix} 1 & 3 \\ 2 & 4 \end{bmatrix}. \quad \text{... (A3.13)}$$

Determinant of a Matrix [A]

The array of numbers constituting a square matrix can also give the determinant of the numbers when expanded as per rules; for example, if

$$[\mathbf{A}] = \begin{bmatrix} 1 & 2 \\ 3 & 4 \end{bmatrix}.$$

$$\mathbf{A} = \begin{vmatrix} 1 & 2 \\ 3 & 4 \end{vmatrix} = 1 \times 4 - 3 \times 2 = -2.$$

where [**A**] and A denote matrix and determinant respectively.

Algebra of Matrices

Matrices can be combined (added, subtracted and multiplied) to give new matrices. Three operations are addition (or subtraction), scalar multiplication and multiplication.

Addition

Two matrices [A] and [**B**] of same dimension (same number of rows and columns) can be added by adding each individual element of [A] to the element in the corresponding position in [B]; for example.

$$\begin{bmatrix} 1 & 2 \\ 3 & 4 \end{bmatrix} + \begin{bmatrix} 1 & 3 \\ 2 & 4 \end{bmatrix} = \begin{bmatrix} 1+1 & 2+3 \\ 3+2 & 4+4 \end{bmatrix} = \begin{bmatrix} 2 & 5 \\ 5 & 8 \end{bmatrix} \quad \text{... (A3.14)}$$

For subtraction, + sign is to be replaced by – sign.

Scalar Multiplication

This means multiplication of a matrix by a number and is accomplished by multiplying each of its elements by that number; for example,

$$3 \times \begin{bmatrix} 1 & 2 \\ 3 & 4 \end{bmatrix} = \begin{bmatrix} 3 & 6 \\ 9 & 12 \end{bmatrix}$$

Matrix Multiplication

Two matrices [A] and [**B**] can be multiplied to give a product matrix [C]; the elements of [C] are obtained by the rule.

$$c_{ij} = \sum_n a_{in} \cdot b_{nj}$$

where c_{ij} is the element at the ith row and jth column of [C] and the summation on the right includes the elements (a_{in}) of all the n columns of the ith row of [A] and those (b_{nj}) of all the n rows of the jth column of [**B**].

For example, if

$$[\mathbf{A}] = \begin{bmatrix} 1 & 2 \\ 3 & 4 \end{bmatrix} \text{ and } [\mathrm{B}] = \begin{bmatrix} 1 & 3 \\ 2 & 4 \end{bmatrix} \text{ and}$$

$[\mathbf{A}] \times [\mathbf{B}] = [\mathbf{C}]$, then

$$[\mathbf{C}] = \begin{bmatrix} 1 & 2 \\ 3 & 4 \end{bmatrix} \times \begin{bmatrix} 1 & 3 \\ 2 & 4 \end{bmatrix} = \begin{bmatrix} (1\times 1)+(2\times 2) & (1\times 3)+(2\times 4) \\ (3\times 1)+(4\times 2) & (3\times 3)+(4\times 4) \end{bmatrix}$$

$$= \begin{bmatrix} 5 & 11 \\ 11 & 25 \end{bmatrix}$$

The elements of the new matrix **[C]** are obtained by the rule,

$$C_{11} = a_{11}\, b_{11} + a_{12}\, b_{21} = 1\times 1 + 2\times 2 = 5$$

$$C_{12} = a_{11}\, b_{12} + a_{12}\, b_{22} = 1\times 3 + 2\times 4 = 11 \qquad \text{... (A3.15)}$$

and so on.

This requires that the number of columns in **[A]** be equal to the number of rows in **[B]**. It is important to note that the product **[B]** × **[A]** will not necessarily be equal to the product **[A]** × **[B]**. In the above example,

$$[\mathbf{B}] \times [\mathbf{A}] = \begin{bmatrix} 1 & 3 \\ 2 & 4 \end{bmatrix} \times \begin{bmatrix} 1 & 2 \\ 3 & 4 \end{bmatrix} = \begin{bmatrix} 10 & 14 \\ 14 & 20 \end{bmatrix}$$

Two matrices **[C]** and **[D]** are equal only if $C_{ij} = D_{ij}$ for all elements.

When **[A]** × **[B]** = **[B]** × **[A]**, the two matrices [A] and [B] are said to be commutative.

Inverse of a Matrix

The inverse $[\mathbf{A}]^{-1}$ of a matrix **[A]** is defined such that

$$[\mathbf{A}]\,[\mathbf{A}]^{-1} = [\mathbf{A}]^{-1}\,[\mathbf{A}] = \mathbf{I},$$

the unit matrix of identity. If suppose [B] is the inverse of [A], then

$$[\mathbf{A}]\,[\mathbf{B}] = [\mathbf{B}]\,[\mathbf{A}] = \mathbf{I} \qquad \text{... (A3.16)}$$

For the inverse **[B]** or **[A]** to exist it is necessary that the determinant $|A| \neq 0$.

The inverse **[B]** of a matrix **[A]** can be constructed by the formula

$$[\mathbf{B}] = \frac{[\tilde{\mathbf{A}}]'}{|A|} \qquad \text{... (A3.17)}$$

where $[\tilde{\mathbf{A}}]'$ is the transpose of the matrix of cofactors of $|A|$.

For example, let

$$[\mathbf{A}] = \begin{bmatrix} 1 & 2 \\ 3 & 4 \end{bmatrix}, \text{ then } [\tilde{\mathbf{A}}]' = \begin{bmatrix} 4 & -2 \\ -3 & 1 \end{bmatrix} \text{ and } |A| = -2$$

So, $$[\mathbf{B}] = [\mathbf{A}]^{-1} = \frac{1}{(-2)}\begin{bmatrix} 4 & -2 \\ -3 & 1 \end{bmatrix}$$

$$= \begin{bmatrix} -2 & 1 \\ 3/2 & -1/2 \end{bmatrix}$$

Matrix inversion for larger matrices is a very tedious process and is often done by computer.

Singular and Non-Singular Matrices

A matrix [**A**] is singular if is determinant $|A| = 0$ and non-singular if the $|A| \neq 0$. Only a non-singular matrix possesses its inverse.

Simultaneous Linear Equations in Matrix Form

A set of n simultaneous equations

$$a_{11} x_1 + a_{12} x_2 + \ldots + a_{1n} x_n = b_1$$
$$a_{21} x_1 + a_{22} x_2 + \ldots + a_{2n} x_n = b_2$$
$$\ldots\ldots\ldots\ldots\ldots\ldots\ldots\ldots\ldots$$
$$\ldots\ldots\ldots\ldots\ldots\ldots\ldots\ldots\ldots$$
$$a_{n1} x_1 + a_{n2} x_2 + \ldots + a_{nn} x_n = b_n \quad \ldots (A3.18)$$

can be written in matrix notation as

$$[\mathbf{A}]\,[x] = [\mathbf{b}] \quad \ldots (A3.19)$$

where $$[\mathbf{A}] = \begin{bmatrix} a_{11} & a_{12} & \cdots & a_{1n} \\ a_{21} & a_{22} & \cdots & a_{2n} \\ \cdots & \cdots & & \cdots \\ \cdots & \cdots & & \cdots \\ a_{n1} & a_{n2} & \cdots & a_{nn} \end{bmatrix} \quad \ldots (A3.20)$$

is the matrix of coefficients, and

$$[x] = \begin{bmatrix} x_1 \\ x_2 \\ \vdots \\ x_n \end{bmatrix} \text{ and } [b] = \begin{bmatrix} b_1 \\ b_2 \\ \vdots \\ b_n \end{bmatrix} \quad \ldots (A3.21)$$

are column vectors, *i.e.*, $n \times 1$ matrices.

Multiplying both sides of $[\mathbf{A}]\,[x] = [b]$ (A 3.19) by $[A]^{-1}$ from left, we get

$$[\mathbf{A}]^{-1}\,[\mathbf{A}]\,[x] = [\mathbf{A}]^{-1}\,[b]$$

or $$[x] = [\mathbf{A}]^{-1}\,[b] \quad \ldots (A3.22)$$

So, if the unknowns $x_1, x_2, \ldots, x_n$ can be expressed in terms of

$$b_1, b_2, \ldots b_n,$$

the inverse $[\mathbf{A}]^{-1}$ of $[\mathbf{A}]$ can be determined; or, conversely, the equations. Equation (A3.19) can be solved if we know the inverse $[\mathbf{A}]^{-1}$ of $[\mathbf{A}]$.

Eigenvalue Equation

If in Equation (A3.19),

$$[b] = \lambda [x],$$

then we have an eigenvalue equation

$$[\mathbf{A}][\boldsymbol{x}] = \lambda [\boldsymbol{x}] \qquad \text{... (A3.23)}$$

with λ as the eigenvalue, and $[\boldsymbol{x}]$ as the "eigenvector". In general, there are n eigenvalues that will satisfy the n simultaneous equations

$$\begin{aligned} (a_{11} - \lambda)\, x_1 + a_{12}\, x_2 + \ldots + a_{1n}\, x_n &= 0 \\ a_{21}\, x_1 + (a_{22} - \lambda)\, x_2 + \ldots + a_{2n}\, x_n &= 0 \\ \ldots\ldots\ldots\ldots\ldots\ldots\ldots\ldots\ldots\ldots \\ \ldots\ldots\ldots\ldots\ldots\ldots\ldots\ldots\ldots\ldots \\ a_{n1}\, x_1 + a_{n1}\, x_2 + \ldots + (a_{nn} - \lambda)\, x_n &= 0 \end{aligned} \qquad \text{... (A3.24)}$$

or in the matrix form

$$[\mathbf{A}] - \lambda [\mathbf{I}] = 0 \qquad \text{... (A3.25)}$$

There will be corresponding n eigenvectors. These have non-trivial solution only if the determinant

$$\begin{vmatrix} (a_{11} - \lambda) & a_{12} & \cdots & a_{1n} \\ a_{21} & (a_{22} - \lambda) & \cdots & a_{2n} \\ \cdots & \cdots & & \cdots \\ \cdots & \cdots & & \cdots \\ a_{n1} & a_n & \cdots & (a_{nn} - \lambda) \end{vmatrix} = 0 \qquad \text{... (A3.26)}$$

or $$|\, [\mathbf{A}] - \lambda [\mathbf{I}] \,| = 0. \qquad \text{... (A3.27)}$$

Appendix 4

VECTORS

Vector $\left(\vec{A}\right)$ is a physical or mathematical quantity which has magnitude and direction. Quantity which has only magnitude is scalar (A). Velocity, momentum etc., are vectors while energy is scalar. Unit vector $\left(\vec{h}\right)$ is a vector whose magnitude is unity; thus

$$\vec{A} = A . \vec{h} \qquad \text{... (A4.1)}$$

A 3-dimensional vector has three cartesian components. The components of unit vectors are denoted as $\vec{i}, \vec{j}$ and $\vec{k}$ along the axes X, Y and Z respectively. In terms of unit vectors, the vector $\vec{A}$ is expressed as

$$\vec{A} = A_x \vec{i} + A_y \vec{j} + A_z \vec{k} \qquad \text{... (A4.2)}$$

where A_x, A_y and A_z are the magnitudes of the projections of $\vec{A}$ along the three axes respectively.

We also write

$$\vec{A} = (A_x, A_y, A_z) \qquad \text{... (A4.3)}$$

Mathematically, any single row or column of a matrix is called vector. The elements of the row or column are the components of the vector, *e.g.*,

$$\vec{V} = (a_1, a_2, a_3, a_4, a_5, a_6)$$

is a vector in a hypothetical 6-dimensional space.

Vector addition: If $\vec{A} = (A_x, A_y, A_z)$ and $\vec{B} = (B_x, B_y, B_z)$ then

$$\vec{A} + \vec{B} = (A_x + B_x, A_y + B_y, A_z + B_z) \qquad \text{... (A4.4)}$$

Vector multiplication: There are two types of vector products (a) scalar product and (b) vector product. Scalar, or dot, product of vectors $\vec{A}$ and $\vec{B}$ is a scalar and is defined as

$$\vec{A} . \vec{B} = |A| \, |B| \cos\theta, \theta = \text{angle between the two vectors} \qquad \text{... (A.45)}$$

Also,

$$\vec{A} . \vec{B} = A_x B_x + A_y B_y + A_z B_z \qquad \text{... (A4.6)}$$

where A_x, B_x etc., are the components of the vectors. If the scalar product of the vector A by itself gives 1, the vector is normalised

$$\vec{A} . \vec{A} = A_x^2 + A_y^2 + A_z^2 = 1 \qquad \text{... (A4.7)}$$

If $\vec{A} \cdot \vec{B} = 0$, the vectors $\vec{A}$ and $\vec{B}$ are orthogonal.

The dot products of the unit vectors are given as

$$\vec{i} \cdot \vec{j} = \vec{j} \cdot \vec{k} = \vec{k} \cdot \vec{i} = 0$$

and

$$\vec{i} \cdot \vec{i} = \vec{j} \cdot \vec{j} = \vec{k} \cdot \vec{k} = 1 \qquad \text{... (A4.8)}$$

Vector, or cross, product of two vectors $\vec{A}$ and $\vec{B}$ is defined as

$$\vec{A} \times \vec{B} = AB \sin\theta\, \vec{n} \qquad \text{... (A4.9)}$$

where θ is the angle between $\vec{A}$ and $\vec{B}$, and $\vec{n}$ is the unit vector perpendicular to the plane containing $\vec{A}$ and $\vec{B}$ in the sense of advancing of a right handed screw rotated from $\vec{A}$ to $\vec{B}$. It follows that

$$\vec{A} \times \vec{A} = 0\ (\theta = 0) \qquad \text{... (A4.10)}$$

$$\vec{i} \times \vec{j} = \vec{k}, \vec{j} \times \vec{k} = \vec{i}, \vec{k} \times \vec{i} = \vec{j}\ \ (\theta = 90°) \qquad \text{... (A4.11)}$$

but

$$\vec{j} \times \vec{i} = -\vec{k} \text{ and so on,}$$

and

$$\vec{i} \times \vec{i} = \vec{j} \times \vec{j} = \vec{k} \times \vec{k} = 0 \qquad \text{... (A4.12)}$$

Also,

$$\vec{A} \times \vec{B} = \begin{vmatrix} \vec{i} & \vec{j} & \vec{k} \\ A_x & A_y & A_z \\ B_x & B_y & B_z \end{vmatrix} \qquad \text{... (A4.13)}$$

Vector operator: The vector differential operator, $\vec{\nabla}$, called 'del' is defined as

$$\vec{\nabla} = \vec{i}\frac{\partial}{\partial x} + \vec{j}\frac{\partial}{\partial y} + \vec{k}\frac{\partial}{\partial z} \qquad \text{... (A4.14)}$$

When applied to a scalar function it is called "gradient" and is given as

$$\text{grad} f = \vec{\nabla} f = \vec{i}\frac{\partial f}{\partial x} + \vec{j}\frac{\partial f}{\partial y} + \vec{k}\frac{\partial f}{\partial z} \qquad \text{... (A4.15)}$$

On squaring, it becomes a scalar operator [by Equations (A4.7) and (A4.8)]

$$\nabla^2 = \vec{\nabla} \cdot \vec{\nabla} = \frac{\partial^2}{\partial x^2} + \frac{\partial^2}{\partial y^2} + \frac{\partial^2}{\partial z^2} \qquad \text{... (A4.16)}$$

Appendix 5

TABLE OF SOME USEFUL INTEGRALS

$$\int x^n \, dx = \frac{x^{n+1}}{n+1}, n \neq -1$$

$$\int \frac{dx}{x} = \log_e x$$

$$\int \exp(ax) \, . \, dx = \frac{\exp(ax)}{a}$$

$$\int_0^\infty x^n \exp(-ax) \, dx = \frac{n!}{a^{n+1}}$$

$$\int_0^\infty \exp(-ax) \, . \, dx = \frac{1}{a}$$

$$\int_0^\infty x \exp(-ax) \, dx = \frac{1}{a^2}$$

$$\int_1^\infty x^2 \exp(-ax) \, . \, dx = \left(\frac{2\exp(-a)}{a^3}\right)\left(1 + a + \frac{a^2}{2}\right)$$

$$\int_0^\infty \exp(-ax^2) \, dx = \frac{1}{2}\sqrt{\frac{\pi}{a}}$$

$$\int_{-\infty}^{+\infty} \exp(-ax^2) \, dx = \int_{-\infty}^{0} \exp(-ax^2) \, dx + \int_0^\infty \exp(-ax^2) \, dx$$

$$= \sqrt{\frac{\pi}{a}}$$

$$\int_0^\infty x \exp(-ax^2) \, dx = \frac{1}{2a}$$

$$\int_0^\infty x^2 \exp(-ax^2) \, . \, dx = \frac{1}{4}\sqrt{\frac{\pi}{a^3}}$$

$$\int_{-\infty}^{\infty} x^2 \exp\left(-ax^2\right) dx = \frac{1}{2}\sqrt{\frac{\pi}{a^3}}$$

$$\int_{0}^{\infty} x^{2n} \exp\left(-ax^2\right) dx = \frac{1.3\cdots(2n-!)}{2^{n+1}}\sqrt{\frac{\pi}{a^{2n+1}}}$$

$$\int_{0}^{\infty} x^{2n+1} \exp\left(-ax^2\right) dx = \frac{n!}{2a^{n+1}}$$

$$\int_{0}^{\infty} \frac{x^3}{e^x - 1} dx = \frac{\pi^4}{15}$$

$$\int \sin x \, dx = -\cos x$$

$$\int \cos x \, dx = \sin x$$

$$\int \sin^2 x \, dx = \frac{1}{2}x - \frac{1}{4}\sin 2x$$

$$\int \cos^2 x \, dx = \frac{1}{2}x + \frac{1}{4}\sin 2x$$

$$\int \sin x \, . \cos x \, dx = \frac{1}{2}\sin^2 x$$

$$\int \sin mx \, . \cos nx \, dx = -\frac{\cos(m-n)x}{2(m-n)} - \frac{\cos(m+n)x}{2(m+n)}$$

$$\int x \sin^2 x \, dx = \frac{x^2}{4} - \frac{x \sin 2x}{4} - \frac{\cos 2x}{8}$$

$$\int_{0}^{\pi} y \sin^2 y \, dy = \frac{\pi^2}{4}$$

$$\int_{0}^{\pi} y \cos y \, dy = \left[\cos y - y \sin y\right]_0^{\pi}$$

$$\int_{0}^{\pi} y \cos^3 y \, dy = \frac{y \sin 3y}{12} + \frac{\cos 3y}{36} + \frac{3}{4} y \sin y + \frac{3}{4}\cos y$$

$$\int_{0}^{\pi} \cos^n \theta \sin \theta \, d\theta = -\left[\frac{\cos^{n+1}\theta}{n+1}\right]_0^{\pi}$$

Appendix 6

SI UNITS AND PHYSICAL CONSTANTS

SI Base Units

Physical quantity	*SI units*
Length	meter (m)
Mass	kilogram (kg)
Time	second (s)
Temperature	kelvin (K)
Electric current	ampere (A)
Light intensity	candela (Cd)
Angle	radian (rad)

SI Derived units

Force	newton (N)
Pressure	pascal (Pa)
Energy	joule (J)
Electric charge	coulomb (C)
Potential difference	volt (V)
Frequency	hertz (Hz)

Relation between SI and other units for Energy

1 eV (electron-volt)	$= 1.602 \times 10^{-19}$ J
1 J	$= 10^{7}$ erg
1 J	$= 6.241 \times 10^{18}$ eV
1 erg	$= 10^{-7}$ J
1 J	$= 1.439 \times 10^{20}$ kcal
1 J	$= 1.509 \times 10^{33}$ Hz
1 cal	$= 4.186$ J
1 kcal	$= 6.947 \times 10^{-21}$ J

Physical Constants

Velocity of light (c)	$= 2.997925 \times 10^8$ ms^{-1}
Electronic charge (e)	$= 1.60218 \times 10^{-19}$ C
	$= 4.80298 \times 10^{-10}$ cm$^{3/2}$ g$^{1/2}$ s^{-1} (e.s.u.)
Avogadro Number (N_A)	$= 6.02214 \times 10^{23}$ mol^{-1}
Atomic mass unit (u)	$= 1.66054 \times 10^{-27}$ kg
Mass of electron (m_e)	$= 9.10939 \times 10^{-31}$ kg
Mass of proton (m_p)	$= 1.67262 \times 10^{-27}$ kg
Mass of neutron (m_n)	$= 1.67403 \times 10^{-27}$ kg
Boltzmann constant (k_B)	$= 1.38066 \times 10^{-23}$ JK^{-1}
Planck's constant (h)	$= 6.62608 \times 10^{-34}$ Js
Vacuum Permittivity (ε_0)	$= 8.85419 \times 10^{-12}$ J^{-1} C^2 m^{-1}
	$= 8.85419 \times 10^{-12}$ C^2 N^2 m^{-2}
(ii)	$4\pi\varepsilon_0 = 1.11265 \times 10^{-10}$ J^{-1} C^2 m^{-1}
	$\dfrac{1}{4\pi\varepsilon_0} = 0.8988 \times 10^{10}$ Jm C^{-2}
Bohr radius (a_0)	$= \dfrac{(4\pi\varepsilon_0)\hbar^2}{me^2} = 5.29177 \times 10^{-11}$ m $\left(\hbar = \dfrac{h}{2\pi}\right)$
Rhydberg constant (R_0)	$= \dfrac{me^4}{8h^3 c \varepsilon_0^2} = 1.09737 \times 10^7$ m^{-1}
Gas constant (R)	$= 8.31451$ JK^{-1} mol^{-1}
Faraday constant (F)	$= 9.648445 \times 10^4$ C mol^{-1}
Bohr magneton (γ_B)	$= \dfrac{e\hbar}{2m_e} = 9.27402 \times 10^{-24}$ J τ^{-1}
Nuclear magneton (μ_N)	$= \dfrac{e\hbar}{2m_p} = 5.05079 \times 10^{-27}$ J τ^{-1}
	(τ = tesla)

Conversion Factors for Energy

$$1 \text{ eV} = 1.60219 \times 10^{-19} \text{ J} = 96.485 \text{ kJ mol}^{-1} = 23.06 \text{ kcal mol}^{-1}$$
$$= 8065.5 \text{ cm}^{-1}$$
$$1 \text{ cm}^{-1} = 1.986 \times 10^{-23} \text{ J} = 11.96 \text{ J mol}^{-1} = 0.1240 \text{ meV} = 1.240 \times 10^{-4} \text{ eV}$$
$$1 \text{ J mol}^{-1} = 1.036 \times 10^{-5} \text{ eV} = 8.359 \times 10^{-2} \text{ cm}^{-1} = 2.390 \times 10^{-4} \text{ kcal mol}^{-1}$$

Numerical Constants

$$\pi = 3.14159265, \; e = 2.718281828$$

$$1\text{ N} = \text{Kg ms}^{-2} = 1\text{ Jm}^{-1} = 10^5\text{ dyne}; 1\text{ W} = 1\text{ Js}^{-1}, 1\,\tau = 1\text{ J c}^{-1}\text{ s m}^{-2}$$

$$1\text{ C} = 1\text{ As}; 1\text{ A} = 1\text{ Cs}^{-1}; 1\text{ J} = 1\text{ A V.s.}; 1\text{ V} = \text{J A}^{-1}\text{ s}^{-1}; 1\text{ J} = 10^7\text{ erg}$$

Prefixes

atto (a)	femto (f)	pico (p)	nano (n)	micro (μ)	milli (m)	centi (c)	deci (d)
10^{-18}	10^{-15}	10^{-12}	10^{-9}	10^{-4}	10^{-3}	10^{-2}	10^{-1}
hecto (h)	kilo (k)	mega (M)	Giga (G)	Tetra (T)	peta (ρ)	Exa (E)	
10^{2}	10^{3}	10^{6}	10^{9}	10^{12}	10^{15}	10^{18}	

Atomic Units and S.I. Units

Atomic units (a.u.)	*S.I. Units (S.I.)*
$m_e = 1$	9.109×10^{-31} kg
$e = 1$	1.602×10^{-19} C
$\dfrac{h}{2\pi} = 1$	1.0545×10^{-34} Js
$4\pi\varepsilon_0 = 1$	1.1126×10^{-10} J^{-1} C^2 m^{-1}
$a_0 = \dfrac{4\pi\varepsilon_0 \hbar^2}{m_e e^2} = 1$ bohr	5.292×10^{-11} m
Velocity of electron in 1st Bohr orbit (a_0) $\dfrac{\frac{e}{\sqrt{4\pi\varepsilon_0}}}{\hbar} = 1$ (a.u.)	2.18764×10^{6} ms^{-1}
V_0 (atomic unit of potential)	27.211 V

$$= \frac{\left(\dfrac{e}{\sqrt{4\pi\varepsilon_0}}\right)^2 a_0}{e} = 1\text{ (a.u.)}$$

Appendix 7

IMPORTANT FORMULAS

Basic formulae:

$\frac{d}{dx} x^n = nx^{n-1}$

$\int x^n dx = \frac{x^{n+1}}{n+1}$

$\frac{d}{dx} cx^n = cnx^{n-1}$

$\int uv\, dx = u\int vdx - \int \left[\frac{du}{dx}\int vdx\right] dx$

$\frac{d}{dx}(uv) = \frac{u.dv}{dx} + \frac{vdu}{dx}$

$\frac{d}{dx} \sin x = \cos x$

$\int \sin x\, dx = -\cos x$

$\frac{d}{dx} \cos x = -\sin x$

$\int \cos x\, dx = \sin x$

$\frac{d}{dx} \sin ax = a \cos ax$

$\int \sin ax = \frac{-\cos ax}{a}$

$\frac{d}{dx} \cos ax = -a \sin ax$

$\int \cos ax\, dx = \frac{\sin ax}{a}$

$\frac{d}{dx} e^x = e^x$

$\int e^x dx = ex$

$\frac{d}{dx} e^{ax} = ae^{ax}$

$\int e^{ax} dx = \frac{e^{ax}}{a}$

$\frac{d}{dx} ln = \frac{1}{x}$

$\int \frac{1}{x} dx = lnx$

Trignometric

1. $\sin 2x = 2 \sin x \cos x$

   $\sin 2ax = 2 \sin ax \cos ax$

2. $\sin^2 x = \frac{1 - \cos 2x}{2}$

$\sin 45° = \cos 45° = \frac{1}{\sqrt{2}}$

$\sin 90° = \cos 0° = 1$

$\cos 90° = \sin 0° = 0$

3. $\cos^2 x = \dfrac{1 + \cos 2x}{2}$

$\cos 60° = \sin 30° = \dfrac{1}{2}$

$\cos 30° = \sin 60° = \dfrac{\sqrt{3}}{2}$

4. $\sin x \cos x = \sin \dfrac{2x}{2}$

$e^{-\infty} = 0 \quad e^{\infty} = \infty$

$\sin n\pi = 0, \sin 2n\pi = 0$

$e^{-0} = 1 \quad e^0 = 1$

$\cos n\pi = -1, \cos 2n\pi = +1$ (n ↓ odd, $2n$ ↓ even)

$a^0 = 1 \quad e = 2.7$

$\int \dfrac{\partial^2}{\partial x^2} \cos ax = -a^2 \cos ax$

$\dfrac{\partial^2}{\partial x^2} \sin ax = -a^2 \sin ax$

$\dfrac{\partial^n}{\partial x^n} e^{\alpha x} = \alpha^n e^{\alpha x}$

$\sin (A + B) = \sin A \cos B + \cos A \sin B$

$\sin \dfrac{\pi}{2} = 1, \sin^{-1}(1) = \dfrac{\pi}{2}$

$\cos (A + B) = \cos A \cos B - \sin A \sin B$

$2 \sin A \sin B = \cos (A - B) - \cos (A + B)$

Important Results:

$$\int_0^l \sin^2\left(\frac{n\pi x}{l}\right) dx = \frac{l}{2} \qquad \int_0^l \cos^2\left(\frac{n\pi x}{l}\right) dx = \frac{l}{2}$$

$$\int_0^l x \sin^2\left(\frac{n\pi x}{l}\right) dx = \frac{l^2}{4} \qquad \int_0^l x \cos^2\left(\frac{n\pi x}{l}\right) dx = \frac{l^2}{4}$$

$$\int_{-l}^{+l} \cos^2\left(\frac{n\pi x}{2l}\right) dx = l \qquad \int_{-l}^{+l} \sin^2\left(\frac{n\pi x}{2l}\right) dx = l$$

$$\int xe^x = (x - 1) e^x \qquad \int_0^l x^2 \sin^2\left(\frac{n\pi x}{l}\right) = \frac{l^3}{6} - \frac{l^3}{4n^2\pi^2}$$

Operator and function: operator that operates a function represented by ^ (cap) and function is a rule that relates two or more variables.

e.g., $z = 3x^2y + mpt$

^ $z = f(x, y, m, p, t)$

1. Operator is Directional
2. Square or cube of operator $\hat{A}^2 f(x) = \hat{A}\hat{A} f(x)$

$\hat{A}^3 f(x) = \hat{A}\hat{A}\hat{A} f(x)$

$\hat{A}^2 f(x) \neq [A f(x)]^2$

Commutation of operator: Commutation of two operator $\hat{A}$ and $\hat{B}$ is represented by $[\hat{A}; \hat{B}]$

$$[\hat{A}, \hat{B}]\, \varphi = AB\, \varphi - BA\, \varphi$$

If $[\hat{A}, \hat{B}] = 0$ $\quad \hat{A}$ & $\hat{B}$ commute

$\neq 0$ $\quad \hat{A}$ & $\hat{B}$ anticommute

Commutative operators do not follow Hesienberg principle means they can be determined simultaneously e.g. $[Lx, x]$ are commute

$[Px, x]$ Anticommute

$\nabla^2 \rightarrow$ laplacian operator.

1. Position (x, y, z), $\hat{x}, \hat{y}, \hat{z}$

   Multiplication operation $\hat{x}\varphi = x\varphi$

2. Momentum (Px, Py, Pz)

$$\hat{P}x = \frac{-i\hbar\partial}{\partial x},\ \hat{P}x\ \varphi_{(x)} = \frac{-i\hbar\ \partial\varphi_{(x)}}{\partial x}$$

3. Kinetic energy (Kx, Ky, Kz)

$$\hat{K}x = \frac{-\hbar^2}{2m}\frac{\partial^2}{\partial x^2},\ K_{Total} = Kx + Ky + Kz$$

$$K_{Total} = \frac{-\hbar^2}{2m}\nabla^2 \qquad \nabla^2 = \frac{\partial^2}{\partial x^2} + \frac{\partial^2}{\partial y^2} + \frac{\partial^2}{\partial z^2}$$

4. Potential energy (Vx, Vy, Vz)

$$\hat{V}x = \frac{1}{2}Kx^2$$

5. Total energy operator ($\hat{H} \rightarrow$ Hamiltonian operator)

$$\hat{H} = K + V$$

$$= \frac{-\hbar^2}{2m}\left(\frac{\partial^2}{\partial x^2} + \frac{\partial^2}{\partial y^2} + \frac{\partial^2}{\partial z^2}\right) + V_{x,y,z}$$

$$\boxed{\hat{H} = \frac{-\hbar^2}{2m}\nabla^2 + V}$$

$$\boxed{\hat{H}_x = \frac{-\hbar^2}{2m}\frac{\partial^2}{\partial x^2} + V(x)}$$

6. Angular Momentum

$$\hat{L}x = -i\hbar\left[y\frac{\partial}{\partial z} - z\frac{\partial}{\partial y}\right]$$

$$\hat{L}y = -i\hbar\left[z\frac{\partial}{\partial x} - x\frac{\partial}{\partial y}\right]$$

$$\hat{L}z = -i\hbar\left[x\frac{\partial}{\partial y} - y\frac{\partial}{\partial x}\right]$$

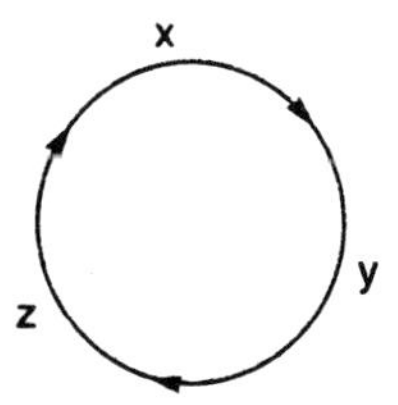

Generally operator with combination of x such as $x\frac{d}{dx}$ and $x\frac{d^2}{dx^2}$ do not commute while operators with x or $\frac{d}{dx}$ separately can commute

$$\left[x^n, \frac{d}{dx}\right] = -nx^{n-1}$$

$$\left[\frac{d}{dx}, x^n\right] = nx^{n-1}$$

$$[x^n, Px] = +i\hbar\ nx^{n-1}$$

$$[Px, x^n] = -i\hbar\ nx^{n-1}$$

$$[\hat{H}, \hat{x}]\varphi = \frac{-\hbar^2}{m}\frac{d\varphi}{dx}$$

$$[kx, x]\varphi = \frac{-\hbar^2}{m}\frac{d\varphi}{dx}$$

Eigen value equation and eigen function

$$\frac{d}{dx}(e^{ax}) = ae^{ax}$$

$\frac{d}{dx}$ → operator; e^{ax} → eigen function; a → eigen value

Expectation value or average value

$$< M > = \int \varphi \hat{M}\varphi\, d\tau$$

1D box	0 to l	$\frac{d\tau}{dx}$
Hydrogen	0 to ∞	$4\pi r^2 dr$
Rigid Rotar	0 to 2π	$d\phi$
S.H.O.	$-\infty$ to $+\infty$	dx

Uncertainty in position

$$\Delta x = \sqrt{< x^2 > - < x >^2}$$

Uncertainty in momentum

$$\Delta px = \sqrt{< Px^2 > - < Px >^2} \qquad \Delta x \,.\, \Delta px \geq \frac{\hbar}{2}$$

Standard deviation form

ID Box $< x > = \frac{l}{2}$ $\qquad < Px > = 0 \qquad \varphi = \sqrt{\frac{2}{l}}\sin\frac{n\pi x}{l}$

$$< x^2 > = \frac{l^2}{3} - \frac{l^2}{2n^2\pi^2} \qquad < Px^2 > = \frac{n^2h^2}{4l^2} \qquad < K.E > = \frac{n^2h^2}{8ml^2}$$

Hydrogen Atom $< r > = \frac{3}{2} a_0$ $\qquad \varphi_{1s} = \frac{1}{\sqrt{\pi a_0^{3/2}}} e^{-r/a_0}$

$$< r^2 > = 3a_0^{\,2}$$

$$\int_0^{\infty} \mu^n e^{-\alpha r}\, dx = \frac{n!}{\alpha^{n+1}}$$

S.H.O

$< x > = 0$ $\qquad < Px > = 0$ $\qquad \varphi_0 = \left(\frac{\beta}{\pi}\right)^{1/4} e^{-\beta x^{2/2}}$

$< x^2 > = \frac{1}{2\beta}$ $\qquad < Px^2 > = \frac{\beta\hbar^2}{2}$

$$\int_{-\infty}^{+\infty} x^n e^{-\alpha x^2} .dx = 0 \text{ when } n \text{ is odd}$$

$$= \frac{\sqrt{\dfrac{n+1}{2}}}{\alpha^{n+1/2}} \text{ when } n \text{ is even}$$

and $\qquad \sqrt{n+1} = n\sqrt{n}$

$$\sqrt{\frac{9}{2}} = \frac{7}{2}\cdot\frac{5}{2}\cdot\frac{3}{2}\cdot\frac{1}{2}\sqrt{\pi}$$

Virial theorem – Energy contributed to ground state energy $\frac{1}{2}$ $(h\nu)$ is equally contributed by K.E & P.F.

$$\boxed{K = V}$$

Normalisation and Probability

$P = \int \varphi^* \varphi d\tau$ for function where $\varphi^* = \varphi$

A function is said to normalised if

$$\int \varphi^* \varphi d\tau = 1$$

Normalise a function: $\varphi = Ax$ find value of A put root of it's inverse on left of function.

i.e., $\qquad A = \frac{1}{\sqrt{\int \varphi\varphi\, d\tau}}$

Normalised function : $\frac{1}{\sqrt{\int \varphi\varphi\, de}} \varphi$

Orthogonal function: $\int \varphi_1 \varphi_2\, d\tau = 0$ then the functions φ_1 and φ_2 are said to be orthogonal.

Orthogonal function: A function satisfy the condition of normal as well as orthogonal forms is orthonormal.

δ m, $n = 1$ if $m = n$ normalised
δ m, $n = 0$ if $m \neq n$ orthogonal } orthonormalised

Unit of φ wave function: $\int \varphi\varphi \, d\tau = 1$ (dimentionally)

$$\varphi^2 d\tau = 1$$

$$\varphi = \frac{1}{\sqrt{d\tau}}$$

1 D Box $\varphi = \frac{1}{\sqrt{L}} = L^{-1/2}$

2 D Box $\varphi = \frac{1}{\sqrt{dx\,dy}} = \frac{L}{\sqrt{L\,.\,L}} = L^{-1}$

3 D Box $\varphi = \frac{1}{\sqrt{dx\,dy\,dz}} = L^{-3/2}$

Hydrogen atom $\varphi = \frac{1}{\sqrt{d\tau}} = \frac{1}{\sqrt{4\pi r^2 dx}} = \frac{1}{\sqrt{L^2 - L}} = L^{-3/2}$

Rigid Rotator $\varphi = \frac{1}{\sqrt{d\tau}} = \frac{1}{\sqrt{d\phi}} = (\text{radian})^{-1/2}$

$\varphi \rightarrow$ **dimentionless** $\left[\theta\,(\text{red}) = \frac{\text{Arc}}{r} = \frac{L}{L} = 1\right]$

S.H.O. $= \varphi = \frac{1}{\sqrt{dx}} = \frac{1}{\sqrt{L}} = L^{-1/2}$

Postulates of quantum mechanics:

1. The state of a quantum mechanical system is completely defined by a wave function $\varphi(r, t)$ or state function and has property

$$\int \varphi^*(r, t) \; \varphi(r, t) \; d\tau$$

is the probability that the particle lies in the volume element $d\tau$ located at r at time t.

$\varphi^* = \varphi$ for 1D box, SHO, H atom systems.

2. To every observable in classical mechanics there is a **Hermitian operator** in quantum mechanics.

3. $\hat{A}\varphi = a\varphi$

4. $\langle a \rangle = \int_{-\infty}^{+\infty} \varphi^* \, \hat{A}\varphi d\tau$ φ is normalised wave function

It φ is not normalised $\langle a \rangle = \dfrac{\int \varphi^* \hat{A} \varphi \, d\tau}{\int \varphi^* \varphi \, d\tau}$

5. φ variation with time is represented by Acc. to time dependent Schrödinger eqn.

$$\hat{H}\varphi(x, t) = \frac{i\hbar \, \partial\varphi}{\partial t}$$

Hermitian operator follows the below condition:

$$\int \varphi^* A\varphi \, d\tau = \int \varphi A^* \varphi^* \, d\tau$$

or

$$\int g^* A f \, d\tau = \int f A^* g^* \, d\tau$$

I Eigenvalue corresponding to Hermitian operator are real

II Eigenfunction of H.O. are orthogonal

III If A is Hermitian, B is Hermitian. Then AB is Hermitian only of A & B commute each other.

Boundary condition – a function vanishes at boundary

$$[\varphi * \varphi]_0 \, \mu = 0, \int_0^l \varphi^* \varphi \, d\tau \neq 0$$

Hermitian Adjoint "Decker" " † "

If $A^+ = A$ then A is Hermitian

Decker is $A^\dagger = (A^*)^\dagger \leftrightarrow (A^+)^\dagger$

$(A^\dagger)^\dagger = A$ $\qquad$ $(A^+)^n = (A^n)^+$

$(aA)^+ = a^* A^+$

$(A + B)^+ = A^+ + B^+$ $\qquad$ $\left(\frac{d}{dx}\right)^+ = -\frac{d}{dx}$

$(AB)^+ = B^+A^+$

$A \mid \varphi >^+ = < \varphi \mid A$ $\qquad$ $e^+ = e$ (Since e = 2.7 = real value)

If $\quad A^+ = A$ (A is Hermitian)

$A^+ = -A$ (A is Anti-Hermitian)

Commutator of two Hermitian operator is Anti-Hermitian

Application of Schrödinger Eqn.

I. One D Box

(*a*) $0 \leq x \leq 1$

$$\varphi = \sqrt{\frac{2}{l}} \sin \frac{n\pi x}{l} \qquad En = \frac{n^2h^2}{8\,ml^2}$$

Zero point energy/Ground state energy

$$E_{Z.P.E} = \frac{h^2}{8\,ml^2} \quad (n = 1)$$

$$E_{n+1} - E_n = (2n + 1)\frac{h^2}{8\,ml^2} \qquad E_x - E_2 - E_1 = \frac{3h^2}{8\,ml^2} \text{ etc.}$$

For same energy level if we change length

$$\boxed{\% \, \Delta E = \frac{2\Delta l}{l} \times 100}$$

$$\text{Probability P} = \frac{N!}{n!(N-n)!}\left(\frac{v}{V}\right)^n\left(\frac{V-v}{V}\right)^{N-n}$$

Occupation of n molecules out of N molecules in volume v out of total volume V.

$$E = \frac{n^2h^2}{8\,ml^2} = \frac{n^2}{l^2}\left(\frac{h^2}{8\,m}\right) = \frac{n^2}{l^2}(5.9\times10^{-38})$$

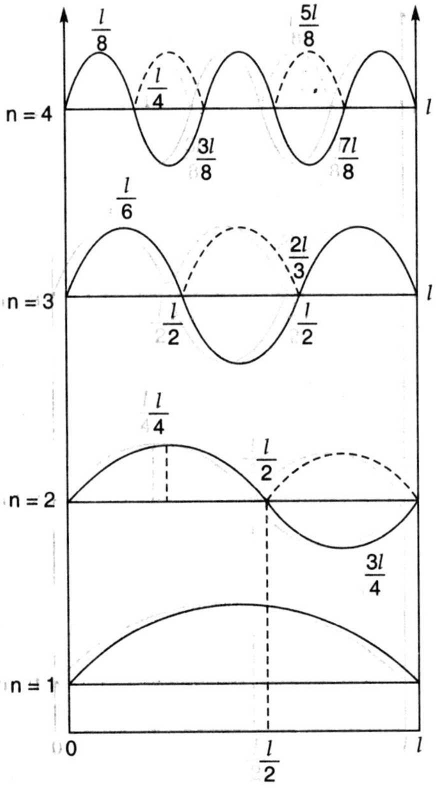

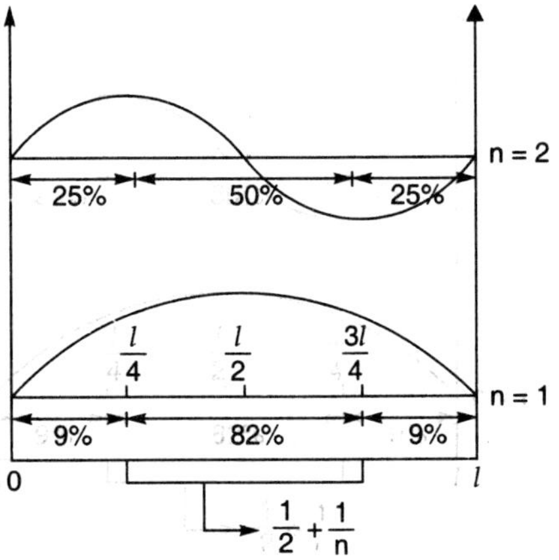

(*b*) 0 to $2l$

$$\varphi = \sqrt{\frac{1}{l}}\sin\frac{n\pi x}{2l} \qquad E_n = \frac{n^2h^2}{32\,ml^2}$$

(*c*) $-l$ to $+l$

$$\varphi = \sqrt{\frac{1}{l}}\cos\frac{n\pi x}{2l} \quad \text{when } n \text{ is odd} \qquad E_n = \frac{n^2h^2}{32\,ml^2}$$

$$\varphi = \sqrt{\frac{1}{l}}\sin\frac{n\pi x}{2l} \quad \text{when } n \text{ is even}$$

$$\text{Ground state } \varphi_1 = \sqrt{\frac{1}{l}}\cos\frac{\pi x}{2l} \quad (n = 1 \text{ odd})$$

First excited state $\varphi_2 = \sqrt{\frac{1}{l}} \sin \frac{\pi x}{l}$ ($n = 2$ even)

Second excited state $\varphi_3 = \sqrt{\frac{1}{l}} \cos \frac{3\pi x}{2l}$ ($n = 3$ odd)

For

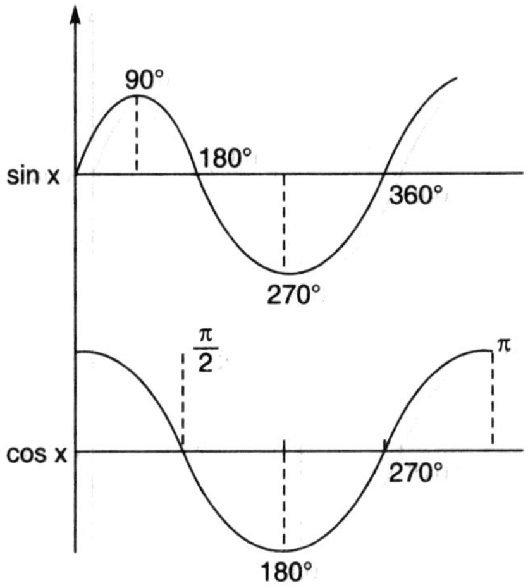

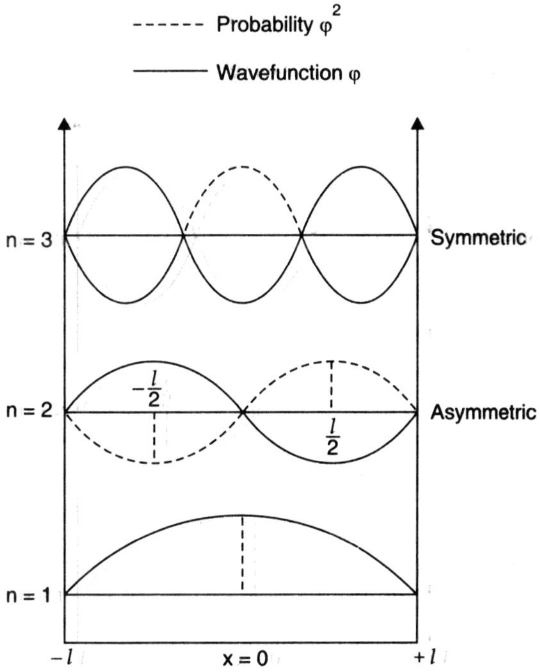

II. Two Dimensional Box (2 D Box)

lx ≠ ly

$$\varphi = \sqrt{\frac{2}{l_x}} \sin \frac{n_x \pi_x}{l_x} \cdot \sqrt{\frac{2}{l_x}} \sin \frac{n_y \pi_y}{l_y}$$

$$E = \frac{h^2}{8\,m} \left[\frac{{n_x}^2}{{l_x}^2} + \frac{{n_y}^2}{{l_y}^2} \right]$$

lx = ly = l

$$\varphi = \sqrt{\frac{2}{l}} \sin \frac{n_x \pi_x}{l} \cdot \sqrt{\frac{2}{l}} \sin \frac{n_y \pi_y}{l}$$

$$E = \frac{h^2}{8\,ml^2} [{n_x}^2 - {n_y}^2]$$

Ground State $\quad E_{11} = \frac{r^2}{4\,ml^2} \quad \varphi_{11} = \sqrt{\frac{2}{l}} \sin \frac{\pi_x}{l} \cdot \sqrt{\frac{2}{l}} \sin \frac{\pi_y}{l}$

First excited state

$n_x = 2 \quad E_{2,1} = \frac{5h^2}{8\,ml^2} \quad nx = 1 \quad E_{1,2} = \frac{5h^2}{8\,ml^2}$

$n_y = 1 \qquad\qquad\qquad\qquad ny = 2$

$$\varphi_{2,1} = \sqrt{\frac{2}{l}} \sin \frac{2\pi x}{l} \cdot \sqrt{\frac{2}{l}} \sin \frac{\pi y}{l} \qquad \varphi_{12} = \sqrt{\frac{2}{l}} \sin \frac{\pi x}{l} \cdot \sqrt{\frac{2}{l}} \sin \frac{2\pi y}{l}$$

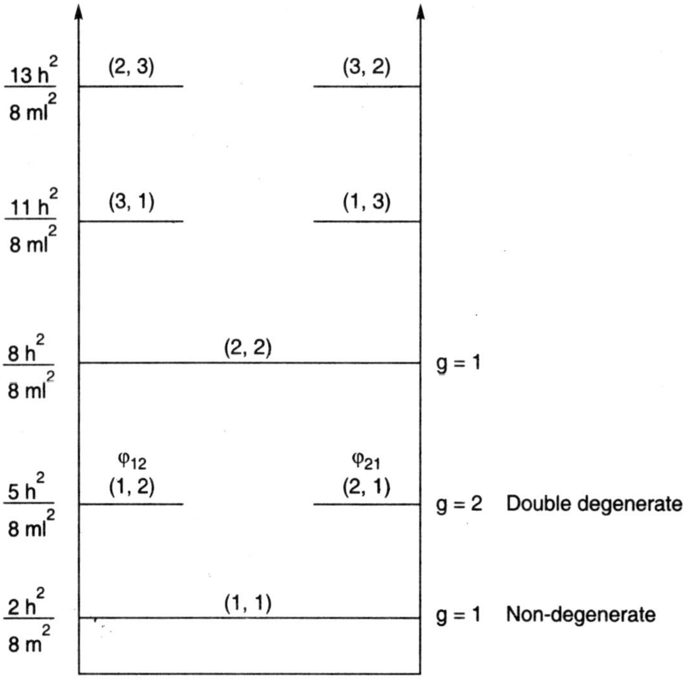

III. Three Dimensional Box (3 D Box)

$lx \neq ly \neq lz$

$$\varphi = \sqrt{\frac{2}{lx}} \sin \frac{nx\pi x}{lx} \cdot \sqrt{\frac{2}{ly}} \sin \frac{ny\pi y}{ly} \cdot \sqrt{\frac{2}{lz}} \sin \frac{nz\pi z}{lz}$$

$$E = \left[\frac{nx^2}{lx^2} + \frac{ny^2}{ly^2} + \frac{nz^2}{lz^2}\right] \frac{h^2}{8\,m}$$

$lx = ly = lz = l$

$$\varphi = \left(\frac{2}{l}\right)^{3/2} \sin \frac{nx\pi x}{l} . \sin \frac{ny\pi y}{l} \sin \frac{nz\pi z}{l}$$

$$E = [nx^2 + ny^2 + nz^2] \frac{h^2}{8\,ml^2}$$

Ground State $\quad nx = 1 \quad E = \frac{3h^2}{8\,ml^2}$

$ny = 1$

$nz = 1$

$$\varphi = \left(\frac{2}{l}\right)^{3/2} \sin\frac{\pi x}{l} \sin\frac{\pi y}{l} . \sin\frac{\pi z}{l}$$

First excited (1, 2, –1) (2, 1, 1) (1, 1, 2)

State $E = \dfrac{6\,h^2}{8\,ml^2}$

$$\varphi_{1,\,2,\,1} = \left(\frac{2}{l}\right)^{3/2} \sin\frac{\pi x}{l} . \sin\frac{\pi y}{l} \sin\frac{\pi z}{l}$$

$$\varphi_{2,\,1,\,1} = \left(\frac{2}{l}\right)^{3/2} \sin\frac{2\pi x}{l} . \sin\frac{\pi y}{l} \sin\frac{\pi z}{l}$$

$$\varphi_{1,\,1,\,2} = \left(\frac{2}{l}\right)^{3/2} \sin\frac{\pi x}{l} \sin\frac{\pi y}{l} . \sin\frac{2\pi z}{l}$$

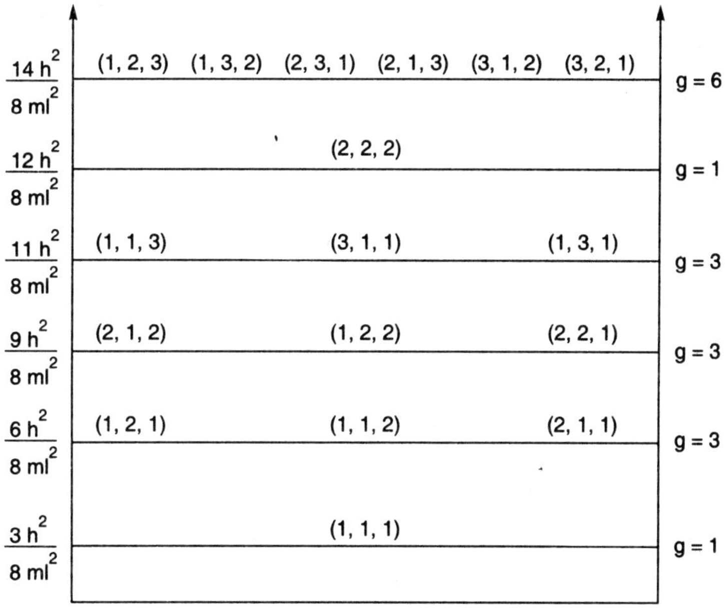

No. of energy states and energy levels below $\dfrac{16\,h^2}{8\,ml^2}$ are 6 and 6 respectively.

Degeneracy:

Accidental degeneracy: Different states with same energy of different energy levels.

e.g., (5, 1, 1) (1, 5, 1) (1, 1, 5) (3, 3, 3) gives $E = \dfrac{27\,h^2}{8\,ml^2}$

The lowest energy level which exists in 2D as well as 3D box

Ans. (4, 1) $\rightarrow$ 2D corresponds to $E = \dfrac{17\,h^2}{8\,ml^2}$

(3, 2, 2) $\rightarrow$ 3D

Some features of particle in a box:

1. Length of the box must be integral multiple of half of wavelength

$$l = \frac{n\lambda}{2}$$

2. The energy associated with a wave function ↑ses with ↑se in the number of node of the function.
3. The symmetry of the wave function w.r.t. the centre of box may be classified into two categories.

   Symmetric function (even function) $\varphi(x) = \varphi(-x)$

   Asymmetric (odd) function $\varphi(x) = -\varphi(-x)$

   $\varphi_1, \varphi_3, \varphi_5, \ldots$ Symmetric function.

   $\varphi_2, \varphi_4, \varphi_6, \ldots$ Antisymmetric function
4. Probability density distribution is not uniform but becomes more and more uniform as n increases and will be completely uniform for very high value of n then the classical behaviour emerges.

   For large value of n prediction of quantum mechanics are identical to prediction by classical mechanics.

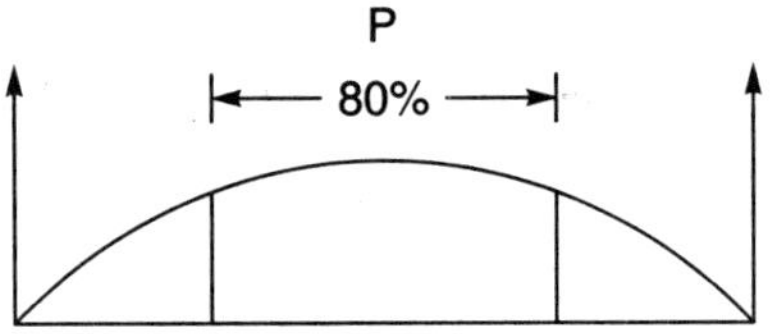

n = 1

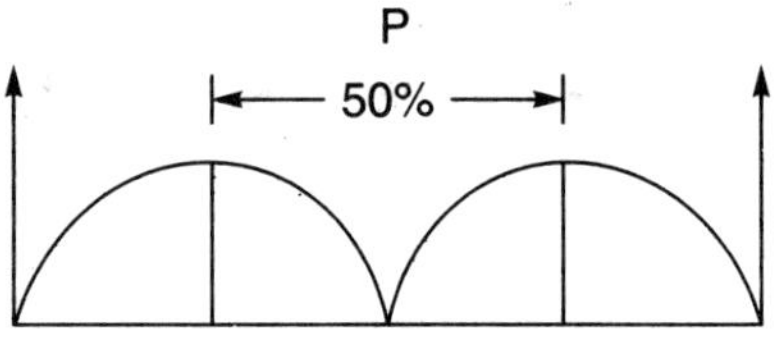

n = 2

	–L to +L	–2L to +2L	$-\frac{L}{2}$ to $+\frac{L}{2}$
N.C.	$\frac{1}{\sqrt{L}}$	$\frac{1}{\sqrt{2L}}$	$\sqrt{\frac{2}{L}}$
φ	$\frac{1}{\sqrt{L}}\cos\frac{n\pi x}{2L}$ n = odd	$\frac{1}{\sqrt{2L}}\cos\frac{n\pi x}{4L}$ n = odd	$\frac{1}{\sqrt{L/2}}\cos\frac{n\pi x}{l}$ n = odd
E	$\frac{1}{\sqrt{2}}\sin\frac{n\pi x}{2L}$ n = even	$\frac{1}{\sqrt{2L}}\sin\frac{n\pi x}{4L}$ n = even	$\frac{1}{\sqrt{L/2}}\sin\frac{n\pi x}{L}$ n = even
	$\frac{nh^2}{8\,m\,(2L)^2} = \frac{n^2h^2}{32\,ml^2}$	$E = \frac{n^2h^2}{32\,(4L)^2} = \frac{n^2h^2}{128\,ml^2}$	$E = \frac{n^2h^2}{8\,ml^2}$

* spin degeneracy = 2X degeneracy

→ $\hat{A} = i(x^2 + 1)\frac{d}{dx} + ix$ is Hermitian

→ For A & its adjoint A^+

AA^+ = is hermitian

$AA^+ + A^+A$ is hermitian

$A + A^+$ is hermitian

$A - A^+$ is Antihermitian

Simple Harmonic Oscillator

For S.H.O $V = \frac{1}{2}kx^2$

Shrödinger wave eqn. for SHO

$$\frac{d^2\varphi}{dx^2} + \frac{8\pi^2 m}{h^2}\left(E - \frac{1}{2}kx^2\right)\varphi = 0$$

$$\frac{d^2\varphi}{dx^2} + \left(\frac{8\pi^2 mE}{h^2} - \frac{8\pi^2 m}{h^2} \times \frac{1}{2}kx^2\right)\varphi = 0$$

$$\frac{d^2\varphi}{dx^2} + [\alpha - \beta x^2]\varphi = 0 \qquad ...(1)$$

$$\boxed{\alpha = \frac{2mE}{\hbar^2}} \qquad \boxed{\beta = \frac{\sqrt{mK}}{\hbar}}$$

xi $\boxed{\xi = \sqrt{\beta}\, x}$

$$\text{Eqn (1)} \quad \frac{\partial^2\varphi}{\partial\xi^2} + \left[\frac{\alpha}{\beta} - \xi^2\right]\varphi = 0 \qquad ...(2)$$

Solution to eqn. (2) is $\phi(\xi) = \phi(\xi)\ e^{-\xi^2/2}$

SHO Equation

Put in (2) $\boxed{\frac{\partial^2\phi}{\partial\xi^2} - 2\xi\frac{\partial\phi}{\partial\xi} + \left(\frac{\alpha}{\beta} - 1\right)\phi = 0}$ ...(3)

(3) is identical to well-known second order differential eqn called HERMITE EQUATION below

$$\boxed{\frac{\partial^2\phi}{\partial\xi^2} - 2\xi\frac{\partial\phi}{\partial\xi} + 2n\phi = 0} \qquad ...(4)$$

Original Hermite eqn. is

$$\frac{d^2H}{d\xi^2} - 2\xi\frac{\partial H}{\partial\xi} + 2nH = 0$$

Hermite polynomial is $Hn(\xi)$

$$Hn(\xi) = (-1)^n e^{\xi^2} \frac{d^n e^{-\xi^2}}{d\xi^n}$$

SHO wave function $\varphi(\xi) = Hn(\xi)\, e^{-\xi^2/2}$

Normalised SHO wave function $\varphi_n(\xi) = \underbrace{\left(\frac{1}{2^n n!}\right)^{1/2}\left(\frac{\beta}{\pi}\right)^{1/4}}_{\text{Normalisation constant}} Hn(\xi)\, e^{-\xi^2/2 = \left(\frac{-\beta x^2}{2}\right)}$

From (3) and (4) $\frac{\alpha}{\beta} - 1 = 2n$

$$\boxed{\frac{\alpha}{\beta} = 2n+1} \qquad \boxed{E = \left(\frac{n+1}{2}\right)hv} \qquad \boxed{\frac{2E}{\hbar}\sqrt{\frac{m}{K}} = 2n+1}$$

$$\xi = \sqrt{\beta x} \qquad \beta = \frac{\sqrt{mK}}{\hbar} \qquad v = \frac{1}{2\pi}\sqrt{\frac{K}{\mu}}$$

To convert gm/mole to kg/molecule multiply by **1.67×10^{-27}**

Ground state function $n = 0$ (allowed)

$$\varphi_0\left(\sqrt{\beta}x\right) = \left(\frac{\beta}{\pi}\right)^{1/4} e^{\frac{-\beta x^2}{2}} \qquad E = \frac{1}{2}hv$$

$$\varphi_1\left(\sqrt{\beta}x\right) = \left(\frac{\beta}{\pi}\right)^{1/4} \sqrt{2\beta}\, x e^{\frac{-\beta x^2}{2}} \qquad E = \frac{3}{2}hv$$

$$\varphi_2\left(\sqrt{\beta}x\right) = \frac{1}{\sqrt{2}}\left(\frac{\beta}{\pi}\right)^{1/4} (2\beta x^2 - 1) e^{\frac{-\beta x^2}{2}} \qquad E = \frac{5}{2}hv$$

2D and 3D SHO,

1D SHO $\quad E = \left(nx + \frac{1}{2}\right)hv$

2D SHO $\quad E = (nx + ny + 1)hv$

3D SHO $\quad E = \left(nx + ny + nz + \frac{3}{2}\right)hv$

1D

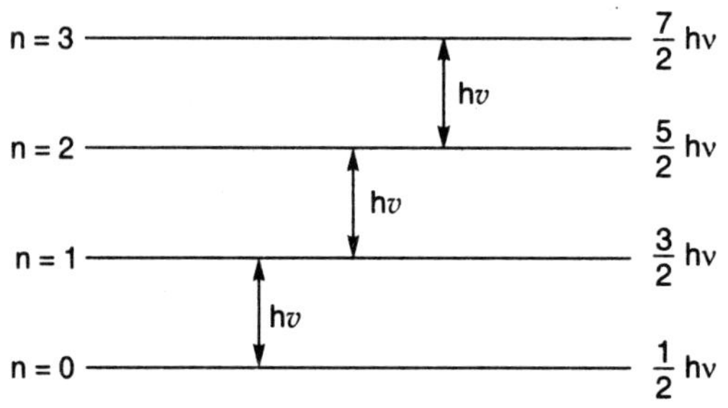

2D

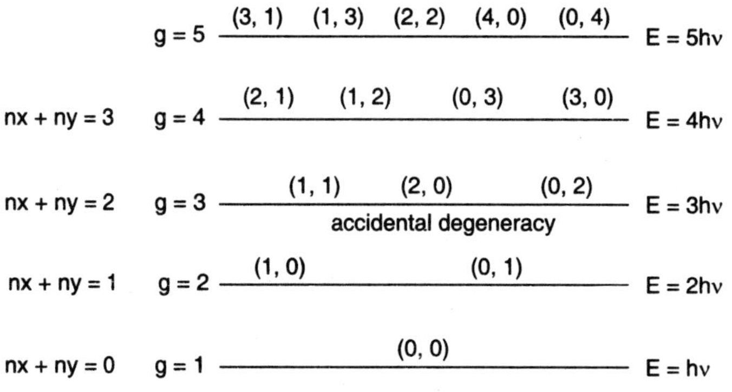

3D

g = 10 — (111) (210) (012) (102) (201) (120) (021) (300) (003) (030) — $\frac{9}{2}$ hν

g = 6 — (011) (101) (110) (200) (020) (002) — $\frac{7}{2}$ hν

g = 3 — (100) (010) (001) — $\frac{5}{2}$ hν

g = 1 — (0 0 0) — $\frac{3}{2}$ hν

SHO $\quad < x > = 0$

$$< x^2 > = \frac{1}{2\beta}$$

$$< Px > = 0$$

$$< Px^2 > = \frac{\beta\hbar^2}{2}$$

$\Rightarrow \quad < E > = < V > = \frac{1}{4} hv$ (Virial theorem)

For 3D SHO degeneracy formula is

$$g_n = \frac{(n+1)(n+2)}{2}$$

Wave function for 3D SHO

$$\varphi_{0,0,0} = \left(\frac{\beta}{\pi}\right)^{3/4} e^{-\beta/2(x^2+y^2+z^2)} \qquad [\varphi = \varphi_x \cdot \varphi_y \cdot \varphi_z]$$

$\Rightarrow \quad \Delta E = E_{n+1} - E_n = h\nu$

Energy of Anharmonic Oscillator

$$E_n = \left(\frac{n+1}{2}\right)h\nu - \left(\frac{n+1}{2}\right)^2 h\nu \, \chi e \text{ anharmonicity constant } (\text{cm}^{-1})$$

Harmonicity lie in lower level

In higher level harmonicity disappear and anharmonicity comes in the system.

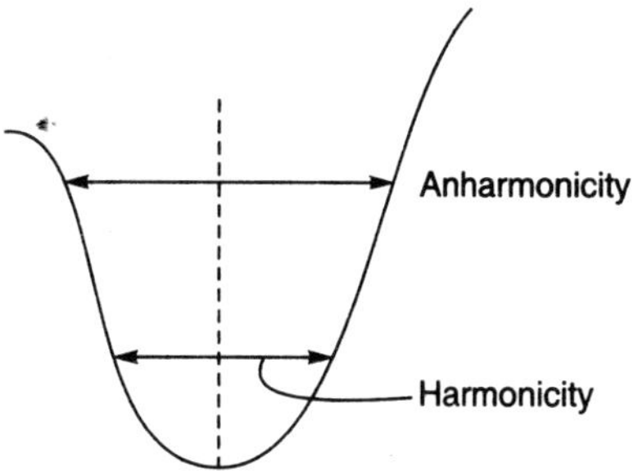

Hydrogen Atom

$$\left[\left(\frac{-h^2}{2m}\nabla^2\right) + V\right]\varphi = E\varphi$$

V for Hydrogen atom = $\frac{-e^2}{4\pi \varepsilon_0 r}$

∇^2 = laplacian operator in polar co-ordinate form (γ, θ, φ)

$$\nabla^2 = \left[\frac{1}{r^2}\frac{\partial}{\partial r}\frac{r^2\partial}{\partial r} + \frac{1}{r^2 \sin\theta}\frac{\partial}{\partial\theta}\sin\theta\frac{\partial}{\partial\theta} + \frac{1}{r^2 \sin^2\theta}\frac{\partial^2}{\partial\phi^2}\right]$$

Schrödinger equation for Hydrogen atom is

$$\boxed{\frac{-\hbar^2}{2m}\left[\frac{1}{r^2}\frac{\partial}{\partial r}r^2\frac{\partial\varphi}{\partial r} + \frac{1}{r^2 \sin\theta}\frac{\partial}{\partial\theta}\sin\theta\frac{\partial\varphi}{\partial\theta} + \frac{1}{r^2\sin^2\theta}\frac{\partial^2\varphi}{\partial\phi^2}\right] - \frac{e^2}{4\pi\varepsilon_0 r} = E\varphi}$$

$$\frac{-\hbar^2}{2m}\nabla^2 + \frac{e^2}{4\pi\varepsilon_0 r}\varphi = -E\varphi$$

$$\nabla^2 + \frac{2m}{\hbar^2}\frac{e^2}{4\pi\varepsilon_0 r}\varphi = \frac{-2m}{\hbar^2}E\varphi$$

$$\nabla^2 + \frac{2m}{\hbar^2}\left[\frac{e^2}{4\pi\varepsilon_0 r} + E\right]\varphi = 0$$

$$\boxed{\frac{1}{r^2}\left[\frac{\partial}{\partial r}\frac{r^2\partial\varphi}{\partial r} + \frac{1}{\sin\theta}\frac{\partial}{\partial\theta}\sin\theta\frac{\partial\varphi}{\partial\theta} + \frac{1}{\sin^2\theta}\frac{\partial^2\varphi}{\partial\phi^2}\right] + \frac{2m}{\hbar^2}\left[\frac{e^2}{4\pi\varepsilon_0 r} + E\right]\varphi} = 0$$

when m and $\hbar$ are replaced by r and $\frac{h}{2\pi}$

$$\boxed{\frac{1}{r^2}\left[\frac{\partial}{\partial r}\frac{r^2\partial\varphi}{\partial r} + \frac{1}{\sin\theta}\frac{\partial}{\partial\theta}\sin\theta\frac{\partial\varphi}{\partial\theta} + \frac{1}{\sin^2\theta}\frac{\partial^2\varphi}{\partial\phi^2}\right] + \frac{8\pi^2 r}{h^2}\left[\frac{e^2}{4\pi\varepsilon_0 r} + E\right]\varphi} = 0$$

Solution of Schrödinger wave eqn. for H-atom, 3 eqns. in three separate variable.

$$\frac{1}{r^2}\frac{\partial}{\partial r}r^2\frac{\partial R}{\partial r} + \frac{2m}{\hbar^2}\left(E + \frac{e^2}{4\pi\varepsilon_0 r}\right) = l(l+1) \quad ...(1)$$

$$\frac{\sin\theta}{\Theta}\frac{\partial}{\partial\theta}\sin\theta\frac{\partial\Theta}{\partial\theta} + l(l+1)\sin^2\theta = m^2 \quad ...(2)$$

$$\frac{1}{\phi}\frac{\partial^2\phi}{\partial\phi^2} = -m^2 \quad ...(3)$$

Solution of ϕ dependent Equation (3)

$$\phi_m = \frac{1}{\sqrt{2\pi}}e^{(im\phi)} \qquad m = 0, \pm1, \pm2, ...$$

$m \rightarrow$ magnetic quantum no. and it represents the quantization of z-component of angular momentum

Solution of θ dependent Equation (2)

$$\phi_{j,m} = \left[\frac{(2J+1)(J-|m|)!}{2(J+|m|)!}\right] P_J|m| \cos\theta$$

$$P_J|m| = \left(1-\xi^2\right)^{|m|/2}\frac{d^{|m|}}{d\xi^{|m|}}P_J$$

$$P_J = \frac{1}{2^J\ J!}\frac{d^J}{d\xi^J}(\xi^2 - 1)J$$

$$\xi = \cos\theta \qquad J = 0, 1, 2, 3...$$

$$m = 0, \pm 1, \pm 2 \ldots \pm J$$

Solution of r-Dependent Equation

$$P^2\frac{d^2L}{dp^2} + (J + 1 - P)\frac{dL}{dP} + (K - J)L = 0$$

Exact expression for Radial function Rn, l:

$$R, n, l = -\left\{\left(\frac{2z}{na_0}\right)^3 \frac{(n-l-1)}{2n[(n+l)!]^3}\right\}^{1/2} P^l\, e^{-P/2} L^{2l+1}_{n+l}$$

$$L^{2l+1}_{n+l} = \frac{d^{2l+1}}{dP^{2l+1}} L_{n+l}$$

$$L_{n+l} = e^P\frac{d^{n+l}}{dP^{n+l}}(P^{n+l}\, e^{-P}) \text{ and } P = \left(\frac{2z}{na_0}\right)r$$

Formula for identification of θ & ϕ

$$e^{\frac{-Zr}{na_0}} \sin\theta^{|m|} \sum_{K=0}^{\frac{l-|m|}{2}} (-1)^K \cos^{l-|m|-2K}\theta\, e^{im\phi}$$

If limit 0 to $\frac{1}{2}$ then K = 0

0 to 3/2 then K = 0, K = 1

0 to 5/2 then K = 0, K = 1, K = 2

$e^{i\phi} = \cos\phi$

$e^{-i\phi} = \sin\phi$

$e^{2i\phi} = \cos 2\phi$

	n	***l***	***Rn, l***
1S	1	0	$2\left(\frac{z}{a_0}\right)^{3/2} \exp\left(\frac{-Zr}{a_0}\right)$
2S	2	0	$\left(\frac{z}{2a_0}\right)^{3/2}\left(\frac{2-zr}{a_0}\right)\exp\left(-\frac{zr}{2a_0}\right)$
2P	2	1	$\frac{1}{\sqrt{3}}\left(\frac{z}{2a_0}\right)^{3/2}\left(\frac{zr}{a_0}\right)\exp\left(-\frac{zr}{2a_0}\right)$

$l = 1$	θ	ϕ	
$m = 0$	$\cos\theta$	0	P_z
$m = +1$	$\sin\theta$	$e^{i\phi}$	P_x
$m = -1$	$\sin\theta$	$e^{-i\phi}$	P_y
$l = 2$	θ	ϕ	
$m = 0$	$\cos^2\theta - 1$	0	dz^2
$m = +1$	$\sin\theta\cos\theta$	$e^{i\phi}$	dxz
$m = -1$	$\sin\theta\cos\theta$	$e^{-i\phi}$	dxy
$m = +2$	$\sin^2\theta$	$e^{2\phi}$	$dx^2 - y^2$
$m = -2$	$\sin^2\theta$	$e^{-2\phi}$	dzy

$\varphi_{r\theta\phi} = R_r\,\Theta_\theta\,\Phi_\phi$

$\varphi_{r\theta\phi} = Rnl\ Ylm$

nlm

$\varphi_{r\theta\phi} = Rr\theta\ Y\theta\phi$

Hamiltonian for H atom

$$\hat{H} = \frac{-\hbar^2}{2m}\left[\frac{1}{\mu^2}\frac{\partial}{\partial\mu}\mu^2\frac{\partial}{\partial\mu} + \frac{1}{r^2\sin\theta}\frac{\partial}{\partial\theta}\sin\theta\frac{\partial}{\partial\theta} + \frac{1}{\mu^2\sin^2\theta}\frac{\partial^2}{\partial\varphi^2} - \frac{e^2}{4\pi\varepsilon_0 r}\right]$$

$$\left.\begin{aligned} V &= 2E \\ V &= -2K \\ K &= -E \end{aligned}\right\} \quad \text{Total energy } E = -\frac{1}{2}\frac{e^2}{4\pi\epsilon_0}\frac{1}{a_0} = \underset{\text{Kinetic energy}}{-K}$$

*For ns orbital only radial function remains θ and ϕ function vanishes

$$\varphi_{1s} = \varphi_{1,0,0} = \frac{1}{\sqrt{\pi}\,a_0^{3/2}}\,e^{-r/a_0}$$

$$\varphi_{2s} = \varphi_{2,0,0} = \frac{1}{\sqrt{32\pi}\,a_0^{3/2}}\left(2 - \frac{r}{a_0}\right)e^{-r/2a_0}$$

*All Radial Node $\varphi = 0$

For 2S orbital node exists at $r = 2a_0$

Average distance of 2S e^- from the nucleus of H atom = $6a_0$

Average distance of 1S e^- from the nucleus of H atom = $\frac{3}{2}a_0$

$$a_0 = \frac{h^2}{4\pi^2 e}\cdot\frac{4\pi\epsilon_o}{e^2} = 0.529\ \text{Å (Bohr radius)}$$

$$\boxed{r = \frac{n^2}{2}a_0}$$

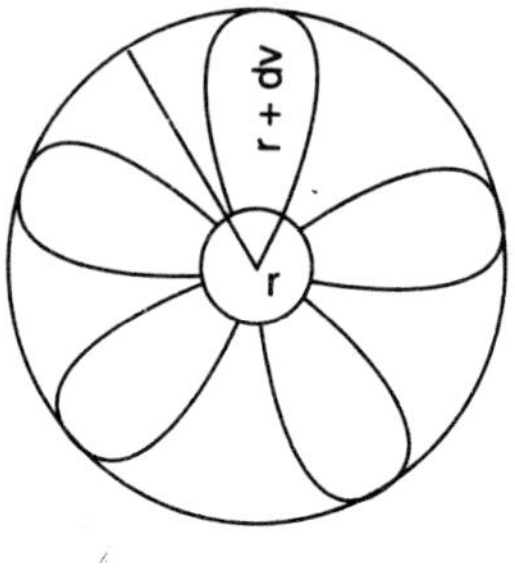

Most probable distance of e^- in orbital is $P(r)$

$$P(r)\,dr = [\varphi(r, \theta, \phi)]^2\,d\tau$$

$$P(r)\,dr = \varphi^2\,4\pi r^2\,du$$

Probability is maximum at most probable distance

$$\frac{dP(r)}{dr} = 0$$

1s For 1s probability is max at $r = a_0$

P (probability) = **0.323** $\underbrace{0 \; to \; a_0}_{P}$

P = 32.3%

2s For 2S probability is max at $r = (3 \pm \sqrt{5})\, a_0$

$$< V > = \frac{-e^2}{4\pi \in a_0} \qquad < r > = \frac{1}{a_0}$$

$$< E > = -\frac{1}{2}\frac{e^2}{4\pi \in_0 a_0} \qquad < T > = \frac{1}{2}\frac{e^2}{4\pi \in_0 a_0}$$

$$< V > = 2 < E >$$

$$< T > = - < E >$$

$$< V > = - 2 < T >$$

Degeneracy of Hydrogen atom

⇒ Energy of n level of Hydrogen $= -\frac{RH}{n^2}$

Degeneracy of nth level $= gn = n^2 = \sum_{l=0}^{n-1}(2l+1)$

Spin degeneracy $= 2n^2$

Hückel Theory of Conjugated Diene's

To find energy states in a diene.

⇒ Corresponding to number of carbon atoms n in diene form a matrix $[n \times n]$

⇒ In matrix put $C_{ii} = \alpha - \varepsilon$

$$C_{11} = C_{22} = C_{33} = C_{44} \ldots C_{nn} = \alpha - \varepsilon$$

Put $C_{\underbrace{2\,3}} = \beta$

If C_2 & C_3 are connected. If not put $C_{23} = 0$

Solve the matrix for x values put $\frac{\alpha - \varepsilon}{\beta} = x$

I. Ethylene system: ($CH_2{=}CH_2$)

2 carbon → [2 × 2] Matrix

$$\begin{bmatrix} C_{11} & C_{12} \\ C_{21} & C_{22} \end{bmatrix} = \begin{bmatrix} \alpha - \xi & \beta \\ \beta & \alpha - \varepsilon \end{bmatrix}$$

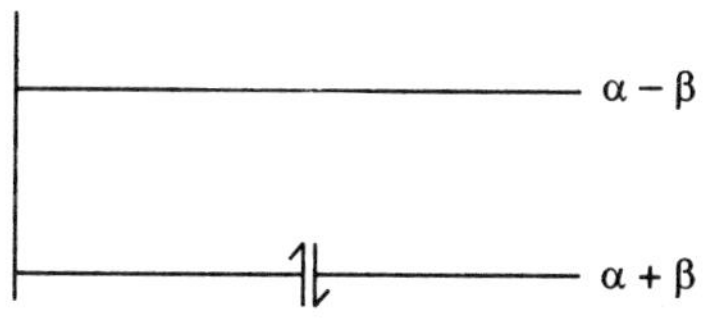

$x = 1$ $\quad \xi = \alpha - \beta$

$x = -1$ $\quad \varepsilon = \alpha + \beta$

Value of β is –75 kJ/mole

II. Allyl system: $\overset{1}{C}H_2{=}\overset{2}{C}H{-}\overset{3}{C}H_3$ 3 × 3 Matrix

$$\begin{bmatrix} C_{11} & C_{12} & C_{13} \\ C_{21} & C_{22} & C_{23} \\ C_{31} & C_{32} & C_{33} \end{bmatrix} = \begin{bmatrix} \alpha-\varepsilon & \beta & 0 \\ \beta & \alpha-\varepsilon & \beta \\ 0 & \beta & \alpha-\varepsilon \end{bmatrix}$$

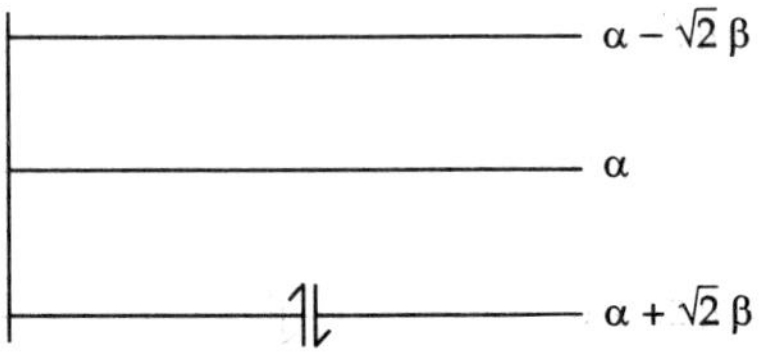

$x = 0$

$x = \pm\sqrt{2}\ \alpha - \sqrt{2}\,\beta,\ \alpha + \sqrt{2}\,\beta, \alpha$

Allyl radical

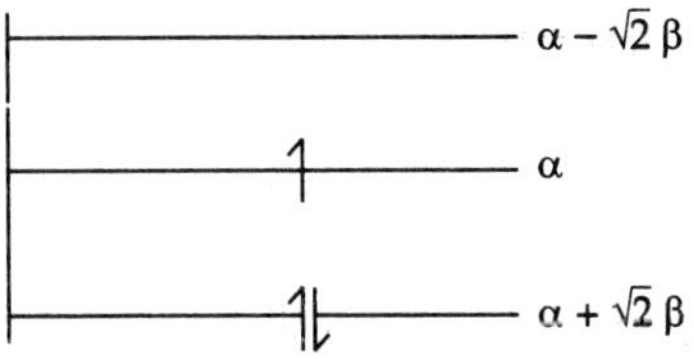

Allyl cation

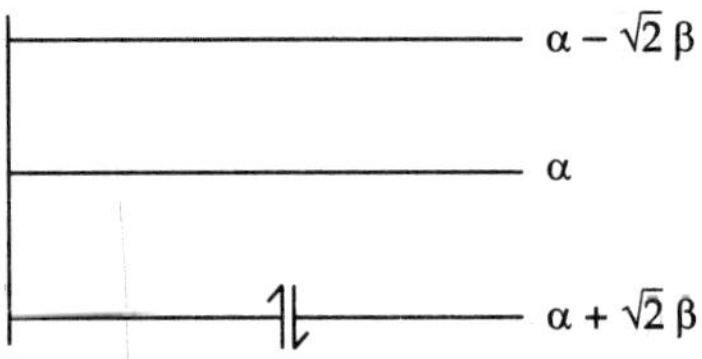

Allyl anion

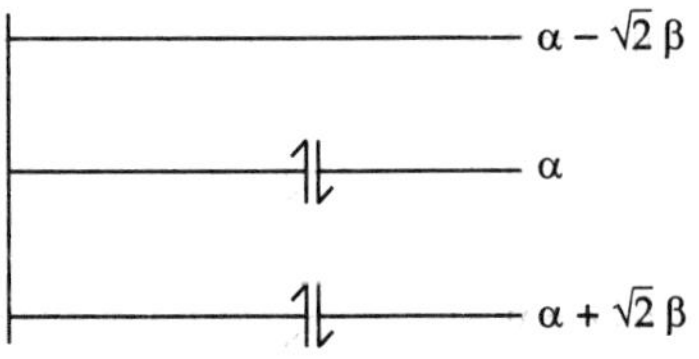

III. Cyclobutadiene: 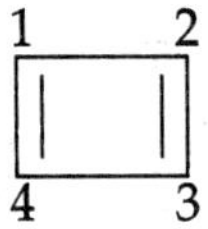

4 × 4 Matrix

$$\begin{bmatrix} C_{11} & C_{12} & C_{13} & C_{14} \\ C_{21} & C_{22} & C_{23} & C_{24} \\ C_{31} & C_{32} & C_{33} & C_{34} \\ C_{41} & C_{42} & C_{43} & C_{44} \end{bmatrix} = \begin{bmatrix} \alpha-\xi & \beta & 0 & \beta \\ \beta & \alpha-\xi & \beta & 0 \\ 0 & \beta & \alpha-\xi & \beta \\ \beta & 0 & \beta & \alpha-\xi \end{bmatrix}$$

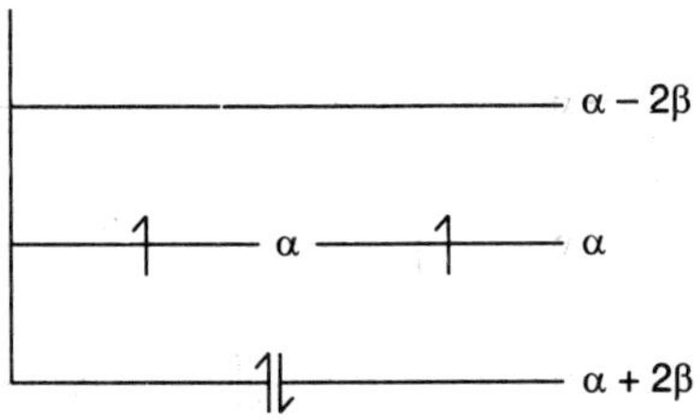

$x^2\,[x^2 - 4] = 0$

$x = 0 \quad \alpha$

$x = 0 \quad \alpha$

$x = \pm 2 \qquad \alpha - 2\beta,\ \ \alpha + 2\beta$

Conjugated Dienes rate considered as formed from in ethylene molecules, and conjugated dienes are more stabilised due to delocalisation of π bonds.

So energy of Dines is the energy due to delocalisation and energy of no. of constituent ethylene molecule e.g. **For Cyclobutadiene**

Delocalisation Energy = Energy of cyclobutadiene – (2 × Energy of one ethylene)

$$= \alpha + \alpha + 2(\alpha + 2\beta) - 2(2(\alpha + \beta)$$

$$= 2\alpha + 2\alpha + 4\beta - 4\alpha - 4\beta$$

$$= 0$$

No. delocalisation energy so it is not stabilised due to delocalisation.

Similarly we can find out delocalisation energy of other conjugated diene system.

Delocalisation energy of conjugated diene	=	Energy of conjugated diene – (n × Energy of one ethylene)

$n \rightarrow$ no. of constituting ethylene molecule in conjugated dienes.

$\beta = -75$ KJ/Mole.

IV. Benzene 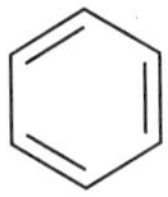 [6 × 6] Matrix

$$\begin{bmatrix} C_{11} & C_{12} & C_{13} & C_{14} & C_{15} & C_{16} \\ C_{21} & C_{22} & C_{23} & C_{24} & C_{25} & C_{26} \\ C_{31} & C_{32} & C_{33} & C_{34} & C_{35} & C_{36} \\ C_{41} & C_{42} & C_{43} & C_{44} & C_{45} & C_{46} \\ C_{51} & C_{52} & C_{53} & C_{54} & C_{55} & C_{56} \\ C_{61} & C_{62} & C_{63} & C_{64} & C_{65} & C_{66} \end{bmatrix} = \begin{vmatrix} x & 1 & 0 & 0 & 0 & 1 \\ 1 & x & 1 & 0 & 0 & 0 \\ 0 & 1 & x & 1 & 0 & 0 \\ 0 & 0 & 1 & x & 1 & 0 \\ 1 & 0 & 0 & 0 & 1 & x \end{vmatrix} = 0$$

$$x^6 - 6x^4 + 9x^2 - 4 = (x^2 - 4)(x^2 - 1)^2 = 0$$

$$x = \pm 2, \pm 1, \pm 1$$

$$E_1 = \alpha + 2\beta \quad \left.\begin{matrix} E_2 \\ E_3 \end{matrix}\right\} = \alpha + \beta \quad \left.\begin{matrix} E_4 \\ E_5 \end{matrix}\right\} = \alpha - \beta \quad E_6 = \alpha - 2\beta$$

V. $CH_2{=}CH{-}CH{=}CH_2$

$$x^2 + x - 1 = 0$$

$$E = \alpha \pm 0.618\ \beta \quad E = \alpha \pm 1.618\ \beta$$

Delocalisation energy = – 35.4 kJ/Mole

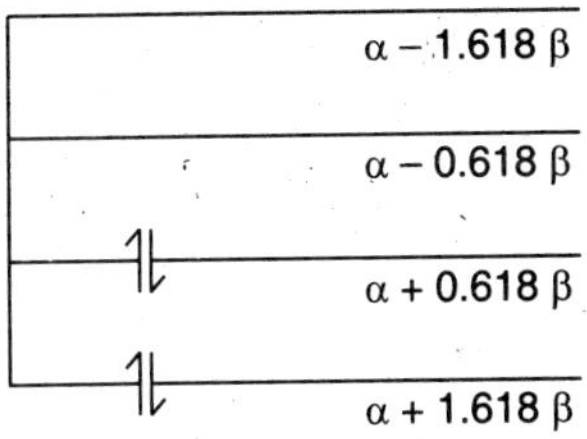

Rigid Rotor

A diatomic molecule rotating about an axis $\perp^r$ to the internuclear axis and passing through the centre of gravity of the molecule is an example of rigid rotor.

$$\text{K.E.} = \frac{1}{2} I\omega^2 = \frac{L^2}{2I} = H = T + V \Rightarrow 0 \text{ for rigid rotor (because rotation is free)}$$

$$\text{K.E.} = \frac{\left[\sqrt{l(l+1)}\,\hbar\right]^2}{2I} \text{ in form of } l$$

$$\text{K.E.} = \frac{\left[\sqrt{J(J+1)}\hbar\right]^2}{2I} \text{ in form of J}$$

$$\text{K.E.} = \frac{\hbar^2}{2I} J(J+1) = \frac{h^2}{8\pi^2 I} J(J+1)$$

$$\text{K.E.} = \frac{h^2}{8\pi^2 I} J(J+1) \textbf{ Joule} \quad \text{K.E.} = \frac{h}{8\pi^2 IC} J(J+1) \textbf{ cm}^{-1}$$

Dividing *hc* to convert in cm^{-1}

$$B = \frac{h^2}{8\pi^2 I}$$

Schrödinger wave eqn. $\frac{-\hbar^2}{2m}\left[\underbrace{\frac{1}{r^2}\frac{\partial}{\partial r}r^2\frac{\partial}{\partial r}} + \frac{1}{r^2 \sin\theta}\frac{\partial}{d\theta}\sin\theta\frac{\partial}{\partial\theta} + \frac{1}{r^2\sin^2\theta}\frac{\partial^2}{\partial\phi^2}\right] = E\varphi$

r is fixed, *r* = constant

then *r* term removed for writing eqn. for rigid rotor

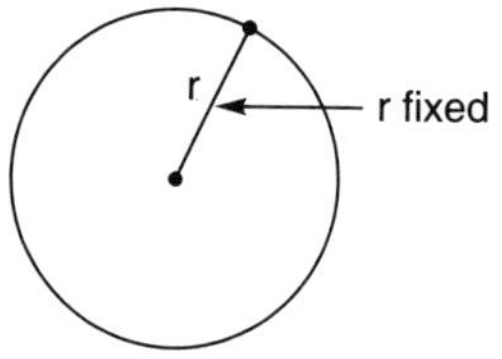

$$\text{Two atom so } \mu = m = \frac{m_1 * m_2}{m_1 + m_2}$$

Equation becomes S eqn. for rigid rotor.

$$\frac{-\hbar^2}{2.\mu}\left[\frac{1}{r^2\sin\theta}\frac{\partial}{\partial\theta}\sin\theta\frac{\partial}{\partial\theta} + \frac{1}{r^2\sin^2\theta}\frac{\partial^2}{\partial\phi^2}\right]\varphi = E\varphi$$

$\mu r^2 = I$

V = 0 Hamiltonian for rigid rotor

$$\text{so, } \hat{H} = \frac{-\hbar^2}{2\mu r^2}\left[\frac{1}{\sin\theta}\frac{\partial}{\partial\theta}\sin\theta\frac{\partial}{\partial\phi} + \frac{1}{\sin^2\theta}\frac{\partial^2}{\partial\phi^2}\right]$$

→ Constant

using $\mu r^2 = I \quad E = \frac{h^2}{8\pi^2 I}J(J+1) = \frac{L^2}{2I}$

Eqn becomes

$$\left[\frac{1}{\sin\theta}\frac{\partial}{\partial\theta}\sin\theta\frac{\partial}{\partial\theta} + \frac{1}{\sin^2\theta}\frac{\partial^2}{\partial\phi^2}\right]Y + J(J+1)Y = 0$$

→ angular function

$$\frac{\partial^2\phi}{\partial\phi^2} + m^2\phi = 0 \qquad ...(1)$$

$$\frac{1}{\sin\theta}\frac{\partial}{\partial\theta}\left(\sin\theta\frac{\partial\Theta}{\partial\theta}\right) + \left(\beta - \frac{m^2}{\sin^2\theta}\right) = 0 \qquad ...(2)$$

$$\beta = \frac{8\pi^2 IE}{h^2} = J(J+1)$$

Solution (1)

$$\Phi_\phi = \frac{1}{\sqrt{2\pi}}e^{im\phi}$$

Solution (2)

$$\Theta(\theta) = \left[\frac{2J + 1 \times (J - |m|)!}{2(J + |m|)!}\right]^{1/2} P_J^{|m|}\cos\theta$$

Same as for Hydrogen atom

Relation b/w J and M $[J\ (J+1) - m^2]^2 \geq 0$

All state with different values of *m* but same value of J are degenerate because energy of system depends on J.

Degeneracy = (2J + 1)

Perturbation Theory

Ist order perturbation or Approximation technique.

$$\left.\begin{aligned} H^0 &= \frac{-\hbar^2}{2m}\frac{\partial^2}{\partial x^2} \\ E^0 &= \frac{n^2h^2}{8\,ml^2} \end{aligned}\right\}\text{1 D box}$$

$$\left.\begin{aligned} H^0 &= \frac{-\hbar^2}{2m}\frac{\partial^2}{\partial x^2} + \frac{1}{2}Kx^2 \\ E^0 &= \left(n + \frac{1}{2}\right)h\nu \end{aligned}\right\}\text{SHO}$$

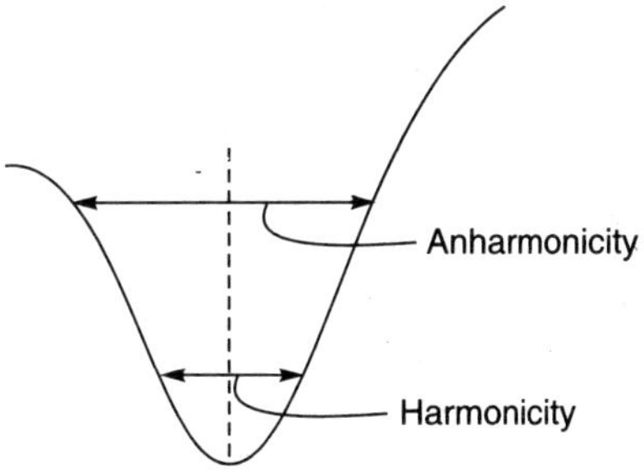

When system is disturbed

$H^1 = H^0 + \underbrace{\Delta H} \rightarrow$ Perturbed value

$E^1 = E^0 + \underbrace{\Delta E} \rightarrow$ Perturbed value

$\varphi = \varphi_0 + \Delta\varphi$

Ist order correction

When φ_n Normalised

$$\Delta E = \int \varphi_n^* \, \Delta H \, \varphi_n \, d\tau$$

same state

Also $\int \varphi_0 \, \Delta\varphi \, d\tau = 0$

When φ_n is not normalised

(No need to normalise)

$$\Delta E = \frac{\int \varphi_0^* \, \Delta H \, \varphi_n \, d\tau}{\int \varphi_n^* \, \varphi_n \, d\tau}$$

IInd order perturbation theory

$$E_n = \sum_{n \neq m} \frac{|< \varphi_n^0 | H | \varphi_m^0 >|^2}{E_n^0 - E_m^0} \quad \text{different state}$$

Correction in function

$$< \phi'_n > = \sum_{m \neq n} \frac{|< \varphi_m | H | \varphi_n | \phi_m >}{E_n - E_m}$$

Generally second order perturbation is *–ve* if $n = m$ then 2nd order perturbation is zero.

Introducting Dirac – Delta function in perturbation

$$\int_{-a}^{+a} f(x)\, \delta(x - L)\, f(x)\, dx$$

$-a < L < +a$

$f(x) = f(a)$

$f(x) = f(L)$

otherwise whole ∫ becomes 0

If variable under and lies b/w the limit of integration then Dirac-remove the integration. If variable under and lies beyond the limit of integration then Dirac makes integration zero.

e.g., $$\int_{-a}^{+a} \frac{1}{\sqrt{a}} \sin\left(\frac{\pi x}{a}\right) 8\left(x - \frac{a}{2}\right) \frac{1}{\sqrt{a}} \sin\left(\frac{\pi x}{a}\right) dx$$

Commutation of Angular Momentum

$$Lx = ypz - zpy$$
$$Ly = zpx - xpz$$
$$Lz = xpy - ypx$$

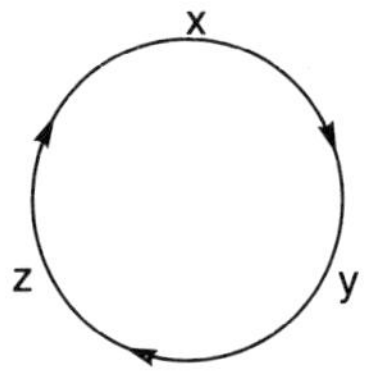

$$Lx = -\,i\hbar\left[y\frac{\partial}{\partial z} - z\frac{\partial}{\partial y}\right]$$

$$Ly = -\,i\hbar\left[z\frac{\partial}{\partial x} - x\frac{\partial}{\partial z}\right]$$

$$Lz = -\,i\hbar\left[x\frac{\partial}{\partial y} - y\frac{\partial}{\partial x}\right]$$

Imp. $[Lx, ly] = i\hbar Lz$
$[Ly, lz] = i\hbar Lx$
$[Lz, lx] = i\hbar Ly$

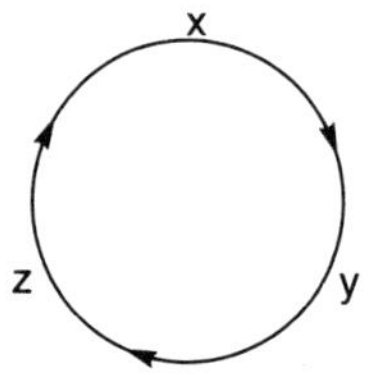

$[Ly, lx] = -\,i\hbar Lz$
$[Lz, ly] = -\,i\hbar Lx$
$[Lx, lz] = -\,i\hbar Ly$

$[Lx, x] = [Ly, y] = [Lz, z] = 0$
$[Lx, y] = i\hbar z$
$[Ly, z] = i\hbar x$
$[Lz, x] = i\hbar y$

$[Lx, Lx] = 0$ $[Lx^2, Lx] = 0$

$[L^2, Lx] = 0$
$[L^2, Ly] = 0$
$[L^2, Lz] = 0$ $L^2 = Lx^2 + Ly^2 + Lz^2$
$[Px, y] = 0$ $[x, y] = 0$
$[Py, z] = 0$ $[Px, Py] = 0$
$[Px, z] = 0$

$[Px, x] = -i\hbar$

$[Py, y] = -i\hbar$

$[Pz, z] = -i\hbar$

$[x^n, px] = i\hbar n x^{n-1}$	$[px, x^n] = i\hbar n x^{n-1}$
$[px^n, x] = -ni\hbar\ px^{n-1}$	$[x, px^n] = ni\hbar\ px^{n-1}$

Ladder Operator

$$L+ = Lx + iLy$$

$$L- = Lx - iLy$$

$[Lz, L_+] = \hbar L+$ $\quad$ $[Lz, L-] = -\hbar L-$

$[L+, Lz] = -\hbar L+$ $\quad$ $[L-, Lz] = -\hbar L-$

$[L^2, L+] = 0$ $\quad$ $[L+, L-] = 2\hbar Lz$

$[L^2, L-] = 0$

Jacobian identity

1. $[A, B] = -[B, A]$
2. $[A, B + C] = [A, B] + [A, C]$
3. $[A + B, C] = [A, C] + [B, C]$
4. $[AB, C] = A[B, C] + [A, C]B$
5. $[A, BC] = [A, B]C + B[A, C]$
6. $[A[B, C]] + [B[C, A]] + [C[A, B]] = 0$

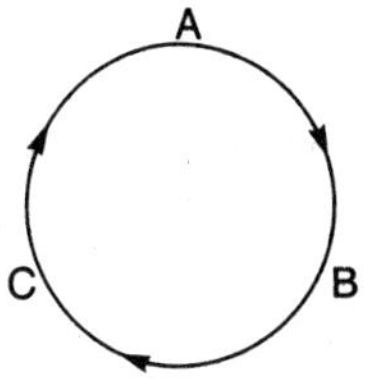

Pauli Spin Principle

spin angular matrix

$$\sigma_x = \begin{bmatrix} 0 & 1 \\ 1 & 0 \end{bmatrix} = -1 \qquad Sx = \frac{1}{2}\hbar \begin{bmatrix} 0 & 1 \\ 1 & 0 \end{bmatrix}$$

$$\sigma_y = \begin{bmatrix} 0 & -i \\ 1 & 0 \end{bmatrix} = -1 \qquad Sy = \frac{1}{2}\hbar \begin{bmatrix} 0 & -i \\ i & 0 \end{bmatrix}$$

$$\sigma_z = \begin{bmatrix} 1 & 0 \\ 0 & -1 \end{bmatrix} = -1 \qquad Sz = \frac{1}{2}\hbar \begin{bmatrix} 1 & 0 \\ 0 & -1 \end{bmatrix}$$

$$E = \begin{bmatrix} 1 & 0 \\ 0 & 1 \end{bmatrix} \text{ identity matrix}$$

$[\sigma_x, \sigma_y] = 2i\sigma_z$ $\quad$ $[\sigma^2, \sigma_x] = 0$

$[\sigma_y, \sigma_z] = 2i\sigma_x$ $\quad$ $[\sigma^2, \sigma_y] = 0$

$[\sigma_z, \sigma_x] = 2i\sigma_y$ $\quad$ $[\sigma^2, \sigma_z] = 0$

$$\sigma^2 = \sigma_x^{\ 2} + \sigma_y^{\ 2} + \sigma_z^{\ 2}$$

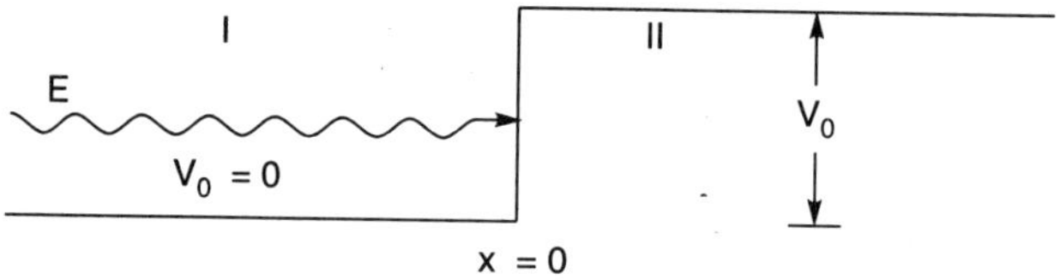

$V_x = 0$ if $x < 0$
$V_x = V0$ if $x > 0$

Ist region $\frac{d^2\varphi_I}{dx^2} + K_1^2\varphi_I = 0$ $K_1 = \frac{\sqrt{2mE}}{\hbar} = \frac{P_1}{\hbar}$ $\frac{\text{Incidence}}{\text{Reflection}}$

IInd region $\frac{d^2\varphi_{II}}{dx^2} + K_2^2\,\varphi_{II} = 0$ $K_2 = \frac{\sqrt{2m(E-V)}}{\hbar} = \frac{P_2}{\hbar}$ transmition

Case I $E > V_0$

Probability current density is defined as

$$J = \frac{\hbar}{2mi}\,[\varphi^*\Delta\varphi - \varphi\Delta\varphi^*]$$

$|R|$, Reflectance $= \frac{(P_1 - P_2)^2}{(P_1 + P_2)^2}$ $P_1 = \sqrt{2\,mE}$

$|T|$, Transmittance $= \frac{4P_1P_2}{(P_1 + P_2)^2}$ $P_2 = \sqrt{2m(E-V)}$

$|R| + |T| = 1$

How much may be the width (*i.e.,* infinite) of barrier R & T both occurs

$E < V_0$ for infinite width only R occurs i.e., quantum mechanics is not effective here.

Case II $E < V_0$ $T = 0,\ R = 1$

Case III $E = V_0$ $T = 0,\ R = 1$

Tunneling

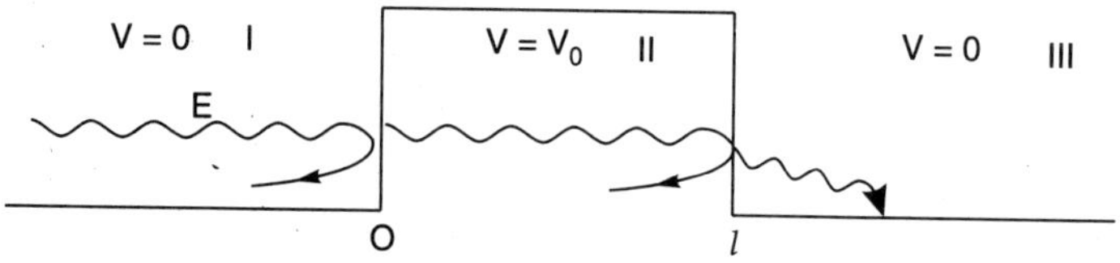

$V = 0$ $x < 0$ ...I

$V = V_0$ $< x < L$ ...II

$V = 0$ $L < x$ ...III

$$\varphi_I = \overbrace{Ae^{ip_1x/\hbar}}^{I} + \overbrace{Be^{-ip_1x/\hbar}}^{R}$$

$$\varphi_{II} = Ce^{ip_2x/\hbar} + De^{-ip_2x/\hbar}$$

$$\varphi_{III} = \underbrace{Ee^{ip_1x/\hbar}}_{T}$$

$$|R| = \frac{|B|^2}{|A|^2} \qquad |T| = \frac{|E|^2}{|A|^2}$$

Relection probability	(R)
Transmission probabity	(T)

1. For $E < V_0$

$$\sin hx = \frac{e^x - e^{-x}}{2} \qquad \boxed{T = \frac{4E(V_0 - E)}{4E(V_0 - E) + V_0^2 \sin h^2\left(\sqrt{\frac{2m(V_0 - E)L^2}{\hbar^2}}\right)}}$$

$$\sin hKl = \frac{e^{Kl} - e^{-Kl}}{2} \qquad \left(\sqrt{K^2L^2}\right) = (KL)$$

2. For $E > V_0$

$$\boxed{T = \frac{4E(V_0 - E)}{4E(V_0 - E) + V_0^2 \sin^2\left(\sqrt{\frac{2m(V_0 - E)L^2}{\hbar^2}}\right)}}$$

If $E < V_0$ Assuming Kl large

$$T \approx e^{-2Kl}$$

$$\boxed{i.e., \quad T = e^{-2\frac{\sqrt{2m(V_0 - E)L^2}}{\hbar}}}$$

If Kl < 1 then use $T = \dfrac{4E(V_0 - E_0)}{4E(V_0 - E) + V_0^2\left[\dfrac{e^{Kl} - e^{-Kl}}{2}\right]^2}$

If $Kl > 1$ then $T = e^{-2Kl}$

$$Kl = \frac{\sqrt{2m(V_0 - E)}}{\hbar}\, l$$

Variation Principle

Trial wave function	Perfect function
↓	↓
E_ϕ	Exactly solvable system
	↓
	E_0

$$\boxed{E_\phi \geq E_0}$$

Minimum value of energy from trial wave function is either greater or equal to that energy obtained from exactly solvable system.

Many problems of quantum mechanics that can't be solved by direct used of wave function of the exact system (pure) so trial wave function is introduced.

Trial wave function must be acceptable within the limits.

$$E\phi = \frac{\int \phi H \phi \, d\tau}{\int \phi\phi \, d\tau}$$

$$\% \text{ error} = \frac{E_\phi - E_0}{E_0} \times 100$$

When trial function is given as a linear combination of functions

$$\phi = c_1\phi_1 + c_2\phi_2$$

To find minimum energy of a system using (trial wave function) variation principle.

Solve the Matrix $\begin{bmatrix} H_{11} - \varepsilon & H_{12} \\ H_{21} & H_{22} - \varepsilon \end{bmatrix}$ E is min energy

where $H_{11} = \int \phi_1 H \phi_1 \, d\tau$ $H_{21} = \int \phi_2 H \phi_1 \, d\tau$

$H_{12} = \int \phi_1 H \phi_2 \, d\tau$ $H_{22} = \int \phi_2 H \phi_2 \, d\tau$

Note: $H_{11} - \varepsilon$ and $H_{22} - \varepsilon$ are equal then find H_{12} (generally becomes zero)

Calculate minimum energy from trial wave function.

$\hat{H} = -\frac{1}{2r^2}\frac{\partial}{\partial r}\left(\frac{r^2\partial}{\partial r}\right)\frac{-1}{r}$ **in a.u.** Normally $\hat{H} = \frac{-\hbar^2}{2m}\frac{\partial^2}{\partial x^2} + V(x)$ (Not in a.u.)

$$E = \langle \hat{H} \rangle = \frac{\int \varphi^* \hat{H} \varphi \, d\tau}{\int \varphi^* \varphi \, d\tau}$$

Calculate E

Setting $\left(\frac{\partial E}{\partial r}\right)_{\alpha_0} = 0$ find α (variational parameter)

Put this value in E you will get $[\mathbf{E_0}]$

Consider a wave function $\varphi = c_1\phi_1 + c_2\phi_2 + c_3\phi_3$

If φ is normalised

$$C_1^2 + C_2^2 + C_3^2 = 1 \text{ (must)}$$

Probability of system is sum of P_1, P_2, P_3

$P_1 = C_1^2$

$P_2 = C_2^2$

$P_3 = C_3^2$

$$P = P_1 + P_2 + P_3 = 1$$

$$P = C_1^2 + C_2^2 + C_3^2 = 1$$

$$E = P_1E_1 + P_2E_2 + P_3E_3$$

Valence Bond Theory

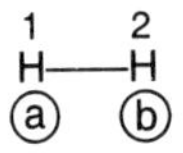

Consider H_2 atom

VB wave function can be written as

$$\varphi_{AB} = C_1\varphi_1 + C_2\varphi_2$$

C_1 and C_2 are the coefficient and φ_1 and φ_2 can be written as

$$\varphi_1 = \phi_a(1)\ \phi_b(2)$$

$$\varphi_2 = \phi_a(2)\ \phi_b(1)$$

$$\varphi_{AB} = C_1\phi_a(1)\ \phi_b(2) + C_2\phi_a(2)\ \phi_b(1)$$

φ_1 wave function correspond to when one e^- is on the atomic orbital $\phi(a)$ centred on nucleus a and 2nd e^- on the atomic orbital $\phi(b)$ centred on nucleus b.

$$C_1 = \pm C_2$$

Bonding: $\varphi_{AB} = \dfrac{1}{\sqrt{2(1+s^2)}}\ [\phi_a(1)\ \phi_b(2) + \phi_a(2)\ \phi_b(1)]$

Antibonding: $\varphi_{AB} = \dfrac{1}{\sqrt{2(1-s^2)}}\ [\phi_a(1)\ \phi_b(2) - \phi_a(2)\ \phi_b(1)]$

(*a*) Purely covalent $\varphi_{COV} = \boldsymbol{\phi_A(1)\ \phi_B(2) + \phi_B(1)\ \phi_A(2)}$

Each of both the e^- has equal probability to be found on atom A or B

(*b*) Purely ionic $\varphi_{ionic} = \boldsymbol{\phi_B(1)\ \phi_B(2)}$

A – (B) → more electronegative atom will have the pair of e^- in bond

(*c*) x% covalent y% ionic

$$\varphi = \underset{\substack{\uparrow\\ \text{covalent}}}{C_1\varphi_1} + \underset{\substack{\uparrow\\ \text{ionic}}}{C_2\varphi_2}$$

$$\varphi = C_1[\phi_A(1)\ \phi_B(2) + \phi_B(1)\ \phi_A(2)] + C_2[\phi_B(1)\ \phi_B(2)]$$

Acceptability of wave function

Condition

(1) function should be finite

1. e^x $(-\infty, +\infty)$ → Unacceptable
2. e^{-x} $(-\infty, +\infty)$ → Unacceptable
3. e^{-x^2} $(0, \infty)$ → Acceptable
4. e^{x^2} $(-\infty, 0)$ → Unacceptable
5. $\sin^{-1} x$ $(0, 1)$ → Unacceptable

6. $\tan^{-1} x$ (0, 1) → Unacceptable

7. $e^{i\theta}$ (0, 2π) → Acceptable

8. $\sin hx$ (0, ∞) → Unacceptable

9. xe^{-x} (0, ∞) → Acceptable

10. $\frac{1}{x}$ (0, ∞) → Unacceptable

11. $e^{-2x} \sin hx$ (0, ∞) → Acceptable

12. $e^{-x} \cos x$ (0, ∞) → Acceptable

13. $\frac{\sin x}{x}$ (0, ∞) → Acceptable

(2) Function should be single valued

(3) Function should be normalised

(4) Function should be continuous and its first derivative should be continuous (whether increasing in +ve or –ve direction).

Time Evaluation of Expectation Value

$$< A > = < \varphi(t) \mid A \mid \phi(t) >$$

Constant $\frac{d\langle A\rangle}{dt} = \frac{1}{i\hbar} \langle [A, H] \rangle + \frac{dA}{dt}$

For constant motion $\frac{d\langle A\rangle}{dt} = 0 \Rightarrow \frac{1}{i\hbar}\langle [A, H] \rangle = -\left(\frac{dA}{dt}\right)$

Commutator of A and H gives <[A, H]> = 0 for constant motion

Wave function of electron

According to pauli wave function of e^- is always **Antisymmetric** $2e^-$ may be arranged in four ways or may have four **Spin parts possible**

↑ ↑ $\alpha(1)\alpha(2)$
↓ ↓ $\beta(1)\beta(2)$
↑↓ + ↓↑ $\alpha(1)(\beta_2) + \beta(2)\alpha(1)$
} Triplet symmetrical

↑↓ – ↓↑ $\alpha(1)\beta(2) - \beta(2)\alpha(1)$ → Singlet antisymmetrical

Wave function = Spin part + Space part

Always anti symmetric =

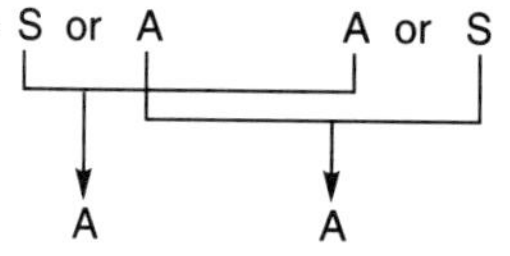

Possible combination

Spin part		Space part
$\alpha(1)\ \alpha(2)$	&	${\varphi_A}^1{\varphi_B}^2 + {\varphi_A}^2 + {\varphi_B}^1 = \varphi_-$
S		A
$\beta(1)\ \beta(2)$	&	$\varphi-$
S		A
$\alpha(1)\ \beta(2) + \alpha(2)\ \beta(1)$	&	$\varphi-$
S		A
$\alpha(1)\ \beta(2) - \alpha(2)\ \beta(1)$	&	φ_+
A		S

Exchange Operator

A particle exchange operator may be written in this form

$$\boxed{\begin{array}{l} P_{12}\ \varphi_S\ =\ \varphi_S \\ P_{12}\ \varphi_A\ =\ -\ \varphi_A \end{array}}$$

The respective eigen function of particle exchange operator corresponding to eigen value **+1 and –1** are **symmetric and antisymmetric**.

Plank's quantum theory $E = hv = \frac{dc}{\lambda} = hc\bar{v}$

Photoelectric effect $hv = \phi + \frac{1}{2}mV^2 \quad \phi = hvc, \ \frac{1}{2}mV^2 = h(V - V_0)$

Bohr's theory of hydrogen atom $mvr = \frac{nh}{2\pi}$

Radius of Bohr's orbit (H) $\partial n = n^2 \times 0.529$ Å
atom

(Ionisation energy) Energy of electron $En = \frac{-13.6}{n^2} eV\, z^2$

$$En = \mathbf{2.18 \times 10^{-18}\ z^2\ (J)}$$

Dual character of electron De Broglie equation $\lambda = \frac{h}{mV} = \frac{b}{P} = \frac{h}{\sqrt{2\,mE}}$

Heisenberg uncertainty principle $\Delta s.\ \Delta p \geq \frac{h}{4\pi},\ \ \Delta x\ .\ \Delta v \geq \frac{h}{\sqrt{2\pi m}}$

Compton effect $\delta\lambda = (2h/mc)\sin^2\theta/2$

↓

increase in wavelength

$$\Delta\lambda = \lambda\Delta\lambda = \frac{h}{mC}(1 - \cos\theta)$$

1. $\theta = 0°$, scattered radiation is ll to incident radiation $\cos\theta = 1$

$$\Delta\lambda = 0$$

2. $\theta = 90°$, $\cos\theta = 0$ $\Delta\lambda = \frac{h}{mC}$ = **0.0242 Å** → compton wavelength

3. $\theta = 180°$, scattered rad opp. to incident rad $\cos\theta = 1$

$$\Delta\lambda = \frac{2h}{mC} = 2 \times 0.0242 \text{ Å} = 0.0484 \text{ Å}$$

From uncertainty principle, $\Delta E\, \Delta t \geq \frac{h}{4\pi}$

$$\Delta V\, \Delta t = \frac{h}{4\pi}$$

$$\Rightarrow \quad \Delta V = \frac{1}{4\pi\, \Delta t} \text{ (sec}^{-1}\text{) and } \Delta V = \frac{\Delta V}{C} \text{ (cm}^{-1}\text{)}.$$

Appendix 8

GREEK ALPHABET

Alpha	Α	α	Iota	Ι	ι	Rho	Ρ	ρ
Beta	Β	β	Kappa	Κ	κ	Sigma	Σ	σ
Gamma	Γ	γ	Lambda	Λ	λ	Tau	Τ	τ
Delta	Δ	δ	Mu	Μ	μ	Upsilon	Υ	υ
Epsilon	Ε	ε	Nu	Ν	ν	Phi	Φ	φ
Zeta	Ζ	ζ	Xi	Ξ	ξ	Chi	Χ	χ
Eta	Η	η	Omicron	Ο	ο	Psi	Ψ	ψ
Theta	Θ	θ	Pi	Π	π	Omega	Ω	ω

Appendix 9

MASSES AND NATURAL ABUNDANCES FOR SELECTED ISOTOPES

Nuclide	*Symbol*	*Mass (amu)*	*Percent Ambundance*
H	^{1}H	1.0078	99.985
	^{2}H	2.0140	0.015
He	^{3}He	3.0160	0.00013
	^{4}He	4.0026	100
Li	^{6}Li	6.0151	7.42
	^{7}Li	7.0160	92.58
B	^{10}B	10.0129	19.78
	^{11}B	11.0093	80.22
C	^{12}C	12 (exact)	98.89
	^{13}C	13.0034	1.11
N	^{14}N	14.0031	99.63
	^{15}N	15.0001	0.37
O	^{16}O	15.9949	99.76
	^{17}O	16.9991	0.037
	^{18}O	17.9992	0.204
F	^{19}F	18.9984	100
P	^{31}P	30.9738	100
S	^{32}S	31.9721	95.0
	^{33}S	32.9715	0.76
	^{34}S	33.9679	4.22
Cl	^{35}Cl	34.9688	75.53
	^{37}Cl	36.9651	24.4
Br	^{79}Br	79.9183	50.54
	^{81}Br	80.9163	49.46
I	^{127}I	126.9045	100

Appendix 10

CONVERSION TABLE FOR UNITS

Length		
meter (SI unit)	m	
centimeter	cm	$= 10^{-2}$ m
ångström	Å	$= 10^{-10}$ m
micron	μ	$= 10^{-6}$ m
Volume		
cubic meter (SI unit)	m^3	
liter	L	$= dm^3 = 10^{-3}\ m^3$
Mass		
kilogram (SI unit)	kg	
gram	g	$= 10^{-3}$ kg
metric ton	t	= 1000 kg
Energy		
joule (SI unit)	J	
erg	erg	$= 10^{-7}$ J
rydberg	Ry	$= 2.179\ 87 \times 10^{-18}$ J
electron volt	eV	$= 1.602\ 176\ 565 \times 10^{-19}$ J
inverse centimeter	cm^{-1}	$= 1.986\ 455\ 684 \times 10^{-23}$ J
calorie (thermochemical)	Cal	= 4.184 J
liter atmosphere	l atm	= 101 325 J
Pressure		
pascal (SI unit)	Pa	
atmosphere	atm	= 101325 Pa
bar	bar	$= 10^5$ Pa
torr	Torr	= 133.322 Pa
pounds per square inch	psi	$= 6.894\ 757 \times 10^3$ Pa
Power		
watt (SI unit)	W	
horsepower	hp	= 745.7 W
Angle		
radian (SI unit)	rad	
degree	°	$= \frac{2\pi}{360}$ rad $= \left(\frac{1}{57.29578}\right)$ rad
Electrical dipole moment		
C m (SI unit)		
debye	D	$= 3.335\ 64 \times 10^{-80}$ C m

Appendix 11

EQUATION LIST

Photon properties	$E = h\nu$ and $\lambda\nu = c$
Schrödinger equation	$\hat{H}\psi_n = E_n\Psi_n$
Orthonormality	$\int\psi_m^2 d\tau = 1$ and $\int\psi_m\psi_n d\tau = 0$ for $m \neq n$
Quantum operators	$\hat{x} = x,\ \hat{p}_x = -i\hbar\partial/\partial x,\ \hat{p}_x^2 = -\hbar^2\partial^2/\partial x^2$
	$\hat{T}_x = \hat{p}_x^2/(2m), \hat{H} = \hat{T} + \hat{V}$
Mean value	$\langle A\rangle = \int\psi(\hat{A}\Psi)\mathrm{d}\tau$
Variance	$\sigma(A) = \left(\langle A^2\rangle - \langle A\rangle^2\right)^{1/2}$
Heisenberg uncertainty principle	$\sigma(x)\sigma(p_x) \geq \hbar/2$
Particle in a wire	$E_n = n^2h^2/(8ma^2)$ for n = 1, 2,...
	$\Psi_n(x) = (2/a)^{1/2}\sin(n\pi x/a)$ for $0 \leq x \leq a$
Particle in a	$E_{n_x,n_y} = h^2\left(n_x^2/a^2 + n_y^2/b^2\right)/(8m)$
rectangular plate	$\Psi_{n_x,n_y}(x,y) = [4/(ab)]^{1/2}\sin(n_x\pi x/a)\sin(n_y\pi y/b)$
	inside the box, for n_x, n_y = 1, 2, ...
Harmonic oscillator	$E_v = (v + 1/2)\hbar\omega$ for v = 0, 1, 2,...; $\omega = \sqrt{k/m}$
	$\Psi_0(x) = (\alpha/\pi)^{1/4}e^{-\alpha x^2/2}$ with $\alpha = m\omega/\hbar$
Particle on a ring	$E_m = \hbar^2m^2/(2I)$ for m = 0, ±1, ±2,...
	$\Psi_0(\phi) = \sqrt{1/(2\pi)}$
Paticle on a sphere	$E_{\ell,m} = \hbar^2\ell(\ell+1)/(2I)$ for ℓ = 0, 1,...; $\ell \geq \lvert m \rvert$
	$\Psi_{0,0}(\theta,\phi) = y_{0,0}(\theta,\phi) = \sqrt{1/(4\pi)}$
	$\langle\hat{L}^2\rangle = \ell(\ell+1)\hbar^2, \langle\hat{L}_z\rangle = m\hbar$
Rigid rotor	$I = \mu R^2$ with $\mu = m_1m_2/(m_1+m_2)$
Cartesian/spherical	$r = (x^2 + y^2 + z^2)^{1/2}$
	$dx\ dy\ dz = r^2 \sin\theta\ dr\ d\theta\ d\phi$

Hydrogen atom	$E_{n,\ell,m} = -E_h/(2n^2)$ for $n = 1, 2, ...; n > \ell \geq \|m\|$
	$\Psi_{1,0,0}(\vec{r}) = 1s(r) = \pi^{-1/2}e^{-r}$
Hydrogen-like ion	$E_{n,\ell,m} = -Z^2E_h/2n^2$ *for* $n = 1, 2,...; n > \ell \geq \|m\|$
	$\Psi_{1,0,0}(\vec{r}) = 1s(r) = (Z^3/\pi)^{1/2}e^{-Zr}$
Variational principle	$\int \Phi(\hat{H}\Phi)d\tau / \int \|\Phi\|^2 d\tau \geq E_{gs}$
Hartree-Fock	$\hat{F}\Phi_k = \varepsilon_k\varphi_k$ for $k = 1, 2, ...$
Matrix Hartree-Fock	$FC_k = \varepsilon_k SC_k$ for $k = 1, 2, ...$
Hartree-Fock electron density	$\rho(\vec{r}) = m_1\|\varphi_1(\vec{r})\|^2 + m_2\|\varphi_2(\vec{r})\|^2 + ... + m_n\|\varphi_n(\vec{r})\|^2$
Hückel matrix	$F = \alpha 1 + \beta A$
Hückel MO (HMO)	$\varphi_k = c_{1k}p_1 + c_{2k}p_2 + ... + c_{Nk}p_N$
HMO normalization	$c_{1k}^2 + c_{2k}^2 + ... + c_{Nk}^2 = 1$
Hückel π-charges	$q_j = m_1\|c_{j1}\|^2 + m_2\|c_{j2}\|^2 + ... + m_N\|c_{jN}\|^2$
Hückel bond orders	$P_{ij} = m_1c_{i1}c_{j1} + m_2c_{i2}c_{j2} + ... + m_Nc_{iN}c_{jN}$
Hückel free valence	$f_k = \sqrt{3} - B_k$

Index